MATRIX METHODS IN ELASTOMECHANICS

MATRIX METHODS IN ELASTO

DR.-ING. EDUARD C. PESTEL

Professor of Mechanics
Technische Hochschule Hannover
Visiting Professor of Engineering
University of California at Los Angeles

FREDERICK A. LECKIE, PH.D.

Lecturer, University of Cambridge, England
Fellow of Pembroke College

McGRAW-HILL BOOK COMPANY, INC.

New York San Francisco Toronto London

MECHANICS

MATRIX METHODS IN ELASTOMECHANICS

 Library of Congress Catalog Card Number 62-19249

4567891011 HDBP 7543210698 49520

To Our Parents

PREFACE

The field of linear elastomechanics has been in a highly developed state for many years, but it was not until the last decade, during which electronic computers were generally available, that the possibilities of matrix calculus were exploited for the static and dynamic treatment of complicated elastic systems. In the authors' opinion these matrix methods, which have proved to be so successful in the study of modern aircraft wings, rocket structures, turbine machinery, etc., have been developed to such a degree that a comprehensive treatise is unlikely to become quickly out of date.

The basic philosophy adopted in the book is based on the idea of breaking up a complicated system into component parts with simple elastic and dynamic properties that can be readily expressed in matrix form. These component matrices are considered as building blocks that, when fitted together according to a set of predetermined rules, provide the static and dynamic properties of the entire system. The matrix formulation of these rules is superbly adapted for consumption by digital computers, and furthermore the concise matrix notation brings to light basic properties of linear elastic systems formerly obscured in a mass of algebraic baroque.

A common type of system occurring in engineering practice consists of a number of elements linked together end to end in the form of a chain. Well-known examples are continuous beams, turbine-generator shafts, crankshafts, etc. The transfer-matrix method is ideally suited to such systems, because only successive matrix multiplications are necessary to fit the elements together. Intermediate conditions and the number of degrees of freedom present no difficulty since they have no effect on the order of the transfer matrices required; in fact, their size is dependent only on the order of the differential equations governing the behavior of the elements of the system.

Although the transfer-matrix method is also suitable for the treatment of branched and coupled systems, its application is inadvisable for systems that lack a predominant chain topology. Then it becomes profitable to employ general methods capable of dealing with any system. Naturally the rules for fitting the building blocks together are more complicated than those of the transfer-matrix method, but nevertheless, with the help of the work principle, a surprisingly efficient and simple formulation is possible. Apart from the demand that the systems must be linearly elastic, no other restrictions are made, so that the methods presented should be of interest to those working in the fields of mechanical, civil, and aeronautical engineering and also to naval architects.

It has been assumed in writing the book that the reader is already acquainted with elementary mechanics and strength of materials. In order to limit the mathematical prerequisites to the knowledge of elementary algebra and calculus, it was felt necessary to present in Chapter 1 an introduction to matrix algebra and matrix calculus. The material covered is strictly limited to that necessary for an understanding of the book, and no attempt has been made to study thoroughly such topics as matrix inversion and matrix iteration, which receive the attention they deserve in other works. No previous knowledge of the theory of mechanical vibrations has been assumed; hence an introduction, in conventional mathematical language, is presented in Chapter 2.

After the two preparatory chapters, attention is focused on the transfer-matrix method, to which Chapters 3 to 7 are devoted. This topic has been treated first because it is the simplest of the matrix methods, both in concept and in application.

During the study of the foregoing chapters the reader is likely to have acquired considerable dexterity in matrix manipulations, so that he should be able to assimilate the somewhat more demanding material covered in Chapters 8 to 10, which are concerned with the most general aspects of linear elastomechanics. For the application of the modal method of vibration analysis which is described in Chapter 8, it is necessary to know the mass matrix and either the stiffness or the flexibility matrix of the system. By and large, it is easy to find the mass matrix for any system, and although it is true that for some systems it is easy to find the stiffness matrix, this is not generally the case for systems of great complexity. The procedures available for determining the flexibility and stiffness matrices of such systems from the flexibility and stiffness of the individual components are known as the matrix force method and matrix displacement method and are described in Chapters 9 and 10, respectively. In these two chapters the authors have drawn heavily from the most remarkable work of Professor J. H. Argyris.

No method can be regarded as satisfactory until it has been applied to numerical problems, and Chapter 11, though adding little or nothing to the theory, may be regarded as the proof of the pudding. It is hoped that this chapter, though by no means complete in its coverage, will give confidence to the reader in the merits of the methods covered in the text.

All the chapters have been liberally provided with examples and problem exercises. It is pointed out, however, that the examples were chosen solely for their illustrative and didactic value, and do not necessarily show up the matrix methods in their best light. In this connection, it might be mentioned that the course presented in this book has been taught for several summer sessions at UCLA by the senior author, who is grateful for the steady encouragement given to him by Professors J. S. Beggs, J. C. Dillon, W. C. Hurty, and W. T. Thomson of UCLA.

The compilation of the Catalogue of Transfer Matrices proved to be an enormous task, which was very considerably lightened by the efforts of Dr.-Ing. S. Spierig. The Catalogue of Transfer Matrices should also prove very valuable for the purpose of deriving the stiffness and flexibility matrices for the individual elements of a system which are required in the matrix force and displacement methods.

Many of the numerical examples worked out were completed by Dr. Spierig, Dr. rer. nat. H. Lippmann, Dr.-Ing. O. Mahrenholtz, and Dr.-Ing. J. Fahr, who, in addition, helped to organize the manuscript. We gratefully acknowledge the unselfish effort exerted by these staff members of the Institute of Mechanics of the Technical University Hannover, Germany. We furthermore thank Mrs. Otto for her great cooperation displayed in writing the entire manuscript in a language foreign to her.

Last but not least, we owe great gratitude to the Deutsche Forschungsgemeinschaft and to the European Office of Aerospace Research of the United States Air Force at Brussels, which for several years provided financial assistance for the pursuit of our research work.

Eduard C. Pestel
Frederick A. Leckie

CONTENTS

Preface vii
List of Symbols xiii

Chapter I
Introduction to Matrix Calculus I

1-1 Definitions 1
1-2 Determinants and Linear Equations 4
1-3 Matrix Algebra 8
1-4 The Eigenvalues of a Square Matrix 18
1-5 Differential Equations 25

Chapter 2
Introduction to the Theory of Undamped Mechanical Vibrations 28

2-1 The Free Vibration of a System with One Degree of Freedom . . 28
2-2 Forced Vibration of a System with One Degree of Freedom . . 32
2-3 Free Vibrations of Systems with Two Degrees of Freedom . . . 37
2-4 Forced Vibrations of Systems with Two Degrees of Freedom . 45

Chapter 3
Introduction to State Vectors and Transfer Matrices 51

3-1 State Vector and Transfer Matrix 51
3-2 Transfer Matrices as a Means of Elimination. Frequency Determinant 60
3-3 Determination of the Normal Modes 68
3-4 Numerical Calculations with Transfer Matrices 71
3-5 Forced Vibrations and Statics 82
3-6 Closed Systems 90

Chapter 4
Introduction to the Theory of Damped Mechanical Vibrations 95

4-1 Damping Models 95
4-2 Free Damped Vibrations of Simple Systems 97
4-3 Transfer Matrices Applied to Free Damped Vibrations . . . 100
4-4 Forced Vibrations 104
4-5 Transfer Matrices Applied to Forced Damped Vibrations . . . 109
4-6 Rotating Shaft with Damping 124

Chapter 5
The Derivation of Transfer Matrices 130

5-1 Derivation of the Transfer Matrix from an *n*th-order Differential Equation 130
5-2 The Solution of *n* First-order Ordinary Differential Equations with Constant Coefficients 137
5-3 The Solution of *n* First-order Nonhomogeneous Differential Equations . 141
5-4 The Solution of *n* First-order Differential Equations with Variable Coefficients 145
5-5 Derivation of the Transfer Matrix from the Stiffness Matrix . . 148

Chapter 6
Intermediate Conditions 153

6-1 Elastic Intermediate Conditions and Branched Systems . . . 153
6-2 Rigid Intermediate Conditions and Releases 169
6-3 Matrix Reduction in the Presence of Releases and Rigid Supports . 176
6-4 Coupled Systems 187

Chapter 7
Variations of the Transfer-matrix Method 192

7-1 The Problem of Numerical Difficulties 192
7-2 The Delta-matrix Method 194
7-3 Modified Transfer-matrix Method 204

Chapter 8
General Theory of Vibrations 214

8-1 The Equation of Motion 214
8-2 Free Vibrations 219
8-3 Forced Undamped Vibrations 227
8-4 Steady-state Forced Damped Vibrations 233
8-5 Free Damped Vibrations, Transients, and General Types of Damped Motions 235

Chapter 9

The Matrix Force Method 240

9-1 General Concepts and Theorems 240
9-2 Basic Theory of the Matrix Force Method 252
9-3 Stress Distribution Due to Thermal and/or Other Initial Strains . . 264
9-4 Generalized Forces, Generalized Displacements, and Force Groups as Redundants 267
9-5 The Effect of Modifications of the Elements on the Stress Distribution and the Flexibility 274
9-6 Recurrence Method for Highly Redundant Systems 280

Chapter 10

The Matrix Displacement Method 286

10-1 Displacement Method Derived by Virtual Work 286
10-2 Condensation of the Stiffness Matrix 297
10-3 Analogy between the Force Method and the Displacement Method . 302
10-4 Some Remarks about the Matrix Force Method and the Matrix Displacement Method 322

Chapter 11

Miscellaneous Applications 323

11-1 Bending Vibrations and Whirling Speeds of a Machine Shaft . . 323
11-2 Coupled Bending and Longitudinal Vibrations of a Circular Arch . 327
11-3 Symmetric Bending Vibrations of Turbine-Generator Shaft on Elastic Steel Foundation 332
11-4 The Application of Transfer Matrices to Plate Vibrations . . . 346
11-5 Shear-lag Problem 351
11-6 The Analysis of a Box Beam and the Effect of Structural Modification . 359
11-7 Calculation of Stresses and Strains in Rotating Disks 365
11-8 Simultaneous Bending and Buckling of Multisectional Straight Beams . 369

Catalogue of Transfer Matrices 375

Straight Beams

C-1 Longitudinal Vibration 376
C-2 Torsional Vibration 377
C-3 Bending Vibration in *xz* or *xy* Plane 378
C-4 Bending Vibration under Constant Axial Stress 382
C-5 Miscellaneous Cases 384
C-6 Forcing Functions 388

Curved and Twisted Beams

C-7 Deformation in the Plane of the Central Axis 390
C-8 Deformation Perpendicular to the Plane of the Central Axis . . 392
C-9 Straight Twisted Beam 395

C-10 Coordinate Transformations 396
C-11 General Case 401
C-12 Forcing Functions 401

Rotating Disks

C-13 Stresses and Deformation Caused by Centrifugal Forces and Thermal Loading 403
C-14 Bending Vibrations of Thick Rotating Disks (Reissner's Theory) . . 404
C-15 The Derivation of Flexibility and Stiffness Matrices from the Transfer Matrix and Remarks on Various Load Conditions 408

References 411

Answers to Selected Problems 417

Index 431

LIST OF SYMBOLS

1. Mathematical Symbols

[ ]	Matrix, row vector
{ }	Column vector, written horizontally
diag [ ]	Diagonal matrix
x, y, z	Cartesian right-handed coordinate system
u, v, w	Displacements in x, y, z directions, respectively
ϕ, ψ, ϑ	Rotations around x, y, z axes, respectively
a_{ik}	Element of matrix $\mathbf{A}$
A_{ik}^{Δ}	Element of Δ matrix $\mathbf{A}^{\Delta}$
$\tilde{\mathbf{A}}$	Extended transfer matrix
$\mathbf{A}^{\Delta_r}$	Reduced Δ matrix
Re	Real part of complex quantity
β^4	$= \dfrac{\mu\omega^2 l^4}{EJ}$
Sin	diag $[\sin \omega_i(t - t_0)]$
Cos	diag $[\cos \omega_i(t - t_0)]$
E	diag $[e^{-\delta_i(t-t_0)}]$

2. General Symbols

$\mathbf{a}$	Amplitude vector
A	Amplitude of vibration
A	Cross-sectional area
$\mathbf{b}$	Amplitude vector
c	Damping constant
c_{ik}	Normal-mode factors
C	Centrifugal force
$\mathbf{C}$	Matrix of damping constants
d	Displacement
$\mathbf{d}$	Displacement vector
e	Elongation
e	Eccentricity
E	Young's modulus
EJ	Bending stiffness
$\mathbf{f}$	(Applied) force vector
F	Force
$\mathbf{F}$	Field matrix

$\mathbf{F}$	Flexibility matrix
$\mathbf{F}_d$	Flexibility matrix of complete structure
$\mathbf{F}_v$	Flexibility matrix of unassembled structural elements
g	Acceleration due to gravity
g	Constant of structural damping
$\mathbf{g}$	Impulse vector
G	Impulse
G	Shear modulus
$\mathbf{G}$	Coordinate transformation matrix
GA_s	Shear stiffness
h	Size of interval
$\mathbf{h}$	Column vector of initial strains on structural elements
i_y	Radius of gyration about the y axis
I	Mass moment of inertia
$\mathbf{I}$	Unit matrix
j	Imaginary unit ($=\sqrt{-1}$)
J_T	Polar second moment of area
J_y	Second moment of area about y axis
$J_T G$	Torsional stiffness
k	Spring stiffness
k_w	Longitudinal spring stiffness (in z direction)
k_ψ	Rotational spring stiffness (about y axis)
K_d	Dynamic stiffness
$\mathbf{K}$	Stiffness matrix
$\mathbf{K}$	Substitute spring matrix
$\mathbf{K}_f$	Stiffness matrix of complete structure
$\mathbf{K}_p$	Stiffness matrix of unassembled structural elements
l	Length
m	Mass
$\bar{m}$	Normalizing constant
M	Bending moment
$\mathbf{M}$	Mass matrix
N	Normal force
O	Origin
p	Complex eigenvalue
p	Variable force
$\mathbf{p}$	Internal-force vector (stresses on structural elements)
P	Force magnitude
P^*	Dimensionless force
$\mathbf{P}$	Point matrix
q	Distributed load
$\mathbf{q}$	Modal vector (generalized coordinates)
r	Radius
$\mathbf{R}_1$, $\mathbf{R}_2$	Square submatrices
$\mathbf{S}$	Spring matrix
$\bar{\mathbf{S}}$	Complex dynamic-stiffness matrix
t	Time
T	Period of vibration
T	Torque
$\mathbf{T}_C$	Column-transposing matrix
$\mathbf{T}_R$	Row-transposing matrix
u	Displacement in x direction

$\mathbf{U}$	Transfer matrix
v	Displacement in y direction
v	Velocity
$\mathbf{v}$	Unknown vector
$\mathbf{v}$	Vector of internal deformations
V	Shear force
w	Displacement in z direction
W	Weight
x	Amplitude of free vibration, measured from undeflected position
x	Displacement
x^*	Dimensionless displacement
$\mathbf{x}$	Displacement vector
$\mathbf{x}$	Redundant-force vector
X	Amplitude of steady-state forced vibration
X_i	ith redundant force
$\mathbf{y}$	Vector of kinematic deficiencies
Y_i	ith kinematic deficiency
$\bar{z}$	Complex impedance
$\mathbf{z}$	State vector

3. Greek Symbols

α	Phase-lag angle
α	Slope change
γ	Shear strain
Γ	Distributed foundation stiffness against displacement of beam
δ	Damping rate
$\boldsymbol{\delta}$	diag $[\delta_i]$
Δ	Frequency determinant
$\boldsymbol{\Delta}$	Transformed damping matrix
ε	Direct strain
ε	Eccentricity angle
ζ	Dimensionless damping factor
$\boldsymbol{\zeta}$	Diagonal matrix of dimensionless damping factors
ϑ	Rotation about z axis
κ	Correction factor
λ	Eigenvalue of matrix
μ	Mass per unit length
μ	Poisson's ratio
ν	Circular frequency of damped vibration
$\boldsymbol{\nu}$	diag $[\nu_i]$
ξ	Displacement measured from equilibrium position
σ	Direct stress
τ	Shear stress
ϕ	Rotation about x axis
$\boldsymbol{\phi}$	Normalized modal vector
Φ	Angular forced deflection
$\boldsymbol{\Phi}$	Modal matrix
ψ	Rotation about y axis
ω	Natural circular frequency of undamped vibration
$\boldsymbol{\omega}$	diag $[\omega_i]$
Ω	Forcing circular frequency

4. Superscripts

E	Equilibrium
i	Imaginary component
L	Left side of cut
r	Real component
R	Right side of cut
0	Indicates initial conditions

5. Subscripts

h	Homogeneous solution
p	Particular solution

1 INTRODUCTION TO MATRIX CALCULUS

1-1. Definitions

Matrix and Column Vector. The chief domain of matrix calculus is in the field of linear relationships which exist between one system of quantities $x_1, x_2, \ldots, x_n$ and another system $y_1, y_2, \ldots, y_m$. We assume that such a relationship is given by

$$\begin{array}{l} a_{11}x_1 + a_{12}x_2 + \cdots + a_{1k}x_k + \cdots + a_{1n}x_n = y_1 \\ a_{21}x_1 + a_{22}x_2 + \cdots + a_{2k}x_k + \cdots + a_{2n}x_n = y_2 \\ \cdots\cdots\cdots\cdots\cdots\cdots\cdots\cdots \\ a_{i1}x_1 + a_{i2}x_2 + \cdots + a_{ik}x_k + \cdots + a_{in}x_n = y_i \\ \cdots\cdots\cdots\cdots\cdots\cdots\cdots\cdots \\ a_{m1}x_1 + a_{m2}x_2 + \cdots + a_{mk}x_k + \cdots + a_{mn}x_n = y_m \end{array} \tag{1-1}$$

Let us represent Eqs. (1-1) in "short-hand" notation as

$$\mathbf{Ax} = \mathbf{y} \tag{1-1a}$$

The symbol **A** stands for the coefficients arranged in the form

$$\mathbf{A} = \begin{bmatrix} a_{11} & a_{12} & \cdots & a_{1k} & \cdots & a_{1n} \\ a_{21} & a_{22} & \cdots & a_{2k} & \cdots & a_{2n} \\ \cdot & \cdot & \cdot & \cdot & \cdot & \cdot \\ a_{i1} & a_{i2} & \cdots & a_{ik} & \cdots & a_{in} \\ \cdot & \cdot & \cdot & \cdot & \cdot & \cdot \\ a_{m1} & a_{m2} & \cdots & a_{mk} & \cdots & a_{mn} \end{bmatrix} = [a_{ik}] \tag{1-2}$$

A is called a matrix of order (m, n), which means that it consists of m rows and n columns. The coefficient in the ith row and kth column is represented by the symbol a_{ik}. It often proves convenient to indicate the number of rows and columns, and therefore, in addition to the symbol **A**, the symbol ${}_m\overset{n}{\mathbf{A}}$ will also be used. When $m = n$, the matrix **A** is called a square matrix of order n.

The symbols **x** and **y** represent the groups of quantities $x_1, x_2, \ldots, x_n$ and $y_1, y_2, \ldots, y_m$ written in the form

$$\mathbf{x} = \begin{bmatrix} x_1 \\ x_2 \\ \cdot \\ \cdot \\ \cdot \\ x_n \end{bmatrix} \qquad \mathbf{y} = \begin{bmatrix} y_1 \\ y_2 \\ \vdots \\ y_m \end{bmatrix} \tag{1-3}$$

and are called column vectors. The quantities $x_1, x_2, \ldots, x_n$ are referred to as the components of the column vector **x**. In order to save space in the text it is advantageous to represent the column vector **x** by $\{x_1 \quad x_2 \quad \cdots \quad x_n\}$.†

Using Eqs. (1-2) and (1-3), Eq. (1-1*a*) takes the form

$$\begin{bmatrix} a_{11} & a_{12} & \cdots & a_{1k} & \cdots & a_{1n} \\ a_{21} & a_{22} & \cdots & a_{2k} & \cdots & a_{2n} \\ \cdot & \cdot & \cdot & \cdot & \cdot & \cdot \\ a_{i1} & a_{i2} & \cdots & a_{ik} & \cdots & a_{in} \\ \cdot & \cdot & \cdot & \cdot & \cdot & \cdot \\ a_{m1} & a_{m2} & \cdots & a_{mk} & \cdots & a_{mn} \end{bmatrix} \cdot \begin{bmatrix} x_1 \\ x_2 \\ \cdot \\ \cdot \\ \cdot \\ x_k \\ \cdot \\ \cdot \\ \cdot \\ x_n \end{bmatrix} = \begin{bmatrix} y_1 \\ y_2 \\ \cdot \\ y_i \\ \vdots \\ y_m \end{bmatrix} \tag{1-1b}$$

Let us now establish the rule which relates Eq. (1-1*b*) to the original equation (1-1). The ith equation is

$$a_{i1}x_1 + a_{i2}x_2 + \cdots + a_{ik}x_k + \cdots + a_{in}x_n = y_i$$

the left side of which may be obtained from Eq. (1-1*b*) by adding the products of each element in the ith row of **A** with its corresponding component in the column vector **x**. The component y_i is thus obtained as the so-called scalar product of the ith row of the matrix **A** and the column vector **x**.

Example 1-1. The relation between the column vectors $\{x_1 \quad x_2 \quad x_3\}$ and $\{y_1 \quad y_2\}$ is given by

$$3x_1 + 2x_2 - 4x_3 = y_1$$
$$5x_1 + \ 0 \ + \ x_3 = y_2$$

or in matrix notation by

$$\begin{bmatrix} 3 & 2 & -4 \\ 5 & 0 & 1 \end{bmatrix} \cdot \begin{bmatrix} x_1 \\ x_2 \\ x_3 \end{bmatrix} = \begin{bmatrix} y_1 \\ y_2 \end{bmatrix}$$

or by $\mathbf{Ax} = \mathbf{y}$, where

$${}_2\overset{3}{\mathbf{A}} = \begin{bmatrix} 3 & 2 & -4 \\ 5 & 0 & 1 \end{bmatrix}$$

† In contrast to the term column vector, the term row vector is used to represent the group of quantities $x_1, x_2, \ldots, x_n$ when arranged in a row $[x_1 \quad x_2 \quad \cdots \quad x_n]$. The column vector is a matrix of order $(n, 1)$, and the row vector is a matrix of order $(1, n)$.

Partitioned Matrix. It is often advantageous to partition a matrix **A** into a number of smaller submatrices. For example, we may partition the matrix ${}^{m}\overset{n}{\mathbf{A}}$ so that

$$ {}^{m}\overset{n}{\mathbf{A}} = \left[\begin{array}{c:c:c} {}^{d}\overset{a}{\mathbf{A}}_1 & {}^{d}\overset{b}{\mathbf{A}}_2 & {}^{d}\overset{c}{\mathbf{A}}_3 \\ \hdashline {}^{e}\overset{a}{\mathbf{A}}_4 & {}^{e}\overset{b}{\mathbf{A}}_5 & {}^{e}\overset{c}{\mathbf{A}}_6 \end{array}\right] \tag{1-4} $$

where $a + b + c = n$ and $d + e = m$.

Null, Unit, and Diagonal Matrices. A null matrix is one that consists only of zero elements:

$$ \mathbf{A} = \mathbf{0} = \begin{bmatrix} 0 & 0 & \cdots & 0 \\ 0 & 0 & \cdots & 0 \\ \cdot & \cdot & \cdot & \cdot \\ 0 & 0 & \cdots & 0 \end{bmatrix} \tag{1-5} $$

Similarly, a null vector (row or column) has only zero components. A unit matrix is a square matrix in which the elements on the *main diagonal*† are unity, all other elements being zero.

$$ \mathbf{A} = {}^{n}\overset{n}{\mathbf{I}} = \begin{bmatrix} 1 & 0 & 0 & 0 & \cdots & 0 \\ 0 & 1 & 0 & 0 & \cdots & 0 \\ 0 & 0 & 1 & 0 & \cdots & 0 \\ 0 & 0 & 0 & 1 & \cdots & 0 \\ \cdot & \cdot & \cdot & \cdot & \cdot & \cdot \\ 0 & 0 & 0 & 0 & \cdots & 1 \end{bmatrix} \tag{1-6} $$

The unit matrix corresponds to the number 1 in ordinary algebra. Therefore, by analogy with $a^0 = 1$, we define ${}^{n}\overset{n}{\mathbf{A}}{}^{0} = {}^{n}\overset{n}{\mathbf{I}}$ for any given square matrix $\mathbf{A} \neq \mathbf{0}$.

A diagonal matrix is a square matrix the elements of which are zero except for those on the main diagonal:

$$ \mathbf{A} = \mathbf{D} = \begin{bmatrix} a_{11} & 0 & \cdots & 0 \\ 0 & a_{22} & \cdots & 0 \\ \cdot & \cdot & \cdot & \cdot \\ 0 & 0 & \cdots & a_{nn} \end{bmatrix} = \text{diag}\,[a_{ii}] \tag{1-7} $$

The unit matrix **I** is, therefore, a special case of the diagonal matrix.

If it is possible to partition the square matrix **A** in the following special way:

$$ \mathbf{A} = \begin{bmatrix} \mathbf{A}_{11} & \mathbf{0} & \mathbf{0} & \cdots & \mathbf{0} \\ \mathbf{0} & \mathbf{A}_{22} & \mathbf{0} & \cdots & \mathbf{0} \\ \mathbf{0} & \mathbf{0} & \cdots & \cdots & \mathbf{0} \\ \cdot & \cdot & \cdot & \cdot & \cdot \\ \mathbf{0} & \mathbf{0} & \mathbf{0} & \cdots & \mathbf{A}_{mm} \end{bmatrix} = \text{diag}\,[\mathbf{A}_{ii}] \qquad m > 1 \tag{1-8} $$

† In a square matrix **A** the main diagonal is formed of all elements a_{ii}, whereas the so-called cross diagonal consists of all elements $a_{i,n+1-i}$.

where $\mathbf{A}_{11}, \mathbf{A}_{22}, \ldots, \mathbf{A}_{mm}$ are square matrices, the main diagonals of which cover without overlapping the main diagonal of the total matrix $\mathbf{A}$, then it is called a diagonally partitioned matrix. For example,

$$\begin{bmatrix} 2 & 1 & 0 & 0 & 0 & 0 \\ 8 & 3 & 0 & 0 & 0 & 0 \\ 0 & 0 & 2 & -1 & 3 & 0 \\ 0 & 0 & 8 & 5 & 1 & 0 \\ 0 & 0 & 2 & 1 & 6 & 0 \\ 0 & 0 & 0 & 0 & 0 & 8 \end{bmatrix} = \begin{bmatrix} \begin{bmatrix} 2 & 1 \\ 8 & 3 \end{bmatrix} & & \\ & \begin{bmatrix} 2 & -1 & 3 \\ 8 & 5 & 1 \\ 2 & 1 & 6 \end{bmatrix} & \\ & & [8] \end{bmatrix}$$

Transposed, Symmetric, and Cross-symmetric Matrices. The transpose $\mathbf{A}'$ of a matrix $\mathbf{A}$ is formed by writing the ith row of $\mathbf{A}$ as the ith column of $\mathbf{A}'$. For example, if

$$\mathbf{A} = \begin{bmatrix} 5 & 7 & 0 \\ 1 & 0 & 4 \end{bmatrix}$$

then

$$\mathbf{A}' = \begin{bmatrix} 5 & 1 \\ 7 & 0 \\ 0 & 4 \end{bmatrix} \tag{1-9}$$

It is obvious that the transpose of $\mathbf{A}'$ is again $\mathbf{A}$, that is, $(\mathbf{A}')' = \mathbf{A}$.

A square matrix $\mathbf{A}$ is said to be symmetric about its main diagonal when the elements satisfy the relation

$$a_{ij} = a_{ji} \tag{1-10}$$

Hence a property of a symmetric matrix is that it is equal to its transpose, that is, $\mathbf{A} = \mathbf{A}'$. For example,

$$\mathbf{A} = \begin{bmatrix} 4 & 7 & 0 \\ 7 & 1 & 2 \\ 0 & 2 & 3 \end{bmatrix} = \mathbf{A}'$$

A square matrix $\mathbf{A}$ is said to be cross-symmetric if it is symmetric about its cross diagonal (bottom left to upper right), e.g.,

$$\mathbf{A} = \begin{bmatrix} 2 & 0 & 4 \\ 8 & 1 & 0 \\ 5 & 8 & 2 \end{bmatrix} \tag{1-11}$$

1-2. Determinants and Linear Equations

Rules for the Evaluation of Determinants. It is assumed that the reader is already familiar with the simple procedure for calculating determinants, but some useful rules associated with determinants are now listed:†

I. Rows and columns can be interchanged without affecting the value of the determinant, i.e.,

$$|\mathbf{A}| = |\mathbf{A}'| \tag{1-12}$$

† For fuller treatment see, for example, Ref. 1.

II. If two columns (or rows) are interchanged, the sign of the determinant is changed. For example,

$$\begin{vmatrix} 3 & 4 \\ 1 & -2 \end{vmatrix} = -\begin{vmatrix} 1 & -2 \\ 3 & 4 \end{vmatrix}$$

III. If a row (or column) is changed by adding to or subtracting from its elements the corresponding elements of any other row (or column), then the determinant remains unaltered, i.e.,

$$\begin{vmatrix} a_{11} & a_{12} & a_{13} & \cdots & a_{1n} \\ \cdot & \cdot & \cdot & \cdot & \cdot \\ a_{i1} & a_{i2} & a_{i3} & \cdots & a_{in} \\ \cdot & \cdot & \cdot & \cdot & \cdot \\ a_{j1} & a_{j2} & a_{j3} & \cdots & a_{jn} \\ \cdot & \cdot & \cdot & \cdot & \cdot \\ a_{n1} & a_{n2} & a_{n3} & \cdots & a_{nn} \end{vmatrix} = \begin{vmatrix} a_{11} & a_{12} & a_{13} & \cdots & a_{1n} \\ \cdot & \cdot & \cdot & \cdot & \cdot \\ a_{i1} + a_{j1} & a_{i2} + a_{j2} & a_{i3} + a_{j3} & \cdots & a_{in} + a_{jn} \\ \cdot & \cdot & \cdot & \cdot & \cdot \\ a_{j1} & a_{j2} & a_{j3} & \cdots & a_{jn} \\ \cdot & \cdot & \cdot & \cdot & \cdot \\ a_{n1} & a_{n2} & a_{n3} & \cdots & a_{nn} \end{vmatrix}$$

IV. If the elements in any row (or column) have a common factor α, then the determinant equals the determinant of the corresponding matrix in which $\alpha = 1$, multiplied by α. For example,

$$\begin{vmatrix} a_{11} & a_{12} & a_{13} & \cdots & a_{1n} \\ \cdot & \cdot & \cdot & \cdot & \cdot \\ \alpha a_{i1} & \alpha a_{i2} & \alpha a_{i3} & \cdots & \alpha a_{in} \\ \cdot & \cdot & \cdot & \cdot & \cdot \\ a_{n1} & a_{n2} & a_{n3} & \cdots & a_{nn} \end{vmatrix} = \alpha \begin{vmatrix} a_{11} & a_{12} & a_{13} & \cdots & a_{1n} \\ \cdot & \cdot & \cdot & \cdot & \cdot \\ a_{i1} & a_{i2} & a_{i3} & \cdots & a_{in} \\ \cdot & \cdot & \cdot & \cdot & \cdot \\ a_{n1} & a_{n2} & a_{n3} & \cdots & a_{nn} \end{vmatrix}$$

Should $\alpha = 0$, then the determinant is zero.

Rules III and IV can often be used in combination to simplify the computation of a determinant:

Example 1-2

$$\begin{vmatrix} 4 & 6 & 1 & 2 \\ 3 & 2 & 1 & 0 \\ 1 & 2 & 2 & 1 \\ 2 & 3 & 1 & 1 \end{vmatrix} = -\tfrac{1}{2}\begin{vmatrix} 4 & 6 & 1 & 2 \\ 3 & 2 & 1 & 0 \\ 1 & 2 & 2 & 1 \\ -4 & -6 & -2 & -2 \end{vmatrix} = -\tfrac{1}{2}\begin{vmatrix} 4-4 & 6-6 & 1-2 & 2-2 \\ 3 & 2 & 1 & 0 \\ 1 & 2 & 2 & 1 \\ -4 & -6 & -2 & -2 \end{vmatrix}$$

$$= -\tfrac{1}{2}\begin{vmatrix} 0 & 0 & -1 & 0 \\ 3 & 2 & 1 & 0 \\ 1 & 2 & 2 & 1 \\ -4 & -6 & -2 & -2 \end{vmatrix} = \tfrac{1}{2}\begin{vmatrix} 3 & 2 & 0 \\ 1 & 2 & 1 \\ -4 & -6 & -2 \end{vmatrix} = 1$$

V. When at least one row (or column) of a determinant is a linear combination of the other rows (or columns), then the determinant is zero. Conversely, if the determinant is zero, then at least one row and one column are linearly dependent on the other rows and columns, respectively.

Consider the determinant

$$\begin{vmatrix} 3 & 2 & 1 \\ 1 & 2 & -1 \\ 2 & -1 & 3 \end{vmatrix}$$

The determinant is zero because the first column is a linear combination of the second and third columns:

$$\text{Column 1} = \text{column 2} + \text{column 3}$$

Furthermore the linear dependence of the first row on the second and third rows is given by the relation

$$\text{Row 1} = \tfrac{7}{5}\,\text{row 2} + \tfrac{4}{5}\,\text{row 3}$$

Solution of Simultaneous Linear Algebraic Equations. The use of determinants provides a systematic way of solving a set of linear algebraic equations.

If the n simultaneous equations are

$$\begin{aligned} a_{11}x_1 + a_{12}x_2 + \cdots + a_{1n}x_n &= y_1 \\ a_{21}x_1 + a_{22}x_2 + \cdots + a_{2n}x_n &= y_2 \\ \cdots\cdots\cdots\cdots\cdots\cdots\cdots & \\ a_{n1}x_1 + a_{n2}x_2 + \cdots + a_{nn}x_n &= y_n \end{aligned} \tag{1-13}$$

and the determinant of the coefficients on the left side of Eqs. (1-13) is not zero, then the solutions for $x_1, x_2, \ldots, x_n$ are uniquely given by

$$x_1 = \frac{\begin{vmatrix} y_1 & a_{12} & a_{13} & \cdots & a_{1n} \\ y_2 & a_{22} & a_{23} & \cdots & a_{2n} \\ \cdots & \cdots & \cdots & \cdots & \cdots \\ y_n & a_{n2} & a_{n3} & \cdots & a_{nn} \end{vmatrix}}{\begin{vmatrix} a_{11} & a_{12} & a_{13} & \cdots & a_{1n} \\ a_{21} & a_{22} & a_{23} & \cdots & a_{2n} \\ \cdots & \cdots & \cdots & \cdots & \cdots \\ a_{n1} & a_{n2} & a_{n3} & \cdots & a_{nn} \end{vmatrix}} \qquad x_2 = \frac{\begin{vmatrix} a_{11} & y_1 & a_{13} & \cdots & a_{1n} \\ a_{21} & y_2 & a_{23} & \cdots & a_{2n} \\ \cdots & \cdots & \cdots & \cdots & \cdots \\ a_{n1} & y_n & a_{n3} & \cdots & a_{nn} \end{vmatrix}}{\begin{vmatrix} a_{11} & a_{12} & a_{13} & \cdots & a_{1n} \\ a_{21} & a_{22} & a_{23} & \cdots & a_{2n} \\ \cdots & \cdots & \cdots & \cdots & \cdots \\ a_{n1} & a_{n2} & a_{n3} & \cdots & a_{nn} \end{vmatrix}} \tag{1-14}$$

and so on. This method of solving the simultaneous equations is known as Cramer's rule.

Should the values of y be such that $y_1 = y_2 = y_3 = \cdots = y_n = 0$, then the set of equations is described as being homogeneous. In this case the numerators of Eqs. (1-14) are all zero, and it follows that

$$x_1 = x_2 = x_3 = \cdots = x_n = 0$$

is the solution of the equations provided

$$|\mathbf{A}| \neq 0$$

When the determinant $|\mathbf{A}|$ is zero, however, it follows from rule V that at least one of Eqs. (1-13) is linearly dependent on the others. If only one equation is linearly dependent, then this equation may be dropped, and we are left with $n - 1$ equations and n unknowns. Suppose† that the subdeterminant of order $n - 1$ is

$$\begin{vmatrix} a_{12} & a_{13} & \cdots & a_{1n} \\ a_{22} & a_{23} & \cdots & a_{2n} \\ \cdots & \cdots & \cdots & \cdots \\ a_{n-1,2} & a_{n-1,3} & \cdots & a_{n-1,n} \end{vmatrix} \neq 0$$

† At least one subdeterminant of order $n - 1$ must be unequal to zero.

Dropping the last of Eqs. (1-13) and dividing throughout by x_1, we obtain the following $n - 1$ nonhomogeneous equations:

$$
\begin{aligned}
a_{12}\frac{x_2}{x_1} + a_{13}\frac{x_3}{x_1} + \cdots + a_{1n}\frac{x_n}{x_1} &= -a_{11} \\
a_{22}\frac{x_2}{x_1} + a_{23}\frac{x_3}{x_1} + \cdots + a_{2n}\frac{x_n}{x_1} &= -a_{21} \\
\cdots\cdots\cdots\cdots\cdots\cdots\cdots\cdots & \\
a_{n-1,2}\frac{x_2}{x_1} + a_{n-1,3}\frac{x_3}{x_1} + \cdots + a_{n-1,n}\frac{x_n}{x_1} &= -a_{n-1,1}
\end{aligned}
\tag{1-15}
$$

These equations can now be solved for $x_2/x_1, x_3/x_1, \ldots, x_n/x_1$. Hence, the solution of a set of homogeneous equations need not be trivial, if $|\mathbf{A}| = 0$. When this is so, it is impossible to find the absolute magnitude of $x_1, x_2, \ldots, x_n$, but it is possible to compute their magnitudes relative to one another.

Example 1-3. Consider the set of homogeneous equations

$$
\begin{aligned}
3x_1 - x_2 - \tfrac{9}{4}x_3 &= 0 \\
2x_1 + x_2 + x_3 &= 0 \\
-2x_1 + x_2 + 2x_3 &= 0
\end{aligned}
$$

Here $|\mathbf{A}| = 0$. A nontrivial solution is possible, for if x_1 is set equal to unity, the first two equations become

$$
\begin{aligned}
-x_2 - \tfrac{9}{4}x_3 &= -3 \\
x_2 + x_3 &= -2
\end{aligned}
$$

from which $x_2 = -6$ and $x_3 = 4$.

Hence $x_1 = 1$, $x_2 = -6$, $x_3 = 4$ is a solution of the equations and similarly $x_1 = k$, $x_2 = -6k$, $x_3 = 4k$ is a solution of the equations, where k is an arbitrary constant.

Singular Matrix and Rank of a Matrix. If the determinant $|\mathbf{A}|$ of a matrix $\mathbf{A}$ is zero, then the matrix is described as being singular. This means that at least one row and one column are linearly dependent on the others. Should the matrix consist of r linearly independent rows and columns,† from which the remaining $n - r$ rows and columns can be formed by linear combination, then the matrix is said to be of rank r.

Example 1-4. The matrix

$$
\mathbf{A} = \begin{bmatrix} 3 & 2 & 2 \\ 1 & 2 & -1 \\ 2 & -1 & 3 \end{bmatrix}
$$

is of rank $r = 3$, since $|\mathbf{A}| \neq 0$.

The matrix

$$
\mathbf{A} = \begin{bmatrix} 3 & 2 & 1 \\ 1 & 2 & -1 \\ 2 & -1 & 3 \end{bmatrix}
$$

is of rank $r = 2$, since the first row (column) can be expressed in terms of the second and third, and the matrix

† That is, none of these r rows and columns can be expressed as a linear combination of the others.

$$\mathbf{A} = \begin{bmatrix} 8 & -4 & 12 \\ 6 & -3 & 9 \\ 2 & -1 & 3 \end{bmatrix}$$

is of rank $r = 1$, since all the rows or columns can be formed from $(2 \quad -1 \quad 3)$ or $(4 \quad 3 \quad 1)$, respectively.

PROBLEMS

1-1. Compute the determinants of the following matrices:

$$\mathbf{A} = \begin{bmatrix} 3 & 2 & 0 \\ 1 & 5 & 2 \\ 0 & -3 & 4 \end{bmatrix} \qquad \mathbf{A} = \begin{bmatrix} 1 & 2 & 2 & 1 \\ 3 & 0 & 1 & -5 \\ -1 & 3 & 2 & 4 \\ -2 & -5 & -5 & 0 \end{bmatrix}$$

$$\mathbf{A} = \begin{bmatrix} +\frac{2}{5} & 1 & 1 & 0 \\ -1 & 3 & 2 & 4 \\ -\frac{1}{2} & -1 & -1 & \frac{1}{2} \\ 6 & 0 & 2 & -10 \end{bmatrix} \qquad \mathbf{A} = \begin{bmatrix} 3 & 0 & 0 & 0 \\ 0 & \frac{1}{2} & 0 & 0 \\ 0 & 0 & 4 & 0 \\ 0 & 0 & 0 & \frac{1}{6} \end{bmatrix}$$

1-2. Solve by Cramer's rule the following set of equations:

$$\begin{aligned} 2x_1 + x_2 + x_3 &= 4 \\ -3x_1 + 2x_2 - x_3 &= -8 \\ x_1 + 3x_2 + 2x_3 &= 4 \end{aligned}$$

1-3. Show that the following set of homogeneous equations has a nontrivial solution:

$$\begin{aligned} x_1 + 2x_2 \qquad &= 0 \\ 4x_1 + 5x_2 + 4x_3 &= 0 \\ - 3x_2 + 4x_3 &= 0 \end{aligned}$$

What is the rank of the coefficient matrix?

1-4. What is the rank of the matrix of the following set of equations?

$$\begin{aligned} x_1 - 4x_2 + 3x_3 \qquad &= 0 \\ - 9x_2 + 7x_3 + 5x_4 &= 0 \\ -2x_1 - x_2 + x_3 + 5x_4 &= 0 \\ -3x_1 - 6x_2 + 5x_3 + 10x_4 &= 0 \end{aligned}$$

Compute a nontrivial solution.

1-3. Matrix Algebra

Addition and Subtraction. The sum (difference) $\mathbf{C}$ of two (m, n) matrices $\mathbf{A}$ and $\mathbf{B}$, that is,

$$\mathbf{A} \pm \mathbf{B} = \mathbf{C} \tag{1-16}$$

is obtained by adding (subtracting) all elements a_{ik} and b_{ik}, thereby obtaining $c_{ik} = a_{ik} \pm b_{ik}$.

For example,

$$\mathbf{A} = \begin{bmatrix} 3 & 1 \\ 4 & 7 \\ 0 & 2 \end{bmatrix} \qquad \mathbf{B} = \begin{bmatrix} 0 & 2 \\ -3 & 5 \\ 1 & -1 \end{bmatrix} \qquad \mathbf{A} + \mathbf{B} = \mathbf{C} = \begin{bmatrix} 3 & 3 \\ 1 & 12 \\ 1 & 1 \end{bmatrix}$$

As an immediate consequence,

$$\mathbf{A} + \mathbf{B} = \mathbf{B} + \mathbf{A}$$

and furthermore

$$(\mathbf{A} + \mathbf{B})' = \mathbf{A}' + \mathbf{B}'$$

Besides we have

$$\mathbf{A} - (\mathbf{B} + \mathbf{C}) = (\mathbf{A} - \mathbf{B}) - \mathbf{C}$$

Multiplication by a Parameter. Multiplication of a matrix **A** by a scalar quantity α yields

$$\mathbf{B} = \alpha\mathbf{A} = [\alpha a_{ik}]$$

For example, when $\alpha = -\frac{1}{5}$ and $\mathbf{A} = \begin{bmatrix} 1 & -3 & 0 \\ 4 & 2 & -1 \end{bmatrix}$, then

$$\mathbf{B} = \begin{bmatrix} -\frac{1}{5} & \frac{3}{5} & 0 \\ -\frac{4}{5} & -\frac{2}{5} & \frac{1}{5} \end{bmatrix}$$

Matrix Multiplication. We shall now consider the operations involved in computing the matrix product

$$\mathbf{AB} = \mathbf{C}$$

The element c_{ik} of the matrix **C** is defined by the following formula involving the elements in the ith row of **A** and the kth column of **B**:

$$c_{ik} = a_{i1}b_{1k} + a_{i2}b_{2k} + a_{i3}b_{3k} + \cdots + a_{in}b_{nk}$$

This operation is carried out most conveniently by using the following scheme [2]:

$$\begin{array}{cc} & \text{column } k \\ & \begin{bmatrix} b_{11} & b_{12} & \cdots & b_{1k} & \cdots & b_{1p} \\ b_{21} & b_{22} & \cdots & b_{2k} & \cdots & b_{2p} \\ \cdot & \cdot & \cdot & \cdot & \cdot & \cdot \\ b_{n1} & b_{n2} & \cdots & b_{nk} & \cdots & b_{np} \end{bmatrix} \\ \begin{array}{r} \\ \\ \\ \text{row } i \\ \\ \\ \end{array} \begin{bmatrix} a_{11} & a_{12} & \cdots & a_{1n} \\ a_{21} & a_{22} & \cdots & a_{2n} \\ \cdot & \cdot & \cdot & \cdot \\ a_{i1} & a_{i2} & \cdots & a_{in} \\ \cdot & \cdot & \cdot & \cdot \\ a_{m1} & a_{m2} & \cdots & a_{mn} \end{bmatrix} & \begin{bmatrix} & & & & & \\ & & & & & \\ & & & & & \\ \cdots & \cdots & \cdots & c_{ik} & & \\ & & & & & \\ & & & & & \end{bmatrix} \end{array} \tag{1-17}$$

Each element in row i of **A** is multiplied by its corresponding element in column k of **B** (note the dashed lines), and the products are summed. For this operation to be possible, the number of columns of **A** must equal the number of rows of **B**. The matrix product is of order (m, p), that is,

$$_m\overset{p}{\mathbf{C}} = {_m\overset{n}{\mathbf{A}}}\ {_n\overset{p}{\mathbf{B}}}$$

Example 1-5. Form the product of the following matrices:

$$ {}_{2}\overset{3}{\mathbf{A}} = \begin{bmatrix} 3 & 0 & 2 \\ 4 & -1 & 5 \end{bmatrix} \qquad {}^{3}\overset{4}{\mathbf{B}} = \begin{bmatrix} 2 & 1 & 0 & -5 \\ 4 & 3 & -1 & 0 \\ 0 & 1 & -7 & 4 \end{bmatrix} $$

The matrix **C** is of order (2, 4) and is computed as follows:

$$ \begin{array}{cc} & \begin{bmatrix} 2 & 1 & 0 & -5 \\ 4 & 3 & -1 & 0 \\ 0 & 1 & -7 & 4 \end{bmatrix} = \mathbf{B} \\ \mathbf{A} = \begin{bmatrix} 3 & 0 & 2 \\ 4 & -1 & 5 \end{bmatrix} & \begin{bmatrix} 6 & 5 & -14 & -7 \\ 4 & 6 & -34 & 0 \end{bmatrix} = \mathbf{C} \end{array} $$

This scheme is particularly useful when several matrices are to be multiplied. Suppose we wish to find the matrix product

$$ \mathbf{D} = \mathbf{A}(\mathbf{BC}) $$

where

$$ \mathbf{A} = \begin{bmatrix} 2 & 4 & 1 & 0 \\ -1 & 2 & 3 & 1 \\ 2 & 5 & -1 & 2 \end{bmatrix} \qquad \mathbf{B} = \begin{bmatrix} 2 & -2 \\ 1 & 0 \\ 4 & 1 \\ 3 & 2 \end{bmatrix} \qquad \mathbf{C} = \begin{bmatrix} 1 & -3 & 2 & 4 & -1 \\ 2 & 0 & 2 & 1 & 2 \end{bmatrix} $$

Then

$$ {}^{3}\overset{4}{\mathbf{A}}\,{}^{4}\overset{2}{\mathbf{B}}\,{}^{2}\overset{5}{\mathbf{C}} = {}^{3}\overset{5}{\mathbf{D}} $$

The matrices **B** and **C** are set out in the manner already described. When the product **BC** has been completed, it is conveniently placed for further multiplication by **A**. The result of this operation is shown below:

$$ \begin{array}{ccc} & & \begin{bmatrix} 1 & -3 & 2 & 4 & -1 \\ 2 & 0 & 2 & 1 & 2 \end{bmatrix} = \mathbf{C} \\ & \mathbf{B} = \begin{bmatrix} 2 & -2 \\ 1 & 0 \\ 4 & 1 \\ 3 & 2 \end{bmatrix} & \begin{bmatrix} -2 & -6 & 0 & 6 & -6 \\ 1 & -3 & 2 & 4 & -1 \\ 6 & -12 & 10 & 17 & -2 \\ 7 & -9 & 10 & 14 & 1 \end{bmatrix} = \mathbf{BC} \\ \mathbf{A} = \begin{bmatrix} 2 & 4 & 1 & 0 \\ -1 & 2 & 3 & 1 \\ 2 & 5 & -1 & 2 \end{bmatrix} & & \begin{bmatrix} 6 & -36 & 18 & 45 & -18 \\ 29 & -45 & 44 & 67 & -1 \\ 9 & -33 & 20 & 43 & -13 \end{bmatrix} = \mathbf{D} \end{array} $$

Multiplication Checks. In all numerical calculations it is desirable to have a simple way of checking the results. In the case of matrix multiplication this is possible by forming an extra column the elements of which are the sums of all elements in the corresponding rows. Consider, for example, the matrix product **C** = **AB**, where

$$ \mathbf{A} = \begin{bmatrix} 3 & 4 & -2 \\ 0 & 1 & 5 \\ 1 & 4 & 0 \end{bmatrix} $$

and

$$\mathbf{B} = \begin{bmatrix} 2 & -1 \\ 0 & 3 \\ 1 & 4 \end{bmatrix}$$

We arrange the matrices in the manner demonstrated previously, but in addition an extra column is formed from the sum of the elements in each row of **B**. The matrix multiplication with the extra column included is carried out in the usual way, as follows:

$$\begin{array}{cc} & \begin{array}{cc} \mathbf{B} & \text{Sum column of } \mathbf{B} \end{array} \\ & \left[\begin{array}{cc|c} 2 & -1 & 1 \\ 0 & 3 & 3 \\ 1 & 4 & 5 \end{array}\right] \\ \mathbf{A} = \begin{bmatrix} 3 & 4 & -2 \\ 0 & 1 & 5 \\ 1 & 4 & 0 \end{bmatrix} & \left[\begin{array}{cc|c} 4 & 1 & 5 \\ 5 & 23 & 28 \\ 2 & 11 & 13 \end{array}\right] \\ & \begin{array}{cc} \mathbf{C} & \text{Sum column of } \mathbf{C} \end{array} \end{array}$$

If the multiplication has been done correctly, each element of the extra column should equal the sum of the elements of its corresponding row in **C**. Indeed we find $4 + 1 = 5$, $5 + 23 = 28$, $2 + 11 = 13$, and the check is satisfied.

The check can also be made by forming an extra row from the sum of the elements in each column. When it is applied to the same matrix product as before, the following scheme can be used:

$$\begin{array}{ccc} & & \begin{bmatrix} 2 & -1 \\ 0 & 3 \\ 1 & 4 \end{bmatrix} \\ & \left[\begin{array}{ccc} 3 & 4 & -2 \\ 0 & 1 & 5 \\ 1 & 4 & 0 \\ \hline 4 & 9 & 3 \end{array}\right] & \left[\begin{array}{cc} 4 & 1 \\ 5 & 23 \\ 2 & 11 \\ \hline 11 & 35 \end{array}\right] \end{array}$$

(Last rows: Sum row of **A** and Sum row of **C**.)

The check is again satisfied, since $4 + 5 + 2 = 11$ and $1 + 23 + 11 = 35$. Both checks can be carried out simultaneously; this has the advantage that any incorrect element can be located.

Consider again the previous matrix product $\mathbf{C} = \mathbf{AB}$, and let us assume that an error is made in computing c_{32} (9 instead of 11). With both checks used, we obtain the following:

$$
\begin{array}{rrrr}
 & & & \left[\begin{array}{rr|r} 2 & -1 & 1 \\ 0 & 3 & 3 \\ 1 & 4 & 5 \end{array}\right] \\
 \left[\begin{array}{rrr} 3 & 4 & -2 \\ 0 & 1 & 5 \\ 1 & 4 & 0 \\ \hline 4 & 9 & 3 \end{array}\right] & & & \left[\begin{array}{rr|r} 4 & 1 & 5 \\ 5 & 23 & 28 \\ 2 & \boxed{9} & 13 \\ \hline 11 & 35 & 46 \end{array}\right] \leftarrow \text{error} \\
 & & & \quad\ \ \uparrow \\
 & & & \quad\ \text{error}
\end{array}
$$

(1) $4 + 1 = 5$

(2) $5 + 23 = 28$

(3) $2 + 9 \neq 13$ error

(4) $4 + 5 + 2 = 11$

(5) $1 + 23 + 9 \neq 35$ error

(6) $5 + 28 + 13 = 46$

Checks 1 to 6 clearly indicate the error in c_{32}. The multiplication checks can be carried through successive matrix products, a typical arrangement being as follows:

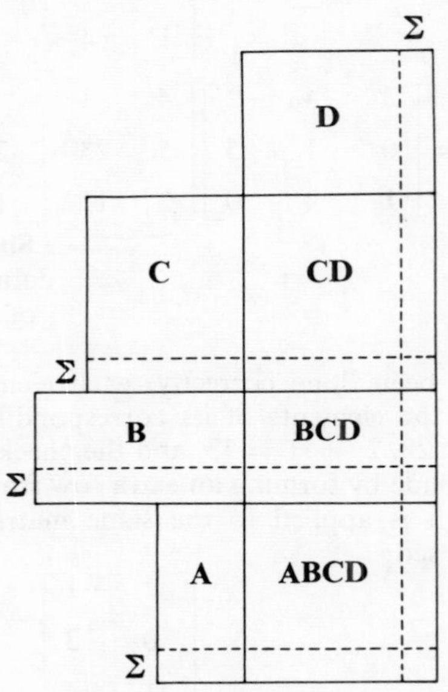

Multiplication of Partitioned Matrices. Partitioned matrices are multiplied in the normal way by treating the submatrices as if they were elements.

Consider the partitioned matrix product ${}^{m}\overset{n}{\mathbf{A}}{}^{n}\overset{p}{\mathbf{B}} = {}^{m}\overset{p}{\mathbf{C}}$. Then

$$
{}^{n}\overset{\quad p}{\begin{bmatrix} {}^{a}\overset{s}{\mathbf{B}}_{11} & \overset{t}{\mathbf{B}}_{12} & \overset{u}{\mathbf{B}}_{13} \\ {}^{b}\mathbf{B}_{21} & \mathbf{B}_{22} & \mathbf{B}_{23} \\ {}^{c}\mathbf{B}_{31} & \mathbf{B}_{32} & \mathbf{B}_{33} \\ {}^{d}\mathbf{B}_{41} & \mathbf{B}_{42} & \mathbf{B}_{43} \end{bmatrix}} \qquad \begin{aligned} s + t + u &= p \\ a + b + c + d &= n \\ v + w &= m \end{aligned} \qquad (1\text{-}18)
$$

$$
{}^{m}\overset{n}{\begin{bmatrix} {}^{v}\overset{a}{\mathbf{A}}_{11} & \overset{b}{\mathbf{A}}_{12} & \overset{c}{\mathbf{A}}_{13} & \overset{d}{\mathbf{A}}_{14} \\ {}^{w}\mathbf{A}_{21} & \mathbf{A}_{22} & \mathbf{A}_{23} & \mathbf{A}_{24} \end{bmatrix}} \begin{bmatrix} {}^{v}\overset{s}{\mathbf{C}}_{11} & \overset{t}{\mathbf{C}}_{12} & \overset{u}{\mathbf{C}}_{13} \\ {}^{w}\mathbf{C}_{21} & \mathbf{C}_{22} & \mathbf{C}_{23} \end{bmatrix}
$$

Here, for example,

$$ {}^{w}\overset{u}{\mathbf{C}}_{23} = {}^{w}\overset{a}{\mathbf{A}}_{21}{}^{a}\overset{u}{\mathbf{B}}_{13} + {}^{w}\overset{b}{\mathbf{A}}_{22}{}^{b}\overset{u}{\mathbf{B}}_{23} + {}^{w}\overset{c}{\mathbf{A}}_{23}{}^{c}\overset{u}{\mathbf{B}}_{33} + {}^{w}\overset{d}{\mathbf{A}}_{24}{}^{d}\overset{u}{\mathbf{B}}_{43} $$

For multiplication of partitioned matrices to be possible, the matrix **A** must be partitioned as to columns in the same way that **B** is partitioned as to rows.

Some Properties of Matrix Products. I. If **B** and **C** are matrices of the same order, then

$$\mathbf{A}(\mathbf{B}+\mathbf{C}) = \mathbf{AB}+\mathbf{AC} \quad \text{and} \quad (\mathbf{B}+\mathbf{C})\mathbf{A} = \mathbf{BA}+\mathbf{CA} \qquad \text{distributive law}$$

Example 1-6

$$\mathbf{A} = \begin{bmatrix} 2 & -1 & 0 \\ 3 & 1 & -2 \end{bmatrix} \qquad \mathbf{B} = \begin{bmatrix} 3 & -2 \\ -1 & 1 \\ 2 & 1 \end{bmatrix} \qquad \mathbf{C} = \begin{bmatrix} 1 & 4 \\ -2 & 0 \\ 1 & 3 \end{bmatrix}$$

$$\begin{bmatrix} 4 & 2 \\ -3 & 1 \\ 3 & 4 \end{bmatrix} = \mathbf{B}+\mathbf{C}$$

$$\mathbf{A} = \begin{bmatrix} 2 & -1 & 0 \\ 3 & 1 & -2 \end{bmatrix}\begin{bmatrix} 11 & 3 \\ 3 & -1 \end{bmatrix} = \mathbf{A}(\mathbf{B}+\mathbf{C})$$

Also

$$\mathbf{AB} = \begin{bmatrix} 7 & -5 \\ 4 & -7 \end{bmatrix} \quad \text{and} \quad \mathbf{AC} = \begin{bmatrix} 4 & 8 \\ -1 & 6 \end{bmatrix}$$

so that

$$\mathbf{AB}+\mathbf{AC} = \begin{bmatrix} 11 & 3 \\ 3 & -1 \end{bmatrix} = \mathbf{A}(\mathbf{B}+\mathbf{C})$$

II. $$\mathbf{A}(\mathbf{BC}) = (\mathbf{AB})\mathbf{C} \qquad \text{associative law}$$

Hence we may delete the parentheses and write **ABC**.

III. $$(\mathbf{AB})' = \mathbf{B}'\mathbf{A}' \tag{1-19}$$

The reader should check this result for

$$\mathbf{A} = \begin{bmatrix} 0 & -2 & 1 \\ 3 & 1 & 4 \end{bmatrix} \qquad \mathbf{B} = \begin{bmatrix} 5 & 0 \\ -3 & 2 \\ 1 & 1 \end{bmatrix}$$

From Eq. (1-19) we can deduce the general result

$$(\mathbf{ABC}\cdots\mathbf{MN})' = \mathbf{N}'\mathbf{M}'\cdots\mathbf{C}'\mathbf{B}'\mathbf{A}'$$

IV. If **B** is a symmetric (m, m) matrix, then the matrix product

$$\mathbf{A}'\mathbf{BA} = \mathbf{S} \tag{1-20}$$

is a symmetric (n, n) matrix, where **A** can be an arbitrary (m, n) matrix provided $\mathbf{BA} \neq \mathbf{0}$ and $\mathbf{A}'\mathbf{B} \neq \mathbf{0}$.

For example, when

$$\mathbf{A} = \begin{bmatrix} 1 & 0 \\ -1 & 2 \\ 2 & 0 \end{bmatrix} \quad \text{and} \quad \mathbf{B} = \begin{bmatrix} 3 & -1 & 4 \\ -1 & 2 & 0 \\ 4 & 0 & 0 \end{bmatrix}$$

then
$$\mathbf{S} = \begin{bmatrix} 23 & -6 \\ -6 & 8 \end{bmatrix}$$

V. The determinant of the product of square matrices satisfies the following relation:

$$|\mathbf{AB}| = |\mathbf{BA}| = |\mathbf{A}||\mathbf{B}| \tag{1-21}$$

From this it follows immediately that, for instance,

$$|\mathbf{ACDB}| = |\mathbf{BCAD}| = \cdots = |\mathbf{A}||\mathbf{B}||\mathbf{C}||\mathbf{D}|$$

VI. If **A** and **B** are square matrices of the same order, then the products **AB** and **BA** are both possible but, in general, $\mathbf{AB} \neq \mathbf{BA}$.

For example,

$$\mathbf{A} = \begin{bmatrix} 1 & 3 \\ -4 & 2 \end{bmatrix} \quad \mathbf{B} = \begin{bmatrix} 3 & 0 \\ 1 & -2 \end{bmatrix} \quad \mathbf{AB} = \begin{bmatrix} 6 & -6 \\ -10 & -4 \end{bmatrix} \quad \mathbf{BA} = \begin{bmatrix} 3 & 9 \\ 9 & -1 \end{bmatrix}$$

Hence, in matrix multiplication the sequence cannot be altered (i.e., the commutative law of multiplication is not valid for matrices). Expressed in other words, the *postmultiplication* of **A** by **B** (that is, **AB**) yields a result different from the *premultiplication* of **A** by **B** (that is, **BA**).

VII. The matrix product of two symmetric matrices does not, in general, yield a symmetric matrix.

For example,

$$\mathbf{A} = \begin{bmatrix} 1 & 2 \\ 2 & 3 \end{bmatrix} \qquad \mathbf{B} = \begin{bmatrix} -1 & 4 \\ 4 & 5 \end{bmatrix}$$

Then
$$\mathbf{AB} = \begin{bmatrix} 7 & 14 \\ 10 & 23 \end{bmatrix} \quad \text{and} \quad \mathbf{BA} = \begin{bmatrix} 7 & 10 \\ 14 & 23 \end{bmatrix}$$

This example demonstrates further that, if **A** and **B** are both symmetric,

$$\mathbf{AB} = \mathbf{A}'\mathbf{B}' = (\mathbf{BA})' \qquad \text{cf. Eq. (1-19)} \tag{1-22}$$

VIII. The matrix product **AB** can be zero, although $\mathbf{A} \neq \mathbf{0}$ and $\mathbf{B} \neq \mathbf{0}$.

For example,

$$\begin{bmatrix} 3 & -6 & -3 \\ 7 & -14 & -7 \\ -1 & 2 & 1 \end{bmatrix} = \mathbf{B}$$

$$\mathbf{A} = \begin{bmatrix} 3 & -1 & 2 \\ 1 & 0 & 3 \\ 3 & -2 & -5 \end{bmatrix} \begin{bmatrix} 0 & 0 & 0 \\ 0 & 0 & 0 \\ 0 & 0 & 0 \end{bmatrix} = \mathbf{AB} = \mathbf{0}$$

In this example $|\mathbf{A}| = |\mathbf{B}| = 0$. This is a necessary condition. That it is not sufficient is shown by the following example:

$$\begin{bmatrix} 12 & 6 \\ 4 & 2 \end{bmatrix} = \mathbf{B}$$

$$\mathbf{A} = \begin{bmatrix} 1 & 3 \\ 2 & 6 \end{bmatrix} \begin{bmatrix} 24 & 12 \\ 48 & 24 \end{bmatrix} \neq \mathbf{0} \qquad \text{although } |\mathbf{A}| = |\mathbf{B}| = 0$$

If **A** is singular, it is possible that $\mathbf{A} \neq \mathbf{0}$, $\mathbf{A}^2 \neq \mathbf{0}, \ldots,$ but $\mathbf{A}^p = \mathbf{0}$.

For example,

$$\mathbf{A} = \begin{bmatrix} 0 & a & b \\ 0 & 0 & c \\ 0 & 0 & 0 \end{bmatrix} \neq \mathbf{0} \qquad \mathbf{A}^2 = \begin{bmatrix} 0 & 0 & ac \\ 0 & 0 & 0 \\ 0 & 0 & 0 \end{bmatrix} \neq \mathbf{0} \quad \text{but} \quad \mathbf{A}^3 = \begin{bmatrix} 0 & 0 & 0 \\ 0 & 0 & 0 \\ 0 & 0 & 0 \end{bmatrix} = \mathbf{0}$$

and

$$\mathbf{A} = \begin{bmatrix} 2 & -1 \\ 4 & -2 \end{bmatrix} \neq \mathbf{0} \qquad \mathbf{A}^2 = \begin{bmatrix} 0 & 0 \\ 0 & 0 \end{bmatrix} = \mathbf{0}$$

Bilinear and Quadratic Forms. The product

$$\overset{1}{{}^1\mathbf{B}} = {}^1\overset{m}{\mathbf{y}'} \, {}^m\overset{n}{\mathbf{A}} \, {}^n\overset{1}{\mathbf{x}} \tag{1-23}$$

formed from the vectors $\mathbf{x}$ and $\mathbf{y}$ and the matrix $\mathbf{A}$, is referred to as the bilinear form. Since $\mathbf{B}' = \mathbf{B}$, then, applying Eq. (1-19), we obtain the result

$$\mathbf{y}'\mathbf{A}\mathbf{x} = \mathbf{x}'\mathbf{A}'\mathbf{y} \tag{1-24}$$

For the special case that $\mathbf{A} = \mathbf{A}'$ and $\mathbf{x} = \mathbf{y}$ the bilinear form becomes the quadratic form

$$Q = \mathbf{x}'\mathbf{A}\mathbf{x} \tag{1-25}$$

The kinetic energy of a system consisting of the masses m_1, m_2, and m_3 is

$$T = \tfrac{1}{2}(m_1 v_1^2 + m_2 v_2^2 + m_3 v_3^2)$$

and can be expressed by the quadratic form

$$T = \tfrac{1}{2}\mathbf{v}'\mathbf{M}\mathbf{v}$$

where

$$\mathbf{M} = \begin{bmatrix} m_1 & 0 & 0 \\ 0 & m_2 & 0 \\ 0 & 0 & m_3 \end{bmatrix} \quad \text{and} \quad \mathbf{v} = \begin{bmatrix} v_1 \\ v_2 \\ v_3 \end{bmatrix}$$

Inversion of a Matrix and Matrix Division. The inverse of a square matrix $\mathbf{A}$ is represented by the symbol $\mathbf{A}^{-1}$ and is defined by the relation

$$\mathbf{A}\mathbf{A}^{-1} = \mathbf{I} \tag{1-26}$$

Premultiplying Eq. (1-26) by $\mathbf{A}^{-1}$ and postmultiplying by $\mathbf{A}$ yield

$$\mathbf{A}^{-1}\mathbf{A}\mathbf{A}^{-1}\mathbf{A} = \mathbf{A}^{-1}\mathbf{I}\mathbf{A} \qquad \text{or} \qquad (\mathbf{A}^{-1}\mathbf{A})^2 = \mathbf{A}^{-1}\mathbf{A}$$

which can hold only if

$$\mathbf{A}^{-1}\mathbf{A} = \mathbf{I}$$

One application of the concept of the inverse matrix can be made with reference to Eqs. (1-13),

$$\mathbf{A}\mathbf{x} = \mathbf{y}$$

Premultiply both sides by $\mathbf{A}^{-1}$; then

$$\mathbf{A}^{-1}\mathbf{A}\mathbf{x} = \mathbf{A}^{-1}\mathbf{y}$$

from which we obtain the expression for $\mathbf{x}$ in terms of $\mathbf{y}$:

$$\mathbf{x} = \mathbf{A}^{-1}\mathbf{y}$$

A great number of methods exist for the numerical computation of the inverse of a square matrix $\mathbf{A}$, but the discussion of these methods is beyond the scope of this introductory chapter.† In any case the inversion could be carried out by the general formula‡

$$\mathbf{A}^{-1} = [a_{ik}]^{-1} = \frac{[A_{ki}]}{|\mathbf{A}|}$$

which could be proved by the use of Cramer's rule [cf. Eqs. (1-14)]. This procedure, however, usually leads to very clumsy expressions, and for this reason it is mostly applied only to the inversion of (2, 2) and (3, 3) matrices.

Inversion Formulas for Second- and Third-order Matrices

$$\mathbf{A} = \begin{bmatrix} a_{11} & a_{12} \\ a_{21} & a_{22} \end{bmatrix} \qquad \mathbf{A}^{-1} = \frac{1}{|\mathbf{A}|}\begin{bmatrix} a_{22} & -a_{12} \\ -a_{21} & a_{11} \end{bmatrix} \tag{1-27}$$

$$\mathbf{A} = \begin{bmatrix} a_{11} & a_{12} & a_{13} \\ a_{21} & a_{22} & a_{23} \\ a_{31} & a_{32} & a_{33} \end{bmatrix} \qquad \mathbf{A}^{-1} = \frac{1}{|\mathbf{A}|}\begin{bmatrix} A_{11} & A_{21} & A_{31} \\ A_{12} & A_{22} & A_{32} \\ A_{13} & A_{23} & A_{33} \end{bmatrix} \tag{1-28}$$

where
$$A_{11} = \begin{vmatrix} a_{22} & a_{23} \\ a_{32} & a_{33} \end{vmatrix} \qquad A_{21} = -\begin{vmatrix} a_{12} & a_{13} \\ a_{32} & a_{33} \end{vmatrix} \qquad A_{31} = \begin{vmatrix} a_{12} & a_{13} \\ a_{22} & a_{23} \end{vmatrix}$$

$$A_{12} = -\begin{vmatrix} a_{21} & a_{23} \\ a_{31} & a_{33} \end{vmatrix} \qquad A_{22} = \begin{vmatrix} a_{11} & a_{13} \\ a_{31} & a_{33} \end{vmatrix} \qquad A_{32} = -\begin{vmatrix} a_{11} & a_{13} \\ a_{21} & a_{23} \end{vmatrix}$$

$$A_{13} = \begin{vmatrix} a_{21} & a_{22} \\ a_{31} & a_{32} \end{vmatrix} \qquad A_{23} = -\begin{vmatrix} a_{11} & a_{12} \\ a_{31} & a_{32} \end{vmatrix} \qquad A_{33} = \begin{vmatrix} a_{11} & a_{12} \\ a_{21} & a_{22} \end{vmatrix}$$

Example 1-7

$$\mathbf{A}^{-1} = \begin{bmatrix} 2 & 4 & 2 \\ 3 & 1 & 1 \\ 1 & 0 & 1 \end{bmatrix}^{-1} = -\tfrac{1}{8}\begin{bmatrix} 1 & -4 & 2 \\ -2 & 0 & 4 \\ -1 & 4 & -10 \end{bmatrix} = \begin{bmatrix} -\frac{1}{8} & \frac{1}{2} & -\frac{1}{4} \\ \frac{1}{4} & 0 & -\frac{1}{2} \\ \frac{1}{8} & -\frac{1}{2} & \frac{5}{4} \end{bmatrix}$$

The reader should check that $\mathbf{AA}^{-1} = \mathbf{I}$.

Some Properties of the Inverse Matrix

I.
$$(\mathbf{A}')^{-1} = (\mathbf{A}^{-1})' \tag{1-29}$$

because
$$\mathbf{AA}^{-1} = (\mathbf{AA}^{-1})' = (\mathbf{A}^{-1})'\mathbf{A}' = \mathbf{I}$$

II. If $\mathbf{A}$ is symmetric, then $(\mathbf{A}')^{-1} = \mathbf{A}^{-1} = (\mathbf{A}^{-1})'$ by property I; hence $\mathbf{A}^{-1}$ is also symmetric.

III.
$$(\mathbf{AB})^{-1} = \mathbf{B}^{-1}\mathbf{A}^{-1} \tag{1-30}$$

because
$$\begin{aligned} (\mathbf{AB})(\mathbf{AB})^{-1} &= \mathbf{I} \\ \mathbf{A}^{-1}(\mathbf{AB})(\mathbf{AB})^{-1} &= \mathbf{A}^{-1} \\ \mathbf{B}(\mathbf{AB})^{-1} &= \mathbf{A}^{-1} \\ \mathbf{B}^{-1}\mathbf{B}(\mathbf{AB})^{-1} &= \mathbf{B}^{-1}\mathbf{A}^{-1} \\ (\mathbf{AB})^{-1} &= \mathbf{B}^{-1}\mathbf{A}^{-1} \qquad \text{Q.E.D.} \end{aligned}$$

IV. For a diagonal matrix $\mathbf{D}$ in which all diagonal elements are different from

† See Refs. 3, 4, and particularly 5.

‡ The elements A_{ki} are the subdeterminants of the matrix $\mathbf{A}$ with row k and column i deleted, multiplied by $(-1)^{i+k}$ [cf. Eqs. (1-28)].

zero (otherwise $|\mathbf{D}| = 0$ and thus **D** would be singular), $\mathbf{D}^{-1}$ is again a diagonal matrix with elements $1/d_{ii}$.

For example,

$$\begin{bmatrix} 1 & 0 & 0 & 0 \\ 0 & 3 & 0 & 0 \\ 0 & 0 & -4 & 0 \\ 0 & 0 & 0 & 5 \end{bmatrix}^{-1} = \begin{bmatrix} 1 & 0 & 0 & 0 \\ 0 & \frac{1}{3} & 0 & 0 \\ 0 & 0 & -\frac{1}{4} & 0 \\ 0 & 0 & 0 & \frac{1}{5} \end{bmatrix}$$

V. Similarly if **D** is a diagonally partitioned matrix,

$$\mathbf{D} = \begin{bmatrix} \mathbf{S}_{11} & \mathbf{0} & \mathbf{0} & \cdots & \mathbf{0} \\ \mathbf{0} & \mathbf{S}_{22} & \mathbf{0} & \cdots & \mathbf{0} \\ \mathbf{0} & \mathbf{0} & \cdots & \cdots & \mathbf{0} \\ \cdot & \cdot & \cdot & \cdot & \cdot \\ \mathbf{0} & \mathbf{0} & \mathbf{0} & \cdots & \mathbf{S}_{nn} \end{bmatrix} = \text{diag}\,[\mathbf{S}_{ii}]$$

then the inverse matrix $\mathbf{D}^{-1}$ is [cf. Eqs. (1-18)]

$$\mathbf{D}^{-1} = \begin{bmatrix} \mathbf{S}_{11}^{-1} & \mathbf{0} & \mathbf{0} & \cdots & \mathbf{0} \\ \mathbf{0} & \mathbf{S}_{22}^{-1} & \mathbf{0} & \cdots & \mathbf{0} \\ \mathbf{0} & \mathbf{0} & \cdots & \cdots & \mathbf{0} \\ \cdot & \cdot & \cdot & \cdot & \cdot \\ \mathbf{0} & \mathbf{0} & \mathbf{0} & \cdots & \mathbf{S}_{nn}^{-1} \end{bmatrix} = \text{diag}\,[\mathbf{S}_{ii}^{-1}] \tag{1-31}$$

PROBLEMS

1-5. Compute the determinant of the matrix $\mathbf{D} = \mathbf{A} + \mathbf{B}$.

$$\mathbf{A} = \begin{bmatrix} 5 & -1 & 2 \\ -4 & -3 & 0 \\ 1 & 4 & 1 \end{bmatrix} \qquad \mathbf{B} = \begin{bmatrix} 0 & 1 & 2 \\ 3 & -1 & 4 \\ 5 & -7 & 2 \end{bmatrix}$$

1-6. Compute the determinant of $\mathbf{B} = 5\mathbf{A}$, where

$$\mathbf{A} = \begin{bmatrix} 2 & 1 \\ 3 & 4 \end{bmatrix}$$

1-7. Compute the product $\mathbf{D} = \mathbf{ABC}$, including row and column checks.

$$\mathbf{A} = \begin{bmatrix} 2 & 1 & 5 & 1 \\ -2 & 3 & 4 & -2 \end{bmatrix} \qquad \mathbf{B} = \begin{bmatrix} 0 & 1 & 5 \\ 5 & -4 & 2 \\ 1 & 0 & -3 \\ -1 & 3 & 1 \end{bmatrix} \qquad \mathbf{C} = \begin{bmatrix} 1 & 4 \\ 2 & -1 \\ -3 & 0 \end{bmatrix}$$

1-8. Form the only possible product **D** of the following matrices:

$$\mathbf{A} = {}^{3}\overset{4}{\mathbf{A}} \qquad \mathbf{B} = {}^{5}\overset{2}{\mathbf{B}} \qquad \mathbf{C} = {}^{4}\overset{5}{\mathbf{C}}$$

1-9. Compute the product $\mathbf{A} = \{-1 \quad 1 \quad 3 \quad -2\} \cdot [2 \quad -1 \quad 1 \quad 4]$. Show that the rank of this so-called dyadic product is 1.

1-10. A skew-symmetric matrix **A** is defined by the relation $\mathbf{A}' = -\mathbf{A}$. Show that

(*a*) **A** is a square matrix.

(*b*) The elements of the main diagonal of **A** vanish.
(*c*) $|\mathbf{A}| = 0$ if the order n of **A** is odd.

1-11. Using partitioned matrices, compute the matrix product **AB**, where

$$\mathbf{A} = \begin{bmatrix} -1 & 3 & 0 & 0 & 0 \\ 4 & 2 & 0 & 0 & 0 \\ 2 & -1 & 0 & 0 & 0 \\ 1 & 2 & 0 & 0 & 0 \\ 0 & 0 & 0 & 2 & 1 \\ 0 & 0 & 0 & 1 & -3 \end{bmatrix} \qquad \mathbf{B} = \begin{bmatrix} 4 & 2 & 1 & 0 & 0 \\ 2 & -1 & 3 & 0 & 0 \\ 1 & 2 & 4 & 0 & 0 \\ 0 & 0 & 0 & 1 & 2 \\ 0 & 0 & 0 & 3 & 4 \end{bmatrix}$$

1-12. Invert the following matrices:

$$\mathbf{A} = \begin{bmatrix} 3 & 1 \\ -2 & -4 \end{bmatrix} \qquad \mathbf{B} = \begin{bmatrix} 6 & -3 \\ -3 & 2 \end{bmatrix}$$

$$\mathbf{C} = \begin{bmatrix} 8 & -1 & 3 \\ 2 & 0 & 4 \\ 5 & 2 & 0 \end{bmatrix} \qquad \mathbf{D} = \begin{bmatrix} 1 & -4 & 0 & 0 & 0 \\ 2 & 3 & 0 & 0 & 0 \\ 0 & 0 & 7 & 2 & 0 \\ 0 & 0 & 0 & 1 & 4 \\ 0 & 0 & 1 & 3 & 0 \end{bmatrix}$$

1-13. Verify property I of the inverse matrix, using the examples of Prob. 1-12.

1-14. Verify property III of the inverse matrix, using the matrices **A** and **B** of Prob. 1-12.

1-15. Solve the matrix equation $\mathbf{Cx} = \mathbf{y}$ for **x**, using the inversion method. **C** is as given in Prob. 1-12, and

(*a*) $\mathbf{y} = \{1 \quad 0 \quad -3\}$ (*b*) $\mathbf{y} = \{-2 \quad 4 \quad 1\}$

1-4. The Eigenvalues of a Square Matrix

Characteristic Equation and Eigenvalues. Equations (1-13) are n simultaneous algebraic equations which can be represented by the equation

$$\mathbf{Ax} = \mathbf{y} \tag{1-13a}$$

where **A** is a square matrix of order n. If the column vector **y** is replaced by a multiple of the column vector **x**, then Eq. (1-13*a*) becomes

$$\mathbf{Ax} = \lambda\mathbf{x} \tag{1-32}$$

or, written in full,

$$\begin{aligned} a_{11}x_1 + a_{12}x_2 + \cdots + a_{1n}x_n &= \lambda x_1 \\ a_{21}x_1 + a_{22}x_2 + \cdots + a_{2n}x_n &= \lambda x_2 \\ \cdots\cdots\cdots\cdots\cdots\cdots \\ a_{n1}x_1 + a_{n2}x_2 + \cdots + a_{nn}x_n &= \lambda x_n \end{aligned} \tag{1-32a}$$

A nontrivial solution of these equations is possible if and only if (cf. Sec. 1-2)

$$\begin{vmatrix} a_{11} - \lambda & a_{12} & \cdots & a_{1n} \\ a_{21} & a_{22} - \lambda & \cdots & a_{2n} \\ \cdots & \cdots & \cdots & \cdots \\ a_{n1} & a_{n2} & \cdots & a_{nn} - \lambda \end{vmatrix} = 0 \qquad \text{or} \qquad |\mathbf{A} - \lambda\mathbf{I}| = 0 \tag{1-33}$$

When this determinant is expanded, we obtain an algebraic equation in λ of the form

$$\lambda^n + a_1\lambda^{n-1} + a_2\lambda^{n-2} + \cdots + a_n = 0 \tag{1-34}$$

which is known as the *characteristic equation of the matrix* **A**. The roots $\lambda_1, \lambda_2, \ldots, \lambda_n$ of the characteristic equation are known as the eigenvalues of the matrix **A**.

Example 1-8. Consider the equations

$$\begin{aligned} 4x_1 + x_2 &= \lambda x_1 \\ -3x_1 + 0x_2 &= \lambda x_2 \end{aligned}$$

These equations are represented by Eq. (1-32), where **A** is the matrix

$$\mathbf{A} = \begin{bmatrix} 4 & 1 \\ -3 & 0 \end{bmatrix}$$

The characteristic equation is given by the determinant

$$\begin{vmatrix} 4-\lambda & 1 \\ -3 & -\lambda \end{vmatrix} = 0$$

which on expansion yields

$$\lambda^2 - 4\lambda + 3 = 0$$

The roots (or the eigenvalues) of this equation are $\lambda_1 = 1$ and $\lambda_2 = 3$. When $\lambda = \lambda_1 = 1$, the original equations become

$$\begin{aligned} 3x_1 + x_2 &= 0 \\ -3x_1 - x_2 &= 0 \end{aligned}$$

Assuming $x_1 = 1$, we then find $x_2 = -3$ (cf. Sec. 1-2). When $\lambda = \lambda_2 = 3$, the equations become

$$\begin{aligned} x_1 + x_2 &= 0 \\ -3x_1 - 3x_2 &= 0 \end{aligned}$$

With $x_1 = 1$ we then find $x_2 = -1$. The vectors $\mathbf{x}_1 = \{1 \quad -3\}$ and $\mathbf{x}_2 = \{1 \quad -1\}$ are described as eigenvectors corresponding to the eigenvalues $\lambda_1 = 1$ and $\lambda_2 = 3$, respectively.

The eigenvalues fulfill two conditions that can serve as valuable checks:

(1)
$$\sum_{i=1}^{n} \lambda_i = \operatorname{tr} \mathbf{A} \tag{1-35}$$

where tr **A** is the trace of the matrix **A** which is defined as $\sum_{i=1}^{n} a_{ii}$. In the above numerical example we have

$$1 + 3 = 4 + 0$$

and the check is satisfied.

(2)
$$\prod_i \lambda_i = |\mathbf{A}| \tag{1-36}$$

where $\prod_i \lambda_i$ is the product of all eigenvalues. In the above numerical example we have

$$(1)(3) = (4)(0) - (-3)(1)$$

and the check is satisfied.

Real Symmetric Matrices. In view of the fact that real† symmetric matrices are of great practical importance in the field of vibrations, we shall investigate the properties of their eigenvalues and eigenvectors somewhat more deeply.

A most important property of the eigenvalues λ_i of a real symmetric matrix is

† The coefficients of the matrix are all real.

that they are always real [5], and an important property of the eigenvectors can be found by considering two different eigenvalues λ_i and λ_k of the matrix $\mathbf{A}$ together with their respective eigenvectors $\mathbf{x}_i$ and $\mathbf{x}_k$. Then we have

$$\mathbf{A}\mathbf{x}_i = \lambda_i \mathbf{x}_i \tag{1-37a}$$

$$\mathbf{A}\mathbf{x}_k = \lambda_k \mathbf{x}_k \tag{1-37b}$$

Now we premultiply Eq. (1-37*a*) by $\mathbf{x}_k'$ and Eq. (1-37*b*) by $\mathbf{x}_i'$ and subtract the second from the first:

$$\mathbf{x}_k'\mathbf{A}\mathbf{x}_i - \mathbf{x}_i'\mathbf{A}\mathbf{x}_k = \mathbf{x}_k'\lambda_i\mathbf{x}_i - \mathbf{x}_i'\lambda_k\mathbf{x}_k$$

With $\quad \mathbf{x}_k'\mathbf{A}\mathbf{x}_i = \mathbf{x}_i'\mathbf{A}\mathbf{x}_k \quad$ and $\quad \mathbf{x}_k'\mathbf{x}_i = \mathbf{x}_i'\mathbf{x}_k \quad$ cf. Eq. (1-24)

we have

$$(\lambda_i - \lambda_k)\mathbf{x}_i'\mathbf{x}_k = 0$$

which for $\lambda_i \neq \lambda_k$ yields the relation

$$\mathbf{x}_i'\mathbf{x}_k = 0 \tag{1-38}$$

Eigenvectors that satisfy Eq. (1-38) are said to be *orthogonal* to each other. The term *orthogonal* stems from a geometric interpretation. In two dimensions, for example, the two unit vectors

$$\mathbf{x}_1 = \{\cos\phi \quad \sin\phi\} \qquad \text{and} \qquad \mathbf{x}_2 = \{-\sin\phi \quad \cos\phi\}$$

are obviously orthogonal to each other (Fig. 1-1); the application of Eq. (1-38),

$$\begin{array}{r} \begin{bmatrix} \cos\phi \\ \sin\phi \end{bmatrix} \\ [-\sin\phi \quad \cos\phi][\quad 0 \quad] \end{array}$$

confirms this obvious statement. It is useful for theoretical considerations to normalize the eigenvectors so that

$$\mathbf{x}_i'\mathbf{x}_k = \begin{cases} 0 & \text{for} \quad i \neq k \\ 1 & \text{for} \quad i = k \end{cases} \tag{1-39}$$

For example, the normalized form of the vector $\{1 \quad -3\}$ is $\{1/\sqrt{10} \quad -3/\sqrt{10}\}$.

So far we assumed that all n eigenvalues of an (n, n) matrix are different from each other. It is clear that we can then also find n eigenvectors that satisfy Eq. (1-39). Sometimes, however, we meet symmetric matrices for which the number of different eigenvalues is smaller than n. For example, the matrix

$$\mathbf{A} = \begin{bmatrix} 40 & -8\sqrt{3} & 48 \\ -8\sqrt{3} & 24 & -16\sqrt{3} \\ 48 & -16\sqrt{3} & 112 \end{bmatrix}$$

possesses the eigenvalue $\lambda_1 = 144$ and the double eigenvalue $\lambda_2 = \lambda_3 = 16$. Whereas the eigenvector $\mathbf{x}_1$ is definitely found from the equations [cf. Eqs. (1-32*a*)]

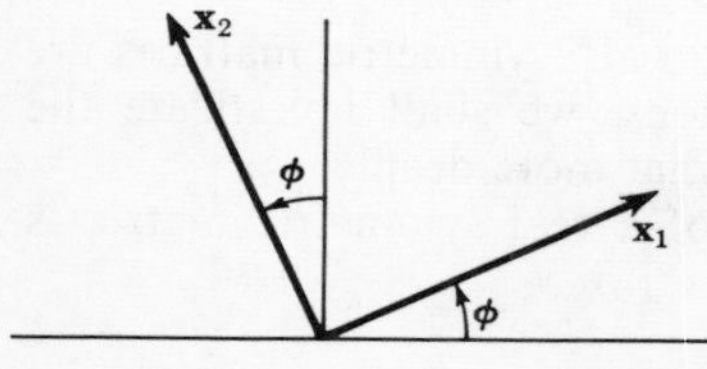

FIG. 1-1. Two orthogonal unit vectors.

$$\begin{aligned} 40x_1 - 8\sqrt{3}x_2 + 48x_3 &= 144x_1 \\ -8\sqrt{3}x_1 + 24x_2 - 16\sqrt{3}x_3 &= 144x_2 \\ 48x_1 - 16\sqrt{3}x_2 + 112x_3 &= 144x_3 \end{aligned}$$

to be in its normalized form,

$$\mathbf{x}_1 = \left\{\frac{\sqrt{3}}{4} \quad -\frac{1}{4} \quad \frac{\sqrt{3}}{2}\right\}$$

we find for $\lambda = 16$ only one linearly independent equation for x_1, x_2, and x_3:

$$24x_1 - 8\sqrt{3}x_2 + 48x_3 = 0 \tag{1-40}$$

Solving this equation for x_1, we obtain

$$x_1 = \frac{1}{\sqrt{3}}x_2 - 2x_3$$

With the choice $x_2 = \sqrt{3}$ and $x_3 = 0$ we obtain $x_1 = 1$; the choice $x_2 = 0$ and $x_3 = -\frac{1}{2}$ gives once more $x_1 = 1$.

Thus we have found, in quite arbitrary fashion, the two linearly independent eigenvectors

$$\mathbf{x}_2^* = \{1 \quad \sqrt{3} \quad 0\} \qquad \text{and} \qquad \mathbf{x}_3^* = \{1 \quad 0 \quad -\tfrac{1}{2}\}$$

Although they are not orthogonal to each other, because

$$\mathbf{x}_2^{*\prime}\mathbf{x}_3^* = 1 \neq 0$$

they are both orthogonal to $\mathbf{x}_1$. In this present three-dimensional example it is therefore apparent that $\mathbf{x}_2^*$ and $\mathbf{x}_3^*$ are in a plane perpendicular to $\mathbf{x}_1$. Any other vector found for $\lambda = 16$ would also lie in the same plane; for example, with $\mathbf{y} = \{-7 \quad \sqrt{3} \quad 4\}$, which also satisfies Eq. (1-40), we have

$$\mathbf{y}'\mathbf{x}_1 = 0$$

Let us now normalize $\mathbf{x}_2^*$ to obtain $\mathbf{x}_2 = \{\frac{1}{2} \quad \sqrt{3}/2 \quad 0\}$ and then find an eigenvector $\mathbf{x}_3$ which is orthogonal to $\mathbf{x}_2$ and $\mathbf{x}_1$. Let us define an eigenvector $\mathbf{y}_3$ normal to $\mathbf{x}_2$ which also lies in the plane of $\mathbf{x}_2$ and $\mathbf{x}_3^*$:

$$\mathbf{y}_3 = c_{23}\mathbf{x}_2 + \mathbf{x}_3^* \tag{1-41}$$

where c_{23} is a constant.

On premultiplying Eq. (1-41) by $\mathbf{x}_2'$, the left side becomes zero since by definition $\mathbf{y}_3$ is orthogonal to $\mathbf{x}_2$:

$$\mathbf{x}_2'\mathbf{y}_3 = 0 = \mathbf{x}_2'c_{23}\mathbf{x}_2 + \mathbf{x}_2'\mathbf{x}_3^*$$

Since $\mathbf{x}_2'\mathbf{x}_2 = 1$, we have

$$c_{23} = -\mathbf{x}_2'\mathbf{x}_3^* = -\tfrac{1}{2}$$

Therefore

$$\mathbf{y}_3 = -\frac{1}{2}\left\{\frac{1}{2} \quad \frac{\sqrt{3}}{2} \quad 0\right\} + \left\{1 \quad 0 \quad -\frac{1}{2}\right\} = \left\{\frac{3}{4} \quad -\frac{\sqrt{3}}{4} \quad -\frac{1}{2}\right\}$$

Normalization of $\mathbf{y}_3$ then shows that $\mathbf{y}_3'\mathbf{y}_3 = 1$, so that

$$\mathbf{x}_3 = \mathbf{y}_3 = \left\{\frac{3}{4} \quad -\frac{\sqrt{3}}{4} \quad -\frac{1}{2}\right\}$$

Hence three normalized vectors $\mathbf{x}_1$, $\mathbf{x}_2$, and $\mathbf{x}_3$ have been found which are orthogonal to each other.

In general, we can set up, for every p repeated eigenvalues λ, p arbitrary linearly independent eigenvectors $\mathbf{x}_1^*, \mathbf{x}_2^*, \ldots, \mathbf{x}_p^*$ from which we can, through linear combination, form p orthogonal eigenvectors.

First we normalize $\mathbf{x}_1^*$ to give $\mathbf{x}_1 = \mathbf{x}_1^*/|\mathbf{x}_1^*|$. Then we obtain

$$\mathbf{y}_2 = c_{12}\mathbf{x}_1 + \mathbf{x}_2^* \tag{1-42}$$

orthogonal to $\mathbf{x}_1$ by determining c_{12}, as shown above. Premultiplication of Eq. (1-42) by $\mathbf{x}_1'$ gives

$$\mathbf{x}_1'\mathbf{y}_2 = 0 = c_{12} + \mathbf{x}_1'\mathbf{x}_2^* \qquad \text{or} \qquad c_{12} = -\mathbf{x}_1'\mathbf{x}_2^*$$

Next, $\mathbf{y}_2$ is normalized to give $\mathbf{x}_2 = \mathbf{y}_2/|\mathbf{y}_2|$. Thereafter we set up $\mathbf{y}_3$ as an eigenvector normal to both $\mathbf{x}_1$ and $\mathbf{x}_2$ by linear combination of $\mathbf{x}_1$, $\mathbf{x}_2$, and $\mathbf{x}_3^*$:

$$\mathbf{y}_3 = c_{13}\mathbf{x}_1 + c_{23}\mathbf{x}_2 + \mathbf{x}_3^* \tag{1-43}$$

Equation (1-43) is premultiplied first by $\mathbf{x}_1'$ to yield

$$\mathbf{x}_1'\mathbf{y}_3 = 0 = c_{13} + \mathbf{x}_1'\mathbf{x}_3^* \qquad \text{or} \qquad c_{13} = -\mathbf{x}_1'\mathbf{x}_3^*$$

and then by $\mathbf{x}_2'$ to yield

$$\mathbf{x}_2'\mathbf{y}_3 = 0 = c_{23} + \mathbf{x}_2'\mathbf{x}_3^* \qquad \text{or} \qquad c_{23} = -\mathbf{x}_2'\mathbf{x}_3^*$$

Hereafter

$$\mathbf{x}_3 = \frac{\mathbf{y}_3}{|\mathbf{y}_3|}$$

Hence, in general,

$$\mathbf{y}_k = c_{1k}\mathbf{x}_1 + c_{2k}\mathbf{x}_2 + \cdots + c_{k-1,k}\mathbf{x}_{k-1} + \mathbf{x}_k^* \qquad k = 1, 2, \ldots, p \tag{1-44}$$

where

$$c_{ik} = -\mathbf{x}_i'\mathbf{x}_k^* \qquad i = 1, 2, \ldots, k-1 \tag{1-45}$$

and normalization yields

$$\mathbf{x}_k = \frac{\mathbf{y}_k}{|\mathbf{y}_k|}$$

The Cayley-Hamilton Theorem.† This theorem states that a matrix satisfies its own characteristic equation. If the characteristic equation is

$$\lambda^n + a_1\lambda^{n-1} + \cdots + a_{n-1}\lambda + a_n = 0$$

then

$$\mathbf{A}^n + a_1\mathbf{A}^{n-1} + \cdots + a_{n-1}\mathbf{A} + a_n\mathbf{I} = \mathbf{0} \tag{1-46}$$

Previously we found that the characteristic equation of the matrix $\mathbf{A} = \begin{bmatrix} 4 & 1 \\ -3 & 0 \end{bmatrix}$ is

$$\lambda^2 - 4\lambda + 3 = 0$$

Now $\mathbf{A}^2 = \begin{bmatrix} 13 & 4 \\ -12 & -3 \end{bmatrix}$, so that, according to Eq. (1-46),

$$\mathbf{A}^2 - 4\mathbf{A} + 3\mathbf{I} = \begin{bmatrix} 13 & 4 \\ -12 & -3 \end{bmatrix} - \begin{bmatrix} 16 & 4 \\ -12 & 0 \end{bmatrix} + \begin{bmatrix} 3 & 0 \\ 0 & 3 \end{bmatrix} = \begin{bmatrix} 0 & 0 \\ 0 & 0 \end{bmatrix} = \mathbf{0}$$

A function $f(\mathbf{A})$ of an (n, n) matrix $\mathbf{A}$ can be replaced by a polynomial $P(\mathbf{A})$ in $\mathbf{A}$ of order $n - 1$:

$$f(\mathbf{A}) = P(\mathbf{A}) = c_0\mathbf{I} + c_1\mathbf{A} + c_2\mathbf{A}^2 + \cdots + c_{n-1}\mathbf{A}^{n-1} \tag{1-47}$$

The constants $c_0, c_1, \ldots, c_{n-1}$ can be determined by using the fact that the eigenvalues λ_i of $\mathbf{A}$ also satisfy Eq. (1-47); that is,

$$f(\lambda_i) = c_0 + c_1\lambda_i + c_2\lambda_i^2 + \cdots + c_{n-1}\lambda_i^{n-1} = P(\lambda_i) \tag{1-48}‡$$

If there are n distinct eigenvalues λ_i of $\mathbf{A}$, then we have n equations (1-48) which can be solved for the constants c_i.

† For proof of this theorem see, for example, Ref. 5.

‡ The function f must be defined for all n eigenvalues λ_i of the matrix $\mathbf{A}$.

Example 1-9. Compute the value of sin **A** when $\mathbf{A} = \begin{bmatrix} 5 & 4 \\ 1 & 2 \end{bmatrix}$.

Since **A** is a square matrix of second order, sin **A** can be replaced by a polynomial of first degree, so that

$$\sin \mathbf{A} = c_0\mathbf{I} + c_1\mathbf{A}$$

The eigenvalues of **A** are $\lambda_1 = 1$ and $\lambda_2 = 6$; hence Eq. (1-48) yields the following two equations for the unknown coefficients c_0 and c_1:

$$\sin 1 = c_0 + c_1$$

$$\sin 6 = c_0 + 6c_1$$

From these two equations we obtain

$$c_0 = \frac{6 \sin 1 - \sin 6}{5} = 1.0657 \qquad c_1 = \frac{\sin 6 - \sin 1}{5} = -0.2242$$

Therefore $\quad \sin \mathbf{A} = 1.0657\begin{bmatrix} 1 & 0 \\ 0 & 1 \end{bmatrix} - 0.2242\begin{bmatrix} 5 & 4 \\ 1 & 2 \end{bmatrix} = \begin{bmatrix} -0.0553 & -0.8968 \\ -0.2242 & 0.6173 \end{bmatrix}$

When λ_j is a multiple eigenvalue, that is, $\lambda_j = \lambda_{j+1} = \cdots = \lambda_{j+m}$ $(m < n)$, we lack m equations of the type of Eq. (1-48). The missing m equations are found by satisfying the requirement that $f(\lambda)$ and the polynomial $P(\lambda)$ possess the same first m derivatives for the eigenvalue $\lambda = \lambda_j$. Hence we have for $\lambda = \lambda_j$, in addition to the equation

$$P(\lambda_j) = c_0 + c_1\lambda_j + \cdots + c_{n-1}\lambda_j^{n-1} = f(\lambda_j)$$

also the following m equations:

$$\begin{aligned} \left(\frac{dP}{d\lambda}\right)_{\lambda=\lambda_j} &= c_1 + \cdots + (n-1)c_{n-1}\lambda_j^{n-2} = \left(\frac{df}{d\lambda}\right)_{\lambda=\lambda_j} \\ &\cdots\cdots\cdots\cdots\cdots\cdots \\ \left(\frac{d^mP}{d\lambda^m}\right)_{\lambda=\lambda_j} &= c_m + \cdots + (n-m)\cdots(n-1)c_{n-1}\lambda_j^{n-m-1} = \left(\frac{d^mf}{d\lambda^m}\right)_{\lambda=\lambda_j} \end{aligned} \tag{1-49}$$

Example 1-10. Compute $e^{\mathbf{A}}$, where

$$\mathbf{A} = \begin{bmatrix} 0 & 1 & 0 & 0 \\ 0 & 0 & 2 & 0 \\ 0 & 0 & 0 & 1 \\ 0 & 0 & 0 & 0 \end{bmatrix}$$

The characteristic equation has the quadruple root $\lambda_i = 0$ $(i = 1, 2, 3, 4)$. The substitute polynomial is

$$e^{\mathbf{A}} = c_0\mathbf{I} + c_1\mathbf{A} + c_2\mathbf{A}^2 + c_3\mathbf{A}^3$$

and from Eqs. (1-48) and (1-49) we obtain, since $de^\lambda/d\lambda = e^\lambda$,

$$\begin{aligned} e^{\lambda i} &= c_0 + c_1\lambda_i + c_2\lambda_i^2 + c_3\lambda_i^3 \\ e^{\lambda i} &= c_1 + 2c_2\lambda_i + 3c_3\lambda_i^2 \\ e^{\lambda i} &= 2c_2 + 3 \times 2c_3\lambda_i \\ e^{\lambda i} &= 6c_3 \end{aligned}$$

Substituting $\lambda_i = 0$ in these equations gives

$$c_0 = 1 \qquad c_1 = 1 \qquad c_2 = \tfrac{1}{2} \qquad c_3 = \tfrac{1}{6}$$

Hence
$$e^{\mathbf{A}} = \mathbf{I} + \mathbf{A} + \tfrac{1}{2}\mathbf{A}^2 + \tfrac{1}{6}\mathbf{A}^3$$

Now
$$\mathbf{A}^2 = \begin{bmatrix} 0 & 0 & 2 & 0 \\ 0 & 0 & 0 & 2 \\ 0 & 0 & 0 & 0 \\ 0 & 0 & 0 & 0 \end{bmatrix} \qquad \mathbf{A}^3 = \begin{bmatrix} 0 & 0 & 0 & 2 \\ 0 & 0 & 0 & 0 \\ 0 & 0 & 0 & 0 \\ 0 & 0 & 0 & 0 \end{bmatrix}$$

so that
$$e^{\mathbf{A}} = \begin{bmatrix} 1 & 0 & 0 & 0 \\ 0 & 1 & 0 & 0 \\ 0 & 0 & 1 & 0 \\ 0 & 0 & 0 & 1 \end{bmatrix} + \begin{bmatrix} 0 & 1 & 0 & 0 \\ 0 & 0 & 2 & 0 \\ 0 & 0 & 0 & 1 \\ 0 & 0 & 0 & 0 \end{bmatrix} + \tfrac{1}{2}\begin{bmatrix} 0 & 0 & 2 & 0 \\ 0 & 0 & 0 & 2 \\ 0 & 0 & 0 & 0 \\ 0 & 0 & 0 & 0 \end{bmatrix} + \tfrac{1}{6}\begin{bmatrix} 0 & 0 & 0 & 2 \\ 0 & 0 & 0 & 0 \\ 0 & 0 & 0 & 0 \\ 0 & 0 & 0 & 0 \end{bmatrix}$$
$$= \begin{bmatrix} 1 & 1 & 1 & \tfrac{1}{3} \\ 0 & 1 & 2 & 1 \\ 0 & 0 & 1 & 1 \\ 0 & 0 & 0 & 1 \end{bmatrix}$$

PROBLEMS

1-16. Set up and solve the characteristic equation for the following eigenvalue problems and determine the eigenvectors:

(*a*) $\begin{bmatrix} 3 & -4 \\ -1 & 3 \end{bmatrix} \cdot \begin{bmatrix} x_1 \\ x_2 \end{bmatrix} = \lambda \begin{bmatrix} x_1 \\ x_2 \end{bmatrix}$ (*b*) $\begin{bmatrix} 1 & 3 \\ 1 & -1 \end{bmatrix} \cdot \begin{bmatrix} x_1 \\ x_2 \end{bmatrix} = \lambda \begin{bmatrix} x_1 \\ x_2 \end{bmatrix}$

(*c*)
$$\begin{aligned} x_1 + 3x_2 - 2x_3 &= \lambda x_1 \\ -x_1 + 2x_2 + x_3 &= \lambda x_2 \\ 3x_2 - x_3 &= \lambda x_3 \end{aligned}$$

1-17. Determine the eigenvalues and normalized eigenvectors for the symmetric matrix

$$\begin{bmatrix} 1 & 0 & 2\sqrt{2} \\ 0 & 1 & 2 \\ 2\sqrt{2} & 2 & 3 \end{bmatrix}$$

Check the orthogonality relation. Check eigenvalues by Eqs. (1-35) and (1-36).

1-18. For the matrix (cf. page 20)

$$\mathbf{A} = \begin{bmatrix} 40 & -8\sqrt{3} & 48 \\ -8\sqrt{3} & 24 & -16\sqrt{3} \\ 48 & -16\sqrt{3} & 112 \end{bmatrix}$$

with the eigenvalues $\lambda_1 = 144$ and $\lambda_2 = \lambda_3 = 16$, find the normalized eigenvectors $\mathbf{x}_2$ and $\mathbf{x}_3$ starting with $\mathbf{x}_2^* = \{-1 \quad \sqrt{3} \quad 1\}$.

1-19. Verify the Cayley-Hamilton theorem for the matrices in Prob. 1-16.

1-20. Compute the matrices $e^{\mathbf{A}}$, cos **A**, cosh **A**, and sinh **A** for

$$\mathbf{A} = \begin{bmatrix} 1 & 3 & -2 \\ -1 & 2 & 1 \\ 0 & 3 & -1 \end{bmatrix}$$

1-5. Differential Equations

Differentiation and Integration with Respect to a Parameter. If the elements a_{ik} of a matrix **A** are functions of a parameter t, we define

$$\frac{d\mathbf{A}}{dt} = \dot{\mathbf{A}} = \begin{bmatrix} \frac{da_{11}}{dt} & \frac{da_{12}}{dt} & \cdots & \frac{da_{1n}}{dt} \\ \frac{da_{21}}{dt} & \frac{da_{22}}{dt} & \cdots & \frac{da_{2n}}{dt} \\ \cdot & \cdot & \cdot & \cdot \\ \frac{da_{n1}}{dt} & \frac{da_{n2}}{dt} & \cdots & \frac{da_{nn}}{dt} \end{bmatrix} \tag{1-50}$$

Likewise
$$\frac{d\mathbf{x}}{dt} = \dot{\mathbf{x}} = \left\{\frac{dx_1}{dt} \quad \frac{dx_2}{dt} \quad \cdots \quad \frac{dx_n}{dt}\right\} \tag{1-51}$$

In an analogous manner we define the integration of **A** with respect to t as

$$\int \mathbf{A}\,dt = \begin{bmatrix} \int a_{11}\,dt & \int a_{12}\,dt & \cdots & \int a_{1n}\,dt \\ \int a_{21}\,dt & \int a_{22}\,dt & \cdots & \int a_{2n}\,dt \\ \cdot & \cdot & \cdot & \cdot \\ \int a_{n1}\,dt & \int a_{n2}\,dt & \cdots & \int a_{nn}\,dt \end{bmatrix} \tag{1-52}$$

Linear Homogeneous First-order Equations with Constant Coefficients. The homogeneous system of first-order differential equations

$$\begin{aligned} \dot{x}_1 &= a_{11}x_1 + \cdots + a_{1n}x_n \\ &\cdots\cdots\cdots \\ \dot{x}_n &= a_{n1}x_1 + \cdots + a_{nn}x_n \end{aligned} \tag{1-53}$$

can, in accordance with Eqs. (1-1*a*) and (1-51), be written in matrix notation as

$$\dot{\mathbf{x}} = \mathbf{A}\mathbf{x} \tag{1-54}$$

If the initial conditions are given by the vector $\mathbf{x}_0$, the solution is

$$\mathbf{x} = e^{\mathbf{A}t}\mathbf{x}_0 \tag{1-55}$$

which is analogous to the solution $x = x_0e^{at}$ of the single differential equation $\dot{x} = ax$ with the initial value x_0.

Example 1-11. $\dot{x}_1 = x_2$, $\dot{x}_2 = 2x_3$, $\dot{x}_3 = x_4$, and $\dot{x}_4 = 0$, with the initial conditions $x_{10} = 0$, $x_{20} = 1$, $x_{30} = -1$, and $x_{40} = 1$. That is,

$$\dot{\mathbf{x}} = \mathbf{A}\mathbf{x} \qquad \text{with } \mathbf{A} = \begin{bmatrix} 0 & 1 & 0 & 0 \\ 0 & 0 & 2 & 0 \\ 0 & 0 & 0 & 1 \\ 0 & 0 & 0 & 0 \end{bmatrix} \text{ and } \mathbf{x} = \{x_1 \quad x_2 \quad x_3 \quad x_4\}$$

Furthermore
$$\mathbf{x}_0 = \{0 \quad 1 \quad -1 \quad 1\}$$

According to Eq. (1-55) we have

$$\mathbf{x} = e^{\mathbf{A}t}\mathbf{x}_0$$

Since the matrix **A** is taken from Example 1-10, we recognize easily that $e^{\mathbf{A}t}$ can be represented by the substitute polynomial

$$e^{\mathbf{A}t} = \mathbf{I} + \mathbf{A}t + \tfrac{1}{2}(\mathbf{A}t)^2 + \tfrac{1}{6}(\mathbf{A}t)^3 \tag{1-56}$$

Using the results found before, we obtain

$$e^{\mathbf{A}t} = \begin{bmatrix} 1 & t & t^2 & \frac{t^3}{3} \\ 0 & 1 & 2t & t^2 \\ 0 & 0 & 1 & t \\ 0 & 0 & 0 & 1 \end{bmatrix}$$

Hence, according to Eq. (1-55),

$$\begin{bmatrix} x_1 \\ x_2 \\ x_3 \\ x_4 \end{bmatrix} = \begin{bmatrix} 1 & t & t^2 & \frac{t^3}{3} \\ 0 & 1 & 2t & t^2 \\ 0 & 0 & 1 & t \\ 0 & 0 & 0 & 1 \end{bmatrix} \cdot \begin{bmatrix} 0 \\ 1 \\ -1 \\ 1 \end{bmatrix} = \begin{bmatrix} t - t^2 + \frac{t^3}{3} \\ 1 - 2t + t^2 \\ -1 + t \\ 1 \end{bmatrix}$$

or $\quad x_1 = t - t^2 + \dfrac{t^3}{3} \qquad x_2 = 1 - 2t + t^2 \qquad x_3 = -1 + t \qquad x_4 = 1$

Nonhomogeneous System of First-order Equations. In this case we consider the following system of differential equations:

$$\dot{x}_1 = a_{11}x_1 + \cdots + a_{1n}x_n + a_1(t)$$
$$\cdots\cdots\cdots\cdots\cdots$$
$$\dot{x}_n = a_{n1}x_1 + \cdots + a_{nn}x_n + a_n(t)$$

or $\quad \dot{\mathbf{x}} = \mathbf{A}\mathbf{x} + \mathbf{a}(t) \qquad \text{where } \mathbf{a}(t) = \{a_1(t) \quad \cdots \quad a_n(t)\} \qquad$ (1-57)

The solution† of Eq. (1-57) is

$$\mathbf{x}(t) = e^{\mathbf{A}t}\mathbf{x}_0 + e^{\mathbf{A}t}\int_0^t e^{-\mathbf{A}\tau}\,\mathbf{a}(\tau)\,d\tau \tag{1-58}$$

Example 1-12. $\dot{x}_1 = x_2 + t$, $\dot{x}_2 = 2x_3$, $\dot{x}_3 = x_4$, and $\dot{x}_4 = t^2$, with the initial conditions $x_{10} = x_{20} = x_{30} = x_{40} = 0$. Here again

$$\mathbf{A} = \begin{bmatrix} 0 & 1 & 0 & 0 \\ 0 & 0 & 2 & 0 \\ 0 & 0 & 0 & 1 \\ 0 & 0 & 0 & 0 \end{bmatrix} \qquad \text{and} \qquad \mathbf{a}(t) = \{t \quad 0 \quad 0 \quad t^2\}$$

From Eq. (1-56) we deduce immediately, that

$$e^{-\mathbf{A}t} = \mathbf{I} - \mathbf{A}t + \tfrac{1}{2}(\mathbf{A}t)^2 - \tfrac{1}{6}(\mathbf{A}t)^3$$

† This solution is analogous to the solution $x(t) = x_0e^{at} + e^{at}\int_0^t e^{-a\tau} f(\tau)\,d\tau$ for the first-order nonhomogeneous differential equation $\dot{x} = ax + f(t)$.

Hence
$$e^{-\mathbf{A}\tau}\mathbf{a}(\tau) = \begin{bmatrix} 1 & -\tau & \tau^2 & -\dfrac{\tau^3}{3} \\ 0 & 1 & -2\tau & \tau^2 \\ 0 & 0 & 1 & -\tau \\ 0 & 0 & 0 & 1 \end{bmatrix} \cdot \begin{bmatrix} \tau \\ 0 \\ 0 \\ \tau^2 \end{bmatrix} = \begin{bmatrix} \tau - \dfrac{\tau^5}{3} \\ \tau^4 \\ -\tau^3 \\ \tau^2 \end{bmatrix}$$

and thus
$$\int_0^t e^{-\mathbf{A}\tau}\mathbf{a}(\tau)\, d\tau = \begin{bmatrix} \dfrac{t^2}{2} - \dfrac{t^6}{18} \\ \dfrac{t^5}{5} \\ -\dfrac{t^4}{4} \\ \dfrac{t^3}{3} \end{bmatrix}$$

With $\mathbf{x}_0 = \mathbf{0}$, Eq. (1-58) yields
$$\begin{bmatrix} x_1 \\ x_2 \\ x_3 \\ x_4 \end{bmatrix} = \begin{bmatrix} 1 & t & t^2 & \dfrac{t^3}{3} \\ 0 & 1 & 2t & t^2 \\ 0 & 0 & 1 & t \\ 0 & 0 & 0 & 1 \end{bmatrix} \cdot \begin{bmatrix} \dfrac{t^2}{2} - \dfrac{t^6}{18} \\ \dfrac{t^5}{5} \\ -\dfrac{t^4}{4} \\ \dfrac{t^3}{3} \end{bmatrix} = \begin{bmatrix} \dfrac{t^2}{2} + \dfrac{t^6}{180} \\ \dfrac{t^5}{30} \\ \dfrac{t^4}{12} \\ \dfrac{t^3}{3} \end{bmatrix}$$

PROBLEMS

1-21. Solve the homogeneous system of differential equations $\dot{\mathbf{x}} = \mathbf{A}\mathbf{x}$ with $\mathbf{x} = \{x_1 \quad x_2 \quad x_3\}$ and
$$\mathbf{A} = \begin{bmatrix} -2 & 2 & -3 \\ 2 & 1 & -6 \\ -1 & -2 & 0 \end{bmatrix}$$
for the initial values $\mathbf{x}_0 = \{8 \quad 0 \quad 0\}$.

1-22. Solve the homogeneous system of differential equations $\dot{\mathbf{x}} = \mathbf{A}\mathbf{x}$ with $\mathbf{x} = \{x_1 \quad x_2\}$ and $\mathbf{A} = \begin{bmatrix} 5 & 4 \\ 1 & 2 \end{bmatrix}$ for the initial values $\mathbf{x}_0 = \{1 \quad -1\}$.

1-23. Solve the nonhomogeneous case of Prob. 1-21 with the disturbing function $\mathbf{a}(t) = \{3 \sin \Omega t \quad 0 \quad 0\}$ for the same initial values.

1-24. Solve the nonhomogeneous case of Prob. 1-22 with $\mathbf{a}(t) = \{5e^t \quad 0\}$ for the initial values $\mathbf{x}_0 = \{-1 \quad 0\}$.

2 INTRODUCTION TO THE THEORY OF UNDAMPED MECHANICAL VIBRATIONS†

2-1. The Free Vibration of a System with One Degree of Freedom

Solution of the Differential Equation. Natural Frequency, Initial Conditions. The spring-mass system of Fig. 2-1, consisting of a mass m and a massless spring of stiffness k, is in equilibrium under the action of a constant force P. Let us now suppose that the mass is displaced from its equilibrium position and then released so that it begins to vibrate. On account of the frictionless guide the position of the mass at any time is fully described by the magnitude of the displacement x from the equilibrium position. Since the position of the mass can be described by one coordinate, the system is said to possess a single degree of freedom. The positive directions of velocity $\dot{x}$ and acceleration $\ddot{x}$ coincide with the positive direction of the displacement x, as shown in Fig. 2-1.

The equation of motion is derived by applying Newton's second law. Since the deflection of the free end of the spring is x and the spring has stiffness k, the force in the spring is $F_s = P + kx$ (Fig. 2-2). The force exerted by the spring on the

† For a thorough treatment of this topic, see, for example, Refs. 6 and 7.

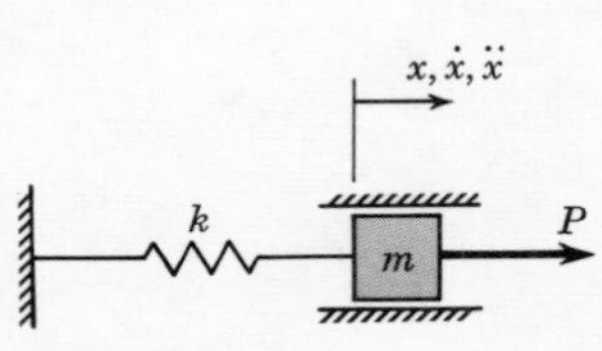

FIG. 2-1. Spring-mass system.

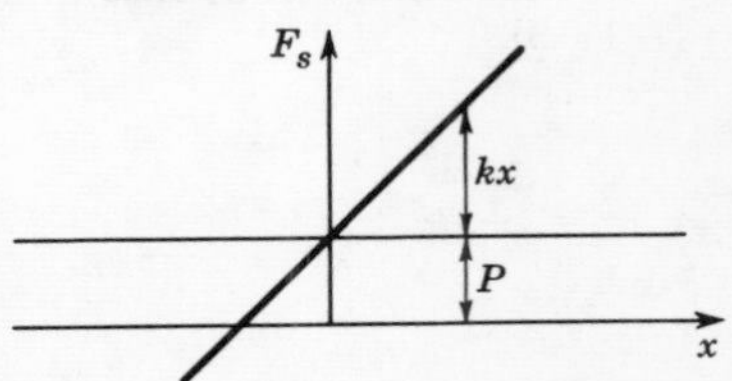

FIG. 2-2. Spring characteristic.

FIG. 2-3. Free-body diagram of vibrating mass.

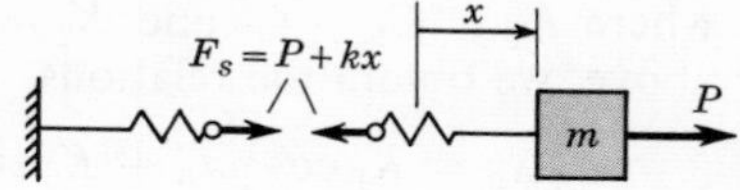

mass is in the opposite direction to the displacement x and the constant force P (Fig. 2-3). Hence the equation of motion is

$$P + [-(P + kx)] = m\ddot{x} \qquad \text{or} \qquad m\ddot{x} + kx = 0 \tag{2-1}$$

We notice that in this case a constant force, such as the weight, will not influence the motion of the mass except that it determines the equilibrium position.

Equation (2-1) can also be formulated from the viewpoint of D'Alembert's principle (Fig. 2-4). The equation of motion is replaced by an equilibrium equation involving, besides the external force P and the force exerted by the deflected spring, the inertia force defined as the negative product of the mass times its linear acceleration. If we take the inertia force as an external force, we are in fact considering a massless† system, consisting of a spring of stiffness k, the free end of which is subjected to the "external" forces P and $-m\ddot{x}$. The free-body diagram is shown in Fig. 2-4. The forces are in equilibrium if

$$P + [-(P + kx)] + (-m\ddot{x}) = 0 \qquad \text{or} \qquad -m\ddot{x} - kx = 0 \tag{2-2}$$

which is, of course, equivalent to Eq. (2-1). We shall appreciate later the advantage of using D'Alembert's principle when setting up the equations for complicated problems.

The differential equation (2-1) is a homogeneous linear differential equation of second order with constant coefficients. Its solution is found by substituting into Eq. (2-1) the expression

$$x = Ce^{\lambda t} \tag{2-3}$$

where C and λ are constants. Hereby we obtain the so-called characteristic equation

$$mC\lambda^2 e^{\lambda t} + kCe^{\lambda t} = 0 \qquad \text{or} \qquad m\lambda^2 + k = 0 \tag{2-4}$$

Equation (2-4) yields

$$\lambda_{1,2} = \pm\sqrt{-\frac{k}{m}} = \pm j\sqrt{\frac{k}{m}} = \pm j\omega \qquad \text{with } j = \sqrt{-1}$$

Then

$$x = C_1 e^{j\omega t} + C_2 e^{-j\omega t} \tag{2-5}$$

is the solution of Eq. (2-1), where C_1 and C_2 are constants to be determined from the initial conditions $x(t = t_0) = x_0$ and $\dot{x}(t = t_0) = \dot{x}_0$. Using Euler's relation

$$e^{\pm j\alpha} = \cos\alpha \pm j\sin\alpha \tag{2-6}$$

we can rewrite Eq. (2-5) in the form

$$x = K_1\cos\omega t + K_2\sin\omega t \tag{2-7}$$

† In the illustrations, bodies with mass are shaded; in contrast, massless bodies are left blank.

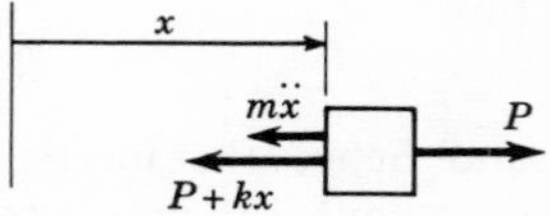

FIG. 2-4. Free-body diagram of vibrating mass using D'Alembert's principle.

where $K_1 = C_1 + C_2$ and $K_2 = j(C_1 - C_2)$. Applying the initial conditions stated above, we obtain the relations

$$x_0 = K_1 \cos \omega t_0 + K_2 \sin \omega t_0 \qquad \dot{x}_0 = -\omega(K_1 \sin \omega t_0 - K_2 \cos \omega t_0)$$

which are then solved for K_1 and K_2 to give

$$K_1 = x_0 \cos \omega t_0 - \frac{\dot{x}_0}{\omega} \sin \omega t_0 \qquad K_2 = x_0 \sin \omega t_0 + \frac{\dot{x}_0}{\omega} \cos \omega t_0$$

Hence for $t \geq t_0$, with the initial conditions as stated, Eq. (2-7) becomes

$$x(t) = \left(x_0 \cos \omega t_0 - \frac{\dot{x}_0}{\omega} \sin \omega t_0\right) \cos \omega t + \left(x_0 \sin \omega t_0 + \frac{\dot{x}_0}{\omega} \cos \omega t_0\right) \sin \omega t$$

or, after some simple rearranging,

$$x(t) = x_0 \cos \omega(t - t_0) + \frac{\dot{x}_0}{\omega} \sin \omega(t - t_0) \tag{2-8a}$$

and

$$\dot{x}(t) = -\omega x_0 \sin \omega(t - t_0) + \dot{x}_0 \cos \omega(t - t_0) \tag{2-8b}$$

These equations may also be written in the form

$$x(t) = A \sin [\omega(t - t_0) + \phi] \tag{2-9a}$$

$$\dot{x}(t) = \omega A \cos [\omega(t - t_0) + \phi] \tag{2-9b}$$

where the amplitude is

$$A = \left[x_0^2 + \left(\frac{\dot{x}_0}{\omega}\right)^2\right]^{\frac{1}{2}} \tag{2-9c}$$

and the phase angle is

$$\phi = \tan^{-1} \frac{x_0 \omega}{\dot{x}_0} \tag{2-9d}$$

This type of motion is described as being harmonic. The displacement and velocity at any moment of time are repeated after the *period of vibration*

$$T = \frac{2\pi}{\omega} \tag{2-10a}$$

has elapsed. Here $\omega = \sqrt{k/m}$ has the dimension $(\text{time})^{-1}$ and is called the *natural circular frequency*. It is related to the natural frequency f by

$$f = \frac{\omega}{2\pi} = \frac{1}{T} \tag{2-10b}$$

Figure 2-5*a* and *b* show the displacement/time graph for the mass when it has the initial conditions of positive displacement and positive velocity.

The Equation of Motion in Algebraic Form. Having found the solution of the differential equation of motion, we can deduce a property of the motion which enables us to set up the equation of motion in algebraic form. If we differentiate Eq. (2-9*b*) once more with respect to time, we obtain the expression for the acceleration:

$$\ddot{x}(t) = -A\omega^2 \sin [\omega(t - t_0) + \phi] = -\omega^2 x$$

and hence the inertia force $-m\ddot{x}$ (Fig. 2-4) becomes $m\omega^2 x$. A new free-body diagram for the mass can be drawn (Fig. 2-6), where the inertia force is now $+m\omega^2 x$. Equilibrium of forces exists if [cf. Eq. (2-2)]

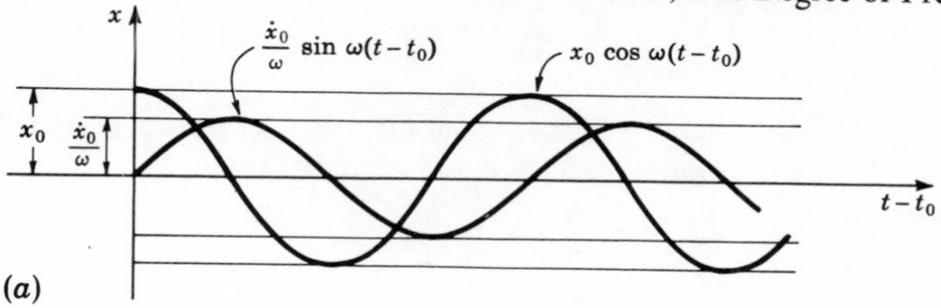

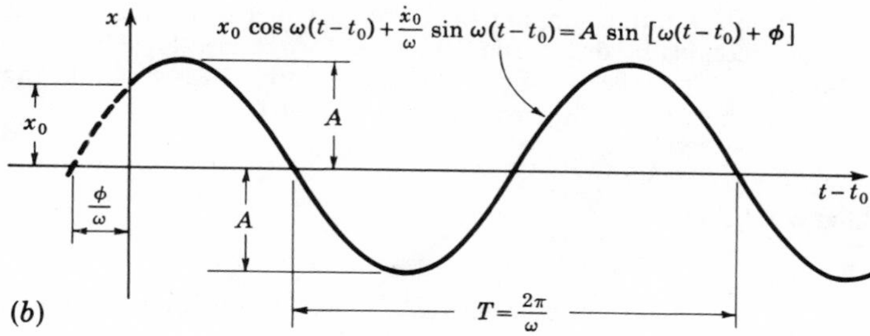

FIG. 2-5. Periodic motion of mass m after initial conditions x_0, $\dot{x}_0 > 0$ at t_0.

$$m\omega^2 x - kx = 0 \tag{2-11}$$

from which we obtain the natural circular frequency

$$\omega = \sqrt{\frac{k}{m}}$$

Hence we see that in a harmonically vibrating system the inertia force can be represented by the positive product of the mass times the square of the circular frequency times the displacement. It is left to the reader to show that this property is also valid for moments when the following correspondence is used:

Mass ↔ moment of inertia

Linear displacement ↔ angular displacement

Inertia force ↔ inertia torque

Example 2-1. We shall use these results to obtain the natural frequency of the system illustrated in Fig. 2-7. The external forces acting on the roller are the reactions F and N at the point of contact C with the ground, its weight W, and the restoring spring force kx

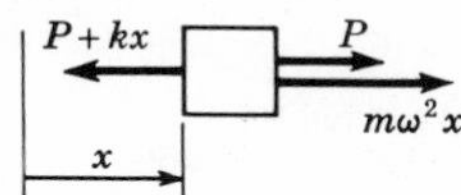

FIG. 2-6. Free-body diagram of vibrating mass using D'Alembert's principle.

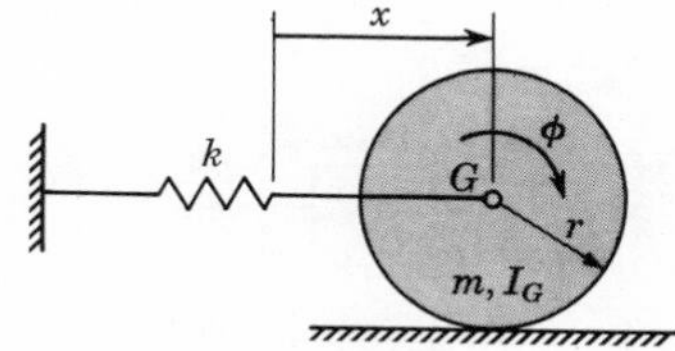

FIG. 2-7. Roller restrained by spring.

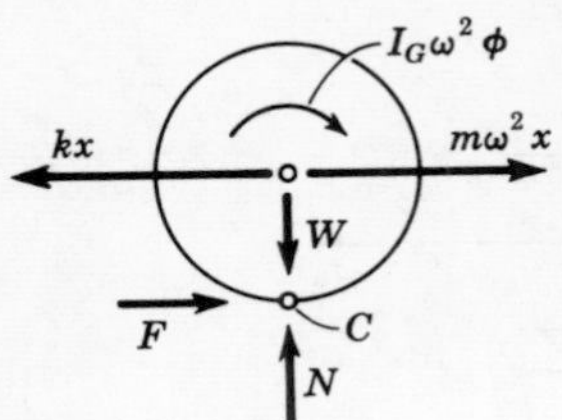

FIG. 2-8. Free-body diagram of Fig. 2-7 using D'Alembert's principle.

(Fig. 2-8). Additionally, the inertia force acting at the center of gravity of the roller is $m\omega^2 x$, and the inertia torque is $I_G\omega^2\phi$, where ϕ is the angle turned through by the disk. Since the roller is to roll without slipping ($x = r\phi$), the inertia torque becomes $I_G\omega^2 x/r$. Note again that the directions of the inertia force and torque are the same as those of the displacements x and ϕ. From the free-body diagram of Fig. 2-8 we obtain the following equation by taking moments about the instantaneous center C:

$$(-kx + m\omega^2 x)r + I_G\omega^2\phi = 0$$

or with the rolling condition $x = r\phi$,

$$\omega^2(I_G + mr^2)x - kr^2 x = 0$$

Thus $\omega = \sqrt{kr^2/(I_G + mr^2)}$. For the case where $I_G = mr^2/2$ (solid cylindrical homogeneous roller), $\omega = \sqrt{2k/3m}$.

With initial conditions x_0 and $\dot{x}_0$ we then obtain from Eqs. (2-8), for $t_0 = 0$,

$$x(t) = x_0 \cos\left(\sqrt{\frac{2k}{3m}}\,t\right) + \frac{\dot{x}_0}{\sqrt{2k/3m}} \sin\left(\sqrt{\frac{2k}{3m}}\,t\right)$$

and $\phi(t) = x(t)/r$.

2-2. Forced Vibration of a System with One Degree of Freedom

We now subject the simple spring-mass system of Fig. 2-9 to a time-varying force $p(t)$. The displacement of the mass is measured from its undeflected position. With reference to the free-body diagram of the mass (Fig. 2-10) we obtain the following nonhomogeneous linear differential equation of second order with constant coefficients:

$$m\ddot{x} + kx = p(t) \tag{2-12}$$

The Effect of an Impulse. A simple case, which can be dealt with by the use of solution (2-8), occurs when at time t_0 a sudden impulse G is applied to mass m in its equilibrium position $x(t_0) = 0$. On account of the impulse G the mass m assumes at time t_0 the initial velocity $\dot{x}_0 = G/m$, and x_0 is zero. Equation (2-8*a*) therefore immediately yields the following result for the motion of mass m:

$$x(t) = \frac{\dot{x}_0}{\omega} \sin\omega(t - t_0) = \frac{G}{m\omega} \sin\omega(t - t_0) \qquad \text{for } t \geq t_0 \tag{2-13}$$

General Case of a Time-varying Force. Equation (2-13) paves the way for finding the effect of a time-varying force $p(t)$ such as is illustrated in Fig. 2-11. Let us first

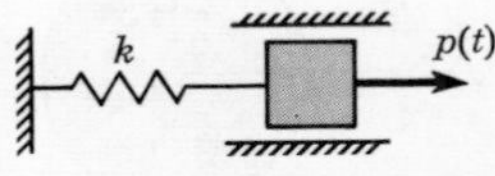

FIG. 2-9. Spring-mass system subjected to time-varying force.

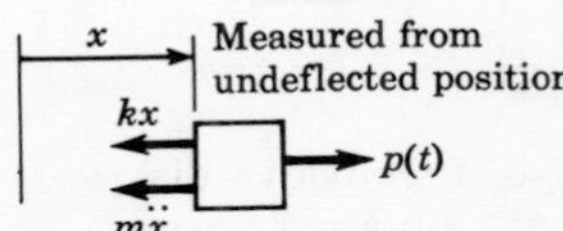

FIG. 2-10. Free-body diagram of mass.

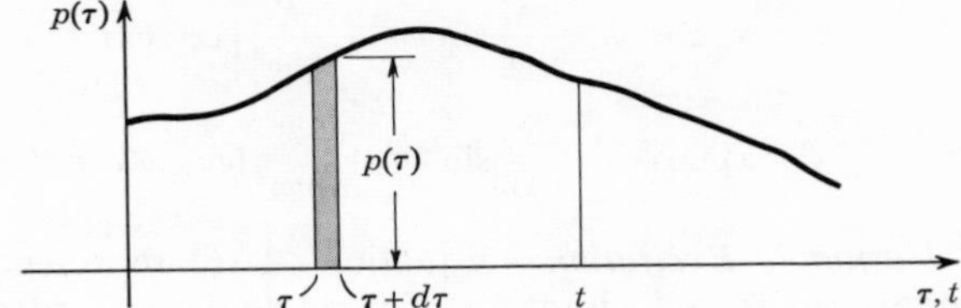

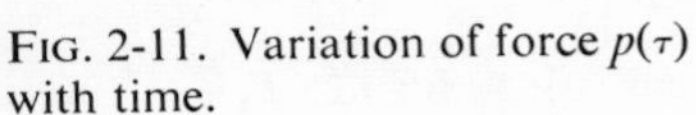

FIG. 2-11. Variation of force $p(\tau)$ with time.

consider an infinitesimal impulse $dG = p(\tau)\,d\tau$ applied at the time $t_0 = \tau$. This impulse will create a velocity increment $d\dot{x} = p(\tau)\,d\tau/m$. If we consider this as an "initial velocity" occurring at time $t_0 = \tau$, the motion of the mass due to this impulse alone is given by Eq. (2-13). That is,

$$x = \frac{d\dot{x}}{\omega}\sin\omega(t-\tau) = \frac{p(\tau)\,d\tau}{m\omega}\sin\omega(t-\tau) \qquad \text{for } t \geq \tau \tag{2-14}$$

Since such "initial velocities" are produced continuously at all times τ between 0 and t, the motion of mass m due to $p(\tau)$ is obtained by summing all incremental motions (2-14) between 0 and t. Hence

$$x = \frac{1}{m\omega}\int_0^t p(\tau)\sin\omega(t-\tau)\,d\tau \tag{2-15}$$

where the integration is performed with respect to τ.

If the initial conditions at time $t = 0$ are x_0 and $\dot{x}_0$, solution (2-8) of the homogeneous equation (2-1) must be added so that the complete motion is described by

$$x = x_0\cos\omega t + \frac{\dot{x}_0}{\omega}\sin\omega t + \frac{1}{m\omega}\int_0^t p(\tau)\sin\omega(t-\tau)\,d\tau \tag{2-16}$$

Example 2-2. The spring-mass system of Fig. 2-9 is subjected to a rectangular pulse load P of duration T_1 (Fig. 2-12). Find the response of the system to this load if the displacement and velocity at $t = 0$ are x_0 and $\dot{x}_0$, respectively.

For $0 \leq t \leq T_1$ the motion is governed by Eq. (2-16):

$$\begin{aligned} x &= x_0\cos\omega t + \frac{\dot{x}_0}{\omega}\sin\omega t + \frac{1}{m\omega}\int_0^t P\sin\omega(t-\tau)\,d\tau \\ &= x_0\cos\omega t + \frac{\dot{x}_0}{\omega}\sin\omega t + \frac{P}{m\omega^2}\Big|\cos\omega(t-\tau)\Big|_0^t \\ &= x_0\cos\omega t + \frac{\dot{x}_0}{\omega}\sin\omega t + \frac{P}{m\omega^2}(1-\cos\omega t) \end{aligned}$$

Since $\omega^2 = k/m$, this expression becomes

$$x = x_0\cos\omega t + \frac{\dot{x}_0}{\omega}\sin\omega t + \frac{P}{k}(1-\cos\omega t) \qquad \text{for } t \leq T_1$$

For $t \geq T_1$ the integral must be split into two portions since $p(\tau) = P$ for $0 < \tau < T_1$ and $p(\tau) = 0$ for $\tau > T_1$. Then

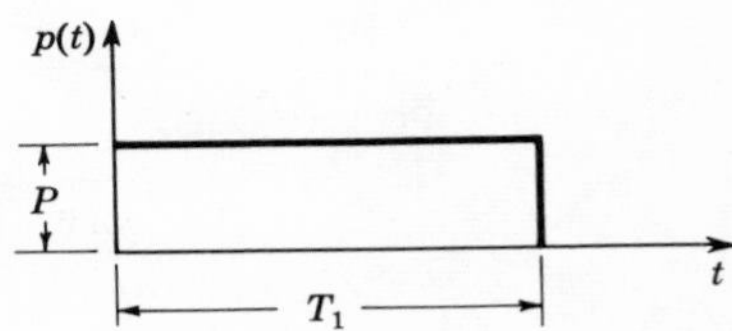

FIG. 2-12. Pulse load of duration T_1.

$$x = x_0 \cos \omega t + \frac{\dot{x}_0}{\omega} \sin \omega t + \frac{P}{m\omega^2} \left| \cos \omega(t - \tau) \right|_0^{T_1} + \frac{0}{m\omega^2} \left| \cos \omega(t - \tau) \right|_{T_1}^{t}$$

$$= x_0 \cos \omega t + \frac{\dot{x}_0}{\omega} \sin \omega t + \frac{P}{m\omega^2} [\cos \omega(t - T_1) - \cos \omega t] \qquad \text{for } t \geq T_1$$

Harmonic Excitation. Equation (2-16) represents the complete solution for the undamped forced vibration of a single-degree-of-freedom system and therefore can be evaluated for any time function of the exciting force $p(\tau)$, including, of course, the case of harmonic excitation:

$$p(\tau) = P \sin \Omega\tau \qquad \text{or} \qquad p(\tau) = P \cos \Omega\tau$$

However, we shall treat this special, but most important, case in a different (the usual) manner. For this purpose we assume that the solution $x(t)$ consists of two parts:

$$x(t) = x_h(t) + x_p(t)\dagger$$

where $x_h(t)$ satisfies homogeneous equation (2-1) and $x_p(t)$ satisfies Eq. (2-12). Hence

$$x(t) = A \cos \omega t + B \sin \omega t + x_p(t) \qquad \text{for } t \geq 0 \tag{2-17}$$

The constants A and B in Eq. (2-17) have to be determined so that $x_h + x_p$ fulfills the initial conditions $x(t = 0) = x_0$ and $\dot{x}(t = 0) = \dot{x}_0$.‡

We now turn to the evaluation of the *particular integral* $x_p(t)$ of Eq. (2-12). It can be verified by direct substitution in the differential equation that, when $p(t) = P \sin \Omega t$, $x_p = X \sin \Omega t$ is a solution. Doing this we find

$$-m\Omega^2 X \sin \Omega t + kX \sin \Omega t = P \sin \Omega t \tag{2-18}$$

from which we deduce that

$$X = \frac{P}{k - m\Omega^2} = \frac{P}{k} \frac{1}{1 - (m/k)\Omega^2} = \frac{P}{k} \frac{1}{1 - (\Omega/\omega)^2} \tag{2-19}$$

Hence the total solution is

$$x(t) = A \cos \omega t + B \sin \omega t + \frac{P}{k} \frac{1}{1 - (\Omega/\omega)^2} \sin \Omega t$$

and
$$\dot{x}(t) = -A\omega \sin \omega t + B\omega \cos \omega t + \frac{P\Omega}{k} \frac{1}{1 - (\Omega/\omega)^2} \cos \Omega t$$

Applying the initial conditions at $t = 0$ we find that

$$x_0 = A \qquad \text{and} \qquad \dot{x}_0 = B\omega + \frac{P\Omega}{k} \frac{1}{1 - (\Omega/\omega)^2}$$

so that the complete solution is now

† In linear systems, where the principle of superposition is valid, this splitting up is always possible. In the present case this is easily shown:

$$m\ddot{x}_h + kx_h = 0 \tag{2-1}$$

$$m\ddot{x}_p + kx_p = p(t) \tag{2-12}$$

$$m(\ddot{x}_h + \ddot{x}_p) + k(x_h + x_p) = p(t)$$

$$m\ddot{x} + kx = p(t)$$

‡ The reader is warned against simply assuming that $A = x_0$ and $B = \dot{x}_0/\omega$.

$$x = x_0 \cos \omega t + \left[\frac{\dot{x}_0}{\omega} - \frac{P\Omega}{k\omega} \frac{1}{1 - (\Omega/\omega)^2} \right] \sin \omega t + \frac{P}{k} \frac{1}{1 - (\Omega/\omega)^2} \sin \Omega t \quad (2\text{-}20)$$

The first two terms describe the free vibration, and the third term describes what is known as the *steady-state forced vibration.* The amplitude X [cf. Eq. (2-19)] of the steady-state forced vibration is dependent on the ratio of the forcing frequency Ω to the natural frequency ω (Fig. 2-13). The change of sign at $\Omega/\omega = 1$ indicates that $x_p(t)$ and $p(t)$ are in equal phase for $\Omega < \omega$ and in opposite phase for $\Omega > \omega$. When $\Omega/\omega = 1$ (resonance), the amplitude X becomes infinitely large. It must be pointed out, however, that when $\Omega = \omega$ the solution (2-20) is not valid.

It is left to the reader to show that, for $p(\tau) = P \sin \omega\tau$ (that is, $\Omega = \omega$) and with the initial conditions x_0 and $\dot{x}_0$, Eq. (2-16) yields the solution

$$x(t) = x_0 \cos \omega t + \frac{\dot{x}_0}{\omega} \sin \omega t + \frac{P}{2k} (\sin \omega t - \omega t \cos \omega t) \quad (2\text{-}21)$$

$$\dot{x}(t) = -x_0\omega \sin \omega t + \dot{x}_0 \cos \omega t + \frac{P\omega^2}{2k} t \sin \omega t \quad (2\text{-}22)$$

These equations reveal immediately that it requires an infinite time for the amplitude to become infinite. For large values of t, Eqs. (2-21) and (2-22) can be reduced to

$$x(t) = -\frac{P\omega}{2k} t \cos \omega t \qquad \text{and} \qquad \dot{x}(t) = \frac{P\omega^2}{2k} t \sin \omega t$$

The last expression for the velocity $\dot{x}(t)$ may serve to explain why the amplitude grows with time: The exciting force $P \sin \omega t$ is in phase with the velocity $\dot{x}(t)$, and hence the power input at all times t is

$$\frac{P^2\omega^2}{2k} t \sin^2 \omega t$$

that is, always positive and increasing with time.

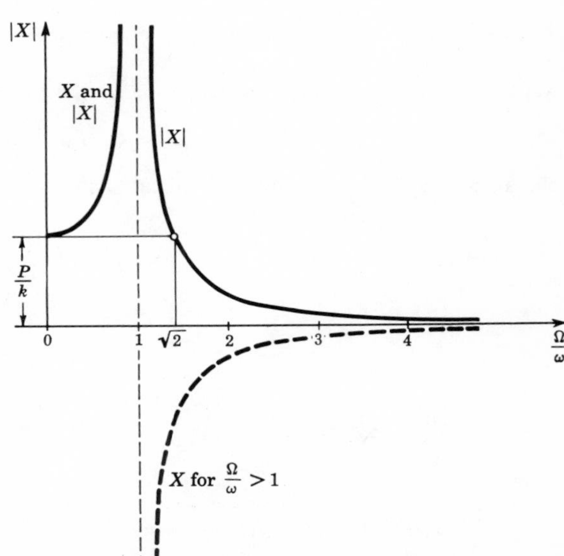

FIG. 2-13. Variation of amplitude of forced vibration with frequency.

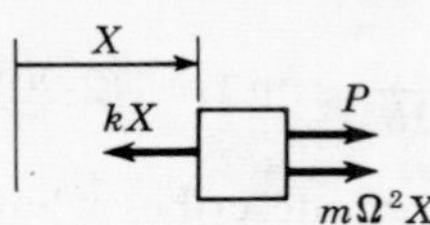

FIG. 2-14. Free-body diagram of mass m in steady-state forced vibration using D'Alembert's principle.

The Steady-state Motion in Algebraic Form. As for free vibrations [cf. Eq. (2-11)], it is possible to devise a simple algebraic technique, so that the steady-state response is obtained without solving the differential equation (2-12) formally. Equation (2-18) can be written in the form

$$m\Omega^2 X - kX + P = 0 \tag{2-23}$$

This equation leads immediately to the result of Eq. (2-19) and can be interpreted as the equation of equilibrium for the mass m under the action of the amplitudes of the inertia force $m\Omega^2 X$, of the spring force $-kX$, and of the external exciting force P (Fig. 2-14). Whereas in the case of free vibrations the D'Alembert equation, repeated here,

$$m\omega^2 x - kx = 0 \tag{2-11}$$

was valid for any $x = x(t)$, Eq. (2-23) is specialized for the times when $\sin \Omega t = 1$, because it is at such times that x_p reaches its amplitude X and $p(t)$ reaches its amplitude P.

Example 2-3. We now apply this approach to the determination of the steady-state forced vibration of the system of Fig. 2-15, which is identical to the one in Fig. 2-7 except that a periodic torque $T \sin \Omega t$ is applied to the roller, which is to roll without slipping. Figure 2-16 shows the corresponding free-body diagram of the roller. Taking moments about C, we obtain

$$-kXr + m\Omega^2 Xr + I_G\Omega^2\Phi + T = 0$$

or with the rolling condition $X = r\Phi$

$$[\Omega^2(I_G + mr^2) - kr^2]X + Tr = 0$$

Hence

$$X = \frac{Tr}{kr^2 - \Omega^2(I_G + mr^2)}$$

With the natural circular frequency ω of the system having been found to be

$$\omega^2 = kr^2(I_G + mr^2)$$

the amplitude of the forced vibration can also be expressed as follows:

$$X = \frac{T}{kr}\frac{1}{1 - (\Omega/\omega)^2}$$

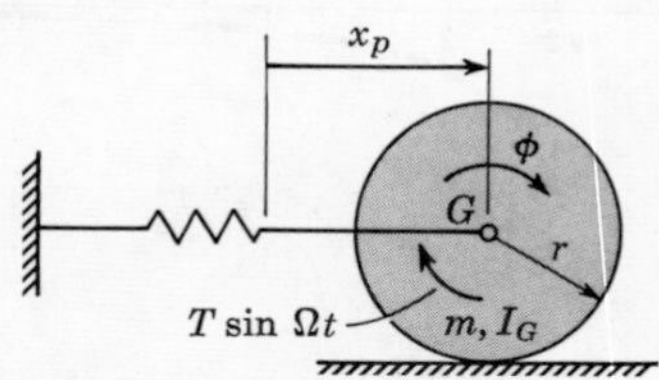

FIG. 2-15. Spring-roller system with harmonic excitation (cf. Fig. 2-7).

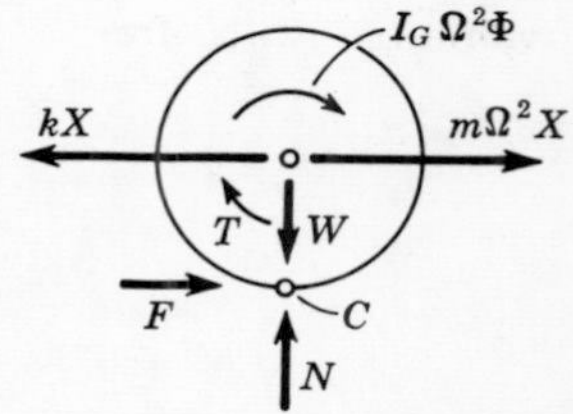

FIG. 2-16. Free-body diagram for mass of Fig. 2-15.

PROBLEMS

2-1. A weight W_1 is attached to a spring of stiffness k and hangs vertically in the equilibrium position. Another weight W_2 falls from rest through a height h and collides with the weight W_1 without rebound (Fig. P 2-1). Deduce the subsequent motion of the weights.

2-2. Assuming small displacements, compute the natural frequency of the pendulum shown in Fig. P 2-2. The rod is massless and infinitely stiff and is hinged at point 0. The mass is restrained by a spring of stiffness k.

2-3. Show that for the pendulum of Fig. P 2-3 to stand upright $k > mg/l$. Assuming this to be the case, compute the natural frequency of the system for small deflections.

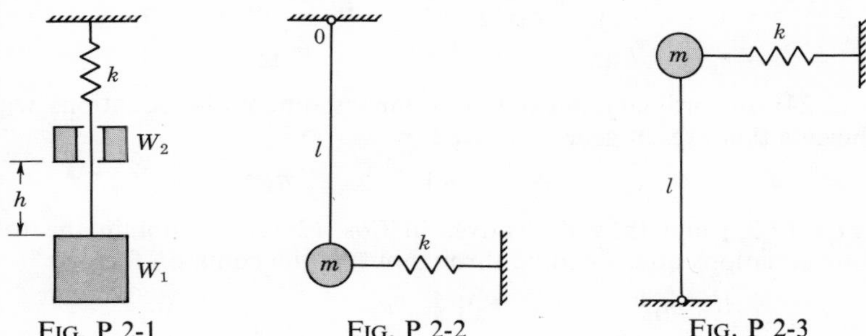

FIG. P 2-1 FIG. P 2-2 FIG. P 2-3

2-4. A mass m is attached to the end of a massless cantilever beam of length l and flexural stiffness EJ. Find the natural frequency of this system. Supposing that initially the mass fell through a height h before attaching itself to the end of the beam, find the resulting motion of the mass.

2-5. A weight W is attached to the middle point of a string of length l (Fig. P 2-5), which is subjected to a tension T. Find the natural frequency for lateral deflections of the weight, assuming that the deflections are small and that the tension in the string remains constant at all times.

2-6. A torque $T \sin \Omega_1 t$ is applied about the center of the disk of Fig. P 2-6. Compute the amplitude of the steady-state motion.

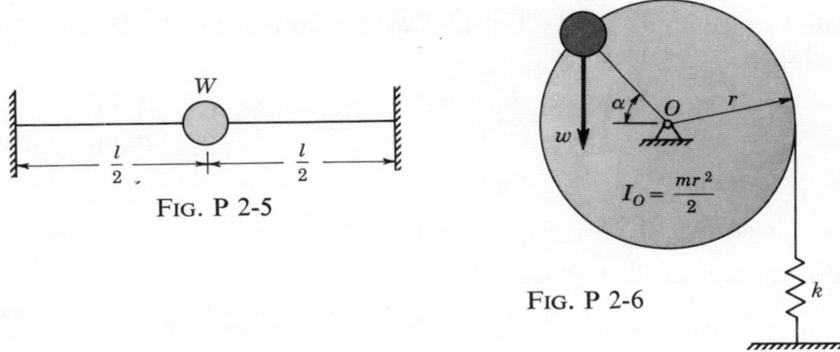

FIG. P 2-5

FIG. P 2-6

2-7. A simple spring-mass system of mass m and spring stiffness k is subjected to a force $P \sin \Omega t$ for the period $0 < t \leq 2\pi/\Omega$. Find the resulting motion of the mass for $t \geq 2\pi/\Omega$ if its initial displacement and velocity are zero.

2-3. Free Vibrations of Systems with Two Degrees of Freedom

Solution of Differential Equations. Natural Frequencies. Normal Modes. The simple spring-mass system of Fig. 2-17 is a two-degree-of-freedom system, since its configuration is fully described by the two displacements x_1 and x_2 that again are

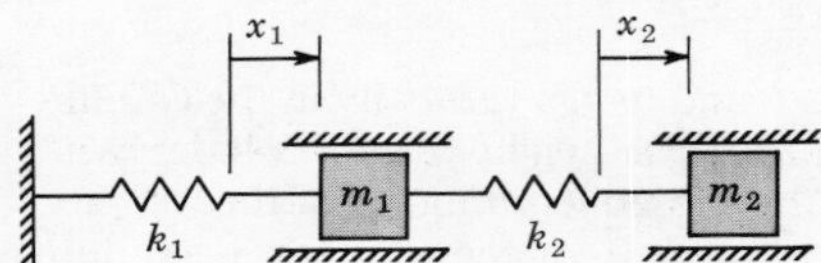

FIG. 2-17. Spring-mass system with two degrees of freedom.

measured, for convenience, from the equilibrium position. The positive directions of the displacements also fix the positive directions of the velocities and accelerations. The spring constants are denoted by k_1 and k_2. The free-body diagram (Fig. 2-18) using D'Alembert's principle yields the following equilibrium equations:

$$-m_1\ddot{x}_1 - k_1x_1 + k_2(x_2 - x_1) = 0 \qquad \text{for mass } m_1 \tag{2-24a}$$

$$-m_2\ddot{x}_2 - k_2(x_2 - x_1) = 0 \qquad \text{for mass } m_2 \tag{2-24b}$$

Equations (2-24) are ordinary linear homogeneous differential equations with constant coefficients that are, in general, solved by

$$x_1 = Ae^{\lambda t} \qquad \text{and} \qquad x_2 = Be^{\lambda t} \tag{2-25}$$

Inserting Eqs. (2-25) and their derivatives in Eqs. (2-24), we obtain the following characteristic equations after dividing throughout by the common factor $e^{\lambda t}$:

$$A[-m_1\lambda^2 - (k_1 + k_2)] + Bk_2 = 0 \tag{2-26a}$$

$$Ak_2 + B(-m_2\lambda^2 - k_2) = 0 \tag{2-26b}$$

From the theory of linear homogeneous equations (cf. Sec. 1-2) we know that a nontrivial solution for A and B is possible only if the determinant of the coefficients of A and B in Eqs. (2-26) vanishes; that is,

$$[m_1\lambda^2 + (k_1 + k_2)](m_2\lambda^2 + k_2) - k_2^2 = 0 \tag{2-27}$$

The values of λ, for which Eq. (2-27) is satisfied, are called the eigenvalues. On expansion, Eq. (2-27) leads to the following quadratic equation in λ^2:

$$\lambda^4 + \left(\frac{k_2}{m_2} + \frac{k_1 + k_2}{m_1}\right)\lambda^2 + \frac{k_1k_2}{m_1m_2} = 0 \tag{2-27a}$$

The two values of λ^2 that satisfy Eq. (2-27*a*) are both negative, because from the properties of quadratic equations

$$\lambda_1^2 + \lambda_2^2 = -\left(\frac{k_2}{m_2} + \frac{k_1 + k_2}{m_1}\right) \qquad \text{and} \qquad \lambda_1^2\lambda_2^2 = \frac{k_1k_2}{m_1m_2}$$

Setting $\lambda_1^2 = -\omega_1^2$ and $\lambda_2^2 = -\omega_2^2$, then

$$\lambda_{11} = j\omega_1 \qquad \lambda_{12} = -j\omega_1 \qquad \text{and} \qquad \lambda_{21} = j\omega_2 \qquad \lambda_{22} = -j\omega_2$$

We therefore have, according to Eqs. (2-25),

$$x_1 = A_1e^{j\omega_1 t} + A_2e^{-j\omega_1 t} + A_3e^{j\omega_2 t} + A_4e^{-j\omega_2 t} \tag{2-28a}$$

$$x_2 = B_1e^{j\omega_1 t} + B_2e^{-j\omega_1 t} + B_3e^{j\omega_2 t} + B_4e^{-j\omega_2 t} \tag{2-28b}$$

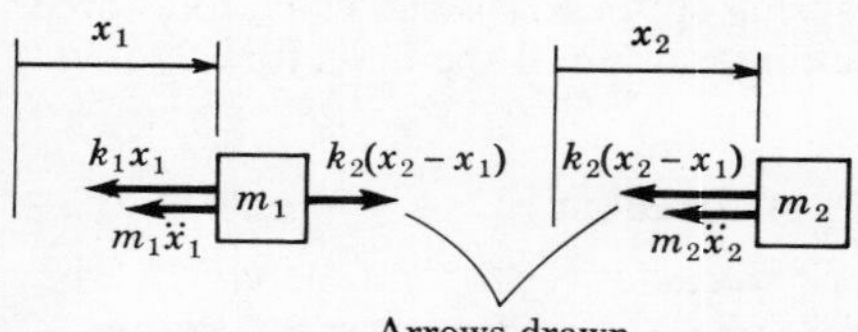

FIG. 2-18. Free-body diagram using D'Alembert's principle.

Before rewriting these equations we note from Eq. (2-26*b*) that the following relation exists between A and B:

$$B = \frac{k_2}{m_2\lambda^2 + k_2} A = cA\dagger \tag{2-29}$$

Equation (2-29) yields for each of the two values of λ^2 a corresponding value of c, both of which are real numbers. Therefore Eq. (2-28*b*) can be written as

$$x_2 = c_1(A_1 e^{j\omega_1 t} + A_2 e^{-j\omega_1 t}) + c_2(A_3 e^{j\omega_2 t} + A_4 e^{-j\omega_2 t}) \tag{2-28c}$$

Again making use of the relation $e^{\pm j\alpha} = \cos\alpha \pm j\sin\alpha$, we obtain, similarly to Sec. 2-1,

$$x_1 = K_1 \cos\omega_1 t + K_2 \sin\omega_1 t + K_3 \cos\omega_2 t + K_4 \sin\omega_2 t \tag{2-30a}$$

$$x_2 = c_1(K_1 \cos\omega_1 t + K_2 \sin\omega_1 t) + c_2(K_3 \cos\omega_2 t + K_4 \sin\omega_2 t) \tag{2-30b}$$

or

$$x_1 = A_1 \sin(\omega_1 t + \phi_1) + A_2 \sin(\omega_2 t + \phi_2) \tag{2-31a}$$

$$x_2 = c_1 A_1 \sin(\omega_1 t + \phi_1) + c_2 A_2 \sin(\omega_2 t + \phi_2) \tag{2-31b}$$

We now see that the motion of m_1 and m_2 consists of the superposition of two harmonic motions, one of which has the circular frequency ω_1 and the other ω_2. If the system is vibrating with the circular frequency ω_1 alone, then x_1 and x_2 are related by the constant c_1. In other words, if the position of one of the masses is defined, then the position of the other is automatically known. This applies equally well to the configuration corresponding to the circular frequency ω_2. Hence, corresponding to each natural frequency, the system vibrates according to a definite shape that is described as the *normal mode*. The number of normal modes is equal to the number of degrees of freedom.

Example 2-4. Let us find the natural frequencies and the corresponding modes for the system of Fig. 2-17 when $k_1 = k_2 = k$ and $m_1 = m_2 = m$.

Solving Eq. (2-27*a*) for this special case, we obtain

$$\lambda_1^2 = \frac{-3+\sqrt{5}}{2}\frac{k}{m} = -0.382\frac{k}{m} \qquad \text{and} \qquad \lambda_2^2 = \frac{-3-\sqrt{5}}{2}\frac{k}{m} = -2.618\frac{k}{m}$$

Hence $\omega_1 = 0.618\sqrt{k/m}$ and $\omega_2 = 1.618\sqrt{k/m}$. Also, from Eq. (2-29) the values of c_1 and c_2 are

$$c_1 = \frac{1}{1-0.382} = 1.618 \qquad c_2 = \frac{1}{1-2.618} = -0.618$$

so that the resulting equations of motion of the masses are

$$x_1 = \left(K_1 \cos 0.618\sqrt{\frac{k}{m}}\,t + K_2 \sin 0.618\sqrt{\frac{k}{m}}\,t\right) + \left(K_3 \cos 1.618\sqrt{\frac{k}{m}}\,t + K_4 \sin 1.618\sqrt{\frac{k}{m}}\,t\right)$$

$$x_2 = 1.618\left(K_1 \cos 0.618\sqrt{\frac{k}{m}}\,t + K_2 \sin 0.618\sqrt{\frac{k}{m}}\,t\right) - 0.618\left(K_3 \cos 1.618\sqrt{\frac{k}{m}}\,t + K_4 \sin 1.618\sqrt{\frac{k}{m}}\,t\right)$$

The normal-mode shapes are shown in Fig. 2-19.

† The relation between A and B as gained from Eq. (2-26*a*) is identical, because Eqs. (2-26) are linearly dependent.

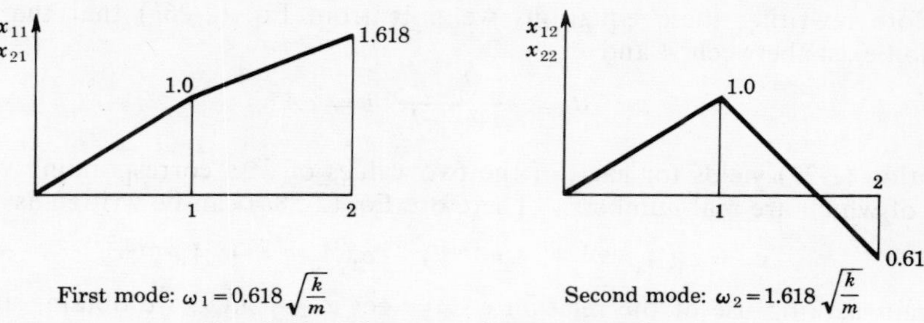

FIG. 2-19. Diagrams of normal modes.

Orthogonality of the Normal Modes. Let the displacements of the masses due to the first normal mode be represented by x_{11} and x_{21} and those due to the second normal mode by x_{12} and x_{22}. Note the order of the subscripts: the first gives the number of the mass and the second the number of the mode. Then

$$x_1 = x_{11} + x_{12} \qquad \text{and} \qquad x_2 = x_{21} + x_{22} \tag{2-32}$$

From Eq. (2-29) we have $x_{21} = c_1x_{11}$ and $x_{22} = c_2x_{12}$.

The normal modes possess the important property

$$m_1x_{11}x_{12} + m_2x_{21}x_{22} = 0 \tag{2-33}$$

or $$m_1x_{11}x_{12} + m_2c_1c_2x_{11}x_{12} = 0 \qquad \text{or} \qquad m_1 + m_2c_1c_2 = 0$$

This property is known as the *orthogonality of the normal modes.*† We can readily check this for the normal modes of Example 2-4. In this case $x_{21} = 1.618x_{11}$ and $x_{22} = -0.618x_{12}$; then applying Eq. (2-33) we obtain

$$mx_{11}x_{12} + m(1.618x_{11})(-0.618x_{12}) = 0$$

The result (2-33) can be shown to be true for the general two-degree-of-freedom system. From Eq. (2-29) we have

$$c_1 = \frac{k_2}{m_2\lambda_1^2 + k_2} \qquad c_2 = \frac{k_2}{m_2\lambda_2^2 + k_2}$$

Hence the left-hand side of Eq. (2-33) becomes

$$x_{11}x_{12}(m_1 + m_2c_1c_2) = x_{11}x_{12}\left[m_1 + \frac{m_2k_2^2}{m_2^2\lambda_1^2\lambda_2^2 + k_2m_2(\lambda_1^2 + \lambda_2^2) + k_2^2}\right] \tag{2-34}$$

Since we noted previously (page 38) that

$$\lambda_1^2 + \lambda_2^2 = -\left(\frac{k_2}{m_2} + \frac{k_1 + k_2}{m_1}\right) \qquad \text{and} \qquad \lambda_1^2\lambda_2^2 = \frac{k_1k_2}{m_1m_2}$$

it is a simple algebraic procedure to show that the expression (2-34) is identically zero.

The physical interpretation of the orthogonality equation (2-33) becomes clear after multiplying this equation by either ω_1^2 or ω_2^2, for example,

$m_1\omega_1^2x_{11}$	$\times$	x_{12}	$+$	$m_2\omega_1^2x_{21}$	$\times$	x_{22}	$= 0$
inertia force of mass m_1 for 1st mode		displacement of mass m_1 for 2d mode		inertia force of mass m_2 for 1st mode		displacement of mass m_2 for 2d mode	

† A general proof of this property is given in Chap. 8.

Equation (2-33) therefore expresses the fact that the work done by the inertia forces that occur in the first normal mode moving through the displacements of the second normal mode is zero. The equivalent statement, vice versa, can be made when Eq. (2-33) is multiplied by ω_2^2. This property of the normal modes explains the reason for describing normal modes as being orthogonal to one another; for we know from elementary mechanics that, if a force does no work in moving through a finite displacement, then the direction of the force is perpendicular to the direction of the displacement; i.e., the line of action of the force and the displacement are orthogonal.

Initial Conditions. Let us now deal with the question of how to determine the constants K_1, K_2, K_3, and K_4 in solutions (2-30) from the initial conditions†

$$x_1(t_0) = x_1^0 \qquad \dot{x}_1(t_0) = \dot{x}_1^0 \qquad x_2(t_0) = x_2^0 \qquad \dot{x}_2(t_0) = \dot{x}_2^0$$

In view of our preceding considerations it appears sensible to split up the initial conditions in normal-mode form [cf. Eqs. (2-32)], which for this reason also fulfill the orthogonality conditions (2-33).

$$x_1^0 = x_{11}^0 + x_{12}^0 \tag{2-35a}$$

$$x_2^0 = x_{21}^0 + x_{22}^0 = c_1 x_{11}^0 + c_2 x_{12}^0 \tag{2-35b}$$

$$\dot{x}_1^0 = \dot{x}_{11}^0 + \dot{x}_{12}^0 \tag{2-35c}$$

$$\dot{x}_2^0 = \dot{x}_{21}^0 + \dot{x}_{22}^0 = c_1 \dot{x}_{11}^0 + c_2 \dot{x}_{12}^0 \tag{2-35d}$$

The solution of these four simultaneous equations yields the initial conditions of the first normal mode x_{11}^0 and $\dot{x}_{11}^0$ and of the second normal mode x_{12}^0 and $\dot{x}_{12}^0$. With reference to Eqs. (2-7) and (2-8), Eqs. (2-30) can now be written

$$x_1(t) = x_{11}^0 \cos \omega_1(t - t_0) + \frac{\dot{x}_{11}^0}{\omega_1} \sin \omega_1(t - t_0) + x_{12}^0 \cos \omega_2(t - t_0) + \frac{\dot{x}_{12}^0}{\omega_2} \sin \omega_2(t - t_0) \tag{2-36a}$$

$$x_2(t) = c_1\left[x_{11}^0 \cos \omega_1(t - t_0) + \frac{\dot{x}_{11}^0}{\omega_1} \sin \omega_1(t - t_0)\right] + c_2\left[x_{12}^0 \cos \omega_2(t - t_0) + \frac{\dot{x}_{12}^0}{\omega_2} \sin \omega_2(t - t_0)\right] \tag{2-36b}$$

For the solution of Eqs. (2-35) we utilize the orthogonality property (2-33). For this purpose we multiply (2-35*a*) by m_1, (2-35*b*) by $c_1 m_2$, and add; thus we obtain

$$m_1 x_1^0 + c_1 m_2 x_2^0 = x_{11}^0(m_1 + c_1^2 m_2) + x_{12}^0(m_1 + m_2 c_1 c_2)$$

In view of Eq. (2-33) the term with x_{12}^0 vanishes; hence

$$x_{11}^0 = \frac{m_1 x_1^0 + c_1 m_2 x_2^0}{m_1 + c_1^2 m_2} \tag{2-37a}$$

Similarly multiplying the same equations by m_1 and $c_2 m_2$, respectively, and adding, we find

$$x_{12}^0 = \frac{m_1 x_1^0 + c_2 m_2 x_2^0}{m_1 + c_2^2 m_2} \tag{2-37b}$$

Repeating exactly the same procedure but using Eqs. (2-35*c*) and (2-35*d*), we obtain

† From now on, the initial conditions will be indicated by the superscript 0.

$$\dot{x}_{11}^{0} = \frac{m_1\dot{x}_1^0 + c_1 m_2 \dot{x}_2^0}{m_1 + c_1^2 m_2} \tag{2-37c}$$

$$\dot{x}_{12}^{0} = \frac{m_1\dot{x}_1^0 + c_2 m_2 \dot{x}_2^0}{m_1 + c_2^2 m_2} \tag{2-37d}$$

Example 2-5. Find the equations of motion of the system of Example 2-4 when the initial conditions at $t_0 = 0$ are

$$x_1^0 = -x_2^0 = \delta \qquad \dot{x}_1^0 = v \qquad \dot{x} \ = 0$$

With $c_1 = 1.618$, $c_2 = -0.618$, the expressions for x_{11}^0, $\dot{x}_{11}^0$, and so forth, are given by the relations (2-37), so that

$$x_{11}^0 = \frac{m(\delta - 1.618\delta)}{m(1 + 1.618^2)} = -0.171\delta \qquad x_{12}^0 = \frac{m(\delta + 0.618\delta)}{m(1 + 0.618^2)} = 1.171\delta$$

$$\dot{x}_{11}^0 = \frac{mv}{m(1 + 1.618^2)} = 0.276v \qquad \dot{x}_{12}^0 = \frac{mv}{m(1 + 0.618^2)} = 0.724v$$

Hence the equations of motion (2-36) for the two masses are

$$x_1(t) = \left(-0.171\delta \cos \omega_1 t + \frac{0.276v}{\omega_1} \sin \omega_1 t\right) + \left(1.171\delta \cos \omega_2 t + \frac{0.724v}{\omega_2} \sin \omega_2 t\right)$$

$$x_2(t) = 1.618\left(-0.171\delta \cos \omega_1 t + \frac{0.276v}{\omega_1} \sin \omega_1 t\right) - 0.618\left(1.171\delta \cos \omega_2 t + \frac{0.724v}{\omega_2} \sin \omega_2 t\right)$$

Algebraic Formulation. For the single-degree-of-freedom case we found, on account of the properties of the harmonic motion, that it is possible to replace the differential equation of motion by an algebraic equation. By this method we could compute the natural frequency without solving the differential equation formally [cf. Eq. (2-11)].

An identical technique can be applied to the two-degree-of-freedom system. We have learned that the motion of the system consists of the superposition of two harmonic motions, each with a different natural frequency. Assuming, then, that the motion is harmonic with circular frequency ω, we have

$$\ddot{x}_1 = -\omega^2 x_1 \qquad \text{and} \qquad \ddot{x}_2 = -\omega^2 x_2$$

so that the differential equations (2-24) become

$$m_1\omega^2 x_1 - k_1 x_1 + k_2(x_2 - x_1) = 0 \tag{2-38a}$$

$$m_2\omega^2 x_2 - k_2(x_2 - x_1) \qquad\qquad = 0 \tag{2-38b}$$

Rearranging the equations according to coefficients of x_1 and x_2,

$$x_1[m_1\omega^2 - (k_1 + k_2)] + x_2 k_2 \qquad = 0$$

$$x_1 k_2 \qquad\qquad + x_2(m_2\omega^2 - k_2) = 0$$

For these equations to have a nontrivial solution the determinant of the coefficients is zero, so that

$$\omega^4 - \left(\frac{k_2}{m_2} + \frac{k_1 + k_2}{m_1}\right)\omega^2 + \frac{k_1 k_2}{m_1 m_2} = 0 \tag{2-39}$$

If we recall that $\lambda^2 = -\omega^2$, this equation corresponds to the characteristic equation (2-27a). The mode constants c_1 and c_2 are given by (2-38b) and are

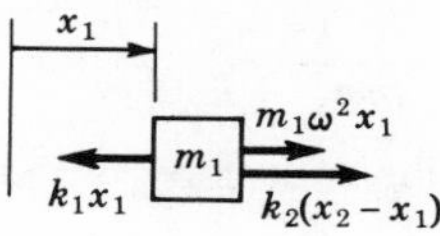

FIG. 2-20. Free-body diagram using D'Alembert's principle.

$$c_1 = \frac{k_2}{k_2 - m_2\omega_1^2} \qquad c_2 = \frac{k_2}{k_2 - m_2\omega_2^2}$$

From this point the procedure follows that from Eqs. (2-30) on.

Recalling that the inertia force may be expressed as the positive product of mass times displacement times the square of the natural circular frequency, we redraw the free-body diagram of Fig. 2-18 to obtain Fig. 2-20. On the basis of Fig. 2-20, Eqs. (2-38) can be formulated immediately.

Example 2-6. A mass m is supported by an elastic string that passes without slipping over a pulley consisting of a disk of radius r having the moment of inertia I_G, and is then attached to a wall (Fig. 2-21). The pulley divides the string into two parts of equal stiffness k. Find the natural frequencies, the normal modes, and the equation of motion when the initial conditions are x_1^0, $\dot{x}_1^0$, x_2^0, and $\dot{x}_2^0$, where x_1 denotes the angular displacement of the pulley and x_2 denotes the linear displacement of the mass. From the free-body diagram of Fig. 2-22 we formulate the equilibrium equations for the pulley and for the mass:

$$I_G\omega^2 x_1 - kx_1r^2 + kr(x_2 - x_1r) = 0$$

$$m\omega^2 x_2 - k(x_2 - x_1r) = 0$$

or

$$x_1(I_G\omega^2 - 2kr^2) + x_2kr = 0 \qquad (2\text{-}40a)$$

$$x_1kr + x_2(m\omega^2 - k) = 0 \qquad (2\text{-}40b)$$

The determinant of Eqs. (2-40) yields the frequency equation for ω_1 and ω_2:

$$(I_G\omega^2 - 2kr^2)(m\omega^2 - k) - k^2r^2 = 0$$

or

$$\omega^4 - \left(\frac{k}{m} + \frac{2kr^2}{I_G}\right)\omega^2 + \frac{k^2r^2}{mI_G} = 0 \qquad (2\text{-}41)$$

When $I_G = 0$ this equation reduces to the equation in ω^2 for a one-degree-of-freedom system with mass m and a spring of stiffness $k/2$, that is, $\omega^2 = k/2m$. Either Eq. (2-40*a*) or (2-40*b*) serves to determine the normal-mode constants c_1 and c_2. Using Eq. (2-40*b*) we obtain

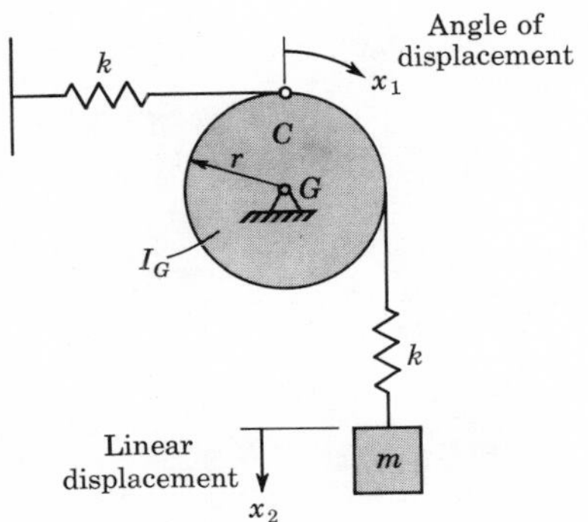

FIG. 2-21. System of two degrees of freedom.

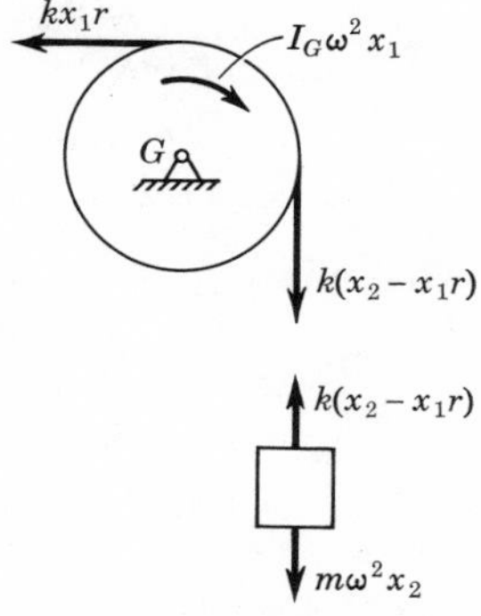

FIG. 2-22. Free-body diagram of system of Fig. 2-21.

$$c_1 = \left(\frac{x_2}{x_1}\right)_1 = -\frac{kr}{m\omega_1^2 - k} \quad \text{and} \quad c_2 = \left(\frac{x_2}{x_1}\right)_2 = -\frac{kr}{m\omega_2^2 - k} \tag{2-42}$$

In order to avoid the writing of lengthy formulas, let us evaluate Eqs. (2-41) and (2-42) for the numerical values:

$$k = 6 \qquad m = 1 \qquad r = 2 \qquad I_G = 6$$

Hence from Eq. (2-41)

$$\omega^4 - (6 + 8)\omega^2 + 24 = 0$$

giving $\omega_{1,2}^2 = 7 \mp \sqrt{49 - 24}$ or $\omega_1^2 = 2,\ \omega_2^2 = 12$

With these values inserted in Eqs. (2-42) the two mode constants become

$$c_1 = \left(\frac{x_2}{x_1}\right)_1 = -\frac{12}{2 - 6} = 3 \quad \text{and} \quad c_2 = \left(\frac{x_2}{x_1}\right)_2 = -\frac{12}{12 - 6} = -2$$

These mode constants reveal that for the lower natural frequency the mass m and the pulley vibrate "in phase" (plus sign of c_1), and while the mass m descends by three length units, the pulley rotates clockwise through an angle equal to 1 radian or, because $r = 2$, the point C on the rim of the pulley (Fig. 2-21) travels clockwise through an arc length of 2. In the higher normal mode belonging to $\omega_2^2 = 12$ the mass m and the pulley vibrate in opposite phase (minus sign of c_2), and while the mass m descends by two length units, the pulley rotates counterclockwise through an angle equal to 1 radian.

Let us see if our results fulfill the orthogonality condition (2-33) for the normal modes:

$$mx_{21}x_{22} + I_G x_{11}x_{12} = 0$$

Putting the proper numerical values in this equation, we see that the above normal modes fulfill the orthogonality condition since

$$(1)(3)(-2) + (6)(1)(1) = 0$$

The initial conditions finally determine the motion of our system. Using Eqs. (2-37) we obtain for the first mode

$$x_{11}^0 = \frac{6x_1^0 + (3)(1)x_2^0}{6 + (9)(1)} = \frac{2x_1^0 + x_2^0}{5} \qquad x_{21}^0 = c_1 x_{11}^0 = \tfrac{3}{5}(2x_1^0 + x_2^0)$$

$$\dot{x}_{11}^0 = \frac{6\dot{x}_1^0 + (3)1\dot{x}_2^0}{6 + (9)(1)} = \frac{2\dot{x}_1^0 + \dot{x}_2^0}{5} \qquad \dot{x}_{21}^0 = c_1 \dot{x}_{11}^0 = \tfrac{3}{5}(2\dot{x}_1^0 + \dot{x}_2^0)$$

and for the second mode

$$x_{12}^0 = \frac{6x_1^0 - (2)(1)x_2^0}{6 + (4)(1)} = \frac{3x_1^0 - x_2^0}{5} \qquad x_{22}^0 = c_2 x_{12}^0 = -\tfrac{2}{5}(3x_1^0 - x_2^0)$$

$$\dot{x}_{12}^0 = \frac{6\dot{x}_1^0 - (2)1\dot{x}_2^0}{6 + (4)(1)} = \frac{3\dot{x}_1^0 - \dot{x}_2^0}{5} \qquad \dot{x}_{22}^0 = c_2 \dot{x}_{12}^0 = -\tfrac{2}{5}(3\dot{x}_1^0 - \dot{x}_2^0)$$

With the initial values $x_1^0 = -1,\ x_2^0 = 1,\ \dot{x}_1^0 = 1,\ \dot{x}_2^0 = 1$ we have

$$x_{11}^0 = -\tfrac{1}{5} \qquad \dot{x}_{11}^0 = \tfrac{3}{5} \qquad x_{12}^0 = -\tfrac{4}{5} \qquad \dot{x}_{12}^0 = \tfrac{2}{5}$$

$$x_{21}^0 = -\tfrac{3}{5} \qquad \dot{x}_{21}^0 = \tfrac{9}{5} \qquad x_{22}^0 = \tfrac{8}{5} \qquad \dot{x}_{22}^0 = -\tfrac{4}{5}$$

Hence Eqs. (2-36) yield the following equations of motion ($t_0 = 0$):

$$x_1 = \left(-\tfrac{1}{5}\cos\sqrt{2}t + \frac{3}{5\sqrt{2}}\sin\sqrt{2}t\right) + \left(-\tfrac{4}{5}\cos\sqrt{12}t + \frac{2}{5\sqrt{12}}\sin\sqrt{12}t\right)$$

$$x_2 = \left(-\tfrac{3}{5}\cos\sqrt{2}t + \frac{9}{5\sqrt{2}}\sin\sqrt{2}t\right) + \left(\tfrac{8}{5}\cos\sqrt{12}t - \frac{4}{5\sqrt{12}}\sin\sqrt{12}t\right)$$

PROBLEMS

2-8. Compute the natural frequencies and normal modes for the spring-mass system shown in Fig. P 2-8. Find the equations of motion if the mass m_1 has an initial displacement x_1^0 and the initial displacement of m_2 and the initial velocities are zero.

2-9. Find the frequency determinant for the system shown in Fig. P 2-9. The pendulum consists of a massless rigid rod with a mass attached to its free end. Compute the natural frequencies and normal modes when $kl/mg = 2$. Assume small oscillations.

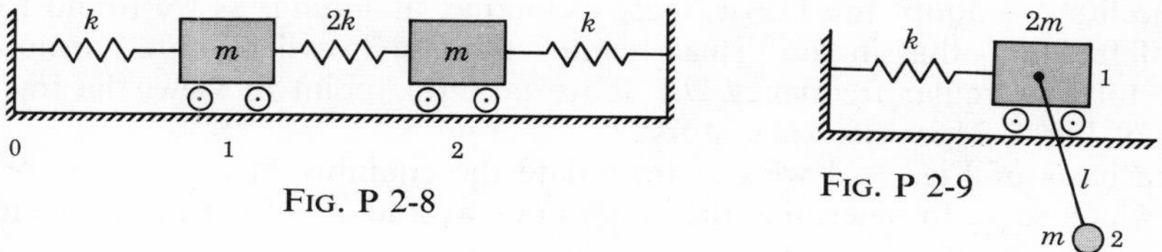

FIG. P 2-8

FIG. P 2-9

2-10. If the initial conditions of the system of Prob. 2-9 are $x_1^0 = \delta$, $x_2^0 = -\delta/2$, $\dot{x}_1^0 = 0$, and $\dot{x}_2^0 = v$, find the expressions for the subsequent motion of the masses.

2-11. Compute the natural frequencies and the normal modes for the system shown in Fig. P 2-11. The built-in cantilever consists of a massless beam of length l and flexural stiffness EJ, the stiffness of the spring being given by the relation $kl^3/EJ = 3$.

2-12. Two weights W are attached to a tight string which is under a tension T (Fig. P 2-12). Compute the natural frequencies for lateral motion of the weights, assuming that the tension remains constant.

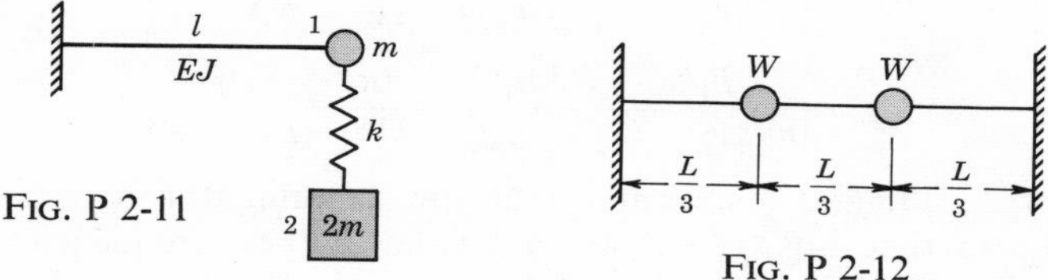

FIG. P 2-11

FIG. P 2-12

2-13. Compute the natural frequencies and normal modes of the system illustrated in Fig. P 2-13. The cylinder rolls without slipping and has a moment of inertia about its center of gravity of $mr^2/2$. Check the orthogonality property of the normal modes.

2-14. In Prob. 2-13 the system is at rest under the action of a horizontal force F applied to the carriage. Find the resulting motion if the force is suddenly removed.

2-15. Two masses are connected by means of a spring of stiffness k (Fig. P 2-15). Compute the natural frequencies and the normal modes. For the initial conditions $x_1^0 = \delta$, $x_2^0 = \delta/2$, $\dot{x}_1^0 = v$, and $\dot{x}_2^0 = -v$, find the subsequent motion. HINT: For the natural frequency $\omega_1 = 0$, Eq. (2-36*a*) becomes, for $t_0 = 0$,

$$x_1(t) = x_{11}^0 + \dot{x}_{11}^0 t + x_{12}^0 \cos \omega_2 t + \frac{\dot{x}_{12}^0}{\omega_2} \sin \omega_2 t$$

since $\cos \omega_1 t = 1$ and $(\sin \omega_1 t)/\omega_1 = t$.

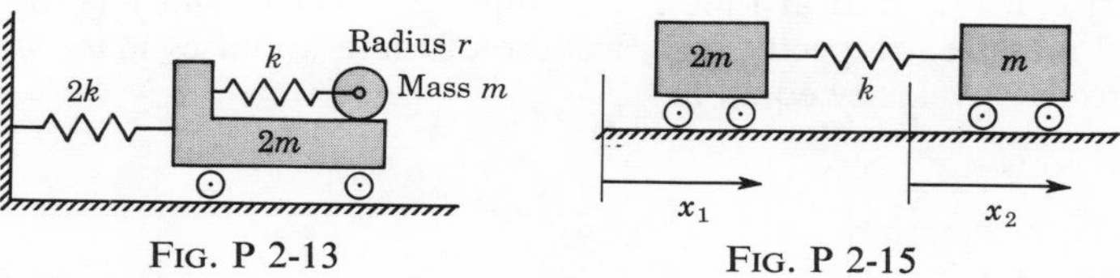

FIG. P 2-13

FIG. P 2-15

2-4. Forced Vibrations of Systems with Two Degrees of Freedom

Steady-state Harmonic Motion. We consider first the steady-state forced undamped vibrations of the simple system shown in Fig. 2-23. When dealing with

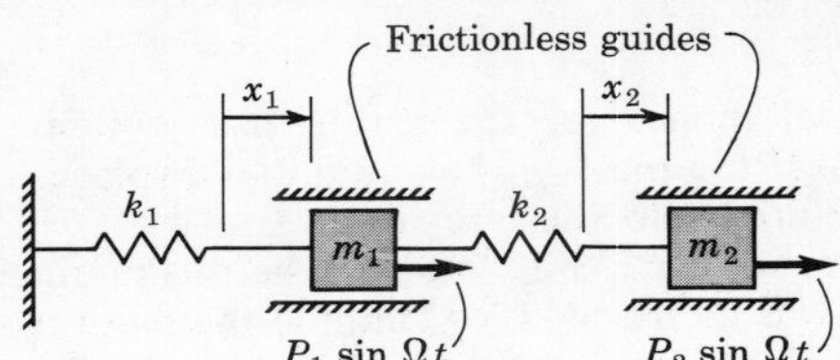

FIG. 2-23. Spring-mass system of two degrees of freedom subjected to harmonic excitation.

the steady-state vibrations alone, the initial conditions are entirely disregarded. From the first we adopt the D'Alembert technique, assuming, as we found for one degree of freedom, that in the "steady state" the system will vibrate harmonically with the forced circular frequency Ω. If we take this point of view, the free-body diagram of Fig. 2-24 is self-explanatory.

On the basis of Fig. 2-24 we can formulate the equilibrium conditions for both masses, which serve to determine the amplitudes X_1 and X_2 of the forced vibration:

$$m_1\Omega^2 X_1 + k_2(X_2 - X_1) - k_1 X_1 + P_1 = 0$$
$$m_2\Omega^2 X_2 - k_2(X_2 - X_1) \qquad + P_2 = 0$$

Hence

$$X_1(-m_1\Omega^2 + k_1 + k_2) + X_2(-k_2) \qquad = P_1 \tag{2-43a}$$
$$X_1(-k_2) \qquad + X_2(-m_2\Omega^2 + k_2) = P_2 \tag{2-43b}$$

Solving these equations for X_1 and X_2, we obtain

$$X_1 = \frac{-P_1(m_2\Omega^2 - k_2) + P_2 k_2}{[m_1\Omega^2 - (k_1 + k_2)](m_2\Omega^2 - k_2) - k_2^2} \tag{2-44a}$$

$$X_2 = \frac{P_1 k_2 - P_2[m_1\Omega^2 - (k_1 + k_2)]}{[m_1\Omega^2 - (k_1 + k_2)](m_2\Omega^2 - k_2) - k_2^2} \tag{2-44b}$$

Comparison with Eq. (2-39) indicates that the denominator becomes zero when $\Omega = \omega_1$ or ω_2, so that Eqs. (2-44) are not valid at these frequencies (resonance). When $P_2 = 0$, Eq. (2-44*a*) shows that, if $k_2/m_2 = \Omega^2$, then $X_1 = 0$ for any value of P_1. Now $\Omega = \sqrt{k_2/m_2}$ equals the natural circular frequency of the system consisting of the mass m_2 and the spring of stiffness k_2, so that, should the forcing frequency Ω coincide with this value, then X_1 is always zero. (This is the principle of the vibration damper.)

Interestingly enough, mass m_2 then vibrates with amplitude $-P_1/k_2$, the negative sign indicating that its phase is opposite to that of the exciting force. Therefore the force exerted by spring k_2 on mass m_1 is equal and opposite to the exciting force $P_1 \sin \Omega t$, explaining the fact that $X_1 \equiv 0$. It may be remarked that this ideal behavior is not reached when damping is present, as is always the case in reality.

Transients. We now turn to the more difficult case when the masses m_1 and m_2 of the system shown in Fig. 2-17 are subjected to forces $p_1(t)$ and $p_2(t)$ which vary arbitrarily with time (Fig. 2-25).

Let us first consider that at time $t = \tau$ impulses $p_1(\tau)\, d\tau$ and $p_2(\tau)\, d\tau$ impinge on mass m_1 and mass m_2, respectively. Because of these impulses mass m_1 will experience an increase in velocity equal to

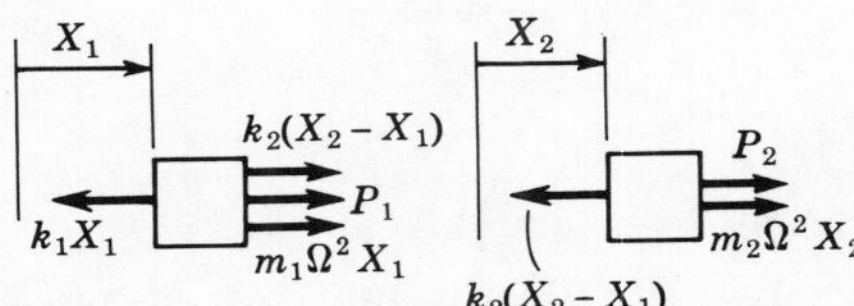

FIG. 2-24. Free-body diagram of system of Fig. 2-23.

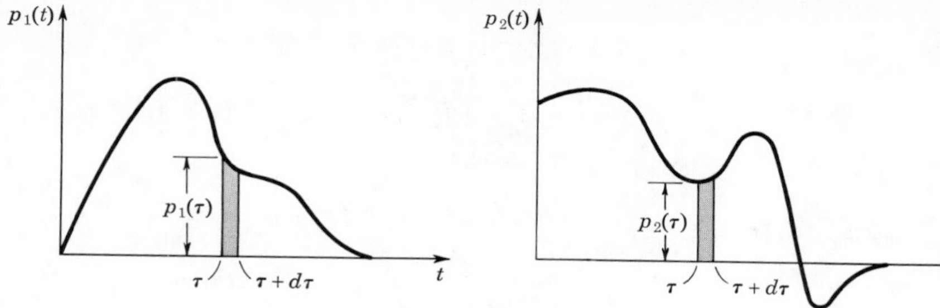

FIG. 2-25. Force functions acting on system of Fig. 2-17.

$$d\dot{x}_1 = \frac{p_1(\tau)\,d\tau}{m_1} \tag{2-45a}$$

and mass m_2 will acquire a velocity increment equal to

$$d\dot{x}_2 = \frac{p_2(\tau)\,d\tau}{m_2} \tag{2-45b}$$

For the present we consider these velocity increments as the initial conditions $\dot{x}_1^0 \equiv d\dot{x}_1$ and $\dot{x}_2^0 \equiv d\dot{x}_2$ at time $t_0 = \tau$. These initial conditions are split up into normal-mode components by means of Eqs. (2-37). Hence

$$\dot{x}_{11}^0 = \frac{m_1\dot{x}_1^0 + c_1 m_2 \dot{x}_2^0}{m_1 + c_1^2 m_2} = \frac{[p_1(\tau) + c_1 p_2(\tau)]\,d\tau}{m_1 + c_1^2 m_2} \tag{2-46a}$$

$$\dot{x}_{21}^0 = \frac{c_1[p_1(\tau) + c_1 p_2(\tau)]\,d\tau}{m_1 + c_1^2 m_2} \tag{2-46b}$$

and

$$\dot{x}_{12}^0 = \frac{m_1\dot{x}_1^0 + c_2 m_2 \dot{x}_2^0}{m_1 + c_2^2 m_2} = \frac{[p_1(\tau) + c_2 p_2(\tau)]\,d\tau}{m_1 + c_2^2 m_2} \tag{2-46c}$$

$$\dot{x}_{22}^0 = \frac{c_2[p_1(\tau) + c_2 p_2(\tau)]\,d\tau}{m_1 + c_2^2 m_2} \tag{2-46d}$$

and the initial displacements are

$$x_{11}^0 = x_{12}^0 = x_{21}^0 = x_{22}^0 = 0$$

The equations of motion of the system resulting from the impulses applied at time τ are found by using the initial conditions (2-46) in Eqs. (2-36) at time $t_0 = \tau$. Hence

$$x_1(t) = \left[\frac{p_1(\tau) + c_1 p_2(\tau)}{\omega_1(m_1 + c_1^2 m_2)} \sin \omega_1(t - \tau) + \frac{p_1(\tau) + c_2 p_2(\tau)}{\omega_2(m_1 + c_2^2 m_2)} \sin \omega_2(t - \tau)\right] d\tau \qquad \text{for } t \geq \tau$$

and the corresponding expression for $x_2(t)$ is

$$x_2(t) = \left[c_1 \frac{p_1(\tau) + c_1 p_2(\tau)}{\omega_1(m_1 + c_1^2 m_2)} \sin \omega_1(t - \tau) + c_2 \frac{p_1(\tau) + c_2 p_2(\tau)}{\omega_2(m_1 + c_2^2 m_2)} \sin \omega_2(t - \tau)\right] d\tau \tag{2-47}$$

Since "initial velocities" as given by Eqs. (2-46) are produced continuously at all times τ between 0 and t, the motion of masses m_1 and m_2, when forced by $p_1(\tau)$ and $p_2(\tau)$, is obtained by summing all incremental motions (2-47) between 0 and t. Hence,

$$x_1(t) = \frac{1}{\omega_1(m_1 + c_1^2 m_2)} \int_0^t [p_1(\tau) + c_1 p_2(\tau)] \sin \omega_1(t - \tau)\, d\tau + \frac{1}{\omega_2(m_1 + c_2^2 m_2)} \int_0^t [p_1(\tau) + c_2 p_2(\tau)] \sin \omega_2(t - \tau)\, d\tau$$

$$x_2(t) = \frac{c_1}{\omega_1(m_1 + c_1^2 m_2)} \int_0^t [p_1(\tau) + c_1 p_2(\tau)] \sin \omega_1(t - \tau)\, d\tau + \frac{c_2}{\omega_2(m_1 + c_2^2 m_2)} \int_0^t [p_1(\tau) + c_2 p_2(\tau)] \sin \omega_2(t - \tau)\, d\tau \tag{2-48}$$

If at time $t = 0$ initial conditions exist, the solutions (2-48) have to be supplemented by the addition of the free vibrations caused by these initial conditions. The expression for the deflection x_1 is then

$$x_1 = x_{11}^0 \cos \omega_1 t + \frac{\dot{x}_{11}^0}{\omega_1} \sin \omega_1 t + \frac{1}{\omega_1(m_1 + c_1^2 m_2)} \int_0^t [p_1(\tau) + c_1 p_2(\tau)] \sin \omega_1(t - \tau)\, d\tau + x_{12}^0 \cos \omega_2 t + \frac{\dot{x}_{12}^0}{\omega_2} \sin \omega_2 t + \frac{1}{\omega_2(m_1 + c_2^2 m_2)} \int_0^t [p_1(\tau) + c_2 p_2(\tau)] \sin \omega_2(t - \tau)\, d\tau \tag{2-49}$$

Example 2-7. The system of Example 2-4 is subjected to suddenly applied loads at time $t = 0$. The force acting on mass m_1 is of constant value P and lasts for a time T_1, and mass m_2 is subjected to a constant force $P/2$ for the time interval $T_2 = 2T_1$. If the system is initially unstretched and at rest, find the resulting motion.

Let us consider the two modes separately. For the first mode [cf. Eqs. (2-48)] corresponding to $\omega_1 = 0.618\sqrt{k/m}$ we have for the time interval $0 < t \leq T_1$

$$\begin{aligned} x_{11} &= \frac{1}{\omega_1 m(1 + c_1^2)} \int_0^t P\left(1 + \frac{c_1}{2}\right) \sin \omega_1(t - \tau)\, d\tau \\ &= \frac{P(1 + c_1/2)}{\omega_1 m(1 + c_1^2)} \left| \frac{\cos \omega_1(t - \tau)}{\omega_1} \right|_0^t = \frac{P(1 + c_1/2)}{m\omega_1^2(1 + c_1^2)} (1 - \cos \omega_1 t) \\ &= 1.31 \frac{P}{k} (1 - \cos \omega_1 t) \end{aligned}$$

on using the values of Example 2-4.

For the time interval $T_1 < t \leq 2T_1$

$$\begin{aligned} x_{11} &= \frac{1}{\omega_1 m(1 + c_1^2)} \left[\int_0^{T_1} \left(P + c_1 \frac{P}{2}\right) \sin \omega_1(t - \tau)\, d\tau + \int_{T_1}^t c_1 \frac{P}{2} \sin \omega_1(t - \tau)\, d\tau \right] \\ &= 1.31 \frac{P}{k} \left| \cos \omega_1(t - \tau) \right|_0^{T_1} + \frac{c_1 P}{2\omega_1 m(1 + c_1^2)} \left| \frac{\cos \omega_1(t - \tau)}{\omega_1} \right|_{T_1}^t \\ &= 1.31 \frac{P}{k} [\cos \omega_1(t - T_1) - \cos \omega_1 t] + 0.588 \frac{P}{k} [1 - \cos \omega_1(t - T_1)] \\ &= \frac{P}{k} [0.588 + 0.722 \cos \omega_1(t - T_1) - 1.31 \cos \omega_1 t] \end{aligned}$$

For time $t > 2T_1$

$$x_{11} = 1.31 \frac{P}{k} \left| \cos \omega_1(t - \tau) \right|_0^{T_1} + 0.588 \frac{P}{k} \left| \cos \omega_1(t - \tau) \right|_{T_1}^{2T_1}$$

$$= 1.31 \frac{P}{k} [\cos \omega_1(t - T_1) - \cos \omega_1 t] + 0.588 \frac{P}{k} [\cos \omega_1(t - 2T_1) - \cos \omega_1(t - T_1)]$$

$$= \frac{P}{k} [0.722 \cos \omega_1(t - T_1) + 0.588 \cos \omega_1(t - 2T_1) - 1.31 \cos \omega_1 t]$$

The corresponding deflections of x_{21} can be found by multiplying x_{11} by $c_1 = 1.618$.

The response of the second mode is now made noting that $\omega_2 = 1.618\sqrt{k/m}$ and $c_2 = -0.618$. For the time interval $0 < t \leq T_1$

$$x_{12} = \frac{1}{\omega_2 m(1 + c_2^2)} \int_0^t P\left(1 + \frac{c_2}{2}\right) \sin \omega_2(t - \tau)\, d\tau$$

$$= \frac{P(1 + c_2/2)}{\omega_2^2 m(1 + c_2^2)} \left| \cos \omega_2(t - \tau) \right|_0^t = 0.190 \frac{P}{k} (1 - \cos \omega_2 t)$$

For $T_1 < t \leq 2T_1$

$$x_{12} = \frac{1}{\omega_2 m(1 + c_2^2)} \int_0^{T_1} P\left(1 + \frac{c_2}{2}\right) \sin \omega_2(t - \tau)\, d\tau + \frac{1}{\omega_2 m(1 + c_2^2)} \int_{T_1}^t c_2 \frac{P}{2} \sin \omega_2(t - \tau)\, d\tau$$

$$= \frac{P(1 + c_2/2)}{\omega_2^2(1 + c_2^2)} \left| \cos \omega_2(t - \tau) \right|_0^{T_1} + \frac{c_2 P}{2\omega_2^2 m(1 + c_2^2)} \left| \cos \omega_2(t - \tau) \right|_{T_1}^t$$

$$= 0.190 \frac{P}{k} [\cos \omega_2(t - T_1) - \cos \omega_2 t] - 0.0853 \frac{P}{k} [1 - \cos \omega_2(t - T_1)]$$

$$= \frac{P}{k} [-0.0853 + 0.275 \cos \omega_2(t - T_1) - 0.190 \cos \omega_2 t]$$

For $t > 2T_1$

$$x_{12} = 0.190 \frac{P}{k} \left| \cos \omega_2(t - \tau) \right|_0^{T_1} - 0.0853 \frac{P}{k} \left| \cos \omega_2(t - \tau) \right|_{T_1}^{2T_1}$$

$$= 0.190 \frac{P}{k} [\cos \omega_2(t - T_1) - \cos \omega_2 t] - 0.0853 \frac{P}{k} [\cos \omega_2(t - 2T_1) - \cos \omega_2(t - T_1)]$$

$$= \frac{P}{k} [-0.190 \cos \omega_2 t + 0.275 \cos \omega_2(t - T_1) - 0.0853 \cos \omega_2(t - 2T_1)]$$

The motion of mass 1 is then given by adding the response of the first and second harmonics, so that, for example, for $0 < t \leq T_1$

$$x_1 = x_{11} + x_{12}$$

$$x_1 = \frac{P}{k} [1.31(1 - \cos \omega_1 t) + 0.190(1 - \cos \omega_2 t)]$$

Also $$x_2 = c_1 x_{11} + c_2 x_{12}$$

and similarly for the other time intervals.

Time-varying Forced Displacements. In the previous sections we considered the response of the system to arbitrary forces applied to the masses. On many occasions it is the movement of one of the masses which is prescribed and it is then required to find the response of the other masses of the system.

Let us suppose that point 2 of the system of Fig. 2-17 is forced to move in the

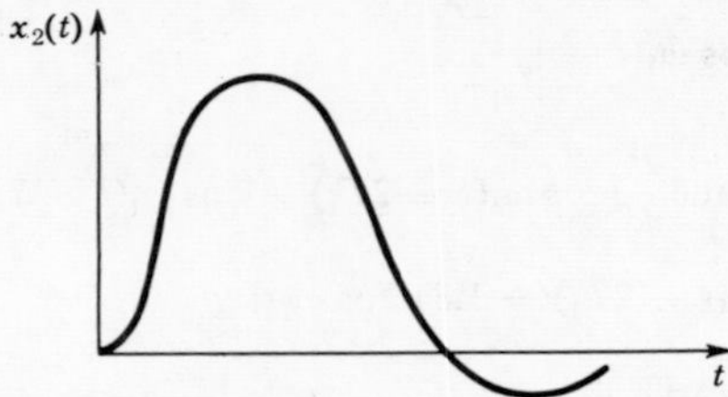

FIG. 2-26. Displacement-time graph.

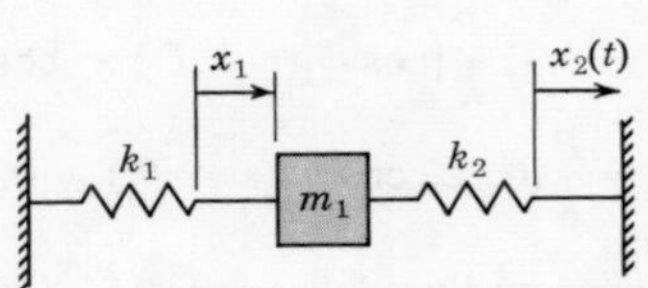

FIG. 2-27. The reduced single-degree-of-freedom system.

manner shown in Fig. 2-26. What was formerly a two-degree-of-freedom system has now been reduced to a single-degree-of-freedom system because only mass m_1 is free to move.

The equation of motion of mass m_1 can be readily found to be (Fig. 2-27)

$$m_1\ddot{x}_1 + k_1x_1 + k_2(x_1 - x_2) = 0$$

or

$$m_1\ddot{x}_1 + x_1(k_1 + k_2) = k_2x_2(t) = p_1(t)$$

The problem is thereby reduced to that of a single degree of freedom with $\omega^2 = (k_1 + k_2)/m$, which was discussed in Sec. 2-2. There we found that the motion resulting from the application of a time-varying force is [cf. Eq. (2-15)]

$$x_1 = \int_0^t \frac{p_1(\tau)}{m_1\omega} \sin \omega(t - \tau)\, d\tau$$

In this case $p_1(\tau) = k_2x_2(\tau)$, so that

$$x_1 = \int_0^t \frac{k_2x_2(\tau)}{m_1\omega} \sin \omega(t - \tau)\, d\tau$$

It is easy to show that for a displacement x_2 the new equilibrium position of mass m_1 becomes

$$x_1^E = \frac{k_2x_2}{k_1 + k_2} = \frac{k_2x_2}{m_1\omega^2}$$

Hence

$$x_1(t) = \int_0^t \omega x_1^E(\tau) \sin \omega(t - \tau)\, d\tau \tag{2-50}$$

In the presence of initial conditions at $t_0 = 0$ the motion of m_1 becomes

$$x_1 = x_1^0 \cos \omega t + \frac{\dot{x}_1^0}{\omega} \sin \omega t + \int_0^t \omega x_1^E(\tau) \sin \omega(t - \tau)\, d\tau \tag{2-50a}$$

PROBLEMS

2-16. A vertical oscillating force $F \cos \Omega t$ is applied to mass m at point 1 of the system illustrated in Fig. P 2-11. Find the value of Ω for which the deflection of the beam is zero. Compute the steady-state deflection of the mass at point 2 at the same frequency.

2-17. A horizontal force $F \cos \Omega t$ is applied to the carriage of Prob. 2-13 (Fig. P 2-13). Find the steady-state deflection of the carriage.

2-18. The mass at point 1 of the system described in Prob. 2-9 (Fig. P 2-9) is subjected to a constant horizontal force of magnitude F for the time duration T_1. Deduce the resulting motion of the system if the initial displacements and velocities are zero.

2-19. The spring-mass system of Fig. P 2-15 is hung vertically by means of a string. Find the motion after the string is cut. HINT: Compare this problem with Prob. 2-15.

3 INTRODUCTION TO STATE VECTORS AND TRANSFER MATRICES

3-1. State Vector and Transfer Matrix

State Vector. The state vector at a point i of an elastic system is a column vector the components of which are the displacements of the point i and the corresponding internal forces. In the simple case of a spring-mass system (Fig. 3-1) the displacement of the point i is clearly the linear displacement x_i, and the corresponding internal force is the direct force N_i in the spring. For this special case the state vector $\mathbf{z}_i$ has the two components x_i and N_i, and in matrix notation $\mathbf{z}_i$ has the form

$$\mathbf{z}_i = \begin{bmatrix} x_i \\ N_i \end{bmatrix} = \begin{bmatrix} x \\ N \end{bmatrix}_i \tag{3-1}$$

Analogous to the spring-mass system is the torsion system, consisting of an elastic

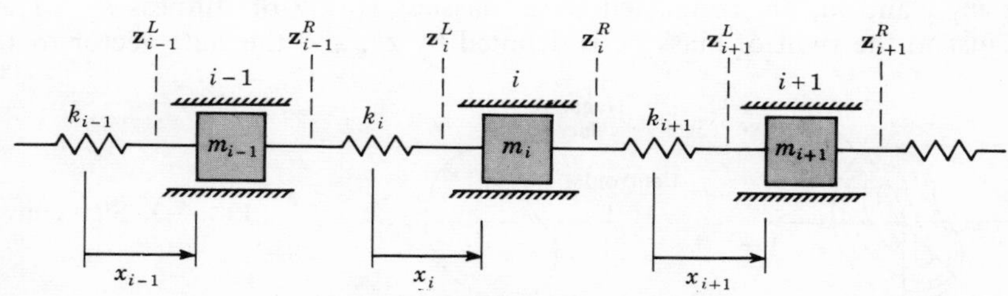

FIG. 3-1. Spring-mass system.

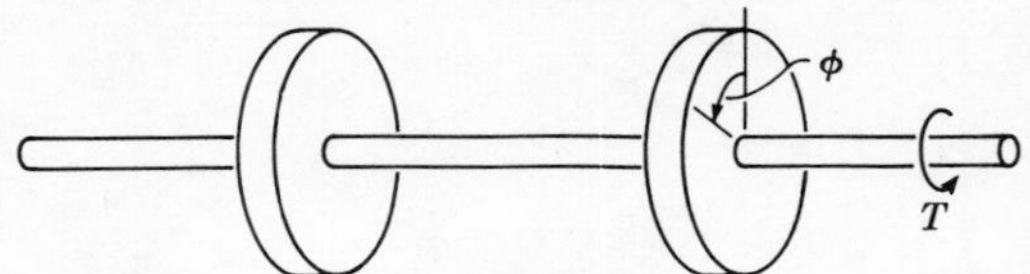

FIG. 3-2. Torsional system.

massless shaft with disks concentrated at different points along its length (Fig. 3-2). The displacement this time is the angle of twist ϕ_i, and the corresponding force is the torque T_i. The state vector is then given by

$$\mathbf{z}_i = \begin{bmatrix} \phi \\ T \end{bmatrix}_i$$

A more complicated case is that of the straight beam. The displacements at the point i are the deflection w_i and the slope ψ_i. The internal forces are the shear force V_i corresponding to the displacement w_i and the moment M_i corresponding to the slope ψ_i. The state vector in this case, therefore, has four components:

$$\mathbf{z}_i = \begin{bmatrix} w \\ \psi \\ M \\ V \end{bmatrix}_i$$

Notice the order in which the components have been written. The displacements are placed in the upper half of the column, and the forces in the lower, in such a way that the force and the corresponding displacement (that is, w and V, ψ and M) are in positions that are mirror images of each other about the center of the column. This arrangement has advantages that will be appreciated later.

Coordinate System and Sign Convention. We shall introduce transfer matrices by referring to the three systems mentioned in the previous section. Before doing so we must define the coordinate system and the sign convention. We shall use the right-handed cartesian coordinate system, the x axis coinciding with the centroidal axis of the elastic body (Fig. 3-3). A cut made across the body will expose two faces, and the face whose outward normal points in the positive direction of the x axis is known as the positive face, the other being the negative face. Positive displacements coincide with positive directions of the coordinate system, and forces are positive if, when acting on the positive (negative) face, their vectors are in the positive (negative) directions. Force vectors are represented by arrows, and moment vectors are represented according to the right-hand-screw rule by a double line with an arrowhead (Fig. 3-4).

Transfer Matrix of Spring-Mass System. Let us consider a spring-mass system of the type shown in Fig. 3-1 which is vibrating with circular frequency ω. The masses m_{i-1} and m_i are connected by a massless spring of stiffness k_i. The state vector just to the right of mass m_i is denoted by $\mathbf{z}_i^R$, and the state vector to the left

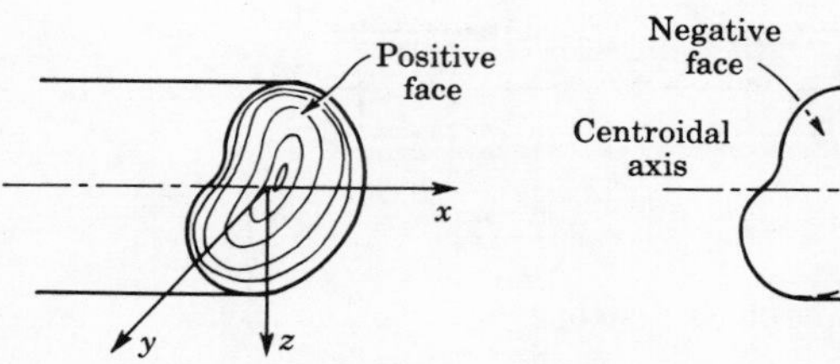

FIG. 3-3. Sign convention.

FIG. 3-4. Vector symbols. Force vector Moment vector

is denoted by $\mathbf{z}_i^L$. If we isolate the spring k_i and use the convention explained above, the positive forces and deflections are as shown in Fig. 3-5.

From the equilibrium of the spring we immediately obtain

$$N_{i-1}^R = N_i^L$$

and from the stiffness property of the spring we have the further relation

$$N_i^L = N_{i-1}^R = k_i(x_i - x_{i-1})$$

Rewriting these equations in the form

$$x_i = x_{i-1} + \frac{N_{i-1}^R}{k_i} \qquad N_i^L = (0)x_{i-1} + N_{i-1}^R$$

we can then take one more step to express the equations in matrix notation,

$$\begin{bmatrix} x \\ N \end{bmatrix}_i^L = \begin{bmatrix} 1 & \dfrac{1}{k_i} \\ 0 & 1 \end{bmatrix} \cdot \begin{bmatrix} x \\ N \end{bmatrix}_{i-1}^R \tag{3-2}$$

or

$$\mathbf{z}_i^L = \mathbf{F}_i \mathbf{z}_{i-1}^R$$

Hence by means of the matrix $\mathbf{F}_i$ we have been able to express the state vector $\mathbf{z}_i^L$ in terms of the state vector $\mathbf{z}_{i-1}^R$. The matrix $\mathbf{F}_i$ is known as the *field transfer matrix*, or more simply as the *field matrix*.

The matrix relation that exists between the state vectors to the left and right of mass i can be found by considering the forces (Fig. 3-6) acting on the mass. The two spring forces are N_i^R and N_i^L, and in addition there is the inertia force $m_i\omega^2 x_i$ acting in the positive direction (cf. Sec. 2-1). Since the mass is rigid, the deflections to the left and right of mass m_i are the same, so that

$$x_i^R = x_i^L$$

and from the equilibrium of the forces we have

$$N_i^R = N_i^L - m_i\omega^2 x_i$$

Rewritten in matrix notation, the above equations become

$$\begin{bmatrix} x \\ N \end{bmatrix}_i^R = \begin{bmatrix} 1 & 0 \\ -m_i\omega^2 & 1 \end{bmatrix} \cdot \begin{bmatrix} x \\ N \end{bmatrix}_i^L \tag{3-3}$$

or

$$\mathbf{z}_i^R = \mathbf{P}_i \mathbf{z}_i^L$$

Again we have found a matrix relation between two adjacent state vectors. This

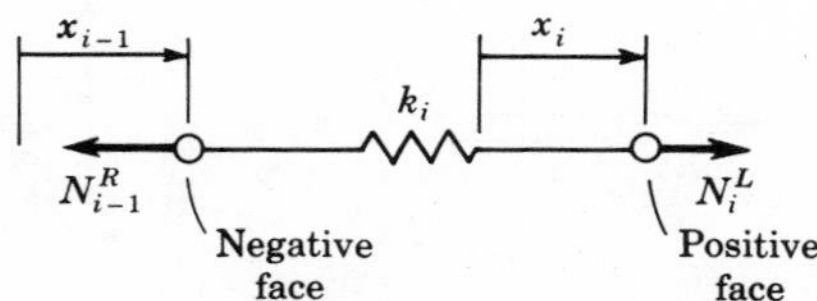

FIG. 3-5. Free-body diagram of spring i.

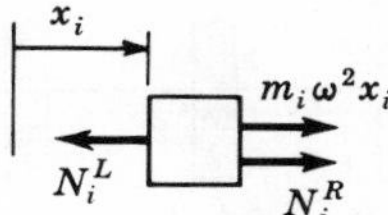

FIG. 3-6. Free-body diagram of mass m_i.

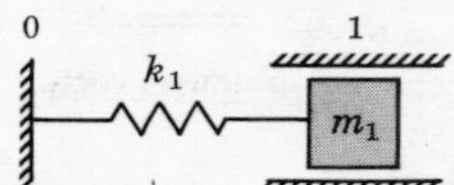

FIG. 3-7. Simple spring-mass system.

time, since we are simply transferring over a point, the matrix $\mathbf{P}_i$ is known as the *point transfer matrix*, or the *point matrix*.

Example 3-1. From the transfer matrices just developed find the natural frequency for the spring-mass system of Fig. 3-7.

From Eqs. (3-2) and (3-3) we have

$$\begin{bmatrix} x \\ N \end{bmatrix}_1^L = \begin{bmatrix} 1 & \frac{1}{k} \\ 0 & 1 \end{bmatrix}_1 \cdot \begin{bmatrix} x \\ N \end{bmatrix}_0^R \quad \text{and} \quad \begin{bmatrix} x \\ N \end{bmatrix}_1^R = \begin{bmatrix} 1 & 0 \\ -m\omega^2 & 1 \end{bmatrix}_1 \cdot \begin{bmatrix} x \\ N \end{bmatrix}_1^L$$

Substituting the first equation in the second, we obtain the relation

$$\begin{bmatrix} x \\ N \end{bmatrix}_1^R = \begin{bmatrix} 1 & 0 \\ -m\omega^2 & 1 \end{bmatrix}_1 \cdot \begin{bmatrix} x \\ N \end{bmatrix}_1^L = \begin{bmatrix} 1 & 0 \\ -m\omega^2 & 1 \end{bmatrix}_1 \cdot \begin{bmatrix} 1 & \frac{1}{k} \\ 0 & 1 \end{bmatrix}_1 \cdot \begin{bmatrix} x \\ N \end{bmatrix}_0^R$$

$$= \begin{bmatrix} 1 & \frac{1}{k} \\ -m\omega^2 & 1 - \frac{m\omega^2}{k} \end{bmatrix}_1 \cdot \begin{bmatrix} x \\ N \end{bmatrix}_0^R$$

Noting that $x_0 = 0$ and $N_1^R = 0$, the above equation yields the results

$$x_1^R = \frac{N_0^R}{k} \qquad 0 = \left(1 - \frac{m_1\omega^2}{k_1}\right) N_0^R$$

For the second of these equations to be satisfied, it follows that $1 - m_1\omega^2/k_1 = 0$, giving the expression for the natural circular frequency $\omega = \sqrt{k_1/m_1}$.

Obviously the matrix method has no special advantage in this simple case, but when the systems are more complicated, the advantages of matrix methods will become obvious.

Transfer Matrix for a Torsional System. We shall now consider the torsional vibrations of an elastic shaft of circular cross section, with disks attached at discrete points along its axis (Fig. 3-8*a*). The shaft is elastic and without rotational inertia, and the disks are rigid and have a rotational moment of inertia I_i. The shaft between $i - 1$ and i is isolated, the end rotations and torques being indicated in Fig. 3-8*b*.†

† In view of the fact that only small deformations are considered throughout, the end rotations ϕ are depicted as axial vectors like the moments.

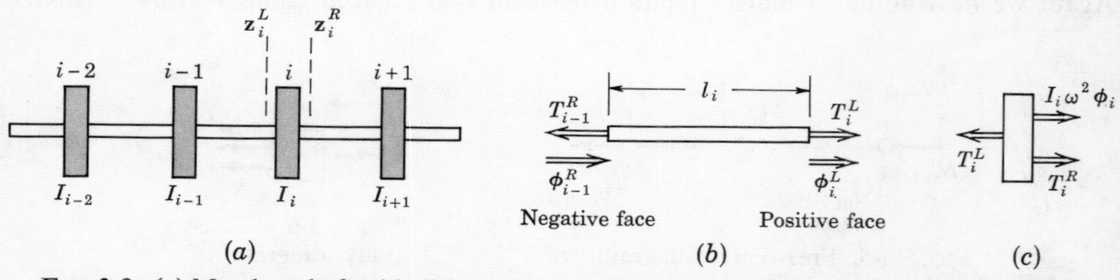

FIG. 3-8. (*a*) Massless shaft with disks; (*b*) free-body diagram of shaft; (*c*) free-body diagram of disk.

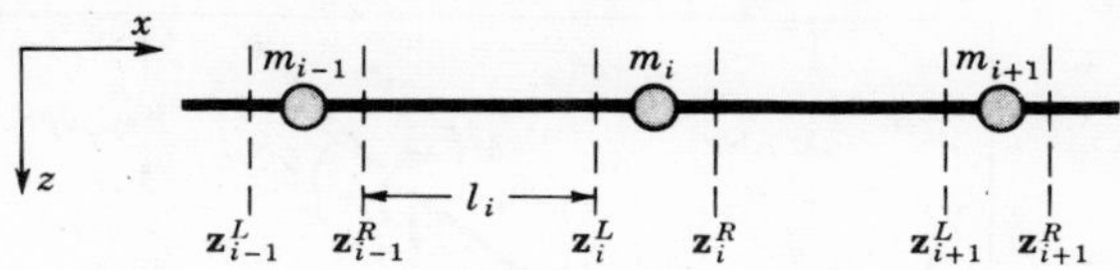

FIG. 3-9. Beam with concentrated masses.

From the equilibrium of the shaft we have

$$T_i^L = T_{i-1}^R$$

and from simple strength of materials the relation

$$\phi_i^L - \phi_{i-1}^R = \frac{T_{i-1}^R l_i}{(J_T G)_i}$$

where J_T is the polar second moment of area of the shaft and G is the shear modulus of the material.

In matrix notation these two equations become

$$\begin{bmatrix} \phi \\ T \end{bmatrix}_i^L = \begin{bmatrix} 1 & \dfrac{l}{J_T G} \\ 0 & 1 \end{bmatrix}_i \cdot \begin{bmatrix} \phi \\ T \end{bmatrix}_{i-1}^R \tag{3-4}$$

or

$$\mathbf{z}_i^L = \mathbf{F}_i \mathbf{z}_{i-1}^R$$

When relating the state vectors $\mathbf{z}_i^R$ and $\mathbf{z}_i^L$ on either side of the disk i, we note that the angle of twist remains unchanged, so that $\phi_i^L = \phi_i^R$, but as a result of the inertia torque of the disk there is a discontinuity in the torque. With reference to Fig. 3-8c, the equilibrium condition yields the expression

$$T_i^R - T_i^L + I_i \omega^2 \phi_i = 0$$

These equations are combined in the single matrix expression

$$\begin{bmatrix} \phi \\ T \end{bmatrix}_i^R = \begin{bmatrix} 1 & 0 \\ -\omega^2 I & 0 \end{bmatrix}_i \cdot \begin{bmatrix} \phi \\ T \end{bmatrix}_i^L \tag{3-5}$$

or

$$\mathbf{z}_i^R = \mathbf{P}_i \mathbf{z}_i^L$$

Plane Flexural Vibrations of a Straight Beam. When computing the flexural vibrations of beams with distributed mass, it is often advisable to follow the technique† of replacing the actual beam by a beam of the same flexural stiffness which is massless between discrete points where the mass is concentrated. Such a system (Fig. 3-9) is easily analyzed by transfer matrices. The first step is to isolate the beam element between the points $i - 1$ and i. The sign convention explained at the beginning of this section is applied to the straight beam, as illustrated in Fig. 3-10.

† Cf., for example, Refs. 7 and 8.

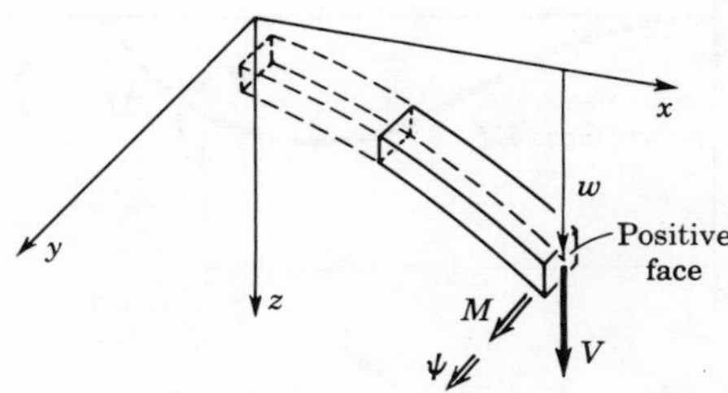

FIG. 3-10. Sign convention for beam.

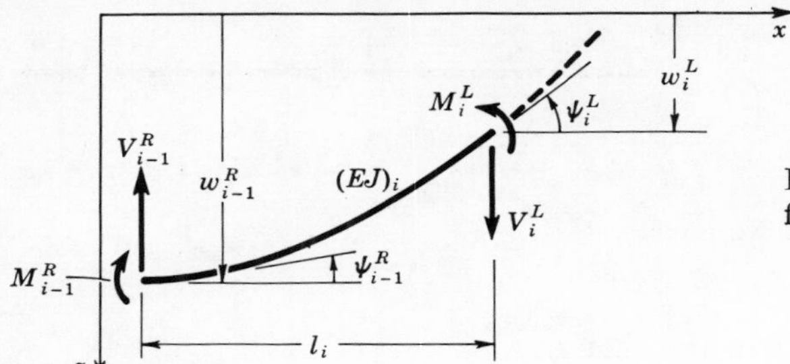

FIG. 3-11. End forces and deflections for massless beam.

The two displacements are the deflection w and the slope ψ, the corresponding forces being the shear force V and the bending moment M. The forces and deflections at the extremities of the beam element are shown in Fig. 3-11. The equilibrium of the element requires that the sum of the vertical forces be zero and that the sum of the moments about, let us say, point $i - 1$ be zero. The two equilibrium equations are then

$$V_i^L - V_{i-1}^R = 0 \tag{3-6a}$$

$$M_i^L - M_{i-1}^R - V_i^L l_i = 0 \tag{3-6b}$$

We obtain two further equations for the end deflection and slope of a cantilever of flexural stiffness EJ subjected to moment M and shear V at its free end (Fig. 3-12) from elementary beam theory:

$$w = -\frac{Ml^2}{2EJ} + \frac{Vl^3}{3EJ} \qquad \psi = \frac{Ml}{EJ} - \frac{Vl^2}{2EJ}$$

Applying these results to the problem at hand and noting that the point $i - 1$ has a deflection w_{i-1} and a slope ψ_{i-1}, we obtain the equations

$$w_i^L = w_{i-1}^R - \psi_{i-1}^R l_i - M_i^L \frac{l_i^2}{2(EJ)_i} + V_i^L \frac{l_i^3}{3(EJ)_i} \tag{3-7a}$$

$$\psi_i^L = \psi_{i-1}^R + M_i^L \frac{l_i}{(EJ)_i} - V_i^L \frac{l_i^2}{2(EJ)_i} \tag{3-7b}$$

We note from Eqs. (3-6) that

$$V_i^L = V_{i-1}^R \qquad \text{and} \qquad M_i^L = M_{i-1}^R + V_{i-1}^R l_i$$

Equations (3-6) and (3-7) can be rewritten such that all the state-vector elements at point i^L can be expressed in terms of those at point $i - 1^R$:

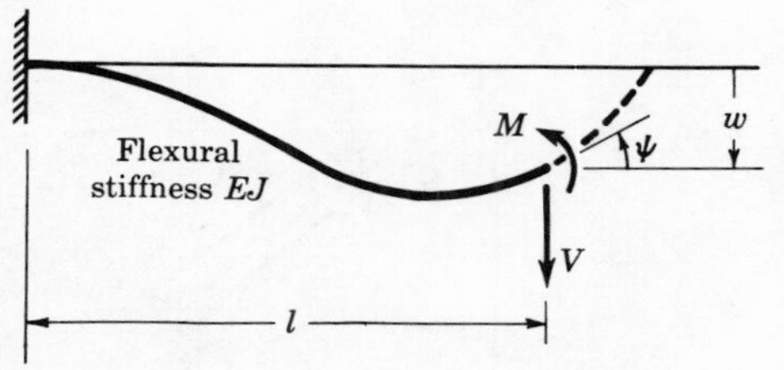

FIG. 3-12. Cantilever subjected to force V and moment M.

$$
\begin{aligned}
-w_i^L\dagger &= -w_i^R + l_i\psi_{i-1}^R + \frac{l_i^2}{2(EJ)_i}M_{i-1}^R + \frac{l_i^3}{6(EJ)_i}V_{i-1}^R \\
\psi_i^L &= \psi_{i-1}^R + \frac{l_i}{(EJ)_i}M_{i-1}^R + \frac{l_i^2}{2(EJ)_i}V_{i-1}^R \\
M_i^L &= M_{i-1}^R + l_iV_{i-1}^R \\
V_i^L &= V_{i-1}^R
\end{aligned}
$$

or, in matrix notation,

$$
\begin{bmatrix} -w \\ \psi \\ M \\ V \end{bmatrix}_i^L = \begin{bmatrix} 1 & l & \frac{l^2}{2EJ} & \frac{l^3}{6EJ} \\ 0 & 1 & \frac{l}{EJ} & \frac{l^2}{2EJ} \\ 0 & 0 & 1 & l \\ 0 & 0 & 0 & 1 \end{bmatrix}_i \cdot \begin{bmatrix} -w \\ \psi \\ M \\ V \end{bmatrix}_{i-1}^R \tag{3-8}
$$

or $\mathbf{z}_i^L = \mathbf{F}_i\mathbf{z}_{i-1}^R$

The point matrix connecting $\mathbf{z}_i^R$ with $\mathbf{z}_i^L$ is found by noting that the deflection, slope, and moment‡ are continuous across the concentrated mass m_i, so that

$$
w_i^R = w_i^L \qquad \psi_i^R = \psi_i^L \qquad M_i^R = M_i^L \tag{3-9}
$$

The vibrating mass, however, introducing an inertia force causes a discontinuity in the shear. The free-body diagram shown in Fig. 3-13 yields from simple equilibrium considerations the relation

$$
V_i^R = V_i^L - m_i\omega^2 w_i \tag{3-10}
$$

In matrix notation Eqs. (3-9) and (3-10) become

$$
\begin{bmatrix} -w \\ \psi \\ M \\ V \end{bmatrix}_i^R = \begin{bmatrix} 1 & 0 & 0 & 0 \\ 0 & 1 & 0 & 0 \\ 0 & 0 & 1 & 0 \\ m\omega^2 & 0 & 0 & 1 \end{bmatrix}_i \cdot \begin{bmatrix} -w \\ \psi \\ M \\ V \end{bmatrix}_i^L \tag{3-11}
$$

or $\mathbf{z}_i^R = \mathbf{P}_i\mathbf{z}_i^L$

Another point matrix that can be easily obtained covers the case when the beam

† Choosing the first element of the state vector to be $-w$ (although this is not necessary) has the advantage that all the elements of the matrix are positive and that the matrix is cross-symmetric.

‡ The moment is continuous only if the radius of gyration of the mass about the y axis is taken to be zero.

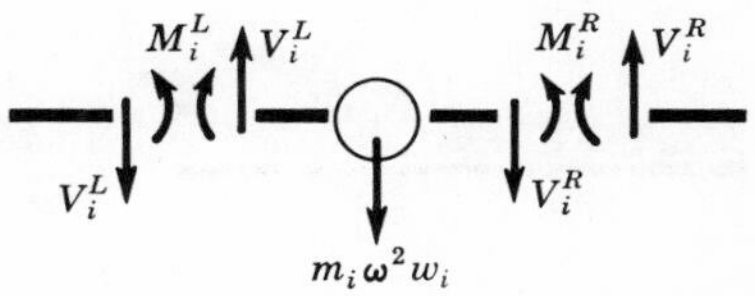

FIG. 3-13. Free-body diagram of mass m_i.

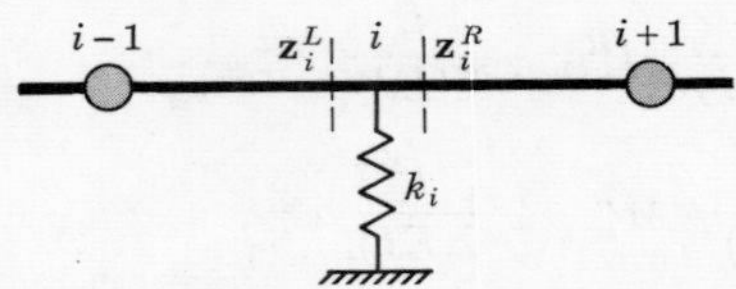

Fig. 3-14. Beam on elastic support.

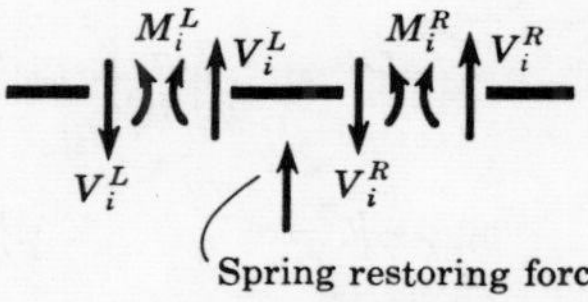

Spring restoring force $k_i w_i$

FIG. 3-15. Free-body diagram of the elastic support.

has a spring support (Fig. 3-14). We can again relate the state vectors $\mathbf{z}_i^R$ and $\mathbf{z}_i^L$ by means of a point matrix. The deflection, slope, and moment are continuous over the point *i*, but on account of the spring restoring force a discontinuity occurs in the shear force. If the spring is deflected by an amount w_i, then the restoring force is $k_i w_i$, where k_i is the stiffness of the spring (Fig. 3-15). The relations of the state-vector elements to the left and right of the spring are then

$$-w_i^R = -w_i^L \qquad \psi_i^R = \psi_i^L \qquad M_i^R = M_i^L \qquad V_i^R = k_i w_i + V_i^L$$

which in matrix notation become

$$\begin{bmatrix} -w \\ \psi \\ M \\ V \end{bmatrix}_i^R = \begin{bmatrix} 1 & 0 & 0 & 0 \\ 0 & 1 & 0 & 0 \\ 0 & 0 & 1 & 0 \\ -k & 0 & 0 & 1 \end{bmatrix}_i \cdot \begin{bmatrix} -w \\ \psi \\ M \\ V \end{bmatrix}_i^L \tag{3-12}$$

or

$$\mathbf{z}_i^R = \mathbf{P}_i \mathbf{z}_i^L$$

Example 3-2. Compute the natural frequency of a massless beam of flexural stiffness *EJ* and length *l*, which is built-in at one end and has a concentrated mass fixed to the other (Fig. 3-16).

Using the results of the previous section, we have the relations

$$\mathbf{z}_1^R = \begin{bmatrix} 1 & 0 & 0 & 0 \\ 0 & 1 & 0 & 0 \\ 0 & 0 & 1 & 0 \\ m\omega^2 & 0 & 0 & 1 \end{bmatrix} \cdot \mathbf{z}_1^L$$

$$\mathbf{z}_1^L = \begin{bmatrix} 1 & l & \dfrac{l^2}{2EJ} & \dfrac{l^3}{6EJ} \\ 0 & 1 & \dfrac{l}{EJ} & \dfrac{l^2}{2EJ} \\ 0 & 0 & 1 & l \\ 0 & 0 & 0 & 1 \end{bmatrix} \cdot \mathbf{z}_0^R$$

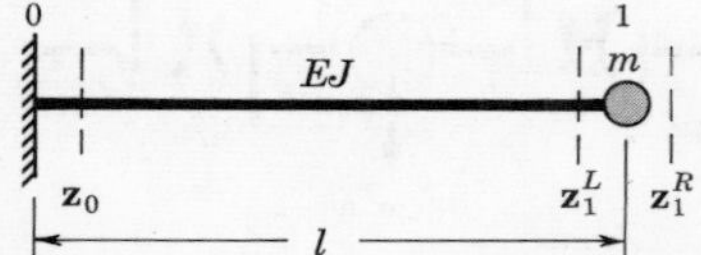

FIG. 3-16. Cantilever with concentrated end mass.

from which we obtain the relation between $\mathbf{z}_1^R$ and $\mathbf{z}_0^R$:

$$\begin{bmatrix} -w \\ \psi \\ M \\ V \end{bmatrix}_1^R = \begin{bmatrix} 1 & 0 & 0 & 0 \\ 0 & 1 & 0 & 0 \\ 0 & 0 & 1 & 0 \\ m\omega^2 & 0 & 0 & 1 \end{bmatrix} \cdot \begin{bmatrix} 1 & l & \frac{l^2}{2EJ} & \frac{l^3}{6EJ} \\ 0 & 1 & \frac{l}{EJ} & \frac{l^2}{2EJ} \\ 0 & 0 & 1 & l \\ 0 & 0 & 0 & 1 \end{bmatrix} \cdot \begin{bmatrix} -w \\ \psi \\ M \\ V \end{bmatrix}_0^R$$

$$= \begin{bmatrix} 1 & l & \frac{l^2}{2EJ} & \frac{l^3}{6EJ} \\ 0 & 1 & \frac{l}{EJ} & \frac{l^2}{2EJ} \\ 0 & 0 & 1 & l \\ m\omega^2 & m\omega^2 l & \frac{m\omega^2 l^2}{2EJ} & 1 + \frac{m\omega^2 l^3}{6EJ} \end{bmatrix} \cdot \begin{bmatrix} -w \\ \psi \\ M \\ V \end{bmatrix}_0^R$$

Noting that $M_1^R = V_1^R = w_0 = \psi_0 = 0$, we obtain from the above matrix equation the relations

$$\begin{aligned} -w_1^R &= \frac{l^2}{2EJ} M_0^R + \frac{l^3}{6EJ} V_0^R \\ \psi_1^R &= \frac{l}{EJ} M_0^R + \frac{l^2}{2EJ} V_0^R \\ 0 &= M_0^R + l V_0^R \\ 0 &= m\omega^2 \frac{l^2}{2EJ} M_0^R + \left(1 + m\omega^2 \frac{l^3}{6EJ}\right) V_0^R \end{aligned}$$

For the last two equations to be satisfied the determinant of the coefficients of M_0^R and V_0^R must be zero (cf. Sec. 1-2):

$$\begin{vmatrix} 1 & l \\ m\omega^2 \frac{l^2}{2EJ} & 1 + m\omega^2 \frac{l^3}{6EJ} \end{vmatrix} = 0$$

On expanding the determinant, the expression for the natural circular frequency is found to be

$$\omega^2 = \frac{3EJ}{ml^3}$$

The transfer matrices just derived have involved us in only simple equilibrium and strength-of-materials relations, but we cannot expect to derive all transfer matrices in such an easy straightforward manner. In Chap. 5, general methods for finding transfer matrices will be discussed, but in the meantime we shall be able to solve a large number of problems with the transfer matrices already at our disposal.

PROBLEMS

3-1. Set up the transfer matrix for a rigid body of mass m and of radius of gyration i_y which is attached to a beam vibrating in the xz plane.

3-2. A beam is supported by a spring of longitudinal stiffness k_w and rotational stiffness k_ψ. Set up the point matrix for this spring. What is the point matrix if at the same point a rigid body of mass m and of radius of gyration i_y is also attached to the beam?

3-3. Compute the natural frequency of the spring-mass system shown in Fig. P 3-3.

3-4. A massless cantilever beam of flexural stiffness EJ and length l has a uniform disk of mass m and radius r attached at its free end (Fig. P 3-4). Compute the natural frequencies for flexural vibrations in the xz plane.

3-5. The cantilever of Fig. P 3-4 is modified by the addition of a prop spring of stiffness k. Compute the new natural frequencies.

3-6. Find the natural frequency of the system illustrated in Fig. P 3-6. What is the natural frequency when the massless beam becomes infinitely stiff?

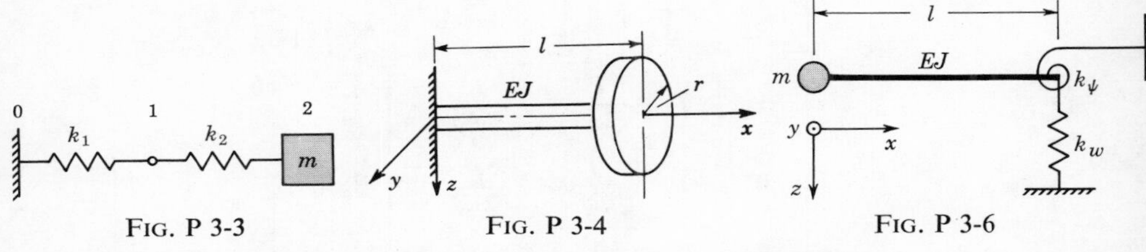

FIG. P 3-3 FIG. P 3-4 FIG. P 3-6

3-2. Transfer Matrices as a Means of Elimination. Frequency Determinant

Elimination of Intermediate State Vectors. The application of transfer matrices to more complicated problems will now be discussed. Let us consider the beam (Fig. 3-17) that is made up of piecewise uniform massless elements, with masses concentrated at discrete points.† The transfer matrices for a uniform massless beam, Eq. (3-8), and for a concentrated mass, Eq. (3-11), have already been derived, so that with the dimensions of the beams and the magnitude of the masses given, the following matrix relations exist between adjacent state vectors:

$$\mathbf{z}_1^L = \mathbf{F}_1\mathbf{z}_0 \quad \mathbf{z}_1^R = \mathbf{P}_1\mathbf{z}_1^L \quad \mathbf{z}_2^L = \mathbf{F}_2\mathbf{z}_1^R \quad \cdots \quad \mathbf{z}_6^L = \mathbf{F}_6\mathbf{z}_5^R \quad \mathbf{z}_6^R = \mathbf{P}_6\mathbf{z}_6^L \quad \mathbf{z}_7 = \mathbf{F}_7\mathbf{z}_6^R$$

From the last two equations $\mathbf{z}_7 = \mathbf{F}_7\mathbf{z}_6^R$ and $\mathbf{z}_6^R = \mathbf{P}_6\mathbf{z}_6^L$, it follows that $\mathbf{z}_7 = \mathbf{F}_7\mathbf{P}_6\mathbf{z}_6^L$. Now using the relation $\mathbf{z}_6^L = \mathbf{F}_6\mathbf{z}_5^R$ we obtain

$$\mathbf{z}_7 = \mathbf{F}_7\mathbf{P}_6\mathbf{F}_6\mathbf{z}_5^R$$

This procedure is continued until we finally obtain the relation between the state vectors at the two ends of the beam:

$$\mathbf{z}_7 = \mathbf{F}_7\mathbf{P}_6\mathbf{F}_6\mathbf{P}_5\mathbf{F}_5\mathbf{P}_4\mathbf{F}_4\mathbf{P}_3\mathbf{F}_3\mathbf{P}_2\mathbf{F}_2\mathbf{P}_1\mathbf{F}_1\mathbf{z}_0$$

$$\mathbf{z}_7 = \mathbf{U}\mathbf{z}_0 \tag{3-13}$$

In this manner all the intermediate state vectors have been eliminated.

Rewriting Eq. (3-13) in full we have

$$\begin{bmatrix} -w \\ \psi \\ M \\ V \end{bmatrix}_7 = \begin{bmatrix} u_{11} & u_{12} & u_{13} & u_{14} \\ u_{21} & u_{22} & u_{23} & u_{24} \\ u_{31} & u_{32} & u_{33} & u_{34} \\ u_{41} & u_{42} & u_{43} & u_{44} \end{bmatrix} \cdot \begin{bmatrix} -w \\ \psi \\ M \\ V \end{bmatrix}_0$$

† This lumped-parameter technique is no prerequisite for the application of transfer matrices. It proves, however, to be practical in most cases.

FIG. 3-17. Beam with discrete masses.

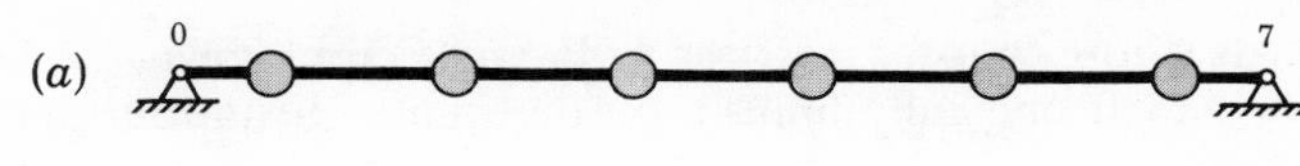

FIG. 3-18. Two cases of boundary conditions.

the coefficients u_{11} to u_{44} all being known functions of the circular frequency ω. Expanding the matrix product gives the four equations

$$-w_7 = -u_{11}w_0 + u_{12}\psi_0 + u_{13}M_0 + u_{14}V_0 \qquad (3\text{-}14a)$$

$$\psi_7 = -u_{21}w_0 + u_{22}\psi_0 + u_{23}M_0 + u_{24}V_0 \qquad (3\text{-}14b)$$

$$M_7 = -u_{31}w_0 + u_{32}\psi_0 + u_{33}M_0 + u_{34}V_0 \qquad (3\text{-}14c)$$

$$V_7 = -u_{41}w_0 + u_{42}\psi_0 + u_{43}M_0 + u_{44}V_0 \qquad (3\text{-}14d)$$

Frequency Determinant. It is by applying the boundary conditions to these equations that we eventually formulate the frequency condition. Consider the following two cases:

Case 1. Beam Simply Supported at Both Ends (Fig. 3-18*a*). The boundary conditions are

$$w_7 = 0 \qquad M_7 = 0 \qquad w_0 = 0 \qquad M_0 = 0$$

Substituting these in Eqs. (3-14*a*) and (3-14*c*), we obtain

$$0 = u_{12}\psi_0 + u_{14}V_0 \qquad 0 = u_{32}\psi_0 + u_{34}V_0$$

For a nontrivial solution of these equations the determinant of the coefficients must be zero, that is,

$$\begin{vmatrix} u_{12} & u_{14} \\ u_{32} & u_{34} \end{vmatrix} = 0$$

Since the elements u_{ik} are known functions of the circular frequency ω, this determinant serves to compute the natural circular frequencies. In view of the fact that the beam possesses six discrete masses, the expansion of the frequency determinant leads to an equation of sixth degree in ω^2.

Case 2. Left Side Built-in, Right Side Free (Fig. 3-18*b*). The boundary conditions

$$M_7 = 0 \qquad V_7 = 0 \qquad w_0 = 0 \qquad \psi_0 = 0$$

yield, after substitution in Eqs. (3-14*c*) and (3-14*d*),

$$0 = u_{33}M_0 + u_{34}V_0 \qquad 0 = u_{43}M_0 + u_{44}V_0$$

and the frequency determinant is

$$\begin{vmatrix} u_{33} & u_{34} \\ u_{43} & u_{44} \end{vmatrix} = 0 \qquad (3\text{-}15)$$

In practice we are usually interested in the natural frequencies of a particular system subjected to only one set of boundary conditions. When this is so, it is not necessary to carry through the complete matrix multiplication. Consider, for example, the beam illustrated in Fig. 3-19, which is, let us say, divided into three

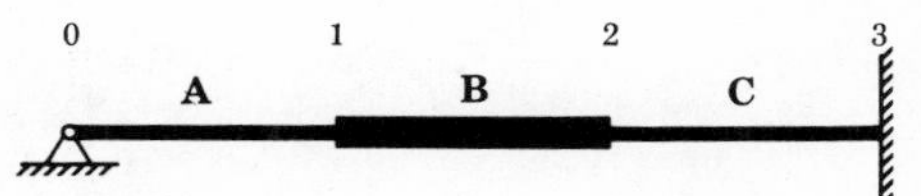

FIG. 3-19. Beam of three sections.

parts whose transfer matrices **A**, **B**, and **C** are known. The beam is simply supported on the left and fully built-in on the right. From our discussion above we have the relations

$$\mathbf{z}_1 = \mathbf{A}\mathbf{z}_0 \qquad \mathbf{z}_2 = \mathbf{B}\mathbf{A}\mathbf{z}_0 \qquad \mathbf{z}_3 = \mathbf{C}\mathbf{B}\mathbf{A}\mathbf{z}_0$$

That is, the state vectors at the points 1, 2, and 3 are found by multiplying the state vector $\mathbf{z}_0$ by the matrices **A**, **BA**, and **CBA**, respectively. Using the method for multiplying matrices described in Sec. 1-3, the matrix layout for this example is shown in Table 3-1. When the matrix multiplication has been completed, we can see that, since the deflection and moment at point 0 are zero, the first and third columns are multiplied by zero, and thus play no part in the calculation. Elements that appear in the first and third columns of the matrices **A**, **BA**, and **CBA** may therefore be dropped. This has been indicated by drawing vertical lines between the unnecessary elements. The abridged layout is indicated in Table 3-2, and from now on it is the abridged version that will be used.

With the boundary conditions at point 3 being $w_3 = \psi_3 = 0$, we obtain the relations

$$e_{12}\psi_0 + e_{14}V_0 = 0 \tag{3-16a}$$

$$e_{22}\psi_0 + e_{24}V_0 = 0 \tag{3-16b}$$

from which the frequency determinant is

$$\begin{vmatrix} e_{12} & e_{14} \\ e_{22} & e_{24} \end{vmatrix} = 0$$

In this problem it is unnecessary to compute e_{32}, e_{34}, e_{42}, and e_{44}.

Example 3-3. Find by the use of transfer matrices the natural frequencies of the spring-mass system shown in Fig. 3-20.

Table 3-1. Scheme for Multiplication of Transfer Matrices

$$\mathbf{A} \downarrow \begin{bmatrix} a_{11} & a_{12} & a_{13} & a_{14} \\ a_{21} & a_{22} & a_{23} & a_{24} \\ a_{31} & a_{32} & a_{33} & a_{34} \\ a_{41} & a_{42} & a_{43} & a_{44} \end{bmatrix} \cdot \begin{bmatrix} 0 \\ \psi \\ 0 \\ V \end{bmatrix}_0 = \mathbf{z}_1$$

$$\mathbf{B} \begin{bmatrix} b_{11} & b_{12} & b_{13} & b_{14} \\ b_{21} & b_{22} & b_{23} & b_{24} \\ b_{31} & b_{32} & b_{33} & b_{34} \\ b_{41} & b_{42} & b_{43} & b_{44} \end{bmatrix} \overrightarrow{} \begin{bmatrix} d_{11} & d_{12} & d_{13} & d_{14} \\ d_{21} & d_{22} & d_{23} & d_{24} \\ d_{31} & d_{32} & d_{33} & d_{34} \\ d_{41} & d_{42} & d_{43} & d_{44} \end{bmatrix} \cdot \begin{bmatrix} 0 \\ \psi \\ 0 \\ V \end{bmatrix}_0 = \mathbf{z}_2$$

$$\mathbf{C} \begin{bmatrix} c_{11} & c_{12} & c_{13} & c_{14} \\ c_{21} & c_{22} & c_{23} & c_{24} \\ c_{31} & c_{32} & c_{33} & c_{34} \\ c_{41} & c_{42} & c_{43} & c_{44} \end{bmatrix} \begin{bmatrix} e_{11} & e_{12} & e_{13} & e_{14} \\ e_{21} & e_{22} & e_{23} & e_{24} \\ e_{31} & e_{32} & e_{33} & e_{34} \\ e_{41} & e_{42} & e_{43} & e_{44} \end{bmatrix} \cdot \begin{bmatrix} 0 \\ \psi \\ 0 \\ V \end{bmatrix}_0 = \mathbf{z}_3$$

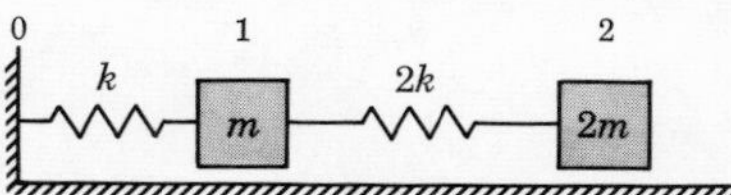

FIG. 3-20. System having two degrees of freedom.

Table 3-2. Abridged Version of Table 3-1

$$\begin{bmatrix} a_{12} & a_{14} \\ a_{22} & a_{24} \\ a_{32} & a_{34} \\ a_{42} & a_{44} \end{bmatrix} \cdot \begin{bmatrix} \psi \\ V \end{bmatrix}_0 = \mathbf{z}_1$$

$$\begin{bmatrix} b_{11} & b_{12} & b_{13} & b_{14} \\ b_{21} & b_{22} & b_{23} & b_{24} \\ b_{31} & b_{32} & b_{33} & b_{34} \\ b_{41} & b_{42} & b_{43} & b_{44} \end{bmatrix} \begin{bmatrix} d_{12} & d_{14} \\ d_{22} & d_{24} \\ d_{32} & d_{34} \\ d_{42} & d_{44} \end{bmatrix} \cdot \begin{bmatrix} \psi \\ V \end{bmatrix}_0 = \mathbf{z}_2$$

$$\begin{bmatrix} c_{11} & c_{12} & c_{13} & c_{14} \\ c_{21} & c_{22} & c_{23} & c_{24} \\ c_{31} & c_{32} & c_{33} & c_{34} \\ c_{41} & c_{42} & c_{43} & c_{44} \end{bmatrix} \begin{bmatrix} e_{12} & e_{14} \\ e_{22} & e_{24} \\ e_{32} & e_{34} \\ e_{42} & e_{44} \end{bmatrix} \cdot \begin{bmatrix} \psi \\ V \end{bmatrix}_0 = \mathbf{z}_3 = \begin{bmatrix} 0 \\ 0 \\ M \\ V \end{bmatrix}_3$$

The transfer matrix for a spring of stiffness k is [cf. Eq. (3-2)]

$$\begin{bmatrix} 1 & \frac{1}{k} \\ 0 & 0 \end{bmatrix}$$

and that for a mass m vibrating with circular frequency ω is [cf. Eq. (3-3)]

$$\begin{bmatrix} 1 & 0 \\ -m\omega^2 & 1 \end{bmatrix}$$

The state vector at point 0 is $\mathbf{z}_0 = \{0 \quad N\}_0$, since the displacement at point 0 is zero, and from the previous discussion we conclude that the first column may be dropped. The abridged version of the matrix multiplication is carried out in Table 3-3 with the substitution $p^2 = m\omega^2/k$.

Since $N_2^R = 0$ we obtain the relation

$$(p^4 - 4p^2 + 1)N_0 = 0$$

which has a nontrivial solution for N_0 if

$$p^4 - 4p^2 + 1 = 0$$

The roots of the equation are

$$p_1^2 = 2 - \sqrt{3} \qquad p_2^2 = 2 + \sqrt{3}$$

so that

$$\omega_1^2 = \frac{k}{m}(2 - \sqrt{3}) \qquad \omega_2^2 = \frac{k}{m}(2 + \sqrt{3})$$

Table 3-3

$$\overset{\mathbf{F}_{\text{spring}}}{\longrightarrow}\downarrow \begin{bmatrix} \dfrac{1}{k} \\ 1 \end{bmatrix} \cdot \begin{bmatrix} N \end{bmatrix}_0^R = \mathbf{z}_1^L$$

$$\mathbf{P}_{\text{mass}} \begin{bmatrix} 1 & 0 \\ -m\omega^2 & 1 \end{bmatrix} \begin{bmatrix} \dfrac{1}{k} \\ 1 - p^2 \end{bmatrix} \cdot \begin{bmatrix} N \end{bmatrix}_0^R = \mathbf{z}_1^R$$

$$\mathbf{F}_{\text{spring}} \begin{bmatrix} 1 & \dfrac{1}{2k} \\ 0 & 1 \end{bmatrix} \begin{bmatrix} \dfrac{3 - p^2}{2k} \\ 1 - p^2 \end{bmatrix} \cdot \begin{bmatrix} N \end{bmatrix}_0^R = \mathbf{z}_2^L$$

$$\mathbf{P}_{\text{mass}} \begin{bmatrix} 1 & 0 \\ -2m\omega^2 & 1 \end{bmatrix} \begin{bmatrix} \dfrac{3 - p^2}{2k} \\ p^4 - 4p^2 + 1 \end{bmatrix} \cdot \begin{bmatrix} N \end{bmatrix}_0^R = \mathbf{z}_2^R = \begin{bmatrix} x \\ 0 \end{bmatrix}_2^R$$

Example 3-4. Compute the natural frequencies of the system shown in Fig. 3-21 in which the two blocks can slide without friction and the uniform disk of radius r and mass m rolls without slipping.

The transfer matrices for the spring and concentrated mass are already known, but before proceeding we must deduce the transfer matrix that relates the state vectors on either side of the rolling disk. This can be done by applying the inertia forces and torques on the disk and considering the equilibrium. The magnitude of the inertia force is $m\omega^2 x_2$, where x_2 is the displacement, and the magnitude of the inertia torque is $(mr^2/2)\omega^2\phi_2$, where $mr^2/2$ is the moment of inertia about the central axis and ϕ_2 is the angle of rotation. With the rolling condition $x_2 = \phi_2 r$ the inertia force and moment acting on the disk are $m\omega^2 x_2$ and $(mr^2/2)\omega^2 x_2/r$. All the forces including the normal reaction R and friction force F are shown in Fig. 3-22.

Taking moments about the instantaneous center C, we have

$$N_2^R r - N_2^L r + m\omega^2 x_2 r + \frac{mr}{2}\,\omega^2 x_2 = 0$$

giving

$$N_2^R = N_2^L - \tfrac{3}{2} m\omega^2 x_2$$

Also, since the displacement remains unchanged,

$$x_2^R = x_2^L$$

Formulating the transfer matrix from these two equations gives

$$\begin{bmatrix} x \\ N \end{bmatrix}_2^R = \begin{bmatrix} 1 & 0 \\ -\tfrac{3}{2}m\omega^2 & 1 \end{bmatrix} \cdot \begin{bmatrix} x \\ N \end{bmatrix}_2^L \tag{3-17}$$

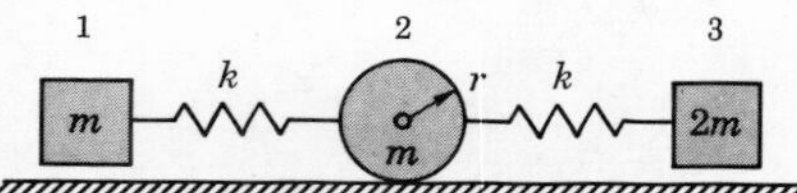

FIG. 3-21. Spring-mass system with roller.

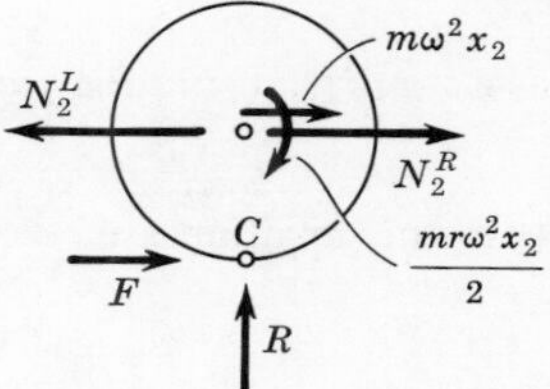

FIG. 3-22. Free-body diagram of roller.

Table 3-4

$$\mathbf{P}_{\text{mass}} \begin{bmatrix} 1 \\ -m\omega^2 \end{bmatrix} \cdot \begin{bmatrix} x \end{bmatrix}_1^L = \mathbf{z}_1^R$$

$$\mathbf{F}_{\text{spring}} \begin{bmatrix} 1 & \frac{1}{k} \\ 0 & 1 \end{bmatrix} \begin{bmatrix} 1 - p^2 \\ -m\omega^2 \end{bmatrix} \cdot \begin{bmatrix} x \end{bmatrix}_1^L = \mathbf{z}_2^L$$

$$\mathbf{P}_{\text{disk}} \begin{bmatrix} 1 & 0 \\ -\frac{3}{2}m\omega^2 & 1 \end{bmatrix} \begin{bmatrix} 1 - p^2 \\ -m\omega^2\left(\frac{5}{2} - \frac{3p^2}{2}\right) \end{bmatrix} \cdot \begin{bmatrix} x \end{bmatrix}_1^L = \mathbf{z}_2^R$$

$$\mathbf{F}_{\text{spring}} \begin{bmatrix} 1 & \frac{1}{k} \\ 0 & 1 \end{bmatrix} \begin{bmatrix} 1 - \frac{7}{2}p^2 + \frac{3}{2}p^4 \\ -m\omega^2\left(\frac{5}{2} - \frac{3p^2}{2}\right) \end{bmatrix} \cdot \begin{bmatrix} x \end{bmatrix}_1^L = \mathbf{z}_3^L$$

$$\mathbf{P}_{\text{mass}} \begin{bmatrix} 1 & 0 \\ -2m\omega^2 & 1 \end{bmatrix} \begin{bmatrix} 1 - \frac{7}{2}p^2 + \frac{3}{2}p^4 \\ -m\omega^2(\frac{9}{2} - \frac{17}{2}p^2 + 3p^4) \end{bmatrix} \cdot \begin{bmatrix} x \end{bmatrix}_1^L = \mathbf{z}_3^R = \begin{bmatrix} x \\ 0 \end{bmatrix}_3^R$$

We now follow the standard procedure, noting on this occasion that the state vector $\mathbf{z}_1^L$ is $\{x \quad 0\}_1^L$. The second column of the matrix products is consequently dropped, and if we again make the substitution $p^2 = m\omega^2/k$, the matrix scheme takes the form shown in Table 3-4.

With $N_3^R = 0$ we obtain from the final matrix equation

$$-m\omega^2(\tfrac{9}{2} - \tfrac{17}{2}p^2 + 3p^4)x_0 = 0$$

the roots of which are, besides $\omega = 0$,

$$p^2 = 0.70 \qquad \text{and} \qquad p^2 = 2.13$$

Hence
$$\omega_1 = 0 \qquad \omega_2^2 = 0.70\,\frac{k}{m} \qquad \omega_3^2 = 2.13\,\frac{k}{m}$$

Example 3-5. Compute the natural frequency for the beam shown in Fig. 3-23 which is built-in at one end and supported on a spring of stiffness k at the other.

The transfer matrices required in this example for a uniform massless beam, concentrated mass, and spring support have already been formulated [Eqs. (3-8), (3-11), (3-12)]. The boundary conditions at the point 0 are $w_0 = 0$ and $\psi_0 = 0$, whereas the boundary conditions at point 2 involve the properties of the spring. The technique to be used in such a case is to multiply the state vector $\mathbf{z}_2^L$ by the spring matrix, Eq. (3-12), to give the state vector $\mathbf{z}_2^R$. The boundary conditions at this point are then simply $M = 0$ and $V = 0$.

The relation between the state vectors $\mathbf{z}_2^R$ and $\mathbf{z}_0$ is

$$\mathbf{z}_2^R = \mathbf{P}_{\text{spring}}\mathbf{F}_{\text{beam}}\mathbf{P}_{\text{mass}}\mathbf{F}_{\text{beam}}\mathbf{z}_0$$

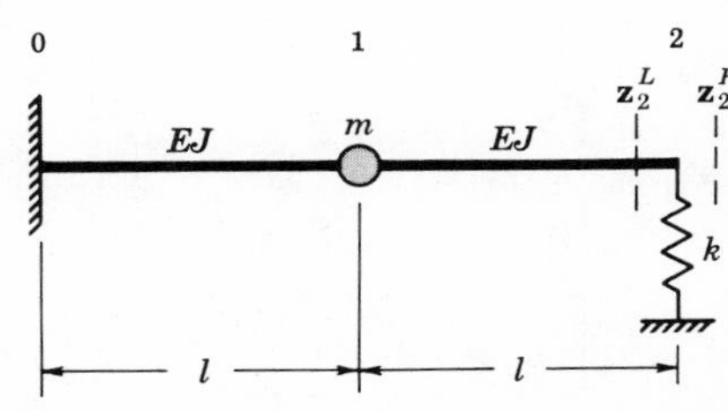

FIG. 3-23. Beam with discrete mass supported on a spring.

and since the first two components of $\mathbf{z}_0$ (w_0 and ψ_0) are zero, only the third and fourth rows of the matrix products are of interest. The matrix scheme is shown in Table 3-5 with the substitution $p^2 = m\omega^2 l^3/EJ$. The frequency determinant is

$$\begin{vmatrix} 1 + \dfrac{p^2}{2} & l\left(2 + \dfrac{p^2}{6}\right) \\ \dfrac{1}{l}\left[\dfrac{p^2}{2} - \dfrac{kl^3}{EJ}\left(2 + \dfrac{p^2}{12}\right)\right] & 1 + \dfrac{p^2}{6} - \dfrac{kl^3}{EJ}\left(\dfrac{4}{3} + \dfrac{p^2}{36}\right) \end{vmatrix} = 0$$

Solving the determinant for p^2, we obtain

$$p^2 = \frac{3 + 8kl^3/EJ}{1 + 7kl^3/12EJ}$$

from which

$$\omega^2 = \frac{EJ}{ml^3}\,\frac{3 + 8kl^3/EJ}{1 + 7kl^3/12EJ}$$

Table 3-5

$$\mathbf{F}_{\text{beam}} \quad \begin{bmatrix} \dfrac{l^2}{2EJ} & \dfrac{l^3}{6EJ} \\ \dfrac{l}{EJ} & \dfrac{l^2}{2EJ} \\ 1 & l \\ 0 & 1 \end{bmatrix} \cdot \begin{bmatrix} M \\ V \end{bmatrix}_0 = \mathbf{z}_1^L$$

$$\mathbf{P}_{\text{mass}} \begin{bmatrix} 1 & 0 & 0 & 0 \\ 0 & 1 & 0 & 0 \\ 0 & 0 & 1 & 0 \\ m\omega^2 & 0 & 0 & 1 \end{bmatrix} \begin{bmatrix} \dfrac{l^2}{2EJ} & \dfrac{l^3}{6EJ} \\ \dfrac{l}{EJ} & \dfrac{l^2}{2EJ} \\ 1 & l \\ \dfrac{p^2}{2l} & 1 + \dfrac{p^2}{6} \end{bmatrix} \cdot \begin{bmatrix} M \\ V \end{bmatrix}_0 = \mathbf{z}_1^R$$

$$\mathbf{F}_{\text{beam}} \begin{bmatrix} 1 & l & \dfrac{l^2}{2EJ} & \dfrac{l^3}{6EJ} \\ 0 & 1 & \dfrac{l}{EJ} & \dfrac{l^2}{2EJ} \\ 0 & 0 & 1 & l \\ 0 & 0 & 0 & 1 \end{bmatrix} \begin{bmatrix} \dfrac{l^2}{EJ}\left(2 + \dfrac{p^2}{12}\right) & \dfrac{l^3}{EJ}\left(\dfrac{4}{3} + \dfrac{p^2}{36}\right) \\ \dfrac{l}{EJ}\left(2 + \dfrac{p^2}{4}\right) & \dfrac{l^2}{EJ}\left(2 + \dfrac{p^2}{12}\right) \\ 1 + \dfrac{p^2}{2} & l\left(2 + \dfrac{p^2}{6}\right) \\ \dfrac{p^2}{2l} & 1 + \dfrac{p^2}{6} \end{bmatrix} \cdot \begin{bmatrix} M \\ V \end{bmatrix}_0 = \mathbf{z}_2^L$$

$$\mathbf{P}_{\text{spring}} \begin{bmatrix} 1 & 0 & 0 & 0 \\ 0 & 1 & 0 & 0 \\ 0 & 0 & 1 & 0 \\ -k & 0 & 0 & 1 \end{bmatrix} \begin{bmatrix} \dfrac{l^2}{EJ}\left(2 + \dfrac{p^2}{12}\right) & \dfrac{l^3}{EJ}\left(\dfrac{4}{3} + \dfrac{p^2}{36}\right) \\ \dfrac{l}{EJ}\left(2 + \dfrac{p^2}{4}\right) & \dfrac{l^2}{EJ}\left(2 + \dfrac{p^2}{12}\right) \\ 1 + \dfrac{p^2}{2} & l\left(2 + \dfrac{p^2}{6}\right) \\ \dfrac{1}{l}\left[\dfrac{p^2}{2} - \dfrac{kl^3}{EJ}\left(2 + \dfrac{p^2}{12}\right)\right] & 1 + \dfrac{p^2}{6} - \dfrac{kl^3}{EJ}\left(\dfrac{4}{3} + \dfrac{p^2}{36}\right) \end{bmatrix} \cdot \begin{bmatrix} M \\ V \end{bmatrix}_0 = \mathbf{z}_2^R = \begin{bmatrix} -w \\ \psi \\ 0 \\ 0 \end{bmatrix}_2^R$$

PROBLEMS

3-7. Using Eqs. (3-14) formulate the frequency determinant for the following sets of boundary conditions: (*a*) built-in, simply supported; (*b*) built-in, built-in; (*c*) simply supported, free; (*d*) free, free.

3-8. Formulate the point matrix relating $\mathbf{z}^L$ and $\mathbf{z}^R$ for the uniform disk of mass m and radius r (Fig. P 3-8). The disk can roll without slipping.

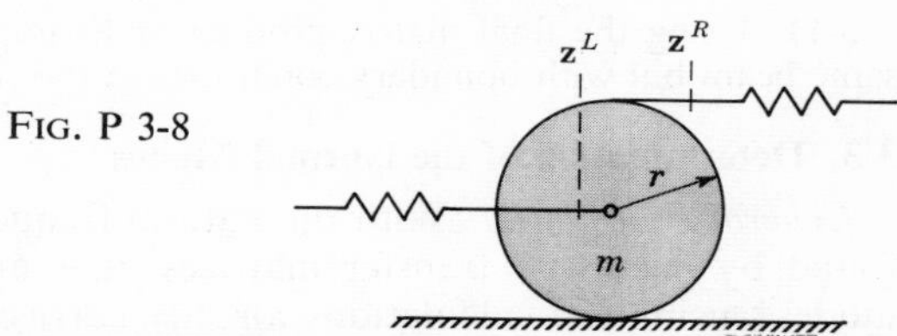

FIG. P 3-8

3-9. Using the transfer matrices that have been derived throughout the text and in the previous problem, derive the expressions for the natural frequencies of the systems shown in Fig. P 3-9.

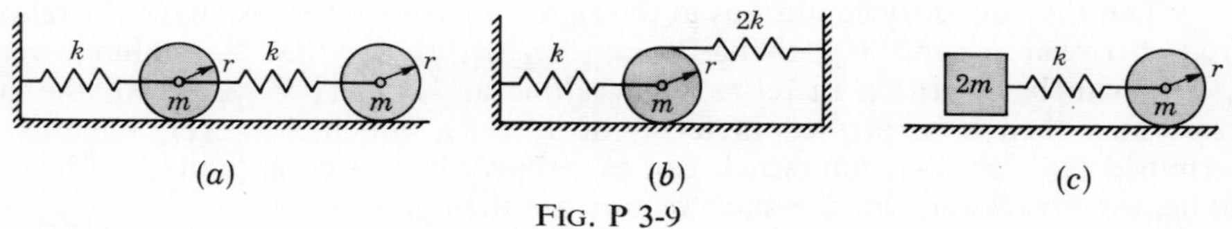

FIG. P 3-9

3-10. Formulate the transfer matrices required and then compute the natural frequencies of the systems shown in Fig. P 3-10. Again assume rolling without slip. HINT: The transfer matrix for the block and roller is found with the aid of Fig. P 3-10*d*. Show that the point matrix is

$$\begin{bmatrix} x \\ \\ N \end{bmatrix}_R = \begin{bmatrix} \frac{5}{2} & \dfrac{-2}{m\omega^2} \\ \\ -\frac{9}{2}m\omega^2 & 3 \end{bmatrix} \cdot \begin{bmatrix} x \\ \\ N \end{bmatrix}_L$$

Note that the displacement is not continuous at point 1.

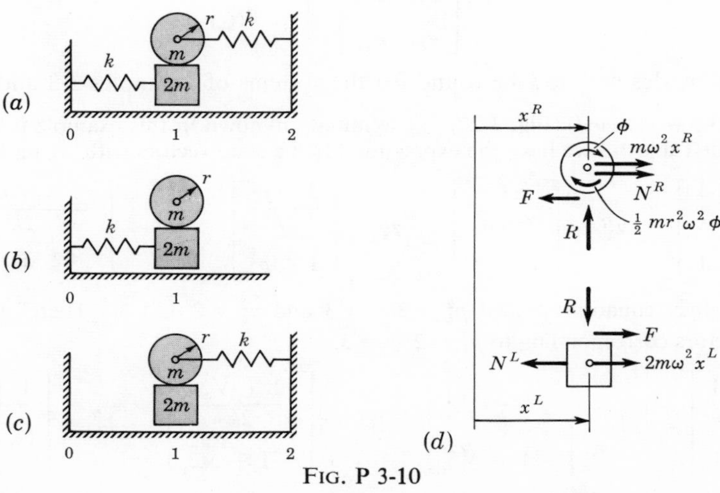

FIG. P 3-10

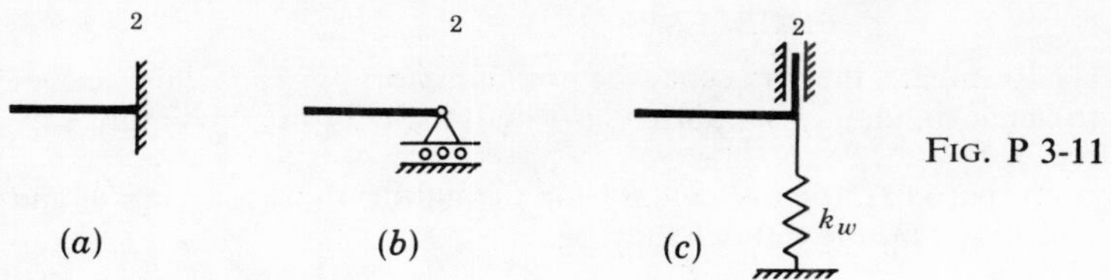

FIG. P 3-11

3-11. Using the final matrix product of Example 3-5, find the natural frequency of the same beam but with boundary conditions at the right end, as shown in Fig. P 3-11.

3-3. Determination of the Normal Modes

General Procedure. With the natural frequencies of an elastic system having been found by means of transfer matrices, it is an easy matter to compute the normal modes† using the calculations already carried out. Let us reconsider the example discussed in Sec. 3-2 which is illustrated in Fig. 3-19. In the abridged version of the matrix layout (Table 3-2) we saw that the state vectors $\mathbf{z}_1$, $\mathbf{z}_2$, and $\mathbf{z}_3$ could be expressed in terms of the unknowns at point 0, namely, the slope ψ_0 and the shear V_0. When the boundary conditions at the right end are applied, we have the relation (3-16*a*) between ψ_0 and V_0, giving $V_0 = -(e_{12}/e_{14})\psi_0$, so that the column vector $\{\psi_0 \quad V_0\}$ can be rewritten in terms of ψ_0 alone as $\{1 \quad -e_{12}/e_{14}\}\psi_0$. All the state vectors may then be expressed in terms of ψ_0 only, which, however, remains undetermined (cf. Sec. 2-3) but which can be arbitrarily chosen as unity. When this is done, the expressions for the state vectors are then given by

$$\mathbf{z}_1 = \begin{bmatrix} a_{12} & a_{14} \\ a_{22} & a_{24} \\ a_{32} & a_{34} \\ a_{42} & a_{44} \end{bmatrix} \cdot \begin{bmatrix} 1 \\ -\dfrac{e_{12}}{e_{14}} \end{bmatrix} \qquad \mathbf{z}_2 = \begin{bmatrix} d_{12} & d_{14} \\ d_{22} & d_{24} \\ d_{32} & d_{34} \\ d_{42} & d_{44} \end{bmatrix} \cdot \begin{bmatrix} 1 \\ -\dfrac{e_{12}}{e_{14}} \end{bmatrix}$$

$$\mathbf{z}_3 = \begin{bmatrix} e_{12} & e_{14} \\ e_{22} & e_{24} \\ e_{32} & e_{34} \\ e_{42} & e_{44} \end{bmatrix} \cdot \begin{bmatrix} 1 \\ -\dfrac{e_{12}}{e_{14}} \end{bmatrix} \tag{3-18}$$

The normal modes will now be found for the systems of Examples 3-3 and 3-5.

Example 3-3 (*continued*) (Fig. 3-20). The initial unknown in this example is the tension N_0, and from Table 3-3 we have the expression for the state vectors with N_0 taken as unity,

$$\mathbf{z}_1^L = \begin{bmatrix} \dfrac{1}{k} \\ 1 \end{bmatrix} \qquad \mathbf{z}_1^R = \begin{bmatrix} \dfrac{1}{k} \\ 1 - p^2 \end{bmatrix} \qquad \mathbf{z}_2^L = \begin{bmatrix} \dfrac{3 - p^2}{2k} \\ 1 - p^2 \end{bmatrix} \qquad \mathbf{z}_2^R = \begin{bmatrix} \dfrac{3 - p^2}{2k} \\ p^4 - 4p^2 + 1 \end{bmatrix}$$

The frequency equation yielded $p_1^2 = 2 - \sqrt{3}$ and $p_2^2 = 2 + \sqrt{3}$. Therefore we have the state vectors corresponding to $p_1^2 = 2 - \sqrt{3}$,

$$\mathbf{z}_1^L = \begin{bmatrix} \dfrac{1}{k} \\ 1 \end{bmatrix} \qquad \mathbf{z}_1^R = \begin{bmatrix} \dfrac{1}{k} \\ -1 + \sqrt{3} \end{bmatrix} \qquad \mathbf{z}_2^L = \begin{bmatrix} \dfrac{1 + \sqrt{3}}{2k} \\ -1 + \sqrt{3} \end{bmatrix} \qquad \mathbf{z}_2^R = \begin{bmatrix} \dfrac{1 + \sqrt{3}}{2k} \\ 0 \end{bmatrix}$$

† For their great practical importance the reader is referred to Sec. 2-3 and Chap. 8.

and to $p_2^2 = 2 + \sqrt{3}$,

$$\mathbf{z}_1^L = \begin{bmatrix} \frac{1}{k} \\ 1 \end{bmatrix} \quad \mathbf{z}_1^R = \begin{bmatrix} \frac{1}{k} \\ -(1 + \sqrt{3}) \end{bmatrix} \quad \mathbf{z}_2^L = \begin{bmatrix} \frac{1 - \sqrt{3}}{2k} \\ -(1 + \sqrt{3}) \end{bmatrix} \quad \mathbf{z}_2^R = \begin{bmatrix} \frac{1 - \sqrt{3}}{2k} \\ 0 \end{bmatrix}$$

Setting the displacement $x_1 = 1$ (multiplication of the displacement elements of the state vectors by k), we obtain the normal modes illustrated in Fig. 3-24.

The results for the normal modes can be checked by using the orthogonality property, Eq. (2-33). In this case

$$\sum_{i=1}^{2} m_i x_{i1} x_{i2} = (1)(1)(1) + (2)(\tfrac{1}{2})(1 + \sqrt{3})(\tfrac{1}{2})(1 - \sqrt{3}) = 0$$

The equations of motion for the two masses are then given by

$$x_1 = x_{11}^0 \cos \omega_1 t + \frac{\dot{x}_{11}^0}{\omega_1} \sin \omega_1 t + x_{12}^0 \cos \omega_2 t + \frac{\dot{x}_{12}^0}{\omega_2} \sin \omega_2 t$$

$$x_2 = c_1\left(x_{11}^0 \cos \omega_1 t + \frac{\dot{x}_{11}^0}{\omega_1} \sin \omega_1 t\right) + c_2\left(x_{12}^0 \cos \omega_2 t + \frac{\dot{x}_{12}^0}{\omega_2} \sin \omega_2 t\right)$$

where $c_1 = (1 + \sqrt{3})/2$ and $c_2 = (1 - \sqrt{3})/2$.

If the initial conditions are $x_1^0 = 1$, $x_2^0 = 0$, $\dot{x}_1^0 = 0$, and $\dot{x}_2^0 = 0$, Eqs. (2-37) yield

$$x_{11}^0 = \frac{m(1) + c_1 2m(0)}{m + c_1^2(2m)} = \frac{1}{3 + \sqrt{3}} \qquad x_{12}^0 = \frac{m(1) + c_2 2m(0)}{m + c_2^2(2m)} = \frac{1}{3 - \sqrt{3}}$$

$$\dot{x}_{11}^0 = 0 \qquad \dot{x}_{12}^0 = 0$$

Hence, the equations of motion are

$$x_1 = \frac{1}{3 + \sqrt{3}} \cos \omega_1 t + \frac{1}{3 - \sqrt{3}} \cos \omega_2 t \qquad x_2 = \frac{1}{2\sqrt{3}} \cos \omega_1 t - \frac{1}{2\sqrt{3}} \cos \omega_2 t$$

Example 3-5 (*continued*) (Fig. 3-23). From Table 3-5 the expressions for the deflections and slopes at the various points in terms of the unknown vector $\{M \quad V\}_0$ are

$$\begin{bmatrix} w \\ \psi \end{bmatrix}_1 = \begin{bmatrix} \frac{l^2}{2EJ} & \frac{l^3}{6EJ} \\ \frac{l}{EJ} & \frac{l^2}{2EJ} \end{bmatrix} \cdot \begin{bmatrix} M \\ V \end{bmatrix}_0 \qquad \begin{bmatrix} w \\ \psi \end{bmatrix}_2 = \begin{bmatrix} \frac{l^2}{EJ}\left(2 + \frac{p^2}{12}\right) & \frac{l^3}{EJ}\left(\frac{4}{3} + \frac{p^2}{36}\right) \\ \frac{l}{EJ}\left(2 + \frac{p^2}{4}\right) & \frac{l^2}{EJ}\left(2 + \frac{p^2}{12}\right) \end{bmatrix} \cdot \begin{bmatrix} M \\ V \end{bmatrix}_0$$

Now from the frequency condition we have the relation between M_0 and V_0:

$$V_0 = -\frac{1 + p^2/2}{(2 + p^2/6)l} M_0$$

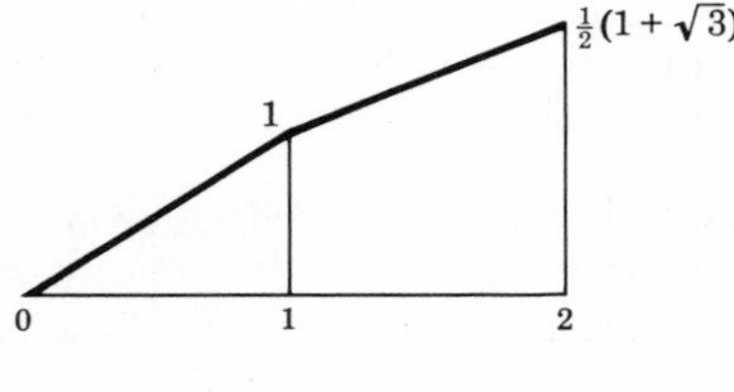

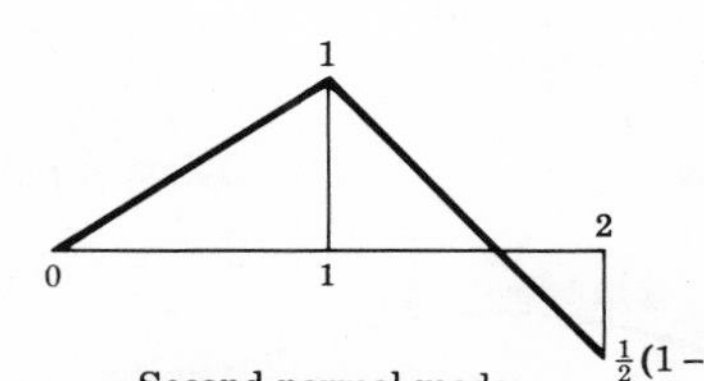

FIG. 3-24. Normal modes of system of Example 3-3.

so that the unknown vector $\{M \quad V\}_0$ can be expressed in terms of M_0 only:

$$\begin{bmatrix} M \\ V \end{bmatrix}_0 = \begin{bmatrix} 1 \\ -\dfrac{1 + p^2/2}{l(2 + p^2/6)} \end{bmatrix} M_0$$

Again taking the unknown M_0 to be unity, the expressions for the deflection vectors become

$$\begin{bmatrix} w \\ \psi \end{bmatrix}_1 = \begin{bmatrix} \dfrac{l^2}{2EJ} & \dfrac{l^3}{6EJ} \\ \dfrac{l}{EJ} & \dfrac{l^2}{2EJ} \end{bmatrix} \cdot \begin{bmatrix} 1 \\ -\dfrac{1 + p^2/2}{l(2 + p^2/6)} \end{bmatrix} = \begin{bmatrix} \dfrac{l^2}{EJ}\left(\dfrac{1}{2} - \dfrac{1 + p^2/2}{12 + p^2}\right) \\ \dfrac{l}{EJ}\left(1 - \dfrac{1 + p^2/2}{4 + p^2/3}\right) \end{bmatrix}$$

$$\begin{bmatrix} w \\ \psi \end{bmatrix}_2 = \begin{bmatrix} \dfrac{l^2}{EJ}\left(2 + \dfrac{p^2}{12}\right) & \dfrac{l^3}{EJ}\left(\dfrac{4}{3} + \dfrac{p^2}{36}\right) \\ \dfrac{l}{EJ}\left(2 + \dfrac{p^2}{4}\right) & \dfrac{l^2}{EJ}\left(2 + \dfrac{p^2}{12}\right) \end{bmatrix} \cdot \begin{bmatrix} 1 \\ -\dfrac{1 + p^2/2}{l(2 + p^2/6)} \end{bmatrix}$$

$$= \begin{bmatrix} \dfrac{l^2}{EJ}\left[2 + \dfrac{p^2}{12} - \dfrac{(\frac{4}{3} + p^2/36)(1 + p^2/2)}{2 + p^2/6}\right] \\ \dfrac{l}{EJ}\left[2 + \dfrac{p^2}{4} - \dfrac{(2 + p^2/12)(1 + p^2/2)}{2 + p^2/6}\right] \end{bmatrix}$$

Suppose, for example, that $kl^3/EJ = 12$. Then $p^2 = \frac{99}{8}$ and the deflection vectors become

$$\begin{bmatrix} w \\ \psi \end{bmatrix}_1 = \begin{bmatrix} \dfrac{l^2}{EJ}(0.205) \\ \dfrac{l}{EJ}(0.115) \end{bmatrix} \qquad \begin{bmatrix} w \\ \psi \end{bmatrix}_2 = \begin{bmatrix} \dfrac{l^2}{EJ}(0.073) \\ \dfrac{l}{EJ}(-0.27) \end{bmatrix}$$

Multiplying throughout by $EJ/0.205l^2$, we obtain

$$\begin{bmatrix} w \\ \psi \end{bmatrix}_1 = \begin{bmatrix} 1.000 \\ \dfrac{0.561}{l} \end{bmatrix} \qquad \begin{bmatrix} w \\ \psi \end{bmatrix}_2 = \begin{bmatrix} 0.355 \\ \dfrac{-1.32}{l} \end{bmatrix}$$

on the basis of which we are able to sketch the vibrating mode (Fig. 3-25).

PROBLEMS

3-12. Compute the normal modes for the system of Fig. P 3-9*a* and demonstrate the orthogonality property.

3-13. A horizontal force F applied at the center of the right-hand disk of the same system as in the preceding problem (Fig. P 3-9*a*) is suddenly released. Find the subsequent motion of the two disks.

3-14. The system of Example 3-3 is supported on a smooth plane inclined at an angle α

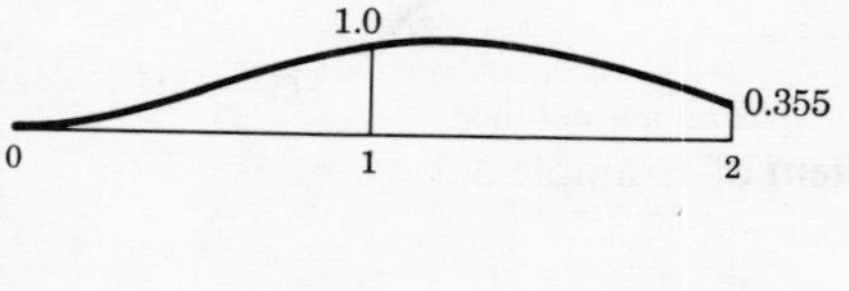

1.0

0.355

0 1 2

FIG. 3-25. Normal mode of system of Example 3-5.

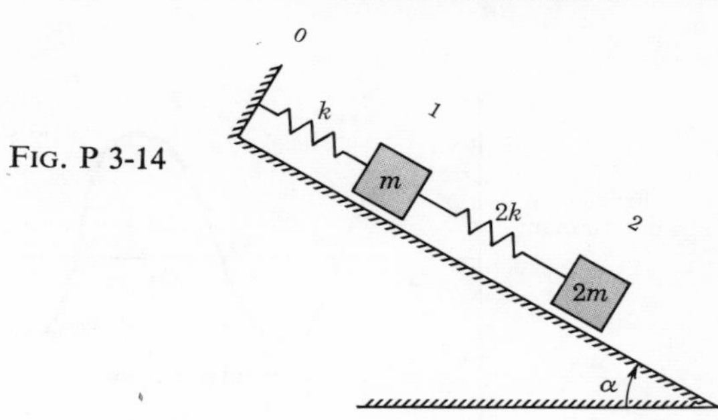

FIG. P 3-14

to the horizontal when suddenly the spring between 0 and 1 breaks. Find the subsequent motion (Fig. P 3-14).

3-4. Numerical Calculations with Transfer Matrices

General Procedure. In the previous examples the matrix multiplications have been made carrying ω^2 through as a free parameter, and by finally applying the boundary conditions we then solved for ω^2 from the resulting frequency equation. In Example 3-5 the amount of algebra was already growing rapidly, and it is easy to imagine that with complicated systems the algebraic labor would become prohibitive. The frequency equation would also be very complicated, and furthermore it would be very cumbersome to extract the roots.. In such cases it is advisable to replace algebraic by numerical computation.

Suppose, for example, that we wish to find the natural frequencies of a massless nonuniform beam with concentrated masses and springs (Fig. 3-26). The state vectors $\mathbf{z}_n$ and $\mathbf{z}_0$ are related by means of the equation

$$\mathbf{z}_n = \mathbf{F}_n\mathbf{P}_{n-1}\mathbf{F}_{n-1}\cdots\mathbf{F}_2\mathbf{P}_1\mathbf{F}_1\mathbf{z}_0 = \mathbf{U}\mathbf{z}_0 \tag{3-19}$$

where $\mathbf{F}_i$ and $\mathbf{P}_i$ are the field and point matrices, which are assumed to be known. If we note that the boundary conditions at point 0 are $w_0 = 0$ and $M_0 = 0$, the first and third columns of the matrix products need not be computed, so that after the matrix multiplication has been completed, Eq. (3-19) becomes

$$\begin{bmatrix} -w \\ \psi \\ M \\ V \end{bmatrix}_n = \begin{bmatrix} u_{12} & u_{14} \\ u_{22} & u_{24} \\ u_{32} & u_{34} \\ u_{42} & u_{44} \end{bmatrix} \cdot \begin{bmatrix} \psi \\ V \end{bmatrix}_0$$

Since, at point n, $w_n = 0$ and $\psi_n = 0$, the frequency condition is

$$\Delta = \begin{vmatrix} u_{12} & u_{14} \\ u_{22} & u_{24} \end{vmatrix} = 0 \tag{3-20}$$

Had the matrix multiplication been carried out algebraically, then the coefficients u_{12}, u_{14}, u_{22}, and u_{24} and consequently the frequency condition would be complicated functions of ω^2. The procedure adopted in practice, however, is to choose certain values for ω^2 and compute the corresponding values of the frequency deter-

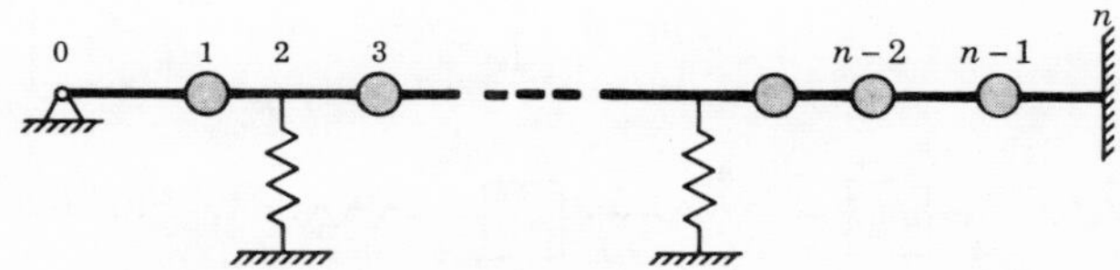

FIG. 3-26. Beam with discrete masses and springs.

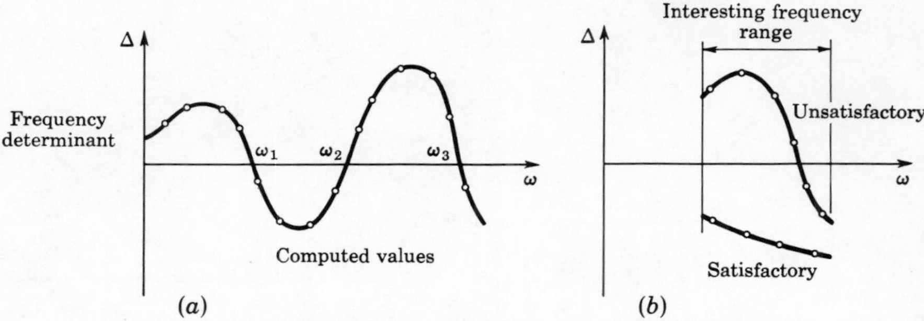

FIG. 3-27. Plot of frequency determinant.

minant $\Delta(\omega)$. The value of the determinant Δ is then plotted against ω, the zero values of Δ occurring at the natural circular frequencies of the system (Fig. 3-27*a*).

Very often the problem is not to find all the natural frequencies of a system, but to discover whether or not it has a natural frequency within a certain frequency range (Fig. 3-27*b*). For example, in the case of a machine foundation, the frequency range of interest is bounded by the maximum and minimum operating speed of the machine, and it is required that no natural frequency occur within this range.

Shifted-matrix Multiplication. In numerical work, especially when using a desk calculator, considerable effort is saved if the so-called "shifted"-matrix multiplication is employed [9]. This matrix operation, which relates the state vectors $\mathbf{z}_{i-1}^R$ and $\mathbf{z}_i^R$, is illustrated here for a spring-mass system (Fig. 3-28).

Let us first carry out this matrix operation in the usual way. The relation between $\mathbf{z}_{i-1}^R$ and $\mathbf{z}_i^L$ is given by

$$\begin{bmatrix} x \\ N \end{bmatrix}_i^L = \begin{bmatrix} 1 & \frac{1}{k} \\ 0 & 1 \end{bmatrix}_i \cdot \begin{bmatrix} x \\ N \end{bmatrix}_{i-1}^R$$

and that between $\mathbf{z}_i^L$ and $\mathbf{z}_i^R$ is

$$\begin{bmatrix} x \\ N \end{bmatrix}_i^R = \begin{bmatrix} 1 & 0 \\ -m\omega^2 & 1 \end{bmatrix}_i \begin{bmatrix} x \\ N \end{bmatrix}_i^L$$

Employing the standard layout for matrix multiplication gives the following result:

$$\begin{array}{ccc} & \begin{bmatrix} 1 & \frac{1}{k} \\ 0 & 1 \end{bmatrix}_i \cdot \begin{bmatrix} x \\ N \end{bmatrix}_{i-1}^R = \begin{bmatrix} x \\ N \end{bmatrix}_i^L \\ \begin{bmatrix} 1 & 0 \\ -\omega^2 m & 1 \end{bmatrix}_i & \begin{bmatrix} 1 & \frac{1}{k} \\ -\omega^2 m & 1 - \frac{\omega^2 m}{k} \end{bmatrix}_i \cdot \begin{bmatrix} x \\ N \end{bmatrix}_{i-1}^R = \begin{bmatrix} x \\ N \end{bmatrix}_i^R \end{array}$$

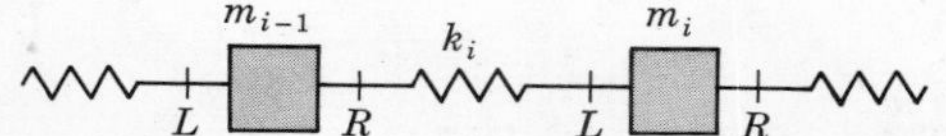

FIG. 3-28. Spring-mass system.

Hence
$$x_i^L = x_i^R = x_{i-1}^R + \frac{N_{i-1}^R}{k_i}$$

and
$$N_i^R = -\omega^2 m_i x_{i-1}^R + \left(1 - \frac{\omega^2 m_i}{k_i}\right) N_{i-1}^R$$
$$= N_{i-1}^R - \omega^2 m_i \left(x_{i-1}^R + \frac{N_{i-1}^R}{k_i}\right) = N_{i-1}^R - \omega^2 m_i x_i^L$$

This same result can be obtained by using the following layout, which combines the field and the point matrix into a single matrix:

$$\begin{array}{cc} & \begin{bmatrix} x \\ \\ N \end{bmatrix}_{i-1}^R \\ \begin{bmatrix} 1 & \dfrac{1}{k} & \vdots & 0 \\ & & \vdots & \\ 0 & 1 & \vdots & -\omega^2 m \end{bmatrix}_i \cdot & \begin{bmatrix} a \\ \\ b \end{bmatrix} = \begin{bmatrix} x \\ \\ N \end{bmatrix}_i^R = \mathbf{z}_i^R \end{array}$$

The element $a \equiv x_i^R = x_i^L$ is found in the usual way:

$$\begin{array}{cc} & \begin{bmatrix} x \\ N \end{bmatrix}_{i-1}^R \\ \begin{bmatrix} 1 & \dfrac{1}{k} \end{bmatrix} \cdot & \begin{bmatrix} a \end{bmatrix} = (1)x_{i-1}^R + \dfrac{N_{i-1}^R}{k_i} = x_i^L = x_i^R \end{array}$$

and the element b is computed as if the element a belonged to the column vector $\mathbf{z}_{i-1}^R$:

$$\begin{array}{cc} & \begin{bmatrix} x_{i-1}^R \\ N_{i-1}^R \\ a \end{bmatrix} \\ \begin{bmatrix} 0 & 1 & -\omega^2 m_i \end{bmatrix} & \begin{bmatrix} b \end{bmatrix} = (0)x_{i-1}^R + N_{i-1}^R - \omega^2 m_i a \end{array}$$

Since $a = x_i^R$, we have indeed

$$b = N_{i-1}^R - \omega^2 m_i x_i^R = N_i^R$$

so that by this matrix operation we have done the equivalent to forming the product $\mathbf{z}_i^R = \mathbf{P}_i \mathbf{F}_i \mathbf{z}_{i-1}^R$.

Example 3-6. The idealized representation of a four-cylinder engine with a flywheel attached is shown in Fig. 3-29. It is required to find the natural torsional frequencies of the system and the corresponding normal modes.

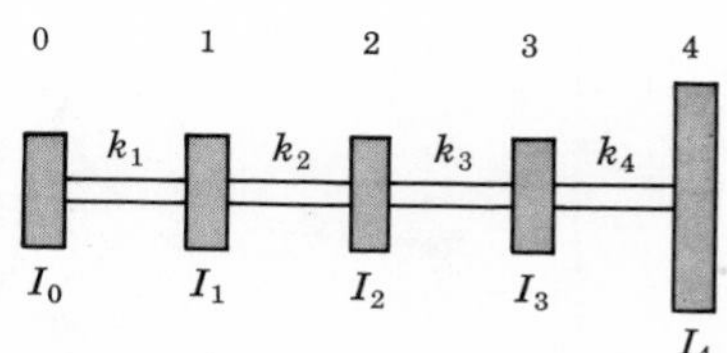

FIG. 3-29. Idealized machine shaft.

$$I_0 = I_1 = I_2 = I_3 = 10 \text{ lb-in.-sec}^2$$

$$I_4 = 20 \text{ lb-in.-sec}^2$$

$$k_1 = k_2 = k_3 = 1.5 \times 10^6 \text{ lb-in./radian}$$

$$k_4 = 2.0 \times 10^6 \text{ lb-in./radian}$$

The relationship between the state vectors $\mathbf{z}_0^L$ and $\mathbf{z}_4^R$ is given by

$$\mathbf{z}_4^R = \mathbf{P}_4\mathbf{F}_4\mathbf{P}_3\mathbf{F}_3\mathbf{P}_2\mathbf{F}_2\mathbf{P}_1\mathbf{F}_1\mathbf{P}_0\mathbf{z}_0^L$$

The initial unknown is the angular displacement ϕ_0, and thus the scheme for the shifted-matrix multiplication is arranged in the manner shown in Table 3-6. If we apply the boundary condition $T_4^R = 0$, the frequency condition is $u_{21} = 0$. The numerical values of the spring stiffnesses are inserted, and with ω chosen as 100 radians/sec the result shown in Table 3-7 is obtained on completion of the matrix multiplications.

These calculations are repeated for the values of ω equal to 200, 300, 400, 500, 600, 700, 800, and 900, the results being given as follows:

ω.....	0	100	200	300	400	500	600	700	800	900
$u_{21}/10^5$	0	−4.27	−2.07	18.61	19.4	−35.9	−44.6	285.0	−931.0	−11,760.0

Any further increase in ω causes u_{21} to become negatively larger. The graph of u_{21} against ω is given in Fig. 3-30. Although the graph is rather coarse on account of the small number of points, we can obtain approximate values of the circular natural frequency. By choosing values of ω in the vicinity of the natural frequencies it is possible to obtain more accurate results.

Taking $\omega = 210$ and 215 we obtain, respectively,

$$u_{21} = -0.6770 \times 10^5 \qquad \text{and} \qquad u_{21} = 0.1035 \times 10^5$$

Interpolating between these two values gives the value

$$\omega_1 = 210.0 + \left(\frac{0.6770}{0.7805}\right)5.0 = 214.337$$

The mode shapes corresponding to $\omega = 210$ and $\omega = 215$ are as follows:

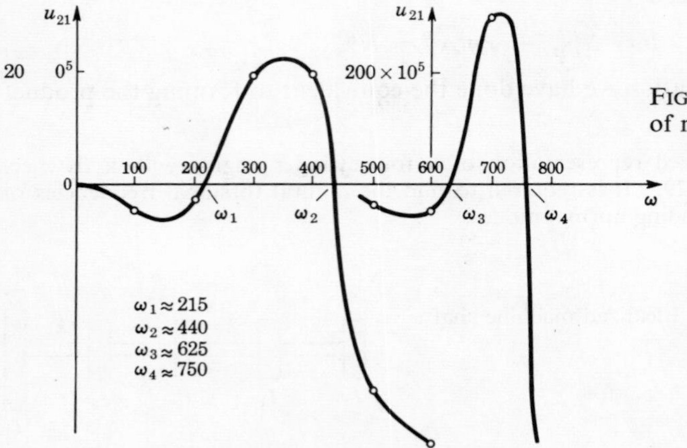

FIG. 3-30. Plot for determination of natural frequencies.

	ϕ_0	ϕ_1	ϕ_2	ϕ_3	ϕ_4
$\omega = 210$	1.00	0.7060	0.2044	−0.3573	−0.6998
$\omega = 215$	1.00	0.6918	0.1704	−0.4034	−0.7406

Table 3-6

$$\begin{bmatrix} 1 \\ -I_0\omega^2 \end{bmatrix} \cdot \begin{bmatrix} \phi \end{bmatrix}_0 = \mathbf{z}_0^R$$

$$\begin{bmatrix} 1 & \frac{1}{k} & 0 \\ 0 & 1 & -I\omega^2 \end{bmatrix}_1 \begin{bmatrix} \\ \\ \end{bmatrix} \cdot \begin{bmatrix} \phi \end{bmatrix}_0 = \mathbf{z}_1^R$$

$$\begin{bmatrix} 1 & \frac{1}{k} & 0 \\ 0 & 1 & -I\omega^2 \end{bmatrix}_2 \begin{bmatrix} \\ \\ \end{bmatrix} \cdot \begin{bmatrix} \phi \end{bmatrix}_0 = \mathbf{z}_2^R$$

$$\begin{bmatrix} 1 & \frac{1}{k} & 0 \\ 0 & 1 & -I\omega^2 \end{bmatrix}_3 \begin{bmatrix} \\ \\ \end{bmatrix} \cdot \begin{bmatrix} \phi \end{bmatrix}_0 = \mathbf{z}_3^R$$

$$\begin{bmatrix} 1 & \frac{1}{k} & 0 \\ 0 & 1 & -I\omega^2 \end{bmatrix}_4 \begin{bmatrix} u_{11} \\ u_{21} \end{bmatrix} \cdot \begin{bmatrix} \phi \end{bmatrix}_0 = \mathbf{z}_4^R = \begin{bmatrix} \phi \\ 0 \end{bmatrix}_4^R$$

Table 3-7

$\omega = 100$

$$\begin{bmatrix} 1 \\ -10^5 \end{bmatrix} \cdot \begin{bmatrix} \phi \end{bmatrix}_0 = \mathbf{z}_0^R$$

$$\begin{bmatrix} 1 & \frac{1}{1.5 \times 10^6} & 0 \\ 0 & 1 & -10^5 \end{bmatrix} \begin{bmatrix} 0.9333 \\ -1.9333 \times 10^5 \end{bmatrix} \cdot \begin{bmatrix} \phi \end{bmatrix}_0 = \mathbf{z}_1^R$$

$$\begin{bmatrix} 1 & \frac{1}{1.5 \times 10^6} & 0 \\ 0 & 1 & -10^5 \end{bmatrix} \begin{bmatrix} 0.8044 \\ -2.7377 \times 10^5 \end{bmatrix} \cdot \begin{bmatrix} \phi \end{bmatrix}_0 = \mathbf{z}_2^R$$

$$\begin{bmatrix} 1 & \frac{1}{1.5 \times 10^6} & 0 \\ 0 & 1 & -10^5 \end{bmatrix} \begin{bmatrix} 0.6219 \\ -3.3596 \times 10^5 \end{bmatrix} \cdot \begin{bmatrix} \phi \end{bmatrix}_0 = \mathbf{z}_3^R$$

$$\begin{bmatrix} 1 & \frac{1}{2.0 \times 10^6} & 0 \\ 0 & 1 & -2 \times 10^5 \end{bmatrix} \begin{bmatrix} 0.4539 \\ -4.2674 \times 10^5 \end{bmatrix} \cdot \begin{bmatrix} \phi \end{bmatrix}_0 = \mathbf{z}_4^R$$

$$u_{21} = -4.2674 \times 10^5$$

1.00
0.694
0.175
0.397
0.735
(a)

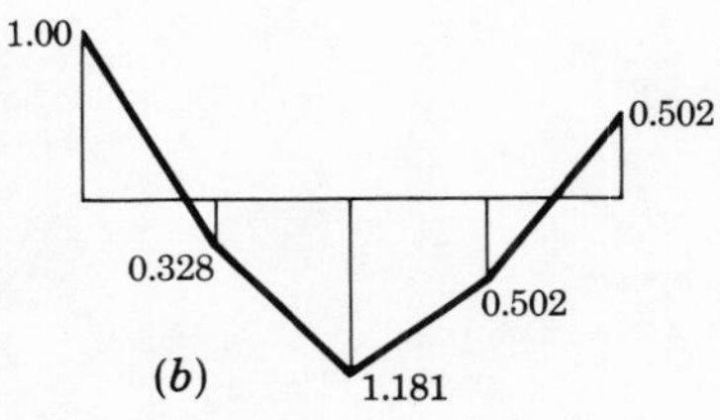

FIG. 3-31. Normal modes for system of Example 3-6. (a) First normal mode; (b) second normal mode.

Interpolating between these two results gives the normal mode corresponding to $\omega_1 = 214.337$ (Fig. 3-31*a*):

ϕ_0	ϕ_1	ϕ_2	ϕ_3	ϕ_4
1.00	0.6937	0.1749	−0.3973	−0.7352

When the identical process is repeated for the second mode, it is found that $\omega_2 = 446.1$ and the second normal mode (Fig. 3-31*b*) is given by

ϕ_0	ϕ_1	ϕ_2	ϕ_3	ϕ_4
1.00	−0.328	−1.181	−0.502	0.502

The orthogonality property of normal modes can be demonstrated with the help of these results. In this case the orthogonality property is

$$\sum_{i=0}^{4} I_i \phi_{i1} \phi_{i2} = 0$$

where ϕ_{i1} is the first-mode displacement of the *i*th disk and ϕ_{i2} is the second-mode displacement of the *i*th disk.

Applying the above results, we find that

$$\begin{aligned}\sum_{i=0}^{4} I_i \phi_{i1} \phi_{i2} &= 10[(1)(1)(1) + (1)(0.694)(-0.328) + (1)(0.175)(-1.181) \\ &\qquad + (1)(-0.397)(-0.502) + (2)(-0.735)(0.502)] \\ &= 10(1.19 - 1.17) \doteq 0\end{aligned}$$

With increased accuracy, this result would be closer to zero, the discrepancy arising owing to slide-rule inaccuracy and rounding-off errors.

Dimensionless Transfer Matrices. Another step in the simplification of numerical work is achieved by using transfer matrices in dimensionless form. We shall illustrate the procedure with reference to the problem of beam vibrations. The relationships between adjacent state vectors of a massless elastic beam are given by Eqs. (3-8). Repeating the second equation, dividing through by l_i in the first, and multiplying by l_i/EJ in the third and by l_i^2/EJ in the fourth, we obtain

$$-\frac{w_i}{l_i} = -\frac{w_{i-1}}{l_i} + \psi_{i-1} + \frac{l_i M_{i-1}}{2EJ_i} + \frac{l_i^2 V_{i-1}}{6EJ_i}$$

$$\psi_i = \psi_{i-1} + \frac{l_i M_{i-1}}{EJ_i} + \frac{l_i^2 V_{i-1}}{2EJ_i}$$

$$\frac{l_i M_i}{EJ_i} = \frac{l_i M_{i-1}}{EJ_i} + \frac{l_i^2 V_{i-1}}{EJ_i}$$

$$\frac{l_i^2 V_i}{EJ_i} = \frac{l_i^2 V_{i-1}}{EJ_i}$$

Letting $\bar{w} = w/l$, $\bar{\psi} = \psi$, $\bar{M} = lM/EJ$, and $\bar{V} = l^2V/EJ$, the above equations expressed in matrix form become

$$\begin{bmatrix} -\bar{w} \\ \bar{\psi} \\ \bar{M} \\ \bar{V} \end{bmatrix}_i^L = \begin{bmatrix} 1 & 1 & \frac{1}{2} & \frac{1}{6} \\ 0 & 1 & 1 & \frac{1}{2} \\ 0 & 0 & 1 & 1 \\ 0 & 0 & 0 & 1 \end{bmatrix} \cdot \begin{bmatrix} -\bar{w} \\ \bar{\psi} \\ \bar{M} \\ \bar{V} \end{bmatrix}_{i-1}^R \qquad (3\text{-}8a)$$

where both the state vector and the transfer matrix are dimensionless.

The effort saved by writing the transfer matrix in this form should be obvious. For beams with flexural stiffness αEJ and length βl (α and β are constants), the field matrix is readily found to be

$$\begin{bmatrix} 1 & \beta & \dfrac{\beta^2}{2\alpha} & \dfrac{\beta^3}{6\alpha} \\ 0 & 1 & \dfrac{\beta}{\alpha} & \dfrac{\beta^2}{2\alpha} \\ 0 & 0 & 1 & \beta \\ 0 & 0 & 0 & 1 \end{bmatrix}$$

By dealing now with the point matrix for the concentrated mass, the shear relation is given by $V_i^R = -\omega^2 m w_i + V_i^L$, and by multiplying through by l^2/EJ the equation becomes

$$\bar{V}_i^R = \bar{V}_i^L - \frac{\omega^2 m l^3}{EJ} \frac{w_i}{l}$$

so that the state vectors on either side of the point mass are related by the matrix equation

$$\begin{bmatrix} -\bar{w} \\ \bar{\psi} \\ \bar{M} \\ \bar{V} \end{bmatrix}_i^R = \begin{bmatrix} 1 & 0 & 0 & 0 \\ 0 & 1 & 0 & 0 \\ 0 & 0 & 1 & 0 \\ \dfrac{\omega^2 m l^3}{EJ} & 0 & 0 & 1 \end{bmatrix} \cdot \begin{bmatrix} -\bar{w} \\ \bar{\psi} \\ \bar{M} \\ \bar{V} \end{bmatrix}_i^L \qquad (3\text{-}11a)$$

where $\omega^2 m l^3/EJ$ is also dimensionless.

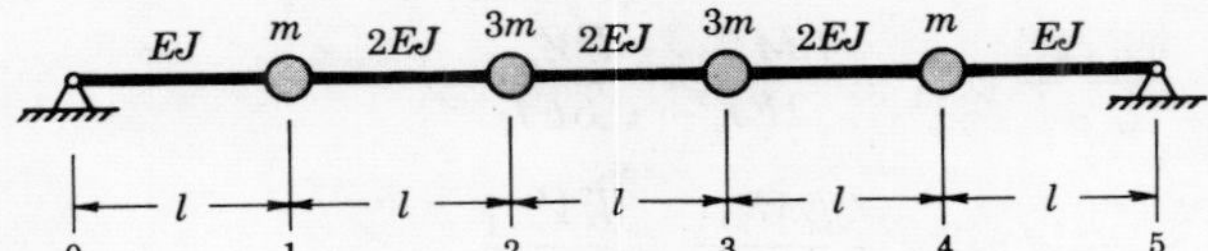

FIG. 3-32. Beam with discrete masses.

Example 3-7. Using these dimensionless matrices, compute the first two natural frequencies and normal modes of the beam illustrated in Fig. 3-32. As in the previous example, the shifted-column-matrix method avoids the multiplication of the field and point matrices. The shifted-column-matrix operation in this case is represented in the following way:

$$\begin{bmatrix} -\bar{w} \\ \bar{\psi} \\ \bar{M} \\ \bar{V} \end{bmatrix}_{i-1}^{R} = \mathbf{z}_{i-1}^{R}$$

$$\left[\begin{array}{cccc|c} 1 & 1 & \frac{1}{2} & \frac{1}{6} & 0 \\ 0 & 1 & 1 & \frac{1}{2} & 0 \\ 0 & 0 & 1 & 1 & 0 \\ 0 & 0 & 0 & 1 & \dfrac{\omega^2 m l^3}{EJ} \end{array}\right]_i \begin{bmatrix} -\bar{w} \\ \bar{\psi} \\ \bar{M} \\ \bar{V} \end{bmatrix}_i^R = \mathbf{z}_i^R$$

The values of $\bar{w}_i^R$, $\bar{\psi}_i^R$, and $\bar{M}_i^R$ are computed in the usual manner because they are continuous at i, but $\bar{V}_i^R$ is found by the following matrix product:

$$\left[\begin{array}{cccc|c} 0 & 0 & 0 & 1 & \dfrac{\omega^2 m l^3}{EJ} \end{array}\right] \left[\begin{array}{c} -\bar{w}_{i-1}^R \\ \bar{\psi}_{i-1}^R \\ \bar{M}_{i-1}^R \\ \bar{V}_{i-1}^R \\ \hline -\bar{w}_i^R \end{array}\right] = \left[\bar{V}_i^R \right]$$

Since in this example $w_0 = M_0 = 0$, the first and third columns of the matrix products are dropped. The complete matrix layout employing the shifted-column method is shown in Table 3-8.

Applying the boundary conditions $\bar{w}_5 = 0$ and $\bar{M}_5 = 0$, the frequency condition is

$$\Delta = \begin{vmatrix} u_{12} & u_{14} \\ u_{32} & u_{34} \end{vmatrix} = 0$$

Following the procedure of the previous problem, we choose certain numerical values for $\omega^2 m l^3/EJ$ and then compute the corresponding values for Δ. In order to find a reasonable starting value for $\omega^2 m l^3/EJ$, let us assume that the total mass of $8m$ is uniformly distributed over the total length of $5l$ and that the beam has an average flexural stiffness of $1.5EJ$. Now $\omega^2 = \pi^4 EJ/ML^3$ is the first natural frequency for a simply supported beam of mass M, length L, and flexural stiffness EJ. In our case, then,

$$\omega_1^2 = \frac{\pi^4 1.5EJ}{(8m)(5l)^3} = 0.15\,\frac{EJ}{ml^3} \qquad \text{that is,} \quad \frac{ml^3\omega_1^2}{EJ} \approx 0.15$$

Table 3-8

$$\begin{bmatrix} 0 & 0 \\ 1 & 0 \\ 0 & 0 \\ 0 & 1 \end{bmatrix} \cdot \begin{bmatrix} \bar{\psi} \\ \bar{V} \end{bmatrix}_0 = \mathbf{z}_0$$

$$\left[\begin{array}{cccc|c} 1 & 1 & \frac{1}{2} & \frac{1}{6} & 0 \\ 0 & 1 & 1 & \frac{1}{2} & 0 \\ 0 & 0 & 1 & 1 & 0 \\ 0 & 0 & 0 & 1 & \dfrac{\omega^2 ml^3}{EJ} \end{array}\right] \begin{bmatrix} \cdots \\ \\ \\ \\ \end{bmatrix} \cdot \begin{bmatrix} \bar{\psi} \\ \bar{V} \end{bmatrix}_0 = \mathbf{z}_1^R$$

$$\left[\begin{array}{cccc|c} 1 & 1 & \frac{1}{4} & \frac{1}{12} & 0 \\ 0 & 1 & \frac{1}{2} & \frac{1}{4} & 0 \\ 0 & 0 & 1 & 1 & 0 \\ 0 & 0 & 0 & 1 & \dfrac{3\omega^2 ml^3}{EJ} \end{array}\right] \begin{bmatrix} \cdots \\ \\ \\ \\ \end{bmatrix} \cdot \begin{bmatrix} \bar{\psi} \\ \bar{V} \end{bmatrix}_0 = \mathbf{z}_2^R$$

$$\left[\begin{array}{cccc|c} 1 & 1 & \frac{1}{4} & \frac{1}{12} & 0 \\ 0 & 1 & \frac{1}{2} & \frac{1}{4} & 0 \\ 0 & 0 & 1 & 1 & 0 \\ 0 & 0 & 0 & 1 & \dfrac{3\omega^2 ml^3}{EJ} \end{array}\right] \begin{bmatrix} \cdots \\ \\ \\ \\ \end{bmatrix} \cdot \begin{bmatrix} \bar{\psi} \\ \bar{V} \end{bmatrix}_0 = \mathbf{z}_3^R$$

$$\left[\begin{array}{cccc|c} 1 & 1 & \frac{1}{4} & \frac{1}{12} & 0 \\ 0 & 1 & \frac{1}{2} & \frac{1}{4} & 0 \\ 0 & 0 & 1 & 1 & 0 \\ 0 & 0 & 0 & 1 & \dfrac{\omega^2 ml^3}{EJ} \end{array}\right] \begin{bmatrix} \cdots \\ \\ \\ \\ \end{bmatrix} \cdot \begin{bmatrix} \bar{\psi} \\ \bar{V} \end{bmatrix}_0 = \mathbf{z}_4^R$$

$$\left[\begin{array}{cccc|c} 1 & 1 & \frac{1}{2} & \frac{1}{6} & 0 \\ 0 & 1 & 1 & \frac{1}{2} & 0 \\ 0 & 0 & 1 & 1 & 0 \\ 0 & 0 & 0 & 1 & 0 \end{array}\right] \begin{bmatrix} u_{12} & u_{14} \\ u_{22} & u_{24} \\ u_{32} & u_{34} \\ u_{42} & u_{44} \end{bmatrix} \cdot \begin{bmatrix} \bar{\psi} \\ \bar{V} \end{bmatrix}_0 = \mathbf{z}_5 = \begin{bmatrix} 0 \\ \bar{\psi} \\ 0 \\ \bar{V} \end{bmatrix}_5$$

A starting value of $ml^3\omega^2/EJ = 0.10$ was chosen, and the result of the calculation using this figure is shown in Table 3-9.

The variation of Δ against $\omega^2 ml^3/EJ$ is shown in Fig. 3-33, and from this graph the first two natural circular frequencies are found as

$$\omega_1^2 = 0.113 \frac{EJ}{ml^3} \quad \text{and} \quad \omega_2^2 = 2.54 \frac{EJ}{ml^3}$$

Table 3-9

$$\frac{ml^3\omega^2}{EJ} = 0.10$$

$$\begin{bmatrix} 0 & 0 \\ 1 & 0 \\ 0 & 0 \\ 0 & 1 \end{bmatrix} \cdot \begin{bmatrix} \bar{\psi} \\ \bar{V} \end{bmatrix}_0 = \mathbf{z}_0$$

$$\left[\begin{array}{cccc:c} 1 & 1 & \frac{1}{2} & \frac{1}{6} & 0 \\ 0 & 1 & 1 & \frac{1}{2} & 0 \\ 0 & 0 & 1 & 1 & 0 \\ 0 & 0 & 0 & 1 & 0.1 \end{array}\right] \left[\begin{array}{cc} 1.0000 & 0.1667 \\ \hdashline 1.0000 & 0.5000 \\ 0.0000 & 1.0000 \\ 0.1000 & 1.0167 \end{array}\right] \cdot \begin{bmatrix} \bar{\psi} \\ \bar{V} \end{bmatrix}_0 = \mathbf{z}_1^R$$

$$\left[\begin{array}{cccc:c} 1 & 1 & \frac{1}{4} & \frac{1}{12} & 0 \\ 0 & 1 & \frac{1}{2} & \frac{1}{4} & 0 \\ 0 & 0 & 1 & 1 & 0 \\ 0 & 0 & 0 & 1 & 0.3 \end{array}\right] \left[\begin{array}{cc} 2.0083 & 1.0014 \\ \hdashline 1.0250 & 1.2542 \\ 0.1000 & 2.0167 \\ 0.7025 & 1.3171 \end{array}\right] \cdot \begin{bmatrix} \bar{\psi} \\ \bar{V} \end{bmatrix}_0 = \mathbf{z}_2^R$$

$$\left[\begin{array}{cccc:c} 1 & 1 & \frac{1}{4} & \frac{1}{12} & 0 \\ 0 & 1 & \frac{1}{2} & \frac{1}{4} & 0 \\ 0 & 0 & 1 & 1 & 0 \\ 0 & 0 & 0 & 1 & 0.3 \end{array}\right] \left[\begin{array}{cc} 3.1168 & 2.8695 \\ \hdashline 1.2506 & 2.5918 \\ 0.8025 & 3.3338 \\ 1.6375 & 2.1780 \end{array}\right] \cdot \begin{bmatrix} \bar{\psi} \\ \bar{V} \end{bmatrix}_0 = \mathbf{z}_3^R$$

$$\left[\begin{array}{cccc:c} 1 & 1 & \frac{1}{4} & \frac{1}{12} & 0 \\ 0 & 1 & \frac{1}{2} & \frac{1}{4} & 0 \\ 0 & 0 & 1 & 1 & 0 \\ 0 & 0 & 0 & 1 & 0.3 \end{array}\right] \left[\begin{array}{cc} 4.7045 & 6.4763 \\ \hdashline 2.0612 & 4.8032 \\ 2.4400 & 5.5118 \\ 3.0489 & 4.1209 \end{array}\right] \cdot \begin{bmatrix} \bar{\psi} \\ \bar{V} \end{bmatrix}_0 = \mathbf{z}_4^R$$

$$\left[\begin{array}{cccc:c} 1 & 1 & \frac{1}{2} & \frac{1}{6} & 0 \\ 0 & 1 & 1 & \frac{1}{2} & 0 \\ 0 & 0 & 1 & 1 & 0 \\ 0 & 0 & 0 & 1 & 0 \end{array}\right] \left[\begin{array}{cc} 8.4938 & 14.7220 \\ 6.0257 & 12.3755 \\ 5.4889 & 9.6327 \\ 3.0489 & 4.1209 \end{array}\right] \cdot \begin{bmatrix} \bar{\psi} \\ \bar{V} \end{bmatrix}_0 = \mathbf{z}_5$$

$$\Delta = \begin{vmatrix} 8.4938 & 14.7220 \\ 5.4889 & 9.6327 \end{vmatrix} = 1.0106$$

In order to find approximately the first normal mode, the matrix calculation was carried out for $\omega_1^2 = 0.120EJ/ml^3$. This calculation yielded the following relation between $\bar{\psi}_0$ and $\bar{V}_0$:

$$9.0176\bar{\psi}_0 + 14.8948\bar{V}_0 = 0$$

giving $\bar{V}_0 = -0.606\bar{\psi}_0$. With $\bar{\psi}_0 = 1$ the value of the deflections at the internal points are computed as follows:

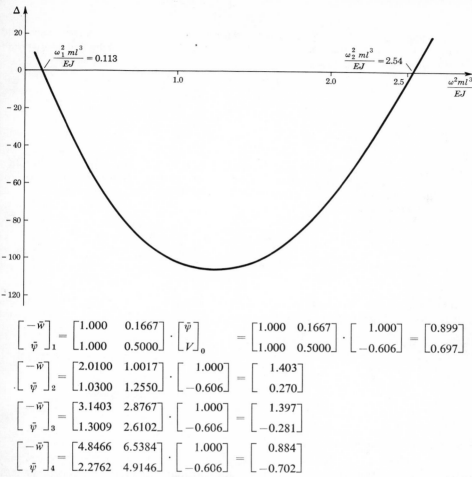

Δ

20, 0, −20, −40, −60, −80, −100, −120

$\frac{\omega_1^2 ml^3}{EJ} = 0.113$

$\frac{\omega_2^2 ml^3}{EJ} = 2.54$

1.0 2.0 2.5 $\frac{\omega^2 ml^3}{EJ}$

$$\begin{bmatrix} -\bar{w} \\ \bar{\psi} \end{bmatrix}_1 = \begin{bmatrix} 1.000 & 0.1667 \\ 1.000 & 0.5000 \end{bmatrix} \cdot \begin{bmatrix} \bar{\psi} \\ V \end{bmatrix}_0 = \begin{bmatrix} 1.000 & 0.1667 \\ 1.000 & 0.5000 \end{bmatrix} \cdot \begin{bmatrix} 1.000 \\ -0.606 \end{bmatrix} = \begin{bmatrix} 0.899 \\ 0.697 \end{bmatrix}$$

$$\begin{bmatrix} -\bar{w} \\ \bar{\psi} \end{bmatrix}_2 = \begin{bmatrix} 2.0100 & 1.0017 \\ 1.0300 & 1.2550 \end{bmatrix} \cdot \begin{bmatrix} 1.000 \\ -0.606 \end{bmatrix} = \begin{bmatrix} 1.403 \\ 0.270 \end{bmatrix}$$

$$\begin{bmatrix} -\bar{w} \\ \bar{\psi} \end{bmatrix}_3 = \begin{bmatrix} 3.1403 & 2.8767 \\ 1.3009 & 2.6102 \end{bmatrix} \cdot \begin{bmatrix} 1.000 \\ -0.606 \end{bmatrix} = \begin{bmatrix} 1.397 \\ -0.281 \end{bmatrix}$$

$$\begin{bmatrix} -\bar{w} \\ \bar{\psi} \end{bmatrix}_4 = \begin{bmatrix} 4.8466 & 6.5384 \\ 2.2762 & 4.9146 \end{bmatrix} \cdot \begin{bmatrix} 1.000 \\ -0.606 \end{bmatrix} = \begin{bmatrix} 0.884 \\ -0.702 \end{bmatrix}$$

Obviously, the first mode shape should be symmetrical about the center, and the slight discrepancy in these results is accounted for by the fact that the estimate we have employed for the natural frequency is more than 5 per cent off. Upon averaging the values and reducing the maximum deflection to unit size, we obtain the first normal mode, shown in Fig. 3-34*a*. The second mode, found by the identical procedure, is shown in Fig. 3-34*b*.

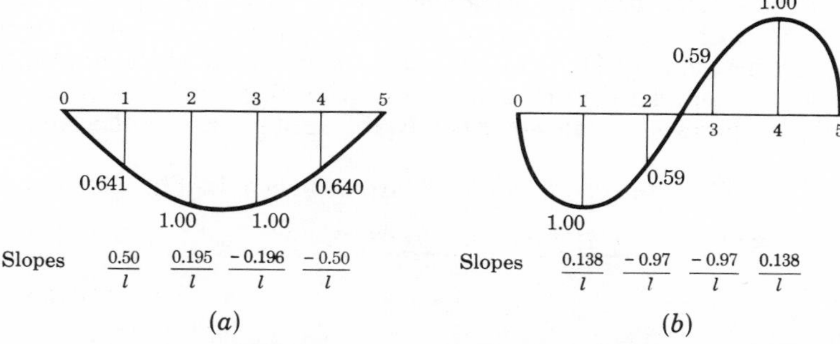

FIG. 3-34. Normal modes of beam in Fig. 3-32. (*a*) First normal mode; (*b*) second normal mode.

PROBLEMS

3-15. Using the method of shifted-matrix multiplication, find the natural frequencies and normal modes of the system of Fig. P 3-15. Check your results using the property of orthogonality.

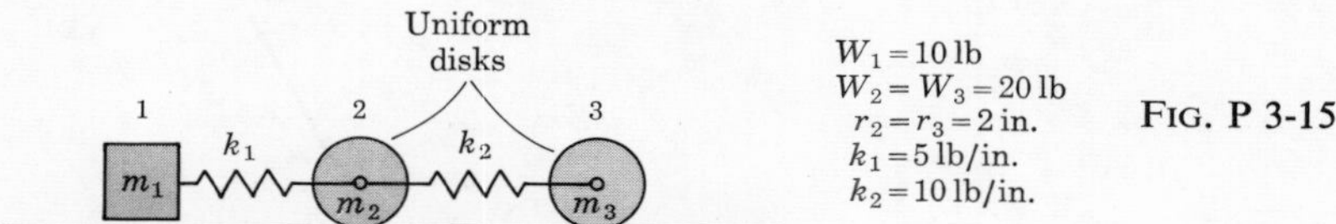

$W_1 = 10$ lb
$W_2 = W_3 = 20$ lb
$r_2 = r_3 = 2$ in.
$k_1 = 5$ lb/in.
$k_2 = 10$ lb/in.

FIG. P 3-15

3-16. When the natural frequencies of generator shafts are estimated, the distributed mass is often replaced by concentrated masses. The substitute system for the generator shaft is illustrated in Fig. P 3-16. Determine its three natural flexural frequencies.

HINT: Observe the symmetry of the shaft.

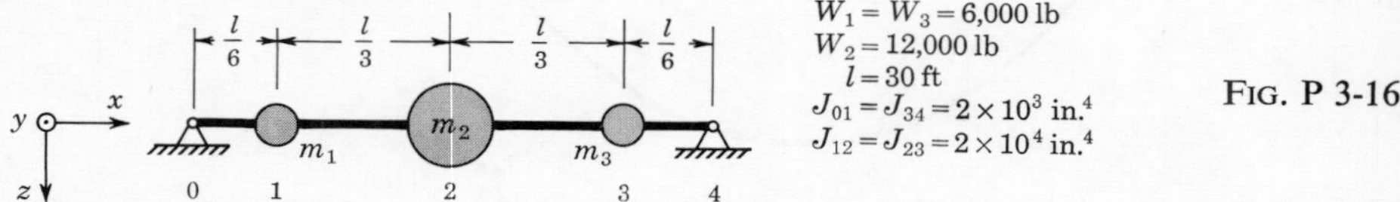

$W_1 = W_3 = 6{,}000$ lb
$W_2 = 12{,}000$ lb
$l = 30$ ft
$J_{01} = J_{34} = 2 \times 10^3$ in.^{4}
$J_{12} = J_{23} = 2 \times 10^4$ in.^{4}

FIG. P 3-16

3-17. Find the two torsional normal modes of the shaft shown in Fig. P 3-17. Check your results using the property of orthogonality.

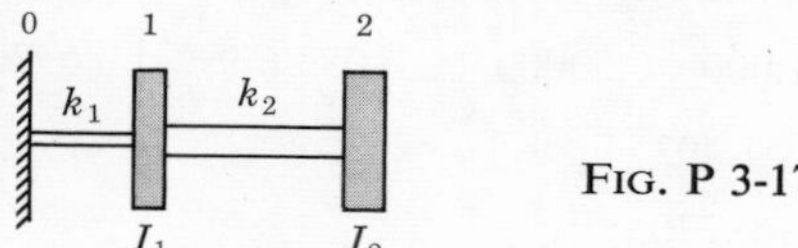

FIG. P 3-17

$k_1 = k_2 = 1.0 \times 10^6$ lb-in./radian
$I_1 = I_2 = 30$ lb-in.-sec^2

3-5. Forced Vibrations and Statics

Steady State. In the previous sections we have seen how transfer matrices may be used to find the natural frequencies and normal modes of an elastic system. Once they are known it is possible, as is demonstrated in Chap. 8, to solve the most general cases of forced undamped vibrations, whether they are of transient or steady-state character. On the other hand, the steady-state condition caused by a harmonic excitation is more readily solved with the aid of a particular integral of the nonhomogeneous differential equation. Using this approach it was shown in Sec. 2-2 that, if the forcing term has a circular frequency Ω, the system will vibrate in its steady state with the same circular frequency, but with an amplitude and phase dependent on the value of Ω. This fact enables us to extend the application of the transfer-matrix method to steady-state forced vibrations and statics ($\Omega = 0$). For explanatory purposes we shall again study the spring-mass system and the elastic beam.

Extended Transfer Matrix for Spring-Mass System. In Fig. 3-35 the illustrated

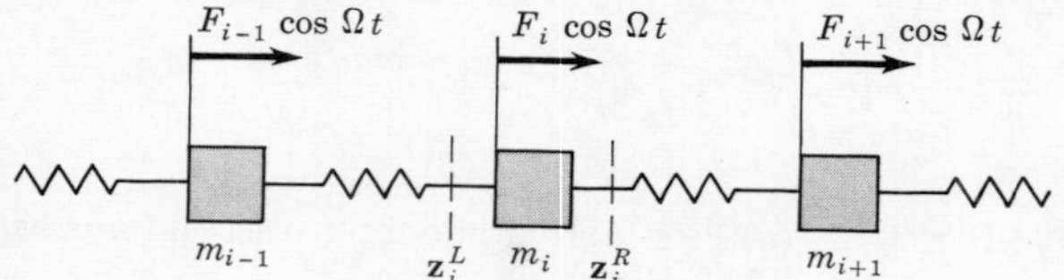

FIG. 3-35. Spring-mass system in forced vibration.

spring-mass system is subjected to the harmonic forces $F_{i-1} \cos \Omega t$, $F_i \cos \Omega t$, $F_{i+1} \cos \Omega t$, and so forth. The system will thereupon vibrate in its steady state with circular frequency Ω. It is desired to ascertain the amplitude response of the system.

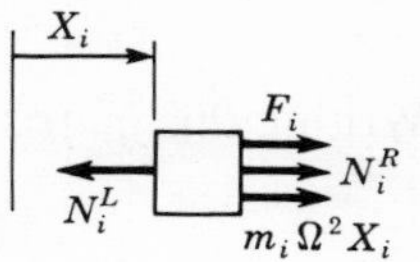

FIG. 3-36. Free-body diagram of mass m_i.

Let us first formulate the point transfer matrix that relates the state vectors $\mathbf{z}_i^R$ and $\mathbf{z}_i^L$. The displacement remains unchanged, so that $X_i^R = X_i^L$. Considering the equilibrium of the applied forces and the inertia force (Fig. 3-36), we have furthermore the following:

$$N_i^R = N_i^L - m_i\Omega^2 X_i^L - F_i$$

These two relations may be expressed in matrix notation as

$$\begin{bmatrix} X \\ N \end{bmatrix}_i^R = \begin{bmatrix} 1 & 0 \\ -m\Omega^2 & 1 \end{bmatrix}_i \cdot \begin{bmatrix} X \\ N \end{bmatrix}_i^L + \begin{bmatrix} 0 \\ -F \end{bmatrix}_i \tag{3-21}$$

This is similar to Eq. (3-3), except for the additional column matrix that has appeared to take account of the forcing term. The two matrix terms on the right-hand side may, however, be brought together as a single term in the following way:

$$\begin{bmatrix} X \\ N \\ \hdashline 1 \end{bmatrix}_i^R = \left[\begin{array}{cc:c} 1 & 0 & 0 \\ -m\Omega^2 & 1 & -F \\ \hdashline 0 & 0 & 1 \end{array}\right]_i \cdot \begin{bmatrix} X \\ N \\ \hdashline 1 \end{bmatrix}_i^L \tag{3-22}$$

or

$$\tilde{\mathbf{z}}_i^R = \tilde{\mathbf{P}}_i \tilde{\mathbf{z}}_i^L$$

If we expand this matrix expression, we obtain

$$\begin{bmatrix} X \\ N \end{bmatrix}_i^R = \begin{bmatrix} 1 & 0 \\ -m\Omega^2 & 1 \end{bmatrix}_i \cdot \begin{bmatrix} X \\ N \end{bmatrix}_i^L + \begin{bmatrix} 0 \\ -F \end{bmatrix}_i$$

and the identity

$$[1] = [0 \quad 0] \cdot \begin{bmatrix} X \\ N \end{bmatrix}_i^L + [1] \cdot [1] = [1]$$

The first equation is identical to Eq. (3-21), and the second equation is simply the identity $1 \equiv 1$. Equation (3-22) is therefore a slightly more complicated way of expressing (3-21) but has the advantage of more compact representation.

The state vector $\tilde{\mathbf{z}}_i$ with components X_i, N_i, and the additional "one" is known as the extended state vector and the transfer matrix $\tilde{\mathbf{P}}_i$ as the extended point matrix. Applying this new concept to the spring matrix, we have the relation

$$\begin{bmatrix} X \\ N \\ \hdashline 1 \end{bmatrix}_i^L = \left[\begin{array}{cc:c} 1 & \frac{1}{k} & 0 \\ 0 & 1 & 0 \\ \hdashline 0 & 0 & 1 \end{array}\right]_i \cdot \begin{bmatrix} X \\ N \\ \hdashline 1 \end{bmatrix}_{i-1}^R \qquad \text{or} \qquad \tilde{\mathbf{z}}_i^L = \tilde{\mathbf{F}}_i \tilde{\mathbf{z}}_{i-1}^R$$

which is simply the original field-matrix equation (3-2), with the addition of the identity $1 \equiv 1$.

The procedure to be adopted for the forced vibrations has now been brought into line with that used to find the natural frequencies and normal modes. Between the first and last of the state vectors we have the relation

$$\tilde{\mathbf{z}}_n = \tilde{\mathbf{F}}_n\tilde{\mathbf{P}}_{n-1}\tilde{\mathbf{F}}_{n-1}\tilde{\mathbf{P}}_{n-2}\cdots\tilde{\mathbf{P}}_1\tilde{\mathbf{F}}_1\tilde{\mathbf{z}}_0 = \tilde{\mathbf{U}}\tilde{\mathbf{z}}_0 \tag{3-23}$$

Writing this matrix product in our usual matrix-multiplication scheme,

$$\left[\begin{array}{c|c} \mathbf{F}_1 & \mathbf{f}_1 \\ \hline \mathbf{0} & 1 \end{array}\right] \cdot \left[\begin{array}{c} \mathbf{z}_0 \\ \hline 1 \end{array}\right] = \left[\begin{array}{c} \mathbf{z}_1^L \\ \hline 1 \end{array}\right]$$

$$\left[\begin{array}{c|c} \mathbf{P}_1 & \mathbf{p}_1 \\ \hline \mathbf{0} & 1 \end{array}\right]\left[\begin{array}{c|c} \mathbf{P}_1\mathbf{F}_1 & \mathbf{g}_1^R \\ \hline \mathbf{0} & 1 \end{array}\right] \cdot \left[\begin{array}{c} \mathbf{z}_0 \\ \hline 1 \end{array}\right] = \left[\begin{array}{c} \mathbf{z}_1^R \\ \hline 1 \end{array}\right]$$

$$\left[\begin{array}{c|c} \mathbf{F}_2 & \mathbf{f}_2 \\ \hline \mathbf{0} & 1 \end{array}\right]\left[\begin{array}{c|c} \mathbf{F}_2\mathbf{P}_1\mathbf{F}_1 & \mathbf{g}_2^L \\ \hline \mathbf{0} & 1 \end{array}\right] \cdot \left[\begin{array}{c} \mathbf{z}_0 \\ \hline 1 \end{array}\right] = \left[\begin{array}{c} \mathbf{z}_2^L \\ \hline 1 \end{array}\right]$$

$$\cdots\cdots\cdots\cdots\cdots\cdots\cdots\cdots$$

$$\left[\begin{array}{c|c} \mathbf{F}_n & \mathbf{f}_n \\ \hline \mathbf{0} & 1 \end{array}\right]\underbrace{\left[\begin{array}{c|c} \mathbf{F}_n\cdots\mathbf{F}_2\mathbf{P}_1\mathbf{F}_1 & \mathbf{g}_n^L \\ \hline \mathbf{0} & 1 \end{array}\right]}_{\tilde{\mathbf{U}}} \cdot \left[\begin{array}{c} \mathbf{z}_0 \\ \hline 1 \end{array}\right] = \left[\begin{array}{c} \mathbf{z}_n \\ \hline 1 \end{array}\right]$$

we recognize that $\tilde{\mathbf{U}}$ differs from $\mathbf{U}$ only on account of the extra column $\mathbf{g}_n^L$. Furthermore ω is now replaced by the forcing frequency Ω. From this fact it follows that, once $\mathbf{U}$ is computed for certain values of ω, as in the case of free vibrations, only the columns $\mathbf{g}$ have to be calculated additionally if the forced vibrations are of interest for the same frequencies.

Equation (3-23) written in long hand is

$$\left[\begin{array}{c} X \\ N \\ \hline 1 \end{array}\right]_n = \left[\begin{array}{cc|c} u_{11} & u_{12} & u_{13} \\ u_{21} & u_{22} & u_{23} \\ \hline 0 & 0 & 1 \end{array}\right] \cdot \left[\begin{array}{c} X \\ N \\ \hline 1 \end{array}\right]_0$$

giving, on expansion,

$$\begin{aligned} X_n &= u_{11}X_0 + u_{12}N_0 + u_{13} \\ N_n &= u_{21}X_0 + u_{22}N_0 + u_{23} \\ 1 &= 1 \end{aligned}$$

In contrast to the equations that arise for free vibrations, these equations are nonhomogeneous, so that when the boundary conditions are applied it is possible to solve explicitly for the unknowns, provided Ω is not equal to a natural circular frequency ω. With the boundary conditions $N_0 = 0$ and $N_n = 0$, for example, the equations yield the results

$$X_0 = -\frac{u_{23}}{u_{21}} \qquad \text{and} \qquad X_n = u_{13} - \frac{u_{11}u_{23}}{u_{21}}$$

With X_0 known, it is now a routine matter to find the deflections and forces at all points in the system.

Example 3-8. The spring-mass system of Example 3-3 is subjected to an oscillating force $F\cos\Omega t$ acting on the mass m_2 (Fig. 3-37). It is required to find the response of the system to this force.

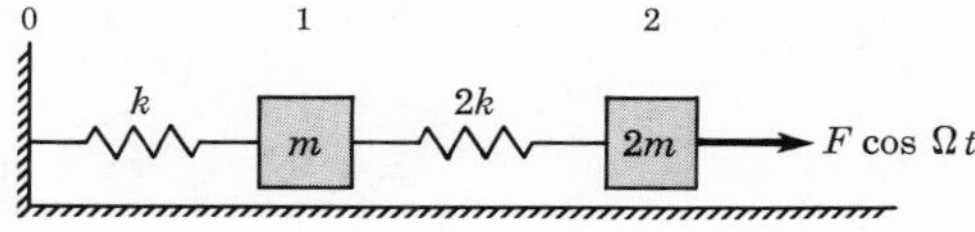

FIG. 3-37. Spring-mass system with two degrees of freedom subjected to a harmonic force.

As in Example 3-3, the deflection at point 0 is zero, so that the first column of the matrix products can be dropped. We shall adopt the same pattern as in Example 3-3 but use extended transfer matrices. In Table 3-10, $p^2 = m\Omega^2/k$. Expanding the final matrix, we obtain the equations

$$\frac{N_0}{2k}(3 - p^2) = X_2^R = X_2 \qquad (p^4 - 4p^2 + 1)N_0 - F = 0$$

from which $$N_0 = \frac{F}{p^4 - 4p^2 + 1} \qquad \text{and} \qquad X_2 = \frac{F(3 - p^2)}{2k(p^4 - 4p^2 + 1)}$$

Also $$X_1 = \frac{N_0}{k} = \frac{F}{k(p^4 - 4p^2 + 1)}$$

When $p^4 - 4p^2 + 1 = 0$, the amplitude of X_1 and X_2 becomes infinitely large. This

Table 3-10

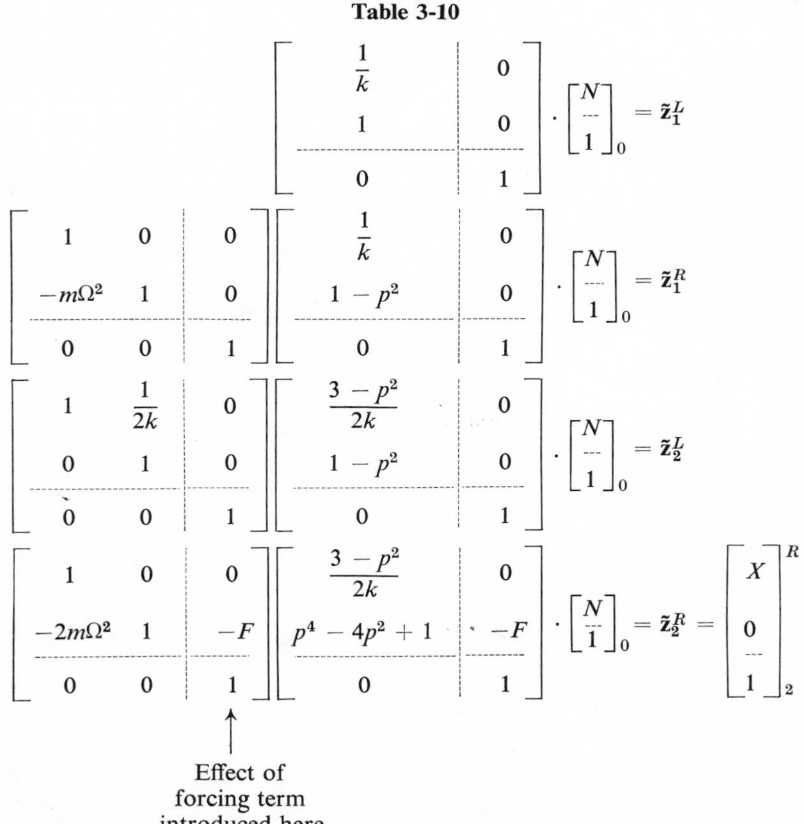

$$\begin{bmatrix} \frac{1}{k} & 0 \\ 1 & 0 \\ 0 & 1 \end{bmatrix} \cdot \begin{bmatrix} N \\ 1 \end{bmatrix}_0 = \tilde{\mathbf{z}}_1^L$$

$$\begin{bmatrix} 1 & 0 & 0 \\ -m\Omega^2 & 1 & 0 \\ 0 & 0 & 1 \end{bmatrix} \begin{bmatrix} \frac{1}{k} & 0 \\ 1 - p^2 & 0 \\ 0 & 1 \end{bmatrix} \cdot \begin{bmatrix} N \\ 1 \end{bmatrix}_0 = \tilde{\mathbf{z}}_1^R$$

$$\begin{bmatrix} 1 & \frac{1}{2k} & 0 \\ 0 & 1 & 0 \\ 0 & 0 & 1 \end{bmatrix} \begin{bmatrix} \frac{3 - p^2}{2k} & 0 \\ 1 - p^2 & 0 \\ 0 & 1 \end{bmatrix} \cdot \begin{bmatrix} N \\ 1 \end{bmatrix}_0 = \tilde{\mathbf{z}}_2^L$$

$$\begin{bmatrix} 1 & 0 & 0 \\ -2m\Omega^2 & 1 & -F \\ 0 & 0 & 1 \end{bmatrix} \begin{bmatrix} \frac{3 - p^2}{2k} & 0 \\ p^4 - 4p^2 + 1 & -F \\ 0 & 1 \end{bmatrix} \cdot \begin{bmatrix} N \\ 1 \end{bmatrix}_0 = \tilde{\mathbf{z}}_2^R = \begin{bmatrix} X \\ 0 \\ 1 \end{bmatrix}_2^R$$

↑ Effect of forcing term introduced here

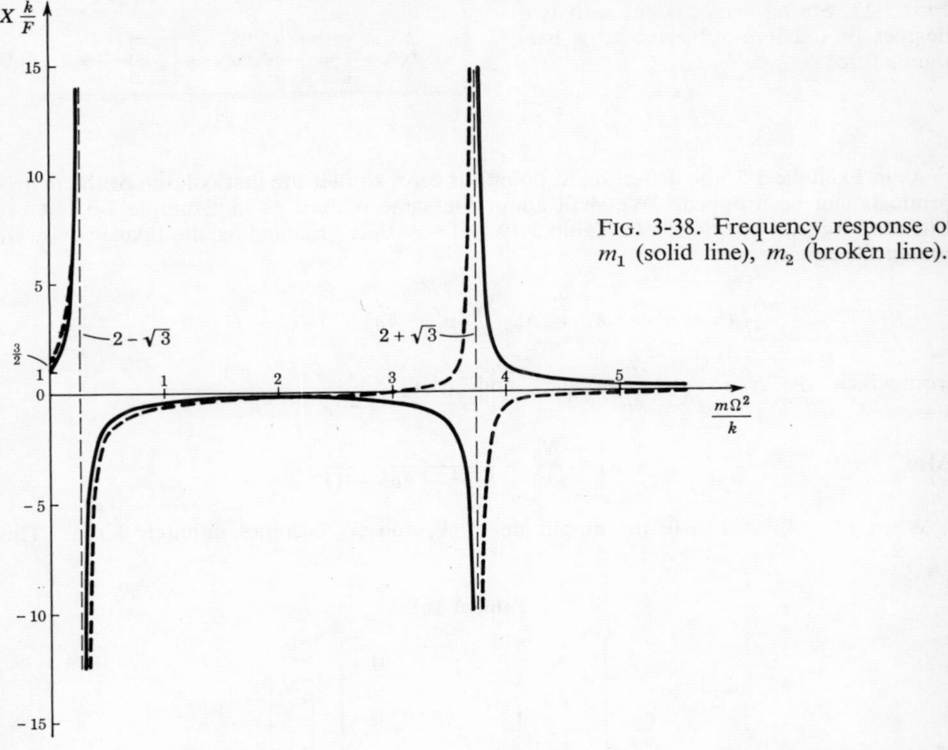

FIG. 3-38. Frequency response of m_1 (solid line), m_2 (broken line).

should be expected, since this is the equation that determines the natural frequencies (cf. Example 3-3). The response graph of the two masses is shown in Fig. 3-38.

Forced Vibrations of a Straight Beam. The transfer matrix relating the state vectors between adjacent points has already been derived in Sec. 3-1. Let us now find the corresponding relations when a length of beam is subjected to a uniformly distributed harmonic load $q \cos \Omega t$ (Fig. 3-39).

From equilibrium conditions we have for the massless beam

$$V_i^L = V_{i-1}^R - q_i l_i \qquad M_i^L = M_{i-1}^R + V_{i-1}^R l_i - \frac{q_i l_i^2}{2}$$

Also, from strength of materials [cf. Eqs. (3-7)], we obtain the relations

$$w_i^L = w_{i-1}^R - \psi_{i-1}^R l_i - M_i^L \frac{l_i^2}{2EJ_i} + V_i^L \frac{l_i^3}{3EJ_i} + \frac{q_i l_i^4}{8EJ_i}$$

$$\psi_i^L = \psi_{i-1}^R + M_i^L \frac{l_i}{EJ_i} - V_i^L \frac{l_i^2}{2EJ_i} - \frac{q_i l_i^3}{6EJ_i}$$

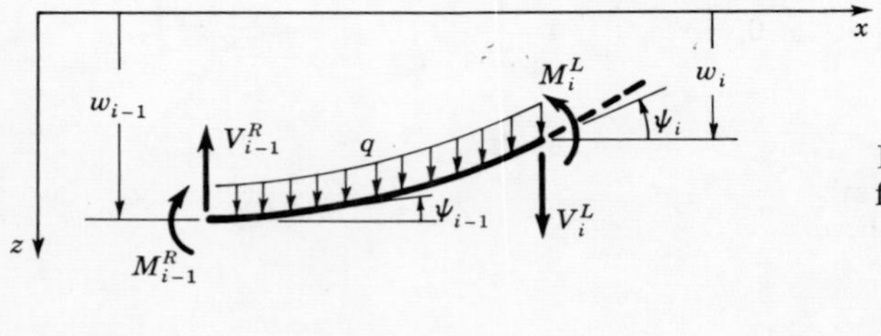

FIG. 3-39. Beam subjected to uniformly distributed load $q \cos \Omega t$.

The elimination of M_i^L and V_i^L from the right-hand side of these equations gives

$$-w_i^L = -w_{i-1}^R + \psi_{i-1}^R l_i + M_{i-1}^R \frac{l_i^2}{2EJ_i} + V_{i-1}^R \frac{l_i^3}{6EJ_i} - \frac{q_i l_i^4}{24EJ_i}$$

$$\psi_i^L = \psi_{i-1}^R + M_{i-1}^R \frac{l_i}{EJ_i} + V_{i-1}^R \frac{l_i^2}{2EJ_i} - \frac{q_i l_i^3}{6EJ_i}$$

Repeating the equilibrium equations

$$M_i^L = M_{i-1}^R + V_{i-1}^R l_i - \frac{q_i l_i^2}{2}$$

$$V_i^L = V_{i-1}^R - q_i l_i$$

and again introducing the identity $1 \equiv 1$, the above equations in matrix form become

$$\begin{bmatrix} -w \\ \psi \\ M \\ V \\ \hline 1 \end{bmatrix}_i^L = \left[\begin{array}{cccc|c} 1 & l & \dfrac{l^2}{2EJ} & \dfrac{l^3}{6EJ} & \dfrac{-ql^4}{24EJ} \\ 0 & 1 & \dfrac{l}{EJ} & \dfrac{l^2}{2EJ} & \dfrac{-ql^3}{6EJ} \\ 0 & 0 & 1 & l & \dfrac{-ql^2}{2} \\ 0 & 0 & 0 & 1 & -ql \\ \hline 0 & 0 & 0 & 0 & 1 \end{array}\right]_i \cdot \begin{bmatrix} -w \\ \psi \\ M \\ V \\ \hline 1 \end{bmatrix}_{i-1}^R \tag{3-24}$$

or

$$\tilde{\mathbf{z}}_i^L = \tilde{\mathbf{F}}_i \tilde{\mathbf{z}}_{i-1}^R$$

where $\tilde{\mathbf{z}}$ is the extended state vector and $\tilde{\mathbf{F}}$ is the extended field transfer matrix.

Example 3-9. A beam of uniform flexural stiffness EJ is simply supported at one end, built-in at the other, and supported by a spring one-third of the distance along its length (Fig. 3-40). It is subjected to a uniformly distributed static load q between points 0 and 1 and a concentrated moment $M = ql^2$ at point 1. Find the bending-moment and shear-force diagrams.

The matrix of Eq. (3-24) relates the state vectors $\tilde{\mathbf{z}}_0$ and $\tilde{\mathbf{z}}_1^L$. At point 1 the effect of the applied moment $M = ql^2$ and the spring of stiffness $k = 2EJ/l^3$ is introduced by means of the point matrix

$$\tilde{\mathbf{z}}_1^R = \left[\begin{array}{cccc|c} 1 & 0 & 0 & 0 & 0 \\ 0 & 1 & 0 & 0 & 0 \\ 0 & 0 & 1 & 0 & +ql^2 \\ \dfrac{-2EJ}{l^3} & 0 & 0 & 1 & 0 \\ \hline 0 & 0 & 0 & 0 & 1 \end{array}\right] \cdot \tilde{\mathbf{z}}_1^L$$

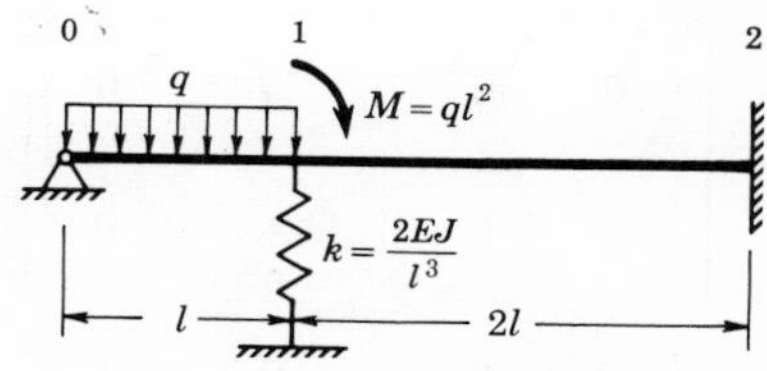

FIG. 3-40. Statically loaded beam.

The field matrix relating the state vectors $\tilde{\mathbf{z}}_1^R$ and $\tilde{\mathbf{z}}_2$ is given by

$$\tilde{\mathbf{z}}_2 = \left[\begin{array}{cccc|c} 1 & 2l & \frac{2l^2}{EJ} & \frac{4l^3}{3EJ} & 0 \\ 0 & 1 & \frac{2l}{EJ} & \frac{2l^2}{EJ} & 0 \\ 0 & 0 & 1 & 2l & 0 \\ 0 & 0 & 0 & 1 & 0 \\ \hline 0 & 0 & 0 & 0 & 1 \end{array}\right] \cdot \tilde{\mathbf{z}}_1^R$$

With the transfer matrices now known, we are in a position to carry out the matrix multiplication. In noting that $w_0 = 0$ and $M_0 = 0$, the first and third columns of the matrix products can be dropped. The matrix calculation is shown in Table 3-11.

Table 3-11

$$\left[\begin{array}{cc|c} l & \frac{l^3}{6EJ} & \frac{-ql^4}{24EJ} \\ 1 & \frac{l^2}{2EJ} & \frac{-ql^3}{6EJ} \\ 0 & l & \frac{-ql^2}{2} \\ 0 & 1 & -ql \\ \hline 0 & 0 & 1 \end{array}\right] \cdot \left[\begin{array}{c} \psi \\ V \\ \hline 1 \end{array}\right]_0 = \tilde{\mathbf{z}}_1^L$$

$$\left[\begin{array}{cccc|c} 1 & 0 & 0 & 0 & 0 \\ 0 & 1 & 0 & 0 & 0 \\ 0 & 0 & 1 & 0 & ql^2 \\ \frac{-2EJ}{l^3} & 0 & 0 & 1 & 0 \\ \hline 0 & 0 & 0 & 0 & 1 \end{array}\right] \left[\begin{array}{cc|c} l & \frac{l^3}{6EJ} & \frac{-ql^4}{24EJ} \\ 1 & \frac{l^2}{2EJ} & \frac{-ql^3}{6EJ} \\ 0 & l & \frac{ql^2}{2} \\ \frac{-2EJ}{l^2} & \frac{2}{3} & -\frac{11}{12}ql \\ \hline 0 & 0 & 1 \end{array}\right] \cdot \left[\begin{array}{c} \psi \\ V \\ \hline 1 \end{array}\right]_0 = \tilde{\mathbf{z}}_1^R$$

$$\left[\begin{array}{cccc|c} 1 & 2l & \frac{2l^2}{EJ} & \frac{4l^3}{3EJ} & 0 \\ 0 & 1 & \frac{2l}{EJ} & \frac{2l^2}{EJ} & 0 \\ 0 & 0 & 1 & 2l & 0 \\ 0 & 0 & 0 & 1 & 0 \\ \hline 0 & 0 & 0 & 0 & 1 \end{array}\right] \left[\begin{array}{cc|c} \frac{l}{3} & \frac{\frac{73}{18}l^3}{EJ} & \frac{-\frac{43}{72}ql^4}{EJ} \\ -3 & \frac{\frac{23}{6}l^2}{EJ} & \frac{-ql^3}{EJ} \\ \frac{-4EJ}{l} & \frac{7}{3}l & -\frac{4}{3}ql^2 \\ \frac{-2EJ}{l^2} & \frac{2}{3} & -\frac{11}{12}ql \\ \hline 0 & 0 & 1 \end{array}\right] \cdot \left[\begin{array}{c} \psi \\ V \\ \hline 1 \end{array}\right]_0 = \tilde{\mathbf{z}}_2^L = \left[\begin{array}{c} 0 \\ 0 \\ M \\ V \\ \hline 1 \end{array}\right]_2^L$$

From the final matrix product we can form the four equations

$$\psi_0 \frac{l}{3} + \frac{73}{18}\frac{V_0 l^3}{EJ} = \frac{43}{72}\frac{ql^4}{EJ}$$

$$-3\psi_0 + \frac{23}{6}\frac{V_0 l^2}{EJ} = \frac{ql^3}{EJ}$$

$$-\frac{4EJ}{l}\psi_0 + \tfrac{7}{3}lV_0 - \tfrac{4}{3}ql^2 = M_2$$

$$-\frac{2EJ}{l^2}\psi_0 + \tfrac{2}{3}V_0 - \tfrac{11}{12}ql = V_2$$

Solving for ψ_0 and V_0 in the first two equations gives the results

$$\psi_0 = -0.132\frac{ql^3}{EJ} \qquad V_0 = 0.158ql$$

Using these results in the two final equations gives the solutions for M_2 and V_2:

$$M_2 = -0.437ql^2 \qquad V_2 = -0.546ql$$

The moment M_1^R and shear V_1^R can be computed from the second matrix product. We have the expressions

$$M_1^R = lV_0 + \frac{ql^2}{2} = 0.658ql^3$$

and
$$V_1^R = -\frac{2EJ}{l^2}\psi_0 + \tfrac{2}{3}V_0 - \tfrac{11}{12}ql = -0.546ql$$

With M_0, V_0, M_1^R, V_1^R, M_2, and V_2 found, the bending-moment and shear-force diagrams can be plotted to give the results shown in Fig. 3-41.

PROBLEMS

3-18. An oscillating force $F\cos\Omega t$ is applied at point 1 of the system described in Prob. 3-3 (Fig. P 3-3). If $k_1 = k_2$, find the deflections of points 1 and 2. At what frequency is X_1 (*a*) infinite and (*b*) zero?

3-19. The beam of Prob. 3-4 is subjected to an end vertical force $F\cos\Omega t$. Compute the resulting end deflection and slope.

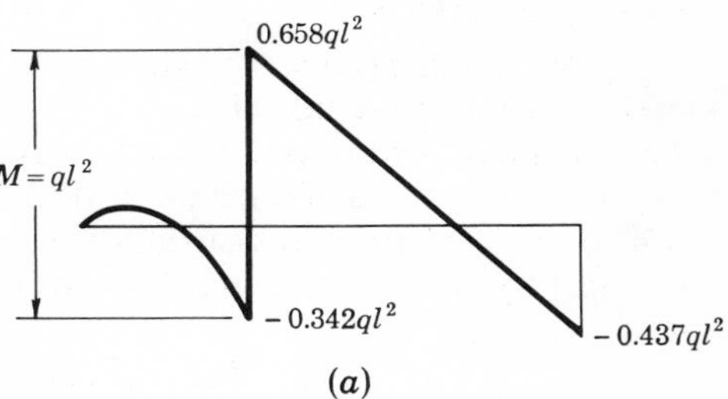

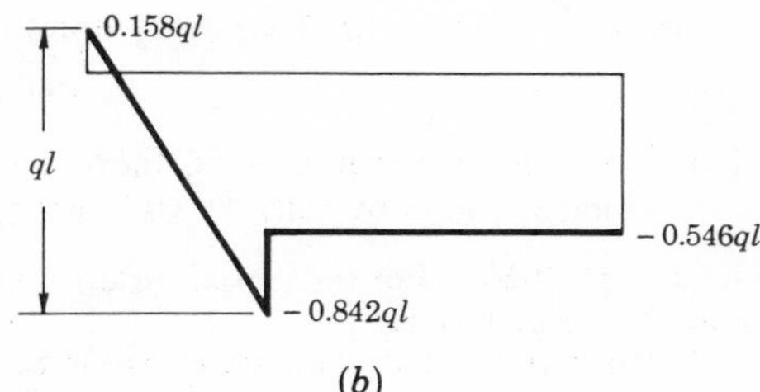

FIG. 3-41. (*a*) Bending-moment and (*b*) shear-force diagrams for the beam of Fig. 3-40.

3-20. Repeat the preceding problem when the beam is subjected to an end moment $M \cos \Omega t$.

3-21. Determine the steady-state displacements of the masses m_1 and m_2 if point 0 is subjected to a harmonic displacement (Fig. P 3-21). What force is necessary to carry out this forced displacement?

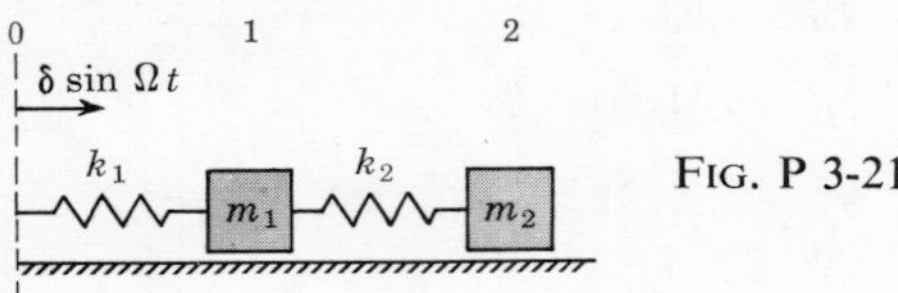

FIG. P 3-21

3-22. Find the bending-moment and shear-force diagrams for the beam of Example 3-9 (Fig. 3-40) when it is (*a*) simply supported at point 2, (*b*) supported by a spring of stiffness $k = 2EJ/l^3$ at point 2.

3-23. The torsional system of Example 3-6 (Fig. 3-29) is subjected to a torque $T_0 \cos \Omega t$ at disk I_0. If $\Omega = 300$ radians/sec, find the response of the system, using shifted-matrix multiplication.

HINT: The shifted extended matrix has the form

$$\left[\begin{array}{cc|c|c} 1 & \dfrac{1}{k} & 0 & 0 \\ 0 & 1 & T & -I\Omega^2 \\ \hline 0 & 0 & 1 & 0 \end{array}\right]$$

3-24. Repeat Prob. 3-23 for the excitation of disk I_1 by torque $T_1 \sin \Omega t$, where $\Omega = 300$ radians/sec.

3-25. With $T_0 = T$ and $T_1 = 2T$, find the total response of the system, using the results obtained in Probs. 3-23 and 3-24.

3-26. The beam of Example 3-7 is subjected to a periodic force $P_2 \cos \Omega t$ acting on mass m_2. Using shifted-matrix multiplication, find the slope amplitude of the beam at point 0 for $\Omega^2 ml^3/EJ = 0.1$.

HINT: Study the matrix scheme on page 80 and avoid unnecessary numerical work.

3-6. Closed Systems

Frequency Determinant. The systems analyzed so far have all been "open" systems, in the sense that there have been two sets of boundary conditions. If the system is closed, however, the boundary conditions are not so obvious. Suppose that we start at any arbitrary point of the closed system, where the state vector is $\mathbf{z}_0$. With the help of transfer matrices it is possible to proceed around the system until we return to the original point from which we started. In this way a relation of the form

$$\mathbf{z}_0 = \mathbf{F}_n\mathbf{F}_{n-1}\mathbf{F}_{n-2}\cdots\mathbf{F}_i\cdots\mathbf{F}_2\mathbf{F}_1\mathbf{z}_0 = \mathbf{U}\mathbf{z}_0$$

or

$$(\mathbf{U} - \mathbf{I})\mathbf{z}_0 = \mathbf{0} \tag{3-25}$$

is obtained, so that the frequency condition is

$$|\mathbf{U} - \mathbf{I}| = 0 \tag{3-26}$$

The frequency determinant is, therefore, of order n of the system and not of order $n/2$, which is the case with "open" systems.

Example 3-10. For the closed system shown in Fig. 3-42, compute the natural frequencies and the normal modes.

Starting at point 0, with state vector $\mathbf{z}_0$, we proceed around the system in the direction

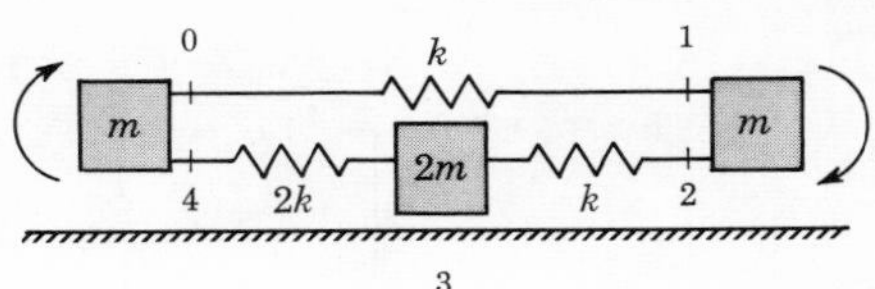

FIG. 3-42. Closed spring-mass system.

indicated by the arrow. The field matrices are simply $\begin{bmatrix} 1 & \frac{1}{k} \\ 0 & 1 \end{bmatrix}$, and the mass point matrix for the mass m at point 3 is $\begin{bmatrix} 1 & 0 \\ -2m\omega^2 & 1 \end{bmatrix}$. However, the point matrices for the masses at points 1 and 2 require examination (cf. Fig. 3-43).

Consider first the relation between state vectors $\mathbf{z}_2$ and $\mathbf{z}_1$. The tensile forces of springs N_1 and N_2 are shown together with the inertia force $m\omega^2 x_1$. With the directions of the arrows in Fig. 3-43 taken to indicate the positive directions for the displacements, then a positive x_1 displacement is a negative x_2 displacement; that is, $x_2 = -x_1$. Also, from equilibrium of forces, $N_2 = -N_1 + m\omega^2 x_1$. The matrix relation between $\mathbf{z}_2$ and $\mathbf{z}_1$ is then

$$\begin{bmatrix} x \\ N \end{bmatrix}_2 = \begin{bmatrix} -1 & 0 \\ m\omega^2 & -1 \end{bmatrix} \cdot \begin{bmatrix} x \\ N \end{bmatrix}_1$$

Following a similar argument for the left-hand mass, the results are

$$x_0 = -x_4 \qquad N_0 = +m\omega^2 x_4 - N_4$$

so that the matrix relation between state vectors $\mathbf{z}_4$ and $\mathbf{z}_0$ is

$$\begin{bmatrix} x \\ N \end{bmatrix}_0 = \begin{bmatrix} -1 & 0 \\ m\omega^2 & -1 \end{bmatrix} \cdot \begin{bmatrix} x \\ N \end{bmatrix}_4$$

The multiplication of the field and point matrices is shown in Table 3-12 ($p^2 = m\omega^2/k$). Subtracting 1's from the main diagonal and forming the frequency determinant, we obtain

$$\begin{vmatrix} p^4 - \frac{5}{2}p^2 & \frac{1}{k}(p^4 - \frac{7}{2}p^2 + \frac{5}{2}) \\ m\omega^2(-p^4 + \frac{9}{2}p^2 - 4) & -p^6 + \frac{11}{2}p^4 - \frac{15}{2}p^2 \end{vmatrix} = 0$$

giving

$$p^2(p^4 - 6.5p^2 + 10) = 0$$

The roots of this equation are

$$p_1^2 = 0 \qquad p_2^2 = 2.5 \qquad p_3^2 = 4.0$$

Hence the natural circular frequencies of the system are $\omega_1^2 = 0$, $\omega_2^2 = 2.5k/m$, and $\omega_3^2 = 4.0k/m$.

If we substitute in the final matrix product of Table 3-12

$$p^2 = p_2^2 = 2.5 \quad \text{and} \quad p^2 = p_3^2 = 4.0$$

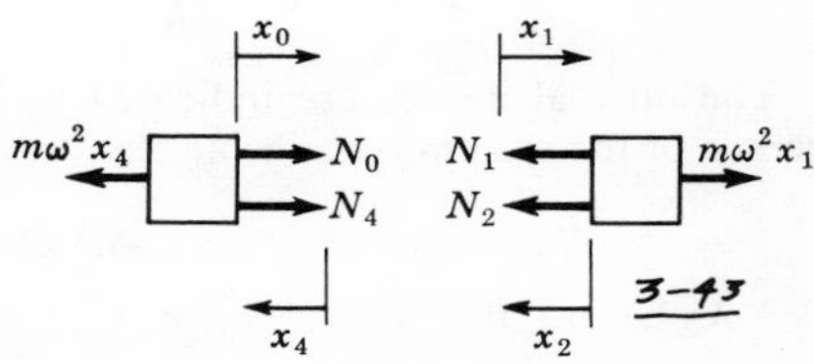

FIG. 3-43. Free-body diagram of system of the masses of Fig. 3-42.

Table 3-12

$$\begin{bmatrix} 1 & \frac{1}{k} \\ 0 & 1 \end{bmatrix} \cdot \mathbf{z}_0 = \mathbf{z}_1$$

$$\begin{bmatrix} -1 & 0 \\ m\omega^2 & -1 \end{bmatrix}\begin{bmatrix} -1 & -\frac{1}{k} \\ m\omega^2 & p^2 - 1 \end{bmatrix} \cdot \mathbf{z}_0 = \mathbf{z}_2$$

$$\begin{bmatrix} 1 & \frac{1}{k} \\ 0 & 1 \end{bmatrix}\begin{bmatrix} p^2 - 1 & \frac{1}{k}(p^2 - 2) \\ m\omega^2 & p^2 - 1 \end{bmatrix} \cdot \mathbf{z}_0 = \mathbf{z}_3^R$$

$$\begin{bmatrix} 1 & 0 \\ -2m\omega^2 & 1 \end{bmatrix}\begin{bmatrix} p^2 - 1 & \frac{1}{k}(p^2 - 2) \\ m\omega^2(3 - 2p^2) & -2p^4 + 5p^2 - 1 \end{bmatrix} \cdot \mathbf{z}_0 = \mathbf{z}_3^L$$

$$\begin{bmatrix} 1 & \frac{1}{2k} \\ 0 & 1 \end{bmatrix}\begin{bmatrix} -p^4 + \frac{5}{2}p^2 - 1 & \frac{1}{k}(-p^4 + \frac{7}{2}p^2 - \frac{5}{2}) \\ m\omega^2(3 - 2p^2) & -2p^4 + 5p^2 - 1 \end{bmatrix} \cdot \mathbf{z}_0 = \mathbf{z}_4$$

$$\begin{bmatrix} -1 & 0 \\ m\omega^2 & -1 \end{bmatrix}\begin{bmatrix} p^4 - \frac{5}{2}p^2 + 1 & \frac{1}{k}(p^4 - \frac{7}{2}p^2 + \frac{5}{2}) \\ m\omega^2(-p^4 + \frac{9}{2}p^2 - 4) & -p^6 + \frac{11}{2}p^4 - \frac{15}{2}p^2 + 1 \end{bmatrix} \cdot \mathbf{z}_0 = \mathbf{z}_0$$

respectively, then we obtain the equations

$$\begin{bmatrix} 1 & 0 \\ m\omega^2 & 1 \end{bmatrix} \cdot \begin{bmatrix} x \\ N \end{bmatrix}_{02} = \begin{bmatrix} x \\ N \end{bmatrix}_{02} \quad \text{and} \quad \begin{bmatrix} 7 & \frac{9}{2k} \\ -2m\omega^2 & -5 \end{bmatrix} \cdot \begin{bmatrix} x \\ N \end{bmatrix}_{03} = \begin{bmatrix} x \\ N \end{bmatrix}_{03}\dagger$$

from which $x_{02} = 0$ for p_2^2, and $x_{03} = -3N_{03}/4k$ for p_3^2.

In general terms the displacements x_1 and x_3 are given by

$$x_1 = x_0 + \frac{N_0}{k} \qquad x_3 = (p^2 - 1)x_0 + \frac{N_0}{k}(p^2 - 2)$$

When $p^2 = p_2^2 = 2.5$, then

$$x_{02} = 0 \qquad x_{12} = \frac{N_{02}}{k} = 1 \text{ (say)} \qquad x_{32} = \frac{1}{2}\frac{N_{02}}{k} = \frac{1}{2}$$

When $p^2 = p_3^2 = 4$, then

$$x_{03} = -\frac{3N_{03}}{4k} = 1 \text{ (say)} \qquad x_{13} = x_{03} + \frac{N_{03}}{k} = 1 - \tfrac{4}{3} = -\tfrac{1}{3}$$

$$x_{33} = 3x_{03} + \frac{2N_{03}}{k} = 3 - \tfrac{8}{3} = \tfrac{1}{3}$$

The normal modes are indicated in Fig. 3-44, from which it is obvious that the mass center of the system remains at rest. A normal-mode check, e.g., for p_2 and p_3 is

$$mx_{02}x_{03} + mx_{12}x_{13} + 2mx_{32}x_{33} = m[(0)(1) + (1)(-\tfrac{1}{3}) + (2)(\tfrac{1}{2})(\tfrac{1}{3})] = 0$$

† As before, the first subscript denotes the position; the second, the mode.

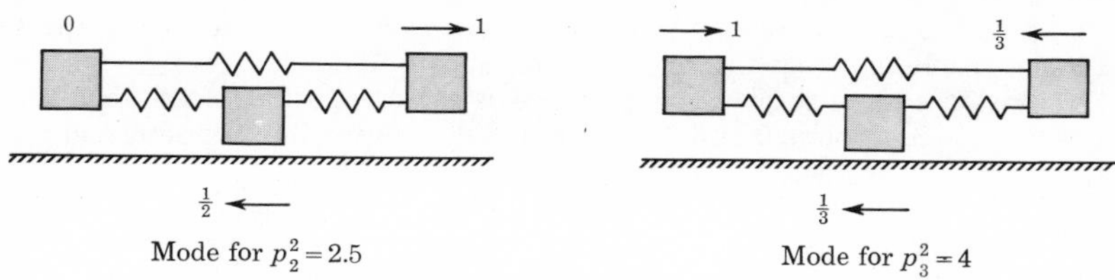

FIG. 3-44. Normal modes of system of Fig. 3-42.

REVIEW PROBLEMS FOR CHAP. 3

3-27. A mass $2m$ is supported by an elastic string which passes over a pulley consisting of a uniform disk of mass m and radius r, and is then attached to a wall (Fig. P 3-27). The pulley divides the string into two parts, each of stiffness k, and the string passes over the pulley without slipping. Find (*a*) the natural frequencies and (*b*) the normal modes of this system, checking your results by means of the orthogonality property.

3-28. Compute the point matrices connecting $\mathbf{z}_2^R$ to $\mathbf{z}_2^L$ for the system shown in Fig. P 3-28. The rod is massless.

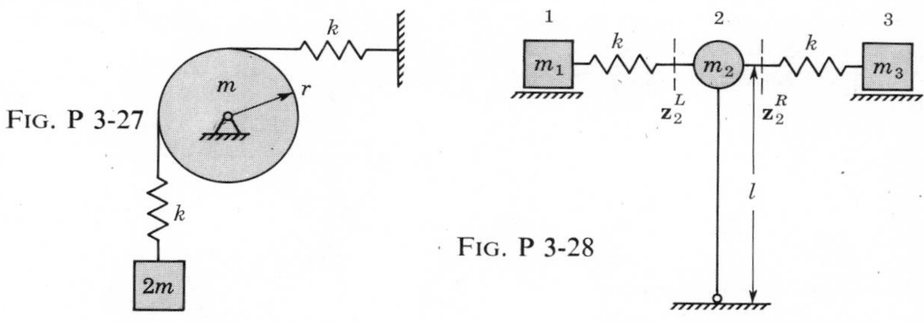

FIG. P 3-27

FIG. P 3-28

3-29. Compute the natural frequencies and normal modes of the system of Fig. P 3-28 when mass $m_1 = 2m$ and the remaining masses are equal to m.

3-30. Compute the point matrices which relate $\mathbf{z}^R$ to $\mathbf{z}^L$ for the systems illustrated in Fig. P 3-30.

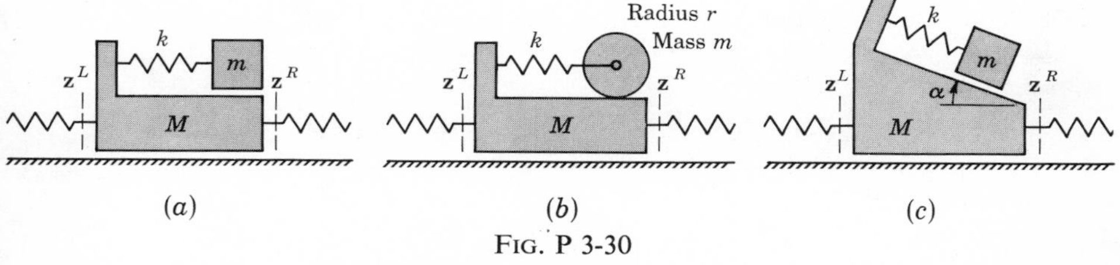

FIG. P 3-30

3-31. Using the point matrices computed in Prob. P 3-30, calculate the natural frequencies and the normal modes of the systems shown in Fig. P 3-31. Check your results by the orthogonality property.

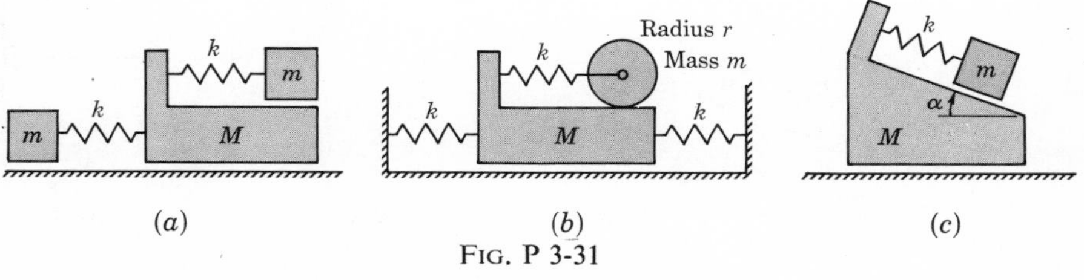

FIG. P 3-31

3-32. Compute the steady-state response of mass m when the left end of the system is subjected to the oscillating displacement indicated in Fig. P 3-32.

3-33. The torsion system shown in Fig. P 3-33 is subjected to a forced angular displacement $\Phi_1 \cos \Omega t$ between points 0 and 2. Compute the amplitudes at points 2 and 3 and the impressed torque.

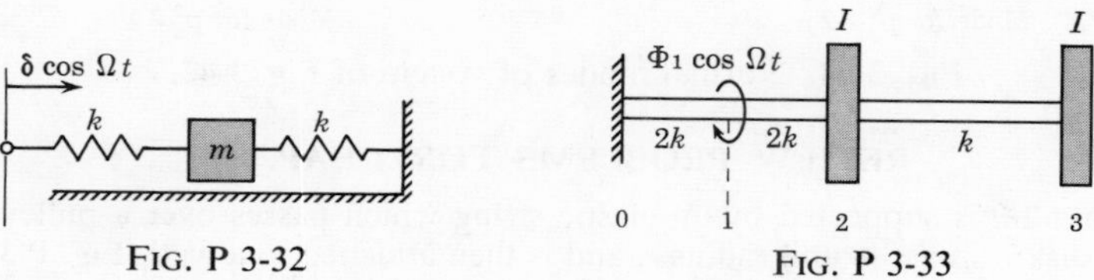

FIG. P 3-32 FIG. P 3-33

3-34. A beam of length $2l$ and constant bending stiffness EJ is built-in at both ends and loaded with a uniform load over half its span. Compute the bending-moment and shear-force diagrams for this beam (Fig. P 3-34).

3-35. Compute the new bending-moment and shear-force diagrams of the beam in Prob. 3-34 if the left-hand end is only partially built-in, the restraining effect being equivalent to a spring of rotational stiffness k.

3-36. Find the natural frequency of the system shown in Fig. P 3-36, assuming that all the pulleys are massless.

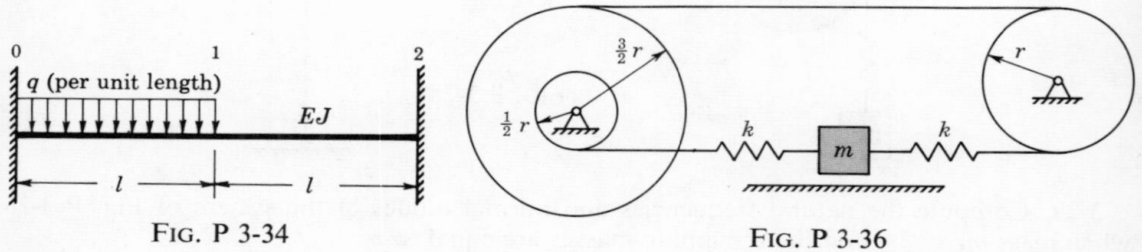

FIG. P 3-34 FIG. P 3-36

3-37. The natural frequencies of the substitute crankshaft of Fig. P 3-37 are to be calculated. Determine the normal mode for the third natural frequency.†

3-38. Compute the natural frequencies of the geared crankshaft shown in Fig. P 3-38.†

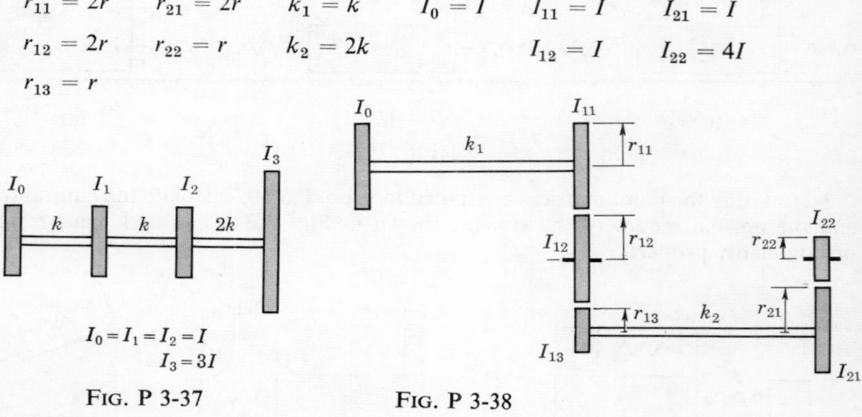

FIG. P 3-37 FIG. P 3-38

† S. Falk, Die Berechnung von Kurbelwellen mit Hilfe von digitalen Rechenautomaten, *VDI-Ber.*, no. 30, pp. 65–69, 1958.

4 INTRODUCTION TO THE THEORY OF DAMPED MECHANICAL VIBRATIONS

4-1. Damping Models

In the preceding chapters we have treated ideal mechanical systems free from internal and external damping. Real systems, however, do not possess perfectly elastic springs, nor are they surrounded by a frictionless medium, and indeed they are often purposely equipped with energy-dissipating elements. For this reason we shall now discuss two simple models that incorporate spring and damping action.†

Simple Viscous Damping. The simplest model of a spring with damping is shown in Fig. 4-1. It consists of an ideal spring with spring constant k and a dashpot in parallel. The dashpot exerts a resistive force c if piston and cylinder are moved relative to each other with unit velocity. When the damping force is proportionate to the relative velocity, the damping is described as viscous. Hence

$$P(t) = kx + c\dot{x} \tag{4-1}$$

where $P(t)$ is a force variable with time t, x is the elongation (displacement), and $\dot{x}$ the velocity.

† For a more complete account, see Refs. 10 and 11.

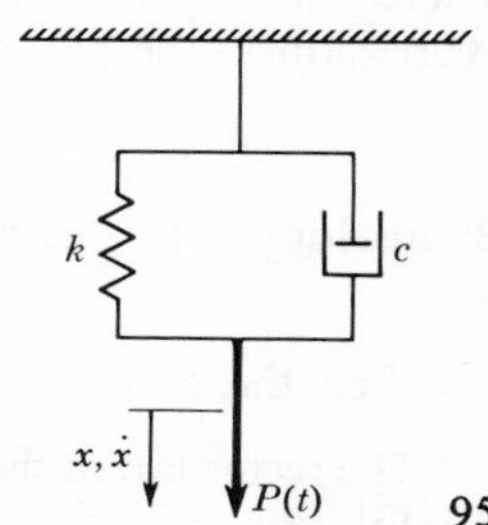

FIG. 4-1. Simple model for spring with damping.

The energy dissipated per cycle in a forced vibration with frequency Ω and amplitude A is

$$\int_0^{2\pi/\Omega} P\dot{x}\,dt = \pi A^2 c\Omega \tag{4-2}$$

From this equation we deduce that for a given value of c the energy dissipated per cycle increases proportionately with the frequency.

Structural Damping. It has been found useful, particularly in the treatment of the damped vibration of aircraft structures, to postulate a damping coefficient which varies with the forcing frequency Ω according to the following relation:

$$c(\Omega) = k\frac{g}{\Omega} \tag{4-3}$$

where k is the spring constant and g is a factor of proportionality, usually very small (0.005 to 0.015). This type of damping, commonly referred to as structural damping, has been shown by Veubeke [10] to be physically unsound, since he proves that the force-displacement relationship is

$$P(t) = kx(t) + \frac{kg}{\pi}\int_{-\infty}^{+\infty} x(\tau)\frac{d\tau}{\tau - t} \tag{4-4}$$

which leads to the conclusion that, if structural damping according to Eq. (4-3) were physically possible, the damping would depend not only on the past history but also on the future of the displacement x. In Ref. 10 it was demonstrated, however, that, if confined to a definite frequency range, structural damping would be quite acceptable. Subjecting a spring-damper system of this type to harmonic excitation,

$$x = A\cos\Omega t \tag{4-5}$$

we obtain easily from Eqs. (4-1) and (4-3)

$$P(t) = A(k\cos\Omega t - kg\sin\Omega t) \tag{4-6}$$

The energy dissipated per cycle,

$$\int_0^{2\pi/\Omega} P\dot{x}\,dt = \pi Akg$$

is a constant independent of the frequency. We conclude further that the energy dissipated by the structural damper per unit time would tend to infinity with $\Omega \to \infty$.

Complex Impedance. In order to introduce the concept of complex impedance, we rewrite Eq. (4-5) in the form

$$x = \operatorname{Re}(Ae^{j\Omega t}) \tag{4-5a}$$

where the symbol Re means that we have to take the real part of the complex expression in the parentheses. Substituting Eq. (4-5*a*) in Eq. (4-1), we obtain

$$P(t) = \operatorname{Re}[(k + j\Omega c)Ae^{j\Omega t}] \tag{4-7}$$

By analogy with electric theory

$$\bar{z}(\Omega) = k + j\Omega c \tag{4-8}$$

is called the complex impedance.† Similarly, we find the complex impedance for

† The reciprocal of the complex impedance is called the *complex admittance*, or *receptance* [12, 13].

structural damping [cf. Eq. (4-6)],

$$\bar{z}(\Omega) \equiv \bar{z} = k(1 + jg) \tag{4-9}$$

A plausible extension of Eq. (4-9) leads to the formulation of the concept of complex shear modulus and complex Young's modulus. For the simple case that Poisson's ratio μ remains real,† we have

$$\bar{G} = G(1 + jg) \tag{4-10}$$

$$\bar{E} = E(1 + jg) \tag{4-11}$$

where the proportionality factor g is the same in both (for a welded structure g may be taken approximately between 0.005 and 0.01).

4-2. Free Damped Vibrations of Simple Systems

Simple Damped Spring-Mass System. Let us consider the simple damped system of Fig. 4-2. On replacing the force $P(t)$ in Eq. (4-1) by the inertia force of mass m, the motion of mass m is described by the differential equation

$$m\ddot{x} + c\dot{x} + kx = 0 \tag{4-12}$$

the solution of which has the form

$$x(t) = e^{-\delta t}(A \cos \nu t + B \sin \nu t) \tag{4-13}$$

The damping rate δ and the natural frequency ν are determined by the constants of the differential equation (4-12), and A and B are found from the initial conditions x_0 and $\dot{x}_0$. In order to determine δ and ν, Eq. (4-13) is differentiated twice with respect to t, giving

$$\dot{x}(t) = e^{-\delta t}[(-A\delta + B\nu) \cos \nu t + (-B\delta - A\nu) \sin \nu t] \tag{4-14}$$

$$\ddot{x}(t) = e^{-\delta t}\{[A(\delta^2 - \nu^2) - 2B\nu\delta] \cos \nu t + [B(\delta^2 - \nu^2) + 2A\nu\delta] \sin \nu t\} \tag{4-15}$$

Inserting Eqs. (4-13) to (4-15) into Eq. (4-12), we obtain

$$e^{-\delta t}\{[m(\delta^2 - \nu^2)A - 2m\nu\delta B - c\delta A + c\nu B + kA] \cos \nu t + [m(\delta^2 - \nu^2)B + 2m\nu\delta A - c\delta B - c\nu A + kB] \sin \nu t\} = 0 \tag{4-16}$$

Since the contents of each set of brackets in Eq. (4-16) has to be zero regardless of initial conditions (i.e., independent of the value of A and B), δ and ν must satisfy the equations

$$m(\delta^2 - \nu^2) - c\delta + k = 0 \qquad \text{and} \qquad 2m\nu\delta - c\nu = 0$$

† We recall the relation between E, G, and μ: $G = E/2(1 + \mu)$.

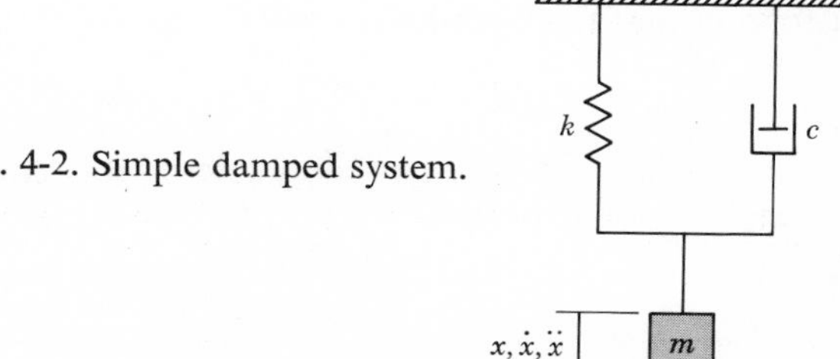

FIG. 4-2. Simple damped system.

from which we obtain

$$\delta = \frac{c}{2m} \tag{4-17}$$

and

$$\nu^2 = \frac{k}{m} - \left(\frac{c}{2m}\right)^2 = \omega^2 - \delta^2 \tag{4-18}$$

ω being the natural circular frequency of the undamped system. Furthermore, applying the initial conditions to Eqs. (4-13) and (4-14), we obtain the expressions for the constants A and B:

$$A = x_0 \qquad B = \frac{\dot{x}_0 + \delta x_0}{\nu} \tag{4-19}$$

We should note that, for this solution to be valid, ν must be real and hence ν^2 positive. It then follows from Eq. (4-18) that $k/m - (c/2m)^2 > 0$, that is, $c < 2\sqrt{mk}$. When the value of c is less than $2\sqrt{km}$, the system is said to be lightly damped. In most structural and mechanical systems the assumption of light damping is justified.

Solution by Complex Numbers. A quicker approach to the solution of Eq. (4-12) is possible by the use of complex numbers. Setting

$$x = \text{Re}\,(\bar{x}_0 e^{pt}) \tag{4-20}$$

where $\bar{x}_0$ is the so-called complex amplitude and p is the complex eigenvalue with dimension T^{-1}, the differential equation (4-12) can be transformed into the algebraic equation

$$mp^2\bar{x}_0 + cp\bar{x}_0 + k\bar{x}_0 = 0 \tag{4-21}$$

which can be interpreted as expressing the equilibrium of the complex amplitudes of the inertia force, the damper force, and the spring force. Dropping the common term $\bar{x}_0$, we obtain the characteristic equation

$$mp^2 + cp + k = 0 \tag{4-21a}$$

which yields the complex eigenvalues

$$p_{1,2} = -\frac{c}{2m} \pm j\sqrt{\frac{k}{m} - \left(\frac{c}{2m}\right)^2} = -\delta \pm j\nu \tag{4-22}$$

This result coincides with Eqs. (4-17) and (4-18) for the case of light damping $[c/(2\sqrt{mk}) = \zeta < 1]$. Therefore, the solution of Eq. (4-12) is

$$x(t) = \bar{x}_{01}e^{p_1 t} + \bar{x}_{02}e^{p_2 t}$$

and in view of the Eulerian relation

$$e^{p_{1,2}t} = e^{(-\delta \pm j\nu)t} = e^{-\delta t}(\cos \nu t \pm j \sin \nu t)$$

it follows that the solution is

$$x(t) = e^{-\delta t}[(\bar{x}_{01} + \bar{x}_{02}) \cos \nu t + j(\bar{x}_{01} - \bar{x}_{02}) \sin \nu t] \tag{4-23}$$

Furthermore, if the right-hand side of this equation is to be real, it follows that $\bar{x}_{01}$ and $\bar{x}_{02}$ are conjugate complex numbers. If we let

$$\bar{x}_{01,2} = \frac{A \pm jB}{2}$$

Eq. (4-23) reduces to Eq. (4-13).

By the use of complex theory we obtain the expressions for δ and ν with greater ease, and henceforth we shall employ solely the complex approach. All quantities such as forces and displacements are introduced in complex form, and will be denoted by the same letters as before, distinguished only by a bar over them.

PROBLEMS

4-1. Determine the natural frequency ν and the damping rate δ for the cantilever beam of Fig. P 4-1.

4-2. Determine the complex impedance of the spring-damper arrangement of Fig. P 4-2.

4-3. The simplified representation of a structure on an elastic foundation with damping is shown in Fig. P 4-3. Find the complex receptance of the spring-damper arrangement for the horizontal vibration of mass m.

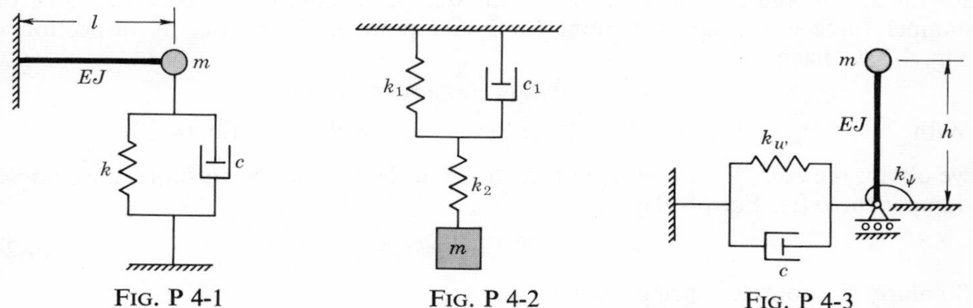

FIG. P 4-1 FIG. P 4-2 FIG. P 4-3

4-4. Determine the natural frequency ν and the damping rate δ for the free oscillation of the solid cylinder shown in Fig. P 4-4. The roller does not slip.

4-5. The air damping on mass m of the shaft of Fig. P 4-5 is represented by a viscous damper. Find the expression for the dimensionless damping constant ζ.

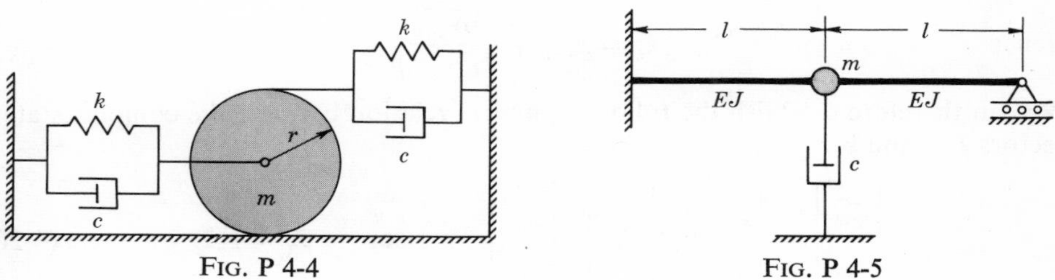

FIG. P 4-4 FIG. P 4-5

4-6. The torsional system with relative damping between the disks of Fig. P 4-6*a* can also be represented by the mass-spring-damper system of Fig. P 4-6*b*. Find the natural frequency ν and the damping rate δ.

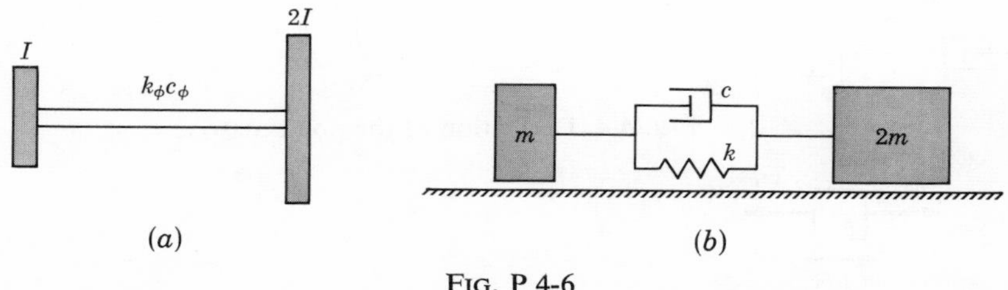

FIG. P 4-6

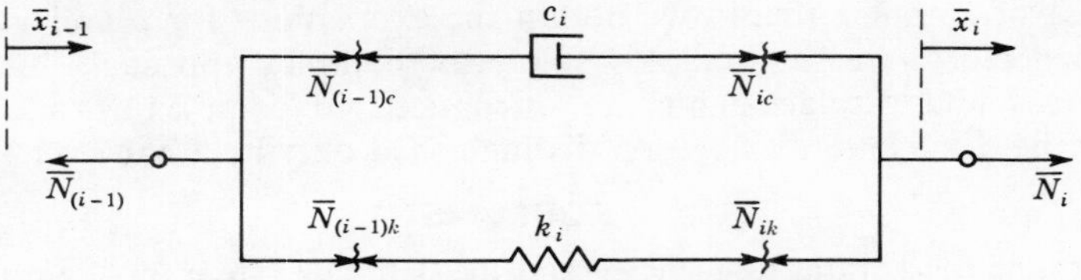

FIG. 4-3. Derivation of the field matrix.

4-3. Transfer Matrices Applied to Free Damped Vibrations

Complex Transfer Matrices. Let us now apply the transfer-matrix method to the simplest case of damped vibrations (Fig. 4-2). We derive first the field matrix for the spring and the damper. Since the damper is considered to be massless, the damper force is the same at point $i - 1$ and point i. Therefore by inspection of Fig. 4-3 we have

$$N_{ic} = N_{(i-1)c} = c_i(\dot{x}_i - \dot{x}_{i-1})$$

With $\quad N_{ic} = \text{Re}\,(\bar{N}_{ic}e^{pt}) = \text{Re}\,[c_i p(\bar{x}_i - \bar{x}_{i-1})e^{pt}] \qquad$ cf. Eq. (4-20)

we obtain the complex amplitude of the force in the damper or, in short, the complex damper force [cf. Eq. (4-21)]

$$\bar{N}_{(i-1)c} = \bar{N}_{ic} = c_i p(\bar{x}_i - \bar{x}_{i-1}) \tag{4-24}$$

Similarly the complex spring force is

$$\bar{N}_{(i-1)k} = \bar{N}_{ik} = k_i(\bar{x}_i - \bar{x}_{i-1}) \tag{4-25}$$

Hence, the total complex force of the parallel spring-damper assembly is

$$\bar{N}_{i-1} = \bar{N}_i = \bar{N}_{ic} + \bar{N}_{ik}$$

Thus
$$\bar{N}_i = \bar{N}_{ic} + \bar{N}_{ik} = (k_i + c_i p)(\bar{x}_i - \bar{x}_{i-1})$$

Hence
$$\bar{x}_i = \bar{x}_{i-1} + \frac{\bar{N}_{i-1}}{k_i + c_i p}$$

We can therefore establish the following matrix relation between the complex state vectors $\bar{\mathbf{z}}_{i-1}$ and $\bar{\mathbf{z}}_i$:

$$\begin{bmatrix} \bar{x} \\ \\ \bar{N} \end{bmatrix}_i = \begin{bmatrix} 1 & \dfrac{1}{k + cp} \\ \\ 0 & 1 \end{bmatrix}_i \cdot \begin{bmatrix} \bar{x} \\ \\ \bar{N} \end{bmatrix}_{i-1} \qquad \text{or} \qquad \bar{\mathbf{z}}_i = \bar{\mathbf{F}}_i \bar{\mathbf{z}}_{i-1} \tag{4-26}$$

Next we set up the point matrix for mass m_i, which is restrained by an "absolute" damper with damping constant r. Inspection of Fig. 4-4 yields

$$\bar{x}_i^R = \bar{x}_i^L \qquad \bar{N}_i^R = \bar{x}_i^L(m_i p^2 + r_i p) + \bar{N}_i^L$$

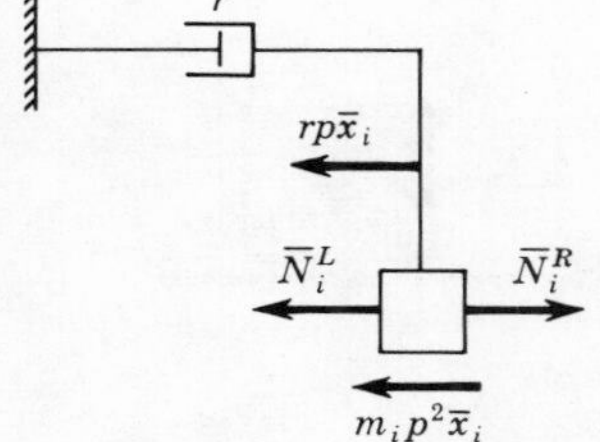

FIG. 4-4. Derivation of the point matrix.

which in matrix notation becomes

$$\begin{bmatrix} \bar{x} \\ \bar{N} \end{bmatrix}_i^R = \begin{bmatrix} 1 & 0 \\ mp^2 + rp & 1 \end{bmatrix}_i \cdot \begin{bmatrix} \bar{x} \\ \bar{N} \end{bmatrix}_i^L \quad \text{or} \quad \bar{\mathbf{z}}_i^R = \bar{\mathbf{P}}_i \bar{\mathbf{z}}_i^L \tag{4-27}$$

Real and Imaginary Parts of Transfer Matrix. We shall now split the state vectors and the transfer matrices into their real and imaginary parts, where the superscripts r and i denote the real and imaginary components, respectively:

$$\bar{\mathbf{z}} = \mathbf{z}^{\mathrm{r}} + j\mathbf{z}^{\mathrm{i}} \tag{4-28a}$$

and

$$\bar{\mathbf{U}} = \mathbf{U}^{\mathrm{r}} + j\mathbf{U}^{\mathrm{i}} \tag{4-28b}$$

Therefore

$$\bar{\mathbf{z}}_i = \bar{\mathbf{U}}_i \bar{\mathbf{z}}_{i-1}$$

$$\mathbf{z}_i^{\mathrm{r}} + j\mathbf{z}_i^{\mathrm{i}} = (\mathbf{U}^{\mathrm{r}} + j\mathbf{U}^{\mathrm{i}})_i(\mathbf{z}^{\mathrm{r}} + j\mathbf{z}^{\mathrm{i}})_{i-1}$$

$$= (\mathbf{U}_i^{\mathrm{r}}\mathbf{z}_{i-1}^{\mathrm{r}} - \mathbf{U}_i^{\mathrm{i}}\mathbf{z}_{i-1}^{\mathrm{i}}) + j(\mathbf{U}_i^{\mathrm{r}}\mathbf{z}_{i-1}^{\mathrm{i}} + \mathbf{U}_i^{\mathrm{i}}\mathbf{z}_{i-1}^{\mathrm{r}})$$

which in matrix notation takes on the following form:

$$\begin{bmatrix} \mathbf{z}^{\mathrm{r}} \\ \mathbf{z}^{\mathrm{i}} \end{bmatrix}_i = \left[\begin{array}{c|c} \mathbf{U}^{\mathrm{r}} & -\mathbf{U}^{\mathrm{i}} \\ \hline \mathbf{U}^{\mathrm{i}} & \mathbf{U}^{\mathrm{r}} \end{array}\right]_i \cdot \begin{bmatrix} \mathbf{z}^{\mathrm{r}} \\ \mathbf{z}^{\mathrm{i}} \end{bmatrix}_{i-1} \tag{4-29}$$

Inserting $p = -\delta + j\nu$ in Eqs. (4-26) and (4-27), we obtain

$$\bar{\mathbf{F}} = \left[\begin{array}{c|c} 1 & \dfrac{1}{k + c(-\delta + j\nu)} \\ \hline 0 & 1 \end{array}\right]$$

$$= \underbrace{\left[\begin{array}{c|c} 1 & \dfrac{k - c\delta}{(k - c\delta)^2 + c^2\nu^2} \\ \hline 0 & 1 \end{array}\right]}_{\mathbf{F}^{\mathrm{r}}} + j \underbrace{\left[\begin{array}{c|c} 0 & \dfrac{-c\nu}{(k - c\delta)^2 + c^2\nu^2} \\ \hline 0 & 0 \end{array}\right]}_{\mathbf{F}^{\mathrm{i}}} \tag{4-30}$$

and

$$\bar{\mathbf{P}} = \left[\begin{array}{c|c} 1 & 0 \\ \hline m(-\delta + j\nu)^2 + r(-\delta + j\nu) & 1 \end{array}\right]$$

$$= \underbrace{\left[\begin{array}{c|c} 1 & 0 \\ \hline m(\delta^2 - \nu^2) - r\delta & 1 \end{array}\right]}_{\mathbf{P}^{\mathrm{r}}} + j \underbrace{\left[\begin{array}{c|c} 0 & 0 \\ \hline r\nu - 2m\delta\nu & 0 \end{array}\right]}_{\mathbf{P}^{\mathrm{i}}} \tag{4-31}$$

In order to shorten the labor of writing we make use of the following abbreviations in Eqs. (4-30) and (4-31):

$$f^{\mathrm{r}} = \frac{k - c\delta}{(k - c\delta)^2 + c^2\nu^2} \qquad f^{\mathrm{i}} = \frac{-c\nu}{(k - c\delta)^2 + c^2\nu^2}$$

$$m^{\mathrm{r}} = m(\delta^2 - \nu^2) - r\delta \qquad m^{\mathrm{i}} = r\nu - 2m\delta\nu$$

so that, when Eqs. (4-30) and (4-31) are written according to Eq. (4-29), we obtain

$$\bar{\mathbf{F}} = \left[\begin{array}{cc|cc} 1 & f^r & 0 & -f^i \\ 0 & 1 & 0 & 0 \\ \hline 0 & f^i & 1 & f^r \\ 0 & 0 & 0 & 1 \end{array}\right] \qquad \bar{\mathbf{P}} = \left[\begin{array}{cc|cc} 1 & 0 & 0 & 0 \\ m^r & 1 & -m^i & 0 \\ \hline 0 & 0 & 1 & 0 \\ m^i & 0 & m^r & 1 \end{array}\right] \tag{4-32}$$

and according to Eq. (4-29) the state vector now consists of four elements:

$$\bar{\mathbf{z}} = \begin{bmatrix} \mathbf{z}^r \\ \mathbf{z}^i \end{bmatrix} = \begin{bmatrix} x^r \\ N^r \\ x^i \\ N^i \end{bmatrix}$$

When square matrices of the type in Eq. (4-29) are multiplied, the result is a square matrix of the same type. This is easily verified, as shown below:

$$\begin{array}{c} \left[\begin{array}{c|c} \mathbf{A} & -\mathbf{B} \\ \hline \mathbf{B} & \mathbf{A} \end{array}\right] \\ \left[\begin{array}{c|c} \mathbf{C} & -\mathbf{D} \\ \hline \mathbf{D} & \mathbf{C} \end{array}\right] \left[\begin{array}{c|c} \mathbf{CA} - \mathbf{DB} & -(\mathbf{CB} + \mathbf{DA}) \\ \hline \mathbf{CB} + \mathbf{DA} & \mathbf{CA} - \mathbf{DB} \end{array}\right] = \left[\begin{array}{c|c} \mathbf{E} & -\mathbf{F} \\ \hline \mathbf{F} & \mathbf{E} \end{array}\right] \end{array} \tag{4-33}$$

It is therefore necessary to carry out only one-half of the matrix multiplication.

Boundary Conditions and Frequency Determinant. The following matrix multiplications have to be completed to solve the simple problem of Fig. 4-5:

$$\bar{\mathbf{z}}_1^R = \bar{\mathbf{P}}_1 \bar{\mathbf{F}}_1 \bar{\mathbf{z}}_0$$

Since $\bar{x}_0 = 0$ (that is, $x_0^r = 0$ and $x_0^i = 0$), the first and third columns of $\bar{\mathbf{F}}_1$ can be left out. In the matrix multiplication scheme below, the following abbreviations are used:

$$a_1 = m^r f^r - m^i f^i + 1 \qquad a_2 = m^i f^r + m^r f^i$$

$$\left[\begin{array}{c|c} f^r & -f^i \\ 1 & 0 \\ \hline f^i & f^r \\ 0 & 1 \end{array}\right]_1 \cdot \begin{bmatrix} N^r \\ N^i \end{bmatrix}_0 = \begin{bmatrix} x^r \\ N^r \\ \hline x^i \\ N^i \end{bmatrix}_1^L$$

$$\left[\begin{array}{cc|cc} 1 & 0 & 0 & 0 \\ m^r & 1 & -m^i & 0 \\ \hline 0 & 0 & 1 & 0 \\ m^i & 0 & m^r & 1 \end{array}\right]_1 \left[\begin{array}{c|c} f^r & -f^i \\ a_1 & -a_2 \\ \hline f^i & f^r \\ a_2 & a_1 \end{array}\right] \cdot \begin{bmatrix} N^r \\ N^i \end{bmatrix}_0 = \begin{bmatrix} x^r \\ N^r \\ \hline x^i \\ N^i \end{bmatrix}_1^R$$

It is readily seen that there is no need for carrying out the multiplication to obtain the second column [cf. Eq. (4-33)].

FIG. 4-5. Simple damped system.

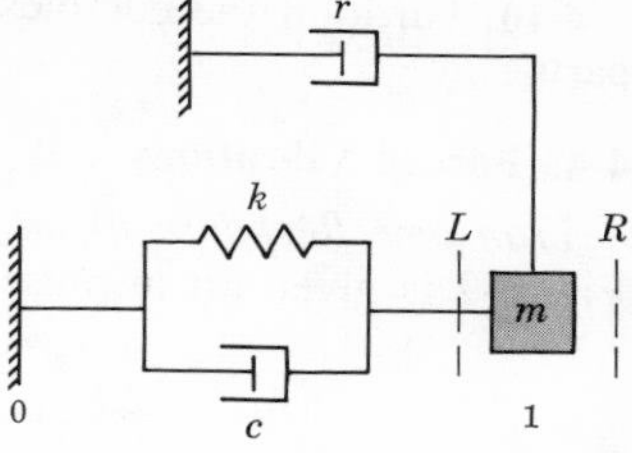

On applying the boundary conditions at point 1^R, $N_1^{rR} = 0$ and $N_1^{iR} = 0$ yield the two equations

$$a_1 N_0^r - a_2 N_0^i = 0 \qquad a_2 N_0^r + a_1 N_0^i = 0$$

which permit a nontrivial solution for N_0^r and N_0^i only if

$$\begin{vmatrix} a_1 & -a_2 \\ a_2 & a_1 \end{vmatrix} = a_1^2 + a_2^2 = 0$$

Since a_1 and a_2 are both real, it follows that

$$a_1 = 0 \qquad a_2 = 0 \tag{4-34}$$

After a short calculation Eqs. (4-34) lead with $r = 0$ to the following values for ν and δ [cf. Eqs. (4-17) and (4-18)]:

$$\nu^2 = \frac{k}{m} - \left(\frac{c}{2m}\right)^2 \qquad \delta = \frac{c}{2m}$$

General Considerations. Although it is theoretically possible to set up in a similar manner the equations for the determination of δ and ν for a multi-degree-of-freedom system, it offers no special advantages. Furthermore a purely numerical calculation is not feasible, because one has to guess simultaneously numerical values for ν and δ so that, as in the above case, a_1 and a_2 both become zero.

This disadvantage does not exist, however, when we consider the steady-state forced vibrations of a damped system. We shall therefore turn to the treatment of forced damped vibrations, which not only are of interest for the steady state but also, in contrast to the case of undamped vibrations, form the basis for the calculation of damped transients, if we consider that the steady state is identical with the frequency response (see, e.g., Ref. 14).

PROBLEMS

4-7. Repeat Probs. 4-1 to 4-6 with transfer matrices in their complex form.

4-8. Repeat Probs. 4-1 to 4-6 with transfer matrices partitioned into their real and imaginary parts.

4-9. Determine the point matrices relating $\bar{\mathbf{z}}^L$ and $\bar{\mathbf{z}}^R$ for the systems illustrated in Fig. P 4-9 in their complex form (cf. Prob. 3-30).

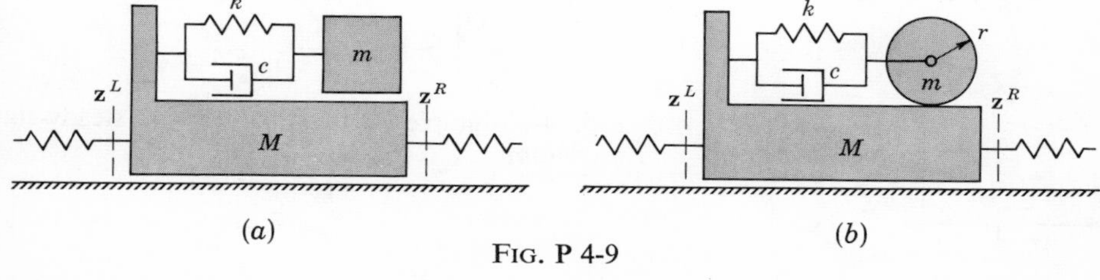

FIG. P 4-9

4-10. Partition the complex point matrices of Prob. 4-9 into their real and imaginary parts.

4-4. Forced Vibrations

Transient Response to an Impulse. The mass m of the simple damped system of Fig. 4-2 is given an impulse G at time t_0, and thereby it assumes the initial velocity

$$\dot{x}_0 = \frac{G}{m}$$

Hence, with $x_0 = 0$, the ensuing motion of mass m is given by [cf. Eqs. (4-13) and (4-19)]

$$x(t) = \frac{G}{m\nu} e^{-\delta(t-t_0)} \sin \nu(t - t_0) \qquad \text{for } t \geq t_0 \tag{4-35}$$

Response to an Arbitrary Time-varying Force. Now we subject the simple damped system to an arbitrary time-varying force $p(t)$. An infinitesimal impulse $p(\tau)\, d\tau$ produces at time τ a velocity increment $p(\tau)\, d\tau/m$. Hence for $t \geq \tau$ the motion of mass m ($x_0 = \dot{x}_0 = 0$) due to the impulse is [cf. Eq. (4-35)]

$$x(t) = \frac{p(\tau)}{m\nu} e^{-\delta(t-\tau)} \sin \nu(t - \tau)\, d\tau \tag{4-36}$$

Since such impulses are acting on m at all times $\tau \geq 0$, the resulting motion is obtained by integrating the right side of Eq. (4-36) with respect to τ:

$$x(t) = \frac{1}{m\nu} \int_0^t p(\tau) e^{-\delta(t-\tau)} \sin \nu(t - \tau)\, d\tau \tag{4-37}$$

If at time $t = 0$ the initial conditions are not zero, we have to add to Eq. (4-37) the effect of the starting conditions:

$$x(t) = \left(x_0 \cos \nu t + \frac{\dot{x}_0 + \delta x_0}{\nu} \sin \nu t \right) e^{-\delta t} \qquad \text{cf. Eqs. (4-13), (4-19)}$$

Steady State with Simple Viscous Damping. The simple damped system shown in Fig. 4-6 is subjected to a harmonic force P with circular frequency Ω,

$$P(t) = P \cos \Omega t$$

which can also be represented as the real part of a complex function, that is,

$$P(t) = \text{Re}\,(Pe^{j\Omega t}) = \text{Re}\,[P(\cos \Omega t + j \sin \Omega t)] = P \cos \Omega t$$

The differential equation of motion for the system in question is therefore

$$m\ddot{x} + c\dot{x} + kx = \text{Re}\,(Pe^{j\Omega t}) \tag{4-38}$$

In view of the right side of Eq. (4-38) the particular solution of the equation that describes the steady-state vibration of mass m is

$$x = \text{Re}\,(\bar{x}e^{j\Omega t}) \tag{4-39}$$

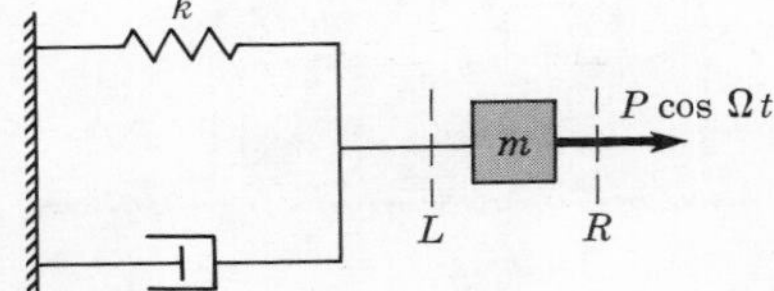

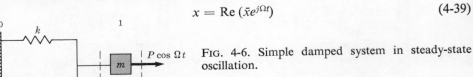

FIG. 4-6. Simple damped system in steady-state oscillation.

where $\bar{x}$ is the complex amplitude of the steady-state forced vibration. When the expression for $\bar{x}$ of Eq. (4-39) is substituted into Eq. (4-38), we obtain

$$(-m\Omega^2 + jc\Omega + k)\bar{x}e^{j\Omega t} = Pe^{j\Omega t} \qquad \text{or} \qquad (-m\Omega^2 + jc\Omega + k)\bar{x} = P \tag{4-40}$$

from which

$$\bar{x} = \frac{P}{k - m\Omega^2 + jc\Omega} \tag{4-41}$$

Equation (4-40) can be represented very conveniently on the complex plane. If the displacement vector is $\bar{x}$ (Fig. 4-7), then the spring force $k\bar{x}$ is parallel to $\bar{x}$. The effect of multiplication by j is to rotate the vector $\bar{x}$ counterclockwise through 90°, so that the force $jc\Omega\bar{x}$ in the damper is at 90° to $\bar{x}$. The inertia force $-m\Omega^2\bar{x}$ is measured in the direction opposite to that of $\bar{x}$. From the diagram we readily deduce that the magnitude of $\bar{x}$ is given by the relation

$$|\bar{x}|\,[(k - m\Omega^2)^2 + c^2\Omega^2]^{\frac{1}{2}} = P \tag{4-42}$$

and the phase-lag angle α by

$$\tan\alpha = \frac{c\Omega}{k - m\Omega^2} \tag{4-43}$$

Hence $\bar{x} = |\bar{x}|e^{-j\alpha}$, so that from Eq. (4-39)

$$x = \text{Re}\,(\bar{x}e^{j\Omega t}) = |\bar{x}|\,\text{Re}\,e^{j(\Omega t - \alpha)} = |\bar{x}|\cos(\Omega t - \alpha)$$

Introducing

$\omega = \sqrt{\dfrac{k}{m}}$ circular frequency of undamped free vibration

$\zeta = \dfrac{c}{2\sqrt{mk}}$ dimensionless damping factor

the magnitude $|\bar{x}|$ can be written [cf. Eq. (4-42)]

$$|\bar{x}| = \frac{P}{k}M$$

where P/k is the static deflection of the system of Fig. 4-7 when subjected to a static load P and

$$M = \left\{\left[1 - \left(\frac{\Omega}{\omega}\right)^2\right]^2 + 4\zeta^2\left(\frac{\Omega}{\omega}\right)^2\right\}^{-\frac{1}{2}} \tag{4-44}$$

is known as the dynamic magnification factor. Similarly we obtain from Eq. (4-43) the phase angle

$$\alpha = \tan^{-1}\frac{2\zeta(\Omega/\omega)}{1 - (\Omega/\omega)^2} \tag{4-45}$$

Graphs showing the variation of M and α with Ω/ω, that is, their frequency

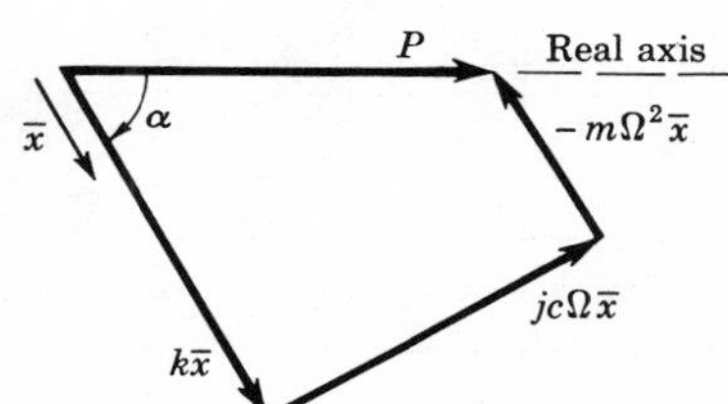

FIG. 4-7. Force vectors in the complex plane.

responses, are plotted in Figs. 4-8 and 4-9. The plot (Fig. 4-9) of the frequency response of α and of the logarithm of M over the logarithm of Ω/ω is known as the Bode diagram.†

We speak of *amplitude resonance* when M is a maximum, which is the case for the excitation frequency $\Omega_M = \omega\sqrt{1 - 2\zeta^2} < \omega$. Then $M = (2\zeta\sqrt{1 - \zeta^2})^{-1}$ or $M \approx (2\zeta)^{-1}$ for light damping. The condition at which $P(t)$ and $\dot{x}(t)$ are in phase is called *phase resonance*, which occurs for $\Omega = \omega$ when $\alpha = \pi/2$.

Inspection of Figs. 4-8 and 4-9 reveals that for light damping the phase-lag angle is very sensitive to frequency changes near $\Omega = \omega$. It therefore offers an ideal means to determine the phase-resonance frequency ω experimentally. Of course, the amplitude may be used as a substitute. It is, however, less sensitive.

Steady State with Structural Damping. For harmonic excitation the case of structural damping is particularly easy to compute, a welcome contrast to the mathematical difficulties that this case presents in free vibrations [cf. Eq. (4-4)]. With the same harmonic excitation as before, we obtain as the differential equation

† The Bode diagram can be used advantageously to determine the transfer function of a damped system from frequency-response data gained by experimental or numerical means. For further information the reader is referred to Ref. 14, among others.

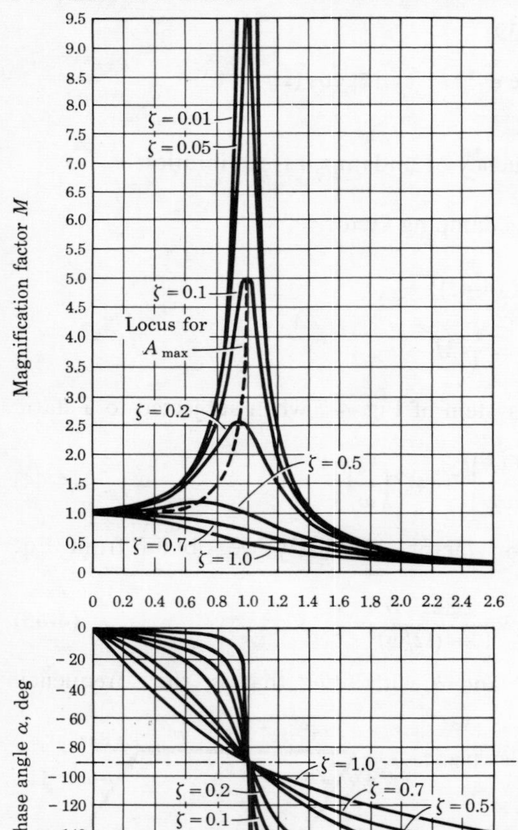

FIG. 4-8. Magnification-factor and phase plot of forced vibration.

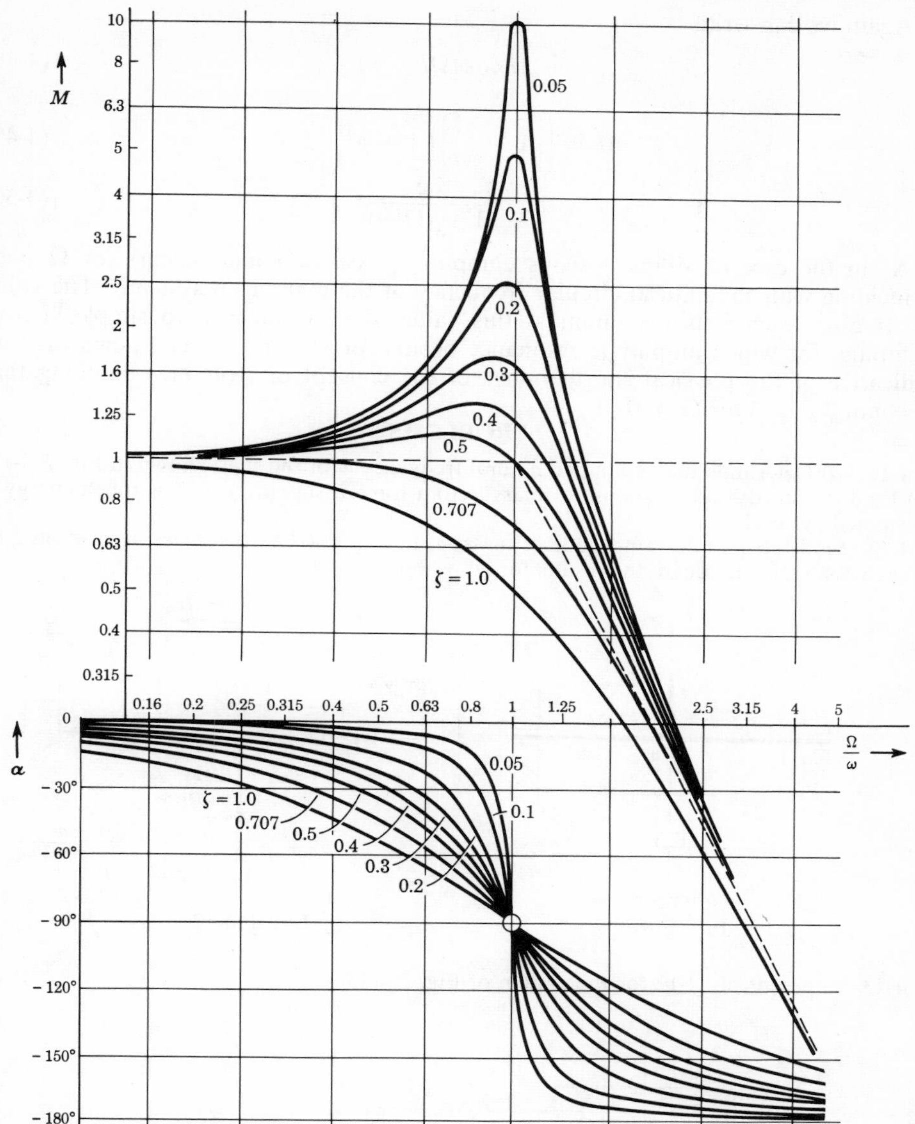

FIG. 4-9. Bode diagram for forced damped vibration.

of motion of mass m

$$m\ddot{x} + \frac{kg}{\Omega}\dot{x} + kx = \text{Re}\,(Pe^{j\Omega t}) \tag{4-46}$$ †

and with $x = \text{Re}\,(\bar{x}e^{j\Omega t})$ we have

$$\bar{x} = \frac{P}{k - m\Omega^2 + jgk} \tag{4-47}$$

† This formulation is permissible only if we confine ourselves to the steady-state solution.

Again we can write

$$x = \frac{P}{k} M \cos (\Omega t - \alpha) \tag{4-48}$$

where

$$M = \left\{\left[1 - \left(\frac{\Omega}{\omega}\right)^2\right]^2 + g^2\right\}^{-\frac{1}{2}} \tag{4-49}$$

$$\alpha = \tan^{-1} \frac{g}{1 - (\Omega/\omega)^2} \tag{4-50}$$

As in the case of simple viscous damping, phase resonance occurs for $\Omega = \omega$, coinciding with the natural circular frequency of the undamped system. The value of M also reaches its maximum at this value of ω in contrast to simple viscous damping, for which amplitude resonance occurs for $\Omega < \omega$. It is noteworthy and indicative of the physical shortcomings of the concept of structural damping that $\alpha = \tan^{-1} g \neq 0$ for $\Omega = 0$.

PROBLEMS

4-11. (*a*) Determine the undamped natural frequency ω of the shaft shown in Fig. P 4-11. (*b*) Find the steady-state response of mass m to a force $P \sin \omega t$. (*c*) How much energy is dissipated per cycle?

4-12. Find the complex amplitude of mass m_1 in Fig. P 4-12 when mass m_1 is excited by a force $P \sin \Omega t$. Evaluate the results for $\Omega^2 = k/m$.

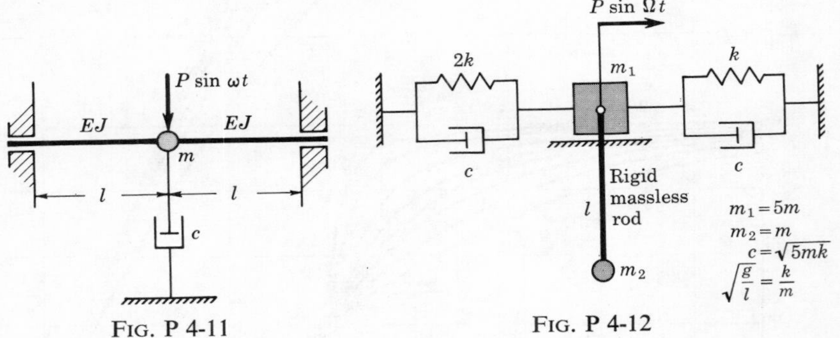

FIG. P 4-11

FIG. P 4-12

4-13. Repeat Prob. 4-12 for the system of Fig. P 4-13.

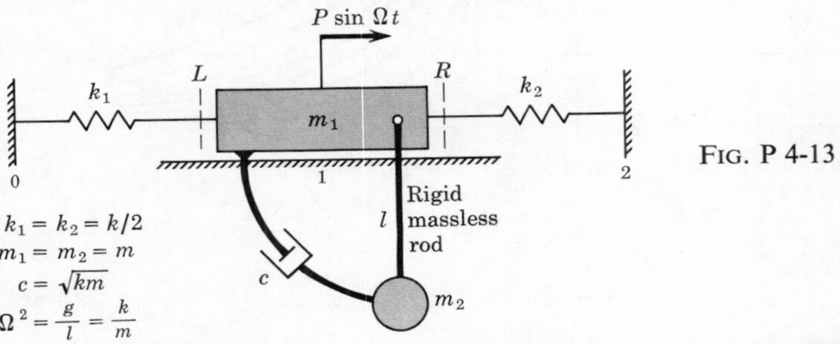

FIG. P 4-13

4-14. The structure of Fig. P 4-3 is excited by periodic aerodynamic forces that are lumped into a single horizontal force $P \sin \Omega t$ at m. Find the steady-state response for

$$\Omega = \frac{1}{2}\sqrt{\frac{EJ}{3ml^3}}$$

when $$k_w = \frac{EJ}{l^3} \qquad k_\varphi = \frac{EJ}{l} \qquad c = 0.3\sqrt{mk_w}$$

4-5. Transfer Matrices Applied to Forced Damped Vibrations

Complex Extended Transfer Matrix. We shall now compute the steady-state vibrations of the system of Fig. 4-6 with the help of transfer matrices. The transfer matrix (4-26) was found for the case of free vibrations, where p has the form

$$p = -\delta + j\nu$$

If we consider that in steady-state forced vibrations $p = j\Omega$ and if we add an extra column to the transfer matrix (4-26), the extended transfer matrix relating $\tilde{\mathbf{z}}_1^L$ and $\tilde{\mathbf{z}}_0$ becomes

$$\begin{bmatrix} \bar{x} \\ \bar{N} \\ 1 \end{bmatrix}_1^L = \begin{bmatrix} 1 & \frac{1}{k + jc\Omega} & 0 \\ 0 & 1 & 0 \\ 0 & 0 & 1 \end{bmatrix} \cdot \begin{bmatrix} \bar{x} \\ \bar{N} \\ 1 \end{bmatrix}_0 \qquad \text{cf. Eq. (4-26)} \tag{4-51}$$

The extended point matrix for the concentrated mass is given by the relation

$$\begin{bmatrix} \bar{x} \\ \bar{N} \\ 1 \end{bmatrix}_1^R = \begin{bmatrix} 1 & 0 & 0 \\ -m\Omega^2 & 1 & -\bar{P} \\ 0 & 0 & 1 \end{bmatrix} \cdot \begin{bmatrix} \bar{x} \\ \bar{N} \\ 1 \end{bmatrix}_1^L \qquad \text{cf. Eq. (4-27)} \tag{4-52}$$

Since in this case $x_0 = 0$, we may drop the first column of Eq. (4-51) and the transfer-matrix product has the form

$$\begin{bmatrix} \frac{1}{k + kc\Omega} & 0 \\ 1 & 0 \\ 0 & 1 \end{bmatrix} \cdot \begin{bmatrix} \bar{N} \\ 1 \end{bmatrix}_0$$

$$\begin{bmatrix} 1 & 0 & 0 \\ -m\Omega^2 & 1 & -\bar{P} \\ 0 & 0 & 1 \end{bmatrix} \begin{bmatrix} \frac{1}{k + jc\Omega} & 0 \\ \frac{-m\Omega^2}{k + jc\Omega} + 1 & -\bar{P} \\ 0 & 1 \end{bmatrix} \cdot \begin{bmatrix} \bar{N} \\ 1 \end{bmatrix}_0 = \begin{bmatrix} \bar{x} \\ \bar{N} \\ 1 \end{bmatrix}_1^R$$

Applying the boundary condition $\bar{N}_1^R = 0$, we obtain the relation

$$\left(1 - \frac{m\Omega^2}{k + jc\Omega}\right)\bar{N}_0 - \bar{P} = 0$$

so that $$\bar{N}_0 = \frac{\bar{P}}{1 - m\Omega^2/(k + jc\Omega)}$$

Thus $$\bar{x}_1 = \frac{\bar{N}_0}{k + jc\Omega} = \frac{\bar{P}}{k + jc\Omega - m\Omega^2} = \frac{\bar{P}}{k - m\Omega^2 + jc\Omega}$$

which coincides with Eq. (4-41).

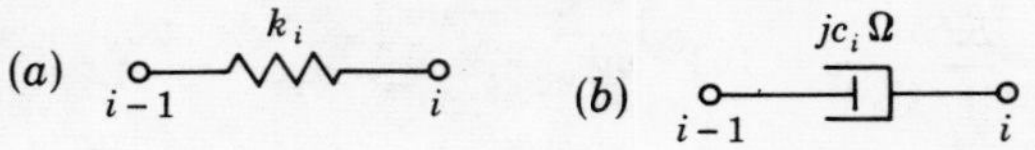

(a) k_i, $i-1$, i (b) $jc_i\Omega$, $i-1$, i

FIG. 4-10. (a) Spring of stiffness k and (b) damper of complex stiffness $jc\Omega$.

Two further simple examples of extended transfer matrices are given by Eqs. (4-53) and (4-54) for the spring (Fig. 4-10a) and the damper (Fig. 4-10b):

$$\begin{matrix} & \bar{x} & \bar{N} & 1 \end{matrix}$$
$$\bar{\mathbf{U}}_i = \left[\begin{array}{c|c|c} 1 & \dfrac{1}{k} & 0 \\ \hline 0 & 1 & 0 \\ \hline 0 & 0 & 1 \end{array}\right]_i$$

which when written in real form is [cf. Eq. (4-29)]

$$\begin{matrix} x^{\mathrm{r}} & N^{\mathrm{r}} & x^{\mathrm{i}} & N^{\mathrm{i}} & 1 \end{matrix}$$
$$\tilde{\mathbf{U}}_i = \left[\begin{array}{cc|cc|c} 1 & \dfrac{1}{k} & 0 & 0 & 0 \\ 0 & 1 & 0 & 0 & 0 \\ \hline 0 & 0 & 1 & \dfrac{1}{k} & 0 \\ 0 & 0 & 0 & 1 & 0 \\ \hline 0 & 0 & 0 & 0 & 1 \end{array}\right]_i \tag{4-53}$$

and for the viscous damper

$$\begin{matrix} & \bar{x} & \bar{N} & 1 \end{matrix}$$
$$\bar{\mathbf{U}}_i = \left[\begin{array}{c|c|c} 1 & \dfrac{1}{jc\Omega} & 0 \\ \hline 0 & 1 & 0 \\ \hline 0 & 0 & 1 \end{array}\right]$$

or in real form

$$\begin{matrix} x^{\mathrm{r}} & N^{\mathrm{r}} & x^{\mathrm{i}} & N^{\mathrm{i}} & 1 \end{matrix}$$
$$\tilde{\mathbf{U}}_i = \left[\begin{array}{cc|cc|c} 1 & 0 & 0 & \dfrac{1}{c\Omega} & 0 \\ 0 & 1 & 0 & 0 & 0 \\ \hline 0 & \dfrac{-1}{c\Omega} & 1 & 0 & 0 \\ 0 & 0 & 0 & 1 & 0 \\ \hline 0 & 0 & 0 & 0 & 1 \end{array}\right]_i \tag{4-54}$$

For easier coordination the elements of the state vector have been written above the associated columns.

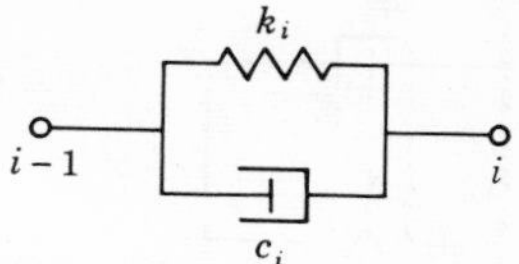

FIG. 4-11. Spring and damper in parallel.

With the terminology introduced in Sec. 4-1 we state that the damper has a *complex impedance* or complex stiffness $\bar{z}(\Omega) = jc\Omega$. The stiffness of two springs in parallel is the sum of the two individual springs, so that the combination shown in Fig. 4-11 has a complex stiffness $k + jc\Omega$. The mechanical admittance or receptance, which is defined as the reciprocal of the complex stiffness, is $1/(k + jc\Omega)$. The extended transfer matrix for the structural unit of Fig. 4-11 is given below in complex as well as in real form [cf. (4-26)]:

$$\tilde{\mathbf{U}}_i = \begin{array}{c} \begin{matrix} \bar{x} & \bar{N} & 1 \end{matrix} \\ \left[\begin{array}{c|c|c} 1 & \dfrac{1}{k + jc\Omega} & 0 \\ \hline 0 & 1 & 0 \\ \hline 0 & 0 & 1 \end{array}\right]_i \end{array} \quad \text{or} \quad \tilde{\mathbf{U}}_i = \begin{array}{c} \begin{matrix} x^r & N^r & x^i & N^i & 1 \end{matrix} \\ \left[\begin{array}{cc|cc|c} 1 & \dfrac{k}{k^2 + c^2\Omega^2} & 0 & \dfrac{c\Omega}{k^2 + c^2\Omega^2} & 0 \\ 0 & 1 & 0 & 0 & 0 \\ \hline 0 & \dfrac{-c\Omega}{k^2 + c^2\Omega^2} & 1 & \dfrac{k}{k^2 + c^2\Omega^2} & 0 \\ 0 & 0 & 0 & 1 & 0 \\ \hline 0 & 0 & 0 & 0 & 1 \end{array}\right]_i \end{array} \tag{4-55}$$

When springs and dampers are connected in series (Fig. 4-12), the total admittance is found by adding the admittances of the individual elements so that the extended transfer matrix becomes

$$\tilde{\mathbf{U}}_i = \begin{array}{c} \begin{matrix} \bar{x} & \bar{N} & 1 \end{matrix} \\ \left[\begin{array}{c|c|c} 1 & \dfrac{1}{k} + \dfrac{1}{jc\Omega} & 0 \\ \hline 0 & 1 & 0 \\ \hline 0 & 0 & 1 \end{array}\right]_i \end{array} \quad \text{or} \quad \tilde{\mathbf{U}}_i = \begin{array}{c} \begin{matrix} x^r & N^r & x^i & N^i & 1 \end{matrix} \\ \left[\begin{array}{cc|cc|c} 1 & \dfrac{1}{k} & 0 & \dfrac{1}{c\Omega} & 0 \\ 0 & 1 & 0 & 0 & 0 \\ \hline 0 & \dfrac{-1}{c\Omega} & 1 & \dfrac{1}{k} & 0 \\ 0 & 0 & 0 & 1 & 0 \\ \hline 0 & 0 & 0 & 0 & 1 \end{array}\right]_i \end{array} \tag{4-56}$$

The reader should check that the same result is obtained by multiplying the matrices of Eqs. (4-53) and (4-54). Whereas the sequence is arbitrary in this case,

FIG. 4-12. Spring and damper in series.

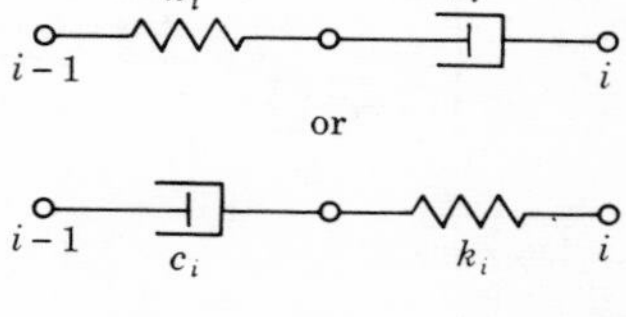

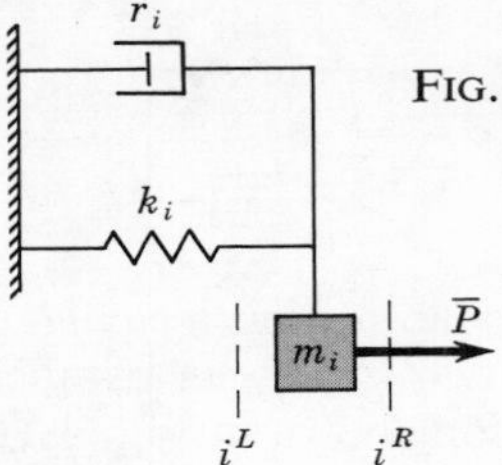

FIG. 4-13. Point mass with harmonic exciting force.

it must be emphasized that in general the sequence of transfer matrices in multiplication is not interchangeable.

Another important "building block" is represented in Fig. 4-13, where a point mass is subjected to a harmonic force of complex amplitude $\bar{P}$ and is restrained by an absolute spring and an absolute damper [cf. Eq. (4-31)]. The extended point matrix is then

$$\begin{array}{cc} & \begin{array}{ccc} \bar{x} & \bar{N} & 1 \end{array} \\ \tilde{\bar{\mathbf{U}}}_i = & \left[\begin{array}{cc|c} 1 & 0 & 0 \\ \hline -m\Omega^2 + k + jr\Omega & 1 & -\bar{P} \\ \hline 0 & 0 & 1 \end{array}\right]_i \end{array}$$

or

$$\tilde{\mathbf{U}}_i = \begin{array}{c} \begin{array}{ccccc} x^{\mathrm{r}} & N^{\mathrm{r}} & x^{\mathrm{i}} & N^{\mathrm{i}} & 1 \end{array} \\ \left[\begin{array}{cc|cc|c} 1 & 0 & 0 & 0 & 0 \\ -m\Omega^2 + k & 1 & -r\Omega & 0 & -P^{\mathrm{r}} \\ \hline 0 & 0 & 1 & 0 & 0 \\ r\Omega & 0 & -m\Omega^2 + k & 1 & -P^{\mathrm{i}} \\ \hline 0 & 0 & 0 & 0 & 1 \end{array}\right]_i \end{array} \tag{4-57}$$

Example 4-1. Determine the extended transfer matrix for the spring-mass combination of Fig. 4-14. The transfer matrix is easily found by multiplying the matrices of Eqs. (4-55) and (4-57) ($r = k = 0$). On account of the general validity of Eq. (4-33) it is necessary only to multiply the first two columns and the "forcing" columns, so that the computational work is just quadrupled, compared with the case of undamped vibrations, as the following scheme shows:

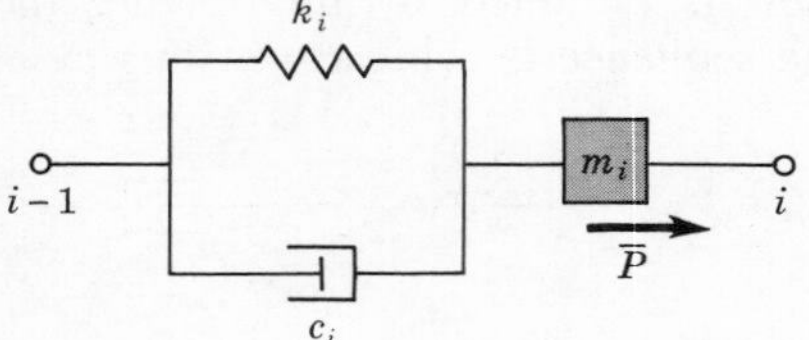

FIG. 4-14. Spring and damper in parallel with point mass in series.

$$\left[\begin{array}{cc:cc:c} 1 & 0 & 0 & 0 & 0 \\ -m\Omega^2 & 1 & 0 & 0 & -P^{\mathrm{r}} \\ \hdashline 0 & 0 & 1 & 0 & 0 \\ 0 & 0 & -m\Omega^2 & 1 & -P^{\mathrm{i}} \\ \hdashline 0 & 0 & 0 & 0 & 1 \end{array}\right] \overset{\begin{matrix} x^{\mathrm{r}} & N^{\mathrm{r}} & x^{\mathrm{i}} & N^{\mathrm{i}} & 1 \end{matrix}}{\left[\begin{array}{cc:cc:c} 1 & \dfrac{k}{k^2+c^2\Omega^2} & 0 & \dfrac{c\Omega}{k^2+c^2\Omega^2} & 0 \\ 0 & 1 & 0 & 0 & 0 \\ \hdashline 0 & \dfrac{-c\Omega}{k^2+c^2\Omega^2} & 1 & \dfrac{k}{k^2+c^2\Omega^2} & 0 \\ 0 & 0 & 0 & 1 & 0 \\ \hdashline 0 & 0 & 0 & 0 & 1 \end{array}\right]}$$

$$= \left[\begin{array}{cc:cc:c} 1 & \dfrac{k}{k^2+c^2\Omega^2} & 0 & \dfrac{c\Omega}{k^2+c^2\Omega^2} & 0 \\ -m\Omega^2 & 1-\dfrac{m\Omega^2 k}{k^2+c^2\Omega^2} & 0 & \dfrac{-mc\Omega^3}{k^2+c^2\Omega^2} & -P^{\mathrm{r}} \\ \hdashline 0 & \dfrac{-c\Omega^2}{k^2+c^2\Omega^2} & 1 & \dfrac{k}{k^2+c^2\Omega^2} & 0 \\ 0 & \dfrac{+mc\Omega^3}{k^2+c^2\Omega^2} & -m\Omega^2 & 1-\dfrac{m\Omega^2 k}{k^2+c^2\Omega^2} & -P^{\mathrm{i}} \\ \hdashline 0 & 0 & 0 & 0 & 1 \end{array}\right]$$

In view of the fact that for a spring with structural damping the complex impedance is simply

$$\bar{z} = k(1 + jg) \qquad \text{cf. Eq. (4-9)}$$

it is easy to set up the extended transfer matrix for the steady-state vibration of such a spring. By analogy with Eq. (4-55)

$$\tilde{\mathbf{U}}_i = \overset{\begin{matrix} \bar{x} & \bar{N} & 1 \end{matrix}}{\left[\begin{array}{c:c:c} 1 & \dfrac{1}{k(1+jg)} & 0 \\ \hdashline 0 & 1 & 0 \\ \hdashline 0 & 0 & 1 \end{array}\right]_i} \quad \text{or } \tilde{\mathbf{U}}_i = \overset{\begin{matrix} x^{\mathrm{r}} & N^{\mathrm{r}} & x^{\mathrm{i}} & N^{\mathrm{i}} & 1 \end{matrix}}{\left[\begin{array}{cc:cc:c} 1 & \dfrac{1}{k(1+g^2)} & 0 & \dfrac{g}{k(1+g^2)} & 0 \\ 0 & 1 & 0 & 0 & 0 \\ \hdashline 0 & \dfrac{-g}{k(1+g^2)} & 1 & \dfrac{1}{k(1+g^2)} & 0 \\ 0 & 0 & 0 & 1 & 0 \\ \hdashline 0 & 0 & 0 & 0 & 1 \end{array}\right]_i} \tag{4-58}$$

Note that Eq. (4-58) is independent of the excitation frequency. Physically this means that the phase-angle shift brought about by structurally damped springs is independent of Ω and therefore that the shift is constant over the entire frequency range.

The extended point matrix for a mass subjected to a harmonic force $\bar{P}$ and restrained by a spring with structural damping is [cf. Eq. (4-57)]

$$\tilde{\mathbf{U}}_i = \begin{bmatrix} 1 & 0 & 0 \\ -m\Omega^2 + k(1+jg) & 1 & -\bar{P} \\ 0 & 0 & 1 \end{bmatrix}_i \qquad (\bar{x},\ \bar{N},\ 1)$$

or

$$\tilde{\mathbf{U}} = \begin{bmatrix} 1 & 0 & 0 & 0 & 0 \\ -m\Omega^2 + k & 1 & -kg & 0 & -P^{\mathrm{r}} \\ 0 & 0 & 1 & 0 & 0 \\ kg & 0 & -m\Omega^2 + k & 1 & -P^{\mathrm{i}} \\ 0 & 0 & 0 & 0 & 1 \end{bmatrix}_i \qquad (x^{\mathrm{r}},\ N^{\mathrm{r}},\ x^{\mathrm{i}},\ N^{\mathrm{i}},\ 1) \tag{4-59}$$

For the case of structural damping it is easy to establish the transfer matrix for a massless beam. According to Eq. (3-8) the transfer matrix for an undamped massless beam is

$$\mathbf{U}_i = \begin{bmatrix} 1 & l & \dfrac{l^2}{2EJ} & \dfrac{l^3}{6EJ} \\ 0 & 1 & \dfrac{l}{EJ} & \dfrac{l^2}{2EJ} \\ 0 & 0 & 1 & l \\ 0 & 0 & 0 & 1 \end{bmatrix}_i \qquad (-w,\ \psi,\ M,\ V)$$

Replacing EJ by $EJ(1 + jg)$ [cf. Eq. (4-11)], we obtain the complex extended transfer matrix of the massless beam with structural damping in steady-state vibration, as follows:

$$\tilde{\mathbf{U}}_i = \begin{bmatrix} 1 & l & \dfrac{l^2}{2EJ(1+jg)} & \dfrac{l^3}{6EJ(1+jg)} & 0 \\ 0 & 1 & \dfrac{l}{EJ(1+jg)} & \dfrac{l^2}{2EJ(1+jg)} & 0 \\ 0 & 0 & 1 & l & 0 \\ 0 & 0 & 0 & 1 & 0 \\ 0 & 0 & 0 & 0 & 1 \end{bmatrix}_i \qquad (-\bar{w},\ \bar{\psi},\ \bar{M},\ \bar{V},\ 1) \tag{4-60}$$

With the aid of Eq. (4-29) we can write Eq. (4-60) in its real form, and with $E^*J = E(1 + g^2)J$ we find

$$\tilde{\mathbf{U}}_i = \begin{array}{c} \begin{array}{ccccccccc} -w^r & \psi^r & M^r & V^r & -w^i & \psi^i & M^i & V^i & 1 \end{array} \\ \left[\begin{array}{cccc:cccc:c} 1 & l & \frac{l^2}{2E^*J} & \frac{l^3}{6E^*J} & 0 & 0 & \frac{gl^2}{2E^*J} & \frac{gl^3}{6E^*J} & 0 \\ 0 & 1 & \frac{l}{E^*J} & \frac{l^2}{2E^*J} & 0 & 0 & \frac{gl}{E^*J} & \frac{gl^2}{2E^*J} & 0 \\ 0 & 0 & 1 & l & 0 & 0 & 0 & 0 & 0 \\ 0 & 0 & 0 & 1 & 0 & 0 & 0 & 0 & 0 \\ \hdashline 0 & 0 & \frac{-gl^2}{2E^*J} & \frac{-gl^3}{6E^*J} & 1 & l & \frac{l^2}{2E^*J} & \frac{l^3}{6E^*J} & 0 \\ 0 & 0 & \frac{-gl}{E^*J} & \frac{-gl^2}{2E^*J} & 0 & 1 & \frac{l}{E^*J} & \frac{l^2}{2E^*J} & 0 \\ 0 & 0 & 0 & 0 & 0 & 0 & 1 & l & 0 \\ 0 & 0 & 0 & 0 & 0 & 0 & 0 & 1 & 0 \\ \hdashline 0 & 0 & 0 & 0 & 0 & 0 & 0 & 0 & 1 \end{array}\right]_i \end{array} \tag{4-61}$$

Boundary Conditions and Frequency Response. If we use the extended transfer matrices in their real form, the extended state vector is [cf. also Eq. (4-29)]

$$\tilde{\mathbf{z}} = \{\mathbf{z}^r \quad \mathbf{z}^i \quad 1\}$$

and

$$\begin{bmatrix} \mathbf{z}^r \\ \mathbf{z}^i \\ \hdashline 1 \end{bmatrix}_i = \left[\begin{array}{cc:c} \mathbf{U}^r & -\mathbf{U}^i & \mathbf{r}^r \\ \mathbf{U}^i & \mathbf{U}^r & \mathbf{r}^i \\ \hdashline \mathbf{0} & \mathbf{0} & 1 \end{array}\right]_i \cdot \begin{bmatrix} \mathbf{z}^r \\ \mathbf{z}^i \\ \hdashline 1 \end{bmatrix}_{i-1} \tag{4-62}$$

As in the undamped case, the relation between the state vectors at the boundaries 0 and n of the system is achieved by the multiplication of the extended transfer matrices. Therefore

$$\tilde{\mathbf{z}}_n = \tilde{\mathbf{U}}_n\tilde{\mathbf{U}}_{n-1} \cdots \tilde{\mathbf{U}}_2\tilde{\mathbf{U}}_1\tilde{\mathbf{z}}_0 = \tilde{\mathbf{P}}\tilde{\mathbf{z}}_0 \tag{4-63}$$

where $\tilde{\mathbf{P}}$ is of the form

$$\tilde{\mathbf{P}} = \left[\begin{array}{cc:c} \mathbf{P}^r & -\mathbf{P}^i & \mathbf{f}^r \\ \mathbf{P}^i & \mathbf{P}^r & \mathbf{f}^i \\ \hdashline \mathbf{0} & \mathbf{0} & 1 \end{array}\right]$$

In an n-order undamped problem there are $n/2$ components of the state vectors $\mathbf{z}_0$ and $\mathbf{z}_n$ equal to zero. In the corresponding damped problem, therefore, we have at either end of the system $n/2$ components of $\mathbf{z}^r$ and $n/2$ components of $\mathbf{z}^i$ equal to zero.

In order to be more specific, let us consider a fourth-order problem of steady-state damped forced vibrations of a straight beam clamped at point 0 and propped at point n. Then

$$\tilde{\mathbf{z}}_0 = \{0 \quad 0 \quad M^r \quad V^r \;|\; 0 \quad 0 \quad M^i \quad V^i \;|\; 1\}_0$$

and

$$\tilde{\mathbf{z}}_n = \{0 \quad \psi^r \quad 0 \quad V^r \;|\; 0 \quad \psi^i \quad 0 \quad V^i \;|\; 1\}_n$$

In view of the boundary conditions at point 0, columns 1, 2, 5, and 6 are disregarded in the multiplication of the extended transfer matrices. The boundary conditions at point n yield the following four nonhomogeneous equations:

$$\begin{aligned} p_{13}M_0^r + p_{14}V_0^r + p_{17}M_0^i + p_{18}V_0^i + f_1^r &= 0 \\ p_{33}M_0^r + p_{34}V_0^r + p_{37}M_0^i + p_{38}V_0^i + f_3^r &= 0 \\ p_{53}M_0^r + p_{54}V_0^r + p_{57}M_0^i + p_{58}V_0^i + f_1^i &= 0 \\ p_{73}M_0^r + p_{74}V_0^r + p_{77}M_0^i + p_{78}V_0^i + f_3^i &= 0 \end{aligned} \tag{4-64}$$

Now in view of Eq. (4-33) we have

$$p_{13} = p_{57} \qquad p_{14} = p_{58} \qquad p_{33} = p_{77} \qquad p_{34} = p_{78}$$

$$p_{53} = -p_{17} \qquad p_{54} = -p_{18} \qquad p_{73} = -p_{37} \qquad p_{74} = -p_{38}$$

Hence Eqs. (4-64) can be written in the following matrix form:

$$\left[\begin{array}{cc|cc} a_{11} & a_{12} & -b_{11} & -b_{12} \\ a_{21} & a_{22} & -b_{21} & -b_{22} \\ \hline b_{11} & b_{12} & a_{11} & a_{12} \\ b_{21} & b_{22} & a_{21} & a_{22} \end{array}\right] \cdot \begin{bmatrix} M^r \\ V^r \\ M^i \\ V^i \end{bmatrix}_0 = \begin{bmatrix} g_1 \\ g_2 \\ g_3 \\ g_4 \end{bmatrix} \tag{4-65}$$

or

$$\mathbf{C}\mathbf{p}_0 = \mathbf{g} \tag{4-66}$$

with

$$\mathbf{g} = \{g_1 \quad g_2 \quad g_3 \quad g_4\} = \{-f_1^r - f_3^r - f_1^i - f_3^i\}$$

Thus we obtain the initial unknowns $\mathbf{p}_0 = \{M^r \quad V^r \quad M^i \quad V^i\}_0$:

$$\mathbf{p}_0 = \mathbf{C}^{-1}\mathbf{g} \tag{4-67}$$

Since the structure of matrix **C** is as shown in Eq. (4-65), we can rewrite Eq. (4-66) after partitioning $\mathbf{p}_0 = \{\mathbf{p}^r \quad \mathbf{p}^i\}$ and $\mathbf{g} = \{\mathbf{g}^r \quad \mathbf{g}^i\}$ in the form†

$$\left[\begin{array}{c|c} \mathbf{A} & -\mathbf{B} \\ \hline \mathbf{B} & \mathbf{A} \end{array}\right] \left[\begin{array}{c} \mathbf{p}^r \\ \hline \mathbf{p}^i \end{array}\right] = \left[\begin{array}{c} \mathbf{g}^r \\ \hline \mathbf{g}^i \end{array}\right]$$

Hence

$$\mathbf{A}\mathbf{p}^r - \mathbf{B}\mathbf{p}^i = \mathbf{g}^r \tag{4-68}$$

and

$$\mathbf{B}\mathbf{p}^r + \mathbf{A}\mathbf{p}^i = \mathbf{g}^i \tag{4-69}$$

Premultiplying Eq. (4-68) by $\mathbf{A}^{-1}$, we liberate $\mathbf{p}^r$.

$$\mathbf{p}^r = \mathbf{A}^{-1}\mathbf{B}\mathbf{p}^i + \mathbf{A}^{-1}\mathbf{g}^r \tag{4-70}$$

Substituting Eq. (4-70) in Eq. (4-69), we obtain

$$(\mathbf{A} + \mathbf{B}\mathbf{A}^{-1}\mathbf{B})\mathbf{p}^i = \mathbf{g}^i - \mathbf{B}\mathbf{A}^{-1}\mathbf{g}^r \tag{4-71}$$

Hence with

$$(\mathbf{A} + \mathbf{B}\mathbf{A}^{-1}\mathbf{B})^{-1} = \mathbf{A}_1 \tag{4-72}$$

Eq. (4-71) yields

$$\mathbf{p}^i = -\mathbf{A}_1\mathbf{B}\mathbf{A}^{-1}\mathbf{g}^r + \mathbf{A}_1\mathbf{g}^i \tag{4-73}$$

† See Ref. 4.

FIG. 4-15. Damped torsional system. Applied torques are $M_2 = M_2^c \cos \Omega t + M_2^s \sin \Omega t = -0.75 \cos \Omega t + 0.70 \sin \Omega t$ and $M_3 = M_3^c \cos \Omega t + M_3^s \sin \Omega t = 0.20 \cos \Omega t + 0.60 \sin \Omega t$; $\Omega^2 = 0.800$.

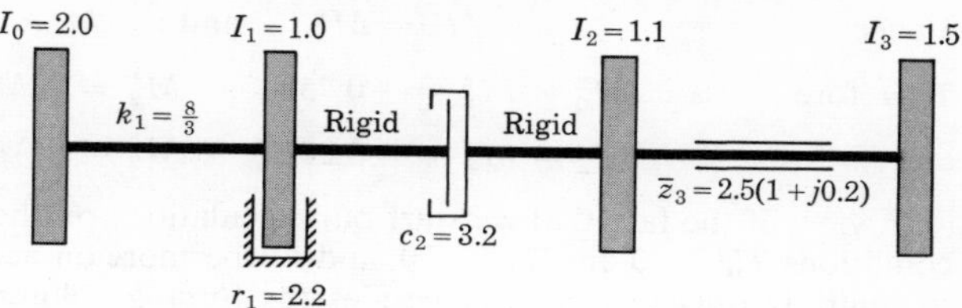

Now if we first liberate $\mathbf{p}^{\mathrm{i}}$ from Eq. (4-69) and then repeat the same elimination process,

$$\mathbf{p}^{\mathrm{r}} = \mathbf{A}_1\mathbf{g}^{\mathrm{r}} + \mathbf{A}_1\mathbf{B}\mathbf{A}^{-1}\mathbf{g}^{\mathrm{i}} \tag{4-74}$$

Therefore, using Eqs. (4-73) and (4-74), we can write

$$\mathbf{C}^{-1} = \left[\begin{array}{c|c} \mathbf{A}_1 & \mathbf{A}_1\mathbf{B}\mathbf{A}^{-1} \\ \hline -\mathbf{A}_1\mathbf{B}\mathbf{A}^{-1} & \mathbf{A}_1 \end{array}\right] \tag{4-75}$$

Thus we see that for the case of damped bending vibration it is not necessary to invert the (4, 4) matrix of Eq. (4-65), two inversions of (2, 2) matrices, namely, $\mathbf{A}^{-1}$ and $(\mathbf{A} + \mathbf{B}\mathbf{A}^{-1}\mathbf{B})^{-1}$, being sufficient.

After the initial unknowns $\mathbf{p}_0$ have been found from Eq. (4-67), the state vectors at all points throughout the system can be calculated according to the techniques described in Sec. 3-5. If we change the excitation, only column $\mathbf{g}$ has to be calculated anew.

Example 4-2. The system† shown in Fig. 4-15 contains practically all the features that a simple "straight-through" torsion system may possibly possess. It was chosen for this reason, although such a combination will hardly occur in practice. The absolute damper r_1 may, for example, represent propeller damping, and the damper c_2 could be an electromagnetic coupling. The spring connecting I_2 and I_3 is to have rather strong structural damping, caused, for example, by a rubber coupling and, as shown previously, having the effect of keeping the phase-lag angle constant, independent of the exciting frequency. The complex impedance of this spring is denoted by $\bar{z}_3 = k_3(1 + jg_3)$.

Figure 4-16 shows the equivalent damped spring-mass system. It is, however, unnecessary to transform the torsional system into such a model. All the transfer matrices of this section can be used immediately when the following correspondence is observed:

$$I \leftrightarrow m \qquad M \leftrightarrow P \qquad \phi \leftrightarrow x \qquad T \leftrightarrow N$$

From the data given with Fig. 4-15 we observe that the exciting torques M_2 and M_3 are given in their cosine and sine components. It is easy to transform these into their corresponding real and imaginary components. For this purpose let us consider

$$\begin{aligned} M^c \cos \Omega t + M^s \sin \Omega t &= \mathrm{Re}\,(\bar{M}e^{j\Omega t}) \\ &= \mathrm{Re}\,[(M^{\mathrm{r}} + jM^{\mathrm{i}})(\cos \Omega t + j \sin \Omega t)] \\ &= \mathrm{Re}\,[M^{\mathrm{r}} \cos \Omega t - M^{\mathrm{i}} \sin \Omega t + j(M^{\mathrm{r}} \sin \Omega t + M^{\mathrm{i}} \cos \Omega t)] \end{aligned}$$

† This example was treated in Ref. 16, where a tabular method was used, a comparison with which will reveal the advantages of the transfer-matrix approach.

FIG. 4-16. System equivalent to Fig. 4-15.

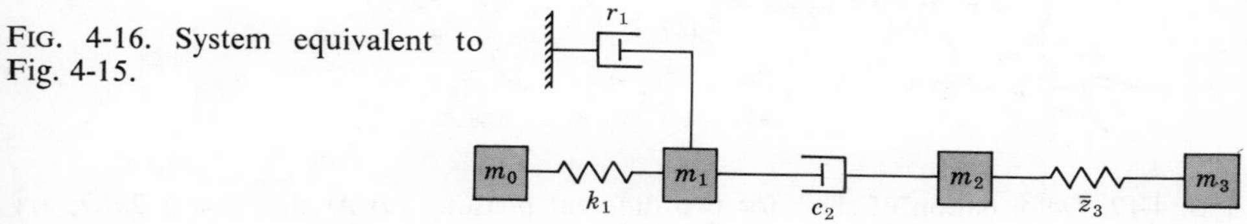

Hence $$M^c = M^r \quad \text{and} \quad M^s = -M^i$$

Therefore $$M_2^r = M_2^c = -0.7500 \qquad M_2^i = -M_2^s = -0.7000$$

and $$M_3^r = M_3^c = +0.2000 \qquad M_3^i = -M_3^s = -0.6000$$

In view of the fact that we start our calculations on the left of disk I_0 with the boundary conditions $T_0^{rL} = 0$ and $T_0^{iL} = 0$, and furthermore on account of Eq. (4-33), it is necessary to multiply only one column besides the forcing column with the field matrices. In the scheme of Table 4-1† the matrix multiplication is demonstrated, using the abbreviations

$$f_3^r = \frac{1}{k_3(1 + g_3^2)} \quad \text{and} \quad f_3^i = \frac{-g_3}{k_3(1 + g_3^2)}$$

The boundary conditions on the right of station 3, $T^r = T^i = 0$, yield the following equations for the determination of ϕ_0^r and ϕ_0^i:

$$u_2\phi_0^r - u_4\phi_0^i + h_2 = 0 \qquad u_4\phi_0^r + u_2\phi_0^i + h_4 = 0$$

Hence
$$\phi_0^r = \frac{u_2h_2 + u_4h_4}{u_2^2 + u_4^2} \tag{4-76a}$$

$$\phi_0^i = \frac{u_4h_2 - u_2h_4}{u_2^2 + u_4^2} \tag{4-76b}$$

Let us now substitute the numerical data given with Fig. 4-15 into the scheme of Table 4-1, together with

$$f_3^r = \frac{1}{k_3(1 + g_3^2)} = \frac{1}{2.5(1 + 0.2^2)} = 0.3846$$

and
$$f_3^i = \frac{-g_3}{k_3(1 + g_3^2)} = \frac{-0.2}{2.5(1 + 0.2^2)} = 0.0769$$

obtaining Table 4-2. While the multiplication is carried out, column 2, headed by ϕ_0^i, is first disregarded because in view of Eq. (4-33) it can be filled in later, taking the corresponding values from column 1. With

$$u_2 = -2.1819 \qquad h_2 = +0.1393$$
$$u_4 = -0.9311 \qquad h_4 = +1.0462$$

Eqs. (4-76) yield $\phi_0^r = \phi_0^c = 0.2271$ and $\phi_0^i = -\phi_0^s = 0.3826$.

Now columns 1 and 2 are multiplied by the above values of ϕ_0^r and ϕ_0^i, respectively, and finally the resulting values of columns 1 and 2 are added, together with the values in column 3, which stand in the same row, to give the final results in column 4. The deformation of the shaft taken from the results listed in column 4 is plotted in Fig. 4-17.

† In order to fit Table 4-1 on one page, the lower-left transfer matrix combines a field matrix and a point matrix. It is obtained from Example 4-1 by setting $c = gk/\Omega$.

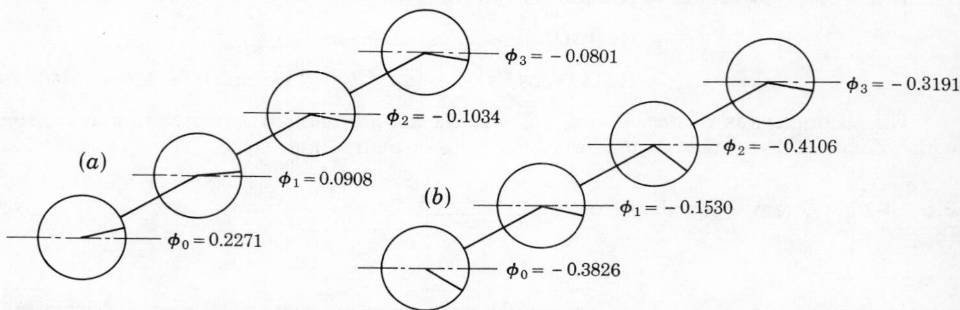

Fig. 4-17. Deformation of shaft for two different phases. (a) At time $t = 0, 2\pi/\Omega, \ldots, 2n\pi/\Omega$; (b) at time $t = \pi/2\Omega, 5\pi/2\Omega, \ldots, (4n + 1)\pi/2\Omega$.

Table 4-1

$$
\begin{array}{ccc} \phi_0^r & \phi_0^i & 1 \end{array}
$$

$$
\left[\begin{array}{cc|c}
1 & 0 & 0 \\
-I\Omega^2 & 0 & 0 \\
0 & 1 & 0 \\
0 & -I\Omega^2 & 0 \\ \hline
0 & 0 & 1
\end{array}\right]_0 \cdot \begin{bmatrix} \phi^r \\ \phi^i \\ \hline 1 \end{bmatrix}_0^L = \begin{bmatrix} \phi^r \\ T^r \\ \phi^i \\ T^i \\ \hline 1 \end{bmatrix}_0^R
$$

$$
\left[\begin{array}{cccc|c}
1 & \frac{1}{k} & 0 & 0 & 0 \\
0 & 1 & 0 & 0 & 0 \\
0 & 0 & 1 & \frac{1}{k} & 0 \\
0 & 0 & 0 & 1 & 0 \\ \hline
0 & 0 & 0 & 0 & 1
\end{array}\right]
\left[\begin{array}{cc|c}
a_1 & -a_3 & 0 \\
a_2 & -a_4 & 0 \\
a_3 & a_1 & 0 \\
a_4 & a_2 & 0 \\ \hline
0 & 0 & 1
\end{array}\right] \cdot \begin{bmatrix} \phi^r \\ \phi^i \\ \hline 1 \end{bmatrix}_0^L = \begin{bmatrix} \phi^r \\ T^r \\ \phi^i \\ T^i \\ \hline 1 \end{bmatrix}_1^L
$$

$$
\left[\begin{array}{cccc|c}
1 & 0 & 0 & 0 & 0 \\
-I\Omega^2 & 1 & -r\Omega & 0 & 0 \\
0 & 0 & 1 & 0 & 0 \\
r\Omega & 0 & -I\Omega^2 & 1 & 0 \\ \hline
0 & 0 & 0 & 0 & 1
\end{array}\right]
\left[\begin{array}{cc|c}
b_1 & -b_3 & 0 \\
b_2 & -b_4 & 0 \\
b_3 & b_1 & 0 \\
b_4 & b_2 & 0 \\ \hline
0 & 0 & 1
\end{array}\right] \cdot \begin{bmatrix} \phi^r \\ \phi^i \\ \hline 1 \end{bmatrix}_0^L = \begin{bmatrix} \phi^r \\ T^r \\ \phi^i \\ T^i \\ \hline 1 \end{bmatrix}_1^R
$$

$$
\left[\begin{array}{cccc|c}
1 & 0 & 0 & \frac{1}{c\Omega} & 0 \\
0 & 1 & 0 & 0 & 0 \\
0 & \frac{-1}{c\Omega} & 1 & 0 & 0 \\
0 & 0 & 0 & 1 & 0 \\ \hline
0 & 0 & 0 & 0 & 1
\end{array}\right]
\left[\begin{array}{cc|c}
c_1 & -c_3 & 0 \\
c_2 & -c_4 & 0 \\
c_3 & c_1 & 0 \\
c_4 & c_2 & 0 \\ \hline
0 & 0 & 1
\end{array}\right] \cdot \begin{bmatrix} \phi^r \\ \phi^i \\ \hline 1 \end{bmatrix}_0^L = \begin{bmatrix} \phi^r \\ T^r \\ \phi^i \\ T^i \\ \hline 1 \end{bmatrix}_2^L
$$

$$
\left[\begin{array}{cccc|c}
1 & 0 & 0 & 0 & 0 \\
-I\Omega^2 & 1 & 0 & 0 & -M^r \\
0 & 0 & 1 & 0 & 0 \\
0 & 0 & -I\Omega^2 & 1 & -M^i \\ \hline
0 & 0 & 0 & 0 & 1
\end{array}\right]
\left[\begin{array}{cc|c}
d_1 & -d_3 & 0 \\
d_2 & -d_4 & -M^r \\
d_3 & d_1 & 0 \\
d_4 & d_2 & -M^i \\ \hline
0 & 0 & 1
\end{array}\right] \cdot \begin{bmatrix} \phi^r \\ \phi^i \\ \hline 1 \end{bmatrix}_0^L = \begin{bmatrix} \phi^r \\ T^r \\ \phi^i \\ T^i \\ \hline 1 \end{bmatrix}_2^R
$$

$$
\left[\begin{array}{cccc|c}
1 & f^r & 0 & -f^i & 0 \\
-I\Omega^2 & 1-I\Omega^2 f^r & 0 & I\Omega^2 f^i & -M^r \\
0 & f^i & 1 & f^r & 0 \\
0 & -I\Omega^2 f^i & -I\Omega^2 & 1-I\Omega^2 f^r & -M^i \\ \hline
0 & 0 & 0 & 0 & 1
\end{array}\right]
\left[\begin{array}{cc|c}
u_1 & -u_3 & h_1 \\
u_2 & -u_4 & h_2 \\
u_3 & u_1 & h_3 \\
u_4 & u_2 & h_4 \\ \hline
0 & 0 & 1
\end{array}\right] \cdot \begin{bmatrix} \phi^r \\ \phi^i \\ \hline 1 \end{bmatrix}_0^L = \begin{bmatrix} \phi^r \\ T^r \\ \phi^i \\ T^i \\ \hline 1 \end{bmatrix}_3^R
$$

Table 4-2

					(1) ϕ_0^r	(2) ϕ_0^i	(3)	(4)
					1	0	0	0.2271
					−1.6000	0	0	−0.3633
					0	1	0	0.3826
					0	−1.6000	0	−0.6121
					0	0	1	

1	0.3750	0	0	0	0.4000	0	0	0.0908
0	1	0	0	0	−1.6000	0	0	−0.3633
0	0	1	0.3750	0	0	0.4000	0	0.1530
0	0	0	1	0	0	−1.6000	0	−0.6121
0	0	0	0	1	0	0	1	

1	0	0	0	0	0.4000	0	0	0.0908
−0.8000	1	−1.9677	0	0	−1.9200	−0.7871	0	−0.7371
0	0	1	0	0	0	0.4000	0	0.1530
1.9677	0	−0.8000	1	0	0.7872	−1.9200	0	−0.5558
0	0	0	0	1	0	0	1	

1	0	0	0.3494	0	0.6750	−0.6708	0	−0.1034
0	1	0	0	0	−1.9200	−0.7871	0	−0.7371
0	−0.3494	1	1	0	0.6708	0.6750	0	0.4106
0	0	0	1	0	0.7871	−1.9200	0	−0.5558
0	0	0	0	1	0	0	1	

1	0	0	0	0	0.6750	−0.6708	0	−0.1034
−0.8800	1	0	0	0.7500	−2.5140	−0.1968	0.7500	0.1039
0	0	1	0	0	0.6708	0.6750	0	0.4106
0	0	−0.8800	1	0.7000	0.1968	−2.5140	0.7000	−0.2171
0	0	0	0	1	0	0	1	

1	0.3846	0	0.0769	0	−0.2768	−0.9399	0.3423	−0.0801
−1.2000	0.5385	0	−0.0923	−0.2000	−2.1819	0.9311	0.1393	0
0	−0.0796	1	0.3846	0	0.9399	−0.2768	0.2115	0.3191
0	0.0923	−1.2000	0.5385	0.6000	−0.9311	−2.1819	1.0462	0
0	0	0	0	1	0	0	1	

FIG. 4-18. Forced vibration with structural damping.

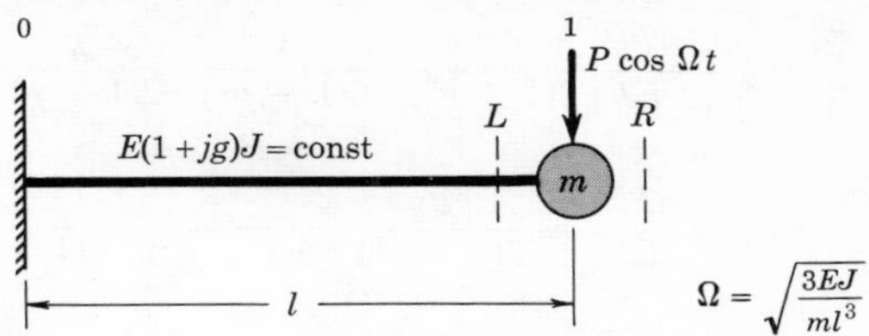

Example 4-3. A uniform massless cantilever beam of length l and bending stiffness EJ has a concentrated mass m attached at its end (Fig. 4-18). The beam has structural damping, the magnitude of which is defined by $g = 0.01$. If a harmonic force $P \cos \Omega t$ is applied to the mass, calculate the resulting end deflection of the beam when $\Omega^2 = 3EJ/ml^3$. (Note that this value of the forcing frequency coincides with the natural frequency of the system without damping.)

The transfer matrix for a beam with structural damping is given in Eq. (4-61). We note that $w_0^{\mathrm{r}} = w_0^{\mathrm{i}} = 0$ and $\psi_0^{\mathrm{r}} = \psi_0^{\mathrm{i}} = 0$, and expressing the transfer matrix in dimensionless form, in which the dimensionless state vector is

$$\left\{ -\frac{w^{\mathrm{r}}}{l} \quad \psi^{\mathrm{r}} \quad \frac{M^{\mathrm{r}}l}{EJ} \quad \frac{V^{\mathrm{r}}l^2}{EJ} \;\Big|\; -\frac{w^{\mathrm{i}}}{l} \quad \psi^{\mathrm{i}} \quad \frac{M^{\mathrm{i}}l}{EJ} \quad \frac{V^{\mathrm{i}}l^2}{EJ} \;\Big|\; 1 \right\}$$

we obtain the matrix scheme shown in Table 4-3.

Applying the boundary conditions at point 1^R, we obtain the equation

$$\begin{bmatrix} 1 & 1 & 0 & 0 \\ \dfrac{m\Omega^2 l^3}{2EJ(1+g^2)} & 1 + \dfrac{m\Omega^2 l^3}{6EJ(1+g^2)} & \dfrac{m\Omega^2 l^3 g}{2EJ(1+g^2)} & \dfrac{m\Omega^2 l^3 g}{6EJ(1+g^2)} \\ 0 & 0 & 1 & 1 \\ -\dfrac{m\Omega^2 l^3 g}{2EJ(1+g^2)} & -\dfrac{m\Omega^2 l^3 g}{6EJ(1+g^2)} & \dfrac{m\Omega^2 l^3}{2EJ(1+g^2)} & 1 + \dfrac{m\Omega^2 l^3}{6EJ(1+g^2)} \end{bmatrix} \cdot \begin{bmatrix} \bar{M}^{\mathrm{r}} \\ \bar{V}^{\mathrm{r}} \\ \bar{M}^{\mathrm{i}} \\ \bar{V}^{\mathrm{i}} \end{bmatrix}_0 = \begin{bmatrix} 0 \\ \dfrac{Pl^2}{EJ} \\ 0 \\ 0 \end{bmatrix}$$

and on setting $m\Omega^2 l^3/EJ = 3$ the equation becomes

$$\begin{bmatrix} 1 & 1 & 0 & 0 \\ \dfrac{3}{2(1+g^2)} & 1 + \dfrac{1}{2(1+g^2)} & \dfrac{3g}{2(1+g^2)} & \dfrac{g}{2(1+g^2)} \\ 0 & 0 & 1 & 1 \\ -\dfrac{3g}{2(1+g^2)} & -\dfrac{g}{2(1+g^2)} & \dfrac{3}{2(1+g^2)} & 1 + \dfrac{1}{2(1+g^2)} \end{bmatrix} \cdot \begin{bmatrix} \bar{M}^{\mathrm{r}} \\ \bar{V}^{\mathrm{r}} \\ \bar{M}^{\mathrm{i}} \\ \bar{V}^{\mathrm{i}} \end{bmatrix}_0 = \frac{Pl^2}{EJ} \begin{bmatrix} 0 \\ 1 \\ 0 \\ 0 \end{bmatrix}$$

On inverting the matrix according to Eq. (4-75), the solution of this equation is

$$\begin{bmatrix} \bar{M}^{\mathrm{r}} \\ \bar{V}^{\mathrm{r}} \\ \bar{M}^{\mathrm{i}} \\ \bar{V}^{\mathrm{i}} \end{bmatrix}_0 = \frac{4Pl^2}{EJ} \begin{bmatrix} -1 \\ 1 \\ \dfrac{1}{g} \\ -\dfrac{1}{g} \end{bmatrix}$$

The deflection at point 1 is then found by substituting this result in Table 4-3 to give

$$\bar{w}_1^r = \frac{4Pl^2}{EJ}\left[\frac{1}{2(1+g^2)} \quad \frac{1}{6(1+g^2)} \quad \frac{g}{2(1+g^2)} \quad \frac{g}{6(1+g^2)}\right]\cdot\left\{-1 \quad 1 \quad \frac{1}{g} \quad -\frac{1}{g}\right\} = 0$$

$$\bar{w}_1^i = \frac{4Pl^2}{EJ}\left[-\frac{g}{2(1+g^2)} \quad \frac{-g}{6(1+g^2)} \quad \frac{1}{2(1+g^2)} \quad \frac{1}{6(1+g^2)}\right]\cdot\left\{-1 \quad 1 \quad \frac{1}{g} \quad -\frac{1}{g}\right\}$$

$$= \frac{4Pl^2}{3EJg} = 40\,\frac{Pl^2}{3EJ}$$

$\bar{w}_1^r$ is zero because, if the forcing frequency is equal to the natural frequency of the undamped system, then the force and the resulting deflection are out of phase by 90°.

Comparison with the static deflection,

$$w_1 = \frac{Pl^3}{3EJ} \qquad \text{or} \qquad \bar{w}_1 = \frac{Pl^2}{3EJ}$$

reveals that the magnification factor is 40.

PROBLEMS

4-15. Find the extended transfer matrix, in its complex and its real partitioned form, relating $\bar{\mathbf{z}}_1^L$ and $\bar{\mathbf{z}}_1^R$ for the system of Fig. P 4-13.

4-16. Repeat Probs. 4-11 to 4-14 with the help of transfer matrices in their partitioned form.

4-17. A turbine on its foundations is represented by the crude substitute system shown in Fig. P 4-17. Compute the steady-state response for the given data, assuming structural damping in the springs.

4-18. The three-story building of Fig. P 4-18 is excited by a horizontal force $P \sin \Omega t$ on the first floor. The floors can be taken as rigid. Assuming structural damping in the massless columns, compute the steady-state response for the following data:

$$l = 12 \text{ ft} \qquad \text{Weight of each floor} = 80 \text{ kips}$$
$$EJ = 9 \times 10^9 \text{ lb-in.}^2 \qquad g = 0.01 \qquad \Omega = 150 \text{ radians/sec}$$

Only translatory motion of the floors need be considered.

4-19. Compute the steady-state response of the system shown in Fig. P 4-19. The pulley should be considered to be a solid uniform disk, and no slipping occurs.

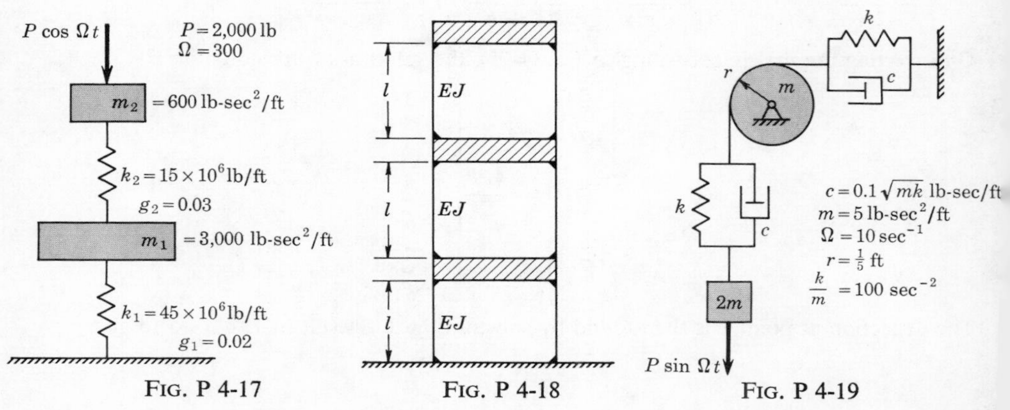

FIG. P 4-17 FIG. P 4-18 FIG. P 4-19

Table 4-3

$$
\left[\begin{array}{cc|cc|c}
\dfrac{1}{2(1+g^2)} & \dfrac{1}{6(1+g^2)} & \dfrac{g}{2(1+g^2)} & \dfrac{g}{6(1+g^2)} & 0 \\
\dfrac{1}{1+g^2} & \dfrac{1}{2(1+g^2)} & \dfrac{g}{1+g^2} & \dfrac{g}{2(1+g^2)} & 0 \\
1 & 1 & 0 & 0 & 0 \\
0 & 1 & 0 & 0 & 0 \\
\hline
-\dfrac{g}{2(1+g^2)} & -\dfrac{g}{6(1+g^2)} & \dfrac{1}{2(1+g^2)} & \dfrac{1}{6(1+g^2)} & 0 \\
-\dfrac{g}{1+g^2} & -\dfrac{g}{2(1+g^2)} & \dfrac{1}{1+g^2} & \dfrac{1}{2(1+g^2)} & 0 \\
0 & 0 & 1 & 1 & 0 \\
0 & 0 & 0 & 1 & 0 \\
\hline
0 & 0 & 0 & 0 & 1
\end{array}\right]
\cdot
\left[\begin{array}{c}
\bar{M}^{r} \\ \bar{V}^{r} \\ \hline \bar{M}^{i} \\ \bar{V}^{i} \\ \hline 1
\end{array}\right]_0
= \tilde{\mathbf{z}}_1^L
$$

$$
\left[\begin{array}{cccc|cccc|c}
1 & 0 & 0 & 0 & & & & & 0 \\
0 & 1 & 0 & 0 & & \mathbf{0} & & & 0 \\
0 & 0 & 1 & 0 & & & & & 0 \\
\dfrac{m\Omega^2 l^3}{EJ} & 0 & 0 & 1 & & & & & -\dfrac{Pl^2}{EJ} \\
\hline
 & & & & 1 & 0 & 0 & 0 & 0 \\
 & \mathbf{0} & & & 0 & 1 & 0 & 0 & 0 \\
 & & & & 0 & 0 & 1 & 0 & 0 \\
 & & & & \dfrac{m\Omega^2 l^3}{EJ} & 0 & 0 & 1 & 0 \\
\hline
0 & 0 & 0 & 0 & 0 & 0 & 0 & 0 & 1
\end{array}\right]
\left[\begin{array}{cc|cc|c}
\dfrac{1}{2(1+g^2)} & \dfrac{1}{6(1+g^2)} & \dfrac{g}{2(1+g^2)} & \dfrac{g}{6(1+g^2)} & 0 \\
\dfrac{1}{1+g^2} & \dfrac{1}{2(1+g^2)} & \dfrac{g}{1+g^2} & \dfrac{g}{2(1+g^2)} & 0 \\
1 & 1 & 0 & 0 & 0 \\
\dfrac{m\Omega^2 l^3}{2EJ(1+g^2)} & 1+\dfrac{m\Omega^2 l^3}{6EJ(1+g^2)} & \dfrac{m\Omega^2 l^3 g}{2EJ(1+g^2)} & \dfrac{m\Omega^2 l^3 g}{6EJ(1+g^2)} & -\dfrac{Pl^2}{EJ} \\
\hline
-\dfrac{g}{2(1+g^2)} & -\dfrac{g}{6(1+g^2)} & \dfrac{1}{2(1+g^2)} & \dfrac{1}{6(1+g^2)} & 0 \\
-\dfrac{g}{1+g^2} & -\dfrac{g}{2(1+g^2)} & \dfrac{1}{1+g^2} & \dfrac{1}{2(1+g^2)} & 0 \\
0 & 0 & 1 & 1 & 0 \\
-\dfrac{m\Omega^2 l^3 g}{2EJ(1+g^2)} & -\dfrac{m\Omega^2 l^3 g}{6EJ(1+g^2)} & \dfrac{m\Omega^2 l^3}{2EJ(1+g^2)} & 1+\dfrac{m\Omega^2 l^3}{6EJ(1+g^2)} & 0 \\
\hline
0 & 0 & 0 & 0 & 1
\end{array}\right]
\cdot
\left[\begin{array}{c}
\bar{M}^{r} \\ \bar{V}^{r} \\ \hline \bar{M}^{i} \\ \bar{V}^{i} \\ \hline 1
\end{array}\right]_0
= \tilde{\mathbf{z}}_1^R
$$

4-20. Compute the steady-state response for the torsional system of Fig. P 4-20 when disk 5 is subjected to a torque $T = C \cos \Omega t$. The data are

$$I_1 = I_2 = I_3 = I_4 = 50 \text{ lb-in.-sec}^2 \qquad I_5 = 1{,}000 \text{ lb-in.-sec}^2$$
$$k_1 = k_2 = k_3 = 2 \times 10^8 \text{ lb-in.} \qquad k_4 = 10^8 \text{ lb-in.}$$
$$\Omega = 2 \times 10^3 \text{ radians/sec} \qquad \text{Structural damping with } g = 0.01$$

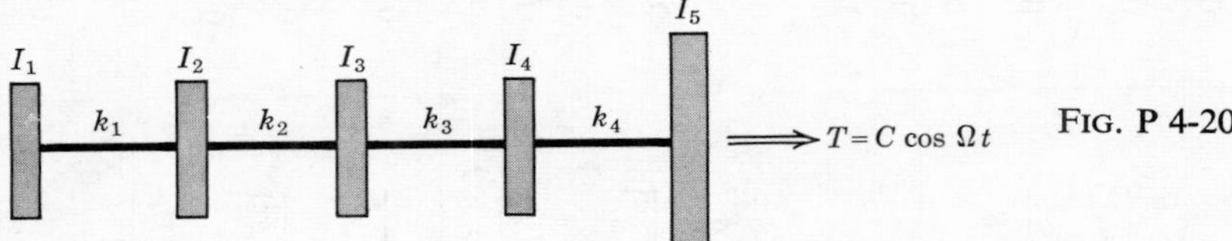

FIG. P 4-20

4-6. Rotating Shaft with Damping

Definition of Problem. From a computational point of view it is advantageous to employ a Myklestad beam as a substitute for the actual shaft. For the sake of simplicity, we assume that it is supported by isotropic bearings that possess equal spring and damping properties in all directions normal to the axis of the shaft (Fig. 4-19). In addition, we suppose that $J_y = J_z = J$. Owing to unavoidable manufacturing inaccuracies the geometric axis of the shaft and the line connecting the centers of mass of all cross sections do not coincide. Since the mass of the substitute shaft is concentrated at discrete points, the eccentricity of the shaft is defined by the eccentricity at each discrete point i. The eccentricity at point i is determined by the normal distance e_i of the center of mass m_i from the geometric axis of the shaft and by the angle ε_i measured from a radial line fixed in the shaft (Fig. 4-20). On account of these eccentricities the rotating shaft whirls. Because the bearings are taken to be isotropic,† each mass will rotate in a circle parallel to the yz plane with angular velocity Ω, which is constant along the length of the beam if we neglect‡ the effect of the moment about the x axis. We assume also that the masses are point masses (no gyroscopic effects) and neglect the effects of shear deformation and gravity. The xyz system rotates about the x axis with angular velocity Ω.

In order to use the transfer-matrix method we establish the three transfer matrices for:

1. The elastic massless shaft between masses m_{i-1} and m_i

† Actually the damping and spring characteristics of a bearing are far too complicated to permit a simple circular whirl. If more realistic bearing properties are to be considered (cf. Ref. 64), the problem leads to 16×16 transfer matrices. Then the motion of the shaft should be described in a space-fixed frame of reference.

‡ This is permissible except in a very narrow region about the natural bending frequencies of the shaft.

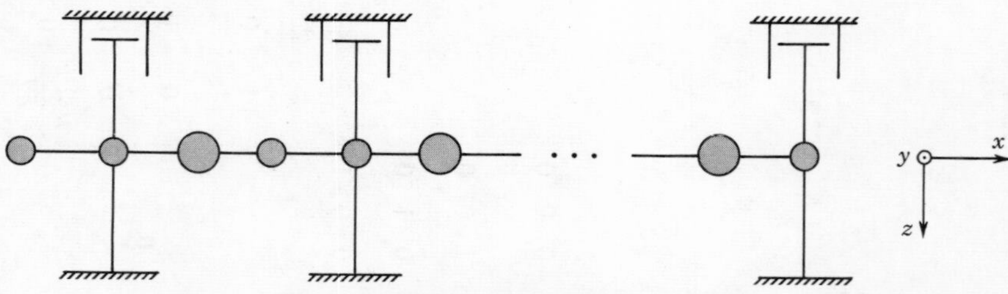

FIG. 4-19. Shaft on isotropic bearings.

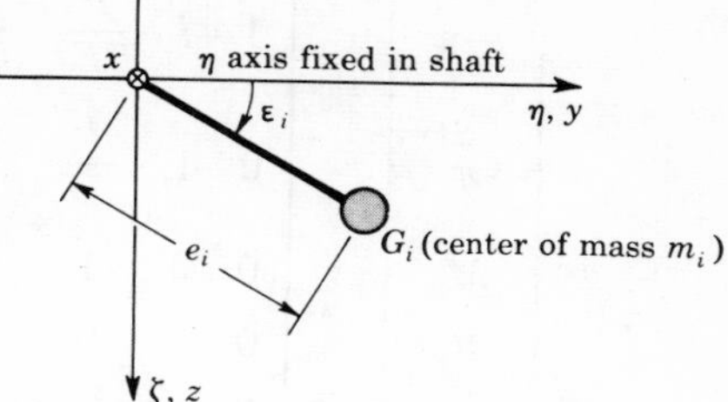

FIG. 4-20. Eccentricity of nonrotating mass m_i.

2. The whirling mass m_i with the eccentricity defined by e_i and ε_i
3. The isotropic bearing

Field Matrix for Whirling Elastic Shaft. Assuming EJ = const for the field i, inspection of Fig. 4-21 and elementary theory of elasticity yield the relations (cf. also the Catalogue of Transfer Matrices at the end of the book)

$$
\begin{aligned}
-w_i &= -w_{i-1} + \psi_{i-1}l_i + M_{y_{i-1}}\frac{l_i^2}{2EJ_i} + V_{z_{i-1}}\frac{l_i^3}{6EJ_i} \\
\psi_i &= \psi_{i-1} + M_{y_{i-1}}\frac{l_i}{EJ_i} + V_{z_{i-1}}\frac{l_i^2}{2EJ_i} \\
M_{y_i} &= M_{y_{i-1}} + V_{z_{i-1}}l_i \\
V_{z_i} &= V_{z_{i-1}} \\
v_i &= v_{i-1} + \vartheta_{i-1}l_i + M_{z_{i-1}}\frac{l_i^2}{2EJ_i} - V_{y_{i-1}}\frac{l_i^3}{6EJ_i} \\
\vartheta_i &= \vartheta_{i-1} + M_{z_{i-1}}\frac{l_i}{EJ_i} - V_{y_{i-1}}\frac{l_i^2}{2EJ_i} \\
M_{z_i} &= M_{z_{i-1}} - V_{y_{i-1}}l_i \\
-V_{y_i} &= -V_{y_{i-1}}
\end{aligned}
$$

from which we derive the following matrix equation for the state vectors $\mathbf{z}_{i-1}^R$ and $\mathbf{z}_i^L$, in which w and V_y are given a minus sign in order to obtain all elements in the field matrix as positive quantities.

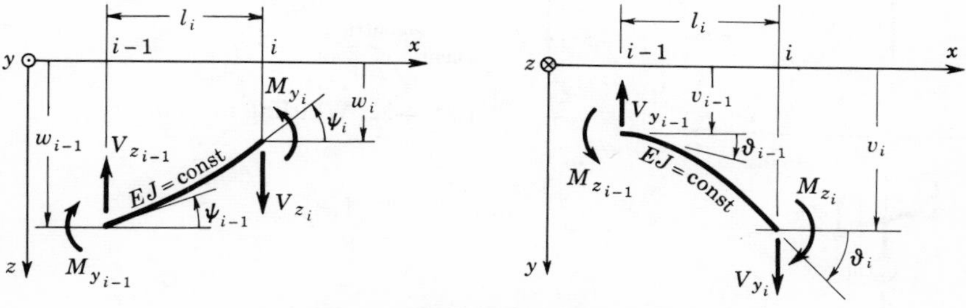

FIG. 4-21. Elastic field i.

$$\begin{bmatrix} -w \\ \psi \\ M_y \\ V_z \\ \hdashline v \\ \vartheta \\ M_z \\ -V_y \end{bmatrix}_i^L = \left[\begin{array}{cccc:cccc} 1 & l & \frac{l^2}{2EJ} & \frac{l^3}{6EJ} & & & & \\ 0 & 1 & \frac{l}{EJ} & \frac{l^2}{2EJ} & & \mathbf{0} & & \\ 0 & 0 & 1 & l & & & & \\ 0 & 0 & 0 & 1 & & & & \\ \hdashline & & & & 1 & l & \frac{l^2}{2EJ} & \frac{l^3}{6EJ} \\ & \mathbf{0} & & & 0 & 1 & \frac{l}{EJ} & \frac{l^2}{2EJ} \\ & & & & 0 & 0 & 1 & l \\ & & & & 0 & 0 & 0 & 1 \end{array}\right]_i \cdot \begin{bmatrix} -w \\ \psi \\ M_y \\ V_z \\ \hdashline v \\ \vartheta \\ M_z \\ -V_y \end{bmatrix}_{i-1}^R \tag{4-77}$$

or

$$\mathbf{z}_i^L = \mathbf{F}_i \mathbf{z}_{i-1}^R$$

Point Matrix for the Whirling Mass m_i. From Fig. 4-22 we can easily obtain the relations

$$w_i^R = w_i^L \qquad \psi_i^R = \psi_i^L \qquad M_{y_i}^R = M_{y_i}^L$$

and

$$v_i^R = v_i^L \qquad \vartheta_i^R = \vartheta_i^L \qquad M_{z_i}^R = M_{z_i}^L$$

The forces acting on mass m_i are the centrifugal forces C_i. The components of the centrifugal forces are

$$C_{z_i} = m_i \Omega^2 (w_i + e_1 \sin \varepsilon_i)$$

$$C_{y_i} = m_i \Omega^2 (v_i + e_1 \cos \varepsilon_i)$$

Hence, from equilibrium (Fig. 4-22)

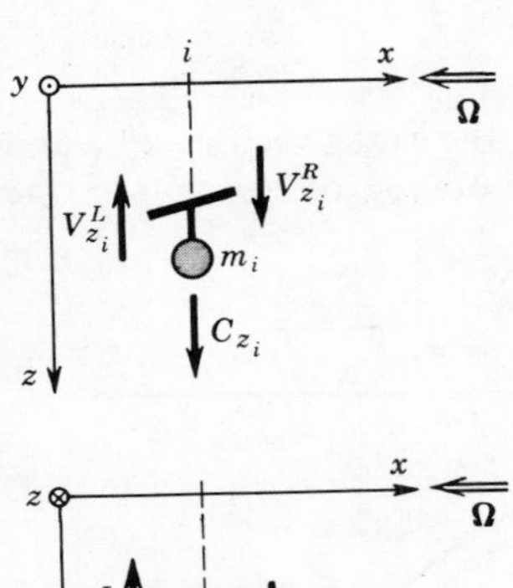

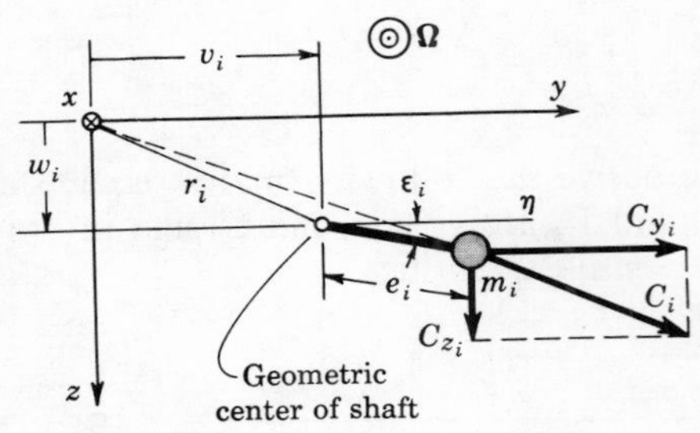

FIG. 4-22. Whirling mass m_i.

$$V_{z_i}^R = V_{z_i}^L - C_{z_i}$$

$$V_{z_i}^R = V_{z_i}^L - w_i m_i \Omega^2 - e_i m_i \Omega^2 \sin \varepsilon_i$$

and

$$-V_{y_i}^R = -V_{y_i}^L + C_{y_i}$$

$$-V_{y_i}^R = -V_{y_i}^L + v_i m_i \Omega^2 + e_i m_i \Omega^2 \cos \varepsilon_i$$

The second and fourth of these equations contain the forcing terms

$$-e_i m_i \Omega^2 \sin \varepsilon_i \qquad \text{in } z \text{ direction}$$

and

$$e_i m_i \Omega^2 \cos \varepsilon_i \qquad \text{in } y \text{ direction}$$

To accommodate these terms in the point matrix we have to extend it by one column so that we obtain the following extended matrix equation for the extended state vectors $\tilde{\mathbf{z}}_i^L$ and $\tilde{\mathbf{z}}_i^R$:

$$\begin{bmatrix} -w \\ \psi \\ M_y \\ V_z \\ \hline v \\ \vartheta \\ M_z \\ -V_y \\ \hline 1 \end{bmatrix}_i^R = \left[\begin{array}{cccc|cccc|c} 1 & 0 & 0 & 0 & 0 & 0 & 0 & 0 & 0 \\ 0 & 1 & 0 & 0 & 0 & 0 & 0 & 0 & 0 \\ 0 & 0 & 1 & 0 & 0 & 0 & 0 & 0 & 0 \\ m\Omega^2 & 0 & 0 & 1 & 0 & 0 & 0 & 0 & -em\Omega^2 \sin \varepsilon \\ \hline 0 & 0 & 0 & 0 & 1 & 0 & 0 & 0 & 0 \\ 0 & 0 & 0 & 0 & 0 & 1 & 0 & 0 & 0 \\ 0 & 0 & 0 & 0 & 0 & 0 & 1 & 0 & 0 \\ 0 & 0 & 0 & 0 & m\Omega^2 & 0 & 0 & 1 & em\Omega^2 \cos \varepsilon \\ \hline 0 & 0 & 0 & 0 & 0 & 0 & 0 & 0 & 1 \end{array}\right]_i \cdot \begin{bmatrix} -w \\ \psi \\ M_y \\ V_z \\ \hline v \\ \vartheta \\ M_z \\ -V_y \\ \hline 1 \end{bmatrix}_i^L \tag{4-78}$$

or

$$\tilde{\mathbf{z}}_i^R = \tilde{\mathbf{P}}_{m_i} \tilde{\mathbf{z}}_i^L$$

Point Matrix for Isotropic Bearing. The spring and damping effects of the oil film in an ideal isotropic bearing are represented by forces B and D (Fig. 4-23). Resolving these in the y and z directions, we have

$$B_y = -kv \qquad B_z = -kw \qquad \text{and} \qquad D_y = -c\Omega w \qquad D_z = c\Omega v$$

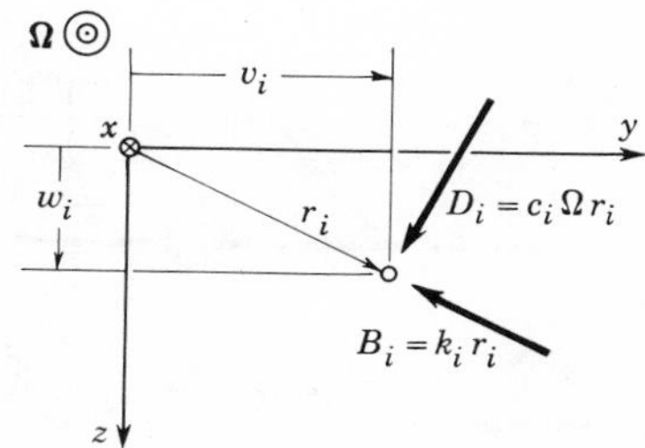

FIG. 4-23. Spring and damping action of isotropic bearing.

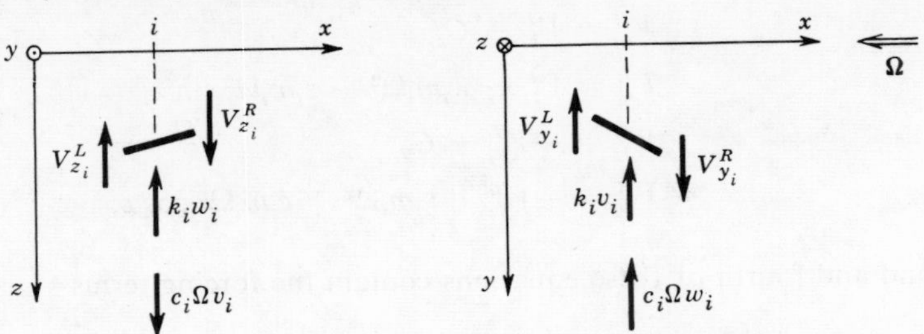

FIG. 4-24. Forces exerted by bearing on rotating shaft.

Hence, by inspection of Fig. 4-24,

$$V_z^R = V_z^L + kw - c\Omega v \qquad \text{and} \qquad -V_y^R = -V_y^L - kv - c\Omega w$$

All other quantities are continuous. Both k and c are functions of Ω.

Thus we obtain the following point matrix:

$$\mathbf{P}_{B_i} = \begin{bmatrix} 1 & 0 & 0 & 0 & 0 & 0 & 0 & 0 \\ 0 & 1 & 0 & 0 & 0 & 0 & 0 & 0 \\ 0 & 0 & 1 & 0 & 0 & 0 & 0 & 0 \\ -k & 0 & 0 & 1 & -c\Omega & 0 & 0 & 0 \\ 0 & 0 & 0 & 0 & 1 & 0 & 0 & 0 \\ 0 & 0 & 0 & 0 & 0 & 1 & 0 & 0 \\ 0 & 0 & 0 & 0 & 0 & 0 & 1 & 0 \\ c\Omega & 0 & 0 & 0 & -k & 0 & 0 & 1 \end{bmatrix}_i \tag{4-79}$$

Comparing these three transfer matrices [Eqs. (4-77), (4-78), (4-79)], we recognize that they possess the same structure:

$$\mathbf{U} = \left[\begin{array}{c|c} \mathbf{A} & -\mathbf{B} \\ \hline \mathbf{B} & \mathbf{A} \end{array}\right]$$

already found in Secs. 4-3 and 4-4.

PROBLEMS

4-21. Compute the steady-state response of the shaft of Fig. P 4-21 when whirling on account of the eccentricity e of mass m. The shaft is constrained by isotropic bearings. Carry out the calculation in dimensionless form using the data

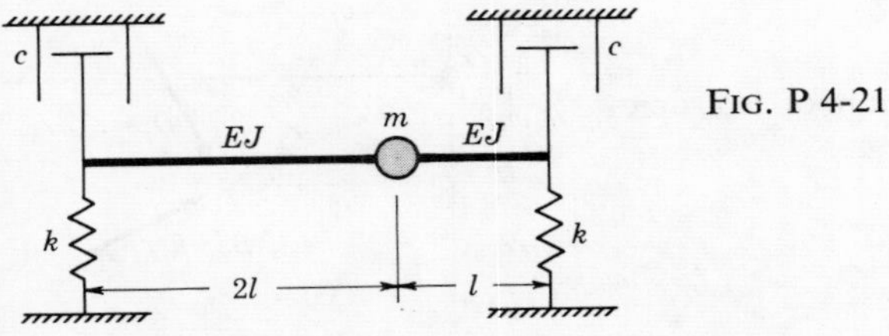

FIG. P 4-21

$$\bar{e} = e\frac{m\Omega^2 l^2}{EJ} = 10^{-5} \qquad \bar{c} = \frac{c\Omega l^3}{EJ} = 0.3$$

$$\bar{k} = \frac{kl^3}{EJ} = 4 \qquad \bar{m} = \frac{m\Omega^2 l^3}{EJ} = 1$$

4-22. Repeat Prob. 4-21 including the gyroscopic effect of the mass (see transfer matrix C-3*f*), with $\bar{I} = I\Omega^2 l/EJ = 1$ (Fig. P 4-22).

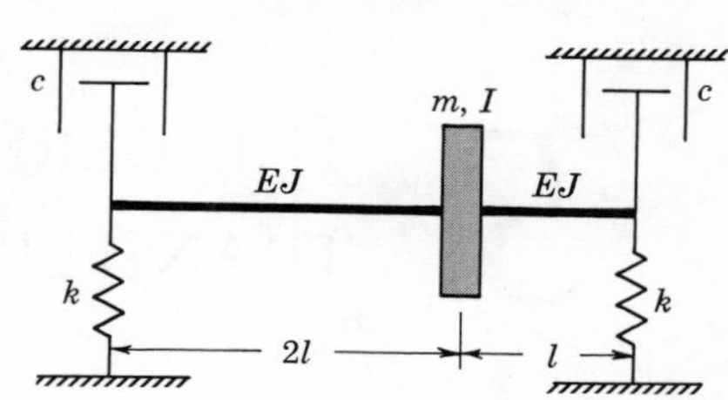

FIG. P 4-22

5 THE DERIVATION OF TRANSFER MATRICES

In Chap. 3 we learned that it is a routine matter to find the natural frequencies and the associated normal modes of a system if the transfer matrices for its elements are known. It is of great practical value to have a catalogue [20, 21] of the most important transfer matrices readily available, so that, when a problem is to be solved, the individual matrices can be linked together as a set of building blocks. Such a Catalogue of Transfer Matrices† is given at the end of this book, and examples of their application to engineering problems are found in Chap. 11. Sometimes, however, the required transfer matrix will not be catalogued, and the various methods that can be used for the calculation of these matrices are now described. It is often possible to find the transfer matrix by using simple statics or by using results that are tabulated in engineering handbooks. We have already used such techniques in Chap. 3. In the following work only methods capable of general application will be considered.

5-1. Derivation of the Transfer Matrix from an *n*th-order Differential Equation

The usual method of solving problems of one independent variable is to eliminate $n - 1$ of the dependent variables to give an nth-order ordinary differential equation in the remaining dependent variable. If it is possible to find n closed solutions of this equation, it is then a straightforward matter to develop the transfer matrix. The n constants associated with the nth-order differential equation are determined by the boundary conditions of the problem. We shall find these constants in terms of the components of the state vector at an arbitrary point $i - 1$ of the system. The technique will be illustrated by means of the two examples that follow.

Transfer Matrix for the Torsional Vibration of an Elastic Shaft. Let us formulate the transfer matrix for a uniform elastic shaft with mass which is undergoing

† When referring to a transfer matrix listed in this Catalogue, the number is preceded by the letter C, for example, "cf. matrix C-1*c*."

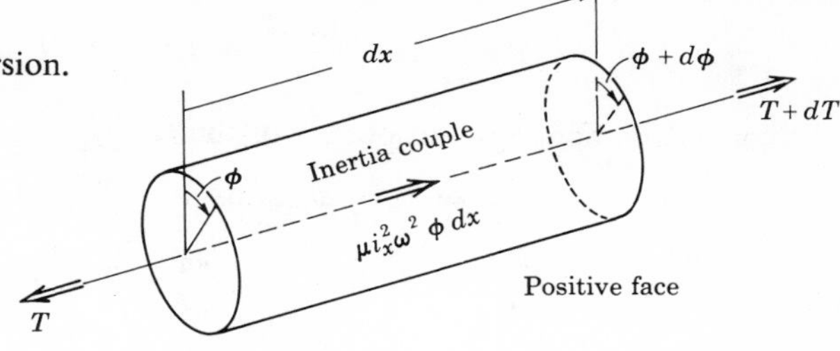

FIG. 5-1. Shaft element under torsion.

torsional vibrations of circular frequency ω. Figure 5-1 illustrates the forces acting on the shaft and the displacements of an element of length dx of the shaft. The inertia couple is $(i_x^2\mu\, dx)\omega^2\phi$, where i_x is the radius of gyration about the x axis and μ is the mass per unit length. From the equilibrium condition we obtain the equation

$$\frac{dT}{dx} + i_x^2\mu\omega^2\phi = 0$$

and from the elastic properties

$$\frac{d\phi}{dx} = \frac{T}{J_T G}$$

where $J_T G$ is the torsional stiffness of the shaft. The elimination of T gives the second-order differential equation in ϕ:

$$\frac{d^2\phi}{dx^2} + \frac{\mu i_x^2\omega^2}{J_T G}\phi = 0 \tag{5-1}$$

the solution of which is, for a shaft portion of length l (Fig. 5-2),

$$\phi = A \sin\left(\lambda\frac{x}{l}\right) + B\cos\left(\lambda\frac{x}{l}\right)$$

where

$$\lambda^2 = \frac{\mu i_x^2 l^2\omega^2}{J_T G}$$

At $x = 0$, coinciding with point $i - 1$ on the shaft, the boundary conditions are $\phi = \phi_{i-1}$ and $T = T_{i-1}$, from which we obtain

$$B = \phi_{i-1} \qquad \text{and} \qquad A = \frac{T_{i-1}l}{\lambda J_T G}$$

The solution of Eq. (5-1) is then

$$\phi = \phi_{i-1}\cos\left(\lambda\frac{x}{l}\right) + T_{i-1}\frac{l}{\lambda J_T G}\sin\left(\lambda\frac{x}{l}\right)$$

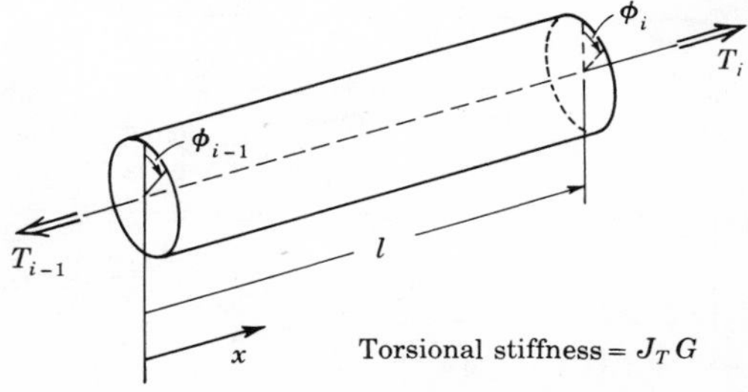

FIG. 5-2. Shaft under torsion.

and the expression for T is

$$T = -\phi_{i-1}\frac{\lambda J_T G}{l}\sin\left(\lambda\frac{x}{l}\right) + T_{i-1}\cos\left(\lambda\frac{x}{l}\right)$$

At $x = l$, coinciding with point i of the shaft,

$$\phi = \phi_i = \phi_{i-1}\cos\lambda + T_{i-1}\frac{l}{\lambda J_T G}\sin\lambda$$

$$T = T_i = -\phi_{i-1}\frac{\lambda J_T G}{l}\sin\lambda + T_{i-1}\cos\lambda$$

Expressed in matrix form, these two equations become

$$\begin{bmatrix}\phi\\ T\end{bmatrix}_i = \begin{bmatrix}\cos\lambda & \dfrac{l}{\lambda J_T G}\sin\lambda\\ -\dfrac{\lambda J_T G}{l}\sin\lambda & \cos\lambda\end{bmatrix}\cdot\begin{bmatrix}\phi\\ T\end{bmatrix}_{i-1}$$

or

$$\mathbf{z}_i = \mathbf{U}_i\mathbf{z}_{i-1} \tag{5-2}$$

If the shaft is massless (that is, $\lambda \to 0$), Eq. (5-2) reduces to the form

$$\begin{bmatrix}\phi\\ T\end{bmatrix}_i = \begin{bmatrix}1 & \dfrac{l}{J_T G}\\ 0 & 1\end{bmatrix}_i\cdot\begin{bmatrix}\phi\\ T\end{bmatrix}_{i-1}$$

which is identical to Eq. (3-4).

Transfer Matrix for the Flexural Vibrations of a Beam Including the Effect of Shear Deflection and Rotary Inertia. To illustrate this method further, we shall solve the problem of the vibrating beam of constant section taking into consideration the effect of shear deflection and rotary inertia. Let us consider a beam of length l, with the following properties that are constant over its length (Fig. 3-11): cross-sectional area A, second moment of area about the y axis J_y, mass per unit length μ, and radius of gyration about the y axis i_y. The slope dw/dx of the center line of the beam is affected by both the bending moment and the shear force. The action of the bending moment rotates the face of the cross section through an angle ψ, and from there the shearing action turns the center line to adopt the slope dw/dx, the angle of the face of the beam remaining unchanged. This can be seen more clearly when we use the analogy of a pack of cards (Fig. 5-3), the face of the pack of cards being the face at the beam. We first rotate the pack through an angle ψ and then slide the cards over one another as in shearing action, so that the angle of the center line is changed without any rotation of the cards having taken place. The angle between the perpendicular to the face and the center line of the beam is caused by the shear force acting on the beam. Inspection of Fig. 5-3 shows that this angle

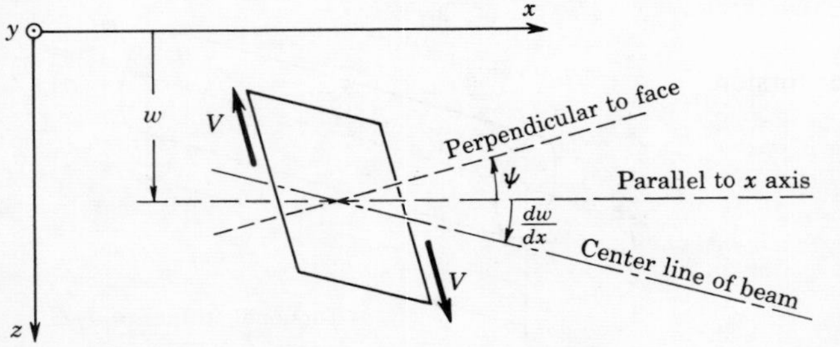

FIG. 5-3. Effect of shear on beam deflection.

is equal to $dw/dx + \psi$. The relation between this angle and the shear force causing it is

$$V = GA_s \left(\frac{dw}{dx} + \psi\right) \tag{5-3a}$$

where $GA_s = GA/\kappa_s$ is the shear stiffness, κ_s being a form factor depending on the shape of the cross section [17]. The usual bending relation for a beam is

$$M = EJ_y \frac{d\psi}{dx} \tag{5-3b}$$

and equilibrium considerations (Fig. 5-4) give the equations

$$\frac{dM}{dx} = V - \mu i_y^2 \omega^2 \psi \dagger \tag{5-3c}$$

and

$$\frac{dV}{dx} = -\mu\omega^2 w \tag{5-3d}$$

Taking the derivative of Eq. (5-3*a*) with respect to x and substituting it and Eq. (5-3*b*) in Eq. (5-3*d*) give the equation

$$\frac{d^2w}{dx^2} + \frac{\mu\omega^2}{GA_s} w + \frac{M}{EJ_y} = 0 \tag{5-4}$$

In the same way, if we differentiate Eq. (5-3*c*), into which we substitute Eqs. (5-3*b*) and (5-3*d*), we obtain the equation

$$\frac{d^2M}{dx^2} + \frac{\mu i_y^2 \omega^2}{EJ_y} M + \mu\omega^2 w = 0 \tag{5-5}$$

Eliminating M from these equations, we obtain the fourth-order differential equation in w:

$$\frac{d^4w}{dx^4} + \frac{\mu\omega^2}{EJ_y}\left(\frac{EJ_y}{GA_s} + i_y^2\right)\frac{d^2w}{dx^2} - \frac{\mu\omega^2}{EJ_y}\left(1 - \frac{\mu i_y^2 \omega^2}{GA_s}\right) w = 0 \tag{5-6}$$

With the substitutions

$$\sigma = \frac{\mu\omega^2}{GA_s} l^2 \qquad \tau = \frac{\mu i_y^2 \omega^2 l^2}{EJ_y} \qquad \beta^4 = \frac{\mu\omega^2 l^4}{EJ_y}$$

Eq. (5-6) becomes

$$\frac{d^4w}{dx^4} + \frac{\sigma + \tau}{l^2}\frac{d^2w}{dx^2} - \frac{\beta^4 - \sigma\tau}{l^4} w = 0 \tag{5-7}$$

† Figure 5-3 illustrates that each cross-sectional face rotates through an angle ψ and hence the inertia couple is $\mu i_y^2 \omega^2 \psi \, dx$.

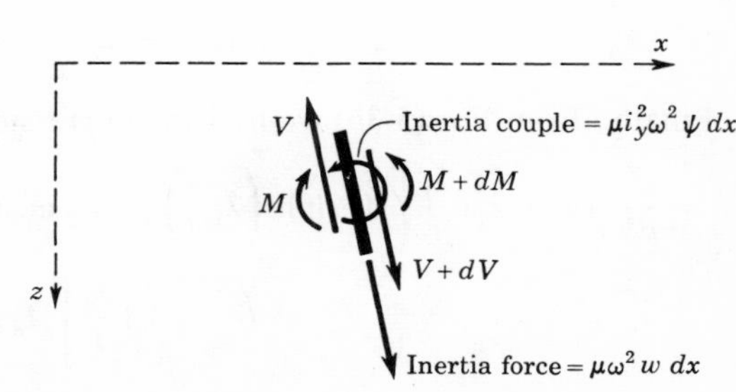

FIG. 5-4. Forces acting on beam element.

It is from this equation that we now determine the transfer matrix. Since Eq. (5-7) is an ordinary differential equation with constant coefficients, its solution is of the form $w = \bar{C}e^{\lambda x/l}$, where $\bar{C}$ is a constant.

This solution, substituted in Eq. (5-7), leads to the characteristic equation in λ:

$$\lambda^4 + (\sigma + \tau)\lambda^2 - (\beta^4 - \sigma\tau) = 0 \tag{5-8}$$

The roots of this equation are $\pm\lambda_1$ and $\pm j\lambda_2$, where

$$\lambda_{1,2} = \sqrt{\sqrt{\beta^4 + \tfrac{1}{4}(\sigma - \tau)^2} \mp \tfrac{1}{2}(\sigma + \tau)} \tag{5-9}$$

and they exhibit the relations

$$\lambda_2^2 - \lambda_1^2 = \sigma + \tau \qquad \lambda_1^2\lambda_2^2 = \beta^4 - \sigma\tau$$

The solution of Eq. (5-7) is therefore

$$w = \bar{C}_1 e^{\lambda_1 x/l} + \bar{C}_2 e^{-\lambda_1 x/l} + \bar{C}_3 e^{j\lambda_2 x/l} + \bar{C}_4 e^{-j\lambda_2 x/l}$$

and using the relations

$$e^{\pm\alpha} = \cosh\alpha \pm \sinh\alpha \qquad \text{and} \qquad e^{\pm j\alpha} = \cos\alpha \pm j\sin\alpha$$

the solution can be written in the form

$$w = C_1 \cosh\left(\lambda_1 \frac{x}{l}\right) + C_2 \sinh\left(\lambda_1 \frac{x}{l}\right) + C_3 \cos\left(\lambda_2 \frac{x}{l}\right) + C_4 \sin\left(\lambda_2 \frac{x}{l}\right)$$

where

$$C_1 = \bar{C}_1 + \bar{C}_2 \qquad C_2 = \bar{C}_1 - \bar{C}_2 \qquad C_3 = \bar{C}_3 + \bar{C}_4 \qquad C_4 = j(\bar{C}_3 - \bar{C}_4)$$

Since the solution for all four dependent variables is of the same form, we can start off most conveniently with the solution for V,

$$V = A_1 \cosh\left(\lambda_1 \frac{x}{l}\right) + A_2 \sinh\left(\lambda_1 \frac{x}{l}\right) + A_3 \cos\left(\lambda_2 \frac{x}{l}\right) + A_4 \sin\left(\lambda_2 \frac{x}{l}\right) \tag{5-10}$$

From Eq. (5-3*d*) we then find the deflection w:

$$w = -\frac{l^4}{\beta^4 EJ_y}\left[A_1 \frac{\lambda_1}{l} \sinh\left(\lambda_1 \frac{x}{l}\right) + A_2 \frac{\lambda_1}{l} \cosh\left(\lambda_1 \frac{x}{l}\right) - A_3 \frac{\lambda_2}{l} \sin\left(\lambda_2 \frac{x}{l}\right) + A_4 \frac{\lambda_2}{l} \cos\left(\lambda_2 \frac{x}{l}\right)\right] \tag{5-11}$$

Using Eq. (5-3*a*), we obtain the expression for ψ in terms of V and dw/dx, so that

$$\psi = \frac{l^2}{\beta^4 EJ_y}\left\{(\sigma + \lambda_1^2)\left[A_1 \cosh\left(\lambda_1 \frac{x}{l}\right) + A_2 \sinh\left(\lambda_1 \frac{x}{l}\right)\right] + (\sigma - \lambda_2^2)\left[A_3 \cos\left(\lambda_2 \frac{x}{l}\right) + A_4 \sin\left(\lambda_2 \frac{x}{l}\right)\right]\right\} \tag{5-12}$$

Finally, from Eq. (5-3*b*) we find the expression for M:

$$M = \frac{l^2}{\beta^4}\left\{(\sigma + \lambda_1^2)\frac{\lambda_1}{l}\left[A_1 \sinh\left(\lambda_1 \frac{x}{l}\right) + A_2 \cosh\left(\lambda_1 \frac{x}{l}\right)\right] - (\sigma - \lambda_2^2)\frac{\lambda_2}{l}\left[A_3 \sin\left(\lambda_2 \frac{x}{l}\right) - A_4 \cos\left(\lambda_2 \frac{x}{l}\right)\right]\right\} \tag{5-13}$$

Equations (5-10) to (5-13) can be expressed in matrix form:

$$\begin{bmatrix} -w \\ \psi \\ M \\ V \end{bmatrix}_x = \begin{bmatrix} \frac{l^3\lambda_1}{\beta^4 EJ_y}\sinh\left(\lambda_1\frac{x}{l}\right) & \frac{l^3\lambda_1}{\beta^4 EJ_y}\cosh\left(\lambda_1\frac{x}{l}\right) & -\frac{l^3\lambda_2}{\beta^4 EJ_y}\sin\left(\lambda_2\frac{x}{l}\right) & \frac{l^3\lambda_2}{\beta^4 EJ_y}\cos\left(\lambda_2\frac{x}{l}\right) \\ \frac{l^2(\sigma+\lambda_1^2)}{\beta^4 EJ_y}\cosh\left(\lambda_1\frac{x}{l}\right) & \frac{l^2(\sigma+\lambda_1^2)}{\beta^4 EJ_y}\sinh\left(\lambda_1\frac{x}{l}\right) & \frac{l^2(\sigma-\lambda_2^2)}{\beta^4 EJ_y}\cos\left(\lambda_2\frac{x}{l}\right) & \frac{l^2(\sigma-\lambda_2^2)}{\beta^4 EJ_y}\sin\left(\lambda_2\frac{x}{l}\right) \\ \frac{l\lambda_1(\sigma+\lambda_1^2)}{\beta^4}\sinh\left(\lambda_1\frac{x}{l}\right) & \frac{l\lambda_1(\sigma+\lambda_1^2)}{\beta^4}\cosh\left(\lambda_1\frac{x}{l}\right) & -\frac{l\lambda_2(\sigma-\lambda_2^2)}{\beta^4}\sin\left(\lambda_2\frac{x}{l}\right) & \frac{l\lambda_2(\sigma-\lambda_2^2)}{\beta^4}\cos\left(\lambda_2\frac{x}{l}\right) \\ \cosh\left(\lambda_1\frac{x}{l}\right) & \sinh\left(\lambda_1\frac{x}{l}\right) & \cos\left(\lambda_2\frac{x}{l}\right) & \sin\left(\lambda_2\frac{x}{l}\right) \end{bmatrix} \cdot \begin{bmatrix} A_1 \\ A_2 \\ A_3 \\ A_4 \end{bmatrix}$$

or

$$\mathbf{z}(x) = \mathbf{B}(x)\mathbf{a} \tag{5-14}$$

At the point $x = 0$ (Fig. 5-5) we have $\mathbf{z}(x) = \mathbf{z}_{i-1}$, and the matrix equation (5-14) becomes

$$\begin{bmatrix} -w \\ \psi \\ M \\ V \end{bmatrix}_{i-1} = \begin{bmatrix} 0 & \frac{l^3\lambda_1}{\beta^4 EJ_y} & 0 & \frac{l^3\lambda_2}{\beta^4 EJ_y} \\ \frac{l^2(\sigma+\lambda_1^2)}{\beta^4 EJ_y} & 0 & \frac{l^2(\sigma-\lambda_2^2)}{\beta^4 EJ_y} & 0 \\ 0 & \frac{l\lambda_1(\sigma+\lambda_1^2)}{\beta^4} & 0 & \frac{l\lambda_2(\sigma-\lambda_2^2)}{\beta^4} \\ 1 & 0 & 1 & 0 \end{bmatrix} \cdot \begin{bmatrix} A_1 \\ A_2 \\ A_3 \\ A_4 \end{bmatrix}$$

or

$$\mathbf{z}_{i-1} = \mathbf{B}(0)\mathbf{a} \tag{5-15}$$

Therefore, solving for the column vector **a**, we obtain

$$\mathbf{a} = \mathbf{B}^{-1}(0)\mathbf{z}_{i-1} \tag{5-16}$$

Substituting Eq. (5-16) into Eq. (5-14) yields

$$\mathbf{z}(x) = \mathbf{B}(x)\mathbf{B}^{-1}(0)\mathbf{z}_{i-1} \tag{5-17}$$

At the point $x = l$, $\mathbf{z}(x) = \mathbf{z}_i$, so that Eq. (5-17) becomes

$$\mathbf{z}_i = \mathbf{B}(l)\mathbf{B}^{-1}(0)\mathbf{z}_{i-1} = \mathbf{U}_i\mathbf{z}_{i-1} \tag{5-18}$$

Hence the transfer matrix is $\mathbf{U}_i = \mathbf{B}(l)\mathbf{B}^{-1}(0)$.

In this case the inversion of $\mathbf{B}(0)$ is rather easy because Eq. (5-15) can be split up into two equations of the form

$$\begin{bmatrix} -w \\ M \end{bmatrix}_{i-1} = \begin{bmatrix} b_{12} & b_{14} \\ b_{32} & b_{34} \end{bmatrix} \cdot \begin{bmatrix} A_2 \\ A_4 \end{bmatrix} \qquad \begin{bmatrix} \psi \\ V \end{bmatrix}_{i-1} = \begin{bmatrix} b_{21} & b_{23} \\ b_{41} & b_{43} \end{bmatrix} \cdot \begin{bmatrix} A_1 \\ A_3 \end{bmatrix}$$

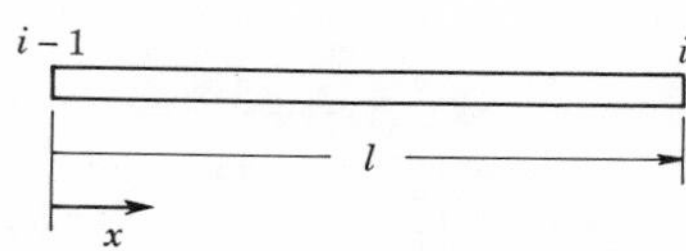

FIG. 5-5. Straight uniform beam.

and from Eqs. (1-27)

$$\begin{bmatrix} A_2 \\ A_4 \end{bmatrix} = \frac{1}{b_{12}b_{34} - b_{14}b_{32}} \begin{bmatrix} b_{34} & -b_{14} \\ -b_{32} & b_{12} \end{bmatrix} \cdot \begin{bmatrix} -w \\ M \end{bmatrix}_{i-1}$$

and

$$\begin{bmatrix} A_1 \\ A_3 \end{bmatrix} = \frac{1}{b_{21}b_{43} - b_{23}b_{41}} \begin{bmatrix} b_{43} & -b_{23} \\ -b_{41} & b_{21} \end{bmatrix} \cdot \begin{bmatrix} \psi \\ V \end{bmatrix}_{i-1}$$

On completing these calculations, the inverse of $\mathbf{B}(0)$ is found to be

$$\mathbf{B}^{-1}(0) = \begin{bmatrix} 0 & \beta^4 \Lambda \dfrac{EJ_y}{l^2} & 0 & \Lambda_2 \\ \beta^4 \dfrac{\Lambda_2}{\lambda_1} \dfrac{EJ_y}{l^3} & 0 & \dfrac{\beta^4 \Lambda}{\lambda_1 l} & 0 \\ 0 & -\beta^4 \Lambda \dfrac{EJ_y}{l^2} & 0 & \Lambda_1 \\ \beta^4 \dfrac{\Lambda_1}{\lambda_2} \dfrac{EJ_y}{l^3} & 0 & -\dfrac{\beta^4 \Lambda}{\lambda_2 l} & 0 \end{bmatrix}$$

where the following abbreviations have been introduced:

$$\Lambda = \frac{1}{\lambda_1^2 + \lambda_2^2} \tag{5-19a}$$

$$\Lambda_1 = \frac{\sigma + \lambda_1^2}{\lambda_1^2 + \lambda_2^2} \tag{5-19b}$$

$$\Lambda_2 = \frac{\lambda_2^2 - \sigma}{\lambda_1^2 + \lambda_2^2} \tag{5-19c}$$

which exhibit the properties

$$\Lambda_1 + \Lambda_2 = 1 \tag{5-19d}$$

$$\Lambda_1 \Lambda_2 = \Lambda^2 \beta^4 \tag{5-19e}$$

The final matrix operation $\mathbf{B}(l)\mathbf{B}^{-1}(0)$ then gives us the transfer matrix, so that

$$\begin{bmatrix} -w \\ \psi \\ M \\ V \end{bmatrix}_i = \begin{bmatrix} c_0 - \sigma c_2 & l[c_1 - (\sigma + \tau)c_3] & \dfrac{l^2 c_2}{EJ_y} & \dfrac{l^3}{\beta^4 EJ_y}[-\sigma c_1 + (\beta^4 + \sigma^2)c_3] \\ \dfrac{\beta^4}{l} c_3 & c_0 - \tau c_2 & \dfrac{l(c_1 - \tau c_3)}{EJ_y} & \dfrac{l^2}{EJ_y} c_2 \\ \beta^4 \dfrac{EJ_y}{l^2} c_2 & \dfrac{EJ_y}{l}[-\tau c_1 + (\beta^4 + \tau^2)c_3] & c_0 - \tau c_2 & l[c_1 - (\sigma + \tau)c_3] \\ \beta^4 \dfrac{EJ_y}{l^3}(c_1 - \sigma c_3) & \beta^4 \dfrac{EJ_y}{l^2} c_2 & \dfrac{\beta^4}{l} c_3 & c_0 - \sigma c_2 \end{bmatrix} \cdot \begin{bmatrix} -w \\ \psi \\ M \\ V \end{bmatrix}_{i-1} \tag{5-20}$$

where

$$c_0 = \Lambda(\lambda_2^2 \cosh \lambda_1 + \lambda_1^2 \cos \lambda_2) \qquad c_1 = \Lambda\left(\frac{\lambda_2^2}{\lambda_1} \sinh \lambda_1 + \frac{\lambda_1^2}{\lambda_2} \sin \lambda_2\right)$$

$$c_2 = \Lambda(\cosh \lambda_1 - \cos \lambda_2) \qquad c_3 = \Lambda\left(\frac{\sinh \lambda_1}{\lambda_1} - \frac{\sin \lambda_2}{\lambda_2}\right) \tag{5-20a}$$

This transfer matrix is identical to that in the Catalogue (Sec. C-3*a*), except that the

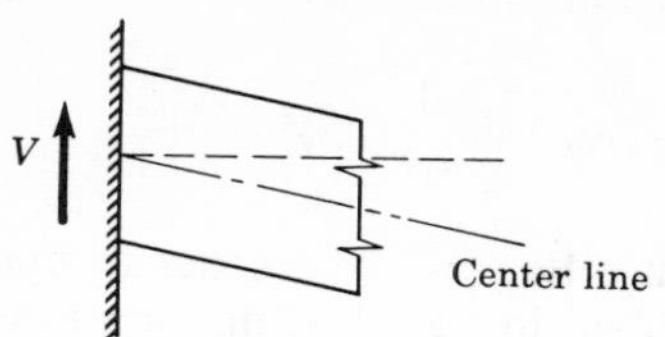

FIG. 5-6. Boundary condition $\psi = 0$.

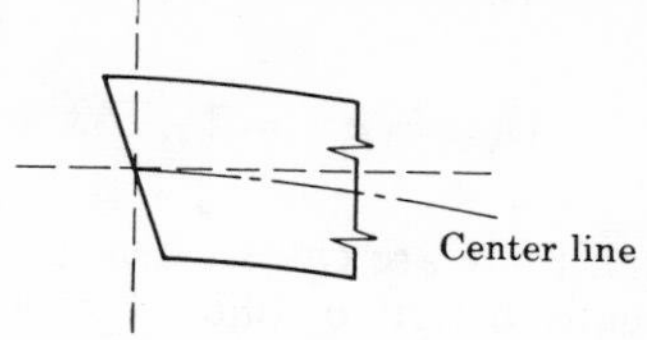

FIG. 5-7. Boundary condition $dw/dx = 0$.

values of β, σ, and τ in the Catalogue are more general than in this particular problem and also cover the case of a beam on elastic foundation and whirling shafts.

It is as well to clarify several points that must be observed when applying this matrix. In considering the state vector, it is natural to ask why the angle ψ has been chosen in preference to the slope of the center line dw/dx. The reason for this is that in a continuous beam ψ is always continuous, whereas dw/dx has a discontinuity wherever there is a discontinuity in the shear force—a condition that occurs frequently. However, although the use of ψ has this advantage, care must be taken when considering the case of a beam that is built-in (Figs. 5-6 and 5-7). If the boundary condition is that the slope of the face of the cross section be zero, then we must take $\psi = 0$, a condition that causes no difficulty. However, it may be demanded that the slope of the center line dw/dx be zero. From Eq. (5-3*a*) it is seen that, if $dw/dx = 0$, then the boundary condition to be used is $\psi = V/GA_s$.

PROBLEMS

5-1. Derive the transfer matrix for the longitudinal vibration of a straight bar of constant section, length l, and mass per unit length μ (cf. matrix C-1*a*).

5-2. Consider a rigid torsional shaft ($G \to \infty$) of length l. Derive its transfer matrix, using the solution of Eq. (5-2) (cf. matrix C-2*b*).

5-3. Find the transfer matrix of the massless beam of length l under axial compression applied at its ends (cf. Sec. C-4*b*).

5-4. Derive the transfer matrix for a whirling shaft of constant section, neglecting shear deformation (cf. Sec. C-3*a*).

5-5. Consider the solution of Prob. 5-4. Find the transfer matrix for a whirling disk by letting $l \to 0$, while $\mu l \to m$ (cf. matrix C-3*f*). Check, using standard methods of dynamics.

5-6. Find the transfer matrix for a massless curved bar ($\mu \to 0$) of constant section and constant radius of curvature for vibration (*a*) in the plane of the central axis and (*b*) perpendicular to this plane (cf. matrices C-7*c* and C-8*c*).

5-2. The Solution of *n* First-order Ordinary Differential Equations with Constant Coefficients

Method of Finding the Transfer Matrix Using the Cayley-Hamilton Theorem. In the previous example we reduced the set of first-order differential equations (5-3) to one of fourth order in w. It is possible, and in many cases it is advantageous, to find the transfer matrix from the set of first-order differential equations directly [18].

Let us consider a set of n first-order differential equations with constant coefficients which in matrix representation [cf. Eq. (1-54)] is written

$$\frac{d\mathbf{z}}{ds} = \mathbf{Az} \tag{5-21}$$

The solution of this equation is [cf. Eq. (1-55)]

$$\mathbf{z} = e^{\mathbf{A}s}\mathbf{z}_0 = \mathbf{U}\mathbf{z}_0 \tag{5-22}$$

where $\mathbf{z}_0$ is the initial state vector at $s = 0$ and $\mathbf{U} = e^{\mathbf{A}s}$ is the transfer matrix.

The transfer matrix $\mathbf{U} = e^{\mathbf{A}s}$ can be expanded as an infinite series:

$$\mathbf{U}(s) = e^{\mathbf{A}s} = \mathbf{I} + \mathbf{A}s + \frac{1}{2!}(\mathbf{A}s)^2 + \frac{1}{3!}(\mathbf{A}s)^3 + \frac{1}{4!}(\mathbf{A}s)^4 + \cdots \tag{5-23}$$

Although there are cases when it is practical to use Eq. (5-23) in order to find $\mathbf{U}(s)$, it is usually better to follow the procedure described in Sec. 1-4, making use of the Cayley-Hamilton theorem.

To illustrate the technique, let us consider the case of a straight, uniform, vibrating beam, neglecting the effect of shear deflection and rotary inertia. Making these assumptions, Eqs. (5-3) reduce to

$$\frac{dw}{dx} = -\psi \qquad \text{since } GA_s = \infty \qquad \frac{d\psi}{dx} = \frac{M}{EJ_y} \qquad \frac{dM}{dx} = V \qquad \frac{dV}{dx} = -\mu\omega^2 w$$

which in matrix form become

$$\frac{d}{dx}\begin{bmatrix} -w \\ \psi \\ M \\ V \end{bmatrix} = \begin{bmatrix} 0 & 1 & 0 & 0 \\ 0 & 0 & \dfrac{1}{EJ_y} & 0 \\ 0 & 0 & 0 & 1 \\ \omega^2\mu & 0 & 0 & 0 \end{bmatrix} \cdot \begin{bmatrix} -w \\ \psi \\ M \\ V \end{bmatrix} \tag{5-24}$$

or

$$\frac{d\mathbf{z}}{dx} = \mathbf{A}\mathbf{z}$$

According to Eq. (5-22) the transfer matrix $\mathbf{U}$ for a beam of length l is given by $\mathbf{U} = e^{\mathbf{A}l}$. The characteristic equation [cf. Eq. (1-33)] for $\mathbf{A}l$ is

$$|\lambda\mathbf{I} - \mathbf{A}l| = \begin{vmatrix} \lambda & -l & 0 & 0 \\ 0 & \lambda & \dfrac{-l}{EJ_y} & 0 \\ 0 & 0 & \lambda & -l \\ -\mu\omega^2 l & 0 & 0 & \lambda \end{vmatrix} = \lambda^4 - \beta^4 = 0 \tag{5-25}$$

where $\beta^4 = \mu\omega^2 l^4/EJ_y$. The eigenvalues of $\mathbf{A}l$ are therefore $\lambda_1 = \beta$, $\lambda_2 = -\beta$, $\lambda_3 = j\beta$, and $\lambda_4 = -j\beta$. Since $\mathbf{A}l$ is a fourth-order square matrix, the function $e^{\mathbf{A}l}$ may be written in the form [cf. Eq. (1-47)]

$$\mathbf{U} = e^{\mathbf{A}l} = c_0\mathbf{I} + c_1\mathbf{A}l + c_2(\mathbf{A}l)^2 + c_3(\mathbf{A}l)^3 \tag{5-26}$$

Replacing $\mathbf{A}l$ by its eigenvalues λ_i ($i = 1, 2, 3, 4$) in this equation [cf. Eq. (1-48)], we obtain

$$\begin{aligned} e^{\beta} &= c_0 + c_1\beta + c_2\beta^2 + c_3\beta^3 \\ e^{-\beta} &= c_0 - c_1\beta + c_2\beta^2 - c_3\beta^3 \\ e^{j\beta} &= c_0 + jc_1\beta - c_2\beta^2 - jc_3\beta^3 \\ e^{-j\beta} &= c_0 - jc_1\beta - c_2\beta^2 + jc_3\beta^3 \end{aligned}$$

which yield

$$c_0 = \tfrac{1}{2}(\cosh\beta + \cos\beta) \qquad c_1 = \frac{1}{2\beta}(\sinh\beta + \sin\beta)$$
$$c_2 = \frac{1}{2\beta^2}(\cosh\beta - \cos\beta) \qquad c_3 = \frac{1}{2\beta^3}(\sinh\beta - \sin\beta) \tag{5-27}$$

Before applying these results to Eq. (5-26) we must form the second and third powers of $\mathbf{A}l$:

$$(\mathbf{A}l)^2 = \begin{bmatrix} 0 & 0 & \dfrac{l^2}{EJ_y} & 0 \\ 0 & 0 & 0 & \dfrac{l^2}{EJ_y} \\ \mu\omega^2 l^2 & 0 & 0 & 0 \\ 0 & \mu\omega^2 l^2 & 0 & 0 \end{bmatrix} \qquad (\mathbf{A}l)^3 = \begin{bmatrix} 0 & 0 & 0 & \dfrac{l^3}{EJ_y} \\ \dfrac{\mu\omega^2 l^3}{EJ_y} & 0 & 0 & 0 \\ 0 & \mu\omega^2 l^3 & 0 & 0 \\ 0 & 0 & \dfrac{\mu\omega^2 l^3}{EJ_y} & 0 \end{bmatrix}$$

The expression for the transfer matrix $\mathbf{U} = e^{\mathbf{A}l}$ is then given by

$$\mathbf{U} = c_0 \begin{bmatrix} 1 & 0 & 0 & 0 \\ 0 & 1 & 0 & 0 \\ 0 & 0 & 1 & 0 \\ 0 & 0 & 0 & 1 \end{bmatrix} + c_1 \begin{bmatrix} 0 & l & 0 & 0 \\ 0 & 0 & \dfrac{l}{EJ_y} & 0 \\ 0 & 0 & 0 & l \\ \mu\omega^2 l & 0 & 0 & 0 \end{bmatrix} + c_2 \begin{bmatrix} 0 & 0 & \dfrac{l^2}{EJ_y} & 0 \\ 0 & 0 & 0 & \dfrac{l^2}{EJ_y} \\ \mu\omega^2 l^2 & 0 & 0 & 0 \\ 0 & \mu\omega^2 l^2 & 0 & 0 \end{bmatrix}$$

$$+ c_3 \begin{bmatrix} 0 & 0 & 0 & \dfrac{l^3}{EJ_y} \\ \dfrac{\mu\omega^2 l^3}{EJ_y} & 0 & 0 & 0 \\ 0 & \mu\omega^2 l^3 & 0 & 0 \\ 0 & 0 & \dfrac{\mu\omega^2 l^3}{EJ_y} & 0 \end{bmatrix} = \begin{bmatrix} c_0 & lc_1 & \dfrac{l^2 c_2}{EJ_y} & \dfrac{l^3 c_3}{EJ_y} \\ \dfrac{\beta^4}{l} c_3 & c_0 & \dfrac{lc_1}{EJ_y} & \dfrac{l^2 c_2}{EJ_y} \\ \beta^4 \dfrac{EJ_y}{l^2} c_2 & \beta^4 \dfrac{EJ_y}{l} c_3 & c_0 & lc_1 \\ \beta^4 \dfrac{EJ_y}{l^3} c_1 & \beta^4 \dfrac{EJ_y}{l^2} c_2 & \dfrac{\beta^4}{l} c_3 & c_0 \end{bmatrix} \tag{5-28}$$

This result can be checked against Eq. (5-20) for the case $i_y = 0$ and $GA_s = \infty$.

The Case of Repeated Eigenvalues. A simple example of repeated eigenvalues occurs in the case of a vibrating massless beam. This is identical with the previous case except that we now have $\mu = 0$. Hence, the characteristic equation for the matrix $\mathbf{A}l$ is

$$|\mathbf{I} - \mathbf{A}l| = \begin{vmatrix} \lambda & -l & 0 & 0 \\ 0 & \lambda & \dfrac{-l}{EJ_y} & 0 \\ 0 & 0 & \lambda & -l \\ 0 & 0 & 0 & \lambda \end{vmatrix} = 0 \tag{5-29}$$

from which, on expansion, we obtain $\lambda^4 = 0$, so that $\lambda = 0$ is a quadruple root. According to Eqs. (1-49) we obtain for $m = 3$ and $f(\lambda_j) = e^{\lambda_j}$ the following set of equations:

$$\begin{aligned} e^{\lambda_j} &= c_0 + c_1\lambda_j + c_2\lambda_j^2 + c_3\lambda_j^3 \\ e^{\lambda_j} &= c_1 + 2c_2\lambda_j + 3c_3\lambda_j^2 \\ e^{\lambda_j} &= 2c_2 + 6c_3\lambda_j \\ e^{\lambda_j} &= 6c_3 \end{aligned}$$

When $\lambda_j = 0$ is substituted into these equations, it is a simple matter to find the following values for c_i:

$$c_0 = 1 \qquad c_1 = 1 \qquad c_2 = \tfrac{1}{2} \qquad c_3 = \tfrac{1}{6}$$

The transfer matrix is then

$$\mathbf{U} = \mathbf{I} + \mathbf{A}l + \tfrac{1}{2}(\mathbf{A}l)^2 + \tfrac{1}{6}(\mathbf{A}l)^3$$

With

$$\mathbf{A}l = \begin{bmatrix} 0 & l & 0 & 0 \\ 0 & 0 & \dfrac{l}{EJ_y} & 0 \\ 0 & 0 & 0 & l \\ 0 & 0 & 0 & 0 \end{bmatrix}$$

we therefore have

$$\mathbf{U} = \begin{bmatrix} 1 & l & \dfrac{l^2}{2EJ_y} & \dfrac{l^3}{6EJ_y} \\ 0 & 1 & \dfrac{l}{EJ_y} & \dfrac{l^2}{2EJ_y} \\ 0 & 0 & 1 & l \\ 0 & 0 & 0 & 1 \end{bmatrix} \tag{5-30}$$

General Case of Bending Vibration and Stability of Beams. Inspection of the differential equations for the various cases of bending vibration and elastic stability of beams reveals that in the most general case the matrix $\mathbf{A}$ of the four homogeneous first-order differential equations possesses the following structure:

$$\mathbf{A} = \begin{bmatrix} 0 & 1 & 0 & \alpha_4 \\ 0 & 0 & \alpha_3 & 0 \\ 0 & \alpha_2 & 0 & 1 \\ \alpha_1 & 0 & 0 & 0 \end{bmatrix} \tag{5-31}$$

where $\alpha_1, \ldots, \alpha_4$ take on different values in accordance with the problem that is being considered. Using the technique outlined above, we obtain the transfer matrix

$$\mathbf{U}_i = \begin{bmatrix} c_0 - \sigma c_2 & l[c_1 - c_3(\sigma + \tau)] & \alpha_3 l^2 c_2 & \alpha_4 l(c_1 - \sigma c_3) + \alpha_3 l^3 c_3 \\ \dfrac{\beta^4}{l} c_3 & c_0 - \tau c_2 & \alpha_3 l(c_1 - \tau c_3) & \alpha_3 l^2 c_2 \\ \alpha_1 l^2 c_2 & \alpha_2 l(c_1 - \tau c_3) + \alpha_1 l^3 c_3 & c_0 - \tau c_2 & l[c_1 - c_3(\sigma + \tau)] \\ \alpha_1 l(c_1 - \sigma c_3) & \alpha_1 l^2 c_2 & \dfrac{\beta^4}{l} c_3 & c_0 - \sigma c_2 \end{bmatrix} \tag{5-32}$$

where $\beta^4 = \alpha_1 \alpha_3 l^4 \qquad \sigma = -\alpha_1 \alpha_4 l^2 \qquad \tau = -\alpha_2 \alpha_3 l^2$

and c_0, c_1, c_2, and c_3 have been given in Eqs. (5-20*a*).

In the Catalogue this transfer matrix has been expanded for a variety of different cases (cf. Secs. C-3 and C-4).

PROBLEMS

5-7. Derive the point matrix for a mass m with rotary inertia I_z which is part of a Myklestad beam, vibrating in the xy plane (cf. matrix C-3*f*).

5-8. Set up the transfer matrix for the elastic stability of a column of length l and constant bending stiffness EJ_y. Check the result with the general solution of Eq. (5-32) (also cf. Sec. C-4*b*).

5-9. Using the result of Prob. 5-8, determine the buckling load for the four Eulerian cases.

5-10. Derive the point matrix for an elastic hinge, using the technique of this section as well as simple statics (cf. matrices C-3*g* and *h*).

5-11. Set up the system of first-order differential equations for a whirling shaft of constant section. Then use Eq. (5-32) to derive the transfer matrix (cf. Sec. C-3*a*).

5-12. Repeat Prob. 5-6, using the technique of Sec. 5-2 (use matrix **A** in Secs. C-7*a* and C-8*a*).

5-13. With the result of Prob. 5-12 derive the transfer matrix for a corner of angle α (cf. matrices C-7*f* and C-8*f*). Check the result by geometrical reasoning.

5-14. Find the transfer matrix for a vibrating rigid ($E \to \infty$) curved bar of constant mass distribution and constant radius of curvature (use matrix **A** in Sec. C-7*a*) (cf. Secs. C-7*b* and C-8*b*).

5-3. The Solution of n First-order Nonhomogeneous Differential Equations

If an elastic system is subjected to harmonic forces, then the differential equations of motion are no longer homogeneous and have the general form

$$\frac{d\mathbf{z}}{ds} = \mathbf{A}\mathbf{z} + \mathbf{a}(s) \tag{5-33}$$

Provided the elements of **A** are all constants, the solution of Eq. (5-33) is [cf. Eq. (1-58)]

$$\mathbf{z}(s) = e^{\mathbf{A}s}\mathbf{z}_0 + e^{\mathbf{A}s} \int_0^s e^{-\mathbf{A}\sigma}\mathbf{a}(\sigma)\, d\sigma \tag{5-34}$$

where $\mathbf{z}_0$ is the initial state vector at the point $s = 0$. If we compare this equation with Eq. (5-22), we notice that $e^{\mathbf{A}s}$ is the transfer matrix **U**, which we shall assume to be known. It remains to evaluate the term under the integral, for which we require the inverse of the transfer matrix, $\mathbf{U}^{-1}(\sigma) = e^{-\mathbf{A}\sigma}$. Since the matrix **A** contains only elements that are constant, then $\mathbf{U}^{-1}(\sigma)$ is found by replacing σ by $-\sigma$ in the transfer matrix $\mathbf{U}$. Hence, for the case in which the matrix $\mathbf{A}$ is independent of the space coordinate, we have the important property

$$\mathbf{U}^{-1}(\sigma) = \mathbf{U}(-\sigma) \tag{5-35}$$

Equation (5-34) therefore becomes

$$\mathbf{z}(s) = \mathbf{U}(s)\mathbf{z}_0 + \mathbf{U}(s)\int_0^s \mathbf{U}(-\sigma)\mathbf{a}(\sigma)\,d\sigma \tag{5-36}$$

or

$$\mathbf{z}(s) = \mathbf{U}(s)\mathbf{z}_0 + \mathbf{r}(s)$$

where

$$\mathbf{U}(s) = e^{\mathbf{A}s} \qquad \text{and} \qquad \mathbf{r}(s) = \mathbf{U}(s)\int_0^s \mathbf{U}(-\sigma)\mathbf{a}(\sigma)\,d\sigma \tag{5-37}$$

We shall illustrate the procedure by considering a straight uniform beam that is subjected to a distributed lateral exciting force $q(x)\sin\Omega t$. The differential equations of motion are

$$\frac{\partial w}{\partial x} = -\psi \tag{5-38a}$$

$$\frac{\partial \psi}{\partial x} = \frac{M}{EJ_y} \tag{5-38b}$$

$$\frac{\partial M}{\partial x} = V \tag{5-38c}$$

$$\frac{\partial V}{\partial x} = \frac{\mu\partial^2 w}{\partial t^2} - q(x)\sin\Omega t \tag{5-38d}$$

Separation of the time and space variables is achieved by means of the substitutions

$$w(x, t) = w(x)\sin\Omega t \qquad \psi(x, t) = \psi(x)\sin\Omega t$$

$$M(x, t) = M(x)\sin\Omega t \qquad V(x, t) = V(x)\sin\Omega t$$

so that Eqs. (5-38) become

$$\frac{dw}{dx} = -\psi \qquad \frac{d\psi}{dx} = \frac{M}{EJ_y} \qquad \frac{dM}{dx} = V \qquad \frac{dV}{dx} = -\mu\Omega^2 w - q(x)$$

or, in matrix form,

$$\frac{d}{dx}\begin{bmatrix} -w \\ \psi \\ M \\ V \end{bmatrix} = \begin{bmatrix} 0 & 1 & 0 & 0 \\ 0 & 0 & \dfrac{1}{EJ_y} & 0 \\ 0 & 0 & 0 & 1 \\ \mu\Omega^2 & 0 & 0 & 0 \end{bmatrix} \cdot \begin{bmatrix} -w \\ \psi \\ M \\ V \end{bmatrix} + \begin{bmatrix} 0 \\ 0 \\ 0 \\ -q(x) \end{bmatrix} \tag{5-39}$$

Comparing Eq. (5-39) with Eq. (5-33), we see that

$$\mathbf{A} = \begin{bmatrix} 0 & 1 & 0 & 0 \\ 0 & 0 & \dfrac{1}{EJ_y} & 0 \\ 0 & 0 & 0 & 1 \\ \mu\Omega^2 & 0 & 0 & 0 \end{bmatrix} \qquad \text{and} \qquad \mathbf{a}(x) = \begin{bmatrix} 0 \\ 0 \\ 0 \\ -q(x) \end{bmatrix}$$

The transfer matrix $\mathbf{U} = e^{\mathbf{A}x}$ has already been found to be

$$\mathbf{U}(x) = \begin{bmatrix} c_0(x) & lc_1(x) & \frac{l^2 c_2(x)}{EJ_y} & \frac{l^3 c_3(x)}{EJ_y} \\ \frac{\beta^4}{l} c_3(x) & c_0(x) & \frac{lc_1(x)}{EJ_y} & \frac{l^2 c_2(x)}{EJ_y} \\ \frac{\beta^4 EJ_y}{l^2} c_2(x) & \frac{\beta^4 EJ_y}{l} c_3(x) & c_0(x) & lc_1(x) \\ \frac{\beta^4 EJ_y}{l^3} c_1(x) & \frac{\beta^4 EJ_y}{l^2} c_2(x) & \frac{\beta^4}{l} c_3(x) & c_0(x) \end{bmatrix} \tag{5-40}$$

where

$$c_0(x) = \tfrac{1}{2}\left[\cosh\left(\beta\frac{x}{l}\right) + \cos\left(\beta\frac{x}{l}\right)\right] \qquad c_1(x) = \frac{1}{2\beta}\left[\sinh\left(\beta\frac{x}{l}\right) + \sin\left(\beta\frac{x}{l}\right)\right]$$

$$c_2(x) = \frac{1}{2\beta^2}\left[\cosh\left(\beta\frac{x}{l}\right) - \cos\left(\beta\frac{x}{l}\right)\right] \qquad c_3(x) = \frac{1}{2\beta^3}\left[\sinh\left(\beta\frac{x}{l}\right) - \sin\left(\beta\frac{x}{l}\right)\right]$$

and on account of the result (5-35), $\mathbf{U}^{-1}(x) = \mathbf{U}(-x)$, then

$$\mathbf{U}^{-1}(x) = \begin{bmatrix} c_0(x) & -lc_1(x) & \frac{l^2 c_2(x)}{EJ_y} & \frac{-l^3}{EJ_y} c_3(x) \\ \frac{-\beta^4}{l} c_3(x) & c_0(x) & \frac{-lc_1(x)}{EJ_y} & \frac{l^2}{EJ_y} c_2(x) \\ \frac{\beta^4 EJ_y}{l^2} c_2(x) & \frac{-\beta^4 EJ_y}{l} c_3(x) & c_0(x) & -lc_1(x) \\ \frac{-\beta^4 EJ_y}{l^3} c_1(x) & \frac{\beta^4 EJ_y}{l^2} c_2(x) & \frac{-\beta^4}{l} c_3(x) & c_0(x) \end{bmatrix} \tag{5-41}$$

The product $\mathbf{U}^{-1}(\xi)\mathbf{a}(\xi)$ gives the column vector

$$\left\{\frac{ql^3}{EJ_y} c_3(\xi) \quad -\frac{ql^2}{EJ_y} c_2(\xi) \quad qlc_1(\xi) \quad -qc_0(\xi)\right\}$$

and if $q(\xi)$ is a constant q, the integral $\int_0^x \mathbf{U}^{-1}(\xi)\mathbf{a}(\xi)\,d\xi$ becomes [cf. Eq. (1-52)]

$$\int_0^x \mathbf{U}^{-1}(\xi)\mathbf{a}(\xi)\,d\xi = \begin{bmatrix} \int_0^x \frac{ql^3}{EJ} c_3(\xi)\,d\xi \\ \int_0^x -\frac{ql^2}{EJ} c_2(\xi)\,d\xi \\ \int_0^x qlc_1(\xi)\,d\xi \\ \int_0^x -qc_0(\xi)\,d\xi \end{bmatrix} = \begin{bmatrix} \frac{ql^4}{\beta^4 EJ}[c_0(x) - 1] \\ -\frac{ql^3}{EJ} c_3(x) \\ ql^2 c_2(x) \\ -qlc_1(x) \end{bmatrix} \tag{5-42}$$

As the final step, the column vector (5-42) is multiplied by the transfer matrix $\mathbf{U}(x)$ [Eq. (5-40)]:

$$\mathbf{r}(x) = \mathbf{U}(x)\int_0^x \mathbf{U}^{-1}(\xi)\mathbf{a}(\xi)\,d\xi = \begin{bmatrix} \dfrac{ql^4}{EJ}\left\{\dfrac{c_0(x)[c_0(x)-1]}{\beta^4} - 2c_1(x)c_3(x) + c_2^2(x)\right\} \\ -\dfrac{ql^3}{EJ}c_3(x) \\ ql^2[2c_0(x)c_2(x) - c_2^2(x) - \beta^4 c_3^2(x) - c_1^2(x)] \\ -qlc_1(x) \end{bmatrix} \tag{5-43}$$

As soon as $\mathbf{r}(x)$ is known, we can set up the extended transfer matrix (cf. Sec. 3-5):

$$\begin{bmatrix} \mathbf{z}(x) \\ \hline 1 \end{bmatrix} = \begin{bmatrix} \mathbf{U}(x) & \mathbf{r}(x) \\ \hline \mathbf{0} & 1 \end{bmatrix} \cdot \begin{bmatrix} \mathbf{z}(0) \\ \hline 1 \end{bmatrix} \tag{5-44}$$

or

$$\tilde{\mathbf{z}}(x) = \tilde{\mathbf{U}}(x)\tilde{\mathbf{z}}(0)$$

PROBLEMS

5-15. Determine the vector $\mathbf{r}(l)$ for the loading shown in Fig. P 5-15 (cf. Sec. C-6). The beam is considered massless. Use the result also for the simple case $q_1 = q_2 = q$.

5-16. Determine the vector $\mathbf{r}(l)$ for the loading shown in Fig. P 5-16. The beam is considered massless. Check the result by forming the product $\tilde{\mathbf{U}}_3\tilde{\mathbf{U}}_2\tilde{\mathbf{U}}_1$.

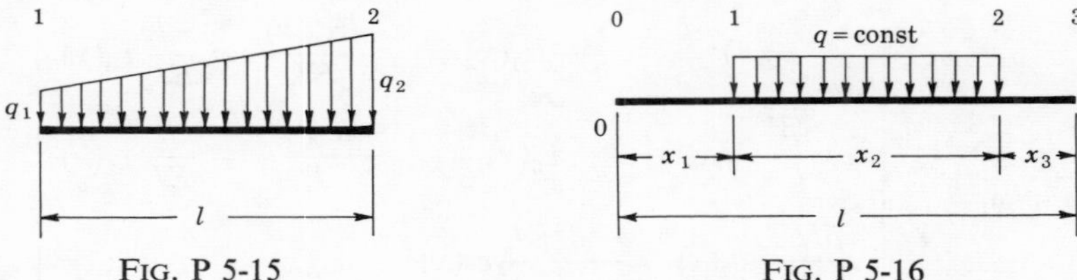

FIG. P 5-15

FIG. P 5-16

5-17. Find the extended transfer matrix for the beam section of Fig. P 5-17 by using elementary methods.

5-18. Derive the extended transfer matrix for the frame corner shown in Fig. P 5-18. The frame corner is massless except for the two point masses. Treat also the case $EA \to \infty$. HINT: Divide the corner into three parts such that for each the transfer matrix is known. Then find the complete extended transfer matrix by multiplication.

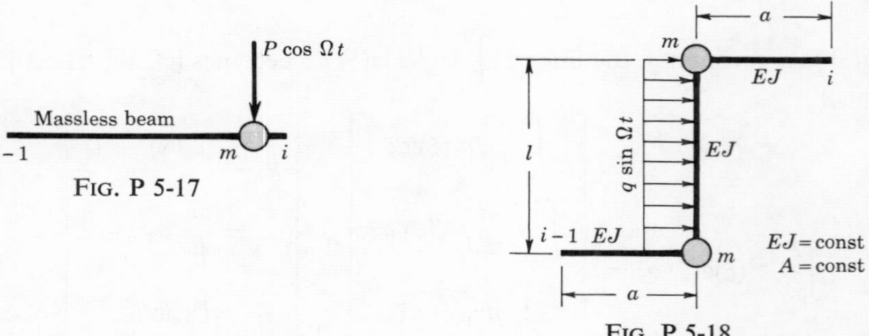

FIG. P 5-17

FIG. P 5-18

5-19. Using the results listed in the Catalogue under Sec. C-12*a*, find the vector $\mathbf{r}$ for the case shown in Fig. P 5-19. Treat also the case $f = 0$.

5-20. For the static loading $q_x = q_z = 0$ and $q_y =$ const of the arc in Fig. P 5-20, determine M_x, M_z, and N_x at point 0. HINT: Set up the extended transfer matrix, using the results given in the Catalogue (cf. Secs. C-8*c* and C-12*b*).

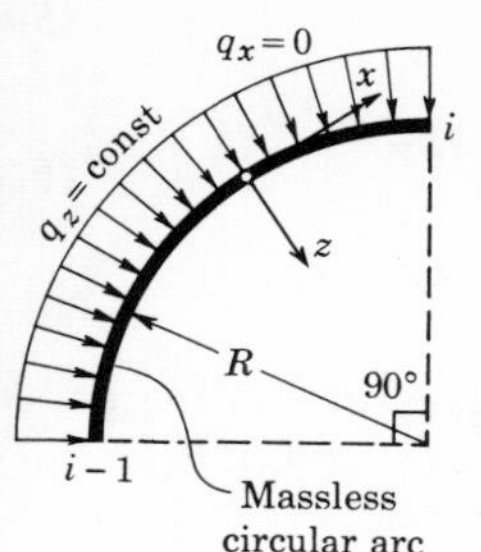

FIG. P 5-19

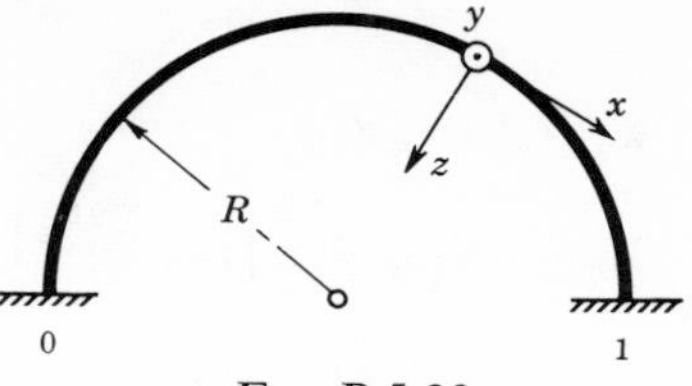

FIG. P 5-20

5-4. The Solution of n First-order Differential Equations with Variable Coefficients

General Considerations. In the previous sections we discussed a method of solving the differential equation (5-21) when the elements of the matrix $\mathbf{A}$ are all constants. This method fails when the elements of $\mathbf{A}$ are variables of the space coordinate s or when it becomes impossible to find the eigenvalues of the matrix $\mathbf{A}l$. In such cases we either replace the system by a substitute system or adopt a numerical procedure to find the elements of the transfer matrix.

For example, when dealing with a beam of variable cross section it is normal practice to replace the beam by a beam consisting of piecewise constant elements (Fig. 5-8). The transfer matrices for the elements of the substitute beam are known, and hence the calculation can proceed in the standard manner to yield very satisfactory results [19].

The differential equations for the vibrations of a curved beam or for the coupled torsional and flexural vibrations of open web beams are virtually impossible to solve on account of the difficulties of finding the eigenvalues of the $\mathbf{A}l$ matrix. Both these problems are greatly simplified if the Myklestad technique of concentrating the mass at discrete points is adopted. The transfer matrices for the massless elements in both of these cases can be readily found by standard elastostatic methods, and this technique again gives satisfactory results [18].

The Runge-Kutta Method. In the rare case that neither of these techniques proves satisfactory, it becomes necessary to adopt a numerical procedure. The Runge-Kutta method is well suited for finding the transfer matrix, but by and large it is necessary to have the services of an electronic computer. If we wish to compute the transfer matrix relating the state vectors $\mathbf{z}_{i-1}$ and $\mathbf{z}_i$, we divide the interval between $i - 1$ and i into a number of small intervals. Let us suppose that the differential equations to be integrated are

$$\frac{d\mathbf{z}}{ds} = \mathbf{A}(s)\mathbf{z} \tag{5-45}$$

and that between sections n and $n + 1$ the interval size is h (Fig. 5-9). The Runge-Kutta method gives the result

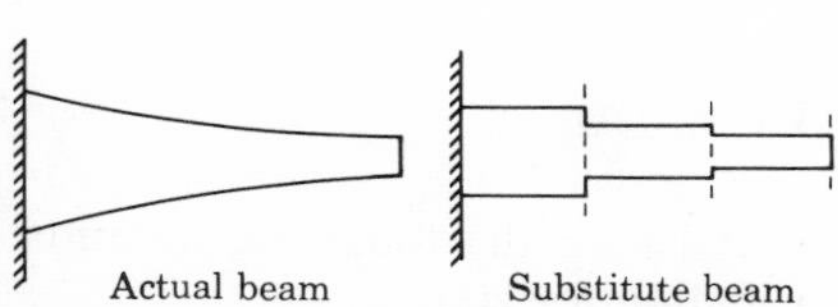

FIG. 5-8. Substitution of beam of variable cross section by one of piecewise constant elements.

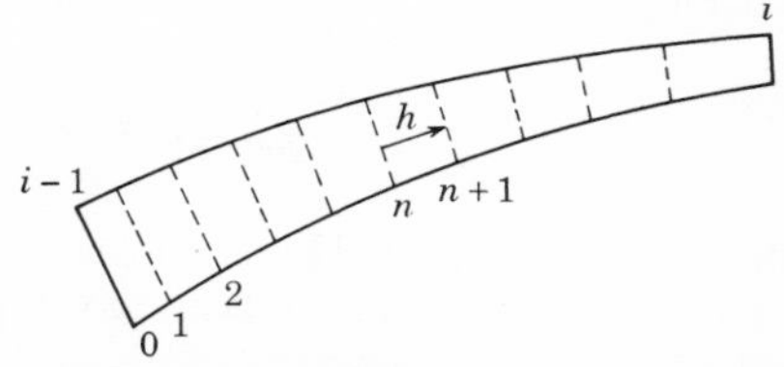

FIG. 5-9. The subdivision of the interval between stations $i - 1$ and i.

$$\mathbf{z}_{n+1} = \mathbf{z}_n + \tfrac{1}{6}(\mathbf{k}_0 + 2\mathbf{k}_1 + 2\mathbf{k}_2 + \mathbf{k}_3) \tag{5-46}$$

where

$$\mathbf{k}_0 = h\mathbf{A}(s_n)\mathbf{z}_n \qquad \mathbf{k}_1 = h\mathbf{A}\left(s_n + \frac{h}{2}\right)\left(\mathbf{z}_n + \frac{\mathbf{k}_0}{2}\right) \tag{5-47}$$

$$\mathbf{k}_2 = h\mathbf{A}\left(s_n + \frac{h}{2}\right)\left(\mathbf{z}_n + \frac{\mathbf{k}_1}{2}\right) \qquad \mathbf{k}_3 = h\mathbf{A}(s_n + h)(\mathbf{z}_n + \mathbf{k}_2)$$

$\mathbf{A}(s_n)$, $\mathbf{A}(s_n + h)$, and $\mathbf{A}(s_n + h/2)$ are, respectively, the values of the matrix $\mathbf{A}(s)$ at the sections n and $n + 1$ and at the section midway between n and $n + 1$.

Substituting expressions (5-47) into Eq. (5-46) gives the relation between $\mathbf{z}_{n+1}$ and $\mathbf{z}_n$:

$$\begin{aligned}\mathbf{z}_{n+1} = \Big\{\mathbf{I} &+ \frac{h}{6}\left[\mathbf{A}(s_n) + 4\mathbf{A}\left(s_n + \frac{h}{2}\right) + \mathbf{A}(s_n + h)\right] \\ &+ \frac{h^2}{6}\left[\mathbf{A}\left(s_n + \frac{h}{2}\right)\mathbf{A}(s_n) + \mathbf{A}(s_n + h)\mathbf{A}\left(s_n + \frac{h}{2}\right) + \mathbf{A}^2\left(s_n + \frac{h}{2}\right)\right] \\ &+ \frac{h^3}{12}\left[\mathbf{A}^2\left(s_n + \frac{h}{2}\right)\mathbf{A}(s_n) + \mathbf{A}(s_n + h)\mathbf{A}^2\left(s_n + \frac{h}{2}\right)\right] \\ &+ \frac{h^4}{24}\mathbf{A}(s_n + h)\mathbf{A}^2\left(s_n + \frac{h}{2}\right)\mathbf{A}(s_n)\Big\}\mathbf{z}_n\end{aligned} \tag{5-48}$$

where the contents of the braces represents the transfer matrix linking the state vectors $\mathbf{z}_n$ and $\mathbf{z}_{n+1}$. By repeating the process for all the intervals between $i - 1$ and i, the transfer matrix $\mathbf{U}_i$ relating $\mathbf{z}_{i-1}$ and $\mathbf{z}_i$ can then be found by multiplication of the braces of Eq. (5-48) in the proper sequence.

It is interesting to note that, if $\mathbf{A}(s)$ contains only constant elements, Eq. (5-48) reduces to the expression

$$\mathbf{z}_{n+1} = \left[\mathbf{I} + \frac{\mathbf{A}h}{1!} + \frac{(\mathbf{A}h)^2}{2!} + \frac{(\mathbf{A}h)^3}{3!} + \frac{(\mathbf{A}h)^4}{4!}\right]\mathbf{z}_n$$

where the brackets contain the first five terms of the infinite expansion of Eq. (5-23).

A disadvantage of the Runge-Kutta method is that it is impossible to estimate the error associated with a given incremental step of size h. One can only select what seems a reasonable value for h, and then compare the result with that obtained for a smaller increment.†

Picard Iteration. Another way of solving the set of homogeneous first-order differential equations with variable coefficients

$$\frac{d\mathbf{z}}{ds} = \mathbf{A}(s)\mathbf{z} \qquad \mathbf{z}(s_0) = \mathbf{z}_0 \tag{5-45}$$

with the aim of obtaining the transfer matrix $\mathbf{U}(s)$, is possible by means of the so-called Picard iteration. Integration of Eq. (5-45) yields

$$\mathbf{z}(s) = \mathbf{z}_0 + \int_0^s \mathbf{A}(\sigma)\mathbf{z}(\sigma)\,d\sigma \tag{5-49}$$

We now use Eq. (5-49) as the rule for establishing the following iteration procedure, where $\mathbf{z}_n(s)$ represents the nth approximation for $\mathbf{z}(s)$:

† For further information regarding the question of accuracy the reader is referred to the literature, e.g., Ref. 22.

$$\mathbf{z}_{n+1}(s) = \mathbf{z}_0 + \int_0^s \mathbf{A}(\sigma)\mathbf{z}_n(\sigma)\,d\sigma \tag{5-50}$$

The first approximation is obtained by taking the initial vector $\mathbf{z}_0$ as the zeroth approximation:

$$\mathbf{z}_1(s) = \mathbf{z}_0 + \int_0^s \mathbf{A}(\sigma)\mathbf{z}_0\,d\sigma = \left[\mathbf{I} + \int_0^s \mathbf{A}(\sigma)\,d\sigma\right]\mathbf{z}_0 \tag{5-51}$$

Hence, according to Eq. (5-50),

$$\begin{aligned}\mathbf{z}_2(s) &= \mathbf{z}_0 + \int_0^s \mathbf{A}(\sigma)\mathbf{z}_1(\sigma)\,d\sigma \\ &= \left\{\mathbf{I} + \int_0^s \mathbf{A}(\sigma)\,d\sigma + \int_0^s \mathbf{A}(\sigma_1)\left[\int_0^{\sigma_1} \mathbf{A}(\sigma)\,d\sigma\right]d\sigma_1\right\}\mathbf{z}_0\end{aligned}$$

and generally with $n \to \infty$

$$\begin{aligned}\mathbf{z}(s) = \Bigg(\mathbf{I} &+ \int_0^s \mathbf{A}(\sigma)\,d\sigma + \int_0^s \mathbf{A}(\sigma_1)\left[\int_0^{\sigma_1} \mathbf{A}(\sigma)\,d\sigma\right]d\sigma_1 \\ &+ \int_0^s \mathbf{A}(\sigma_2)\left\{\int_0^{\sigma_2} \mathbf{A}(\sigma_1)\left[\int_0^{\sigma_1} \mathbf{A}(\sigma)\,d\sigma\right]d\sigma_1\right\}d\sigma_2 + \cdots\Bigg)\mathbf{z}_0\end{aligned} \tag{5-52}$$

It is immediately apparent that the infinite series within the outer parentheses represents the transfer matrix $\mathbf{U}(s)$,† which can also be written as follows:

$$\mathbf{U}(s) = \mathbf{I} + \mathbf{A}^{(1)} + \mathbf{A}^{(2)} + \mathbf{A}^{(3)} + \cdots \tag{5-53}$$

in which the iterated matrices $\mathbf{A}^{(n)}$ are found according to the following rule:

$$\begin{aligned}\mathbf{A}^{(1)}(s) &= \int_0^s \mathbf{A}(\sigma)\,d\sigma \quad \to \mathbf{B}^{(1)}(s) = \mathbf{A}(s)\mathbf{A}^{(1)}(s) \\ \mathbf{A}^{(2)}(s) &= \int_0^s \mathbf{B}^{(1)}(\sigma)\,d\sigma \to \mathbf{B}^{(2)}(s) = \mathbf{A}(s)\mathbf{A}^{(2)}(s) \\ \mathbf{A}^{(3)}(s) &= \int_0^s \mathbf{B}^{(2)}(\sigma)\,d\sigma \to \mathbf{B}^{(3)}(s) = \mathbf{A}(s)\mathbf{A}^{(3)}(s)\end{aligned} \tag{5-54}$$

and so on.

If $\mathbf{A} = \text{const}$, we recognize easily that the series (5-53) becomes the exponential series

$$\mathbf{U}(s) = \mathbf{I} + \mathbf{A}s + \frac{(\mathbf{A}s)^2}{2!} + \frac{(\mathbf{A}s)^3}{3!} + \cdots = e^{\mathbf{A}s}$$

This result has already been obtained in Sec. 1-5.

By differentiating Eq. (5-52) with respect to s, we see that

$$\begin{aligned}\frac{d\mathbf{z}}{ds} &= \left\{\mathbf{A}(s) + \mathbf{A}(s)\int_0^s \mathbf{A}(\sigma)\,d\sigma + \mathbf{A}(s)\int_0^s \mathbf{A}(\sigma_1)\left[\int_0^{\sigma_1} \mathbf{A}(\sigma)\,d\sigma\right]d\sigma_1 + \cdots\right\}\mathbf{z}_0 \\ &= \mathbf{A}(s)\left\{\mathbf{I} + \int_0^s \mathbf{A}(\sigma)\,d\sigma + \int_0^s \mathbf{A}(\sigma_1)\left[\int_0^{\sigma_1} \mathbf{A}(\sigma)\,d\sigma\right]d\sigma_1 + \cdots\right\}\mathbf{z}_0\end{aligned} \tag{5-55}$$

Substituting Eqs. (5-52) and (5-55) in Eq. (5-45), we realize that this differential matrix equation is satisfied.

† This expression is called the *Matrizant* [3].

It has been proved [3] that the series (5-53) converges uniformly for every matrix **A** if its elements are continuous functions of s, but naturally this method of obtaining the transfer matrix is applicable only if the convergence is rapid, which in general can be achieved by taking small steps, i.e., by making the interval s small. Once the transfer matrix is obtained for the homogeneous problem, the corresponding nonhomogeneous set of differential equations

$$\frac{d\mathbf{z}}{ds} = \mathbf{A}(s)\mathbf{z} + \mathbf{a}(s)$$

is solved in the already well-known manner (cf. Secs. 1-5 and 5-3) by means of the equation

$$\mathbf{z}(s) = \mathbf{U}(s)\mathbf{z}_0 + \mathbf{U}(s)\int_0^s \mathbf{U}^{-1}(\sigma)\mathbf{a}(\sigma)\,d\sigma \tag{5-56}$$

5-5. Derivation of the Transfer Matrix from the Stiffness Matrix

This method is especially useful for the derivation of the transfer matrix of complicated structures, such as grid works, for which it is easy to find the end forces in terms of the end displacements. So far it has been successfully applied to problems in aircraft structures and plate theory (cf. Chap. 11).

It is demonstrated here for the case of the simple straight massless beam of uniform cross section. Inspection of Fig. 5-10 yields the following relations between the deflections and slopes of the beam at its ends $i - 1$ and i:

$$w_i = w_{i-1} - \psi_{i-1}l_i + w_1 \tag{5-57}$$

$$\psi_i = \psi_{i-1} + \psi_1 \tag{5-58}$$

where w_1 and ψ_1 are the deflection and slope, respectively, at the free end of a clamped beam subjected to end moment M_1 and shear force V_1 (Fig. 5-11). Using the sign convention shown in Fig. 5-11, we have the following relations for the cantilever beam:

$$V_1 = V_0 = \frac{6EJ}{l_i^3}(2w_1 + \psi_1 l_i) \tag{5-59}$$

$$M_0 = \frac{2EJ}{l_i^2}(-3w_1 - \psi_1 l_i) \tag{5-60}$$

$$M_1 = \frac{2EJ}{l_i^2}(3w_1 + 2\psi_1 l_i) \tag{5-61}$$

The expressions for w_1 and ψ_1 from Eqs. (5-57) and (5-58),

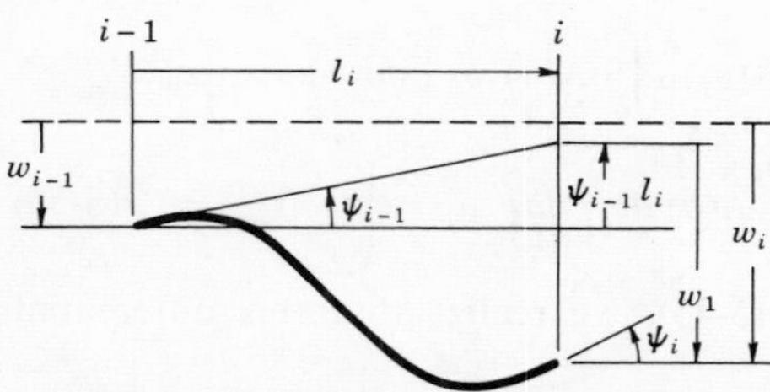

FIG. 5-10. Deflected form of beam.

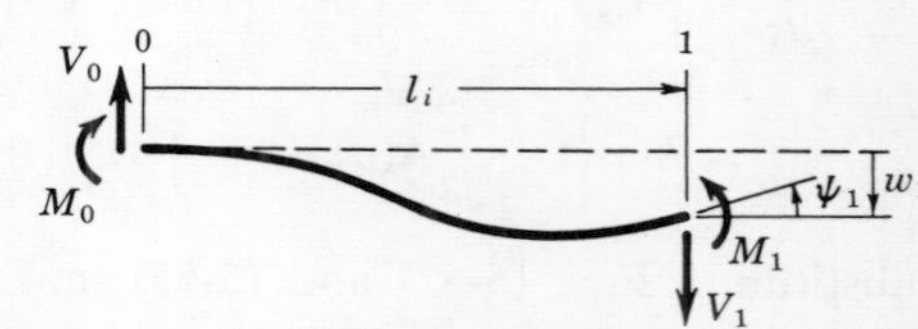

FIG. 5-11. Cantilever subjected to end moment and shear.

$$w_1 = w_i - w_{i-1} + \psi_{i-1} l_i \tag{5-57a}$$

$$\psi_1 = \psi_i - \psi_{i-1} \tag{5-58a}$$

are inserted into Eqs. (5-59) to (5-61), and finally making the substitutions

$$V_1 = V_i \qquad V_0 = V_{i-1} \qquad M_1 = M_i \qquad M_0 = M_{i-1}$$

we obtain the equations

$$V_i = V_{i-1} = \frac{6EJ}{l_i^3}(-2w_{i-1} + \psi_{i-1}l_i + 2w_i + \psi_i l_i) \tag{5-62}$$

$$M_{i-1} = \frac{2EJ}{l_i^2}(3w_{i-1} - 2\psi_{i-1}l_i - 3w_i - \psi_i l_i) \tag{5-63}$$

$$M_i = \frac{2EJ}{l_i^2}(-3w_{i-1} + \psi_{i-1}l_i + 3w_i + 2\psi_i l_i) \tag{5-64}$$

In matrix form these equations are given by the equation

$$\begin{bmatrix} M_{i-1} \\ V_{i-1} \\ M_i \\ V_i \end{bmatrix} = \begin{bmatrix} \frac{6EJ}{l^2} & -\frac{4EJ}{l} & -\frac{6EJ}{l^2} & -\frac{2EJ}{l} \\ -\frac{12EJ}{l^3} & \frac{6EJ}{l^2} & \frac{12EJ}{l^3} & \frac{6EJ}{l^2} \\ -\frac{6EJ}{l^2} & \frac{2EJ}{l} & \frac{6EJ}{l^2} & \frac{4EJ}{l} \\ -\frac{12EJ}{l^3} & \frac{6EJ}{l^2} & \frac{12EJ}{l^3} & \frac{6EJ}{l^2} \end{bmatrix}_i \cdot \begin{bmatrix} w_{i-1} \\ \psi_{i-1} \\ w_i \\ \psi_i \end{bmatrix} \tag{5-65}$$

The square matrix in Eq. (5-65) which relates the forces to the displacements is known as the stiffness matrix.

In order to find the relationship between the state vectors $\mathbf{z}_i$ and $\mathbf{z}_{i-1}$, we partition the column vectors and the square matrix into the form

$$\begin{bmatrix} \mathbf{p}_{i-1} \\ \hline \mathbf{p}_i \end{bmatrix} = \left[\begin{array}{c|c} \mathbf{A} & \mathbf{B} \\ \hline \mathbf{C} & \mathbf{D} \end{array}\right]_i \cdot \begin{bmatrix} \mathbf{d}_{i-1} \\ \hline \mathbf{d}_i \end{bmatrix} \tag{5-66}$$

where

$$\begin{bmatrix} \frac{6EJ}{l^2} & \frac{-4EJ}{l} \\ \frac{-12EJ}{l^3} & \frac{6EJ}{l^2} \end{bmatrix}_i = \mathbf{A}_i \qquad \begin{bmatrix} \frac{-6EJ}{l^2} & \frac{-2EJ}{l} \\ \frac{12EJ}{l^3} & \frac{6EJ}{l^2} \end{bmatrix}_i = \mathbf{B}_i$$

$$\begin{bmatrix} \frac{-6EJ}{l^2} & \frac{2EJ}{l} \\ \frac{-12EJ}{l^3} & \frac{6EJ}{l^2} \end{bmatrix}_i = \mathbf{C}_i \qquad \begin{bmatrix} \frac{6EJ}{l^2} & \frac{4EJ}{l} \\ \frac{12EJ}{l^3} & \frac{6EJ}{l^2} \end{bmatrix}_i = \mathbf{D}_i$$

and

$$\mathbf{p}_{i-1} = \{M_{i-1} \quad V_{i-1}\} \qquad \mathbf{p}_i = \{M_i \quad V_i\}$$

$$\mathbf{d}_{i-1} = \{w_{i-1} \quad \psi_{i-1}\} \qquad \mathbf{d}_i = \{w_i \quad \psi_i\}$$

Expanding Eq. (5-66) yields

$$\mathbf{p}_{i-1} = \mathbf{A}_i\mathbf{d}_{i-1} + \mathbf{B}_i\mathbf{d}_i \qquad \text{and} \qquad \mathbf{p}_i = \mathbf{C}_i\mathbf{d}_{i-1} + \mathbf{D}_i\mathbf{d}_i$$

Solving for $\mathbf{d}_i$ from the first of these equations, we obtain

$$\mathbf{d}_i = -\mathbf{B}_i^{-1}\mathbf{A}_i\mathbf{d}_{i-1} + \mathbf{B}_i^{-1}\mathbf{p}_{i-1} \tag{5-67}$$

This expression is substituted in the second equation to give

$$\mathbf{p}_i = (\mathbf{C} - \mathbf{D}\mathbf{B}^{-1}\mathbf{A})_i\mathbf{d}_{i-1} + \mathbf{D}_i\mathbf{B}_i^{-1}\mathbf{p}_{i-1} \tag{5-68}$$

Equations (5-67) and (5-68) are combined into a single equation to give

$$\begin{bmatrix} \mathbf{d} \\ \hline \mathbf{p} \end{bmatrix}_i = \left[\begin{array}{c|c} -\mathbf{B}^{-1}\mathbf{A} & \mathbf{B}^{-1} \\ \hline \mathbf{C} - \mathbf{D}\mathbf{B}^{-1}\mathbf{A} & \mathbf{D}\mathbf{B}^{-1} \end{array}\right]_i \cdot \begin{bmatrix} \mathbf{d} \\ \hline \mathbf{p} \end{bmatrix}_{i-1} \tag{5-69}$$

which is the relation defining the transfer matrix. The inversion of $\mathbf{B}$ in this illustrative example is easily found to be [cf. Eqs. (1-27)]

$$\mathbf{B}^{-1} = \begin{bmatrix} -\dfrac{l^2}{2EJ} & -\dfrac{l^3}{6EJ} \\ \dfrac{l}{EJ} & \dfrac{l^2}{2EJ} \end{bmatrix}$$

The evaluation of Eq. (5-69) yields the already well-known transfer-matrix relation for a massless straight uniform beam:

$$\begin{bmatrix} w \\ \psi \\ M \\ V \end{bmatrix}_i = \begin{bmatrix} 1 & -l & -\dfrac{l^2}{2EJ} & -\dfrac{l^3}{6EJ} \\ 0 & 1 & \dfrac{l}{EJ} & \dfrac{l^2}{2EJ} \\ 0 & 0 & 1 & l \\ 0 & 0 & 0 & 1 \end{bmatrix}_i \cdot \begin{bmatrix} w \\ \psi \\ M \\ V \end{bmatrix}_{i-1} \tag{5-70}$$

The minus signs in the transfer matrix disappear if w is replaced by $-w$ (cf. first footnote on page 57).

The concept used here for the derivation of the transfer matrix can, of course, also be used for structures with distributed mass, the static stiffness matrix [Eq. (5-65)] being replaced by a dynamic stiffness matrix. The idea of the procedure demonstrated in this section is extensively used in the following chapter in order to take into account elastic branches and coupling ties.

A General Relationship for Transfer Matrices. If Eq. (5-65) is rewritten so that the components of the displacement vector are arranged in a sequence following that of the associated force vector, that is,

$$\mathbf{d} = \{\mathbf{d}_{i-1} \quad \mathbf{d}_i\} = \{\psi_{i-1} \quad w_{i-1} \quad \psi_i \quad w_i\}$$

for

$$\mathbf{p} = \{\mathbf{p}_{i-1} \quad \mathbf{p}_i\} = \{M_{i-1} \quad V_{i-1} \quad M_i \quad V_i\} \tag{5-71}$$

then the stiffness-matrix relation of Eq. (5-65) would assume the following form,†

† Complete symmetry would be brought about if the forces on the negative face (station $i - 1$) were also taken to be positive in the positive directions of the displacements (cf. Sec. 9-1).

which holds quite generally on account of the Betti-Maxwell theorem,

$$\begin{bmatrix} \mathbf{p}_{i-1} \\ \hdashline \mathbf{p}_i \end{bmatrix} = \begin{bmatrix} \mathbf{Q} & \mathbf{R} \\ \hdashline -\mathbf{R}' & \mathbf{S} \end{bmatrix}_i \cdot \begin{bmatrix} \mathbf{d}_{i-1} \\ \hdashline \mathbf{d}_i \end{bmatrix} \tag{5-72}$$

Proceeding as shown in Eqs. (5-67) and (5-68), we obtain the transfer-matrix relation

$$\begin{bmatrix} \mathbf{d} \\ \hdashline \mathbf{p} \end{bmatrix}_i = \begin{bmatrix} \mathbf{U}_1 & \mathbf{U}_2 \\ \hdashline \mathbf{U}_3 & \mathbf{U}_4 \end{bmatrix}_i \cdot \begin{bmatrix} \mathbf{d} \\ \hdashline \mathbf{p} \end{bmatrix}_{i-1}$$

where

$$\mathbf{U}_1 = -\mathbf{R}^{-1}\mathbf{Q} \qquad \mathbf{U}_2 = \mathbf{R}^{-1}$$
$$\mathbf{U}_3 = -\mathbf{R}' - \mathbf{S}\mathbf{R}^{-1}\mathbf{Q} \qquad \mathbf{U}_4 = \mathbf{S}\mathbf{R}^{-1}$$

Hence we deduce the general relationship for transfer matrices:

$$\mathbf{U}_1'\mathbf{U}_4 - \mathbf{U}_3'\mathbf{U}_2 = \mathbf{I} \tag{5-73}$$

Equation (5-73) provides a valuable check on the correct derivation of a transfer matrix. For its application, however, it is, in view of Eq. (5-71), necessary to reverse the sequence of the columns in the left half of our normal transfer matrices as well as the sequence of the rows in their upper half. Besides, all components in the state vector must have the positive sign.

Rectangular† *Transfer Matrix.* Occasionally it occurs that the number n of state vector components at station i is less than the corresponding number m at station $i - 1$. Nevertheless we can establish the stiffness matrix [cf. Eq. (5-72)]

$$\begin{matrix} m/2 \\ n/2 \end{matrix}\begin{bmatrix} \mathbf{p}_{i-1} \\ \hdashline \mathbf{p}_i \end{bmatrix} = \begin{matrix} m/2 \\ n/2 \end{matrix}\overset{\quad m/2 \qquad\quad n/2}{\begin{bmatrix} \mathbf{Q} & \mathbf{R} \\ \hdashline -\mathbf{R}' & \mathbf{S} \end{bmatrix}_i} \cdot \begin{matrix} m/2 \\ n/2 \end{matrix}\begin{bmatrix} \mathbf{d}_{i-1} \\ \hdashline \mathbf{d}_i \end{bmatrix} \tag{5-74}$$

Now **R** is no longer a square submatrix as in Eq. (5-72). However, with the concept of the "left inverse"‡ of a rectangular matrix, defined by

$$\mathbf{R}^{-L} = (\mathbf{R}'\mathbf{R})^{-1}\mathbf{R}' \tag{5-75}$$

so that

$$\mathbf{R}^{-L}\mathbf{R} = \mathbf{I}$$

we can, by means of the same technique as shown in Eqs. (5-67) and (5-68), derive the rectangular transfer-matrix relation

$$\begin{matrix} n/2 \\ n/2 \end{matrix}\begin{bmatrix} \mathbf{d} \\ \hdashline \mathbf{p} \end{bmatrix}_i = \begin{matrix} n/2 \\ n/2 \end{matrix}\overset{\quad m/2 \qquad m/2}{\begin{bmatrix} \mathbf{U}_1 & \mathbf{U}_2 \\ \hdashline \mathbf{U}_3 & \mathbf{U}_4 \end{bmatrix}_i} \cdot \begin{matrix} m/2 \\ m/2 \end{matrix}\begin{bmatrix} \mathbf{d} \\ \hdashline \mathbf{p} \end{bmatrix}_{i-1} \tag{5-76}$$

where

$$\begin{aligned} \mathbf{U}_1 &= -\mathbf{R}^{-L}\mathbf{Q} \qquad & \mathbf{U}_2 &= \mathbf{R}^{-L} \\ \mathbf{U}_3 &= -\mathbf{R}' - \mathbf{S}\mathbf{R}^{-L}\mathbf{Q} \qquad & \mathbf{U}_4 &= \mathbf{S}\mathbf{R}^{-L} \end{aligned} \tag{5-77}$$

Discussion of the Application of the Rectangular Transfer Matrix [66]. Let us

† To our knowledge this concept was first introduced by S. Rubin in a general investigation of the relation between transfer and admittance (impedance) matrices [65].

‡ It is necessary that **R** be a matrix of rank $n/2$. Furthermore $n < m$; otherwise only the "right inverse" is possible.

consider a problem where we start out with an initial state vector $\mathbf{z}_0$ consisting of $m/2$ unknown components. Proceeding then in normal fashion, we express the state vectors $\mathbf{z}_i$ in terms of the initial state vector $\mathbf{z}_0$. At the right-hand boundary there usually exist $m/2$ boundary conditions by which we can determine the m components of $\mathbf{z}_0$. If, however, from station i on, the state vectors contain only n components ($n < m$) and if, therefore, we have only $n/2$ right-hand boundary conditions, we are short of $(m - n)/2$ equations to determine the $m/2$ components of the initial state vector $\mathbf{z}_0$. Obviously we must have lost information while we went from station $i - 1$ to station i by means of an (n, m) rectangular transfer matrix because comparison of the stiffness-matrix relation [Eq. (5-74)] with the corresponding transfer-matrix relation [Eq. (5-76)] shows that the latter represents $(m - n)/2$ equations less than Eq. (5-74). How do we recover these "lost" equations?

In the following scheme we depict the transfer-matrix procedure leading to the state vectors at stations $i - 1$ and i:

$$\begin{bmatrix} \mathbf{P}_1 \\ \hdashline \mathbf{P}_2 \end{bmatrix} \cdot \begin{bmatrix} \mathbf{z} \end{bmatrix}_0 = \begin{bmatrix} \mathbf{d} \\ \hdashline \mathbf{p} \end{bmatrix}_{i-1}$$

(row blocks $m/2$, $m/2$; column block $m/2$)

$$\begin{bmatrix} \mathbf{U}_1 & \mathbf{U}_2 \\ \mathbf{U}_3 & \mathbf{U}_4 \end{bmatrix}_i \begin{bmatrix} \mathbf{V}_1 \\ \hdashline \mathbf{V}_2 \end{bmatrix} \cdot \begin{bmatrix} \mathbf{z} \end{bmatrix}_0 = \begin{bmatrix} \mathbf{d} \\ \hdashline \mathbf{p} \end{bmatrix}_i$$

(row blocks $n/2$, $n/2$; column blocks $m/2$, $m/2$)

We can now express $\mathbf{p}_{i-1}$ in two ways. From the transfer-matrix scheme above we have

$$\mathbf{p}_{i-1} = \mathbf{P}_2\mathbf{z}_0 \tag{5-78}$$

By means of the stiffness-matrix relation [Eq. (5-74)] we obtain

$$\mathbf{p}_{i-1} = \mathbf{Q}\mathbf{d}_{i-1} + \mathbf{R}\mathbf{d}_i$$

or since the scheme above yields

$$\mathbf{d}_{i-1} = \mathbf{P}_1\mathbf{z}_0 \qquad \mathbf{d}_i = \mathbf{V}_1\mathbf{z}_0$$

we have

$$\mathbf{p}_{i-1} = (\mathbf{Q}\mathbf{P}_1 + \mathbf{R}\mathbf{V}_1)\mathbf{z}_0 \tag{5-79}$$

Hence, from Eqs. (5-78) and (5-79) we find the $m/2$ equations

$$(\mathbf{Q}\mathbf{P}_1 + \mathbf{R}\mathbf{V}_1 - \mathbf{P}_2)\mathbf{z}_0 = \mathbf{0} \tag{5-80}$$

It can be shown† that among these $m/2$ homogeneous equations there are $(m - n)/2$ linearly independent equations which constitute the "lost" information.

† Expansion of Eq. (5-80) using the above transfer-matrix scheme and Eqs. (5-77) leads to the $m/2$ equations

$$(\mathbf{I} - \mathbf{R}\mathbf{R}^{-L})(\mathbf{Q}\mathbf{P}_1 - \mathbf{P}_2)\mathbf{z}_0 = \mathbf{0}$$

Since $\mathbf{R}\mathbf{R}^{-L}$ is at most of rank $n/2$, the difference $\mathbf{I} - \mathbf{R}\mathbf{R}^{-L}$ is of rank $\geq (m - n)/2$. At the same time

$$\mathbf{R}'(\mathbf{I} - \mathbf{R}\mathbf{R}^{-L}) = \mathbf{R}' - \mathbf{R}'\mathbf{R}(\mathbf{R}'\mathbf{R})^{-1}\mathbf{R}' = \mathbf{0}$$

Since $\mathbf{R}'$ is of rank $n/2$, the difference $\mathbf{I} - \mathbf{R}\mathbf{R}^{-L}$ must be of rank $\leq (m - n)/2$. Hence $\mathbf{I} - \mathbf{R}\mathbf{R}^{-L}$ is exactly of rank $(m - n)/2$.

6 INTERMEDIATE CONDITIONS

6-1. Elastic Intermediate Conditions and Branched Systems

Elementary Procedure. In Chap. 3 we have already dealt with a beam supported on a spring at an intermediate point [Eq. (3-12)], and we learned that its effect could be introduced into the calculation by means of a simple point matrix. In this section we shall consider more complicated elastic supports and branched systems.

Suppose, for example, we intend to compute the natural frequencies and normal modes of the frame shown in Fig. 6-1 which is vibrating in its plane. Therefore we include the two axial components u and N in addition to the four bending components w, ψ, M, and V, so that the state vector consists of the six vector components u, $-w$, ψ, M, V, N (Fig. 6-2). The (6, 6) transfer matrices for this frame are composed from those in Secs. C-1 and C-3. Regarding $ABDE$ as the main member of the structure, we can proceed from A to E in the usual manner provided we know the point matrix that is to be used at point B. To facilitate this problem it is assumed at present that member BC is without mass, although when the general theory is developed, the introduction of mass causes no difficulty.

Let us assume that, starting from A, we have found the state vector $\mathbf{z}_B^L$ and now wish to compute $\mathbf{z}_B^R$. Whereas the deflections and slope (u, $-w$, ψ) are continuous,

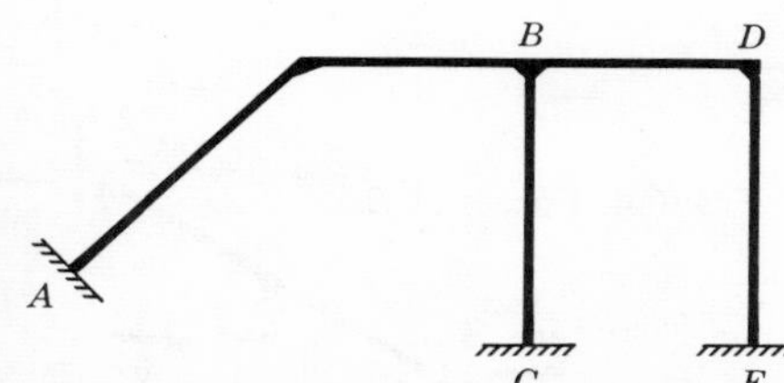

FIG. 6-1. Frame vibrating in its plane.

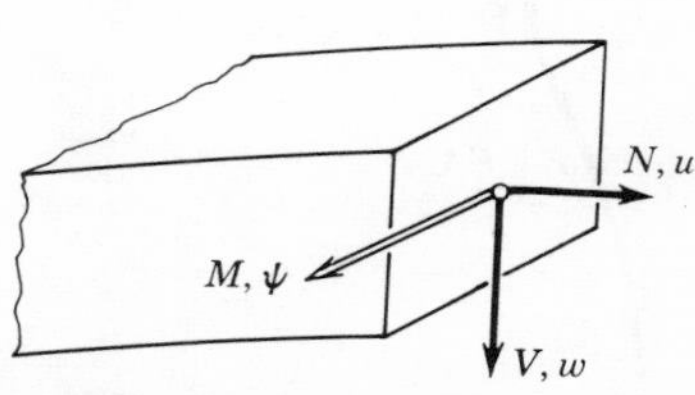

FIG. 6-2. State vector components.

there will be discontinuities in M, V, and N on account of member BC. From simple strength of materials we have the relations for a built-in beam (Fig. 6-3):

$$\hat{M}_B = \frac{6EJ}{l^2}\, u_B + \frac{4EJ}{l}\, \psi_B$$

$$\hat{V}_B = \frac{12EJ}{l^3}\, u_B + \frac{6EJ}{l^2}\, \psi_B$$

$$\hat{N}_B = -\frac{EA}{l}\, w_B$$

Also from equilibrium considerations at the joint (Fig. 6-4)

$$V^R = V^L - \hat{N}_B = V^L + EA\frac{w_B}{l}$$

$$M^R = M^L + \hat{M}_B = M^L + \frac{6EJ}{l^2}\, u_B + \frac{4EJ}{l}\, \psi_B$$

$$N^R = N^L + \hat{V}_B = N^L + \frac{12EJ}{l^3}\, u_B + \frac{6EJ}{l^2}\, \psi_B$$

so that we have been able to express V^R, M^R, and N^R in terms of the vector components of the state vector at the left of B and the elastic properties of member BC. In matrix notation the above relations yield the following point matrix:

$$\mathbf{z}_B^R = \begin{bmatrix} u \\ -w \\ \psi \\ \hdashline M \\ V \\ N \end{bmatrix}_B^R = \left[\begin{array}{ccc:ccc} 1 & 0 & 0 & 0 & 0 & 0 \\ 0 & 1 & 0 & 0 & 0 & 0 \\ 0 & 0 & 1 & 0 & 0 & 0 \\ \hdashline \dfrac{6EJ}{l^2} & 0 & \dfrac{4EJ}{l} & 1 & 0 & 0 \\ 0 & \dfrac{-EA}{l} & 0 & 0 & 1 & 0 \\ \dfrac{12EJ}{l^3} & 0 & \dfrac{6EJ}{l^2} & 0 & 0 & 1 \end{array}\right] \cdot \begin{bmatrix} u \\ -w \\ \psi \\ \hdashline M \\ V \\ N \end{bmatrix}_B^L \tag{6-1}$$

$$\mathbf{z}_B^R = \mathbf{P}_B \mathbf{z}_B^L$$

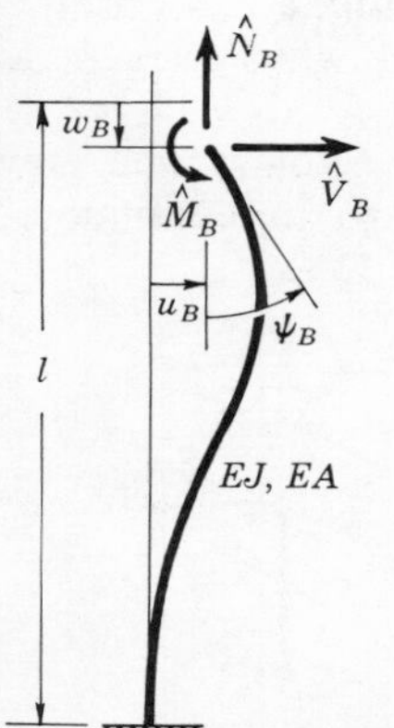

FIG. 6-3. Forces and displacements for branch BC.

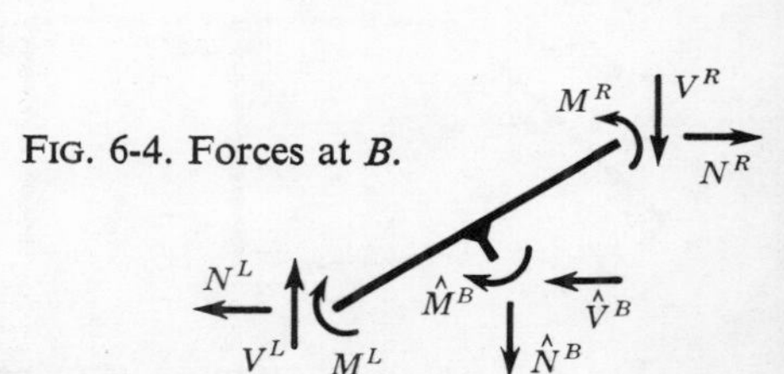

FIG. 6-4. Forces at B.

The matrix can be partitioned into four submatrices, of which the top left and lower right are unit matrices, the top right is a null matrix, and the bottom left contains terms derived from the elastic and geometric properties of member BC. This final submatrix is known as the *spring matrix*, and it contains the terms that, when multiplied by the deflections, give the discontinuities in the forces M, V, and N.

Matrix Procedure. We shall now illustrate how the same spring matrix may be found by adopting a matrix procedure. In view of the boundary conditions at C the state vector at end B of branch BC is given by the matrix relation† (cf. matrices C-1c and C-3c)

$$\begin{bmatrix} \hat{u} \\ -\hat{w} \\ \hat{\psi} \\ \hdashline \hat{M} \\ \hat{V} \\ \hat{N} \end{bmatrix}_B = \begin{bmatrix} 0 & 0 & \dfrac{l}{EA} \\ \dfrac{l^2}{2EJ} & \dfrac{l^3}{6EJ} & 0 \\ \dfrac{l}{EJ} & \dfrac{l^2}{2EJ} & 0 \\ \hdashline 1 & l & 0 \\ 0 & 1 & 0 \\ 0 & 0 & 1 \end{bmatrix} \cdot \begin{bmatrix} \hat{M} \\ \hat{V} \\ \hat{N} \end{bmatrix}_C$$

The transfer matrix is partitioned into two square submatrices by the dashed line, so that

$$\begin{bmatrix} \hat{u} \\ -\hat{w} \\ \hat{\psi} \end{bmatrix}_B = \begin{bmatrix} 0 & 0 & \dfrac{l}{EA} \\ \dfrac{l^2}{2EJ} & \dfrac{l^3}{6EJ} & 0 \\ \dfrac{l}{EJ} & \dfrac{l^2}{2EJ} & 0 \end{bmatrix} \cdot \begin{bmatrix} \hat{M} \\ \hat{V} \\ \hat{N} \end{bmatrix}_C = \mathbf{R}_1 \begin{bmatrix} \hat{M} \\ \hat{V} \\ \hat{N} \end{bmatrix}_C \tag{6-2a}$$

and

$$\begin{bmatrix} \hat{M} \\ \hat{V} \\ \hat{B} \end{bmatrix}_B = \begin{bmatrix} 1 & l & 0 \\ 0 & 1 & 0 \\ 0 & 0 & 1 \end{bmatrix} \cdot \begin{bmatrix} \hat{M} \\ \hat{V} \\ \hat{N} \end{bmatrix}_C = \mathbf{R}_2 \begin{bmatrix} \hat{M} \\ \hat{V} \\ \hat{N} \end{bmatrix}_C \tag{6-2b}$$

† The symbol ^ refers to the fact that the vector components are expressed in terms of the coordinates of branch BC (cf. Fig. 6-5).

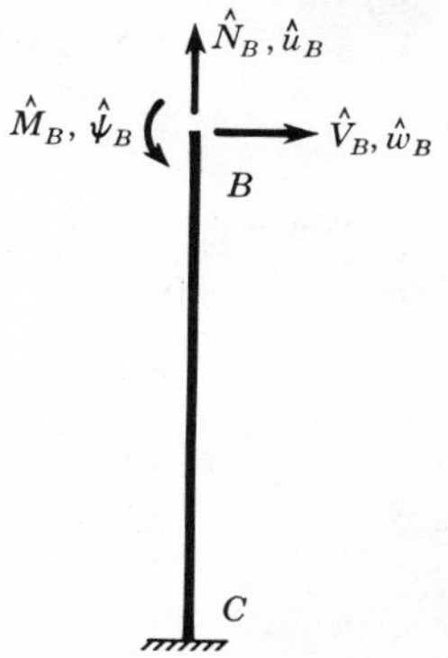

FIG. 6-5. State vector components at point B of branch.

The forces at B can be found in terms of the deflections at B by eliminating the vector $\{\hat{M} \quad \hat{V} \quad \hat{N}\}_C$. From Eq. (6-2*a*)

$$\begin{bmatrix} \hat{M} \\ \hat{V} \\ \hat{N} \end{bmatrix}_C = \mathbf{R}_1^{-1} \begin{bmatrix} \hat{u} \\ -\hat{w} \\ \hat{\psi} \end{bmatrix}_B$$

and substituting this result in Eq. (6-2*b*) we obtain

$$\begin{bmatrix} \hat{M} \\ \hat{V} \\ \hat{N} \end{bmatrix}_B = \mathbf{R}_2 \begin{bmatrix} \hat{M} \\ \hat{V} \\ \hat{N} \end{bmatrix}_C = \mathbf{R}_2\mathbf{R}_1^{-1} \begin{bmatrix} \hat{u} \\ -\hat{w} \\ \hat{\psi} \end{bmatrix}_B \tag{6-3}$$

Now,

$$\mathbf{R}_1^{-1} = \begin{bmatrix} 0 & \dfrac{6EJ}{l^2} & -\dfrac{2EJ}{l} \\ 0 & -\dfrac{12EJ}{l^3} & \dfrac{6EJ}{l^2} \\ \dfrac{EA}{l} & 0 & 0 \end{bmatrix} \quad \text{and} \quad \mathbf{R}_2\mathbf{R}_1^{-1} = \begin{bmatrix} 0 & -\dfrac{6EJ}{l^2} & \dfrac{4EJ}{l} \\ 0 & -\dfrac{12EJ}{l^3} & \dfrac{6EJ}{l^2} \\ \dfrac{EA}{l} & 0 & 0 \end{bmatrix}$$

so that Eq. (6-3) becomes

$$\begin{bmatrix} \hat{M} \\ \hat{V} \\ \hat{N} \end{bmatrix}_B = \begin{bmatrix} 0 & -\dfrac{6EJ}{l^2} & \dfrac{4EJ}{l} \\ 0 & -\dfrac{12EJ}{l^3} & \dfrac{6EJ}{l^2} \\ \dfrac{EA}{l} & 0 & 0 \end{bmatrix} \cdot \begin{bmatrix} \hat{u} \\ -\hat{w} \\ \hat{\psi} \end{bmatrix}_B \tag{6-4}$$

Equation (6-4) relates the forces and the displacements at end B of branch BC. As a final operation we must transform the above vector components so that they are consistent with those of the main member.

The relations between the displacement components are, by inspection of Fig. 6-6, seen to be

$$u = \hat{w} \qquad w = -\hat{u} \qquad \psi = \hat{\psi}$$

or

$$\begin{bmatrix} \hat{u} \\ -\hat{w} \\ \hat{\psi} \end{bmatrix}_B = \begin{bmatrix} 0 & 1 & 0 \\ -1 & 0 & 0 \\ 0 & 0 & 1 \end{bmatrix} \cdot \begin{bmatrix} u \\ -w \\ \psi \end{bmatrix}_B \tag{6-5}$$

The force vector $\{\hat{M} \quad \hat{V} \quad \hat{N}\}_B$ is related to the positive forces of the main member by the following equations (cf. Fig. 6-6):

$$\hat{V} = N \qquad \hat{M} = M \qquad \hat{N} = -V$$

or

$$\begin{bmatrix} M \\ V \\ N \end{bmatrix}_B = \begin{bmatrix} 1 & 0 & 0 \\ 0 & 0 & -1 \\ 0 & 1 & 0 \end{bmatrix} \cdot \begin{bmatrix} \hat{M} \\ \hat{V} \\ \hat{N} \end{bmatrix}_B \tag{6-6}$$

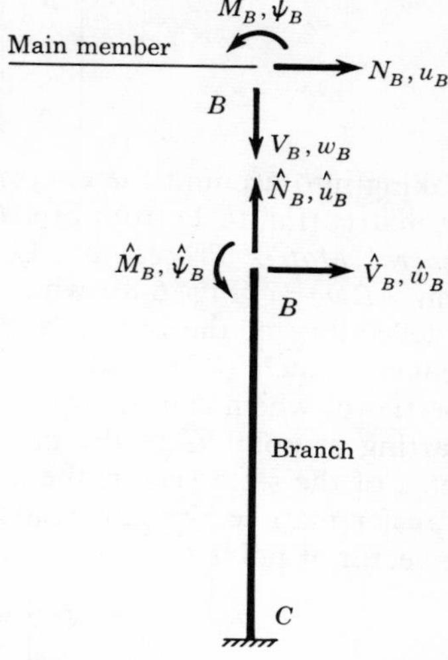

FIG. 6-6. State vector transformation.

Therefore Eq. (6-4) becomes, in terms of the coordinates of the main system,

$$\begin{bmatrix} M \\ V \\ N \end{bmatrix}_B = \begin{bmatrix} 1 & 0 & 0 \\ 0 & 0 & -1 \\ 0 & 1 & 0 \end{bmatrix} \cdot \begin{bmatrix} 0 & -\dfrac{6EJ}{l^2} & \dfrac{4EJ}{l} \\ 0 & -\dfrac{12EJ}{l^3} & \dfrac{6EJ}{l^2} \\ \dfrac{EA}{l} & 0 & 0 \end{bmatrix} \cdot \begin{bmatrix} 0 & 1 & 0 \\ -1 & 0 & 0 \\ 0 & 0 & 1 \end{bmatrix} \cdot \begin{bmatrix} u \\ -w \\ \psi \end{bmatrix}_B$$

so that

$$\begin{bmatrix} M \\ V \\ N \end{bmatrix}_B = \begin{bmatrix} \dfrac{6EJ}{l^2} & 0 & \dfrac{4EJ}{l} \\ 0 & -\dfrac{EA}{l} & 0 \\ \dfrac{12EJ}{l^3} & 0 & \dfrac{6EJ}{l^2} \end{bmatrix} \cdot \begin{bmatrix} u \\ -w \\ \psi \end{bmatrix}_B \tag{6-7}$$

The square matrix of Eq. (6-7) is identical with the spring matrix, which appears as a submatrix in Eq. (6-1). With reference to Fig. 6-7 we have the equilibrium relation

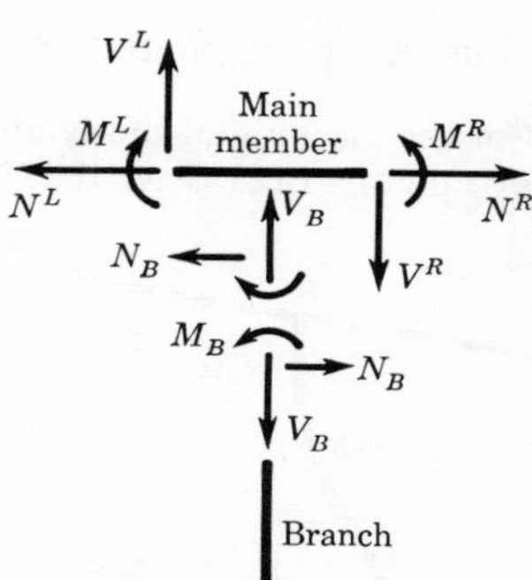

FIG. 6-7. Forces at point B.

$$\begin{bmatrix} M \\ V \\ N \end{bmatrix}_B^R = \begin{bmatrix} M \\ V \\ N \end{bmatrix}_B^L + \begin{bmatrix} M \\ V \\ N \end{bmatrix}_B \tag{6-8}$$

On taking into account the continuity of the displacements, the construction of the point matrix [Eq. (6-1) from Eqs. (6-7) and (6-8)] is obvious.

General Matrix Procedure. Let us suppose we are dealing with the nth-order system $ABD \cdots$ (Fig. 6-8), which has a branch CB joining the main system at B. The deflections of the branch and the main system are identical at B. The aim is to reduce branch BC (which may have mass) to an equivalent elastic support, the properties of which can be expressed by means of a spring matrix [23].

Starting at point C of the branch, there are $n/2$ unknown and $n/2$ known components of the state vector, the latter generally being equal to zero. With the help of transfer matrices we can relate the state vector at point B of the branch to the state vector at point C:

$$\begin{bmatrix} \hat{\mathbf{d}} \\ \hat{\mathbf{p}} \end{bmatrix}_B = \begin{bmatrix} \mathbf{R}_1 \\ \mathbf{R}_2 \end{bmatrix} \cdot \begin{bmatrix} \hat{\mathbf{v}} \end{bmatrix}_C \tag{6-9}\dagger$$

(dimensions: $\hat{\mathbf{d}}$, $\hat{\mathbf{p}}$: $n/2 \times 1$; $\mathbf{R}_1$, $\mathbf{R}_2$: $n/2 \times n/2$; $\hat{\mathbf{v}}$: $n/2 \times 1$)

where the state vector $\hat{\mathbf{z}}_B$ is partitioned in such a way that $\hat{\mathbf{d}}_B$ denotes the deflections and $\hat{\mathbf{p}}_B$ denotes the corresponding forces at B. $\hat{\mathbf{v}}$ is the column vector consisting of the $n/2$ unknown components of the state vector at point C. The matrices $\mathbf{R}_1$ and $\mathbf{R}_2$ are square matrices of order $n/2$. Equation (6-9) can be expanded to give the following two matrix equations:

$$\hat{\mathbf{d}}_B = \mathbf{R}_1\hat{\mathbf{v}}_C \tag{6-10a}$$

$$\hat{\mathbf{p}}_B = \mathbf{R}_2\hat{\mathbf{v}}_C \tag{6-10b}$$

From Eq. (6-10a) we have $\mathbf{R}_1^{-1}\hat{\mathbf{d}}_B = \hat{\mathbf{v}}_C$, and substituting this in Eq. (6-10b) gives

$$\hat{\mathbf{p}}_B = \mathbf{R}_2\mathbf{R}_1^{-1}\hat{\mathbf{d}}_B$$

In order to find the spring matrix $\mathbf{S}_B$ we must now transform the components of $\hat{\mathbf{d}}_B$ and $\hat{\mathbf{p}}_B$ into those of the main system. We have seen above that these transformations can be performed by means of the matrix operations‡

$$\hat{\mathbf{d}}_B = \mathbf{G}_1\mathbf{d}_B \tag{6-11}$$

and

$$\mathbf{p}_B = \mathbf{G}_2\hat{\mathbf{p}}_B \tag{6-12}$$

Then

$$\mathbf{p}_B = \mathbf{G}_2\hat{\mathbf{p}}_B = \mathbf{G}_2\mathbf{R}_2\mathbf{R}_1^{-1}\mathbf{G}_1\mathbf{d}_B$$

and thus the spring matrix is

† For the meaning of the symbol ^ over the vectors, see the footnote on page 155.

‡ For the matrices **G** see the Catalogue (Sec. C-10).

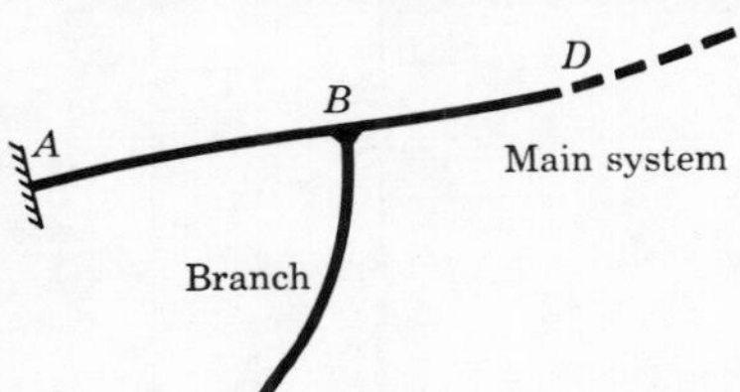

FIG. 6-8. Main system with branch.

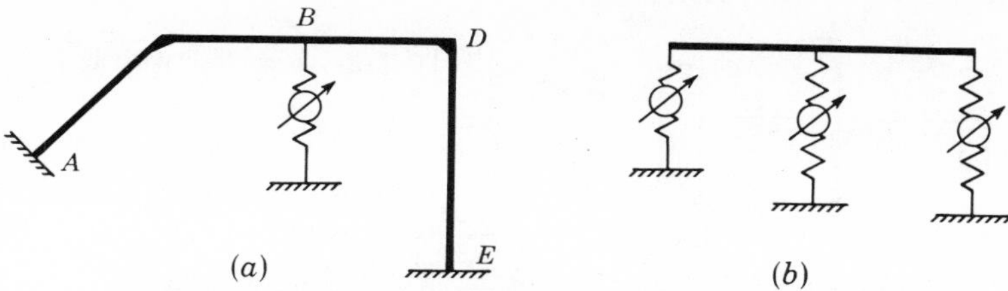

FIG. 6-9. Symbolic representations of structure of Fig. 6-1.

$$\mathbf{S}_B = \mathbf{G}_2\mathbf{R}_2\mathbf{R}_1^{-1}\mathbf{G}_1 \tag{6-13}$$

Hence, by using this method, a branch may be reduced to an equivalent spring with the same elastic and inertia properties. For example, the structure shown in Fig. 6-1 can be reduced to a system that consists of the main part *ABDE* with a "general" spring of known properties attached at point *B*. Therefore the branch *CB* can be represented symbolically as shown in Fig. 6-9*a*.† Of course, the structure of Fig. 6-1 could also be reduced to a straight beam on three general springs (Fig. 6-9*b*). If two or more springs are attached to the same point (Fig. 6-10), their combined effect is found by simply adding the spring matrices.‡ We have the relation for each of the springs:

$$\mathbf{p}_1 = \mathbf{S}_1\mathbf{d} \qquad \mathbf{p}_2 = \mathbf{S}_2\mathbf{d} \qquad \mathbf{p}_j = \mathbf{S}_j\mathbf{d} \qquad \cdots \qquad \mathbf{p}_n = \mathbf{S}_n\mathbf{d}$$

and since the deflection $\mathbf{d}$ is the same for each,

$$\mathbf{p} = \sum_{j=1}^{n} \mathbf{p}_j = \sum_{j=1}^{n} \mathbf{S}_j\mathbf{d} = \left(\sum_{j=1}^{n} \mathbf{S}_j\right)\mathbf{d} = \mathbf{S}\mathbf{d}$$

where

$$\mathbf{S} = \sum_{j=1}^{n} \mathbf{S}_j \tag{6-14}$$

The relation between the state vectors on either side of a point i is then

$$\mathbf{z}_i^R = \mathbf{P}_i\mathbf{z}_i^L$$

where

$$\mathbf{P}_i = \left[\begin{array}{c|c} \mathbf{I} & \mathbf{0} \\ \hline \mathbf{S} & \mathbf{I} \end{array}\right] \tag{6-15}$$

Example 6-1. Compute the natural frequencies of the torsional system shown in Fig. 6-11. Gear wheels 1 and 5 have the same radius.

† The arrow through the spring indicates that the properties of the spring with mass vary with the frequency [23, 24].

‡ Note that for all $\mathbf{p}_j$ the same coordinate system must be used.

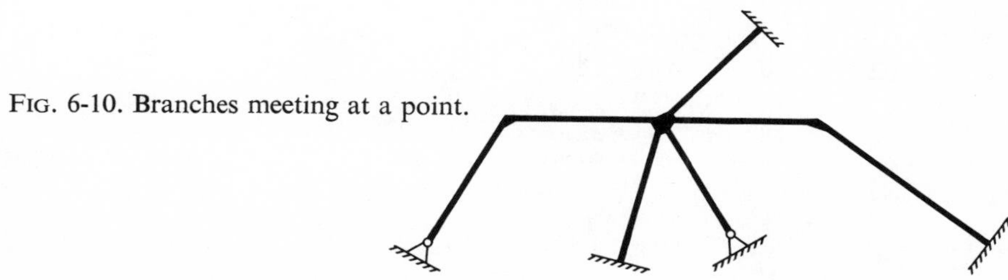

FIG. 6-10. Branches meeting at a point.

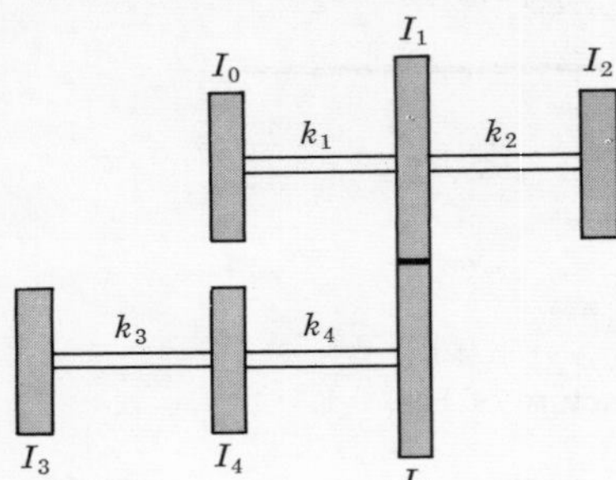

FIG. 6-11. Torsion system with branch.

We choose 012 as the main system, with 345 as the branch. For explanatory purposes it is advantageous to represent the system as shown in Fig. 6-12, where the gears are separated into disks with mass (shaded) and massless gears (blank).

The relation between $\hat{\mathbf{z}}_5^R$ and $\hat{\mathbf{z}}_3^L = \{\hat{\phi} \quad 0\}_3$ has the form

$$\begin{bmatrix} \hat{\phi} \\ \hat{T} \end{bmatrix}_5^R = \begin{bmatrix} \mathbf{R}_1 \\ \mathbf{R}_2 \end{bmatrix} \cdot \begin{bmatrix} \hat{\phi} \end{bmatrix}_3$$

from which we obtain, by elimination of $\hat{\phi}_3$,

$$\hat{T}_5^R = \mathbf{R}_2\mathbf{R}_1^{-1}\hat{\phi}_5$$

Since the gear wheels are of the same size, we have the following relations (Fig. 6-13):

$$\phi_1 = -\hat{\phi}_5 \qquad T_1^R = T_1^M - \hat{T}_5^R$$

Thus

$$T_1^R = T_1^M + \mathbf{R}_2\mathbf{R}_1^{-1}\phi_1$$

and the point matrix is

$$\begin{bmatrix} 1 & 0 \\ \mathbf{R}_2\mathbf{R}_1^{-1} & 1 \end{bmatrix}$$

The numerical calculation is made using the shifted-column technique developed in Sec. 3-4. A typical calculation for $\omega = 50$ radians/sec is shown in Tables 6-1 and 6-2.

The variation of T_2^R with ω is plotted in Fig. 6-14*b*. In the usual way the natural frequencies are found where $T_2^R = 0$. However, an interesting feature of the graph is that it has infinities at $\omega = 239$ and $\omega = 626$. From the plot of ϕ_5 against ω in Fig. 6-14*a* we note that ϕ_5 is zero at these frequencies. Thus the branch has the effect of acting as an infinitely stiff spring at these two frequencies. The change of sign of ϕ_5 also accounts for the sudden change of sign of T_2^R. This feature of branched systems is discussed more fully later under the heading Singularities Occurring in the Spring Matrix.

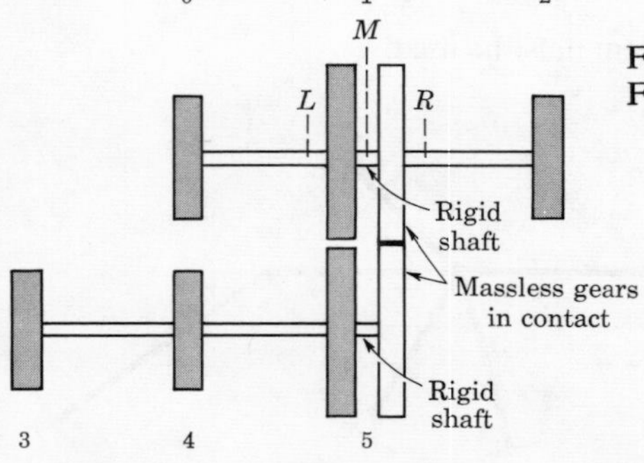

FIG. 6-12. Substitute system replacing that of Fig. 6-11.

FIG. 6-13. Transmission of torque of the branch connection.

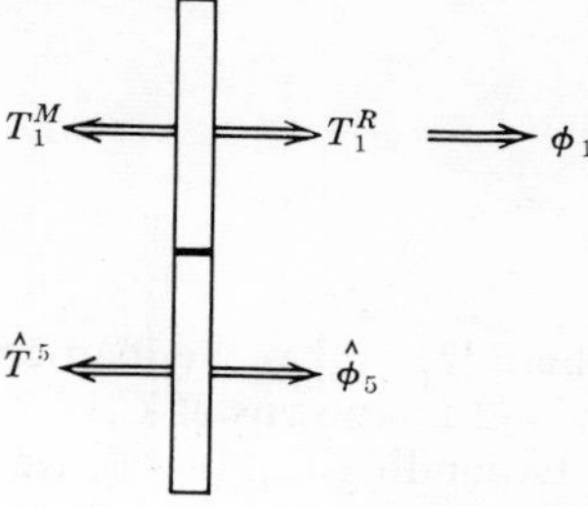

Table 6-1. Branch

$$\begin{bmatrix} 1.00 \\ -2.5\times 10^4 \end{bmatrix}\cdot\begin{bmatrix}\phi\end{bmatrix}_3 = \hat{\mathbf{z}}_3^R = \begin{bmatrix}\hat{\phi} \\ \hat{T}\end{bmatrix}_3^R$$

$$\left[\begin{array}{cc|cc} 1 & \frac{1}{1.5}\times 10^{-6} & & 0 \\ 0 & 1 & & -2.5\times 10^4 \end{array}\right]\begin{bmatrix} 0.9833 \\ -4.958\times 10^4 \end{bmatrix}\cdot\begin{bmatrix}\phi\end{bmatrix}_3 = \hat{\mathbf{z}}_4^R$$

$$\left[\begin{array}{cc|cc} 1 & \frac{1}{1.5}\times 10^{-6} & & 0 \\ 0 & 1 & & -5.0\times 10^4 \end{array}\right]\begin{bmatrix} 0.9503 \\ -9.710\times 10^4 \end{bmatrix}\cdot\begin{bmatrix}\phi\end{bmatrix}_3 = \hat{\mathbf{z}}_5^R$$

$$\mathbf{R}_2\mathbf{R}_1^{-1} = -\frac{9.710}{0.9503}\times 10^4 = -10.22\times 10^4$$

Table 6-2. Main System

$$\begin{bmatrix} 1.00 \\ -2.5\times 10^4 \end{bmatrix}\cdot\begin{bmatrix}\phi\end{bmatrix}_0 = \mathbf{z}_0^R = \begin{bmatrix}\phi \\ T\end{bmatrix}_0^R$$

$$\left[\begin{array}{cc|cc} 1 & \frac{1}{1.5}\times 10^{-6} & & 0 \\ 0 & 1 & & -2.5\times 10^4 \end{array}\right]\begin{bmatrix} 0.9833 \\ -4.958\times 10^4 \end{bmatrix}\cdot\begin{bmatrix}\phi\end{bmatrix}_0 = \mathbf{z}_1^M$$

Point matrix from branch →

$$\left[\begin{array}{cc|cc} 1 & 0 & & 0 \\ -10.22\times 10^4 & 1 & & 0 \end{array}\right]\begin{bmatrix} 0.9833 \\ -15.01\times 10^4 \end{bmatrix}\cdot\begin{bmatrix}\phi\end{bmatrix}_0 = \mathbf{z}_1^R$$

$$\left[\begin{array}{cc|cc} 1 & \frac{1}{1.5}\times 10^{-6} & & 0 \\ 0 & 1 & & -5.0\times 10^4 \end{array}\right]\begin{bmatrix} 0.8833 \\ -19.42\times 10^4 \end{bmatrix}\cdot\begin{bmatrix}\phi\end{bmatrix}_0 = \mathbf{z}_2^R = \begin{bmatrix}\phi \\ 0\end{bmatrix}_2^R$$

Branched Systems Subjected to Forced Vibrations. It is possible to extend the general matrix procedure to forced vibrations and statics. Consider that branch BC (Fig. 6-15) is subjected to forces that are either harmonic or static. Using the extended transfer matrix, the relation between the extended state vectors at points B and C is [cf. (Eq. 6-9)]

$$\begin{matrix} n/2 \\ n/2 \\ 1 \end{matrix}\begin{bmatrix} \hat{\mathbf{d}} \\ \hline \hat{\mathbf{p}} \\ \hline 1 \end{bmatrix}_B = \begin{matrix} n/2 \\ n/2 \\ \ \end{matrix}\begin{bmatrix} \mathbf{R}_1 & \hat{\mathbf{r}}_d \\ \hline \mathbf{R}_2 & \hat{\mathbf{r}}_p \\ \hline \mathbf{0} & 1 \end{bmatrix} \cdot \begin{matrix} n/2 \\ \ \end{matrix}\begin{bmatrix} \hat{\mathbf{v}} \\ \hline 1 \end{bmatrix}_C \tag{6-16}$$

where $\{\hat{\mathbf{r}}_d \quad \hat{\mathbf{r}}_p\}$ is the load column vector $\hat{\mathbf{r}}$ and $\hat{\mathbf{v}}_C$ is the column vector consisting of the $n/2$ unknowns at C.

Expanding Eq. (6-16), we obtain the equations

$$\hat{\mathbf{d}}_B = \mathbf{R}_1\hat{\mathbf{v}}_C + \hat{\mathbf{r}}_d \qquad \hat{\mathbf{p}}_B = \mathbf{R}_2\hat{\mathbf{v}}_C + \hat{\mathbf{r}}_p$$

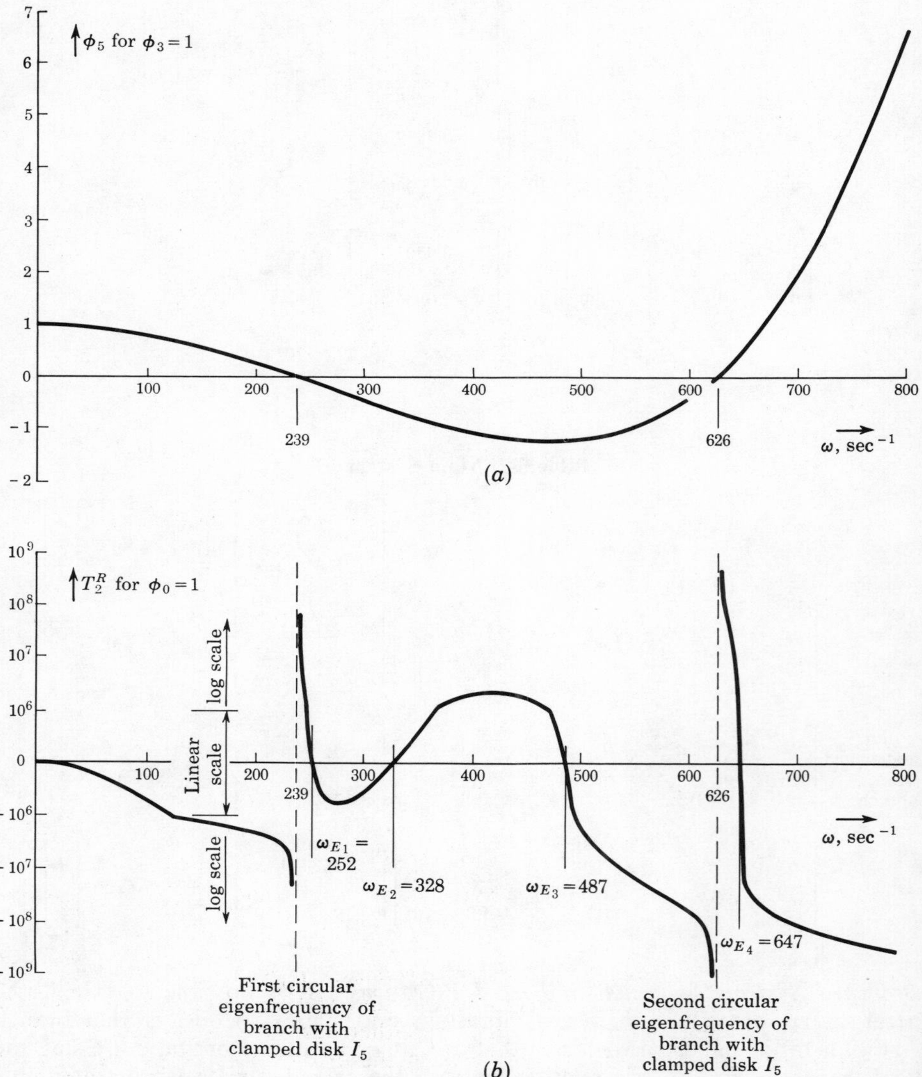

FIG. 6-14. Frequency diagram (a) of branch, (b) of main system.

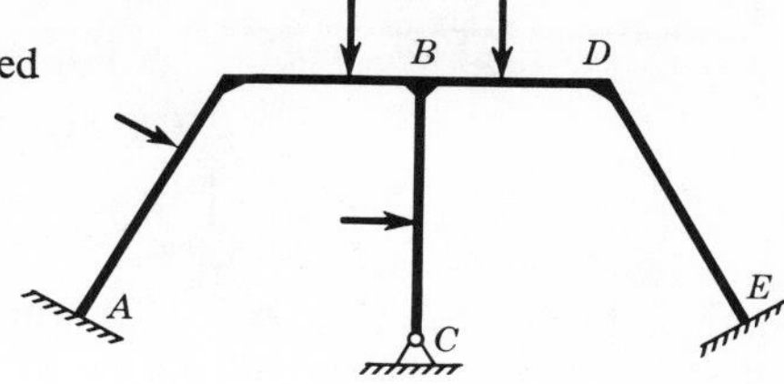

FIG. 6-15. Branched system subjected to forced vibrations.

By elimination of $\hat{\mathbf{v}}_C$ the relation between the forces and displacements at B is found to be

$$\hat{\mathbf{p}}_B = \mathbf{R}_2\mathbf{R}_1^{-1}(\hat{\mathbf{d}}_B - \hat{\mathbf{f}}_d) + \hat{\mathbf{f}}_p = \mathbf{R}_2\mathbf{R}_1^{-1}\hat{\mathbf{d}}_B - (\mathbf{R}_2\mathbf{R}_1^{-1}\hat{\mathbf{f}}_d - \hat{\mathbf{f}}_p) \tag{6-17}$$

Finally, we transform the coordinate system of the branch into that of the main member. These transformations are [Eqs. (6-11) and (6-12)]

$$\hat{\mathbf{d}}_B = \mathbf{G}_1\mathbf{d}_B \qquad \text{and} \qquad \mathbf{p}_B = \mathbf{G}_2\hat{\mathbf{p}}_B$$

and substituting these equations into Eq. (6-17) we obtain the result

$$\begin{aligned}\mathbf{p}_B &= \mathbf{G}_2\hat{\mathbf{p}}_B = \mathbf{G}_2\mathbf{R}_2\mathbf{R}_1^{-1}\hat{\mathbf{d}}_B + \mathbf{G}_2(\hat{\mathbf{f}}_p - \mathbf{R}_2\mathbf{R}_1^{-1}\hat{\mathbf{f}}_d)\\ &= \mathbf{G}_2\mathbf{R}_2\mathbf{R}_1^{-1}\mathbf{G}_1\mathbf{d}_B + \mathbf{G}_2(\hat{\mathbf{f}}_p - \mathbf{R}_2\mathbf{R}_1^{-1}\hat{\mathbf{f}}_d)\end{aligned} \tag{6-18}$$

The extended point matrix is then

$$\begin{bmatrix}\mathbf{d}\\ \mathbf{p}\\ 1\end{bmatrix}_B^R = \begin{bmatrix}\mathbf{I} & \mathbf{0} & \mathbf{0}\\ \mathbf{S} = \mathbf{G}_2\mathbf{R}_2\mathbf{R}_1^{-1}\mathbf{G}_1 & \mathbf{I} & \mathbf{G}_2(\hat{\mathbf{f}}_p - \mathbf{R}_2\mathbf{R}_1^{-1}\hat{\mathbf{f}}_d)\\ 0 & 0 & 1\end{bmatrix}\cdot\begin{bmatrix}\mathbf{d}\\ \mathbf{p}\\ 1\end{bmatrix}_B^L \tag{6-19}$$

(row and column dimensions: $n/2$, $n/2$, 1)

It should be noted that $\mathbf{G}_2(\hat{\mathbf{f}}_p - \mathbf{R}_2\mathbf{R}_1^{-1}\hat{\mathbf{f}}_d)$ is a column vector and that the spring matrix $\mathbf{S} = \mathbf{G}_2\mathbf{R}_2\mathbf{R}_1^{-1}\mathbf{G}_1$ remains as in Eq. (6-13).

Singularities Occurring in the Spring Matrix. In forming the spring matrix for a branch it is necessary to form the inverse of the $\mathbf{R}_1$ matrix in order to eliminate the unknown vector $\hat{\mathbf{v}}_c$ from Eqs. (6-10). When $\mathbf{R}_1$ is singular, it follows that the circular frequency ω satisfies the equation $|\mathbf{R}_1| = 0$, which is in fact the frequency condition for the branch when $\hat{\mathbf{d}}_B = 0$. Should the frequency be such as to satisfy this condition, then the branch behaves as if it were rigidly held at its junction with the main system. Furthermore, when the main system is subjected to oscillatory forces with a circular frequency that corresponds to the natural frequency of the branch, then the deflections at the point of connection with the branch remain zero and the branch behaves as an ideal vibration absorber.

Suppose now that the branch itself is subjected to an oscillatory force with circular frequency equal to one of its own natural frequencies. Then, repeating Eq. (6-16),

$$\hat{\mathbf{d}}_B = \mathbf{R}_1\hat{\mathbf{v}}_c + \hat{\mathbf{f}}_d$$

But since $\mathbf{R}_1\hat{\mathbf{v}}_c = 0$ it follows that

$$\hat{\mathbf{d}}_B = \hat{\mathbf{f}}_d$$

Therefore, in effect, the main system is subjected to a forced displacement, the magnitude of which depends only upon the mass and elastic properties of the branch and its loading.

As an illustration let us consider the cantilever beam with a spring-mass system

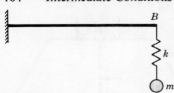

FIG. 6-16. Cantilever beam with vibration absorber.

hanging at its end (Fig. 6-16). Should a force $P \cos \Omega t$ be applied to the beam such that $\Omega^2 = k/m$, then point B does not move. However, if the same force is applied downward to mass m, then it is found that

$$w_B = -\frac{P}{k} \cos \Omega t$$

so that the beam is subjected to a forced deflection at B. Naturally all these observations apply only to the "steady state."

Example 6-2. Determine the lowest frequency Ω of excitation at which the unloaded branch BC of the system of Fig. 6-15 behaves as a vibration absorber, having the same effect as an external constraint that inhibits rotation and lateral displacement of joint B. Branch BC of length l possesses uniform bending stiffness EJ and mass distribution $\mu =$ const.

According to the theory discussed in the preceding paragraph, Ω is the frequency at which the square submatrix $\mathbf{R}_1$ of branch BC becomes singular. In view of the boundary conditions at points B ($\hat{w}_B = \hat{\varphi}_B = 0$) and C ($\hat{\varphi}_c \neq 0$ and $\hat{V}_c \neq 0$) we extract from transfer matrix C-3*b*

$$\mathbf{R}_1 = \begin{bmatrix} lc_1 & alc_3 \\ c_0 & ac_2 \end{bmatrix}$$

Hence

$$|\mathbf{R}_1| = al(c_1c_2 - c_0c_3) = 0$$

yields the frequency equation

$$c_1c_2 - c_0c_3 = 0$$

$$(\sinh \beta + \sin \beta)(\cosh \beta - \cos \beta) - (\cosh \beta + \cos \beta)(\sinh \beta - \sin \beta) = 0$$

or

$$\tanh \beta = \tan \beta$$

where

$$\beta^4 = \frac{\mu l^4}{EJ} \Omega^2$$

From the above frequency equation we obtain as the lowest $\beta \neq 0$

$$\beta = 3.9266$$

For example, with $EJ/\mu l^4 = 100 \text{ sec}^{-2}$ we find

$$\Omega = 154 \text{ sec}^{-1}$$

Note that when $\Omega = 154 \text{ sec}^{-1}$ the branch has the constraining effect shown in Fig. 6-17. Of course, the "ideal" behavior as a vibration absorber is true only in the absence of damping.

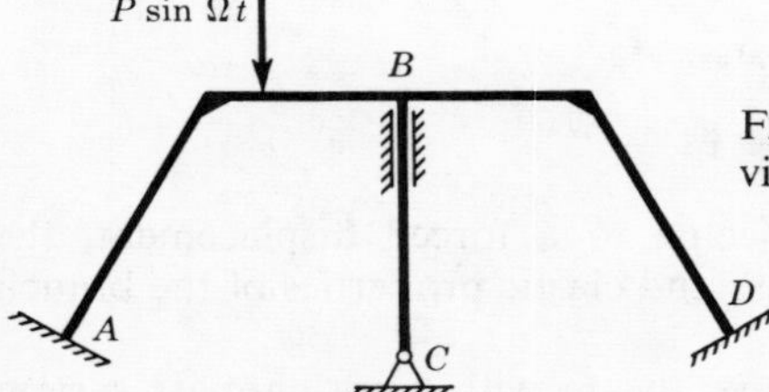

FIG. 6-17. Branched system subjected to forced vibrations.

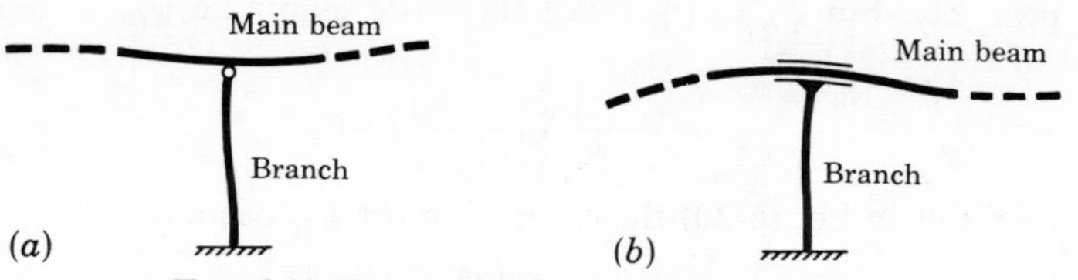

FIG. 6-18. Examples of release in a branch.

Elastic Supports with Releases. So far it has been assumed that the branch is rigidly connected to the main structure. However, this may not always be the case, as can be seen in Fig. 6-18*a*, for example, where the bending moment in the elastic support is zero at its upper end on account of the hinge. Another example of a release is shown in Fig. 6-18*b*, where the shear in the branch is zero because of the frictionless guide connection. In the presence of such releases the theory must be somewhat extended [24].

Let us discuss the procedure using as an example the frame shown in Fig. 6-19 which is vibrating in its plane. Branch *CB* is connected to the frame by means of a pin, so that no moment is transmitted from the branch into the main system.

As in the preceding section, we aim at expressing the reactions of the hinged support in terms of the deflections of the main branch *ABD* at point *B*. Again we denote all components of the state vector of branch *CB* by the symbol ^ over the letter.

The state vector $\hat{\mathbf{z}}_B$ is expressed in terms of the unknowns at point *C* by the matrix equation

$$\begin{bmatrix} \hat{\mathbf{d}} \\ \hline \hat{\mathbf{p}} \end{bmatrix}_B = \begin{bmatrix} \mathbf{R}_1 \\ \hline \mathbf{R}_2 \end{bmatrix} \cdot \begin{bmatrix} \hat{\mathbf{v}} \end{bmatrix}_C \tag{6-9}$$

and following the method described earlier we obtain the relation between the forces and deflections at point *B*:

$$\hat{\mathbf{p}}_B = \mathbf{R}_2\mathbf{R}_1^{-1}\hat{\mathbf{d}}_B = \mathbf{S}\hat{\mathbf{d}}_B$$

In the case under consideration this relation is

$$\begin{bmatrix} \hat{M} \\ \hat{V} \\ \hat{N} \end{bmatrix}_B = \begin{bmatrix} s_{11} & s_{12} & s_{13} \\ s_{21} & s_{22} & s_{23} \\ s_{31} & s_{32} & s_{33} \end{bmatrix} \cdot \begin{bmatrix} \hat{u} \\ -\hat{w} \\ \hat{\varphi} \end{bmatrix}_B \tag{6-20}$$

Since $\hat{M}_B = 0$, the displacements are linearly dependent according to the equation

$$0 = s_{11}\hat{u}_B + s_{12}(-\hat{w}_B) + s_{13}\hat{\varphi}_B \tag{6-21}$$

On account of the type of connection $\hat{u}_B$ and $+\hat{w}_B$ are equal to the deflections $-w_B$

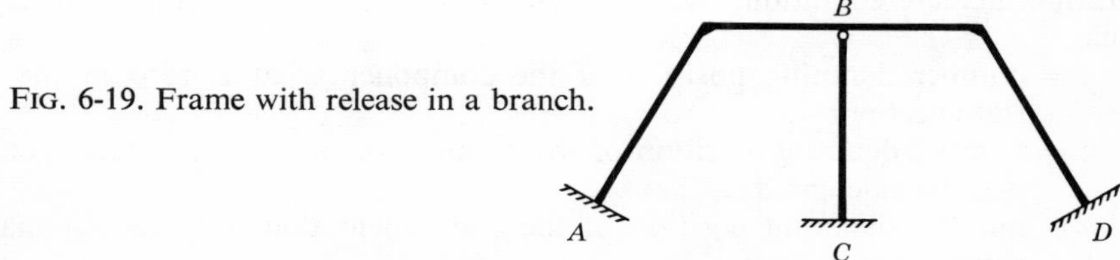

FIG. 6-19. Frame with release in a branch.

and u_B, respectively, but $\hat{\psi}_B \neq \psi_B$. We therefore eliminate $\hat{\psi}_B$, which is possible with the aid of Eq. (6-21):

$$\hat{\psi}_B = -\frac{s_{11}}{s_{13}}\hat{u}_B - \frac{s_{12}}{s_{13}}(-\hat{w}_B)$$

and using this result in Eq. (6-20) the expression for $\hat{V}_B$ becomes

$$\begin{aligned}\hat{V}_B &= s_{21}\hat{u}_B + s_{22}(-\hat{w})_B + s_{23}\left[-\frac{s_{11}}{s_{13}}\hat{u}_B - \frac{s_{12}}{s_{13}}(-\hat{w})_B\right] \\ &= \frac{1}{s_{13}}[(s_{21}s_{13} - s_{23}s_{11})\hat{u}_B + (s_{22}s_{13} - s_{23}s_{12})(-\hat{w})_B]\end{aligned}$$

By using the following short-hand notation [18, 24] for the determinant:

$$\frac{1}{s_{jq}}\begin{vmatrix} s_{jq} & s_{jr} \\ s_{kq} & s_{kr} \end{vmatrix} = \frac{s_{jq}s_{kr} - s_{jr}s_{kq}}{s_{jq}} = |jk \quad qr| \tag{6-22}$$

the expression for $\hat{V}_B$ becomes

$$\hat{V}_B = |12 \quad 31|\,\hat{u}_B + |12 \quad 32|\,(-\hat{w}_B) \tag{6-23}$$

In a similar manner the expression for $\hat{N}_B$ is

$$\hat{N}_B = |13 \quad 31|\,\hat{u}_B + |13 \quad 32|\,(-\hat{w}_B) \tag{6-24}$$

and the relation (6-20) becomes

$$\begin{bmatrix} \hat{M} \\ \hat{V} \\ \hat{N} \end{bmatrix}_B = \begin{bmatrix} 0 & 0 & 0 \\ |12 \quad 31| & |12 \quad 32| & 0 \\ |13 \quad 31| & |13 \quad 32| & 0 \end{bmatrix} \cdot \begin{bmatrix} \hat{u} \\ -\hat{w} \\ \hat{\psi} \end{bmatrix}_B$$

This may also be written in the form

$$\begin{bmatrix} \hat{M} \\ \hat{V} \\ \hat{N} \end{bmatrix}_B = \begin{bmatrix} |11 \quad 31| & |11 \quad 32| & |11 \quad 33| \\ |12 \quad 31| & |12 \quad 32| & |12 \quad 33| \\ |13 \quad 31| & |13 \quad 32| & |13 \quad 33| \end{bmatrix} \cdot \begin{bmatrix} \hat{u} \\ -\hat{w} \\ \hat{\psi} \end{bmatrix}_B \tag{6-25}$$

since $|11 \quad 31| = 0$, etc., from the definition of Eq. (6-22). The number sequence now becomes more obvious.

The letter j denotes the position of the force that is zero. In this case $j = 1$ because the force M_B stands in first position. The letter k denotes the row of the matrix in which the element $|jk \quad qr|$ stands. The letter q denotes the position of the displacement complementary to the force that is zero. In this case $q = 3$ because displacement $\hat{\psi}_B$, complementary to $\hat{M}_B$, stands in third position. The letter r denotes the column of the matrix in which the element $|jk \quad qr|$ stands.

This notation can also be used in a more general sense when a component of a state vector is to be eliminated because another component is zero on account of an intermediate condition. In that case we would formulate the following general rule:

$j =$ number denoting position of the component that is zero in the complete state vector $\mathbf{z}_i$

$k =$ number denoting position of the component of complete state vector $\mathbf{z}_i$ that is to be calculated

$q =$ number denoting position of the component that is to be eliminated from complete state vector $\mathbf{z}_{i-1}$

r = number denoting position of the component of complete state vector $\mathbf{z}_{i-1}$ that is multiplied by $|jk \quad qr|$

It should be noted that it is very easy to locate the elements of the original matrix that are used to compute the element $|jk \quad qr|$ in the new matrix. The elements are found at the points of intersection of rows j and k with columns q and r. This is illustrated in Fig. 6-20.

Modifying the spring matrix (6-4) in this way, we obtain the new matrix

$$\begin{bmatrix} \hat{M} \\ \hat{V} \\ \hat{N} \end{bmatrix} = \begin{bmatrix} 0 & 0 & 0 \\ 0 & -\dfrac{3EJ}{l^3} & 0 \\ \dfrac{EA}{l} & 0 & 0 \end{bmatrix} \cdot \begin{bmatrix} \hat{u} \\ -\hat{w} \\ \hat{\psi} \end{bmatrix}$$

and on applying the coordinate transformations as in Eq. (6-7) the new spring matrix becomes

$$\begin{bmatrix} 0 & 0 & 0 \\ 0 & -\dfrac{EA}{l} & 0 \\ \dfrac{3EJ}{l^3} & 0 & 0 \end{bmatrix}$$

In general, if the forces and displacements at the connecting end of a branch are related by the equation

$$\hat{\mathbf{p}} = \mathbf{S}\hat{\mathbf{d}}$$

and if on account of a release the force $\hat{p}_j = 0$ and its complementary displacement to be eliminated is $\hat{d}_q$, then the spring matrix becomes

$$\begin{bmatrix} |j1 \quad q1| & |j1 \quad q2| & \cdots & |j1 \quad qm| \\ |j2 \quad q1| & |j2 \quad q2| & \cdots & |j2 \quad qm| \\ \cdot & \cdot & \cdots & \cdot \\ |jm \quad q1| & |jm \quad q2| & \cdots & |jm \quad qm| \end{bmatrix} \tag{6-26}$$

The position of the spring matrix as submatrix of the point matrix remains unchanged.

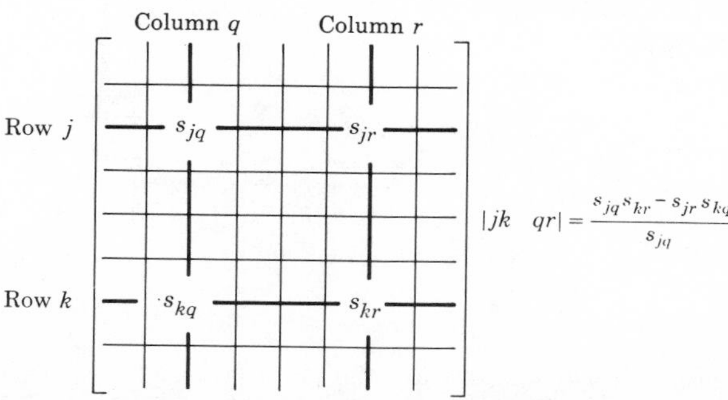

FIG. 6-20. Scheme for locating elements in matrix.

PROBLEMS

6-1. Compute the spring matrix of the massless member shown in Fig. P 6-1.

6-2. For the torsional system of Fig. P 6-2 find the transfer matrix relating $\mathbf{z}^L$ and $\mathbf{z}^R$.

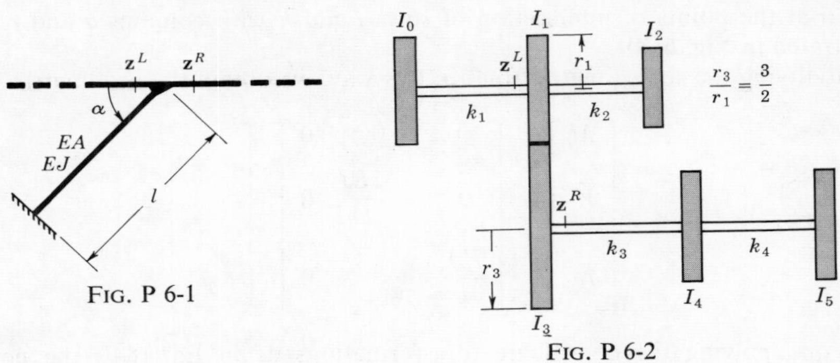

FIG. P 6-1

FIG. P 6-2

6-3. The main system 012 of Fig. P 6-3 is regarded as having a branch 341 which is shown surrounded by the dashed line. Determine the point matrix $\mathbf{P}_1$ for the branch. Find the natural frequencies and the normal modes of the system using the abbreviation $p^2 = m\omega^2/k$. Plot the frequency condition against p^2 and discuss its infinity at $p^2 = 2$.

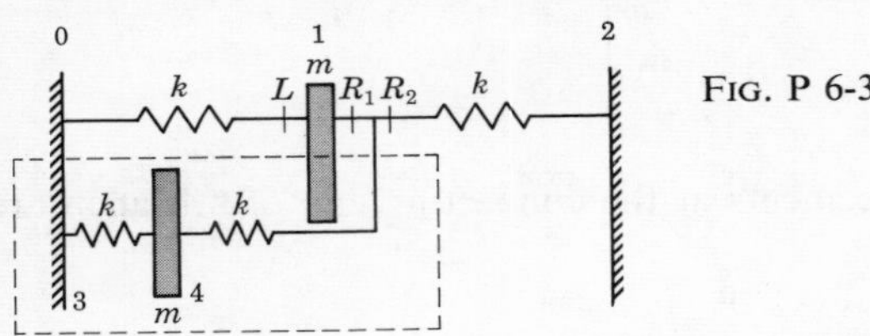

FIG. P 6-3

6-4. The disk I_0 of Fig. P 6-2 is excited by the harmonic torque $T \cos \Omega t$. For what values of Ω are the disks I_1 and I_3 stationary?

6-5. Find the natural frequencies and the normal modes of the system shown in Fig. P 6-5. Regard the spring support as a branch.

6-6. The beam member A shown in Fig. P 6-6 is a branch of a main frame system. The beam A is of uniform mass and stiffness. If the main beam is subjected to harmonic excitation of frequency Ω, determine the frequencies at which the branch will behave as the partly rigid supports shown in parts a and b of the figure.

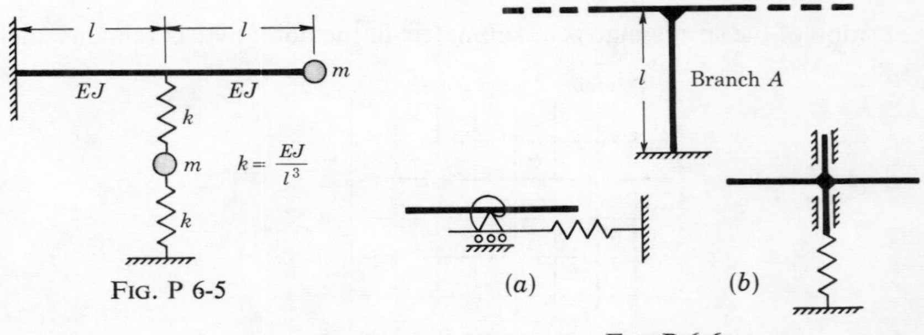

FIG. P 6-5

FIG. P 6-6

6-7. Repeat Prob. 6-6 for the case where the lower end of branch A is free.

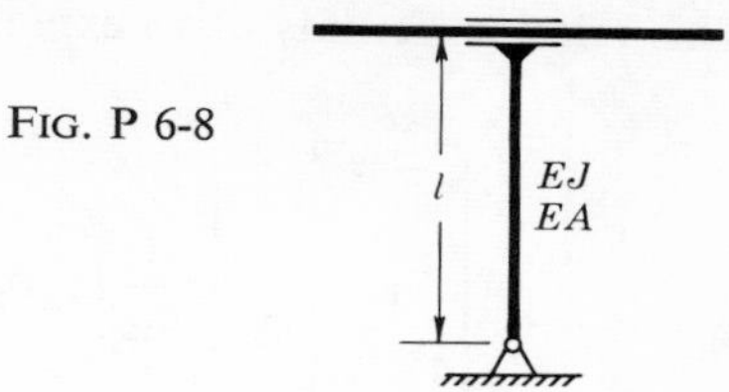

FIG. P 6-8

6-8. The branch shown in Fig. P 6-8 cannot transmit a horizontal force to the main system. Determine the spring matrix if the branch is massless.

6-9. Find the spring stiffness for the branch shown in Fig. P 6-8 if the lower end is built-in.

6-2. Rigid Intermediate Conditions and Releases

Simple Case of Elimination. The methods discussed previously for elastic springs break down when the spring becomes infinitely stiff or when there is a release in the structure. As an example we consider the beam shown in Fig. 6-21, which has a rigid support at point 1 and a frictionless hinge (release) at point 2, whereas at ends 0 and 3 it is pinned and built-in, respectively. In this case there are two internal unknown discontinuities, the reaction P_1 at (1) and the slope change α_2 at (2). Corresponding to these unknowns, however, we have the conditions that the deflection at (1) and the bending moment at (2) are zero. Let us consider the case of free vibrations and assume that the transfer matrices **A**, **B**, and **C** for the beam between (0) and (1), (1) and (2), (2) and (3), respectively, are already known; therefore

$$\mathbf{z}_1^L = \mathbf{A}\mathbf{z}_0 \tag{6-27a}$$

$$\mathbf{z}_2^L = \mathbf{B}\mathbf{z}_1^R \tag{6-27b}$$

$$\mathbf{z}_3 = \mathbf{C}\mathbf{z}_2^R \tag{6-27c}$$

The matrices relating $\mathbf{z}_1^L$ to $\mathbf{z}_1^R$, and $\mathbf{z}_2^L$ to $\mathbf{z}_2^R$ are missing, however.

Since $w_0 = M_0 = 0$, Eq. (6-27*a*) gives the expression relating the state vector $\mathbf{z}_1^L$ to the unknowns ψ_0 and V_0:

$$\begin{bmatrix} -w \\ \psi \\ M \\ V \end{bmatrix}_1^L = \begin{bmatrix} a_{11} & a_{12} \\ a_{21} & a_{22} \\ a_{31} & a_{32} \\ a_{41} & a_{42} \end{bmatrix} \cdot \begin{bmatrix} \psi \\ V \end{bmatrix}_0$$

Setting $w_1^L = 0$, we obtain the relation between ψ_0 and V_0:

$$0 = a_{11}\psi_0 + a_{12}V_0 \qquad \text{so that } V_0 = -\frac{a_{11}}{a_{12}}\psi_0$$

FIG. 6-21. Beam with intermediate rigid support and release.

This relation permits us to express the state vector $\mathbf{z}_1^L$ in terms of ψ_0 alone, so that

$$\begin{bmatrix} -w \\ \psi \\ M \\ V \end{bmatrix}_1^L = \begin{bmatrix} 0 \\ \dfrac{1}{a_{12}}(a_{12}a_{21} - a_{11}a_{22}) \\ \dfrac{1}{a_{12}}(a_{12}a_{31} - a_{11}a_{32}) \\ \dfrac{1}{a_{12}}(a_{12}a_{41} - a_{11}a_{42}) \end{bmatrix} \cdot \begin{bmatrix} \psi_0 \end{bmatrix} = \begin{bmatrix} |11 \;\; 21| \\ |12 \;\; 21| \\ |13 \;\; 21| \\ |14 \;\; 21| \end{bmatrix} \cdot \begin{bmatrix} \psi \end{bmatrix}_0$$

where the determinants are defined by Eq. (6-22). The deflection, slope, and moment are continuous over point 1, but the shear $V_1^R = V^L + P_1$ is discontinuous, with P_1 as the unknown reaction. The state vector $\mathbf{z}_1^R$ is then expressed by the relation

$$\begin{bmatrix} -w \\ \psi \\ M \\ V \end{bmatrix}_1^R = \begin{bmatrix} |11 \;\; 21| & 0 \\ |12 \;\; 21| & 0 \\ |13 \;\; 21| & 0 \\ |14 \;\; 21| & 1 \end{bmatrix} \cdot \begin{bmatrix} \psi_0 \\ P_1 \end{bmatrix}$$

Hence we have eliminated one of the initial unknowns and introduced the new unknown P_1. We proceed now in the established manner to find the state vector $\mathbf{z}_2^L$:

$$\begin{bmatrix} |11 \;\; 21| & 0 \\ |12 \;\; 21| & 0 \\ |13 \;\; 21| & 0 \\ |14 \;\; 21| & 1 \end{bmatrix} \cdot \begin{bmatrix} \psi_0 \\ P_1 \end{bmatrix} = \begin{bmatrix} -w \\ \psi \\ M \\ V \end{bmatrix}_1^R$$

$$\begin{bmatrix} b_{11} & b_{12} & b_{13} & b_{14} \\ b_{21} & b_{22} & b_{23} & b_{24} \\ b_{31} & b_{32} & b_{33} & b_{34} \\ b_{41} & b_{42} & b_{43} & b_{44} \end{bmatrix} \begin{bmatrix} d_{11} & d_{12} \\ d_{21} & d_{22} \\ d_{31} & d_{32} \\ d_{41} & d_{42} \end{bmatrix} \cdot \begin{bmatrix} \psi_0 \\ P_1 \end{bmatrix} = \begin{bmatrix} -w \\ \psi \\ M \\ V \end{bmatrix}_2^L$$

This time $M_2^L = 0$, and hence

$$d_{31}\psi_0 + d_{32}P_1 = 0 \qquad \text{so that } P_1 = -\frac{d_{31}}{d_{32}}\psi_0$$

Eliminating P_1 and introducing the new unknown α_2 in the manner illustrated earlier, we find $\mathbf{z}_2^R$ in terms of the unknowns ψ_0 and α_2. The calculation then proceeds in the usual way:

$$\begin{bmatrix} |31 \ \ 21| & 0 \\ |32 \ \ 21| & 1 \\ |33 \ \ 21| & 0 \\ |34 \ \ 21| & 0 \end{bmatrix} \cdot \begin{bmatrix} \psi_0 \\ \alpha_2 \end{bmatrix} = \mathbf{z}_2^R$$

$$\begin{bmatrix} c_{11} & c_{12} & c_{13} & c_{14} \\ c_{21} & c_{22} & c_{23} & c_{24} \\ c_{31} & c_{32} & c_{33} & c_{34} \\ c_{41} & c_{42} & c_{43} & c_{44} \end{bmatrix}_4 \begin{bmatrix} e_{11} & e_{12} \\ e_{21} & e_{22} \\ e_{31} & e_{32} \\ e_{41} & e_{42} \end{bmatrix} \cdot \begin{bmatrix} \psi_0 \\ \alpha_2 \end{bmatrix} = \begin{bmatrix} 0 \\ 0 \\ M \\ V \end{bmatrix}_3$$

from which we obtain the frequency determinant

$$\Delta = \begin{vmatrix} e_{11} & e_{12} \\ e_{21} & e_{22} \end{vmatrix} = 0$$

The complete matrix scheme is shown in Table 6-3.

Table 6-3

$$\begin{bmatrix} a_{11} & a_{12} \\ a_{21} & a_{22} \\ a_{31} & a_{32} \\ a_{41} & a_{42} \end{bmatrix} \cdot \begin{bmatrix} \psi_0 \\ V_0 \end{bmatrix} = \mathbf{z}_1^L$$

Condition
$a_{11}\psi_0 + a_{12}V_0 = -w_1 = 0$

$$\begin{bmatrix} |11 \ \ 21| & 0 \\ |12 \ \ 21| & 0 \\ |13 \ \ 21| & 0 \\ |14 \ \ 21| & 1 \end{bmatrix} \cdot \begin{bmatrix} \psi_0 \\ P_1 \end{bmatrix} = \mathbf{z}_1^R$$

Elimination of V_0 and introduction of P_1

$$\begin{bmatrix} b_{11} & b_{12} & b_{13} & b_{14} \\ b_{21} & b_{22} & b_{23} & b_{24} \\ b_{31} & b_{32} & b_{33} & b_{34} \\ b_{41} & b_{42} & b_{43} & b_{44} \end{bmatrix} \begin{bmatrix} d_{11} & d_{12} \\ d_{21} & d_{22} \\ d_{31} & d_{32} \\ d_{41} & d_{42} \end{bmatrix} \cdot \begin{bmatrix} \psi_0 \\ P_1 \end{bmatrix} = \mathbf{z}_2^L$$

Condition
$d_{31}\psi_0 + d_{32}P_1 = M_2 = 0$

$$\begin{bmatrix} |31 \ \ 21| & 0 \\ |32 \ \ 21| & 1 \\ |33 \ \ 21| & 0 \\ |34 \ \ 21| & 0 \end{bmatrix} \cdot \begin{bmatrix} \psi_0 \\ \alpha_2 \end{bmatrix} = \mathbf{z}_2^R$$

Elimination of P_1 and introduction of α_2

$$\begin{bmatrix} c_{11} & c_{12} & c_{13} & c_{14} \\ c_{21} & c_{22} & c_{23} & c_{24} \\ c_{31} & c_{32} & c_{33} & c_{34} \\ c_{41} & c_{42} & c_{43} & c_{44} \end{bmatrix} \begin{bmatrix} e_{11} & e_{12} \\ e_{21} & e_{22} \\ e_{31} & e_{32} \\ e_{41} & e_{42} \end{bmatrix} \cdot \begin{bmatrix} \psi_0 \\ \alpha_2 \end{bmatrix} = \mathbf{z}_3$$

General Formulation of the Elimination Technique. In order to preserve full generality we shall consider an nth-order nonhomogeneous system. Suppose that the first discontinuities occur at point i and that the extended state vector $\tilde{\mathbf{z}}_i^L$ is related to the initial unknowns $\mathbf{v}$ at point 0 by the equation

$$\begin{bmatrix} \mathbf{z} \\ \hline 1 \end{bmatrix}_i^L = \left[\begin{array}{c|c} \mathbf{U} & \mathbf{r} \\ \hline \mathbf{0} & 1 \end{array}\right] \cdot \begin{bmatrix} \mathbf{v} \\ \hline 1 \end{bmatrix}_0 \tag{6-28}$$

At point i, k components ($k < n/2$) of the state vector are zero, and consequently the k complementary components will be discontinuous (cf. the previous example). We partition Eq. (6-28) in the following manner:†

$$\left[\begin{array}{c|c|c} \mathbf{B}_m & \mathbf{B}_k & \mathbf{r}_a \\ \hline \mathbf{C}_m & \mathbf{C}_k & \mathbf{r}_b \\ \hline \multicolumn{2}{c|}{\mathbf{0}} & 1 \end{array}\right] \cdot \begin{bmatrix} \mathbf{m} \\ \hline \mathbf{k} \\ \hline 1 \end{bmatrix}_0 = \begin{bmatrix} \mathbf{h} \\ \hline \mathbf{g} \\ \hline \mathbf{0} \\ \hline 1 \end{bmatrix}_i^L \begin{array}{l} \} \; n-2k \text{ variables that are continuous at point } i \\ \} \; k \text{ variables that are discontinuous at point } i \text{ because of the intermediate conditions there} \\ \} \; k \text{ variables (corresponding to the } k \text{ discontinuous variables) that become zero at point } i\text{: intermediate conditions at point } i \end{array} \tag{6-29}$$

(Row dimensions: $n-k$, k, 1; column dimensions: m, k, 1; vector dimensions: m, k, 1 and $n-2k$, k, k, 1.)

As can be seen from Eq. (6-29), the vector $\mathbf{v}_0$ is partitioned into (1) the vector $\mathbf{m}_0$, containing m components that are retained, and (2) the vector $\mathbf{k}_0$, consisting of the k components that are to be eliminated by means of the k intermediate conditions at point i. The k components to be eliminated can be chosen arbitrarily.

The vector $\tilde{\mathbf{z}}_i^L$ is partitioned into (1) the vector $\mathbf{h}_i^L$, which consists of the $n - 2k$ components that are continuous at point i, (2) the vector $\mathbf{g}_i^L$, containing the k components discontinuous at point i, and (3) a null vector with k components that are zero on account of the intermediate conditions at point i.

Now the column vector $\mathbf{k}_0$ can be eliminated because

$$\mathbf{C}_m\mathbf{m}_0 + \mathbf{C}_k\mathbf{k}_0 + \mathbf{r}_b = \mathbf{0}$$

Thus

$$\mathbf{k}_0 = -\mathbf{C}_k^{-1}(\mathbf{C}_m\mathbf{m}_0 + \mathbf{r}_b) \tag{6-30}$$

It is therefore possible to reformulate Eq. (6-29) so that $\tilde{\mathbf{z}}_i^L$ can be expressed in terms of the vector $\mathbf{m}_0$ alone:

$$\left[\begin{array}{c|c|c} \mathbf{B}_m - \mathbf{B}_k\mathbf{C}_k^{-1}\mathbf{C}_m & \mathbf{0} & \mathbf{r}_a - \mathbf{B}_k\mathbf{C}_k^{-1}\mathbf{r}_b \\ \hline \mathbf{0} & \mathbf{0} & \mathbf{0} \\ \hline \multicolumn{2}{c|}{\mathbf{0}} & 1 \end{array}\right] \cdot \begin{bmatrix} \mathbf{m} \\ \hline \mathbf{0} \\ \hline 1 \end{bmatrix}_0 = \begin{bmatrix} \mathbf{h} \\ \hline \mathbf{g} \\ \hline \mathbf{0} \\ \hline 1 \end{bmatrix}_i^L \tag{6-31}$$

† $m + k = n/2$.

In order to obtain the state vector $\mathbf{z}_i^R$ the k unknowns at point i must now be introduced. The k unknowns are represented by the column matrix $\mathbf{g}_i$, which takes the place of the null vector in $\tilde{\mathbf{z}}_0$ [in Eq. (6-31)]. In order to add $\mathbf{g}_i$ to $\mathbf{g}_i^L$ a unit matrix is inserted into the transfer matrix of Eq. (6-31). This operation results in

$$\begin{array}{r} \\ n-k \\ \\ k \\ 1 \end{array}\begin{bmatrix} \overset{m}{\mathbf{B}_m - \mathbf{B}_k\mathbf{C}_k^{-1}\mathbf{C}_m} & \overset{k}{\mathbf{0}} & \overset{1}{\mathbf{r}_a - \mathbf{B}_k\mathbf{C}_k^{-1}\mathbf{r}_b} \\ & \mathbf{I} & \\ \mathbf{0} & \mathbf{0} & \mathbf{0} \\ \multicolumn{2}{c}{\mathbf{0}} & 1 \end{bmatrix} \cdot \begin{array}{r} m \\ k \\ 1 \end{array}\begin{bmatrix} \overset{1}{\mathbf{m}_0} \\ \mathbf{g}_i \\ 1 \end{bmatrix} = \begin{array}{r} n-2k \\ k \\ k \\ 1 \end{array}\begin{bmatrix} \overset{1}{\mathbf{h}} \\ \mathbf{g} \\ \mathbf{0} \\ 1 \end{bmatrix}_i^{R} \quad \begin{array}{l} \mathbf{h}_i^R = \mathbf{h}_i^L \\ \mathbf{g}_i^R = \mathbf{g}_i^L + \mathbf{g}_i \end{array} \tag{6-32}$$

Hereafter the matrix multiplication continues in the usual manner, using, however, the column vector $\{\mathbf{m}_0 \quad \mathbf{g}_i \quad 1\}$ instead of $\{\mathbf{v}_0 \quad 1\}$ until we arrive at the left of a point in the system where new discontinuities arise.

Rearranging Transfer Matrices. When the general method of elimination is applied, it is usually necessary to rearrange the transfer matrices in a form different from the standard scheme. It is possible to matricize this procedure, as illustrated in the following simple example.

Let us consider the transfer matrix connecting points $i - 1$ and i of a simple massless beam:

$$\begin{bmatrix} -w \\ \psi \\ M \\ V \end{bmatrix}_i = \begin{bmatrix} 1 & l & \dfrac{l^2}{2EJ} & \dfrac{l^3}{6EJ} \\ 0 & 1 & \dfrac{l}{EJ} & \dfrac{l^2}{2EJ} \\ 0 & 0 & 1 & l \\ 0 & 0 & 0 & 1 \end{bmatrix}_i \cdot \begin{bmatrix} -w \\ \psi \\ M \\ V \end{bmatrix}_{i-1}$$

For some reason we want to change the sequence and the sign of the components in the state vectors, for example, to

$$\mathbf{z}_{i-1} = \{\psi \quad M \quad +w \quad V\}_{i-1} \qquad \text{and} \qquad \mathbf{z}_i = \{M \quad V \quad +w \quad \psi\}_i$$

We easily recognize that the columns of the transfer matrix have to correspond to the new sequence of the state vector $\mathbf{z}_{i-1}$, and that the rows have to be rearranged in accordance with the new sequence of the state vector $\mathbf{z}_i$. In our example the first column is shifted to third place, the second to first, the third to second, and the fourth remains. Similarly, the first row moves into third place, the second into fourth, the third into first, and the fourth into second. Now the column shifting can be achieved by postmultiplying the above transfer matrix by a square matrix $\mathbf{T}_C$ and the row shifting can be achieved by means of a premultiplication by $\mathbf{T}_R$; that is, the matrix product $\mathbf{U}_i^* = \mathbf{T}_R\mathbf{U}_i\mathbf{T}_C$ must be formed. In addition, the following scheme achieves the desired sign change:

$$\begin{bmatrix} 0 & 0 & -1 & 0 \\ 1 & 0 & 0 & 0 \\ 0 & 1 & 0 & 0 \\ 0 & 0 & 0 & 1 \end{bmatrix} = \mathbf{T}_C$$

$$\mathbf{U}_i = \begin{bmatrix} 1 & l & \dfrac{l^2}{2EJ} & \dfrac{l^3}{6EJ} \\ 0 & 1 & \dfrac{l}{EJ} & \dfrac{l^2}{2EJ} \\ 0 & 0 & 1 & l \\ 0 & 0 & 0 & 1 \end{bmatrix} \begin{bmatrix} l & \dfrac{l^2}{2EJ} & -1 & \dfrac{l^3}{6EJ} \\ 1 & \dfrac{l}{EJ} & 0 & \dfrac{l^2}{2EJ} \\ 0 & 1 & 0 & l \\ 0 & 0 & 0 & 1 \end{bmatrix} = \mathbf{U}_i\mathbf{T}_C$$

$$\mathbf{T}_R = \begin{bmatrix} 0 & 0 & 1 & 0 \\ 0 & 0 & 0 & 1 \\ -1 & 0 & 0 & 0 \\ 0 & 1 & 0 & 0 \end{bmatrix} \begin{bmatrix} 0 & 1 & 0 & l \\ 0 & 0 & 0 & 1 \\ -l & \dfrac{-l^2}{2EJ} & 1 & \dfrac{-l^3}{6EJ} \\ 1 & \dfrac{l}{EJ} & 0 & \dfrac{l^2}{2EJ} \end{bmatrix} = \mathbf{T}_R\mathbf{U}_i\mathbf{T}_C = \mathbf{U}_i^*$$

Hence

$$\begin{bmatrix} M \\ V \\ w \\ \psi \end{bmatrix}_i = \begin{bmatrix} 0 & 1 & 0 & l \\ 0 & 0 & 0 & 1 \\ -l & \dfrac{-l^2}{2EJ} & 1 & \dfrac{-l^3}{6EJ} \\ 1 & \dfrac{l}{EJ} & 0 & \dfrac{l^2}{2EJ} \end{bmatrix} \begin{bmatrix} \psi \\ M \\ w \\ V \end{bmatrix}_{i-1}$$

The following general rules can be extracted from this example:

If in the state vector $\mathbf{z}_{i-1}$ the kth component is moved to position l, the element t_{kl} in the matrix $\mathbf{T}_C$ is unity.

If in the state vector $\mathbf{z}_i$ the pth component is moved to position q, the element t_{qp} in the matrix $\mathbf{T}_R$ is unity.

The elements t_{kl} and t_{qp} are negative if the corresponding state-vector component changes its sign.

The Use of Extra Columns for the Unknowns. The system illustrated in Fig. 6-21 can also be analyzed by carrying extra columns in the transfer matrices [25]. We start at point 0 with the unknowns ψ_0 and V_0, and as we proceed along the beam the unknowns P_1 and α_2 must be introduced. Hence the vector containing all the unknowns is $\{\psi_0 \quad V_0 \quad P_1 \quad \alpha_2\}$. The scheme of matrix multiplication is illustrated below. The transfer matrix $\mathbf{A}$ is used in the normal way (dropping the first and third columns since $w_0 = M_0 = 0$) to find the state vector at point 1^L. At point 1 the deflections, slope, and bending moment are continuous, but the reaction P_1 causes a discontinuity in the shear according to the relation $V_1^R = V_1^L + P_1$. In order to introduce the reaction P_1, we simply attach a 1 to the fourth row of transfer matrix $\mathbf{A}$, thereby taking account of the discontinuity of the shear. Using this device we transfer directly from point 0 to the right of point 1. Multiplication of this enlarged matrix $\mathbf{A}$ by transfer matrix $\mathbf{B}$ takes us to the point 2^L. At point 2 (hinge) there is a discontinuity in the slope, so that $\psi_2^R = \psi_2^L + \alpha_2$. By inserting a 1 for the element d_{24}, the slope discontinuity α_2 is introduced and thereby we go in one step from 1^R to 2^R. The multiplication of matrix **D** by transfer matrix **C** completes the process. The crossed elements need not be computed.

$$\begin{bmatrix} a_{12} & a_{14} & 0 & 0 \\ a_{22} & a_{24} & 0 & 0 \\ a_{32} & a_{34} & 0 & 0 \\ a_{42} & a_{44} & 1 & 0 \end{bmatrix} \cdot \begin{bmatrix} \psi_0 \\ V_0 \\ P_1 \\ \alpha_2 \end{bmatrix} = \begin{bmatrix} w \\ \psi \\ M \\ V \end{bmatrix}_1^R \begin{matrix} = 0 \\ \\ \\ \\ \end{matrix}$$

$$\begin{bmatrix} b_{11} & b_{12} & b_{13} & b_{14} \\ b_{21} & b_{22} & b_{23} & b_{24} \\ b_{31} & b_{32} & b_{33} & b_{34} \\ b_{41} & b_{42} & b_{43} & b_{44} \end{bmatrix} \begin{bmatrix} d_{11} & d_{12} & d_{13} & 0 \\ d_{21} & d_{22} & d_{23} & 1 \\ d_{31} & d_{32} & d_{33} & 0 \\ d_{41} & d_{42} & d_{43} & 0 \end{bmatrix} \cdot \begin{bmatrix} \psi_0 \\ V_0 \\ P_1 \\ \alpha_2 \end{bmatrix} = \begin{bmatrix} w \\ \psi \\ M \\ V \end{bmatrix}_2^R \begin{matrix} \\ \\ = 0 \\ \\ \end{matrix}$$

$$\begin{bmatrix} c_{11} & c_{12} & c_{13} & c_{14} \\ c_{21} & c_{22} & c_{23} & c_{24} \\ c_{31} & c_{32} & c_{33} & c_{34} \\ c_{41} & c_{42} & c_{43} & c_{44} \end{bmatrix} \begin{bmatrix} e_{11} & e_{12} & e_{13} & e_{14} \\ e_{21} & e_{22} & e_{23} & e_{24} \\ \times & \times & \times & \times \\ \times & \times & \times & \times \end{bmatrix} \cdot \begin{bmatrix} \psi_0 \\ V_0 \\ P_1 \\ \alpha_2 \end{bmatrix} = \begin{bmatrix} w \\ \psi \\ \times \\ \times \end{bmatrix}_3 \begin{matrix} = 0 \\ = 0 \\ \\ \\ \end{matrix}$$

Applying the internal and boundary conditions as indicated above, we then obtain the following system of four homogeneous equations in the unknowns ψ_0, V_0, P_1, and α_2:

$$\begin{aligned} a_{12}\psi_0 + a_{14}V_0 \qquad\qquad\qquad\qquad &= 0 \\ d_{31}\psi_0 + d_{32}V_0 + d_{33}P_1 \qquad\qquad &= 0 \\ e_{11}\psi_0 + e_{12}V_0 + e_{13}P_1 + e_{14}\alpha_2 &= 0 \\ e_{21}\psi_0 + e_{22}V_0 + e_{23}P_1 + e_{24}\alpha_2 &= 0 \end{aligned}$$

and the frequency condition is therefore

$$\Delta = \begin{vmatrix} a_{12} & a_{14} & 0 & 0 \\ d_{31} & d_{32} & d_{33} & 0 \\ e_{11} & e_{12} & e_{13} & e_{14} \\ e_{21} & e_{22} & e_{23} & e_{24} \end{vmatrix} = 0$$

It will be noticed that this determinant is of fourth order, in contrast to the usual second-order determinants that occur in beam problems. In general, for each additional internal condition the order of the frequency determinant is increased by 1.

PROBLEMS

6-10. Find the natural frequency for the beam-mass system shown in Fig. P 6-10.

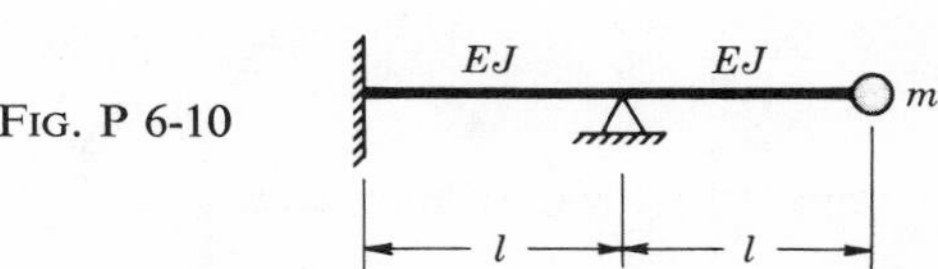

FIG. P 6-10

6-11. Repeat the previous problem for a hinged left-hand support.

6-12. An exciting couple $M \sin \Omega t$ is applied to the beam of Fig. P 6-10 at the intermediate support. Find the steady-state amplitude of the mass when Ω is 90 and 110 per cent of the natural circular frequency ω.

6-13. Repeat Prob. 6-12, taking into consideration structural damping; $g = 0.015$.

6-14. Determine the bending-moment and shear-force diagrams for the continuous beam under load P, as shown in Fig. P 6-14.

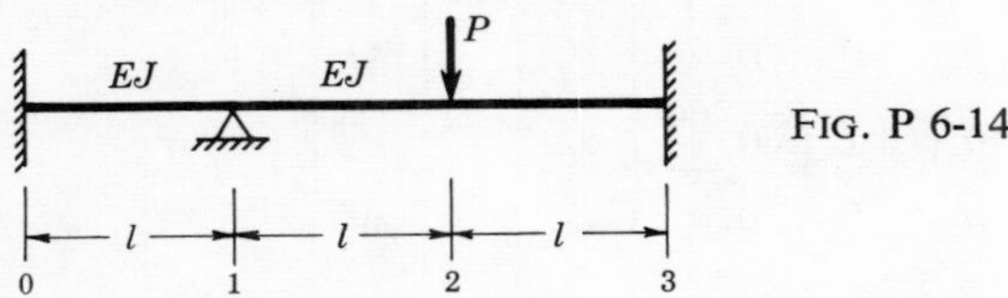

FIG. P 6-14

6-15. Determine the additional bending moments and shear forces in the beam of Fig. P 6-14 if the intermediate support sags by an amount $\delta = Pl^3/20EJ$.

6-3. Matrix Reduction in the Presence of Releases and Rigid Supports

If an elastic system contains a sequence of intermediate rigid supports and releases, such that at each of these an equal number k of state-vector components become zero, it is possible to reduce the n components of the state vector to $n - 2k$ components and accordingly the (n, n) transfer matrices to $(n - 2k, n - 2k)$ *reduced transfer matrices*. A general method for this matrix reduction will be presented for the most common fourth- and sixth-order problems.

Fourth-order Problem. Beam in Plane Bending. The beam shown in Fig. 6-22 illustrates a system for which the transfer matrices can be reduced from order $n = 4$ to order $n - 2k = 4 - 2 = 2$, because at each intermediate rigid support and release one component of the state vector becomes zero [24, 26].

Referring again to Fig. 6-22, we have the following relations between the components of the state vectors $\mathbf{z}_1^R$ and $\mathbf{z}_2^L$:

$$-w_2^L = b_{11}(-w_1^R) + b_{12}\psi_1^R + b_{13}M_1^R + b_{14}V_1^R$$
$$\psi_2^L = b_{21}(-w_1^R) + b_{22}\psi_1^R + b_{23}M_1^R + b_{24}V_1^R$$
$$M_2^L = b_{31}(-w_1^R) + b_{32}\psi_1^R + b_{33}M_1^R + b_{34}V_1^R$$
$$V_2^L = b_{41}(-w_1^R) + b_{42}\psi_1^R + b_{43}M_1^R + b_{44}V_1^R$$

Since $w_1^R = M_2^L = 0$, the above equations become

$$-w_2^L = b_{12}\psi_1^R + b_{13}M_1^R + b_{14}V_1^R$$
$$\psi_2^L = b_{22}\psi_1^R + b_{23}M_1^R + b_{24}V_1^R$$
$$0 = b_{32}\psi_1^R + b_{33}M_1^R + b_{34}V_1^R$$
$$V_2^L = b_{42}\psi_1^R + b_{43}M_1^R + b_{44}V_1^R$$

In these equations ψ_1^R and M_1^R are known to us in terms of the components of the state vector $\mathbf{z}_0$, since

$$\mathbf{z}_1^L = \mathbf{A}\mathbf{z}_0$$

and $\psi_1^R = \psi_1^L$ and $M_1^R = M_1^L$. However, $V_1^R \neq V_1^L$, since the intermediate con-

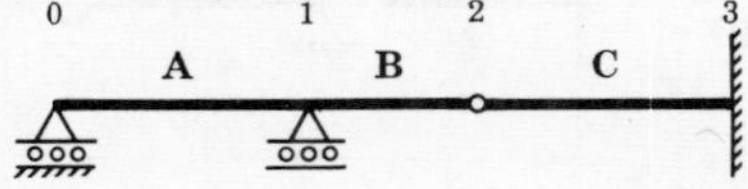

FIG. 6-22. Beam with intermediate rigid support and release.

dition $w_1 = 0$ introduces an unknown reaction at this intermediate support. We note further that w_1 and V_1 are complementary to each other, and we can readily deduce that in general the component complementary to a zero component at an intermediate support or release is discontinuous there. For this reason we use the third of the above equations in order to eliminate V_1^R from the other three equations. Then

$$V_1^R = -\frac{b_{32}}{b_{34}}\psi_1^R - \frac{b_{33}}{b_{34}}M_1^R$$

so that

$$-w_2^L = \frac{b_{12}b_{34} - b_{14}b_{32}}{b_{34}}\psi_1^R + \frac{b_{13}b_{34} - b_{14}b_{33}}{b_{34}}M_1^R$$

$$\psi_2^L = \frac{b_{22}b_{34} - b_{24}b_{31}}{b_{34}}\psi_1^R + \frac{b_{23}b_{34} - b_{24}b_{33}}{b_{34}}M_1^R$$

$$V_2^L = \frac{b_{42}b_{34} - b_{44}b_{32}}{b_{34}}\psi_1^R + \frac{b_{43}b_{34} - b_{44}b_{33}}{b_{34}}M_1^R$$

Using the short-hand symbols defined by Eq. (6-22), these equations become

$$-w_2^L = |31 \quad 42|\,\psi_1^R + |31 \quad 43|\,M_1^R$$

$$\psi_2^L = |32 \quad 42|\,\psi_1^R + |32 \quad 43|\,M_1^R$$

$$V_2^L = |34 \quad 42|\,\psi_1^R + |34 \quad 43|\,M_1^R$$

Since the three components $-w_2^L$, ψ_2^L, and V_2^L can be expressed in terms of the two components ψ_1^R and M_1^R, it follows that $-w_2^L$, ψ_2^L, and V_2^L are linearly dependent on each other. In view of the fact that ψ_2 is discontinuous at point 2 we drop ψ_2^L and form the following matrix equation:

$$\begin{bmatrix} -w \\ V \end{bmatrix}_2 = \begin{bmatrix} |31 \quad 42| & |31 \quad 43| \\ |34 \quad 42| & |34 \quad 43| \end{bmatrix}_2 \cdot \begin{bmatrix} \psi \\ M \end{bmatrix}_1 \tag{6-33}$$

Note the absence of the superscripts L and R, because the reduced state vectors $\{-w \quad V\}_2$ and $\{\psi \quad M\}_1$ are continuous at their respective points.

The elements $|jk \quad qr|$ of the reduced transfer matrix which are derived from the transfer matrix relating the complete state vectors $\mathbf{z}_{i-1}^R$ and $\mathbf{z}_i^L$ can be found by applying the general rules that were stated on page 166. In the example above we have

$j = 3$ because in $\mathbf{z}_2$ we have $M_2 = 0$, and M is the third component in the complete state vector

$k = 1$ in the row corresponding to $-w_2$, since w is the first component in the complete state vector $\mathbf{z}_2$

$k = 4$ in the row corresponding to V_2, since V is the fourth component in the complete state vector $\mathbf{z}_2$

$q = 4$ because V_1 is discontinuous and hence to be eliminated from $\mathbf{z}_1$ and V is the fourth component of the complete state vector

$r = 2$ in the column corresponding to ψ_1, since ψ is the second component in the complete state vector

$r = 3$ in the column corresponding to M_1, since M is the third component in the complete state vector

FIG. 6-23

Let us illustrate the procedure with reference to two adjacent intermediate rigid supports (Fig. 6-23). Here we have the following complete state vectors:

$$\mathbf{z}_{i-1} = \begin{bmatrix} w = 0 \\ \psi \\ M \\ V\dagger \end{bmatrix}_{i-1} \quad \text{and} \quad \mathbf{z}_i = \begin{bmatrix} w = 0 \\ \psi \\ M \\ V\dagger \end{bmatrix}_i$$

Hence, according to the above rule, $j = 1$ and $q = 4$. Since we relate only continuous components that are different from zero, we have in this case

$$\begin{matrix} k = 2 \\ k = 3 \end{matrix} \quad \begin{bmatrix} \psi \\ M \end{bmatrix}_i = \begin{bmatrix} |12 \;\; 42| & |12 \;\; 43| \\ |13 \;\; 42| & |13 \;\; 43| \end{bmatrix}_i \cdot \begin{bmatrix} \psi \\ M \end{bmatrix}_{i-1} \quad \begin{matrix} r = 2 \\ r = 3 \end{matrix}$$

Returning to the system of Fig. 6-22, the relations between the adjacent state vectors are

$$\begin{bmatrix} \psi \\ M \end{bmatrix}_1 = \begin{bmatrix} |12 \;\; 42| & |12 \;\; 43| \\ |13 \;\; 42| & |13 \;\; 43| \end{bmatrix}_1 \cdot \begin{bmatrix} \psi \\ M \end{bmatrix}_0$$

$$\begin{bmatrix} -w \\ V \end{bmatrix}_2 = \begin{bmatrix} |31 \;\; 42| & |31 \;\; 43| \\ |34 \;\; 42| & |34 \;\; 43| \end{bmatrix}_2 \cdot \begin{bmatrix} \psi \\ M \end{bmatrix}_1$$

$$\begin{bmatrix} \psi \\ M \end{bmatrix}_3^{\ddagger} = \begin{bmatrix} |12 \;\; 21| & |12 \;\; 24| \\ |13 \;\; 21| & |13 \;\; 24| \end{bmatrix}_3 \cdot \begin{bmatrix} -w \\ V \end{bmatrix}_2$$

Since $M_0 = 0$, the matrix multiplication scheme takes the form

$$\begin{bmatrix} |12 \;\; 42| \\ |13 \;\; 42| \end{bmatrix}_1 \cdot \begin{bmatrix} \psi \end{bmatrix}_0 = \begin{bmatrix} \psi \\ M \end{bmatrix}_1$$

$$\begin{bmatrix} |31 \;\; 42| & |31 \;\; 43| \\ |34 \;\; 42| & |34 \;\; 43| \end{bmatrix}_2 \begin{bmatrix} \mathrm{x} \\ \mathrm{x} \end{bmatrix} \cdot \begin{bmatrix} \psi \end{bmatrix}_0 = \begin{bmatrix} -w \\ V \end{bmatrix}_2$$

$$\begin{bmatrix} |12 \;\; 21| & |12 \;\; 24| \\ |13 \;\; 21| & |13 \;\; 24| \end{bmatrix}_3 \begin{bmatrix} \mathrm{x} \\ \mathrm{x} \end{bmatrix} \cdot \begin{bmatrix} \psi \end{bmatrix}_0 = \begin{bmatrix} \psi \\ M \end{bmatrix}_3 = \begin{bmatrix} 0 \\ M \end{bmatrix}_3$$

Table 6-4 gives the reduced transfer matrices for all possible combinations of adjacent intermediate releases and rigid supports. Tables 6-5 and 6-6 give the reduced transfer matrices for all possible combinations of boundary conditions and intermediate releases and rigid supports, respectively.

† Discontinuous.

‡ At point 3 we could also have used $\{-w \quad V\}$ as the state vector, in which case we would obtain the relation

$$\begin{bmatrix} -w \\ V \end{bmatrix}_3 = \begin{bmatrix} |21 \;\; 21| & |21 \;\; 24| \\ |24 \;\; 21| & |24 \;\; 24| \end{bmatrix} \cdot \begin{bmatrix} -w \\ V \end{bmatrix}_2$$

Table 6-4. Reduced Transfer Matrices for All Possible Combinations of Intermediate Rigid Supports and Releases ($|jk \quad qr|$)

	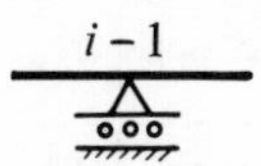		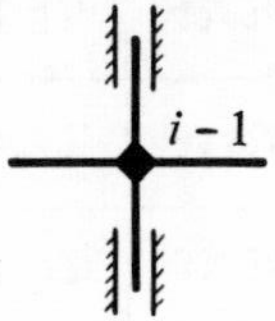		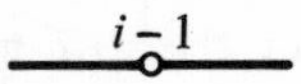		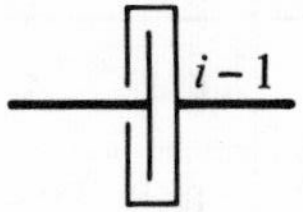					
q	4		3		2		1					
r	2	3	1	4	1	4	2	3				
State vector $\mathbf{z}_{i-1}$	ψ_{i-1}	M_{i-1}	$-w_{i-1}$	V_{i-1}	$-w_{i-1}$	V_{i-1}	ψ_{i-1}	M_{i-1}	$\mathbf{z}_i$	k	j	
	|12 42|	|12 43|	|12 31|	|12 34|	|12 21|	|12 24|	|12 12|	|12 13|	ψ_i	2	1	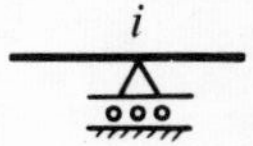
	|13 42|	|13 43|	|13 31|	|13 34|	|13 21|	|13 24|	|13 12|	|13 13|	M_i	3		
	|21 42|	|21 43|	|21 31|	|21 34|	|21 21|	|21 24|	|21 12|	|21 13|	$-w_i$	1	2	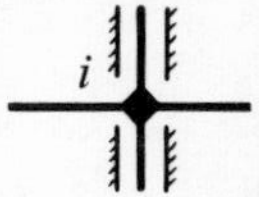
	|24 42|	|24 43|	|24 31|	|24 34|	|24 21|	|24 24|	|24 12|	|24 13|	V_i	4		
	|31 42|	|31 43|	|31 31|	|31 34|	|31 21|	|31 24|	|31 12|	|31 13|	$-w_i$	1	3	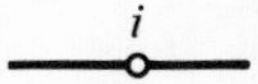
	|34 42|	|34 43|	|34 31|	|34 34|	|34 21|	|34 24|	|34 12|	|34 13|	V_i	4		
	|42 42|	|42 43|	|42 31|	|42 34|	|42 21|	|42 24|	|42 12|	|42 13|	ψ_i	2	4	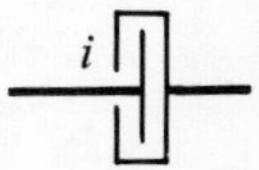
	|43 42|	|43 43|	|43 31|	|43 34|	|43 21|	|43 24|	|43 12|	|43 13|	M_i	3		

Table 6-5. Reduced Transfer Matrices for All Possible Combinations of the Left-hand (Point Zero) Boundary Conditions and Intermediate Rigid Supports and Releases at Point 1 ($|jk \quad qr|$)

	0 (fixed)		0 (simple support)		0 (free)					
q	Either 4	Or 3	Either 4	Or 2	Either 2	Or 1				
r	3	4	2	4	1	2				
Initial unknown	M_0	V_0	ψ_0	V_0	$-w_0$	ψ_0	$\mathbf{z}_1$	k	j	
	$\|12 \quad 43\|$	$\|12 \quad 34\|$	$\|12 \quad 42\|$	$\|12 \quad 24\|$	$\|12 \quad 21\|$	$\|12 \quad 12\|$	ψ_1	2	1	1 (support)
	$\|13 \quad 43\|$	$\|13 \quad 34\|$	$\|13 \quad 42\|$	$\|13 \quad 24\|$	$\|13 \quad 21\|$	$\|13 \quad 12\|$	M_1	3		
	$\|21 \quad 43\|$	$\|21 \quad 34\|$	$\|21 \quad 42\|$	$\|21 \quad 24\|$	$\|21 \quad 21\|$	$\|21 \quad 12\|$	$-w_1$	1	2	1
	$\|24 \quad 43\|$	$\|24 \quad 34\|$	$\|24 \quad 42\|$	$\|24 \quad 24\|$	$\|24 \quad 21\|$	$\|24 \quad 12\|$	V_1	4		
	$\|31 \quad 43\|$	$\|31 \quad 34\|$	$\|31 \quad 42\|$	$\|31 \quad 24\|$	$\|31 \quad 21\|$	$\|31 \quad 12\|$	$-w_1$	1	3	1
	$\|34 \quad 43\|$	$\|34 \quad 34\|$	$\|34 \quad 42\|$	$\|34 \quad 24\|$	$\|34 \quad 21\|$	$\|34 \quad 12\|$	V_1	4		
	$\|42 \quad 43\|$	$\|42 \quad 34\|$	$\|42 \quad 42\|$	$\|42 \quad 24\|$	$\|42 \quad 21\|$	$\|42 \quad 12\|$	ψ_1	2	4	1
	$\|43 \quad 43\|$	$\|43 \quad 34\|$	$\|43 \quad 42\|$	$\|43 \quad 24\|$	$\|43 \quad 21\|$	$\|43 \quad 12\|$	M_1	3		

Table 6-6. Reduced Transfer Matrices for All Possible Combinations of Intermediate Rigid Supports and Releases at Point $n-1$ and Right-hand Boundary Conditions ($|jk \quad qr|$)

	$n-1$		$n-1$		$n-1$		$n-1$						
q	4		3		2		1						
r	2	3	1	4	1	4	2	3					
State vector $\mathbf{z}_{n-1}$	ψ_{n-1}	M_{n-1}	$-w_{n-1}$	V_{n-1}	$-w_{n-1}$	V_{n-1}	ψ_{n-1}	M_{n-1}	Boundary condition	k	j		
	|12 42|	|12 43|	|12 31|	|12 34|	|12 21|	|12 24|	|12 12|	|12 13|	$\psi_n = 0$	2	1	Either	n
	|21 42|	|21 43|	|21 31|	|21 34|	|21 21|	|21 24|	|21 12|	|21 13|	$-w_n = 0$	1	2	Or	
	|13 42|	|13 43|	|13 31|	|13 34|	|13 21|	|13 24|	|13 12|	|13 13|	$M_n = 0$	3	1	Either	n
	|31 42|	|31 43|	|31 31|	|31 34|	|31 21|	|31 24|	|31 12|	|31 13|	$-w_n = 0$	1	3	Or	
	|34 42|	|34 43|	|34 31|	|34 34|	|34 21|	|34 24|	|34 12|	|34 13|	$V_n = 0$	4	3	Either	n
	|43 42|	|43 43|	|43 31|	|43 34|	|43 21|	|43 24|	|43 12|	|43 13|	$M_n = 0$	3	4	Or	

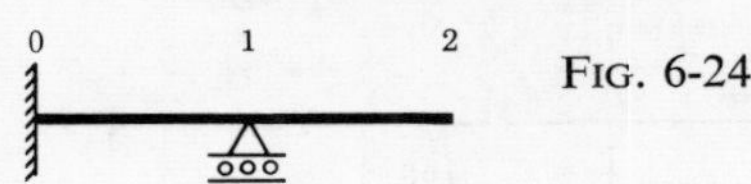

FIG. 6-24

Example 6-3. Find the frequency equation for the uniform beam shown in Fig. 6-24. At the clamped end we have $w_0 = \psi_0 = 0$, $M_0 \neq 0$, and $V_0 \neq 0$, whereas at the free end $M_2 = V_2 = 0$, $w_2 \neq 0$, and $\psi_2 \neq 0$. If we choose M_0 as the initial unknown and utilize $V_2 = 0$ as the right boundary condition, we compose the following reduced matrix scheme from Tables 6-5 and 6-6:

$$\begin{bmatrix} |12 \quad 43| \\ |13 \quad 43| \end{bmatrix} \cdot M_0 = \begin{bmatrix} \psi \\ M \end{bmatrix}_1 \tag{a}$$

$$[|34 \quad 42| \quad |34 \quad 43|][\quad \text{x} \quad] \cdot M_0 = V_2 = 0$$

Choosing $M_2 = 0$ as the right boundary condition, we have from Tables 6-5 and 6-6 the scheme

$$\begin{bmatrix} |12 \quad 43| \\ |13 \quad 43| \end{bmatrix} \cdot M_0 = \begin{bmatrix} \psi \\ M \end{bmatrix}_1 \tag{b}$$

$$[|43 \quad 42| \quad |43 \quad 43|][\quad \text{x} \quad] \cdot M_0 = M_2 = 0$$

If, on the other hand, V_0 is taken as the initial unknown, the following two matrix schemes are derived from Tables 6-5 and 6-6 for $V_2 = 0$ and $M_2 = 0$, respectively, as the right boundary condition:

$$\begin{bmatrix} |12 \quad 34| \\ |13 \quad 34| \end{bmatrix} \cdot V_0 = \begin{bmatrix} \psi \\ M \end{bmatrix}_1 \tag{c}$$

$$[|34 \quad 42| \quad |34 \quad 43|][\quad \text{x} \quad] \cdot V_0 = V_2 = 0$$

or

$$\begin{bmatrix} |12 \quad 34| \\ |13 \quad 34| \end{bmatrix} \cdot V_0 = \begin{bmatrix} \psi \\ M \end{bmatrix}_1 \tag{d}$$

$$[|43 \quad 42| \quad |43 \quad 43|][\quad \text{x} \quad] \cdot V_0 = M_2 = 0$$

Naturally, with all these matrix schemes we arrive at the same result. Let us show this for schemes (*a*) and (*c*). The transfer matrix for the plane flexural vibrations of a uniform beam is (cf. Sec. C-3*b*)

$$\begin{bmatrix} c_0 & lc_1 & \dfrac{l^2c_2}{EJ} & \dfrac{l^3c_3}{EJ} \\ \dfrac{\beta^4c_3}{l} & c_0 & \dfrac{lc_1}{EJ} & \dfrac{l^2c_2}{EJ} \\ \dfrac{\beta^4EJc_2}{l^2} & \dfrac{\beta^4EJc_3}{l} & c_0 & lc_1 \\ \dfrac{\beta^4EJc_1}{l^3} & \dfrac{\beta^4EJc_2}{l^2} & \dfrac{\beta^4c_3}{l} & c_0 \end{bmatrix}$$

Applying the rule of Eq. (6-22), we obtain

$$|12 \quad 43| = \frac{(l^3c_3/EJ)(lc_1/EJ) - (l^2c_2/EJ)(l^2c_2/EJ)}{l^3c_3/EJ} = \frac{l}{EJ}\frac{c_3c_1 - c_2^2}{c_3}$$

$$|13 \quad 43| = \frac{(l^3c_3/EJ)c_0 - (l^2c_2/EJ)lc_1}{l^3c_3/EJ} = \frac{c_3c_0 - c_2c_1}{c_3}$$

$$|34 \quad 42| = \frac{lc_1\beta^4EJc_2/l^2 - \beta^4EJc_3c_0/l}{lc_1} = \frac{\beta^4EJ}{l^2}\frac{c_1c_2 - c_3c_0}{c_1}$$

$$|34 \quad 43| = \frac{lc_1\beta^4c_3/l - c_0^2}{lc_1} = \frac{\beta^4c_1c_3 - c_0^2}{lc_1}$$

Thus scheme (*a*) is as follows:

$$\begin{bmatrix} \dfrac{(l/EJ)(c_3c_1 - c_2^2)}{c_3} \\ \\ \dfrac{c_3c_0 - c_2c_1}{c_3} \end{bmatrix}$$

$$\left[\frac{\beta^4EJ}{l^2}\frac{c_1c_2 - c_0c_3}{c_1} \;\middle|\; \frac{\beta^4c_1c_3 - c_0^2}{lc_1}\right]\left[\frac{\beta^4}{lc_1c_3}(c_0c_2^2c_3 - c_1c_2^3) + \frac{c_0^2c_1c_2 - c_0^3c_3}{lc_1c_3}\right]$$

Hence, the frequency equation is

$$\beta^4(c_0c_2^2c_3 - c_1c_2^3) + c_0^2c_1c_2 - c_0^3c_3 = 0$$

For the application of scheme (*c*) we need in addition the following elements:

$$|12 \quad 34| = \frac{(l^2c_2/EJ)(l^2c_2/EJ) - (l^3c_3/EJ)(lc_1/EJ)}{l^2c_2/EJ} = \frac{l^2}{EJ}\frac{c_2^2 - c_3c_1}{c_2}$$

$$|13 \quad 34| = \frac{(l^2c_2/EJ)lc_1 - (l^3c_3/EJ)c_0}{l^2c_2/EJ} = l\,\frac{c_2c_1 - c_3c_0}{c_2}$$

Thus we have the scheme

$$\begin{bmatrix} \dfrac{l^2}{EJ}\dfrac{c_2^2 - c_3c_1}{c_2} \\ \\ l\,\dfrac{c_2c_1 - c_3c_0}{c_2} \end{bmatrix}$$

$$\left[\frac{\beta^4EJ}{l^2}\frac{c_1c_2 - c_3c_0}{c_1} \;\middle|\; \frac{\beta^4c_1c_3 - c_0^2}{lc_1}\right]\left[\frac{\beta^4}{c_1c_2}(c_1c_2^3 - c_0c_2^2c_3) + \frac{c_0^3c_3 - c_0^2c_1c_2}{c_1c_2}\right]$$

which yields, of course, the same frequency equation

$$\beta^4(c_1c_2^3 - c_0c_2^2c_3) + c_0^3c_3 - c_0^2c_1c_2 = 0$$

Sixth-order Problems. Frames and Arches. We shall now apply the method of matrix reduction when releases and rigid supports occur in frames and arches. Here the transfer matrix is of sixth order (see the Catalogue) if in-plane and normal-to-plane deformations are not coupled. We have to distinguish between the following two cases:

1. All intermediate releases and rigid supports are such that at each of them only one component of the state vector becomes zero, and hence only one—its complementary—component is discontinuous there. Then the (6, 6) transfer matrix can be reduced to a (4, 4) matrix.

2. All intermediate releases and rigid supports are such that at each of them two components of the state vector become zero, and hence two—their complementary—components are discontinuous there. Then the (6, 6) transfer matrix can be reduced to a (2, 2) matrix.

Let us first deal with case 1 by considering in-plane vibrations of an arch with the state vector $\mathbf{z} = \{u \quad -w \quad \psi \quad M \quad V \quad N\}$. A portion of this arch is shown in Fig. 6-25. At point $i-1$ we have $N = 0$, and consequently u is discontinuous, whereas at point i we have $w = 0$, and consequently V is discontinuous.

If we follow the same procedure as before and apply the same rules for the abbreviated determinant notation $|jk \quad qr|$ which were laid down for the fourth-order problem (see page 177), we obtain the following reduced matrix relation between the reduced state vectors $\mathbf{z}_{i-1}$ and $\mathbf{z}_i$. Here $j = 2$ and $q = 1$, and the numbers k and r have been written beside the corresponding components of the state vectors.

$$\begin{matrix} k=1 \\ k=3 \\ k=4 \\ k=6 \end{matrix} \begin{bmatrix} u \\ \psi \\ M \\ N \end{bmatrix}_i = \begin{bmatrix} |21 \quad 12| & |21 \quad 13| & |21 \quad 14| & |21 \quad 15| \\ |23 \quad 12| & |23 \quad 13| & |23 \quad 14| & |23 \quad 15| \\ |24 \quad 12| & |24 \quad 13| & |24 \quad 14| & |24 \quad 15| \\ |26 \quad 12| & |26 \quad 13| & |26 \quad 14| & |26 \quad 15| \end{bmatrix}_i \cdot \begin{bmatrix} -w \\ \psi \\ M \\ V \end{bmatrix}_{i-1} \begin{matrix} r=2 \\ r=3 \\ r=4 \\ r=5 \end{matrix}$$

The procedure is completely identical in the case of vibrations normal to the plane.

Let us now turn to case 2. Here again the procedures for in-plane and normal-to-plane deformations are identical. For each there are $[n(n-2)/2]^2 = 144$ different possible combinations of adjacent intermediate releases and rigid supports. As an example we consider the in-plane deformation of an arch, a portion of which is shown in Fig. 6-26. At point $i-1$ we have $-w = 0$, and consequently V is discontinuous, and $M = 0$, and consequently ψ is discontinuous, whereas at point i we have $u = 0$, and consequently N is discontinuous, and $-w = 0$, and consequently V is discontinuous.

Between sections $i - 1^R$ and i^L we can then write the following linear relations between the components of the state vectors:

$$u_i = 0 = a_{11}u_{i-1} + a_{13}\psi^R_{i-1} + a_{15}V^R_{i-1} + a_{16}N_{i-1} \tag{6-34a}$$

$$-w_i = 0 = a_{21}u_{i-1} + a_{23}\psi^R_{i-1} + a_{25}V^R_{i-1} + a_{26}N_{i-1} \tag{6-34b}$$

$$\psi_i = a_{31}u_{i-1} + a_{33}\psi^R_{i-1} + a_{35}V^R_{i-1} + a_{36}N_{i-1} \tag{6-34c}$$

$$M_i = a_{41}u_{i-1} + a_{43}\psi^R_{i-1} + a_{45}V^R_{i-1} + a_{46}N_{i-1} \tag{6-34d}$$

$$V^L_i = a_{51}u_{i-1} + a_{53}\psi^R_{i-1} + a_{55}V^R_{i-1} + a_{56}N_{i-1} \tag{6-34e}$$

$$N^L_i = a_{61}u_{i-1} + a_{63}\psi^R_{i-1} + a_{65}V^R_{i-1} + a_{66}N_{i-1} \tag{6-34f}$$

With the aid of Eqs. (6-34*a*) and (6-34*b*) we eliminate the discontinuous components at point $i-1$, namely, ψ^R_{i-1} and V^R_{i-1}, from Eqs. (6-34*c*) and (6-34*d*), which can then, using the abbreviations

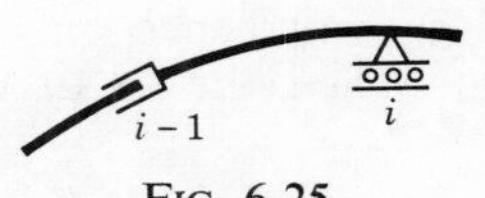

FIG. 6-25

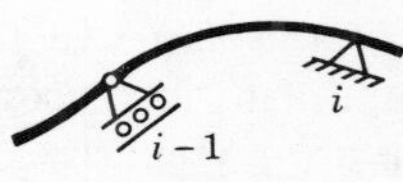

FIG. 6-26

$$\frac{\begin{vmatrix} a_{ip} & a_{iq} & a_{ir} \\ a_{jp} & a_{jq} & a_{jr} \\ a_{kp} & a_{kq} & a_{kr} \end{vmatrix}}{\begin{vmatrix} a_{ip} & a_{iq} \\ a_{jp} & a_{jq} \end{vmatrix}} = |ijk \quad pqr|$$

be written in the form

$$\begin{aligned} \psi_i &= |123 \quad 351|\, u_{i-1} + |123 \quad 356|\, N_{i-1} \\ M_i &= |124 \quad 351|\, u_{i-1} + |124 \quad 356|\, N_{i-1} \end{aligned} \tag{6-35}$$

For V_i^L and N_i^L we obtain

$$\begin{aligned} V_i^L &= |125 \quad 351|\, u_{i-1} + |125 \quad 356|\, N_{i-1} \\ N_i^L &= |126 \quad 351|\, u_{i-1} + |126 \quad 356|\, N_{i-1} \end{aligned}$$

We are, however, interested only in Eqs. (6-35) because they alone connect the continuous components of the state vectors $\mathbf{z}_{i-1}$ and $\mathbf{z}_i$. In matrix notation we then have

$$\begin{bmatrix} \psi \\ M \end{bmatrix}_i = \begin{bmatrix} |123 \quad 351| & |123 \quad 356| \\ |124 \quad 351| & |124 \quad 356| \end{bmatrix} \cdot \begin{bmatrix} u \\ N \end{bmatrix}_{i-1}$$

From the above example we note that the rules for the formation of $|ijk \quad pqr|$ can be gained by amplifying the rules for $|jk \quad qr|$ (see page 177). The letters j, k, q, and r have the same meaning as before, but in addition we have:

i = number denoting, just like j, the position of one of the two components that are zero in the complete state vector $\mathbf{z}_i$; in the example above we have $u = 0$ and $-w = 0$; hence $i = 1$ and $j = 2$

p = number denoting, just like q, the position of one of the two components that are to be eliminated from the complete state vector $\mathbf{z}_{i-1}$; in the example above ψ and V are discontinuous and hence to be eliminated at point $i - 1$; therefore $p = 3$ and $q = 5$

Inhomogeneous Problems. For the treatment of inhomogeneous problems the transfer matrix is enlarged by one extra column, which contains the forcing terms, and one row consisting of zero elements with the exception of the element $u_{n+1,n+1}$, which is equal to unity.

Considering the rules given earlier, the formation of the reduced extended transfer matrix is obvious, as can readily be seen from the few examples below:

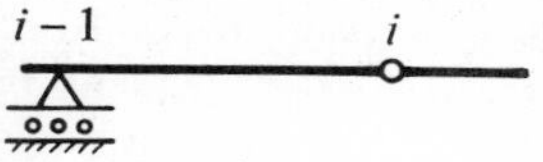

$i-1$ $\qquad$ i

$$j = 3\begin{cases} M_i = 0 \\ \psi_i \text{ discontinuous} \end{cases} \qquad q = 4\begin{cases} -w_{i-1} = 0 \\ V_{i-1} \text{ discontinuous} \end{cases}$$

$$\begin{matrix} k=1 \\ k=4 \\ k=5 \end{matrix} \begin{bmatrix} -w \\ V \\ \hline 1 \end{bmatrix}_i = \left[\begin{array}{cc|c} |31 \quad 42| & |31 \quad 43| & |31 \quad 45| \\ |34 \quad 42| & |34 \quad 43| & |34 \quad 45| \\ \hline 0 & 0 & 1 \end{array}\right] \cdot \begin{bmatrix} \psi \\ M \\ \hline 1 \end{bmatrix}_{i-1} \begin{matrix} r=2 \\ r=3 \\ r=5 \end{matrix}$$

i

$i-1$

$$j = 3\begin{cases}\psi_i = 0 \\ M_i \text{ discontinuous}\end{cases} \qquad q = 5\begin{cases}-w_{i-1} = 0 \\ V_{i-1} \text{ discontinuous}\end{cases}$$

$$\begin{matrix} k=1 \\ k=2 \\ k=5 \\ k=6 \\ k=7 \end{matrix}\begin{bmatrix} u \\ -w \\ V \\ N \\ \hline 1 \end{bmatrix}_i = \left[\begin{array}{cccc|c} |31\ \ 51| & |31\ \ 53| & |31\ \ 54| & |31\ \ 56| & |31\ \ 57| \\ |32\ \ 51| & |32\ \ 53| & |32\ \ 54| & |32\ \ 56| & |32\ \ 57| \\ |35\ \ 51| & |35\ \ 53| & |35\ \ 54| & |35\ \ 56| & |35\ \ 57| \\ |36\ \ 51| & |36\ \ 53| & |36\ \ 54| & |36\ \ 56| & |36\ \ 57| \\ \hline 0 & 0 & 0 & 0 & 1 \end{array}\right] \cdot \begin{bmatrix} u \\ \psi \\ M \\ N \\ \hline 1 \end{bmatrix}_{i-1} \begin{matrix} r=1 \\ r=3 \\ r=4 \\ r=6 \\ r=7 \end{matrix}$$

i

$i-1$

$$\begin{matrix} i = 1 \\ j = 2 \end{matrix}\begin{cases} u_i = 0 \\ -w_i = 0 \\ V_i \text{ discontinuous} \\ N_i \text{ discontinuous}\end{cases} \qquad \begin{matrix} p = 3 \\ q = 5 \end{matrix}\begin{cases} M_{i-1} = 0 \\ -w_{i-1} = 0 \\ \psi_{i-1} \text{ discontinuous} \\ V_{i-1} \text{ discontinuous}\end{cases}$$

$$\begin{matrix} k=3 \\ k=4 \\ k=7 \end{matrix}\begin{bmatrix} \psi \\ M \\ \hline 1 \end{bmatrix}_i = \left[\begin{array}{cc|c} |123\ \ 351| & |123\ \ 356| & |123\ \ 357| \\ |124\ \ 351| & |124\ \ 356| & |124\ \ 357| \\ \hline 0 & 0 & 1 \end{array}\right] \cdot \begin{bmatrix} u \\ N \\ \hline 1 \end{bmatrix}_{i-1} \begin{matrix} r=1 \\ r=6 \\ r=7 \end{matrix}$$

PROBLEMS

6-16. With the help of Tables 6-4 to 6-6 find the reduced transfer matrix for the massless beam elements shown in Fig. P 6-16.

6-17. Find the frequency equation for the uniform continuous beam shown in Fig. P 6-17.

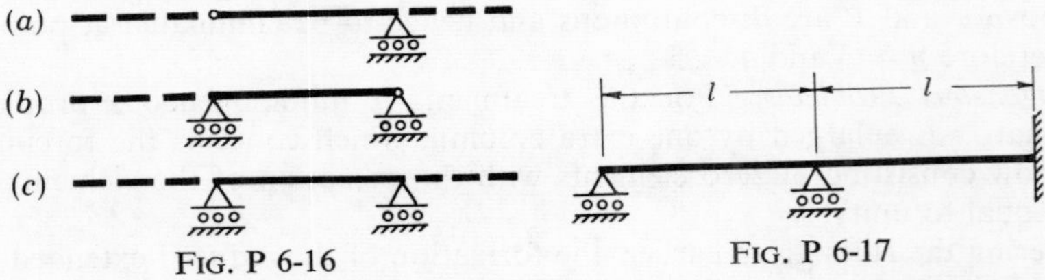

FIG. P 6-16

FIG. P 6-17

6-18. The idealization of a pontoon bridge is illustrated in Fig. P 6-18. The buoyancy forces of the water are represented by continuously distributed springs, and the bridge is considered to be rigid and connected by perfect hinges. Find the reactions at the supports and the hinges caused by load P (cf. transfer matrix C-3e in the Catalogue, $\Gamma^* = 0$).

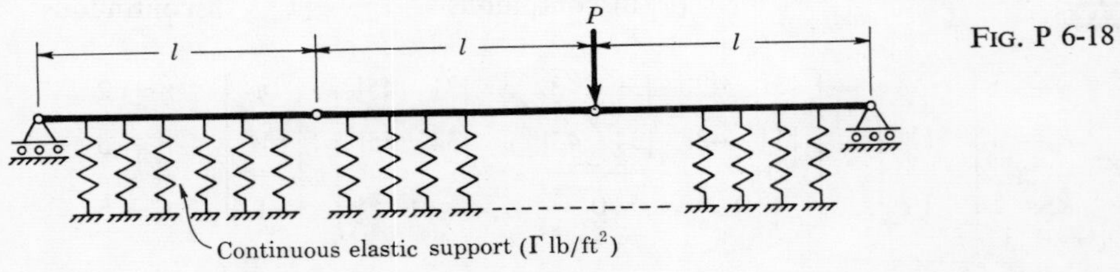

FIG. P 6-18

FIG. P 6-19

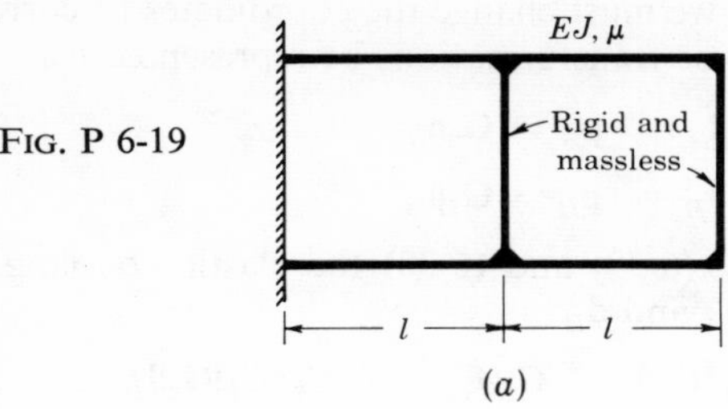

(a)

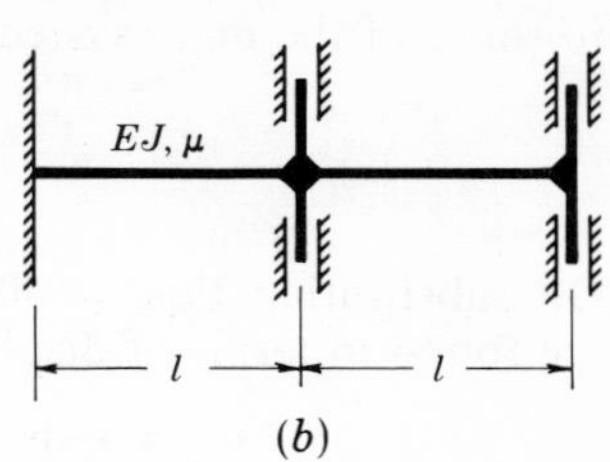

(b)

6-19. Determine the frequency equation for the Vierendeel truss of Fig. P 6-19*a*. The longitudinal stiffness is assumed to be infinite, and the connecting members are rigid. On this account the truss can be reduced to the system of Fig. P 6-19*b*.

6-4. Coupled Systems

General Treatment of Elastic Coupling. We shall now consider two systems I and II coupled by an elastic tie at points A and B (Fig. 6-27). We can proceed in the usual way along members I and II until points A and B are reached. In crossing over from left to right the displacements are unchanged but the coupling tie introduces discontinuities in the forces [24, 26, 27]. Since the displacements are known, these forces may be computed from the elastic and mass properties of the coupling tie. Let us suppose that we have computed the transfer matrix $\mathbf{C}$ of the coupling system BA so that we may relate the state vectors at A and B in the coordinate system of the tie as follows:

$$\hat{\mathbf{z}}_A = \mathbf{C}\hat{\mathbf{z}}_B$$

We rewrite this equation in the form

$$\begin{bmatrix} \hat{\mathbf{d}}_A \\ \hat{\mathbf{p}}_A \end{bmatrix} = \begin{bmatrix} \mathbf{C}_1 & \mathbf{C}_2 \\ \mathbf{C}_3 & \mathbf{C}_4 \end{bmatrix} \begin{bmatrix} \hat{\mathbf{d}}_B \\ \hat{\mathbf{p}}_B \end{bmatrix} \tag{6-36}$$

where $\mathbf{C}_1$, $\mathbf{C}_2$, $\mathbf{C}_3$, and $\mathbf{C}_4$ are square submatrices and $\hat{\mathbf{d}}$ and $\hat{\mathbf{p}}$ represent the displacement and force components of the state vector. Equation (6-36) can be expanded into the two equations

$$\hat{\mathbf{d}}_A = \mathbf{C}_1\hat{\mathbf{d}}_B + \mathbf{C}_2\hat{\mathbf{p}}_B \tag{6-37a}$$

$$\hat{\mathbf{p}}_A = \mathbf{C}_3\hat{\mathbf{d}}_B + \mathbf{C}_4\hat{\mathbf{p}}_B \tag{6-37b}$$

Multiplying Eq. (6-37*a*) by $\mathbf{C}_2^{-1}$, we obtain the relation for $\hat{\mathbf{p}}_B$ in terms of displacements $\hat{\mathbf{d}}_A$ and $\hat{\mathbf{d}}_B$:

$$\hat{\mathbf{p}}_B = \mathbf{C}_2^{-1}\hat{\mathbf{d}}_A - \mathbf{C}_2^{-1}\mathbf{C}_1\hat{\mathbf{d}}_B \tag{6-38}$$

and substituting this equation into Eq. (6-37*b*), we find the expression for $\hat{\mathbf{p}}_A$ to be as follows:

$$\hat{\mathbf{p}}_A = \mathbf{C}_3\hat{\mathbf{d}}_B + \mathbf{C}_4\mathbf{C}_2^{-1}\hat{\mathbf{d}}_A - \mathbf{C}_4\mathbf{C}_2^{-1}\mathbf{C}_1\hat{\mathbf{d}}_B = \mathbf{C}_4\mathbf{C}_2^{-1}\hat{\mathbf{d}}_A + (\mathbf{C}_3 - \mathbf{C}_4\mathbf{C}_2^{-1}\mathbf{C}_1)\hat{\mathbf{d}}_B \tag{6-39}$$

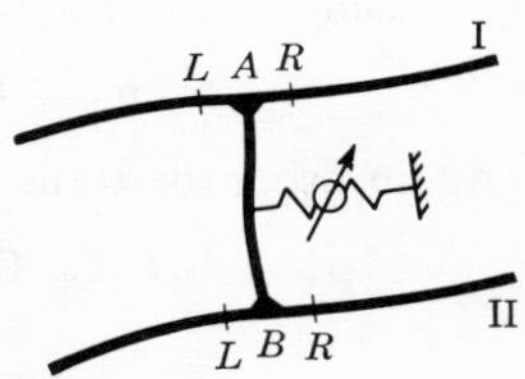

FIG. 6-27. Coupled system.

As in the case of branched systems, we must change the coordinates to correspond to those of the main systems. Let these transformations be represented by

$$\begin{aligned} \hat{\mathbf{d}}_A &= \mathbf{G}_1\mathbf{d}_A \qquad \mathbf{p}_A = \mathbf{G}_2\hat{\mathbf{p}}_A \\ \hat{\mathbf{d}}_B &= \mathbf{G}_3\mathbf{d}_B \qquad \mathbf{p}_B = \mathbf{G}_4\hat{\mathbf{p}}_B \end{aligned} \tag{6-40}$$

On substituting Eqs. (6-40) into Eqs. (6-39) and (6-38) the elastic coupling forces are found in terms of displacements $\mathbf{d}_A$ and $\mathbf{d}_B$:

$$\mathbf{p}_A = \mathbf{G}_2\hat{\mathbf{p}}_A = \mathbf{G}_2\mathbf{C}_4\mathbf{C}_2^{-1}\mathbf{G}_1\mathbf{d}_A + \mathbf{G}_2(\mathbf{C}_3 - \mathbf{C}_4\mathbf{C}_2^{-1}\mathbf{C}_1)\mathbf{G}_3\mathbf{d}_B$$

$$\mathbf{p}_B = \mathbf{G}_4\hat{\mathbf{p}}_B = \mathbf{G}_4\mathbf{C}_2^{-1}\mathbf{G}_1\mathbf{d}_A - \mathbf{G}_4\mathbf{C}_2^{-1}\mathbf{C}_1\mathbf{G}_3\mathbf{d}_B$$

Thus the elastic coupling matrix is

$$\begin{bmatrix} \mathbf{p}_A \\ \hline \mathbf{p}_B \end{bmatrix} = \left[\begin{array}{c|c} \mathbf{G}_2\mathbf{C}_4\mathbf{C}_2^{-1}\mathbf{G}_1 & \mathbf{G}_2(\mathbf{C}_3 - \mathbf{C}_4\mathbf{C}_2^{-1}\mathbf{C}_1)\mathbf{G}_3 \\ \hline \mathbf{G}_4\mathbf{C}_2^{-1}\mathbf{G}_1 & -\mathbf{G}_4\mathbf{C}_2^{-1}\mathbf{C}_1\mathbf{G}_3 \end{array}\right] \cdot \begin{bmatrix} \mathbf{d}_A \\ \hline \mathbf{d}_B \end{bmatrix} \tag{6-41}$$

The point matrix that transfers displacements and forces for both systems I and II from the left to the right of the coupling point is then

$$\begin{bmatrix} \overset{\mathrm{I}}{\mathbf{d}} \\ \hline \overset{\mathrm{II}}{\mathbf{d}} \\ \hline \overset{\mathrm{II}}{\mathbf{p}} \\ \hline \overset{\mathrm{I}}{\mathbf{p}} \end{bmatrix}_R = \left[\begin{array}{c|c|c|c} \mathbf{I} & \mathbf{0} & \mathbf{0} & \mathbf{0} \\ \hline \mathbf{0} & \mathbf{I} & \mathbf{0} & \mathbf{0} \\ \hline \mathbf{G}_4\mathbf{C}_2^{-1}\mathbf{G}_1 & -\mathbf{G}_4\mathbf{C}_2^{-1}\mathbf{C}_1\mathbf{G}_3 & \mathbf{I} & \mathbf{0} \\ \hline \mathbf{G}_2\mathbf{C}_4\mathbf{C}_2^{-1}\mathbf{G}_1 & \mathbf{G}_2(\mathbf{C}_3 - \mathbf{C}_4\mathbf{C}_2^{-1}\mathbf{C}_1)\mathbf{G}_3 & \mathbf{0} & \mathbf{I} \end{array}\right] \cdot \begin{bmatrix} \overset{\mathrm{I}}{\mathbf{d}} \\ \hline \overset{\mathrm{II}}{\mathbf{d}} \\ \hline \overset{\mathrm{II}}{\mathbf{p}} \\ \hline \overset{\mathrm{I}}{\mathbf{p}} \end{bmatrix}_L \tag{6-42}$$

In a similar way the expression for the extended coupling matrix can be found. Following Eq. (6-36) we have the extended matrix relation

$$\begin{bmatrix} \hat{\mathbf{d}}_A \\ \hline \hat{\mathbf{p}}_A \\ \hline 1 \end{bmatrix} = \left[\begin{array}{c|c|c} \mathbf{C}_1 & \mathbf{C}_2 & \hat{\mathbf{f}}_d \\ \hline \mathbf{C}_3 & \mathbf{C}_4 & \hat{\mathbf{f}}_p \\ \hline 0 & 0 & 1 \end{array}\right] \cdot \begin{bmatrix} \hat{\mathbf{d}}_B \\ \hline \hat{\mathbf{p}}_B \\ \hline 1 \end{bmatrix}$$

from which we obtain

$$\hat{\mathbf{d}}_A = \mathbf{C}_1\hat{\mathbf{d}}_B + \mathbf{C}_2\hat{\mathbf{p}}_B + \hat{\mathbf{f}}_d \tag{6-43a}$$

$$\hat{\mathbf{p}}_A = \mathbf{C}_3\hat{\mathbf{d}}_B + \mathbf{C}_4\hat{\mathbf{p}}_B + \hat{\mathbf{f}}_p \tag{6-43b}$$

On multiplying Eq. (6-43*a*) by $\mathbf{C}_2^{-1}$ the expression for $\hat{\mathbf{p}}_B$ in terms of the displacements at *A* and *B* is given by

$$\hat{\mathbf{p}}_B = \mathbf{C}_2^{-1}\hat{\mathbf{d}}_A - \mathbf{C}_2^{-1}\mathbf{C}_1\hat{\mathbf{d}}_B - \mathbf{C}_2^{-1}\hat{\mathbf{f}}_d$$

On using this in Eq. (6-43*b*) the expression for $\hat{\mathbf{p}}_A$ becomes

$$\hat{\mathbf{p}}_A = \mathbf{C}_4\mathbf{C}_2^{-1}\hat{\mathbf{d}}_A + (\mathbf{C}_3 - \mathbf{C}_4\mathbf{C}_2^{-1}\mathbf{C}_1)\hat{\mathbf{d}}_B - \mathbf{C}_4\mathbf{C}_2^{-1}\hat{\mathbf{f}}_d + \hat{\mathbf{f}}_p$$

Again using the transformations (6-40), we obtain

$$\mathbf{p}_A = \mathbf{G}_2\mathbf{C}_4\mathbf{C}_2^{-1}\mathbf{G}_1\mathbf{d}_A + \mathbf{G}_2(\mathbf{C}_3 - \mathbf{C}_4\mathbf{C}_2^{-1}\mathbf{C}_1)\mathbf{G}_3\mathbf{d}_B - \mathbf{G}_2\mathbf{C}_4\mathbf{C}_2^{-1}\hat{\mathbf{f}}_d + \mathbf{G}_2\hat{\mathbf{f}}_p$$

and $$\mathbf{p}_B = \mathbf{G}_4\mathbf{C}_2^{-1}\mathbf{G}_1\mathbf{d}_A - \mathbf{G}_4\mathbf{C}_2^{-1}\mathbf{C}_1\mathbf{G}_3\mathbf{d}_B - \mathbf{G}_4\mathbf{C}_2^{-1}\hat{\mathbf{r}}_d$$

From these equations we can then form the extended point matrix:

$$\begin{bmatrix} \overset{\mathrm{I}}{\mathbf{d}} \\ \overset{\mathrm{II}}{\mathbf{d}} \\ \overset{\mathrm{II}}{\mathbf{p}} \\ \overset{\mathrm{I}}{\mathbf{p}} \\ 1 \end{bmatrix} = \left[\begin{array}{c|c|c|c|c} \mathbf{I} & \mathbf{0} & \mathbf{0} & \mathbf{0} & \mathbf{0} \\ \hline \mathbf{0} & \mathbf{I} & \mathbf{0} & \mathbf{0} & \mathbf{0} \\ \hline \mathbf{G}_4\mathbf{C}_2^{-1}\mathbf{G}_1 & -\mathbf{G}_4\mathbf{C}_2^{-1}\mathbf{C}_1\mathbf{G}_3 & \mathbf{I} & \mathbf{0} & -\mathbf{G}_4\mathbf{C}_2^{-1}\hat{\mathbf{r}}_d \\ \hline \mathbf{G}_2\mathbf{C}_4\mathbf{C}_2^{-1}\mathbf{G}_1 & \mathbf{G}_2(\mathbf{C}_3 - \mathbf{C}_4\mathbf{C}_2^{-1}\mathbf{C}_1)\mathbf{G}_3 & \mathbf{0} & \mathbf{I} & -\mathbf{G}_2\mathbf{C}_4\mathbf{C}_2^{-1}\hat{\mathbf{r}}_d + \mathbf{G}_2\hat{\mathbf{r}}_p \\ \hline \mathbf{0} & \mathbf{0} & \mathbf{0} & \mathbf{0} & 1 \end{array}\right] \cdot \begin{bmatrix} \overset{\mathrm{I}}{\mathbf{d}} \\ \overset{\mathrm{II}}{\mathbf{d}} \\ \overset{\mathrm{II}}{\mathbf{p}} \\ \overset{\mathrm{I}}{\mathbf{p}} \\ 1 \end{bmatrix}$$

Example 6-4. In order to illustrate the application of this general method let us derive the point matrix for two straight beams I and II connected by an elastic tie *AB* (Fig. 6-28).

For the sake of simplicity the elastic tie *AB* is considered to be massless. The relation between the state vectors $\hat{\mathbf{z}}_A$ and $\hat{\mathbf{z}}_B$ is

$$\left[\begin{array}{ccc|ccc} 1 & 0 & 0 & 0 & 0 & \dfrac{l}{EA} \\ 0 & 1 & l & \dfrac{l^2}{2EJ} & \dfrac{l^3}{6EJ} & 0 \\ 0 & 0 & 1 & \dfrac{l}{EJ} & \dfrac{l^2}{2EJ} & 0 \\ \hline 0 & 0 & 0 & 1 & l & 0 \\ 0 & 0 & 0 & 0 & 1 & 0 \\ 0 & 0 & 0 & 0 & 0 & 1 \end{array}\right] \cdot \begin{bmatrix} \hat{u} \\ -\hat{w} \\ \hat{\varphi} \\ \hline \hat{M} \\ \hat{V} \\ \hat{N} \end{bmatrix}_B = \begin{bmatrix} \hat{u} \\ -\hat{w} \\ \hat{\varphi} \\ \hline \hat{M} \\ \hat{V} \\ \hat{N} \end{bmatrix}_A$$

The inverse of $\mathbf{C}_2$ is easily found to be

$$\mathbf{C}_2^{-1} = \begin{bmatrix} 0 & \dfrac{6EJ}{l^2} & \dfrac{-2EJ}{l} \\ 0 & \dfrac{-12EJ}{l^3} & \dfrac{6EJ}{l^2} \\ \dfrac{EA}{l} & 0 & 0 \end{bmatrix}$$

With $$\mathbf{G}_1 = \mathbf{G}_3 = \begin{bmatrix} 0 & 1 & 0 \\ -1 & 0 & 0 \\ 0 & 0 & 1 \end{bmatrix} \quad \text{and} \quad \mathbf{G}_2 = -\mathbf{G}_4 = \begin{bmatrix} 1 & 0 & 0 \\ 0 & 0 & -1 \\ 0 & 1 & 0 \end{bmatrix}$$

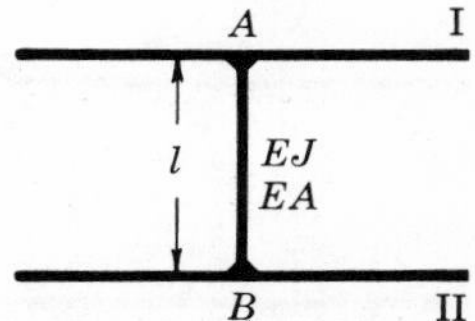

FIG. 6-28. Two beams coupled by straight massless beam.

the square submatrices of Eq. (6-42) are then computed without difficulty:

$$\mathbf{G}_4\mathbf{C}_2^{-1}\mathbf{G}_1 = \begin{bmatrix} \frac{6EJ}{l^2} & 0 & \frac{2EJ}{l} \\ 0 & \frac{EA}{l} & 0 \\ \frac{-12EJ}{l^3} & 0 & \frac{-6EJ}{l^2} \end{bmatrix} \qquad -\mathbf{G}_4\mathbf{C}_2^{-1}\mathbf{C}_1\mathbf{G}_3 = \begin{bmatrix} \frac{-6EJ}{l^2} & 0 & \frac{4EJ}{l} \\ 0 & \frac{-EA}{l} & 0 \\ \frac{12EJ}{l^3} & 0 & \frac{-6EJ}{l^2} \end{bmatrix}$$

$$\mathbf{G}_2\mathbf{C}_4\mathbf{C}_2^{-1}\mathbf{G}_1 = \begin{bmatrix} \frac{6EJ}{l^2} & 0 & \frac{4EJ}{l} \\ 0 & \frac{-EA}{l} & 0 \\ \frac{12EJ}{l^3} & 0 & \frac{6EJ}{l^2} \end{bmatrix} \qquad \mathbf{G}_2(\mathbf{C}_3 - \mathbf{C}_4\mathbf{C}_2^{-1}\mathbf{C}_1)\mathbf{G}_3 = \begin{bmatrix} \frac{-6EJ}{l^2} & 0 & \frac{2EJ}{l} \\ 0 & \frac{EA}{l} & 0 \\ \frac{-12EJ}{l^3} & 0 & \frac{6EJ}{l^2} \end{bmatrix}$$

Coupling Spring with Release. The treatment of a coupling spring with a release follows that adopted for a release in a spring matrix (Sec. 6-2). The displacement complementary to the force that is released is eliminated by using the condition that the force is zero. Consider Example 6-4 when the coupling tie is pinned at A (Fig. 6-29).

If the coupling spring is rigidly connected to the two beams, then the spring forces acting on the main beams are computed with the aid of the following coupling matrix [cf. Eq. (6-41)], the submatrices of which were determined in Example 6-4:

$$\left[\begin{array}{ccc:ccc} \frac{6EJ}{l^2} & 0 & \frac{2EJ}{l} & \frac{-6EJ}{l^2} & 0 & \frac{4EJ}{l} \\ 0 & \frac{EA}{l} & 0 & 0 & \frac{-EA}{l} & 0 \\ \frac{-12EJ}{l^3} & 0 & \frac{-6EJ}{l^2} & \frac{12EJ}{l^3} & 0 & \frac{-6EJ}{l^2} \\ \hdashline \frac{6EJ}{l^2} & 0 & \frac{4EJ}{l} & \frac{-6EJ}{l^2} & 0 & \frac{2EJ}{l} \\ 0 & \frac{-EA}{l} & 0 & 0 & \frac{EA}{l} & 0 \\ \frac{12EJ}{l^3} & 0 & \frac{6EJ}{l^2} & \frac{-12EJ}{l^3} & 0 & \frac{6EJ}{l^2} \end{array}\right] \cdot \left[\begin{array}{c} \overset{\text{I}}{u} \\ -\overset{\text{I}}{w} \\ \overset{\text{I}}{\psi} \\ \hdashline \overset{\text{II}}{u} \\ -\overset{\text{II}}{w} \\ \overset{\text{II}}{\psi} \end{array}\right] = \left[\begin{array}{c} \overset{\text{II}}{M} \\ \overset{\text{II}}{V} \\ \overset{\text{II}}{N} \\ \hdashline \overset{\text{I}}{M} \\ \overset{\text{I}}{V} \\ \overset{\text{I}}{N} \end{array}\right] \tag{6-44}$$

Now, on account of the pin connection, $\overset{\text{I}}{M} = 0$ and the angular rotation of the coupling spring at A is not the same as that for beam I. Hence, using the fact that

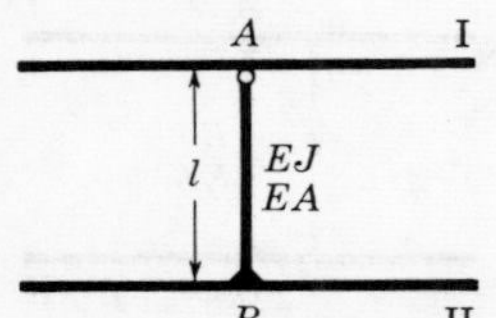

FIG. 6-29. Elastic coupling with release.

$\overset{\mathrm{I}}{M} = 0$, we can eliminate $\overset{\mathrm{I}}{\psi}$ by using Eqs. (6-22) and (6-26) with $m = 6$, $j = 4$, and $q = 3$. Doing this, we obtain the new spring matrix

$$\begin{bmatrix} |41\ \ 31| & |41\ \ 32| & 0 & |41\ \ 34| & |41\ \ 35| & |41\ \ 36| \\ |42\ \ 31| & |42\ \ 32| & 0 & |42\ \ 34| & |42\ \ 35| & |42\ \ 36| \\ |43\ \ 31| & |43\ \ 32| & 0 & |43\ \ 34| & |43\ \ 35| & |43\ \ 36| \\ 0 & 0 & 0 & 0 & 0 & 0 \\ |45\ \ 31| & |45\ \ 32| & 0 & |45\ \ 34| & |45\ \ 35| & |45\ \ 36| \\ |46\ \ 31| & |46\ \ 32| & 0 & |46\ \ 34| & |46\ \ 35| & |46\ \ 36| \end{bmatrix} \cdot \begin{bmatrix} \overset{\mathrm{I}}{u} \\ -\overset{\mathrm{I}}{w} \\ \overset{\mathrm{I}}{\psi} \\ \overset{\mathrm{II}}{u} \\ -\overset{\mathrm{II}}{w} \\ \overset{\mathrm{II}}{\psi} \end{bmatrix} = \begin{bmatrix} \overset{\mathrm{II}}{M} \\ \overset{\mathrm{II}}{V} \\ \overset{\mathrm{II}}{N} \\ \overset{\mathrm{I}}{M} \\ \overset{\mathrm{I}}{V} \\ \overset{\mathrm{I}}{N} \end{bmatrix}$$

For a special case of rigid coupling [24, 26, 27] see Sec. 11-3.

PROBLEMS

6-20. A spring-coupled beam is subjected to a loading, as shown in Fig. P 6-20. Working in dimensionless quantities, determine the bending-moment and shear-force diagrams.

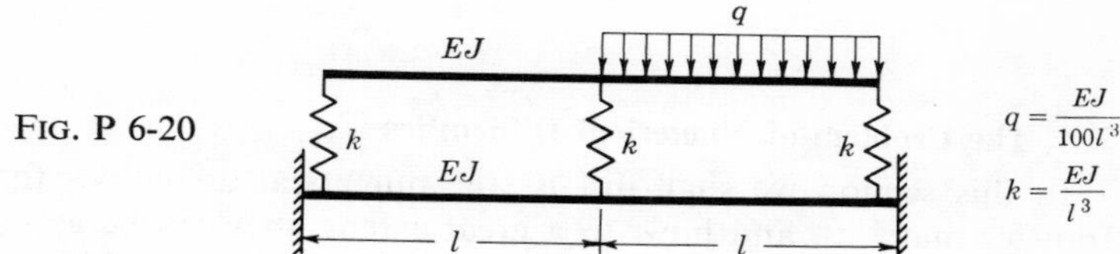

FIG. P 6-20

6-21. The crankshafts of Figs. P 3-37 and P 3-38 are coupled by a straight shaft built-in on its left side (Fig. P 6-21). Compute the dynamic "spring constant" of branches II and III.†

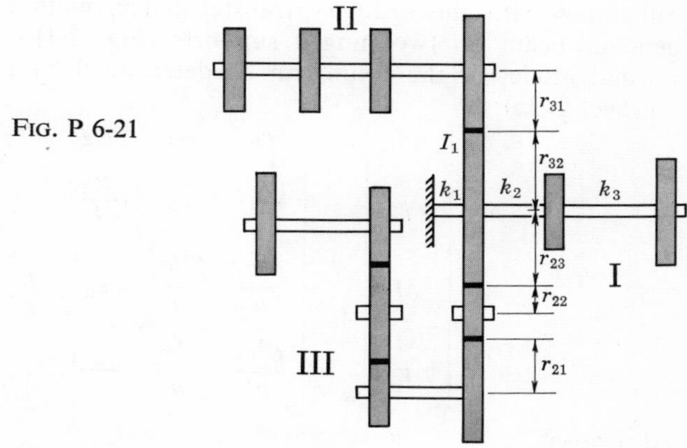

FIG. P 6-21

† S. Falk, Die Berechnung von Kurbelwellen mit Hilfe von digitalen Rechenautomaten, *VDI-Ber.*, no. 30, pp. 65–69, 1958.

7 VARIATIONS OF THE TRANSFER-MATRIX METHOD

7-1. The Problem of Numerical Difficulties

In this section we shall discuss the numerical difficulties that can arise in using transfer matrices, and how, to a great extent, they can be avoided. They normally occur under two circumstances: first, when computing higher natural frequencies, and second, when intermediate elastic supports are very stiff. The following discussion is to be considered as more or less qualitative in character. A thorough investigation of the fundamental difficulties associated with the method of transfer matrices was recently carried out by Marguerre and Uhrig [67].

Computing Higher Natural Frequencies. In order to demonstrate the numerical difficulties with the ordinary transfer-matrix method, let us consider the homogeneous beam on two hinged supports (Fig. 7-1). The natural frequencies and normal modes of the beam can be determined by the following matrix equation (cf. Sec. C-3*b*):

$$\begin{bmatrix} -w \\ \psi \\ M \\ V \end{bmatrix}_B = \begin{bmatrix} c_0 & lc_1 & ac_2 & alc_3 \\ \dfrac{\beta^4 c_3}{l} & c_0 & \dfrac{ac_1}{l} & ac_2 \\ \dfrac{\beta^4 c_2}{a} & \dfrac{\beta^4 lc_3}{a} & c_0 & lc_1 \\ \dfrac{\beta^4 c_1}{al} & \dfrac{\beta^4 c_2}{a} & \dfrac{\beta^4 c_3}{l} & c_0 \end{bmatrix} \cdot \begin{bmatrix} -w \\ \psi \\ M \\ V \end{bmatrix}_A \tag{7-1}$$

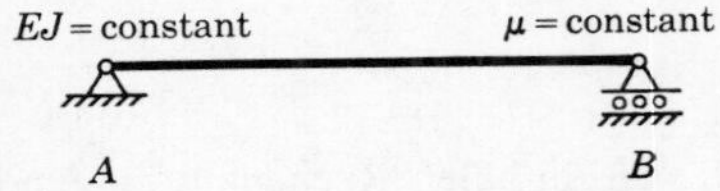

EJ = constant $\quad \mu$ = constant

A $\quad$ B

FIG. 7-1. Beam on hinged supports.

where

$$c_0 = \tfrac{1}{2}(\cosh\beta + \cos\beta) \qquad \beta^4 = \frac{\mu\omega^2 l^4}{EJ}$$

$$c_1 = \frac{1}{2\beta}(\sinh\beta + \sin\beta) \qquad a = \frac{1}{EJ}$$

$$c_2 = \frac{1}{2\beta^2}(\cosh\beta - \cos\beta) \qquad \mu = \text{mass per unit length} \tag{7-2}$$

$$c_3 = \frac{1}{2\beta^3}(\sinh\beta - \sin\beta)$$

With boundary conditions $w_A = M_A = w_B = M_B = 0$ the frequency determinant is

$$0 = \Delta = \begin{vmatrix} lc_1 & alc_3 \\ \dfrac{\beta^4 lc_3}{a} & lc_1 \end{vmatrix} = l^2c_1^2 - \beta^4 l^2 c_3^2$$

$$= l^2\left[\frac{1}{4\beta^2}(\sinh\beta + \sin\beta)^2 - \frac{1}{4\beta^2}(\sinh\beta - \sin\beta)^2\right] = 0 \tag{7-3}$$

On expanding the parentheses the frequency equation reduces to the form

$$0 = \Delta = \frac{l^2}{4\beta^2}(4\sinh\beta\sin\beta)$$

That is, $\sin\beta = 0$ or $\beta_\kappa = \kappa\pi$, giving

$$\omega^2 = \frac{\kappa^4\pi^4}{\mu a l^4} \qquad \kappa = 1, 2, 3, \ldots$$

It is obvious that $\sin\beta$ is responsible for the zero of the frequency determinant. Now the question arises whether the all-important influence of $\sin\beta$ is not lost when we carry out numerical computations with transfer matrices. For then we must consider the fact that the elements in the frequency determinant (7-3) are numbers, and the influence of $\sin\beta$ can be swamped by $\sinh\beta$ as soon as β is much larger than 1 and insufficient digits are carried along in the computation. For example, when β equals 17, we have

$$\sinh\beta = \sinh 17 = 12{,}077{,}476$$

This means that when only eight digits are carried along on the computer the influence of the sine functions is lost. Since for a simple beam the sixth eigenfrequency corresponds to $\beta = 18.85$, it is impossible to find more than the five lowest frequencies when only eight digits are carried in the numerical computation.

This consideration leads to a simple estimate for the least number of digits: the number of digits carried along must be larger than the number of digits of

$$\sinh\beta \approx \cosh\beta \approx \frac{e^\beta}{2}\ \dagger$$

In the determination of β the overall length of the beam, average mass distribution, and average bending stiffness may be used.

Stiff Intermediate Elastic Supports. It was mentioned before that grave numerical difficulties may arise when the stiffness of elastic supports is very large compared

† This rule was first stated by Schumpich in 1955 (unpublished).

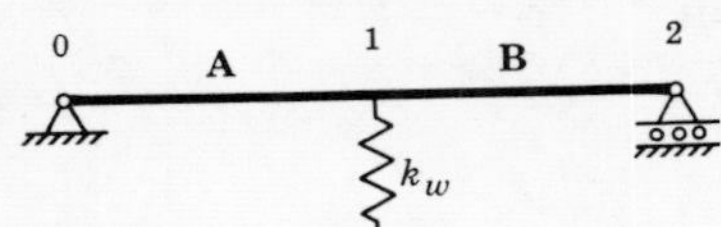

FIG. 7-2. Hinged beam with intermediate spring support.

with the bending stiffness of the beam. In order to illustrate this point let us consider the vibration of the beam illustrated in Fig. 7-2 [28].

The beam is pinned at both ends and is also supported by a spring of stiffness k_w. Let us assume that the transfer matrices of the two divided parts of the beam are **A** and **B**. The matrix multiplications are followed through in the scheme shown in Table 7-1. At the end of the matrix multiplication we apply the boundary conditions at point 2, and this results in the frequency determinant

$$\Delta = \begin{vmatrix} c_{12} & c_{14} \\ c_{32} & c_{34} \end{vmatrix} = 0$$

When this determinant is expanded, we obtain after some algebraic manipulations the result

$$\begin{aligned}\Delta &= k_w^2(a_{12}a_{14}b_{14}b_{34} - a_{12}a_{14}b_{14}b_{34}) \\ &+ k_w\left(\begin{vmatrix} b_{12} & b_{14} \\ b_{32} & b_{34} \end{vmatrix} \cdot \begin{vmatrix} a_{12} & a_{14} \\ a_{22} & a_{24} \end{vmatrix} + \begin{vmatrix} b_{13} & b_{14} \\ b_{33} & b_{34} \end{vmatrix} \cdot \begin{vmatrix} a_{12} & a_{14} \\ a_{32} & a_{34} \end{vmatrix}\right) \\ &+ \left(\begin{vmatrix} b_{11} & b_{12} \\ b_{31} & b_{32} \end{vmatrix} \cdot \begin{vmatrix} a_{12} & a_{14} \\ a_{22} & a_{24} \end{vmatrix} + \begin{vmatrix} b_{11} & b_{13} \\ b_{31} & b_{33} \end{vmatrix} \cdot \begin{vmatrix} a_{12} & a_{14} \\ a_{32} & a_{34} \end{vmatrix} + \begin{vmatrix} b_{11} & b_{14} \\ b_{31} & b_{34} \end{vmatrix} \cdot \begin{vmatrix} a_{12} & a_{14} \\ a_{42} & a_{44} \end{vmatrix}\right. \\ &+ \left.\begin{vmatrix} b_{12} & b_{13} \\ b_{32} & b_{33} \end{vmatrix} \cdot \begin{vmatrix} a_{22} & a_{24} \\ a_{32} & a_{34} \end{vmatrix} + \begin{vmatrix} b_{12} & b_{14} \\ b_{32} & b_{34} \end{vmatrix} \cdot \begin{vmatrix} a_{22} & a_{24} \\ a_{42} & a_{44} \end{vmatrix} + \begin{vmatrix} b_{13} & b_{14} \\ b_{33} & b_{34} \end{vmatrix} \cdot \begin{vmatrix} a_{32} & a_{34} \\ a_{42} & a_{44} \end{vmatrix}\right) \qquad (7\text{-}4)\end{aligned}$$

We see that k_w^2, the square of the spring constant, is multiplied by a factor that is identically zero. However, in numerical work this factor will not be exactly zero, and since it is multiplied by k_w^2, the error introduced could be very high, especially if the spring is rather stiff.

7-2. The Delta-matrix Method

General Formulation of Delta Matrices (*Determinant Matrices or* Δ *Matrices*) [28–35]. From Eq. (7-4) we can see that the expression for Δ is made up of 2×2 determinants the elements of which come either from matrix **A** or from matrix **B**. This result suggests that it may be possible to formulate all possible boundary conditions in terms of these 2×2 subdeterminants. Admitting that this is so, it is still reasonable to ask, before committing ourselves to an extensive study problem, whether working with the subdeterminants has any advantage. We shall show that they have two important points in their favor. For this purpose we choose quite arbitrarily the first one that appears, namely, $\begin{vmatrix} b_{12} & b_{14} \\ b_{32} & b_{34} \end{vmatrix}$. From the transfer matrix in Eq. (7-1) we obtain the elements of this determinant as follows:

$$\begin{vmatrix} \dfrac{l}{2\beta}(\sinh\beta + \sin\beta) & \dfrac{al}{2\beta^3}(\sinh\beta - \sin\beta) \\ \dfrac{\beta l}{2a}(\sinh\beta - \sin\beta) & \dfrac{l}{2\beta}(\sinh\beta + \sin\beta) \end{vmatrix}$$

If the value of β is large, as it can be for the higher modes, the hyperbolic functions will, as mentioned before, completely dominate the natural sines and cosines, the result being that, unless many digits are carried, the value of the determinant is quite inaccurate. However, if we know such a determinant is going to occur, we can reduce it mathematically before introducing numbers:

$$\begin{vmatrix} b_{12} & b_{14} \\ b_{32} & b_{34} \end{vmatrix} = \frac{l^2}{4\beta^2}(\sinh^2\beta + 2\sinh\beta\sin\beta + \sin^2\beta - \sinh^2\beta + 2\sinh\beta\sin\beta - \sin^2\beta)$$

$$= \frac{l^2}{4\beta}(4\sinh\beta\sin\beta)$$

This expression is quite easy to compute accurately enough with a reasonable number of digits even for high values of β. Furthermore, we have seen that serious errors may occur when we carry through the simple transfer-matrix multiplications in cases where intermediate elastic supports are very stiff. However, when the frequency determinant is found in terms of the subdeterminants, we can easily spot the terms that are identically zero and also we can calculate the others with much greater accuracy.

From the 16 elements of the (4, 4) transfer matrix it is possible to form 36 sub-

Table 7-1

$$\begin{bmatrix} a_{12} & a_{14} \\ a_{22} & a_{24} \\ a_{32} & a_{34} \\ a_{42} & a_{44} \end{bmatrix} \cdot \begin{bmatrix} \psi \\ V \end{bmatrix}_0 = \begin{bmatrix} -w \\ \psi \\ M \\ V \end{bmatrix}_1^L$$

$$\begin{bmatrix} 1 & 0 & 0 & 0 \\ 0 & 1 & 0 & 0 \\ 0 & 0 & 1 & 0 \\ -k_w & 0 & 0 & 1 \end{bmatrix} \begin{bmatrix} a_{12} & a_{14} \\ a_{22} & a_{24} \\ a_{32} & a_{34} \\ -k_w a_{12} + a_{42} & -k_w a_{14} + a_{44} \end{bmatrix} \cdot \begin{bmatrix} \psi \\ V \end{bmatrix}_0 = \begin{bmatrix} -w \\ \psi \\ M \\ V \end{bmatrix}_1^R$$

$$\begin{bmatrix} b_{11} & b_{12} & b_{13} & b_{14} \\ b_{21} & b_{22} & b_{23} & b_{24} \\ b_{31} & b_{32} & b_{33} & b_{34} \\ b_{41} & b_{42} & b_{43} & b_{44} \end{bmatrix} \begin{bmatrix} c_{12} & c_{14} \\ c_{22} & c_{24} \\ c_{32} & c_{34} \\ c_{42} & c_{44} \end{bmatrix} \cdot \begin{bmatrix} \psi \\ V \end{bmatrix}_0 = \begin{bmatrix} -w \\ \psi \\ M \\ V \end{bmatrix}_2$$

$$c_{12} = a_{12}b_{11} + a_{22}b_{12} + a_{32}b_{13} + b_{14}(-k_w a_{12} + a_{42})$$

$$c_{32} = a_{12}b_{31} + a_{22}b_{32} + a_{32}b_{33} + b_{34}(-k_w a_{12} + a_{42})$$

$$c_{14} = a_{14}b_{11} + a_{24}b_{12} + a_{34}b_{13} + b_{14}(-k_w a_{14} + a_{44})$$

$$c_{34} = a_{14}b_{31} + a_{24}b_{32} + a_{34}b_{33} + b_{34}(-k_w a_{14} + a_{44})$$

determinants of order (2, 2). In general, it is possible to form from an n-order matrix $\binom{n}{n/2}^2$ subdeterminants of $n/2$ order. For example, when $n = 6$,

$$\binom{n}{n/2} = \frac{(6)(5)(4)}{(3)(2)(1)} = 20$$

It is therefore apparent that the practical application of the method of delta matrices is limited to cases that would normally be dealt with by (4, 4) transfer matrices. Here the 36 subdeterminants will be arranged as the elements of a (6, 6) delta matrix. This arrangement may be carried out as we please, provided, however, the method remains consistent.

Let us consider matrix **A**:

$$\mathbf{A} = \begin{bmatrix} a_{11} & a_{12} & a_{13} & a_{14} \\ a_{21} & a_{22} & a_{23} & a_{24} \\ a_{31} & a_{32} & a_{33} & a_{34} \\ a_{41} & a_{42} & a_{43} & a_{44} \end{bmatrix}$$

We wish to form a matrix from the 36 subdeterminants of this matrix. Each (2, 2) subdeterminant is made up of four elements, and the elements to be used are fixed after we have selected two rows and two columns of the original transfer matrix. Both rows and columns can be selected in pairs in the following six ways according to the arbitrarily chosen correspondence shown:

Number of row and column, respectively, of delta matrix . . .	1	2	3	4	5	6
Number pair of row and column, respectively, of transfer matrix	1, 2	1, 3	1, 4	2, 3	2, 4	3, 4

Hence if we wish to have a short-hand notation for the subdeterminant

$$\begin{vmatrix} a_{21} & a_{23} \\ a_{41} & a_{43} \end{vmatrix}$$

we note first that rows 2 and 4 and columns 1 and 3 fix the number pairs 2, 4 and 1, 3 and second that these number pairs belong (according to the above table) to the numbers 5 and 2. Thus, in this case, the subdeterminant may be represented by the "short-hand" symbol A^{Δ}_{52}.

As further examples of this short-hand notation we have

$$A^{\Delta}_{24} = \begin{vmatrix} a_{12} & a_{13} \\ a_{32} & a_{33} \end{vmatrix} \qquad A^{\Delta}_{13} = \begin{vmatrix} a_{11} & a_{14} \\ a_{21} & a_{24} \end{vmatrix} \qquad A^{\Delta}_{36} = \begin{vmatrix} a_{13} & a_{14} \\ a_{43} & a_{44} \end{vmatrix}$$

Using this nomenclature, we can now form the (6, 6) delta matrix:

$$\mathbf{A}^{\Delta} = \begin{bmatrix} A^{\Delta}_{11} & A^{\Delta}_{12} & A^{\Delta}_{13} & A^{\Delta}_{14} & A^{\Delta}_{15} & A^{\Delta}_{16} \\ A^{\Delta}_{21} & A^{\Delta}_{22} & A^{\Delta}_{23} & A^{\Delta}_{24} & A^{\Delta}_{25} & A^{\Delta}_{26} \\ A^{\Delta}_{31} & A^{\Delta}_{32} & A^{\Delta}_{33} & A^{\Delta}_{34} & A^{\Delta}_{35} & A^{\Delta}_{36} \\ A^{\Delta}_{41} & A^{\Delta}_{42} & A^{\Delta}_{43} & A^{\Delta}_{44} & A^{\Delta}_{45} & A^{\Delta}_{46} \\ A^{\Delta}_{51} & A^{\Delta}_{52} & A^{\Delta}_{53} & A^{\Delta}_{54} & A^{\Delta}_{55} & A^{\Delta}_{56} \\ A^{\Delta}_{61} & A^{\Delta}_{62} & A^{\Delta}_{63} & A^{\Delta}_{64} & A^{\Delta}_{65} & A^{\Delta}_{66} \end{bmatrix} \tag{7-5}$$

If we express Eq. (7-4) by means of delta matrices, we obtain

$$B_{21}^{\Delta}A_{15}^{\Delta} + B_{22}^{\Delta}A_{25}^{\Delta} + B_{23}^{\Delta}A_{35}^{\Delta} + B_{24}^{\Delta}A_{45}^{\Delta} + B_{25}^{\Delta}A_{55}^{\Delta} + B_{26}^{\Delta}A_{65}^{\Delta} + k_w(B_{25}^{\Delta}A_{15}^{\Delta} + B_{26}^{\Delta}A_{25}^{\Delta}) = 0 \tag{7-6}$$

In the case where $k_w = \infty$ (rigid simple support), we obtain the condition for the natural frequencies by dividing throughout by k_w and then letting k_w go to infinity:

$$B_{25}^{\Delta}A_{15}^{\Delta} + B_{26}^{\Delta}A_{25}^{\Delta} = 0 \tag{7-7}$$

Let us now suppose that we first carry out the matrix multiplication $\mathbf{C} = \mathbf{BU}_P\mathbf{A}$ and then find the delta matrix of **C**. Such procedure, however, would lead to the same numerical difficulties as before. Therefore it would be better to work directly with delta matrices, which would be possible if we could formulate a rule for their multiplication. This is fortunately so, and the rule† is as follows:

$$\text{If } \mathbf{H} = \mathbf{GF} \qquad \text{then } \mathbf{H}^{\Delta} = (\mathbf{GF})^{\Delta} = \mathbf{G}^{\Delta}\mathbf{F}^{\Delta} \tag{7-8}$$

Hence, we can find the delta matrix of **C** by multiplying the delta matrices of **B**, $\mathbf{U}_P$, and **A**.

Boundary Conditions. Considering the fact that the delta matrices contain 36 elements compared with the 16 elements of the corresponding transfer matrix, one is inclined to assume that the amount of numerical computation is larger than in the case of ordinary transfer matrices. This, however, is not true because in the multiplication of delta matrices only one column has to be computed instead of two columns as in the case of transfer matrices. We shall illustrate this point for a straight beam with any arbitrary intermediate conditions.

If the transfer matrix relating the state vectors at the two ends is **U**, the frequency determinant for a beam built-in at both ends is $\begin{vmatrix} u_{13} & u_{14} \\ u_{23} & u_{24} \end{vmatrix} = 0$ or $U_{16}^{\Delta} = 0$ according to the correspondence scheme given earlier. Similarly the condition for the beam simply supported at each end is $\begin{vmatrix} u_{12} & u_{14} \\ u_{32} & u_{34} \end{vmatrix} = 0$ or $U_{25}^{\Delta} = 0$. All possible boundary conditions and the corresponding subdeterminants are conveniently assembled in Table 7-2. The symbols on the right side of the delta matrix are the boundary

Table 7-2

Left-hand boundary conditions

$$\mathbf{U}^{\Delta} = \begin{bmatrix} U_{11}^{\Delta} & U_{12}^{\Delta} & U_{13}^{\Delta} & U_{14}^{\Delta} & U_{15}^{\Delta} & U_{16}^{\Delta} \\ U_{21}^{\Delta} & U_{22}^{\Delta} & U_{23}^{\Delta} & U_{24}^{\Delta} & U_{25}^{\Delta} & U_{26}^{\Delta} \\ U_{31}^{\Delta} & U_{32}^{\Delta} & U_{33}^{\Delta} & U_{34}^{\Delta} & U_{35}^{\Delta} & U_{36}^{\Delta} \\ U_{41}^{\Delta} & U_{42}^{\Delta} & U_{43}^{\Delta} & U_{44}^{\Delta} & U_{45}^{\Delta} & U_{46}^{\Delta} \\ U_{51}^{\Delta} & U_{52}^{\Delta} & U_{53}^{\Delta} & U_{54}^{\Delta} & U_{55}^{\Delta} & U_{56}^{\Delta} \\ U_{61}^{\Delta} & U_{62}^{\Delta} & U_{63}^{\Delta} & U_{64}^{\Delta} & U_{65}^{\Delta} & U_{66}^{\Delta} \end{bmatrix}$$

Right-hand boundary conditions

† For its proof, see Ref. 29.

conditions existing on the right end of the beam (built-in, hinged, clamped but not supported, and free), and those on top of the delta matrix are the boundary conditions at the left end of the beam. For example, $U_{26}^{\Delta} = 0$ is the condition for the natural frequency when the beam is built-in at the left end and pinned at the right.

In the multiplication of delta matrices it is therefore, in view of Table 7-2, necessary only to compute the column that corresponds to the left-hand boundary conditions. For example, in the case of a built-in support at the left end of the beam, only the sixth column has to be computed. Furthermore, in the delta matrix leading from point $n - 1$ to point n on the right end of the beam, we need only that row which corresponds to the boundary condition at point n; for example, if the right end of the beam rests on a fixed hinge, we need only the second row of the last delta matrix (cf. Table 7-2).

Example 7-1. Let us turn to the problem of Fig. 7-2. Since the beam is hinged at both ends, we are concerned only with the term C_{25}^{Δ}, which is to be zero for all natural frequencies. The matrix multiplication is illustrated in Table 7-3, where the terms represented by a cross are unnecessary in the calculation. The delta matrix $\mathbf{P}^{\Delta}$ for the spring is easily obtained from the corresponding transfer matrix [cf. Eq. (3-12)]. Hence the frequency condition is

$$C_{25}^{\Delta} = B_{21}^{\Delta}A_{15}^{\Delta} + B_{22}^{\Delta}A_{25}^{\Delta} + B_{23}^{\Delta}A_{35}^{\Delta} + B_{24}^{\Delta}A_{45}^{\Delta} + B_{25}^{\Delta}A_{55}^{\Delta} + B_{26}^{\Delta}A_{65}^{\Delta} + k_w(B_{25}^{\Delta}A_{15}^{\Delta} + B_{26}^{\Delta}A_{25}^{\Delta}) = 0$$

Even when the spring is very stiff, the numerical calculation of the frequency equation offers no difficulty since the value of each determinant is accurately known. In the special case when $k_w = \infty$ we have the following condition for the natural frequencies:

$$B_{25}^{\Delta}A_{15}^{\Delta} + B_{26}^{\Delta}A_{25}^{\Delta} = 0$$

This result can be obtained very easily if we use the special delta matrix for an infinitely stiff spring which is obtained by dividing $\mathbf{P}^{\Delta}$ throughout by k_w and then letting k_w go to infinity. The layout of the matrix multiplication is indicated in Table 7-4. Therefore the frequency condition for a straight beam on three fixed hinged supports is

$$C_{25}^{\Delta} = B_{25}^{\Delta}A_{15}^{\Delta} + B_{26}^{\Delta}A_{25}^{\Delta} = 0$$

Whereas the advantage of delta matrices in avoiding the difference of nearly equal large numbers and in handling stiff spring supports is obvious, they are not suitable for the direct calculation of the normal modes.

The Reduced Delta Matrix. It was shown in Table 7-2 that each element of the delta matrix corresponds to a definite set of boundary conditions. However, not all these boundary conditions are physically feasible. For example, the simultaneous conditions $\psi = 0$ and $M = 0$ are impossible. The elements of the middle two columns and the middle two rows therefore have no physical meaning, and their role is such that they play only a part when the delta matrices are being multiplied. Fuhrke [31, 37] found that it was possible to reduce the size of the (6, 6) delta matrix because, in general, the elements of the third and fourth columns of this matrix are related as follows ($U^{\Delta} = U_{34}^{\Delta}$):

$$\mathbf{U}^{\Delta} = \left[\begin{array}{cc|c|cc} U_{11}^{\Delta} & U_{12}^{\Delta} & U_{13}^{\Delta} = U_{14}^{\Delta} & U_{15}^{\Delta} & U_{16}^{\Delta} \\ U_{21}^{\Delta} & U_{22}^{\Delta} & U_{23}^{\Delta} = U_{24}^{\Delta} & U_{25}^{\Delta} & U_{26}^{\Delta} \\ \hline U_{31}^{\Delta} & U_{32}^{\Delta} & U^{\Delta}+1 \quad U^{\Delta} & U_{35}^{\Delta} & U_{36}^{\Delta} \\ U_{41}^{\Delta} & U_{42}^{\Delta} & U^{\Delta} \quad U^{\Delta}+1 & U_{45}^{\Delta} & U_{46}^{\Delta} \\ \hline U_{51}^{\Delta} & U_{52}^{\Delta} & U_{53}^{\Delta} = U_{54}^{\Delta} & U_{55}^{\Delta} & U_{56}^{\Delta} \\ U_{61}^{\Delta} & U_{62}^{\Delta} & U_{63}^{\Delta} = U_{64}^{\Delta} & U_{65}^{\Delta} & U_{66}^{\Delta} \end{array}\right]$$

Table 7-3

$$\mathbf{A}^{\Delta}=\begin{bmatrix} x & x & x & x & A^{\Delta}_{15} & x \\ x & x & x & x & A^{\Delta}_{25} & x \\ x & x & x & x & A^{\Delta}_{35} & x \\ x & x & x & x & A^{\Delta}_{45} & x \\ x & x & x & x & A^{\Delta}_{55} & x \\ x & x & x & x & A^{\Delta}_{65} & x \end{bmatrix}$$

$$\mathbf{P}^{\Delta}=\begin{bmatrix} 1 & 0 & 0 & 0 & 0 & 0 \\ 0 & 1 & 0 & 0 & 0 & 0 \\ 0 & 0 & 1 & 0 & 0 & 0 \\ 0 & 0 & 0 & 1 & 0 & 0 \\ k_w & 0 & 0 & 0 & 1 & 0 \\ 0 & k_w & 0 & 0 & 0 & 1 \end{bmatrix} \begin{bmatrix} x & x & x & x & A^{\Delta}_{15} & x \\ x & x & x & x & A^{\Delta}_{25} & x \\ x & x & x & x & A^{\Delta}_{35} & x \\ x & x & x & x & A^{\Delta}_{45} & x \\ x & x & x & x & k_wA^{\Delta}_{15}+A^{\Delta}_{55} & x \\ x & x & x & x & k_wA^{\Delta}_{25}+A^{\Delta}_{65} & x \end{bmatrix}$$

$$\mathbf{B}^{\Delta}=\begin{bmatrix} x & x & x & x & x & x \\ B^{\Delta}_{21} & B^{\Delta}_{22} & B^{\Delta}_{23} & B^{\Delta}_{24} & B^{\Delta}_{25} & B^{\Delta}_{26} \\ x & x & x & x & x & x \\ x & x & x & x & x & x \\ x & x & x & x & x & x \\ x & x & x & x & x & x \end{bmatrix} \begin{bmatrix} & & & & \vdots & \\ \cdots & \cdots & \cdots & \cdots & C^{\Delta}_{25} & \\ & & & \mathbf{C}^{\Delta} & & \\ & & & & & \\ & & & & & \\ & & & & & \end{bmatrix}$$

We can now form a (5, 5) matrix in which the middle two columns are replaced by one column that is the sum of the two columns replaced. One of the central rows is removed, so that we obtain the so-called "reduced delta matrix":

$$\mathbf{U}^{\Delta_r}=\begin{bmatrix} U^{\Delta}_{11} & U^{\Delta}_{12} & 2U^{\Delta}_{13} & U^{\Delta}_{15} & U^{\Delta}_{16} \\ U^{\Delta}_{21} & U^{\Delta}_{22} & 2U^{\Delta}_{23} & U^{\Delta}_{25} & U^{\Delta}_{26} \\ U^{\Delta}_{31} & U^{\Delta}_{32} & 2U^{\Delta}+1 & U^{\Delta}_{35} & U^{\Delta}_{36} \\ U^{\Delta}_{51} & U^{\Delta}_{52} & 2U^{\Delta}_{53} & U^{\Delta}_{55} & U^{\Delta}_{56} \\ U^{\Delta}_{61} & U^{\Delta}_{62} & 2U^{\Delta}_{63} & U^{\Delta}_{65} & U^{\Delta}_{66} \end{bmatrix} \quad \text{cf. Table 7-2}$$

Table 7-4

$$\mathbf{A}^\Delta = \begin{bmatrix} x & x & x & x & A^\Delta_{15} & x \\ x & x & x & x & A^\Delta_{25} & x \\ x & x & x & x & A^\Delta_{35} & x \\ x & x & x & x & A^\Delta_{45} & x \\ x & x & x & x & A^\Delta_{55} & x \\ x & x & x & x & A^\Delta_{65} & x \end{bmatrix}$$

$$\mathbf{P}^\Delta = \begin{bmatrix} 0 & 0 & 0 & 0 & 0 & 0 \\ 0 & 0 & 0 & 0 & 0 & 0 \\ 0 & 0 & 0 & 0 & 0 & 0 \\ 0 & 0 & 0 & 0 & 0 & 0 \\ 1 & 0 & 0 & 0 & 0 & 0 \\ 0 & 1 & 0 & 0 & 0 & 0 \end{bmatrix} \quad \begin{bmatrix} 0 & 0 & 0 & 0 & 0 & 0 \\ 0 & 0 & 0 & 0 & 0 & 0 \\ 0 & 0 & 0 & 0 & 0 & 0 \\ 0 & 0 & 0 & 0 & 0 & 0 \\ 0 & 0 & 0 & 0 & A^\Delta_{15} & 0 \\ 0 & 0 & 0 & 0 & A^\Delta_{25} & 0 \end{bmatrix}$$

$$\mathbf{B}^\Delta = \begin{bmatrix} x & x & x & x & x & x \\ B^\Delta_{21} & B^\Delta_{22} & B^\Delta_{23} & B^\Delta_{24} & B^\Delta_{25} & B^\Delta_{26} \\ x & x & x & x & x & x \\ x & x & x & x & x & x \\ x & x & x & x & x & x \\ x & x & x & x & x & x \end{bmatrix} \quad \begin{bmatrix} & & & & & \\ & & & & & C^\Delta_{25} \\ & & & & & \\ & & & \mathbf{C}^\Delta_{25} & & \\ & & & & & \\ & & & & & \end{bmatrix}$$

The use of the reduced delta matrix does not affect the result of the multiplication. In order to facilitate the application of the reduced delta matrices, a small catalogue of the most important ones is compiled below. The extension of the delta-matrix method to nonhomogeneous problems was demonstrated by Pestel [36]. The interested reader is referred to this paper.

Catalogue of Reduced Delta Matrices. This catalogue is based chiefly on the work by Fuhrke [37]. For the reasons explained above, it is concerned solely with the bending vibration of straight beams. The symbols used are those of the Catalogue of Transfer Matrices at the end of the book (cf. Sec. C-3). As a special feature of the delta matrices this catalogue also contains the reduced delta matrices of rigid intermediate conditions.

a. Homogeneous field on elastic foundation (cf. Sec. C-3*b*)

$$\mathbf{U}^{\Delta_r} = \begin{bmatrix} C & \frac{a}{l}A & 2aD & alB & \frac{a^2}{\beta^4}(1-C) \\ -\frac{\beta^4 l}{a}B & 2C-1 & 2lA & 2l^2D & alB \\ -\frac{\beta^4}{a}D & -\frac{\beta^4}{l}B & 2C-1 & lA & aD \\ -\frac{\beta^4}{al}A & -\frac{2\beta^4}{l^2}D & -\frac{2\beta^4}{l}B & 2C-1 & \frac{a}{l}A \\ \frac{\beta^4}{a^2}(1-C) & -\frac{\beta^4}{al}A & -\frac{2\beta^4}{a}D & -\frac{\beta^4 l}{a}B & C \end{bmatrix}^{\dagger}$$

$$\beta^4 = \frac{\omega^2\mu - \Gamma}{EJ}l^4 \qquad \beta^4 = \frac{\omega^2\mu l^4}{EJ} \quad \text{without elastic foundation}$$

$$a = \frac{l^2}{EJ}$$

$$A = \frac{1}{2\beta}(\cosh\beta\sin\beta + \sinh\beta\cos\beta)$$

$$B = \frac{1}{2\beta^3}(\cosh\beta\sin\beta - \sinh\beta\cos\beta)$$

$$C = \tfrac{1}{2}(1 + \cosh\beta\cos\beta)$$

$$D = \frac{1}{2\beta^2}\sinh\beta\sin\beta$$

b. Elastic massless field (cf. Sec. C-3*c*)

$$\mathbf{U}^{\Delta_r} = \begin{bmatrix} 1 & \frac{a}{l} & a & al(\frac{1}{3}+b) & a^2(\frac{1}{12}+b) \\ 0 & 1 & 2l & l^2 & al(\frac{1}{3}+b) \\ 0 & 0 & 1 & l & \frac{a}{2} \\ 0 & 0 & 0 & 1 & \frac{a}{l} \\ 0 & 0 & 0 & 0 & 1 \end{bmatrix}$$

$$a = \frac{l^2}{EJ} \qquad b = \frac{EJ}{l^2GA_s}$$

† The dashed lines frame the parts of the reduced delta matrix which pertain to feasible boundary conditions (cf. Table 7-2).

c. Rigid field (cf. Sec. C-3*d*)

$$\mathbf{U}^{\Delta_r} = \begin{bmatrix} 1 & 0 & 0 & 0 & 0 \\ m\omega^2\left(hi^2 - \frac{l^2}{3}\right) & 1 & 2l & l^2 & 0 \\ -m\omega^2\frac{l}{2} & 0 & 1 & l & 0 \\ -m\omega^2 & 0 & 0 & 1 & 0 \\ m^2\omega^4\left(\frac{l^2}{12} - hi^2\right) & -m\omega^2 & -m\omega^2 l & m\omega^2\left(hi^2 - \frac{l^2}{3}\right) & 1 \end{bmatrix}$$

$$h = \begin{cases} -1 & \text{for bending vibration} \\ +1 & \text{for rotating shaft (equal angular direction of whirl and rotation)} \\ -3 & \text{for rotating shaft (opposite angular direction of whirl and rotation [38; 39])} \end{cases}$$

d. Point mass with rotary inertia (cf. Sec. C-3*f*)

$$\mathbf{U}^{\Delta_r} = \begin{bmatrix} 1 & 0 & 0 & 0 & 0 \\ hI\omega^2 & 1 & 0 & 0 & 0 \\ 0 & 0 & 1 & 0 & 0 \\ -m\omega^2 & 0 & 0 & 1 & 0 \\ -hmI\omega^4 & -m\omega^2 & 0 & hI\omega^2 & 1 \end{bmatrix}$$

(For h, see section *c* above.)

e. Spring (linear and rotary) (cf. Sec. C-3*f*)

$$\mathbf{U}^{\Delta_r} = \begin{bmatrix} 1 & 0 & 0 & 0 & 0 \\ k^* & 1 & 0 & 0 & 0 \\ 0 & 0 & 1 & 0 & 0 \\ k & 0 & 0 & 1 & 0 \\ +kk^* & k & 0 & k^* & 1 \end{bmatrix}$$

f. Elastic hinge (rotary) (cf. Sec. C-3*g*)

$$\mathbf{U}^{\Delta_r} = \begin{bmatrix} 1 & \frac{1}{k^*} & 0 & 0 & 0 \\ 0 & 1 & 0 & 0 & 0 \\ 0 & 0 & 1 & 0 & 0 \\ 0 & 0 & 0 & 1 & \frac{1}{k^*} \\ 0 & 0 & 0 & 0 & 1 \end{bmatrix} \qquad \begin{matrix} l \to 0 \\ \\ \frac{l}{EJ} \to \frac{1}{k^*} \end{matrix}$$

g. Elastic hinge (linear) (cf. Sec. C-3*h*)

$$\mathbf{U}^{\Delta_r} = \begin{bmatrix} 1 & 0 & 0 & \frac{1}{k} & 0 \\ 0 & 1 & 0 & 0 & \frac{1}{k} \\ 0 & 0 & 1 & 0 & 0 \\ 0 & 0 & 0 & 1 & 0 \\ 0 & 0 & 0 & 0 & 1 \end{bmatrix} \qquad \begin{array}{l} l \to 0 \\ \\ \dfrac{l}{GA_s} \to \dfrac{1}{k} \end{array}$$

h. Spring-coupled mass (cf. Secs. C-3*i* and *j*)

$$\mathbf{U}^{\Delta_r} = \begin{bmatrix} 1 & 0 & 0 & 0 & 0 \\ 0 & 1 & 0 & 0 & 0 \\ 0 & 0 & 1 & 0 & 0 \\ K_d & 0 & 0 & 1 & 0 \\ 0 & K_d & 0 & 0 & 1 \end{bmatrix} \qquad K_d = \text{dynamic stiffness}$$

i. Rigid intermediate conditions

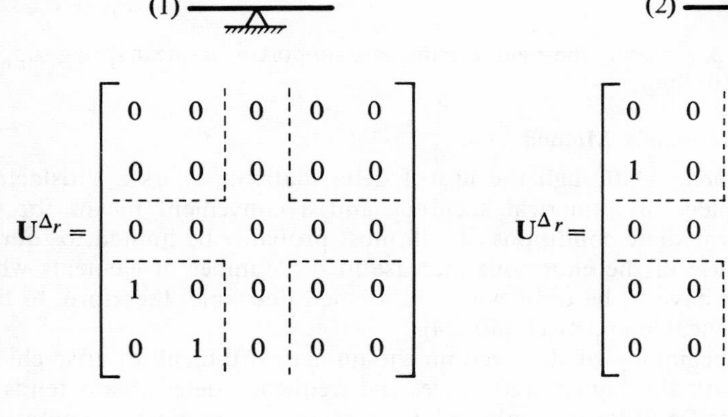

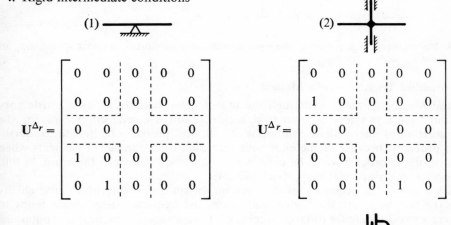

(1)

$$\mathbf{U}^{\Delta_r} = \begin{bmatrix} 0 & 0 & 0 & 0 & 0 \\ 0 & 0 & 0 & 0 & 0 \\ 0 & 0 & 0 & 0 & 0 \\ 1 & 0 & 0 & 0 & 0 \\ 0 & 1 & 0 & 0 & 0 \end{bmatrix}$$

(2)

$$\mathbf{U}^{\Delta_r} = \begin{bmatrix} 0 & 0 & 0 & 0 & 0 \\ 1 & 0 & 0 & 0 & 0 \\ 0 & 0 & 0 & 0 & 0 \\ 0 & 0 & 0 & 0 & 0 \\ 0 & 0 & 0 & 1 & 0 \end{bmatrix}$$

(3)

$$\mathbf{U}^{\Delta_r} = \begin{bmatrix} 0 & 1 & 0 & 0 & 0 \\ 0 & 0 & 0 & 0 & 0 \\ 0 & 0 & 0 & 0 & 0 \\ 0 & 0 & 0 & 0 & 1 \\ 0 & 0 & 0 & 0 & 0 \end{bmatrix}$$

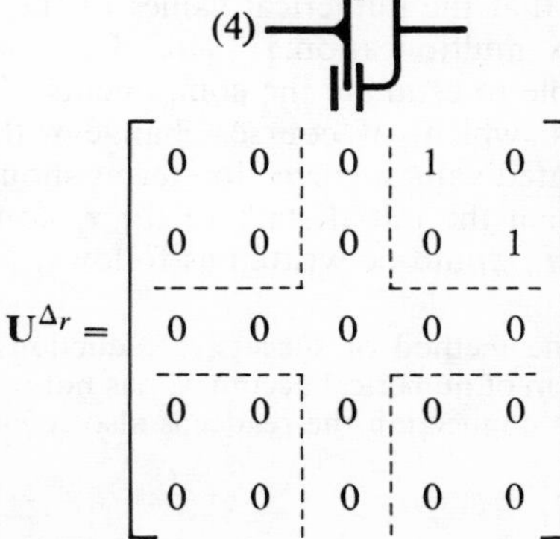

$$\mathbf{U}^{\Delta_r} = \begin{bmatrix} 0 & 0 & 0 & 1 & 0 \\ 0 & 0 & 0 & 0 & 1 \\ 0 & 0 & 0 & 0 & 0 \\ 0 & 0 & 0 & 0 & 0 \\ 0 & 0 & 0 & 0 & 0 \end{bmatrix}$$

PROBLEMS

7-1. With the help of delta matrices, find the natural frequency for the beam-mass system shown in Fig. P 7-1.

FIG. P 7-1

7-2. Repeat Prob. 7-1, replacing the rigid intermediate support by a spring support of stiffness k_w.

7-3. Figure P 7-3 shows a simple substitute system for a machine shaft on three rigid supports. The data are as follows:

$$l_1 = l_2 = 8 \text{ ft} \qquad l_3 = l_4 = 10 \text{ ft}$$

$$m_1 = 50 \text{ lb-sec}^2/\text{ft} \qquad m_2 = 40 \text{ lb-sec}^2/\text{ft}$$

$$(EJ)_1 = 4 \times 10^{10} \text{ lb-in.}^2 \qquad (EJ)_2 = 5 \times 10^{10} \text{ lb-in.}^2$$

Using delta matrices, complete the calculations for $\omega = 25$, 30, and 35 cps, and hence estimate the first critical speed.

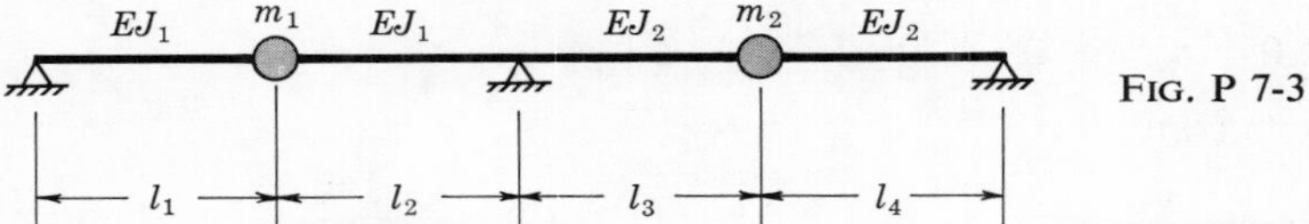

FIG. P 7-3

7-4. Repeat Prob. 7-3, replacing the rigid intermediate support by a linear spring support of stiffness $k_w = 3 \times 10^5$ lb/in.

7-3. Modified Transfer-matrix Method

Basic Idea of Method. Although the use of delta matrices offers a satisfactory solution to the problem of numerical accuracy and a convenient means for the consideration of intermediate conditions, it will most probably be limited to fourth-order problems because of the enormous increase in the number of elements when cases of higher order have to be dealt with. It seemed desirable, therefore, to find another generally applicable approach [40, 24].

As we saw in the beginning of this section, the numerical difficulties arise chiefly from the fact that with the higher frequencies the frequency determinant tends to become a small difference of large numbers. Furthermore, numerical computations show that the numerical values of the matrix elements increase with each successive matrix multiplication.† This dilemma could be resolved in most cases if it were possible to estimate the components of the initial state vector $\mathbf{z}_0$ close to their actual values, which, of course, change with ω. In order to allow a correction of the estimated values, correction terms should be added so that, for the nth-order problem in which the initial state vector $\mathbf{z}_0$ consists, in general, of $n/2$ components equal to zero, $\mathbf{z}_0$ would be written as follows:

† The method of successive reductions [41, 59], which is also capable of handling the problem of numerical accuracy, has not been included in this chapter, in order to save space. In this connection the reader is also referred to Ref. 67.

$$
\mathbf{z}_0 = \begin{bmatrix} \left.\begin{matrix} 0 \\ 0 \\ \cdot \\ \cdot \\ \cdot \\ 0 \end{matrix}\right\} \frac{n}{2} \\ \lambda_0 = 1 \\ \lambda_1 \\ \lambda_2 \\ \cdot \\ \cdot \\ \cdot \\ \cdot \\ \lambda_{n/2-1} \end{bmatrix} + \kappa_1 \begin{bmatrix} \left.\begin{matrix} 0 \\ 0 \\ \cdot \\ \cdot \\ \cdot \\ 0 \end{matrix}\right\} \frac{n}{2} \\ 0 \\ 1 \\ 0 \\ \cdot \\ \cdot \\ \cdot \\ \cdot \\ 0 \end{bmatrix} + \kappa_2 \begin{bmatrix} \left.\begin{matrix} 0 \\ 0 \\ \cdot \\ \cdot \\ \cdot \\ 0 \end{matrix}\right\} \frac{n}{2} \\ 0 \\ 0 \\ 1 \\ 0 \\ \cdot \\ \cdot \\ \cdot \\ 0 \end{bmatrix} + \cdots + \kappa_{n/2-1} \begin{bmatrix} \left.\begin{matrix} 0 \\ 0 \\ \cdot \\ \cdot \\ \cdot \\ 0 \end{matrix}\right\} \frac{n}{2} \\ 0 \\ 0 \\ 0 \\ \cdot \\ \cdot \\ \cdot \\ 0 \\ 1 \end{bmatrix} \tag{7-9}
$$

In this scheme the letters λ_i represent actual numbers that are the estimated values for the corresponding physical quantities constituting the state vector $\mathbf{z}_0$, whereas the correction factors κ_i are unknown. Since we are considering a problem of free vibrations, λ_0 is arbitrarily taken equal to unity. The components are arranged in such a way that those equal to zero on account of the boundary conditions are assembled† in the upper half of the state vector $\mathbf{z}_0$.

Fourth-order Problem. In order to demonstrate the application and the merits of this basic idea, let us consider the simple problem of free vibrations of the Myklestad beam in Fig. 7-3. With

$$l = 1 \qquad \text{and} \qquad EJ = \tfrac{1}{6}$$

the transfer matrix is (cf. matrix C-3k)

$$
\begin{bmatrix} 1 & 1 & 3 & 1 \\ 0 & 1 & 6 & 3 \\ 0 & 0 & 1 & 1 \\ m\omega^2 & m\omega^2 & 3m\omega^2 & 1 + m\omega^2 \end{bmatrix}
$$

If we carry out the ordinary transfer-matrix multiplication for the case $m\omega^2 = 3$, the frequency determinant is

$$82 \times 289 - 558 \times 42 = 262$$

† This is done here only to facilitate the writing of the mathematical proofs given later. In actual computing practice the components remain in their usual position, so that the elements of the transfer matrix need not be rearranged.

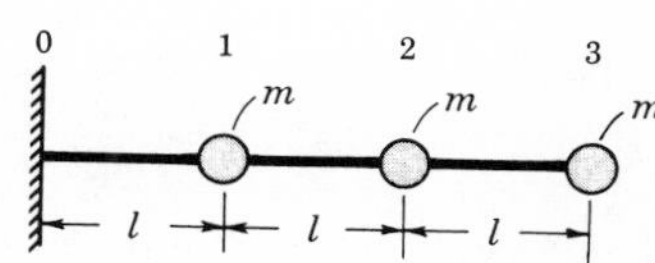

FIG. 7-3. Clamped beam.

which, considering the small numbers in the transfer matrix, constitutes a difference of surprisingly large numbers.

Since we have a fourth-order problem, Eq. (7-9) reduces to

$$\mathbf{z}_0 = \begin{bmatrix} 0 \\ 0 \\ 1 \\ \lambda_1 \end{bmatrix} + \kappa_1 \begin{bmatrix} 0 \\ 0 \\ 0 \\ 1 \end{bmatrix}$$

Let us start with a frequency corresponding to $m\omega^2 = 1$. Since we begin with a small frequency, no numerical difficulties need be expected even though our estimate of λ_1 may be quite inaccurate. For simplicity's sake we take $\lambda_1 = 1$; therefore

$$\mathbf{z}_0 = \begin{bmatrix} 0 \\ 0 \\ 1 \\ 1 \end{bmatrix} + \kappa_1 \begin{bmatrix} 0 \\ 0 \\ 0 \\ 1 \end{bmatrix}$$

This state vector is then successively multiplied by the transfer matrices:

$$\begin{aligned}
& \begin{bmatrix} 0 \\ 0 \\ 1 \\ 1 \end{bmatrix}_0 + \kappa_1 \begin{bmatrix} 0 \\ 0 \\ 0 \\ 1 \end{bmatrix}_0 \\
\begin{bmatrix} 1 & 1 & 3 & 1 \\ 0 & 1 & 6 & 3 \\ 0 & 0 & 1 & 1 \\ 1 & 1 & 3 & 2 \end{bmatrix} & \begin{bmatrix} 4 \\ 9 \\ 2 \\ 5 \end{bmatrix}_1 + \kappa_1 \begin{bmatrix} 1 \\ 3 \\ 1 \\ 2 \end{bmatrix}_1 \\
\begin{bmatrix} 1 & 1 & 3 & 1 \\ 0 & 1 & 6 & 3 \\ 0 & 0 & 1 & 1 \\ 1 & 1 & 3 & 2 \end{bmatrix} & \begin{bmatrix} 24 \\ 36 \\ 7 \\ 29 \end{bmatrix}_2 + \kappa_1 \begin{bmatrix} 9 \\ 15 \\ 3 \\ 11 \end{bmatrix}_2 \\
\begin{bmatrix} 1 & 1 & 3 & 1 \\ 0 & 1 & 6 & 3 \\ 0 & 0 & 1 & 1 \\ 1 & 1 & 3 & 2 \end{bmatrix} & \begin{bmatrix} 110 \\ 165 \\ 36 \\ 139 \end{bmatrix}_3 + \kappa_1 \begin{bmatrix} 44 \\ 66 \\ 14 \\ 55 \end{bmatrix}_3 \begin{matrix} \\ \\ = 0 \\ = 0 \end{matrix}
\end{aligned}$$

The boundary conditions at point 3 lead to the following two equations for κ_1:

$$36 + 14\kappa_1 = 0 \qquad 139 + 55\kappa_1 = 0$$

If both equations would yield the same value for κ_1, they would not be independent of each other; i.e., their determinant (which is the frequency determinant) would be equal to zero. In such a case the value of ω used in the numerical computation would correspond to an eigenfrequency of the beam. As will generally be the case, the above equations each yield a different value for κ_1; therefore let us denote the value obtained from the second equation by x_1 and the one from the first equation by y_1. Then

$$x_1 = -\tfrac{139}{55} = -2.527 \qquad y_1 = -\tfrac{36}{14} = -2.571$$

$$R = x_1 - y_1 = +0.044 \tag{7-10}$$

Since $x_1 - y_1 \neq 0$, the value of ω used above is not a natural frequency. We now compute the mean value of x_1 and y_1 and use it as our correction factor:

$$\bar{\kappa}_1 = \frac{x_1 + y_1}{2} = -2.55$$

Adding this value to λ_1 in the state vector $\mathbf{z}_0$, we obtain

$$\mathbf{z}_0 = \begin{bmatrix} 0 \\ 0 \\ 1 \\ 1 + (-2.55) \end{bmatrix} + \kappa_1' \begin{bmatrix} 0 \\ 0 \\ 0 \\ 1 \end{bmatrix} = \begin{bmatrix} 0 \\ 0 \\ 1 \\ -1.55 \end{bmatrix} + \kappa_1' \begin{bmatrix} 0 \\ 0 \\ 0 \\ 1 \end{bmatrix}$$

We now repeat the numerical computation for the same $m\omega^2 = 1$:

$$\begin{bmatrix} 0 \\ 0 \\ 1 \\ -1.55 \end{bmatrix} + \kappa_1' \begin{bmatrix} 0 \\ 0 \\ 0 \\ 1 \end{bmatrix} = \mathbf{z}_0$$

$$\begin{bmatrix} 1 & 1 & 3 & 1 \\ 0 & 1 & 6 & 3 \\ 0 & 0 & 1 & 1 \\ 1 & 1 & 3 & 2 \end{bmatrix} \begin{bmatrix} 1.45 \\ 1.35 \\ -0.55 \\ -0.10 \end{bmatrix} + \kappa_1' \begin{bmatrix} 1 \\ 3 \\ 1 \\ 2 \end{bmatrix} = \mathbf{z}_1$$

$$\begin{bmatrix} 1 & 1 & 3 & 1 \\ 0 & 1 & 6 & 3 \\ 0 & 0 & 1 & 1 \\ 1 & 1 & 3 & 2 \end{bmatrix} \begin{bmatrix} 1.05 \\ -2.25 \\ -0.65 \\ 0.95 \end{bmatrix} + \kappa_1' \begin{bmatrix} 9 \\ 15 \\ 3 \\ 11 \end{bmatrix} = \mathbf{z}_2$$

$$\begin{bmatrix} 1 & 1 & 3 & 1 \\ 0 & 1 & 6 & 3 \\ 0 & 0 & 1 & 1 \\ 1 & 1 & 3 & 2 \end{bmatrix} \begin{bmatrix} -2.20 \\ -3.30 \\ 0.30 \\ -1.25 \end{bmatrix} + \kappa_1' \begin{bmatrix} 44 \\ 66 \\ 14 \\ 55 \end{bmatrix} = \mathbf{z}_3$$

It is easily recognized that the elements of the first columns of the state vectors $\mathbf{z}_0$, $\mathbf{z}_1$, $\mathbf{z}_2$, and $\mathbf{z}_3$ remain consistently small in contrast to their numerical increase when the first column of $\mathbf{z}_0$ was taken to be $\{0 \;\; 0 \;\; 1 \;\; 1\}$. The boundary conditions at point 3 now yield the following equations for κ_1':

$$0.30 + 14\kappa_1' = 0 \qquad -1.25 + 55\kappa_1' = 0$$

Hence we obtain

$$x_1' = +\frac{1.25}{55} = +0.0227 \qquad y_1' = -\frac{0.30}{14} = -0.0214$$

$$R = 0.0227 - (-0.0214) = +0.0441 \tag{7-10a}$$

Whereas R remains unchanged,

$$\bar{\kappa}_1' = \frac{x_1' + y_1'}{2} = 0.00065$$

is much smaller. Later it will be shown theoretically that $\bar{\kappa}_1'$ should have been equal to zero, the deviation being due to rounding-off errors.

Since R remained unchanged, it is actually unnecessary to repeat the calculation for the same value of ω. However, comparison of Eqs. (7-10) and (7-10a) reveals that in the second computation, where the correct initial values for the chosen value of ω were used, the value of R is found by subtracting two equal numbers of opposite sign, thereby avoiding numerical difficulties.

We now proceed with the computation by choosing a new value for ω. If this is taken close to the preceding one, it can be expected that the value -1.55 is a good estimate for the new λ_1.

Let us carry out the next matrix multiplication for $m\omega^2 = 2$:

$$\begin{bmatrix} 0 \\ 0 \\ 1 \\ -1.55 \end{bmatrix}_0 + \kappa_1 \begin{bmatrix} 0 \\ 0 \\ 0 \\ 1 \end{bmatrix}_0$$

$$\begin{bmatrix} 1 & 1 & 3 & 1 \\ 0 & 1 & 6 & 3 \\ 0 & 0 & 1 & 1 \\ 2 & 2 & 6 & 3 \end{bmatrix} \begin{bmatrix} 1.45 \\ 1.35 \\ -0.55 \\ 1.35 \end{bmatrix}_1 + \kappa_1 \begin{bmatrix} 1 \\ 3 \\ 1 \\ 3 \end{bmatrix}_1$$

$$\begin{bmatrix} 1 & 1 & 3 & 1 \\ 0 & 1 & 6 & 3 \\ 0 & 0 & 1 & 1 \\ 2 & 2 & 6 & 3 \end{bmatrix} \begin{bmatrix} 2.50 \\ 2.10 \\ 0.80 \\ 6.35 \end{bmatrix}_2 + \kappa_1 \begin{bmatrix} 10 \\ 18 \\ 4 \\ 23 \end{bmatrix}_2$$

$$\begin{bmatrix} 1 & 1 & 3 & 1 \\ 0 & 1 & 6 & 3 \\ 0 & 0 & 1 & 1 \\ 2 & 2 & 6 & 3 \end{bmatrix} \begin{bmatrix} 13.55 \\ 25.95 \\ 7.15 \\ 33.05 \end{bmatrix}_3 + \kappa_1 \begin{bmatrix} 63 \\ 111 \\ 27 \\ 149 \end{bmatrix}_3$$

The fact that $\lambda_1 = -1.55$ was not a poor estimate is borne out by the fact that the elements in the first-column vectors did not rise† too rapidly with each successive matrix multiplication, although the step from $m\omega^2 = 1$ to $m\omega^2 = 2$ was quite large. The boundary conditions at point 3 again yield the following two equations:

† The numbers in the first column are less than one-tenth of the size they would assume if λ_1 had been taken equal to unity.

$$7.15 + 27\kappa_1 = 0 \qquad 33.05 + 149\kappa_1 = 0$$

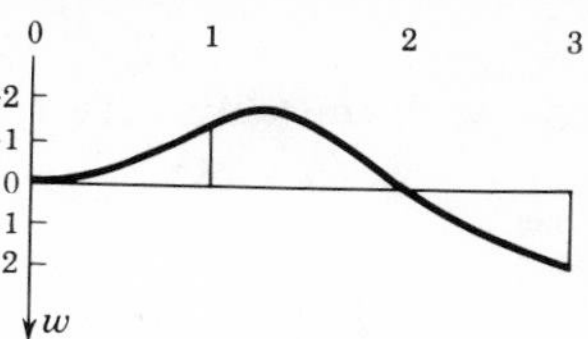

FIG. 7-4. Deflection of beam in Fig. 7-3 for $m\omega^2 = 2$.

from which we obtain

$$x_1 = -\frac{33.05}{149} = -0.222$$

$$y_1 = -\frac{7.15}{27} = -0.265$$

Hence $\quad R = x_1 - y_1 = +0.043 \quad$ and $\quad \bar{\kappa}_1 = \dfrac{x_1 + y_1}{2} = -0.243$

Multiplying the right-hand columns in the last multiplication table by $\kappa_1 = -0.243$ and adding the result to the corresponding left-hand columns, we obtain the values for $-w$, ψ, M, and Q at points 0, 1, 2, and 3:

$$\mathbf{z}_0 = \begin{bmatrix} -w_0 = 0 \\ \psi_0 = 0 \\ M_0 = 1 \\ Q_0 = -1.79 \end{bmatrix} \qquad \mathbf{z}_1 = \begin{bmatrix} -w_1 = 1.21 \\ \psi_1 = 0.62 \\ M_1 = -0.79 \\ Q_1 = 0.62 \end{bmatrix}$$

$$\mathbf{z}_2 = \begin{bmatrix} -w_2 = 0.07 \\ \psi_2 = -2.27 \\ M_2 = -0.17 \\ Q_2 = 0.67 \end{bmatrix} \qquad \mathbf{z}_3 = \begin{bmatrix} -w_3 = -1.96 \\ \psi_3 = -1.05 \\ M_3 = 0.59 \\ Q_3 = -3.15 \end{bmatrix}$$

From the plot of the deflection w in Fig. 7-4 we can readily see that $m\omega^2 = 2$ corresponds to a frequency between the second natural frequency and the third natural frequency.

In the same way the calculation was continued for higher values of $m\omega^2$. In every case slide-rule accuracy was sufficient. The result of the frequency computation is plotted in Fig. 7-5.

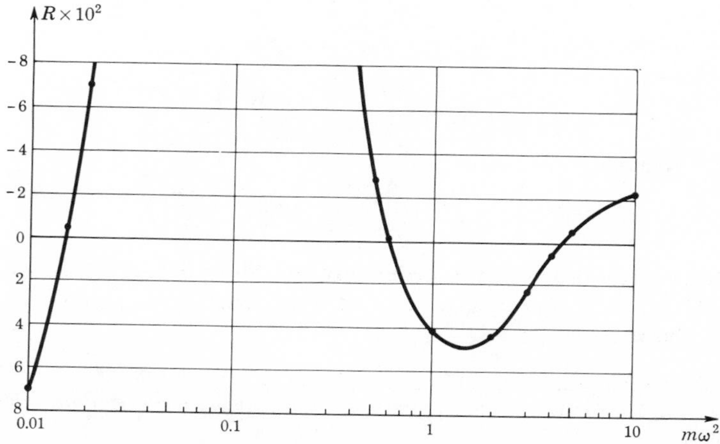

FIG. 7-5. Plot of $R(\omega)$ for beam in Fig. 7-3.

Sixth-order Problem. Since many engineering problems are of sixth order, we deal with this case before considering the general case. Here we have

$$\mathbf{z}_1 = \begin{bmatrix} 0 \\ 0 \\ 0 \\ 1 \\ \lambda_1 \\ \lambda_2 \end{bmatrix} + \kappa_1 \begin{bmatrix} 0 \\ 0 \\ 0 \\ 0 \\ 1 \\ 0 \end{bmatrix} + \kappa_2 \begin{bmatrix} 0 \\ 0 \\ 0 \\ 0 \\ 0 \\ 1 \end{bmatrix}$$

If the product of all transfer matrices between the boundaries 0 and n is denoted by $\mathbf{P}$ and if the matrices are so arranged that the elements of the column vector at n, which are zero on account of the boundary conditions at n, occupy the top three positions (see footnote on page 205), then we obtain the following three nonhomogeneous equations for κ_1 and κ_2:

$$\begin{aligned} p_{14} + p_{15}(\lambda_1 + \kappa_1) + p_{16}(\lambda_2 + \kappa_2) &= 0 \\ p_{24} + p_{25}(\lambda_1 + \kappa_1) + p_{26}(\lambda_2 + \kappa_2) &= 0 \\ p_{34} + p_{35}(\lambda_1 + \kappa_1) + p_{36}(\lambda_2 + \kappa_2) &= 0 \end{aligned} \tag{7-11}$$

The first two equations of (7-11) now yield for κ_1 and κ_2 the following two values:

$$x_1 = -\lambda_1 + \frac{\Delta_1}{\Delta_3} \qquad \text{and} \qquad x_2 = -\lambda_2 + \frac{\Delta_2}{\Delta_3}\dagger$$

with
$$\Delta_1 = \begin{vmatrix} p_{16} & p_{14} \\ p_{26} & p_{24} \end{vmatrix} \qquad \Delta_2 = \begin{vmatrix} p_{14} & p_{15} \\ p_{24} & p_{25} \end{vmatrix} \qquad \Delta_3 = \begin{vmatrix} p_{15} & p_{16} \\ p_{25} & p_{26} \end{vmatrix}$$

Inserting x_1 for κ_1 in the third equation of (7-11) yields in general another value y_2 for κ_2, unless $\omega = \omega_E$, because then the frequency determinant

$$\Delta(\omega) = \begin{vmatrix} p_{14} & p_{15} & p_{16} \\ p_{24} & p_{25} & p_{26} \\ p_{34} & p_{35} & p_{36} \end{vmatrix}$$

vanishes. Hence,

$$y_2 = -\lambda_2 - \left[\left(p_{34} + \frac{p_{35}\Delta_1}{\Delta_3}\right)\frac{1}{p_{36}}\right]\ddagger$$

Therefore the remainder

$$R = x_2 - y_2 = \frac{\Delta_2}{\Delta_3} + \frac{1}{p_{36}}\left(p_{34} + \frac{p_{35}\Delta_1}{\Delta_3}\right)$$

is, as we already saw in the fourth-order problem, independent of the estimates for λ_1 and λ_2. Its value, however, is a function of ω, since $p_{i\kappa} = p_{i\kappa}(\omega)$. If $R(\omega) = 0$, then $\omega = \omega_E$ because

† If $\Delta_3 = 0$, another pair of Eqs. (7-11) is to be taken.

‡ If $\omega \neq \omega_E$, at least either p_{35} or p_{36} must be $\neq 0$. If p_{36} were zero, we would calculate y_1 instead of y_2.

$$R(\omega)p_{36}\,\Delta_3 = \Delta(\omega) = p_{34}\,\Delta_3 + p_{35}\,\Delta_1 + p_{36}\,\Delta_2$$

Setting $\kappa_1 = x_1$ and $\kappa_2 = (x_2 + y_2)/2$, we have for the corrected estimates

$$\lambda_1' = \lambda_1 + \kappa_1 = \frac{\Delta_1}{\Delta_3} \qquad \text{and} \qquad \lambda_2' = \lambda_2 + \kappa_2 = \frac{1}{2}\left[\frac{\Delta_2}{\Delta_3} - \frac{1}{p_{36}}\left(p_{34} + p_{35}\frac{\Delta_1}{\Delta_3}\right)\right]$$

which are also independent of the first estimates λ_1 and λ_2. Therefore λ_1' and λ_2' are already the final corrected values, whence it follows that $\kappa_1' = 0$ and $(x_2' + y_2')/2 = \kappa_2' = 0$. Hence,

$$x_2' = -y_2'$$

and because of $R(\omega) = x_2' - y_2'$

$$x_2' = -y_2' = \tfrac{1}{2}R(\omega)$$

The values λ_1' and λ_2' are then used as estimates in the state vector $\mathbf{z}_0$ for the next chosen ω.

General Theory. We shall now prove that in the general case of an nth-order problem all κ_i' become zero, which means that all λ_i' $(n = 1, 2, 3, \ldots, n/2 - 1)$ are independent of the first estimate λ_i. After the initial state vector $\mathbf{z}_0$ of Eq. (7-9) has been multiplied by the n consecutive transfer matrices, the right-hand boundary conditions yield the following system of $n/2$ nonhomogeneous linear equations for the correction factors κ_i $(i = 1, 2, \ldots, n/2 - 1)$:

$$\begin{aligned}
&(1)\quad p_{11}(\lambda_1 + \kappa_1) + \cdots + p_{1i}(\lambda_i + \kappa_i) + \cdots + p_{1s}(\lambda_s + \kappa_s)\\
&\qquad\qquad + \cdots + p_{1,n/2-1}(\lambda_{n/2-1} + \kappa_{n/2-1}) + p_1 = 0\\
&\cdots\cdots\cdots\cdots\cdots\cdots\cdots\cdots\cdots\cdots\\
&(i)\quad p_{i1}(\lambda_1 + \kappa_1) + \cdots + p_{ii}(\lambda_i + \kappa_i) + \cdots + p_{is}(\lambda_s + \kappa_s)\\
&\qquad\qquad + \cdots + p_{i,n/2-1}(\lambda_{n/2-1} + \kappa_{n/2-1}) + p_i = 0\\
&\cdots\cdots\cdots\cdots\cdots\cdots\cdots\cdots\cdots\cdots\\
&(s)\quad p_{s1}(\lambda_1 + \kappa_1) + \cdots + p_{si}(\lambda_i + \kappa_i) + \cdots + p_{ss}(\lambda_s + \kappa_s)\\
&\qquad\qquad + \cdots + p_{s,n/2-1}(\lambda_{n/2-1} + \kappa_{n/2-1}) + p_s = 0\\
&\cdots\cdots\cdots\cdots\cdots\cdots\cdots\cdots\cdots\cdots\\
&\left(\frac{n}{2}\right)\quad p_{n/2,1}(\lambda_1 + \kappa_1) + \cdots + p_{n/2,i}(\lambda_i + \kappa_i) + \cdots + p_{n/2,s}(\lambda_s + \kappa_s)\\
&\qquad\qquad + \cdots + p_{n/2,n/2-1}(\lambda_{n/2-1} + \kappa_{n/2-1}) + p_{n/2} = 0
\end{aligned} \tag{7-12}$$

That is, we have one equation too many for the solution of the $n/2 - 1$ unknown correction factors κ_i. Using all of Eqs. (7-12) except (7-12*s*) we obtain the following solution for the correction factors κ_i $(i = 1, 2, \ldots, n/2 - 1)$:

$$\kappa_i = x_i = -\lambda_i + \frac{\Delta_i}{\Delta} \tag{7-13}$$

and in particular the correction factor κ_s is

$$\kappa_s = x_s = -\lambda_s + \frac{\Delta_s}{\Delta} \tag{7-13a}$$

In Eq. (7-13) the determinants Δ_i and Δ are

$$\Delta_i = \begin{vmatrix} p_{11} & p_{12} & \cdots & p_{1,i-1} & -p_1 & p_{1,i+1} & \cdots & p_{1,n/2-1} \\ p_{21} & p_{22} & \cdots & p_{2,i-1} & -p_2 & p_{2,i+1} & \cdots & p_{2,n/2-1} \\ \cdot & \cdot & \cdot & \cdot & \cdot & \cdot & \cdot & \cdot \\ p_{s-1,1} & p_{s-1,2} & \cdots & p_{s-1,i-1} & -p_{s-1} & p_{s-1,i+1} & \cdots & p_{s-1,n/2-1} \\ p_{s+1,1} & p_{s+1,2} & \cdots & p_{s+1,i-1} & -p_{s+1} & p_{s+1,i+1} & \cdots & p_{s+1,n/2-1} \\ \cdot & \cdot & \cdot & \cdot & \cdot & \cdot & \cdot & \cdot \\ p_{n/2,1} & p_{n/2,2} & \cdots & p_{n/2,i-1} & -p_{n/2} & p_{n/2,i+1} & \cdots & p_{n/2,n/2-1} \end{vmatrix}$$

and

$$\Delta = \begin{vmatrix} p_{11} & p_{12} & \cdots & p_{1i} & \cdots & p_{1,n/2-1} \\ p_{21} & p_{22} & \cdots & p_{2i} & \cdots & p_{2,n/2-1} \\ \cdot & \cdot & \cdot & \cdot & \cdot & \cdot \\ p_{s-1,1} & p_{s-1,2} & \cdots & p_{s-1,i} & \cdots & p_{s-1,n/2-1} \\ p_{s+1,1} & p_{s+1,2} & \cdots & p_{s+1,i} & \cdots & p_{s+1,n/2-1} \\ \cdot & \cdot & \cdot & \cdot & \cdot & \cdot \\ p_{n/2,1} & p_{n/2,2} & \cdots & p_{n/2,i} & \cdots & p_{n/2,n/2-1} \end{vmatrix}$$

A second value for κ_s can be obtained by substituting the values obtained for κ_i $(i \neq s)$ in Eq. (7-12*s*). This second value for κ_s will be represented by y_s and is given by

$$y_s = -\lambda_s - \left\{\frac{1}{p_{ss}}\left(p_s + p_{s1}\frac{\Delta_1}{\Delta} + p_{s2}\frac{\Delta_2}{\Delta} + \cdots + p_{s,s-1}\frac{\Delta_{s-1}}{\Delta} + p_{s,s+1}\frac{\Delta_{s+1}}{\Delta} + \cdots + p_{s,n/2-1}\frac{\Delta_{n/2-1}}{\Delta}\right)\right\} \qquad (7\text{-}14)$$

We recall from Eq. (7-13*a*) that the first value x_s for κ_s is

$$x_s = -\lambda_s + \frac{\Delta_s}{\Delta}$$

The difference of the two values obtained for κ_s is

$$R_s = x_s - y_s = \frac{\Delta_s}{\Delta} + \{\ \} \qquad \text{cf. Eq. (7-14)}$$

which is independent of the first estimates λ_i. The difference R_s then depends only on the value chosen for ω, and when the value selected for ω coincides with a natural frequency of the system, then $R_s = 0$. This, then, is the frequency condition, but we are still not certain whether R_s is to be the difference of large or small numbers.

We shall now improve our initial estimates for λ_i. Except when $i = s$, the improved values are

$$\lambda_i' = \lambda_i + \kappa_i = \lambda_i + \left(-\lambda_i + \frac{\Delta_i}{\Delta}\right) = \frac{\Delta_i}{\Delta}$$

which is again independent of the initial estimate of λ_i. The improved estimate for λ_s is taken as

$$\lambda_s' = \lambda_s + \frac{x_s + y_s}{2}$$

$$\lambda_s' = \lambda_s + \frac{1}{2}\left(-\lambda_s + \frac{\Delta_s}{\Delta} - \lambda_s - \{\ \}\right) = \frac{1}{2}\left(\frac{\Delta_s}{\Delta} - \{\ \}\right)$$

The new expressions that we then obtain for x' and y' are

$$x_s' = -\lambda_s' + \frac{\Delta_s}{\Delta} = \frac{1}{2}\left(\frac{\Delta_s}{\Delta} + \{\ \}\right) = \frac{R_s}{2} \qquad \text{cf. Eq. (7-13}a\text{)}$$

and

$$y_s' = -\lambda_s' - \{\ \} = -\frac{1}{2}\left(\frac{\Delta_s}{\Delta} + \{\ \}\right) = -\frac{R_s}{2} \qquad \text{cf. Eq. (7-14)}$$

Thus, x_s' and y_s' are again independent of the initial values λ_i. Besides, they are of opposite sign. Hence, if we choose good values for λ_i, then the frequency condition $R_s = x_s - y_s$ becomes the sum of two numbers of the same sign. In actual computing work reasonable estimates λ_i are obtained if for the frequency $\omega = \omega_r$ the corrected values $\lambda_i' = \lambda_i + \kappa_i$ of the preceding computing operation for ω_{r-1} are taken and if the step $\omega_r - \omega_{r-1}$ is relatively small. The normal modes are easily found by multiplying all columns by their respective κ_i, after which the corresponding elements of all columns are added to yield the components of the state vectors $\mathbf{z}_j$ $(j = 0, 1, 2, \ldots, n)$. For an application of this procedure in the presence of "rigid" intermediate conditions, the reader is referred to Sec. 11-3.

PROBLEMS

7-5. The representation of a turbine shaft is shown in Fig. P 7-5. Using the modified transfer-matrix method in dimensionless form, find the first two natural frequencies and the corresponding normal modes.

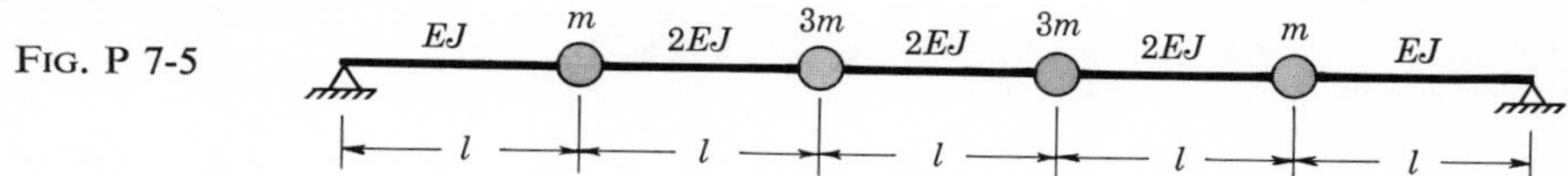

FIG. P 7-5

7-6. Repeat Prob. 7-5 when the shaft rests on spring supports of stiffness $k_w = EJ/l^3$.

7-7. Find the natural frequencies for the spring-supported cantilever of Fig. P 7-7.

FIG. P 7-7

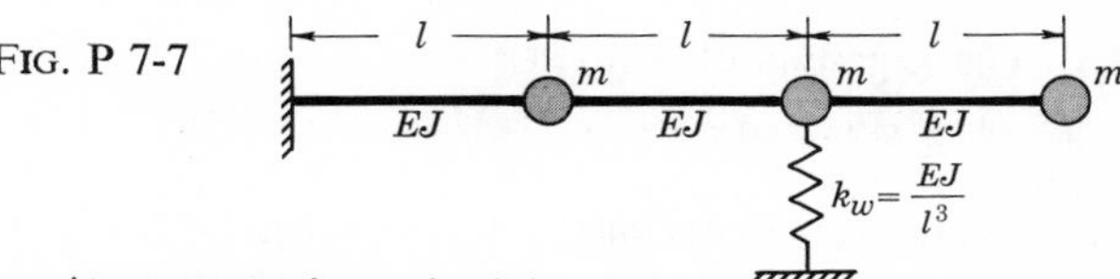

7-8. Repeat Prob. 7-7 when the spring support is made rigid.

8 GENERAL THEORY OF VIBRATIONS

In this chapter matrix algebra is used for a restatement (Secs. 8-2 and 8-3) and expansion of the material discussed in Chap. 2 as well as for the formulation of the general theory of damped vibrations (Secs. 8-4 and 8-5).

8-1. The Equation of Motion

The Stiffness and Flexibility Matrix. Figure 8-1 illustrates an elastic body subjected to static forces $F_1, F_2, \ldots, F_n$, and as a result of these forces the body deflects. Let the displacements of the body at the points of application and in the directions of the forces be $d_1, d_2, \ldots, d_n$. The relation between the displacements and the forces causing them has the form

$$\begin{bmatrix} F_1 \\ F_2 \\ \cdots \\ F_n \end{bmatrix} = \begin{bmatrix} k_{11} & k_{12} & \cdots & k_{1n} \\ k_{21} & k_{22} & \cdots & k_{2n} \\ \cdots & \cdots & \cdots & \cdots \\ k_{n1} & k_{n2} & \cdots & k_{nn} \end{bmatrix} \cdot \begin{bmatrix} d_1 \\ d_2 \\ \cdots \\ d_n \end{bmatrix}$$

or

$$\mathbf{f} = \mathbf{K}\mathbf{d} \tag{8-1}$$

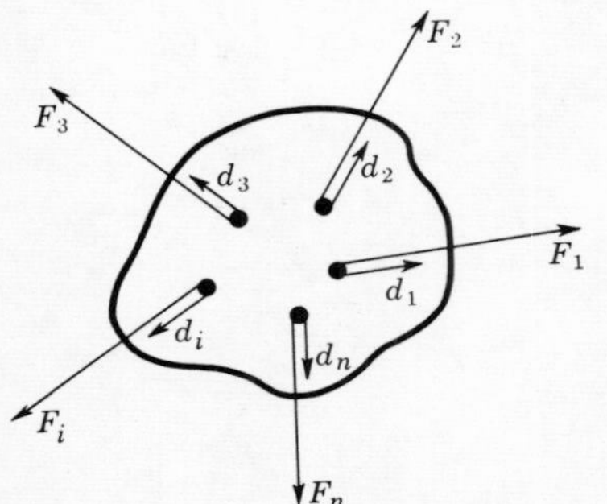

FIG. 8-1. Forces acting on an elastic body and their displacements.

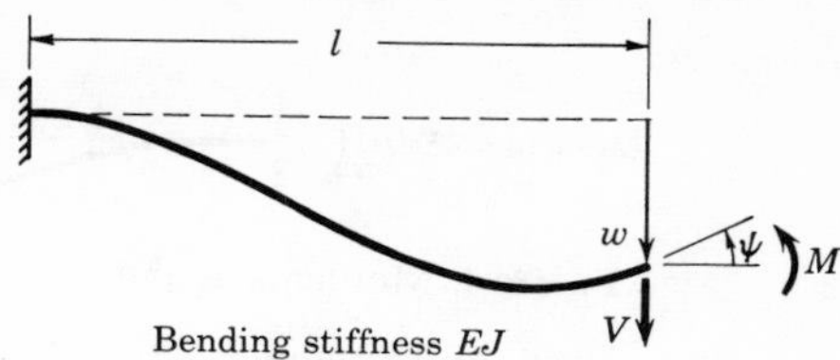

FIG. 8-2. Cantilever subjected to end moment and shear.

where **K** is known as the *stiffness matrix*. On account of the Maxwell-Betti reciprocal theorem [17], we have $k_{ij} = k_{ji}$, so that the stiffness matrix is symmetric about the main diagonal.

On premultiplying both sides of Eq. (8-1) by $\mathbf{K}^{-1}$ we obtain the displacements in terms of the loads,

$$\mathbf{d} = \mathbf{K}^{-1}\mathbf{f} = \mathbf{F}\mathbf{f} \tag{8-2}$$

The matrix **F**, which is the inverse of the stiffness matrix, is known as the *flexibility matrix*, and it is also symmetric about the main diagonal.

The elements k_{ij} in the jth column of the stiffness matrix are found by calculating the forces necessary to hold the body in the deformed shape given by $d_j = 1$, the other displacements being zero. On the other hand, the elements f_{ij} in the jth column of the flexibility matrix are found by calculating the displacements due to a force $F_j = 1$, the other forces being zero.

As an illustration, it is easy to show that the following relations hold for the cantilever of Fig. 8-2:†

$$\begin{bmatrix} w \\ \psi \end{bmatrix} = \begin{bmatrix} \dfrac{l^3}{3EJ} & \dfrac{-l^2}{2EJ} \\ \dfrac{-l^2}{2EJ} & \dfrac{l}{EJ} \end{bmatrix} \cdot \begin{bmatrix} V \\ M \end{bmatrix}$$

$$\begin{bmatrix} V \\ M \end{bmatrix} = \begin{bmatrix} \dfrac{l^3}{3EJ} & \dfrac{-l^2}{2EJ} \\ \dfrac{-l^2}{2EJ} & \dfrac{l}{EJ} \end{bmatrix}^{-1} \cdot \begin{bmatrix} w \\ \psi \end{bmatrix} = \begin{bmatrix} \dfrac{12EJ}{l^3} & \dfrac{6EJ}{l^2} \\ \dfrac{6EJ}{l^2} & \dfrac{4EJ}{l} \end{bmatrix} \cdot \begin{bmatrix} w \\ \psi \end{bmatrix}$$

As our next example we determine the stiffness matrix relating the external moments and the rotations at the rigid supports of the continuous beam shown in Fig. 8-3. It is found by calculating the moments required to cause unit rotation at each of the supports in turn,

† The reader unfamiliar with such calculation is referred, for example, to Ref. 42, pp. 339–340.

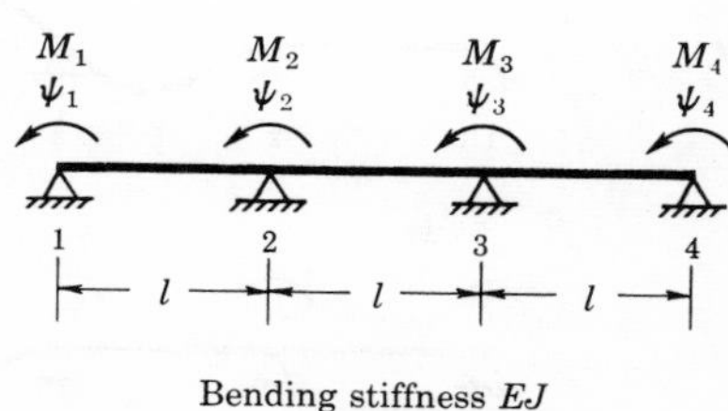

FIG. 8-3. Uniform beam on rigid supports.

FIG. 8-4. Moments acting on propped cantilever to give unit rotation.

the other rotations remaining zero. In order to do this we first consider the external moments that must be applied to a propped cantilever beam in order to give it unit rotation at the propped end. The result of this calculation is shown in Fig. 8-4.† Using this result, one can then, by superposition, calculate the moments required to give unit rotations at points 1, 2, 3, and 4 of the structure under consideration. These moments are illustrated in Fig. 8-5, and hence the first column of the stiffness matrix (obtained from Fig. 8-5*a*) is $\{4EJ/l^2 \quad 2EJ/l^2 \quad 0 \quad 0\}$. The second, third, and fourth columns, obtained by referring to Fig. 8-5*b*, *c*, and *d*, are, respectively, $\{2EJ/l^2 \quad 8EJ/l^2 \quad 2EJ/l^2 \quad 0\}$, $\{0 \quad 2EJ/l^2 \quad 8EJ/l^2 \quad 2EJ/l^2\}$, and $\{0 \quad 0 \quad 2EJ/l^2 \quad 4EJ/l^2\}$. The stiffness matrix is then given by the relation

$$\begin{bmatrix} M_1 \\ M_2 \\ M_3 \\ M_4 \end{bmatrix} = \begin{bmatrix} \frac{4EJ}{l^2} & \frac{2EJ}{l^2} & 0 & 0 \\ \frac{2EJ}{l^2} & \frac{8EJ}{l^2} & \frac{2EJ}{l^2} & 0 \\ 0 & \frac{2EJ}{l^2} & \frac{8EJ}{l^2} & \frac{2EJ}{l^2} \\ 0 & 0 & \frac{2EJ}{l^2} & \frac{4EJ}{l^2} \end{bmatrix} \cdot \begin{bmatrix} \psi_1 \\ \psi_2 \\ \psi_3 \\ \psi_4 \end{bmatrix}$$

The flexibility matrix for this system would be quite tedious to compute directly (we would have to compute the rotations at all points for a unit moment applied at each rigid

† See *ibid.*

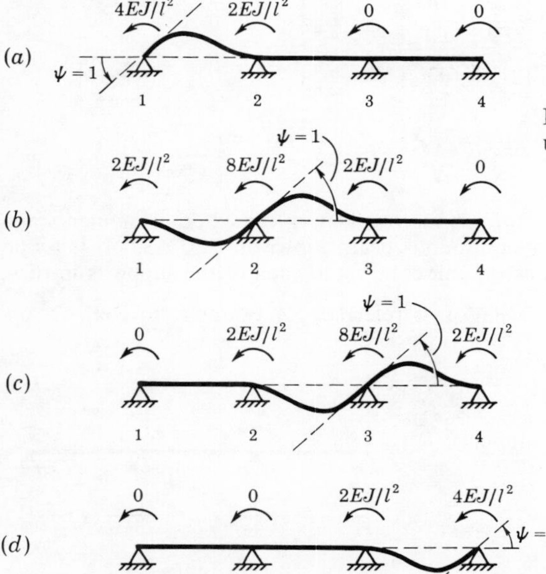

FIG. 8-5. Moments required to produce unit rotations at each support.

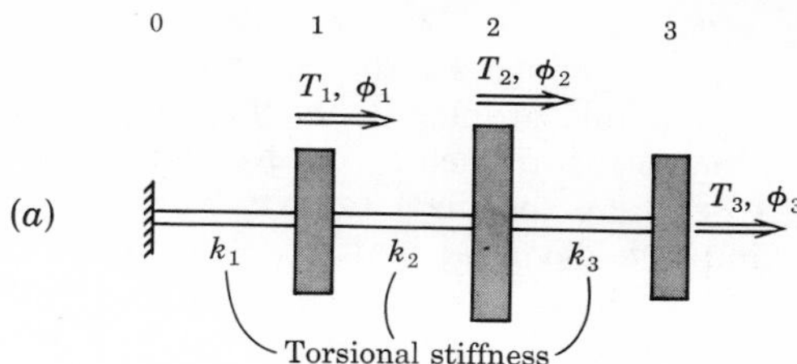

FIG. 8-6. Torsional system.

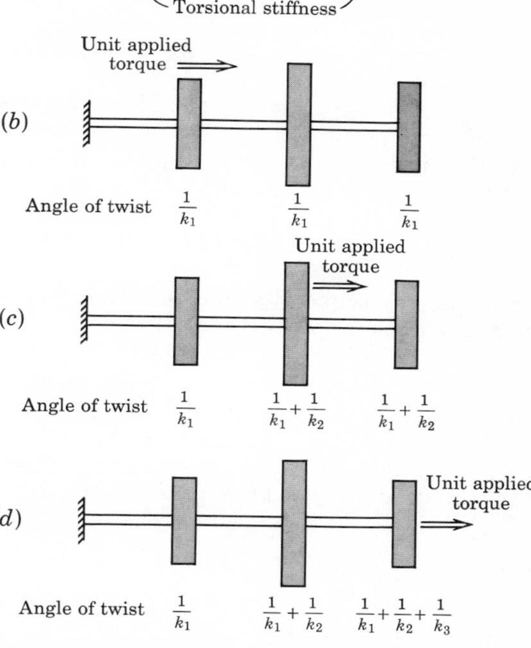

support in turn) and is best calculated by inverting the stiffness matrix. However, when the system is statically determinate, it is easy to calculate the flexibility matrix. Such an example is the torsional shaft shown in Fig. 8-6*a*.

The rotations produced by unit torques applied at points 1, 2, and 3 are shown in Fig. 8-6*b*, *c*, and *d*, so that the first column of the flexibility matrix is $\{1/k_1 \quad 1/k_1 \quad 1/k_1\}$ and the second and third columns are

$$\left\{\frac{1}{k_1} \quad \frac{1}{k_1}+\frac{1}{k_2} \quad \frac{1}{k_1}+\frac{1}{k_2}\right\} \qquad \text{and} \qquad \left\{\frac{1}{k_1} \quad \frac{1}{k_1}+\frac{1}{k_2} \quad \frac{1}{k_1}+\frac{1}{k_2}+\frac{1}{k_3}\right\}$$

respectively. The relation between the rotations and torques in terms of the flexibility matrix is

$$\begin{bmatrix} \phi_1 \\ \phi_2 \\ \phi_3 \end{bmatrix} = \begin{bmatrix} \frac{1}{k_1} & \frac{1}{k_1} & \frac{1}{k_1} \\ \frac{1}{k_1} & \frac{1}{k_1}+\frac{1}{k_2} & \frac{1}{k_1}+\frac{1}{k_2} \\ \frac{1}{k_1} & \frac{1}{k_1}+\frac{1}{k_2} & \frac{1}{k_1}+\frac{1}{k_2}+\frac{1}{k_3} \end{bmatrix} \cdot \begin{bmatrix} T_1 \\ T_2 \\ T_3 \end{bmatrix}$$

The Mass Matrix and the Equation of Motion. We consider an elastic system with concentrated masses at discrete points that are subjected to arbitrary time-varying forces. Let the displacements of these points be defined by the column vector $\mathbf{x}(t) = \{x_1 \quad x_2 \quad \cdots \quad x_n\}$, and let the forces corresponding to these displacements be defined by the column vector $\mathbf{f}(t) = \{F_1 \quad F_2 \quad \cdots \quad F_n\}$. When we view this dynamic problem from the standpoint of D'Alembert's principle, we have in addition to the applied forces $\mathbf{f}(t)$ the inertia forces $-\mathbf{M}\ddot{\mathbf{x}}$ (cf. Secs. 2-1 and 2-3), with $\mathbf{M}$ denoting the mass matrix, which is nearly always† a symmetric and very often simply a diagonal matrix. The forces $\mathbf{f}(t)$ and the inertia forces $-\mathbf{M}\ddot{\mathbf{x}}$ are balanced by the elastic reactions $-\mathbf{K}\mathbf{x}(t)$ induced by the displacements $\mathbf{x}(t)$. Hence we have the equilibrium equation

$$-\mathbf{K}\mathbf{x} + (-\mathbf{M}\ddot{\mathbf{x}}) + \mathbf{f}(t) = \mathbf{0}$$

or

$$\mathbf{M}\ddot{\mathbf{x}} + \mathbf{K}\mathbf{x} = \mathbf{f}(t) \tag{8-3}$$

If the flexibility matrix $\mathbf{F}$ is determined instead of the stiffness matrix $\mathbf{K}$, the corresponding equation is obtained by premultiplying Eq. (8-3) by $\mathbf{F} = \mathbf{K}^{-1}$:

$$\mathbf{F}\mathbf{M}\ddot{\mathbf{x}} + \mathbf{x} = \mathbf{F}\mathbf{f}(t) = \mathbf{x}_{\text{stat}}(t) \tag{8-4}$$

where $\mathbf{x}_{\text{stat}}(t)$ would describe the deflection of the massless structure under the time-varying load $\mathbf{f}(t)$.

PROBLEMS

8-1. Find the stiffness, flexibility, and mass matrices for the torsional system of Fig. P 8-1, using the displacements indicated in the figure.

8-2. Find the stiffness and mass matrices for the torsional system of Fig. P 8-2. Why is it impossible to compute the flexibility matrix?

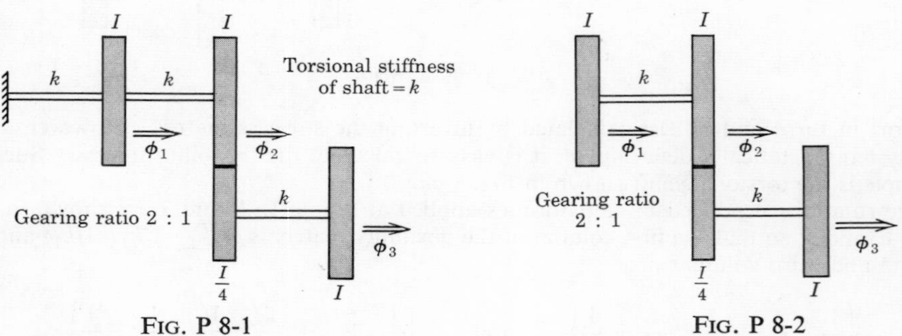

FIG. P 8-1 FIG. P 8-2

8-3. Find the relation between the applied moments and the joint rotations of the system shown in Fig. P 8-3.

8-4. Find the flexibility and mass matrices for the simply supported uniform beam shown in Fig. P 8-4.

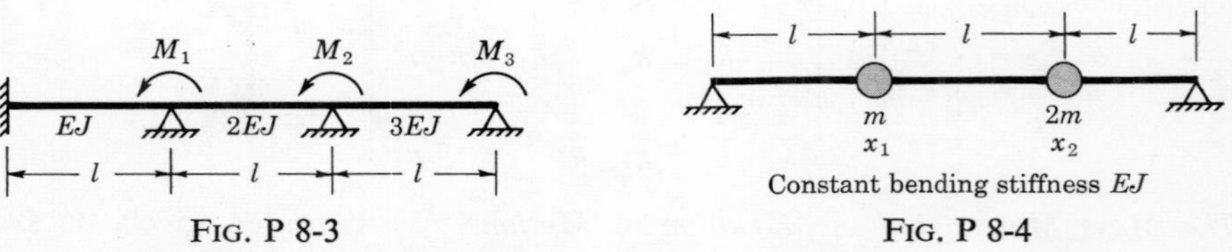

FIG. P 8-3 FIG. P 8-4

† Examples of nonsymmetric mass matrices are given in Ref. 43, p. 244.

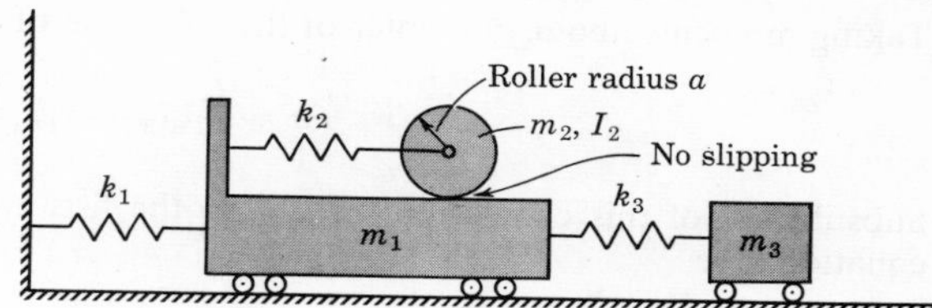

FIG. 8-7. Spring-mass system of Example 8-1.

8-2. Free Vibrations

Frequency Equation. For the case of free vibration we have $\mathbf{f}(t) = 0$, and Eq. (8-3) becomes

$$\mathbf{M}\ddot{\mathbf{x}} + \mathbf{K}\mathbf{x} = \mathbf{0} \tag{8-3a}$$

This differential equation is solved by assuming a solution of the form $\mathbf{x}(t) = \mathbf{a}e^{\pm j\omega t}$, the column vector $\mathbf{a}$ being referred to as the *amplitude matrix*. Then $\ddot{\mathbf{x}} = -\mathbf{a}\omega^2 e^{\pm j\omega t}$, and substituting these equations in Eq. (8-3a) we obtain the result

$$-\omega^2\mathbf{M}\mathbf{a} + \mathbf{K}\mathbf{a} = \mathbf{0}$$

or

$$(\mathbf{K} - \omega^2\mathbf{M})\mathbf{a} = \mathbf{0} \tag{8-5}†$$

In order for Eq. (8-5) to have a nontrivial solution, it is necessary that

$$|\mathbf{K} - \omega^2\mathbf{M}| = 0 \tag{8-6}†$$

This determinant is known as the frequency determinant. Upon expansion it gives a polynomial in ω^2, the roots ω_e of which are known as the natural circular frequencies of the system. For each value of ω_e it is possible to compute an amplitude matrix $\mathbf{a}_e$‡ that is referred to as the normal mode corresponding to ω_e.

Example 8-1. Derive the equation of motion for the system shown in Fig. 8-7, and find the natural circular frequencies and normal modes. It is assumed that the roller does not slip. The free-body diagrams for each of the masses are shown in Fig. 8-8, where x_1, x_2, and x_3 denote the displacements of masses m_1, m_2, and m_3, respectively.

Consideration of horizontal equilibrium of masses m_1, m_2, and m_3, respectively, gives the equations

$$\begin{aligned} m_1\ddot{x}_1 + k_1x_1 - k_3(x_3 - x_1) - k_2(x_2 - x_1) - F &= 0 \\ m_2\ddot{x}_2 + k_2(x_2 - x_1) + F \qquad &= 0 \\ m_3\ddot{x}_3 + k_3(x_3 - x_1) \qquad &= 0 \end{aligned}$$

† When the flexibility matrix $\mathbf{F}$ is known instead of $\mathbf{K}$, Eqs. (8-5) and (8-6) are replaced by

$$\left(\frac{1}{\omega^2}\mathbf{I} - \mathbf{F}\mathbf{M}\right)\mathbf{a} = \mathbf{0} \tag{8-5a}$$

and

$$\left|\frac{1}{\omega^2}\mathbf{I} - \mathbf{F}\mathbf{M}\right| = 0 \tag{8-6a}$$

‡ Cf. Sec. 1-4 under Real Symmetric Matrices.

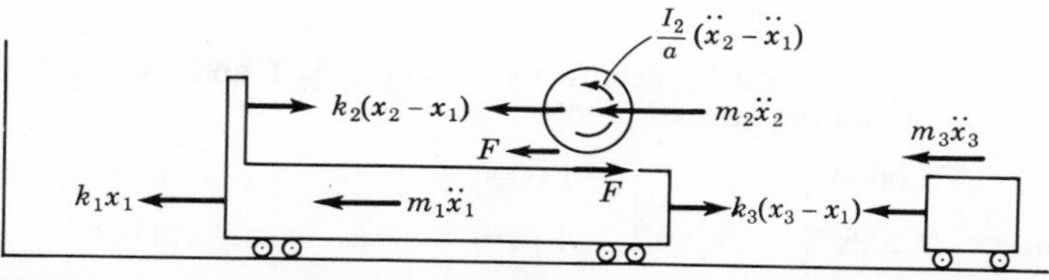

FIG. 8-8. Free-body diagram of forces acting on the masses of the system in Fig. 8-7.

Taking moments about the center of the roller, we obtain

$$Fa = \frac{I_2}{a}(\ddot{x}_2 - \ddot{x}_1)$$

Substitution of this expression for F into the first two equations and repeating the third equation give

$$\begin{aligned}
\left(m_1 + \frac{I_2}{a^2}\right)\ddot{x}_1 - \frac{I_2}{a^2}\ddot{x}_2 + (k_1 + k_2 + k_3)x_1 - k_2x_2 - k_3x_3 &= 0 \\
-\frac{I_2}{a^2}\ddot{x}_1 + \left(m_2 + \frac{I_2}{a^2}\right)\ddot{x}_2 - k_2x_1 + k_2x_2 &= 0 \\
m_3\ddot{x}_3 - k_3x_1 + k_3x_3 &= 0
\end{aligned}$$

or in matrix notation

$$\begin{bmatrix} m_1 + \frac{I_2}{a^2} & -\frac{I_2}{a^2} & 0 \\ -\frac{I_2}{a^2} & m_2 + \frac{I_2}{a^2} & 0 \\ 0 & 0 & m_3 \end{bmatrix} \cdot \begin{bmatrix} \ddot{x}_1 \\ \ddot{x}_2 \\ \ddot{x}_3 \end{bmatrix} + \begin{bmatrix} k_1 + k_2 + k_3 & -k_2 & -k_3 \\ -k_2 & k_2 & 0 \\ -k_3 & 0 & k_3 \end{bmatrix} \cdot \begin{bmatrix} x_1 \\ x_2 \\ x_3 \end{bmatrix} = \begin{bmatrix} 0 \\ 0 \\ 0 \end{bmatrix} \tag{8-7}$$

or

$$\mathbf{M}\ddot{\mathbf{x}} + \mathbf{K}\mathbf{x} = \mathbf{0}$$

When we set $k_1 = k$, $k_2 = k_3 = 2k$, and $m_1 = m$, $m_2 = m_3 = 2m$, and if furthermore $I_2 = ma^2$ (that is, the roller is a very thin walled pipe), then we have

$$\mathbf{M} = \begin{bmatrix} 2m & -m & 0 \\ -m & 3m & 0 \\ 0 & 0 & 2m \end{bmatrix} \quad \text{and} \quad \mathbf{K} = \begin{bmatrix} 5k & -2k & -2k \\ -2k & 2k & 0 \\ -2k & 0 & 2k \end{bmatrix}$$

so that Eq. (8-5) becomes

$$\begin{bmatrix} 5k - 2m\omega^2 & -2k + m\omega^2 & -2k \\ -2k + m\omega^2 & 2k - 3m\omega^2 & 0 \\ -2k & 0 & 2k - 2m\omega^2 \end{bmatrix} \cdot \begin{bmatrix} a_1 \\ a_2 \\ a_3 \end{bmatrix} = \begin{bmatrix} 0 \\ 0 \\ 0 \end{bmatrix} \tag{8-8}$$

With $p^2 = m\omega^2/k$, expansion of the frequency determinant (8-6) yields the polynomial

$$5p^6 - 20p^4 + 15p^2 - 2 = 0$$

the roots of which are

$$p_1^2 = 0.17040 \qquad p_2^2 = 0.76629 \qquad p_3^2 = 3.0633$$

so that the natural circular frequencies are

$$\omega_1 = 0.412\sqrt{\frac{k}{m}} \qquad \omega_2 = 0.874\sqrt{\frac{k}{m}} \qquad \omega_3 = 1.75\sqrt{\frac{k}{m}}$$

The normal modes are found by arbitrarily setting $a_1 = 1$ and solving Eq. (8-8) for a_2 and a_3. Hence we obtain the normal modes

$$\mathbf{a}_1 = \begin{bmatrix} 1.0000 \\ 1.2289 \\ 1.2054 \end{bmatrix} \qquad \mathbf{a}_2 = \begin{bmatrix} 1.0000 \\ -4.1286 \\ 4.2788 \end{bmatrix} \qquad \mathbf{a}_3 = \begin{bmatrix} 1.0000 \\ 0.14789 \\ -0.48466 \end{bmatrix}$$

Orthogonality of the Normal Modes. Let $\mathbf{a}_r$ and $\mathbf{a}_s$ be the normal modes corresponding to the two different natural circular frequencies ω_r and ω_s. Then from Eq. (8-5) we have

$$\omega_r^2 \mathbf{M}\mathbf{a}_r = \mathbf{K}\mathbf{a}_r \tag{8-9a}$$

and

$$\omega_s^2 \mathbf{M}\mathbf{a}_s = \mathbf{K}\mathbf{a}_s \tag{8-9b}$$

Premultiplying Eq. (8-9*a*) by $\mathbf{a}_s'$ and Eq. (8-9*b*) by $\mathbf{a}_r'$,

$$\omega_r^2 \mathbf{a}_s' \mathbf{M}\mathbf{a}_r = \mathbf{a}_s' \mathbf{K}\mathbf{a}_r \tag{8-10a}$$

and

$$\omega_s^2 \mathbf{a}_r' \mathbf{M}\mathbf{a}_s = \mathbf{a}_r' \mathbf{K}\mathbf{a}_s \tag{8-10b}$$

The product $\mathbf{a}_s'\mathbf{M}\mathbf{a}_r$ can be regarded as a (1, 1) matrix, so that it is equal to its transpose and hence [cf. Eq. (1-19)]

$$\mathbf{a}_s'\mathbf{M}\mathbf{a}_r = (\mathbf{a}_s'\mathbf{M}\mathbf{a}_r)' = \mathbf{a}_r'\mathbf{M}'(\mathbf{a}_s')'$$

However, $(\mathbf{a}_s')' = \mathbf{a}_s$, and since $\mathbf{M}$ is a symmetric matrix ($\mathbf{M} = \mathbf{M}'$), this becomes

$$\mathbf{a}_s'\mathbf{M}\mathbf{a}_r = \mathbf{a}_r'\mathbf{M}\mathbf{a}_s$$

Similarly, since $\mathbf{K}$ is also symmetric, $\mathbf{a}_s'\mathbf{K}\mathbf{a}_r = \mathbf{a}_r'\mathbf{K}\mathbf{a}_s$, so that, subtracting Eq. (8-10*b*) from Eq. (8-10*a*), we obtain the result

$$(\omega_r^2 - \omega_s^2)\mathbf{a}_s'\mathbf{M}\mathbf{a}_r = 0 \tag{8-11}$$

For $\omega_r \neq \omega_s$, Eq. (8-11) is satisfied only if

$$\mathbf{a}_s'\mathbf{M}\mathbf{a}_r = 0 \tag{8-12a}$$

which expresses the orthogonality property of the normal modes $\mathbf{a}_s$ and $\mathbf{a}_r$. Also, in view of Eqs. (8-10), we have

$$\mathbf{a}_s'\mathbf{K}\mathbf{a}_r = 0 \qquad \text{for } r \neq s \tag{8-12b}$$

When the system has two (or more) equal natural frequencies, then there are two (or more) different mode shapes associated with this particular frequency. The method that ensures that the chosen mode shapes are orthogonal is described in Sec. 1-4 under the heading Real Symmetric Matrices.

Example 8-1 (*continued*). Forming the matrix product Eq. (8-12*a*) for the first and second modes of the system of Example 8-1, we obtain

$$[1.0000 \quad 1.2289 \quad 1.2054] \cdot \begin{bmatrix} 2m & -m & 0 \\ -m & 3m & 0 \\ 0 & 0 & 2m \end{bmatrix} \cdot \begin{bmatrix} 1.0000 \\ -4.1286 \\ 4.2788 \end{bmatrix} = 0$$

that is,

$$\mathbf{a}_1'\mathbf{M}\mathbf{a}_2 = 0$$

Similarly we can demonstrate the relations $\mathbf{a}_1'\mathbf{M}\mathbf{a}_3 = 0$ and $\mathbf{a}_2'\mathbf{M}\mathbf{a}_3 = 0$, as well as $\mathbf{a}_1'\mathbf{K}\mathbf{a}_2 = 0$, etc.

Normalized Characteristic Functions and the Modal Matrix. When calculating the normal modes $\mathbf{a}_i$ we mostly assume that the amplitude of some chosen point is unity (cf. Example 8-1). This method proves to be inconvenient, however, in matrix calculations, and another method of standardization, which leads to normalized eigenvectors or modal vectors, is usually adopted.

The normalized modal vector $\boldsymbol{\phi}_i$ is a dimensionless column vector whose n components describe the relative amplitudes of the various points of the system when it vibrates freely in its ith mode with circular frequency ω_i. The modal vector

$\boldsymbol{\phi}_i$ is therefore proportional to the normal mode $\mathbf{a}_i$, so that

$$\boldsymbol{\phi}_i = c_i\mathbf{a}_i$$

where c_i is a constant. The common factor c_i is so chosen that

$$\boldsymbol{\phi}_i'\mathbf{M}\boldsymbol{\phi}_i = \bar{m} \tag{8-13}$$

The value for the constant $\bar{m}$ is selected for the convenience of the problem on hand. Note that, since $\boldsymbol{\phi}_i$ is dimensionless, $\bar{m}$ has the dimension of mass.

The vibration of the system in its ith mode can thus be described by the displacement vector

$$\mathbf{x}_i(t) = [a_i \sin \omega_i(t - t_0) + b_i \cos \omega_i(t - t_0)]\boldsymbol{\phi}_i \qquad i = 1, 2, \ldots, n \tag{8-14}$$

where the amplitudes a_i and b_i depend on the initial conditions applied at time t_0.

When the modal vectors are collected in a single square matrix of order n, the resulting matrix is called the *modal matrix* $\boldsymbol{\Phi}$. Hence

$$\boldsymbol{\Phi} = [\boldsymbol{\phi}_1 \quad \boldsymbol{\phi}_2 \quad \cdots \quad \boldsymbol{\phi}_n] \tag{8-15}$$

We now derive some properties of the modal matrix $\boldsymbol{\Phi}$. Recalling the property of orthogonality [Eqs. (8-12)],

$$\boldsymbol{\phi}_r'\mathbf{M}\boldsymbol{\phi}_s = 0 \qquad \text{for } r \neq s$$

and using Eq. (8-13), we can easily show that

$$\boldsymbol{\Phi}'\mathbf{M}\boldsymbol{\Phi} = \begin{bmatrix} \boldsymbol{\phi}_1'\mathbf{M}\boldsymbol{\phi}_1 & \boldsymbol{\phi}_1'\mathbf{M}\boldsymbol{\phi}_2 & \cdots & \boldsymbol{\phi}_1'\mathbf{M}\boldsymbol{\phi}_n \\ \boldsymbol{\phi}_2'\mathbf{M}\boldsymbol{\phi}_1 & \boldsymbol{\phi}_2'\mathbf{M}\boldsymbol{\phi}_2 & \cdots & \boldsymbol{\phi}_2'\mathbf{M}\boldsymbol{\phi}_n \\ \cdot & \cdot & \cdot & \cdot \\ \boldsymbol{\phi}_n'\mathbf{M}\boldsymbol{\phi}_1 & \boldsymbol{\phi}_n'\mathbf{M}\boldsymbol{\phi}_2 & \cdots & \boldsymbol{\phi}_n'\mathbf{M}\boldsymbol{\phi}_n \end{bmatrix}$$

$$= \begin{bmatrix} \bar{m} & 0 & \cdots & 0 \\ 0 & \bar{m} & \cdots & 0 \\ \cdot & \cdot & \cdot & \cdot \\ 0 & 0 & \cdots & \bar{m} \end{bmatrix} = \bar{m}\mathbf{I}$$

Thus

$$\boldsymbol{\Phi}'\mathbf{M}\boldsymbol{\Phi} = \bar{m}\mathbf{I} \tag{8-16}$$

Another relation involving the stiffness matrix $\mathbf{K}$ is found by noting that $\boldsymbol{\phi}_r$ satisfies Eq. (8-5), so that

$$\mathbf{K}\boldsymbol{\phi}_r = \omega_r^2\mathbf{M}\boldsymbol{\phi}_r$$

Premultiplying both sides by $\boldsymbol{\phi}_s'$, then, on account of Eqs. (8-12),

$$\boldsymbol{\phi}_s'\mathbf{K}\boldsymbol{\phi}_r = \omega_r^2\boldsymbol{\phi}_s'\mathbf{M}\boldsymbol{\phi}_r = 0 \qquad \text{for } r \neq s$$

and with $r = s$

$$\boldsymbol{\phi}_r'\mathbf{K}\boldsymbol{\phi}_r = \omega_r^2\boldsymbol{\phi}_r'\mathbf{M}\boldsymbol{\phi}_r = \bar{m}\omega_r^2$$

Now, forming the product $\boldsymbol{\Phi}'\mathbf{K}\boldsymbol{\Phi}$, we have

$$\mathbf{\Phi}'\mathbf{K}\mathbf{\Phi} = \begin{bmatrix} \boldsymbol{\phi}_1'\mathbf{K}\boldsymbol{\phi}_1 & \boldsymbol{\phi}_1'\mathbf{K}\boldsymbol{\phi}_2 & \cdots & \boldsymbol{\phi}_1'\mathbf{K}\boldsymbol{\phi}_n \\ \boldsymbol{\phi}_2'\mathbf{K}\boldsymbol{\phi}_1 & \boldsymbol{\phi}_2'\mathbf{K}\boldsymbol{\phi}_2 & \cdots & \boldsymbol{\phi}_2'\mathbf{K}\boldsymbol{\phi}_n \\ \cdot & \cdot & \cdot & \cdot \\ \boldsymbol{\phi}_n'\mathbf{K}\boldsymbol{\phi}_1 & \boldsymbol{\phi}_n'\mathbf{K}\boldsymbol{\phi}_2 & \cdots & \boldsymbol{\phi}_n'\mathbf{K}\boldsymbol{\phi}_n \end{bmatrix}$$

$$= \begin{bmatrix} \bar{m}\omega_1^2 & 0 & \cdots & 0 \\ 0 & \bar{m}\omega_2^2 & \cdots & 0 \\ \cdot & \cdot & \cdot & \cdot \\ 0 & 0 & \cdots & \bar{m}\omega_n^2 \end{bmatrix} = \bar{m} \begin{bmatrix} \omega_1^2 & 0 & \cdots & 0 \\ 0 & \omega_2^2 & \cdots & 0 \\ \cdot & \cdot & \cdot & \cdot \\ 0 & 0 & \cdots & \omega_n^2 \end{bmatrix}$$

$$= \bar{m}\boldsymbol{\omega}^2 \tag{8-17}$$

where

$$\boldsymbol{\omega} = \begin{bmatrix} \omega_1 & 0 & \cdots & 0 \\ 0 & \omega_2 & \cdots & 0 \\ \cdot & \cdot & \cdot & \cdot \\ 0 & 0 & \cdots & \omega_n \end{bmatrix} = \text{diag } [\omega_i] \tag{8-18}$$

Example 8-2. Form the modal matrix for the system of Example 8-1. The normal modes have already been computed and are

$$\mathbf{a}_1 = \begin{bmatrix} 1.000 \\ 1.2289 \\ 1.2054 \end{bmatrix} \qquad \mathbf{a}_2 = \begin{bmatrix} 1.0000 \\ -4.1286 \\ 4.2788 \end{bmatrix} \qquad \mathbf{a}_3 = \begin{bmatrix} 1.0000 \\ 0.14789 \\ -0.48466 \end{bmatrix}$$

Now let

$$\boldsymbol{\phi}_1 = c_1\mathbf{a}_1 \qquad \boldsymbol{\phi}_2 = c_2\mathbf{a}_2 \qquad \boldsymbol{\phi}_3 = c_3\mathbf{a}_3$$

and forming the matrix product $\boldsymbol{\phi}_1'\mathbf{M}\boldsymbol{\phi}_1 = \bar{m}$ we obtain

$$c_1^2[1.0000 \quad 1.2289 \quad 1.2054] \cdot \begin{bmatrix} 2m & -m & 0 \\ -m & 3m & 0 \\ 0 & 0 & 2m \end{bmatrix} \cdot \begin{bmatrix} 1.0000 \\ 1.2289 \\ 1.2054 \end{bmatrix} = \bar{m} = 6.9788mc_1^2$$

Hence

$$c_1 = \sqrt{\frac{1}{6.9788} \frac{\bar{m}}{m}}$$

and therefore

$$\boldsymbol{\phi}_1 = c_1\mathbf{a}_1 = \{0.3780 \quad 0.4645 \quad 0.4556\} \cdot \sqrt{\frac{\bar{m}}{m}}$$

In the same way we find the expressions for c_2 and c_3, so that

$$\boldsymbol{\phi}_2 = \{0.1010 \quad -0.4169 \quad 0.4321\}\sqrt{\frac{\bar{m}}{m}} \quad \text{and} \quad \boldsymbol{\phi}_3 = \{0.6680 \quad 0.0987 \quad -0.3237\}\sqrt{\frac{\bar{m}}{m}}$$

The modal matrix is then

$$\mathbf{\Phi} = \sqrt{\frac{\bar{m}}{m}} \begin{bmatrix} 0.3780 & 0.1010 & 0.6680 \\ 0.4645 & -0.4169 & 0.0987 \\ 0.4556 & 0.4321 & -0.3237 \end{bmatrix}$$

Checking the results, using Eqs. (8-16) and (8-17), we obtain

$$\mathbf{\Phi}'\mathbf{M}\mathbf{\Phi} = \frac{\bar{m}}{m}\begin{bmatrix} 0.3780 & 0.4645 & 0.4556 \\ 0.1010 & -0.4169 & 0.4321 \\ 0.6680 & 0.0987 & -0.3237 \end{bmatrix} \cdot \begin{bmatrix} 2m & -m & 0 \\ -m & 3m & 0 \\ 0 & 0 & 2m \end{bmatrix} \cdot \begin{bmatrix} 0.3780 & 0.1010 & 0.6680 \\ 0.4645 & -0.4169 & 0.0987 \\ 0.4556 & 0.4321 & -0.3237 \end{bmatrix}$$

$$= \bar{m}\begin{bmatrix} 0.9970 & -0.0001 & 0.0000 \\ -0.0001 & 0.9994 & 0.0002 \\ 0.0000 & 0.0003 & 0.9994 \end{bmatrix} \approx \bar{m}\mathbf{I}$$

and

$$\mathbf{\Phi}'\mathbf{K}\mathbf{\Phi} = \frac{\bar{m}}{m}\begin{bmatrix} 0.3780 & 0.4645 & 0.4556 \\ 0.1010 & -0.4169 & 0.4321 \\ 0.6680 & 0.0987 & -0.3237 \end{bmatrix} \cdot \begin{bmatrix} 5k & -2k & -2k \\ -2k & 2k & 0 \\ -2k & 0 & 2k \end{bmatrix} \cdot \begin{bmatrix} 0.3780 & 0.1010 & 0.6680 \\ 0.4645 & -0.4169 & 0.0987 \\ 0.4556 & 0.4321 & -0.3237 \end{bmatrix}$$

$$= \bar{m}\frac{k}{m}\begin{bmatrix} 0.1698 & 0.0000 & 0.0001 \\ 0.0000 & 0.7658 & 0.0003 \\ 0.0001 & 0.0004 & 3.0613 \end{bmatrix} \approx \bar{m}\begin{bmatrix} \omega_1^2 & 0 & 0 \\ 0 & \omega_2^2 & 0 \\ 0 & 0 & \omega_3^2 \end{bmatrix} = \bar{m}\boldsymbol{\omega}^2$$

Initial Conditions. The equation of motion for an elastic system undergoing free vibrations is

$$\mathbf{M}\ddot{\mathbf{x}} + \mathbf{K}\mathbf{x} = \mathbf{0} \tag{8-3a}$$

Let the initial displacements at time $t = t_0$ be represented by $\mathbf{x}_0$ and the initial velocities by $\dot{\mathbf{x}}_0$, where

$$\mathbf{x}_0 = \{x_1^0 \quad x_2^0 \quad \cdots \quad x_n^0\} \qquad \text{and} \qquad \dot{\mathbf{x}}_0 = \{\dot{x}_1^0 \quad \dot{x}_2^0 \quad \cdots \quad \dot{x}_n^0\} \tag{8-19}$$

The solution of Eq. (8-3*a*) is found by superposition of all n solutions [Eq. (8-14)]

$$\mathbf{x} = \boldsymbol{\phi}_1[a_1 \sin \omega_1(t - t_0) + b_1 \cos \omega_1(t - t_0)] + \boldsymbol{\phi}_2[a_2 \sin \omega_2(t - t_0) + b_2 \cos \omega_2(t - t_0)] + \cdots + \boldsymbol{\phi}_n[a_n \sin \omega_n(t - t_0) + b_n \cos \omega_n(t - t_0)]$$

or

$$\mathbf{x} = \mathbf{\Phi}(\mathbf{Sin\,a} + \mathbf{Cos\,b}) \tag{8-20}$$

where

$$\mathbf{Sin} = \text{diag }[\sin \omega_i(t - t_0)] \tag{8-21a}$$

$$\mathbf{Cos} = \text{diag }[\cos \omega_i(t - t_0)] \tag{8-21b}$$

$$\mathbf{a} = \{a_1 \quad a_2 \quad \cdots \quad a_n\} \tag{8-21c}$$

$$\mathbf{b} = \{b_1 \quad b_2 \quad \cdots \quad b_n\} \tag{8-21d}$$

We note that

$$\mathbf{Sin}\,(t = t_0) = \mathbf{0} \qquad \text{and} \qquad \mathbf{Cos}\,(t = t_0) = \mathbf{I}$$

The column vectors **a** and **b** are found by applying the initial conditions, Eqs. (8-19), at time $t = t_0$.

Differentiating Eq. (8-20) with respect to t gives

$$\dot{\mathbf{x}} = \mathbf{\Phi}(\dot{\mathbf{Sin}}\,\mathbf{a} + \dot{\mathbf{Cos}}\,\mathbf{b}) \tag{8-22}$$

where

$$\dot{\mathbf{Sin}} = \text{diag }[\omega_i \cos \omega_i(t - t_0)]$$

or

$$\dot{\mathbf{Sin}} = \boldsymbol{\omega}\,\mathbf{Cos} = \mathbf{Cos}\,\boldsymbol{\omega} \tag{8-23}$$

and (found in an identical manner)

$$\dot{\mathbf{Cos}} = -\boldsymbol{\omega}\,\mathbf{Sin} = -\mathbf{Sin}\,\boldsymbol{\omega} \tag{8-24}$$

Applying the conditions (8-19) at $t = t_0$, we obtain

$$\mathbf{x}(t = t_0) = \mathbf{\Phi}(\mathbf{0a} + \mathbf{Ib}) = \mathbf{x}_0 \qquad \text{and} \qquad \dot{\mathbf{x}}(t = t_0) = \mathbf{\Phi}(\boldsymbol{\omega}\mathbf{Ia} - \boldsymbol{\omega}\mathbf{0b}) = \dot{\mathbf{x}}_0$$

from which we obtain

$$\mathbf{\Phi b} = \mathbf{x}_0 \tag{8-25a}$$

and

$$\mathbf{\Phi}\boldsymbol{\omega}\mathbf{a} = \dot{\mathbf{x}}_0 \tag{8-25b}$$

so that

$$\mathbf{b} = \mathbf{\Phi}^{-1}\mathbf{x}_0 \tag{8-26a}$$

and

$$\mathbf{a} = (\mathbf{\Phi}\boldsymbol{\omega})^{-1}\dot{\mathbf{x}}_0 \tag{8-26b}$$

These expressions involve the inverse of the modal matrix $\mathbf{\Phi}$, an operation that would usually be rather difficult and time-consuming for large n. Much more convenient expressions can be found when use is made of Eq. (8-16).

Premultiplying both sides of Eqs. (8-25) by $\mathbf{\Phi}'\mathbf{M}$,

$$\mathbf{\Phi}'\mathbf{M}\mathbf{x}_0 = \mathbf{\Phi}'\mathbf{M}\mathbf{\Phi}\mathbf{b} = \bar{m}\mathbf{b} \qquad \text{and} \qquad \mathbf{\Phi}'\mathbf{M}\dot{\mathbf{x}}_0 = \mathbf{\Phi}'\mathbf{M}\mathbf{\Phi}\boldsymbol{\omega}\mathbf{a} = \bar{m}\boldsymbol{\omega}\mathbf{a}$$

Hence

$$\mathbf{b} = \frac{1}{\bar{m}}\mathbf{\Phi}'\mathbf{M}\mathbf{x}_0 \tag{8-27a}$$

and

$$\mathbf{a} = \frac{1}{\bar{m}}\boldsymbol{\omega}^{-1}\mathbf{\Phi}'\mathbf{M}\dot{\mathbf{x}}_0 \tag{8-27b}$$

Since $\boldsymbol{\omega}$ is a diagonal matrix, its inverse is simply

$$\boldsymbol{\omega}^{-1} = \text{diag } [\omega_i^{-1}]$$

Equation (8-20), which describes the free vibrations with initial conditions $\mathbf{x}_0$ and $\dot{\mathbf{x}}_0$, then becomes

$$\mathbf{x}(t) = \frac{1}{\bar{m}}\mathbf{\Phi}(\mathbf{Sin}\,\boldsymbol{\omega}^{-1}\mathbf{\Phi}'\mathbf{M}\dot{\mathbf{x}}_0 + \mathbf{Cos}\,\mathbf{\Phi}'\mathbf{M}\mathbf{x}_0) \tag{8-28}$$

and

$$\dot{\mathbf{x}}(t) = \frac{1}{\bar{m}}\mathbf{\Phi}(\mathbf{Cos}\,\mathbf{\Phi}'\mathbf{M}\dot{\mathbf{x}}_0 - \boldsymbol{\omega}\,\mathbf{Sin}\,\mathbf{\Phi}'\mathbf{M}\mathbf{x}_0) \tag{8-29}$$

These results require only matrix multiplications and can therefore be obtained with relative ease.

Equations (8-28) and (8-29) might induce the reader to believe that the arbitrary choice of $\bar{m}$ affects the result of our calculation. This is not the case. From Eqs. (8-16) and (8-17), as well as from our calculations in Example 8-2, one can easily see that the modal matrix $\mathbf{\Phi}$ contains $\sqrt{\bar{m}}$ as a common factor, so that $\bar{m}$ cancels out in Eqs. (8-28) and (8-29).

Example 8-3. Find the equation of motion for the system of Example 8-1 when the initial conditions at $t = t_0$ are $\mathbf{x}_0 = d\{1 \quad 1 \quad 1\}$ and $\dot{x}_0 = v\{1 \quad 0 \quad -1\}$.

For this purpose we have to determine the vectors **a** and **b** according to Eqs. (8-27), which are then inserted in the solution, Eq. (8-20). From Example 8-2 the modal matrix $\mathbf{\Phi}$ is already known. Using the results previously gained in Examples 8-1 and 8-2, we obtain the following product:

$$\frac{1}{\bar{m}}\mathbf{\Phi}'\mathbf{M} = \frac{1}{\bar{m}}\sqrt{\frac{\bar{m}}{m}}\begin{bmatrix} 0.3780 & 0.4645 & 0.4556 \\ 0.1010 & -0.4169 & 0.4321 \\ 0.6680 & 0.0987 & -0.3237 \end{bmatrix} \cdot \begin{bmatrix} 2m & -m & 0 \\ -m & 3m & 0 \\ 0 & 0 & 2m \end{bmatrix}$$

$$= \sqrt{\frac{m}{\bar{m}}} \cdot \begin{bmatrix} 0.2915 & 1.0155 & 0.9112 \\ 0.6189 & -1.3517 & 0.8642 \\ 1.2373 & -0.3719 & -0.6474 \end{bmatrix}$$

so that from Eqs. (8-27)

$$\mathbf{b} = \frac{1}{\bar{m}}\mathbf{\Phi}'\mathbf{M}\mathbf{x}_0 = \sqrt{\frac{m}{\bar{m}}}\, d \begin{bmatrix} 2.2182 \\ 0.1314 \\ 0.2180 \end{bmatrix}$$

and

$$\mathbf{a} = \frac{1}{\bar{m}}\boldsymbol{\omega}^{-1}\mathbf{\Phi}'\mathbf{M}\dot{\mathbf{x}}_0$$

$$= v\sqrt{\frac{m}{\bar{m}}}\sqrt{\frac{m}{k}} \begin{bmatrix} 2.427 & 0 & 0 \\ 0 & 1.143 & 0 \\ 0 & 0 & 0.572 \end{bmatrix} \cdot \begin{bmatrix} 0.2915 & 1.0155 & 0.9112 \\ 0.6189 & -1.3517 & 0.8642 \\ 1.2373 & -0.3719 & -0.6474 \end{bmatrix} \cdot \begin{bmatrix} 1 \\ 0 \\ -1 \end{bmatrix}$$

$$\mathbf{a} = \frac{vm}{\sqrt{k\bar{m}}} \begin{bmatrix} -1.5040 \\ -0.2804 \\ 1.0936 \end{bmatrix}$$

The equation of motion, Eq. (8-20), is therefore

$$\mathbf{x} = \sqrt{\frac{\bar{m}}{m}} \begin{bmatrix} 0.3780 & 0.1010 & 0.6680 \\ 0.4645 & -0.4169 & 0.0987 \\ 0.4556 & 0.4321 & -0.3237 \end{bmatrix} \cdot \begin{bmatrix} \sin\omega_1(t-t_0) & 0 & 0 \\ 0 & \sin\omega_2(t-t_0) & 0 \\ 0 & 0 & \sin\omega_3(t-t_0) \end{bmatrix}$$

$$\cdot \frac{vm}{\sqrt{k\bar{m}}} \begin{bmatrix} -1.5040 \\ -0.2804 \\ 1.0936 \end{bmatrix} + \sqrt{\frac{\bar{m}}{m}} \begin{bmatrix} 0.3780 & 0.1010 & 0.6680 \\ 0.4645 & -0.4169 & 0.0987 \\ 0.4556 & 0.4321 & -0.3237 \end{bmatrix}$$

$$\cdot \begin{bmatrix} \cos\omega_1(t-t_0) & 0 & 0 \\ 0 & \cos\omega_2(t-t_0) & 0 \\ 0 & 0 & \cos\omega_3(t-t_0) \end{bmatrix} \cdot d\sqrt{\frac{m}{\bar{m}}} \begin{bmatrix} 2.2182 \\ 0.1314 \\ 0.2180 \end{bmatrix}$$

$$\mathbf{x} = \begin{bmatrix} +0.5685\sin\omega_1(t-t_0) - 0.0283\sin\omega_2(t-t_0) + 0.4492\sin\omega_3(t-t_0) \\ -0.6986\sin\omega_1(t-t_0) + 0.1168\sin\omega_2(t-t_0) + 0.1079\sin\omega_3(t-t_0) \\ -0.6852\sin\omega_1(t-t_0) - 0.1212\sin\omega_2(t-t_0) - 0.3540\sin\omega_3(t-t_0) \end{bmatrix} \cdot v\sqrt{\frac{m}{k}}$$

$$+ \begin{bmatrix} 1.0652\cos\omega_1(t-t_0) + 0.0133\cos\omega_2(t-t_0) + 0.1456\cos\omega_3(t-t_0) \\ 1.3090\cos\omega_1(t-t_0) - 0.0548\cos\omega_2(t-t_0) + 0.0215\cos\omega_3(t-t_0) \\ 1.2839\cos\omega_1(t-t_0) + 0.0286\cos\omega_2(t-t_0) - 0.0706\cos\omega_3(t-t_0) \end{bmatrix} \cdot d$$

with $\omega_1 = 0.412\sqrt{k/m}$, $\omega_2 = 0.874\sqrt{k/m}$, and $\omega_3 = 1.75\sqrt{k/m}$.

PROBLEMS

8-5. Compute the frequency and modal matrices for the system shown in Fig. P 8-5. Verify, also, Eqs. (8-16) and (8-17).

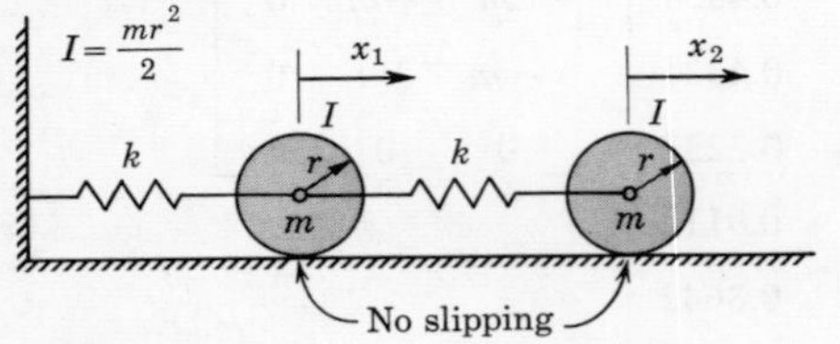

FIG. P 8-5

8-6. Find the response of the system of the previous problem to the following initial conditions:

(*a*) $\mathbf{x} = d\{1 \quad -1\}$, $\dot{\mathbf{x}} = \mathbf{0}$
(*b*) $\mathbf{x} = \mathbf{0}$, $\dot{\mathbf{x}} = v\{-2 \quad 1\}$
(*c*) $\mathbf{x} = d\{1 \quad 1\}$, $\dot{\mathbf{x}} = v\{1 \quad 1\}$

8-7. Compute the frequency and modal matrices for the system shown in Fig. P 8-7, and verify Eqs. (8-16) and (8-17).

FIG. P 8-7

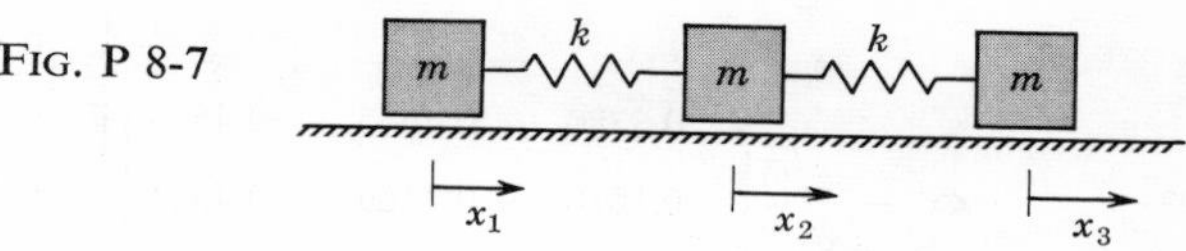

8-8. Find the response of the system of the previous problem to the following initial conditions:

(*a*) $\mathbf{x} = d\{1 \quad 0 \quad 0\}$, $\dot{\mathbf{x}} = \mathbf{0}$
(*b*) $\mathbf{x} = \mathbf{0}$, $\dot{\mathbf{x}} = v\{1 \quad 0 \quad 0\}$

8-3. Forced Undamped Vibrations

Steady-state Harmonic Motion. The differential equation of motion for a system subjected to forces $\mathbf{f}(t)$ is

$$\mathbf{M}\ddot{\mathbf{x}} + \mathbf{K}\mathbf{x} = \mathbf{f}(t) \tag{8-30}$$

If $\mathbf{f}(t) = \mathbf{f}\,\text{Re}\,\{e^{j\Omega t}\}$, where $\mathbf{f} = \{F_1 \quad F_2 \quad \cdots \quad F_n\}$, then the steady-state solution has the form

$$\mathbf{x}(t) = \text{Re}\,(\mathbf{x}e^{j\Omega t})$$

and the equation in $\mathbf{x}$ becomes

$$(-\Omega^2\mathbf{M} + \mathbf{K})\mathbf{x} = \mathbf{f} \tag{8-31}$$

so that

$$\mathbf{x} = (-\Omega^2\mathbf{M} + \mathbf{K})^{-1}\mathbf{f} \tag{8-32}$$

The inversion required in Eq. (8-32) can be avoided if the modal matrix $\mathbf{\Phi}$ of the system is available. The column vector $\mathbf{x}$ can then be expressed as a linear combination of the modal vectors according to the relation

$$\mathbf{x} = c_1\boldsymbol{\phi}_1 + c_2\boldsymbol{\phi}_2 + \cdots + c_n\boldsymbol{\phi}_n = [\boldsymbol{\phi}_1 \quad \boldsymbol{\phi}_2 \quad \cdots \quad \boldsymbol{\phi}_n]\cdot\{c_1 \quad c_2 \quad \cdots \quad c_n\} = \mathbf{\Phi}\mathbf{c} \tag{8-33}$$

Substituting Eq. (8-33) in Eq. (8-31) gives

$$(-\Omega^2\mathbf{M} + \mathbf{K})\mathbf{\Phi}\mathbf{c} = \mathbf{f}$$

and premultiplying throughout by $\mathbf{\Phi}'$ yields

$$(-\Omega^2\mathbf{\Phi}'\mathbf{M}\mathbf{\Phi} + \mathbf{\Phi}'\mathbf{K}\mathbf{\Phi})\mathbf{c} = \mathbf{\Phi}'\mathbf{f}$$

Using Eqs. (8-16) and (8-17), we obtain

$$\bar{m}(\boldsymbol{\omega}^2 - \Omega^2\mathbf{I})\mathbf{c} = \mathbf{\Phi}'\mathbf{f}$$

Hence

$$\mathbf{c} = \frac{1}{\bar{m}}(\boldsymbol{\omega}^2 - \Omega^2\mathbf{I})^{-1}\mathbf{\Phi}'\mathbf{f} \tag{8-34}$$

where

$$(\boldsymbol{\omega}^2 - \Omega^2\mathbf{I})^{-1} = \text{diag}\ \ [(\omega_i^2 - \Omega^2)^{-1}]$$

Note that the matrix $(\boldsymbol{\omega}^2 - \Omega^2\mathbf{I})^{-1}$ becomes singular whenever $\Omega = \omega_i$ (resonance).

Substituting Eq. (8-34) in Eq. (8-33), we obtain

$$\mathbf{x} = \frac{1}{\bar{m}}\mathbf{\Phi}(\boldsymbol{\omega}^2 - \Omega^2\mathbf{I})^{-1}\mathbf{\Phi}'\mathbf{f} \tag{8-35}$$

Example 8-4. Determine the steady-state behavior of the system in Example 8-1 when it is excited by $\mathbf{f} = \{0 \quad 1 \quad 0\}ka$ with $\Omega = 1.00\sqrt{k/m}$.

The problem is solved with the aid of Eq. (8-35), in which the matrices $\mathbf{\Phi}$ and $\boldsymbol{\omega}$ are known from Example 8-2. Equation (8-35) is evaluated in tabular form as follows:

$$\begin{bmatrix} 0 \\ 1 \\ 0 \end{bmatrix} \cdot ka = \mathbf{f}$$

$$\mathbf{\Phi}' = \sqrt{\frac{\bar{m}}{m}}\begin{bmatrix} 0.3780 & 0.4645 & 0.4556 \\ 0.1010 & -0.4169 & 0.4321 \\ 0.6680 & 0.0987 & -0.3237 \end{bmatrix}\begin{bmatrix} 0.4645 \\ -0.4169 \\ 0.0987 \end{bmatrix} \cdot ka\sqrt{\frac{\bar{m}}{m}} = \mathbf{\Phi}'\mathbf{f}$$

$$(\boldsymbol{\omega}^2 - \Omega^2\mathbf{I})^{-1} = \frac{m}{k} \cdot \begin{bmatrix} -1.2045 & 0 & 0 \\ 0 & -4.2699 & 0 \\ 0 & 0 & 0.4851 \end{bmatrix}\begin{bmatrix} -0.5595 \\ 1.7800 \\ 0.0478 \end{bmatrix} \cdot a\sqrt{\bar{m}m} = (\boldsymbol{\omega}^2 - \Omega^2\mathbf{I})^{-1}\mathbf{\Phi}'\mathbf{f}$$

$$\mathbf{\Phi} = \sqrt{\frac{\bar{m}}{m}}\begin{bmatrix} 0.3780 & 0.1010 & 0.6680 \\ 0.4645 & -0.4169 & 0.0987 \\ 0.4556 & 0.4321 & -0.3237 \end{bmatrix}\begin{bmatrix} 0.0002 \\ -0.9973 \\ 0.4988 \end{bmatrix} \cdot a\bar{m} = \mathbf{\Phi}(\boldsymbol{\omega}^2 - \Omega^2\mathbf{I})^{-1}\mathbf{\Phi}'\mathbf{f}$$

where $(\boldsymbol{\omega}^2 - \Omega^2\mathbf{I})^{-1}$ was obtained by inverting the corresponding matrix found in Example 8-2. Thus we have [cf. Eq. (8-35)]

$$\mathbf{x} \approx \begin{bmatrix} 0 \\ -1 \\ \frac{1}{2} \end{bmatrix} \cdot a$$

The reader is advised to check the solution by physical reasoning (cf. Fig. 8-9).

Motion Resulting from Impulsive Forces. The system is subjected to impulsive forces at time $t = t_0$ which are represented by the column vector $\mathbf{g}$. The initial velocities are therefore given by the relation

$$\mathbf{M}\dot{\mathbf{x}}_0 = \mathbf{g} \qquad \text{or} \qquad \dot{\mathbf{x}}_0 = \mathbf{M}^{-1}\mathbf{g} \tag{8-36}$$

Using this expression for $\dot{\mathbf{x}}_0$ in Eq. (8-28), while setting $\mathbf{x}_0 = \mathbf{0}$, the expression for the resulting motion is

$$\mathbf{x}(t) = \frac{1}{\bar{m}}\mathbf{\Phi}\,\mathbf{Sin}\,\boldsymbol{\omega}^{-1}\mathbf{\Phi}'\mathbf{M}\mathbf{M}^{-1}\mathbf{g} = \frac{1}{\bar{m}}\mathbf{\Phi}\,\mathbf{Sin}\,\boldsymbol{\omega}^{-1}\mathbf{\Phi}'\mathbf{g} \tag{8-37}$$

General Case of a Time-varying Force. Now suppose that the system is subjected to time-varying forces $\mathbf{f}(t)$. We consider the effect of an infinitesimal impulse $d\mathbf{g} = \mathbf{f}(\tau)\,d\tau$ applied at time $t_0 = \tau$. The motion due to this impulse according to Eq. (8-37) is

$$\mathbf{x} = \frac{1}{\bar{m}}\mathbf{\Phi}\,\mathbf{Sin}_\tau\,\boldsymbol{\omega}^{-1}\mathbf{\Phi}'\mathbf{f}(\tau)\,d\tau \qquad \text{for } t \geq \tau \tag{8-38}$$

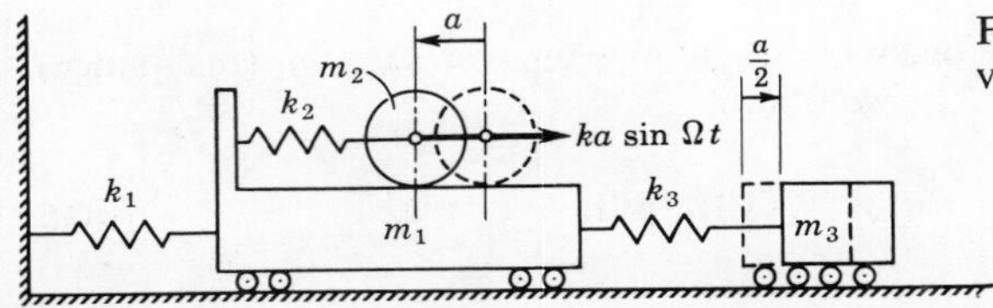

FIG. 8-9. Configuration of forced vibration in Example 8-4.

where
$$\mathbf{Sin}_\tau = \text{diag}\ [\sin \omega_i(t - \tau)] \tag{8-39}$$

Since the impulses are being produced continuously for all times τ between 0 and t, the motion due to the forces $\mathbf{f}(t)$ is found by integrating Eq. (8-38) between 0 and t. Hence

$$\mathbf{x}(t) = \frac{1}{\bar{m}} \mathbf{\Phi} \int_0^t \mathbf{Sin}_\tau\, \boldsymbol{\omega}^{-1} \mathbf{\Phi}' \mathbf{f}(\tau)\, d\tau$$

and allowing for the initial conditions $\mathbf{x}_0$ and $\dot{\mathbf{x}}_0$ at $t = 0$, the complete expression for the motion becomes

$$\mathbf{x}(t) = \frac{1}{\bar{m}} \mathbf{\Phi} \left[\mathbf{Sin}_0\, \boldsymbol{\omega}^{-1} \mathbf{\Phi}' \mathbf{M} \dot{\mathbf{x}}_0 + \mathbf{Cos}_0\, \mathbf{\Phi}' \mathbf{M} \mathbf{x}_0 + \int_0^t \mathbf{Sin}_\tau\, \boldsymbol{\omega}^{-1} \mathbf{\Phi}' \mathbf{f}(\tau)\, d\tau \right] \tag{8-40}$$

where $\mathbf{Sin}_0$ and $\mathbf{Cos}_0$ are obtained from Eqs. (8-21*a*) and (8-21*b*) for $t_0 = 0$.

Example 8-5. A horizontal constant force F is applied to mass m_1 of the system of Example 8-1 (Fig. 8-7) for a length of time T_1. If the system starts from rest with zero displacement, find the resulting motion.

The differential equation of motion of the system is given by Eq. (8-7), except that now the right side is formed not by the column vector $\mathbf{0} = \{0 \quad 0 \quad 0\}$ but by $\mathbf{f} = \{F_1 \quad F_2 \quad F_3\}$; that is, for $0 < t < T_1$, $\mathbf{f}(t) = \{F_1 \quad 0 \quad 0\}$ and $\mathbf{f}(t) = \mathbf{0}$ for $t > T_1$. Since $\mathbf{x}_0 = \mathbf{0}$ and $\dot{\mathbf{x}}_0 = \mathbf{0}$, then for the period $0 < t \le T_1$ the motion is, in view of Eq. (8-40),

$$\mathbf{x}(t) = \frac{1}{\bar{m}} \mathbf{\Phi} \int_0^t \mathbf{Sin}_\tau\, \boldsymbol{\omega}^{-1} \mathbf{\Phi}' \mathbf{f}(\tau)\, d\tau$$

The modal matrix $\mathbf{\Phi}$ was already computed in Example 8-2. Hence

$$\mathbf{x}(t) = \frac{1}{\sqrt{k\bar{m}}} \mathbf{\Phi} \int_0^t \begin{bmatrix} \sin \omega_1(t-\tau) & 0 & 0 \\ 0 & \sin \omega_2(t-\tau) & 0 \\ 0 & 0 & \sin \omega_3(t-\tau) \end{bmatrix} \cdot \begin{bmatrix} 2.427 & 0 & 0 \\ 0 & 1.143 & 0 \\ 0 & 0 & 0.572 \end{bmatrix}$$
$$\cdot \begin{bmatrix} 0.3780 & \mathrm{x} & \mathrm{x} \\ 0.1010 & \mathrm{x} & \mathrm{x} \\ 0.6680 & \mathrm{x} & \mathrm{x} \end{bmatrix} \cdot \begin{bmatrix} F_1 \\ 0 \\ 0 \end{bmatrix} d\tau$$

$$= \frac{F_1}{\sqrt{k\bar{m}}} \mathbf{\Phi} \int_0^t \begin{bmatrix} 0.917 \sin \omega_1(t-\tau) \\ 0.115 \sin \omega_2(t-\tau) \\ 0.382 \sin \omega_3(t-\tau) \end{bmatrix} d\tau = \frac{F_1}{\sqrt{k\bar{m}}} \mathbf{\Phi} \begin{bmatrix} \frac{0.917}{\omega_1} (\cos \omega_1 t - 1) \\ \frac{0.115}{\omega_2} (\cos \omega_2 t - 1) \\ \frac{0.382}{\omega_3} (\cos \omega_3 t - 1) \end{bmatrix}$$

$$\mathbf{x}(t) = \frac{F_1}{k} \begin{bmatrix} 0.841(\cos \omega_1 t - 1) + 0.010(\cos \omega_2 t - 1) + 0.146(\cos \omega_3 t - 1) \\ 1.033(\cos \omega_1 t - 1) - 0.042(\cos \omega_2 t - 1) + 0.021(\cos \omega_3 t - 1) \\ 1.014(\cos \omega_1 t - 1) + 0.044(\cos \omega_2 t - 1) - 0.071(\cos \omega_3 t - 1) \end{bmatrix}$$

for $0 \leq t \leq T_1$. When $t \geq T_1$, then the motion is

$$\mathbf{x}(t) = \frac{1}{\bar{m}} \mathbf{\Phi} \int_0^{T_1} \mathbf{Sin}_\tau\, \boldsymbol{\omega}^{-1} \mathbf{\Phi}' \mathbf{f}(\tau)\, d\tau$$

since, for $t > T_1$, $\mathbf{f}(\tau) = \mathbf{0}$. Therefore

$$\mathbf{x}(t) = \frac{F_1}{k} \begin{bmatrix} 0.814[\cos \omega_1 t - \cos \omega_1(t - T_1)] + 0.010[\cos \omega_2 t - \cos \omega_2(t - T_1)] \\ + 0.146[\cos \omega_3 t - \cos \omega_3(t - T_1)] \\ 1.033[\cos \omega_1 t - \cos \omega_1(t - T_1)] - 0.042[\cos \omega_2 t - \cos \omega_2(t - T_1)] \\ + 0.021[\cos \omega_3 t - \cos \omega_3(t - T_1)] \\ 1.014[\cos \omega_1 t - \cos \omega_1(t - T_1)] + 0.044[\cos \omega_2 t - \cos \omega_2(t - T_1)] \\ - 0.071[\cos \omega_3 t - \cos \omega_3(t - T_1)] \end{bmatrix}$$

for $t \geq T_1$.

General Case of Time-varying Forced Displacements.† The differential equation of motion for a system with n degrees of freedom is

$$\mathbf{M}\ddot{\mathbf{x}} + \mathbf{K}\mathbf{x} = \mathbf{f}(t) \tag{8-30}$$

Let us suppose that f of the displacements are forced to vary in a defined manner. Equation (8-30) can then be partitioned so that the differential equation of motion for the remaining s displacements ($n = s + f$) can be determined. Let Eq. (8-30) be partitioned in the following way:

$$\left[\begin{array}{c|c} \mathbf{M}_1 & \mathbf{M}_2 \\ \hline \mathbf{M}_3 & \mathbf{M}_4 \end{array}\right] \cdot \left[\begin{array}{c} \ddot{\mathbf{x}}_f \\ \hline \ddot{\mathbf{x}}_s \end{array}\right] + \left[\begin{array}{c|c} \mathbf{K}_1 & \mathbf{K}_2 \\ \hline \mathbf{K}_3 & \mathbf{K}_4 \end{array}\right] \cdot \left[\begin{array}{c} \mathbf{x}_f \\ \hline \mathbf{x}_s \end{array}\right] = \left[\begin{array}{c} \mathbf{f}_f \\ \hline \mathbf{f}_s \end{array}\right] \tag{8-41}$$

where $\mathbf{x}_f$ is the column vector representing the displacements that move in a prescribed manner and $\mathbf{x}_s$ are the remaining displacements. Furthermore $\mathbf{f}_f$ are the unknown reactions at the f points in the directions of $\mathbf{x}_f$, whereas $\mathbf{f}_s$ are the given forces at the s points in the directions of $\mathbf{x}_s$. Mostly we have $\mathbf{f}_s = \mathbf{0}$.

Equation (8-41) leads to the two equations

$$\mathbf{M}_1\ddot{\mathbf{x}}_f + \mathbf{M}_2\ddot{\mathbf{x}}_s + \mathbf{K}_1\mathbf{x}_f + \mathbf{K}_2\mathbf{x}_s = \mathbf{f}_f \tag{8-42}$$

and

$$\mathbf{M}_3\ddot{\mathbf{x}}_f + \mathbf{M}_4\ddot{\mathbf{x}}_s + \mathbf{K}_3\mathbf{x}_f + \mathbf{K}_4\mathbf{x}_s = \mathbf{f}_s \tag{8-43}$$

Equation (8-43) can be written in the form

$$\mathbf{M}_4\ddot{\mathbf{x}}_s + \mathbf{K}_4\mathbf{x}_s = \mathbf{f}_s - (\mathbf{M}_3\ddot{\mathbf{x}}_f + \mathbf{K}_3\mathbf{x}_f) \tag{8-44}$$

in which the right-hand side is a given function of time. This is the required differential equation for the remaining s displacements. In Eq. (8-44), $\mathbf{M}_4$ and $\mathbf{K}_4$ are symmetric and are the mass and spring matrices, respectively, for the reduced system that is obtained from the original system simply by introducing additional constraints so that $\mathbf{x}_f = \mathbf{0}$. The natural frequencies and the associated normal modes can be found from these matrices according to standard practice, and it is assumed in the further development that this has been done, i.e., that the modal matrix $\mathbf{\Phi}_s$ for the reduced system as well as the frequency matrix $\boldsymbol{\omega}_s$ has been determined in the manner demonstrated in Sec. 8-2.

If we let $\mathbf{f}(t) = \mathbf{f}_s - (\mathbf{M}_3\ddot{\mathbf{x}}_f + \mathbf{K}_3\mathbf{x}_f)$, then Eq. (8-44) becomes

$$\mathbf{M}_4\ddot{\mathbf{x}}_s + \mathbf{K}_4\mathbf{x}_s = \mathbf{f}(t) \qquad \text{cf. Eq. (8-30)}$$

† For a treatment of this topic limited to the forced displacements of the supports of a structure, see Ref. 44.

and its solution has already been given by Eq. (8-40). Hence

$$\mathbf{x}_s = \frac{1}{\bar{m}}\boldsymbol{\Phi}_s\left[\mathbf{Sin}_0\,\boldsymbol{\omega}_s^{-1}\boldsymbol{\Phi}_s'\mathbf{M}_4\dot{\mathbf{x}}_{0s} + \mathbf{Cos}_0\,\boldsymbol{\Phi}_s'\mathbf{M}_4\mathbf{x}_{0s} + \int_0^t \mathbf{Sin}_\tau\,\boldsymbol{\omega}_s^{-1}\boldsymbol{\Phi}_s'\mathbf{f}(\tau)\,d\tau\right] \tag{8-45}$$

where $\mathbf{x}_{0s}$ and $\dot{\mathbf{x}}_{0s}$ are arbitrary initial conditions at the points s. We could now substitute the values for $\mathbf{x}_f$, $\mathbf{x}_s$, and their derivatives into Eq. (8-42) and thereby compute the forces $\mathbf{f}_f$ necessary to cause the required displacements.

It sometimes proves convenient to reformulate Eq. (8-45) when $\mathbf{M}_3 = \mathbf{0}$ and $\mathbf{f}_s = \mathbf{0}$. When displacements $\mathbf{x}_f$ are imposed on the system, then its time-varying equilibrium position $\mathbf{x}_s^E(t)$ is defined by the relation [cf. Eq. (8-43) for $\mathbf{M}_3 = \mathbf{M}_4 = \mathbf{0}$]

$$\mathbf{K}_4\mathbf{x}_s^E(t) = -\mathbf{K}_3\mathbf{x}_f(t)$$

Thus

$$\mathbf{f}(t) = \mathbf{K}_4\mathbf{x}_s^E(t)$$

and Eq. (8-45) can then be written

$$\begin{aligned}\mathbf{x}_s(t) &= \frac{1}{\bar{m}}\boldsymbol{\Phi}_s\left[\mathbf{Sin}_0\,\boldsymbol{\omega}_s^{-1}\boldsymbol{\Phi}_s'\mathbf{M}_4\dot{\mathbf{x}}_{0s} + \mathbf{Cos}_0\,\boldsymbol{\Phi}_s'\mathbf{M}_4\mathbf{x}_{0s} + \int_0^t \mathbf{Sin}_\tau\,\boldsymbol{\omega}_s^{-1}\boldsymbol{\Phi}_s'\mathbf{K}_4\mathbf{x}_s^E(\tau)\,d\tau\right] \\ &= \frac{1}{\bar{m}}\boldsymbol{\Phi}_s\left[\mathbf{Sin}_0\,\boldsymbol{\omega}_s^{-1}\boldsymbol{\Phi}_s'\mathbf{M}_4\dot{\mathbf{x}}_{0s} + \mathbf{Cos}_0\,\boldsymbol{\Phi}_s'\mathbf{M}_4\mathbf{x}_{0s} + \int_0^t \mathbf{Sin}_\tau\,\boldsymbol{\omega}_s\boldsymbol{\Phi}_s'\mathbf{M}_4\mathbf{x}_s^E(\tau)\,d\tau\right]^{\dagger}\end{aligned} \tag{8-46}$$

This formulation is practical, for example, when calculating the response of a tall building to earthquake movement. If the earthquake causes lateral movement and rotation about its base, then it is easy to calculate the column vector $\mathbf{x}_s^E(t)$ (Fig. 8-10).

The Differential Equation Using the Normal Modes as Coordinates. The differential equation of motion of the system is

$$\mathbf{M}\ddot{\mathbf{x}} + \mathbf{K}\mathbf{x} = \mathbf{f}(t) \tag{8-30}$$

We express the displacement vector $\mathbf{x}(t)$ as a linear combination of the modal vectors according to the relation

$$\begin{aligned}\mathbf{x}(t) &= q_1(t)\,\boldsymbol{\phi}_1 + q_2(t)\,\boldsymbol{\phi}_2 + \cdots + q_n(t)\,\boldsymbol{\phi}_n \\ &= \begin{bmatrix}\boldsymbol{\phi}_1 & \boldsymbol{\phi}_2 & \cdots & \boldsymbol{\phi}_n\end{bmatrix}\cdot\begin{bmatrix} q_1(t) \\ q_2(t) \\ \cdot \\ \cdot \\ \cdot \\ q_n(t)\end{bmatrix} = \boldsymbol{\Phi}\mathbf{q}(t)\end{aligned} \tag{8-47}$$

† Since from Eqs. (8-17) and (8-16)

$$\boldsymbol{\Phi}_s'\mathbf{K}_4 = \bar{m}\boldsymbol{\omega}_s^2\boldsymbol{\Phi}_s^{-1} = \frac{\bar{m}\boldsymbol{\omega}_s^2\boldsymbol{\Phi}_s'\mathbf{M}_4}{\bar{m}} = \boldsymbol{\omega}_s^2\boldsymbol{\Phi}_s'\mathbf{M}_4$$

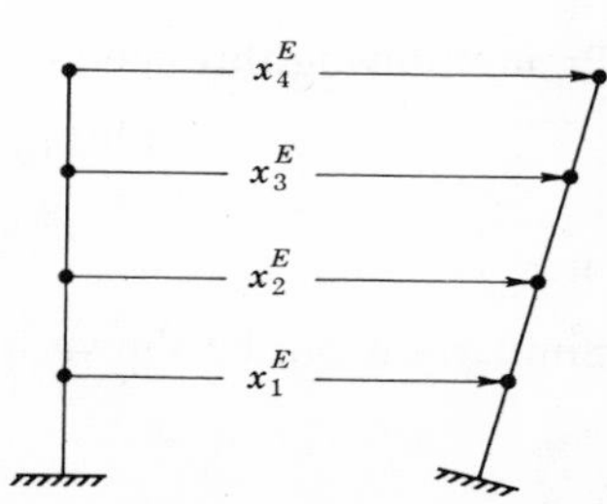

FIG. 8-10. Static displacement of tall building due to ground movement.

where the vector $\mathbf{q}(t) = \{q_1 \quad q_2 \quad \cdots \quad q_n\}$ contains as components the so-called generalized coordinates $q_i(t)$.

The second derivative of x with respect to time is then

$$\ddot{\mathbf{x}} = \mathbf{\Phi}\ddot{\mathbf{q}}$$

Substituting this expression and Eq. (8-47) in Eq. (8-30) gives

$$\mathbf{M\Phi}\ddot{\mathbf{q}} + \mathbf{K\Phi q} = \mathbf{f}(t)$$

Premultiplying throughout by $\mathbf{\Phi}'$, we obtain

$$\mathbf{\Phi}'\mathbf{M\Phi}\ddot{\mathbf{q}} + \mathbf{\Phi}'\mathbf{K\Phi q} = \mathbf{\Phi}'\mathbf{f}(t)$$

and on recalling the results of Eqs. (8-16) and (8-17) the equation can be reduced to the form

$$\bar{m}\ddot{\mathbf{q}} + \bar{m}\boldsymbol{\omega}^2\mathbf{q} = \mathbf{\Phi}'\mathbf{f}(t)$$

or

$$\ddot{\mathbf{q}} + \boldsymbol{\omega}^2\mathbf{q} = \frac{1}{\bar{m}}\mathbf{\Phi}'\mathbf{f}(t) = \mathbf{f}_g(t) \tag{8-48}$$

where

$$\mathbf{f}_g(t) = \{F_{g1} \quad F_{g2} \quad \cdots \quad F_{gn}\} = \frac{1}{\bar{m}}\mathbf{\Phi}'\mathbf{f}(t)$$

is a vector the components of which are called the generalized forces $F_{gi}(t)$ corresponding to the normal modes $\boldsymbol{\phi}_i$.

Since $\boldsymbol{\omega}^2$ is a diagonal matrix [cf. Eq. (8-18)], Eq. (8-48) can be written in the form

$$\begin{bmatrix} \ddot{q}_1 \\ \ddot{q}_2 \\ \cdot \\ \cdot \\ \cdot \\ \ddot{q}_n \end{bmatrix} + \begin{bmatrix} \omega_1^2 q_1 \\ \omega_2^2 q_2 \\ \cdot \\ \cdot \\ \cdot \\ \omega_n^2 q_n \end{bmatrix} = \begin{bmatrix} F_{g1}(t) \\ F_{g2}(t) \\ \cdot \\ \cdot \\ \cdot \\ F_{gn}(t) \end{bmatrix}$$

or, in general, for the ith mode

$$\ddot{q}_i + \omega_i^2 q_i = F_{gi}(t) \tag{8-49}$$

from which we note that the equations of motion have been decoupled by the introduction of the generalized coordinates.

The solution of this equation is [cf. Eq. (2-16)]

$$q_i(t) = q_{i0}\cos\omega_i t + \frac{\dot{q}_{i0}}{\omega_i}\sin\omega_i t + \frac{1}{\omega_i}\int_0^t F_{gi}(\tau)\sin\omega_i(t-\tau)\,d\tau \tag{8-50}$$

where q_{i0} and $\dot{q}_{i0}$ are the initial values of q_i at time $\tau = 0$. These initial values are found from the initial values of $\mathbf{x}$ by means of Eq. (8-47):

$$\mathbf{x}_0 = \mathbf{\Phi q}_0 \qquad \dot{\mathbf{x}}_0 = \mathbf{\Phi}\dot{\mathbf{q}}_0$$

Premultiplying throughout by $\mathbf{\Phi}'\mathbf{M}$ gives

$$\mathbf{\Phi}'\mathbf{M}\mathbf{x}_0 = \mathbf{\Phi}'\mathbf{M\Phi q}_0 = \bar{m}\mathbf{q}_0 \qquad \text{cf. Eq. (8-16)}$$

or

$$\mathbf{q}_0 = \frac{1}{\bar{m}}\mathbf{\Phi}'\mathbf{M}\mathbf{x}_0 \tag{8-51}$$

Similarly it can be shown that

$$\dot{\mathbf{q}}_0 = \frac{1}{\bar{m}}\mathbf{\Phi}'\mathbf{M}\dot{\mathbf{x}}_0 \tag{8-52}$$

Hence with the help of Eqs. (8-50), (8-51), and (8-52) the variation of q_i ($i = 1, 2, \ldots, n$) with time can be calculated. Indeed, the variation of q_i can be found very conveniently on the phase plane [68]. Conversion back to the original displacements is achieved with the help of Eq. (8-47).

Now combining all equations of the type of Eq. (8-50) into a single matrix equation gives

$$\mathbf{q} = \mathbf{Cos}_0\, \mathbf{q}_0 + \mathbf{Sin}_0\, \boldsymbol{\omega}^{-1}\dot{\mathbf{q}}_0 + \frac{1}{\bar{m}} \int_0^t \mathbf{Sin}_\tau\, \boldsymbol{\omega}^{-1}\boldsymbol{\Phi}'\mathbf{f}(\tau)\, d\tau$$

and hence

$$\mathbf{x} = \boldsymbol{\Phi}\mathbf{q} = \frac{1}{\bar{m}} \boldsymbol{\Phi}\left[\mathbf{Cos}_0\, \boldsymbol{\Phi}'\mathbf{M}\mathbf{x}_0 + \mathbf{Sin}_0\, \boldsymbol{\omega}^{-1}\boldsymbol{\Phi}'\mathbf{M}\dot{\mathbf{x}}_0 + \int_0^t \mathbf{Sin}_\tau\, \boldsymbol{\omega}^{-1}\boldsymbol{\Phi}'\mathbf{f}(t)\, d\tau\right]$$

which agrees with Eq. (8-40).

PROBLEMS

8-9. The spring-mass system of Fig. P 8-7 is suspended from one end in a vertical position and then suddenly released. Compute the expressions for the subsequent displacement of the masses.

8-10. The right-hand roller of the system of Fig. P 8-5 is subjected to a horizontal force $P \cos \Omega t$ applied at its center. Compute the steady-state amplitudes of x_1 and x_2 when $\Omega^2 = k/m$, using (*a*) the usual inversion technique, (*b*) the normal-mode method.

8-11. The left-hand mass of the system shown in Fig. P 8-7 is subjected to forced lateral displacements. Find the new frequency and modal matrices, and compute the response of the system, if the left-hand mass is given a displacement $x_1 = at$.

8-12. The rollers of the system of Fig. P 8-5 are subjected to horizontal forces F_1 and F_2 applied at the centers and also to couples C_1 and C_2. Compute the generalized forces acting on the system.

8-4. Steady-state Forced Damped Vibrations

Equations of Motion. In view of our experience with damped vibrations gained in Chap. 4, we shall first investigate steady-state forced vibrations, which are easier to deal with than free damped vibrations. The differential equation for the vibration of an undamped system under harmonic excitation was found to be

$$\mathbf{M}\ddot{\mathbf{x}} + \mathbf{K}\mathbf{x} = \mathbf{f}\, \mathrm{Re}\, e^{j\Omega t} \tag{8-30}$$

If it is assumed that the damping forces act directly on the discrete masses of the system, then depending on the type of damping present the differential equations are as follows:

a. Simple viscous damping

$$\mathbf{M}\ddot{\mathbf{x}} + \mathbf{C}\dot{\mathbf{x}} + \mathbf{K}\mathbf{x} = \mathbf{f}\, \mathrm{Re}\, e^{j\Omega t} \tag{8-53}$$

where $\mathbf{C}$ is an (n, n) matrix containing as elements the constants for viscous damping, and the matrices $\mathbf{M}$ and $\mathbf{K}$ are the same mass and stiffness matrices, respectively, as were found for the undamped system.

b. Structural damping

$$\mathbf{M}\ddot{\mathbf{x}} + \mathbf{K}\left(\mathbf{x} + \frac{g}{\Omega}\dot{\mathbf{x}}\right) = \mathbf{f}\, \mathrm{Re}\, e^{j\Omega t} \tag{8-54}$$

Many authors drop the proportionality of stiffness and damping and write

$$\mathbf{M}\ddot{\mathbf{x}} + \frac{\mathbf{D}}{\Omega}\dot{\mathbf{x}} + \mathbf{K}\mathbf{x} = \mathbf{f}\, \mathrm{Re}\, e^{j\Omega t} \tag{8-55}$$

$\mathbf{D}/\Omega$ is then usually called the matrix of hysteretic damping.

When the trial solution as used in Sec. 8-3,

$$\mathbf{x}(t) = \mathrm{Re}\,(\bar{\mathbf{x}}e^{j\Omega t})$$

where $\bar{\mathbf{x}}$ denotes the complex amplitude of the displacement vector $\mathbf{x}(t)$, is substituted into Eqs. (8-53), (8-54), and (8-55), respectively, we obtain

$$[(\mathbf{K} - \Omega^2\mathbf{M}) + j\Omega\mathbf{C}]\bar{\mathbf{x}} = \mathbf{f} \tag{8-53a}$$

or

$$\bar{\mathbf{S}}_v\bar{\mathbf{x}} = \mathbf{f}$$

$$[-\Omega^2\mathbf{M} + \mathbf{K}(1 + jg)]\bar{\mathbf{x}} = \mathbf{f} \tag{8-54a}$$

or

$$\bar{\mathbf{S}}_{st}\bar{\mathbf{x}} = \mathbf{f}$$

and

$$[(\mathbf{K} - \Omega^2\mathbf{M}) + j\mathbf{D}]\bar{\mathbf{x}} = \mathbf{f} \tag{8-55a}$$

or

$$\bar{\mathbf{S}}_{hy}\bar{\mathbf{x}} = \mathbf{f}$$

The matrices $\bar{\mathbf{S}}$ are referred to as the complex dynamic stiffness matrix of the system. If the flexibility matrix $\mathbf{F}$ is known instead of the stiffness matrix $\mathbf{K}$, the above equations have to be premultiplied by $\mathbf{F} = \mathbf{K}^{-1}$ [cf. Eq. (8-4)]. Then

$$[(\mathbf{I} - \Omega^2\mathbf{FM}) + j\Omega\mathbf{FC}]\bar{\mathbf{x}} = \mathbf{Ff} = \mathbf{x}_{\mathrm{stat}} \tag{8-53b}$$

$$[-\Omega^2\mathbf{FM} + \mathbf{I}(1 + jg)]\bar{\mathbf{x}} = \mathbf{Ff} = \mathbf{x}_{\mathrm{stat}} \tag{8-54b}$$

or

$$[(\mathbf{I} - \Omega^2\mathbf{FM}) + j\mathbf{FD}]\bar{\mathbf{x}} = \mathbf{Ff} = \mathbf{x}_{\mathrm{stat}} \tag{8-55b}$$

Here $\mathbf{x}_{\mathrm{stat}}$ describes the displacements of the structure if it is statically loaded by $\mathbf{f}$. With $\mathbf{F}^* = \mathbf{F}/(1 + jg)$, Eq. (8-54*b*) could also be written

$$(-\Omega^2\mathbf{F}^*\mathbf{M} + \mathbf{I})\bar{\mathbf{x}} = \mathbf{F}^*\mathbf{f} \tag{8-54c}$$

Equations (8-54) are not limited to lumped damping but can also be used if the structural damping is considered to be uniformly distributed in the springs (struts, beams, etc.). The matrices $\mathbf{K}^*$ and $\mathbf{F}^*$ are then easily obtained from the matrices $\mathbf{K}$ and $\mathbf{F}$ listed in Sec. 9-1 if Young's modulus E and the shear modulus G are replaced by $E(1 + jg)$ and $G(1 + jg)$, respectively [cf. also Eqs. (4-10) and (4-11)].

Solution of Equations of Motion. The complex amplitudes $\bar{\mathbf{x}}$ of the forced vibration $\mathbf{x}(t)$ under the harmonic load $\mathbf{f}(t)$ are found from the above equations $\bar{\mathbf{S}}\bar{\mathbf{x}} = \mathbf{f}$ to be

$$\bar{\mathbf{x}} = \bar{\mathbf{S}}^{-1}\mathbf{f} \tag{8-56}$$

where $\bar{\mathbf{S}}^{-1}$ is the inverse of the complex dynamic stiffness matrix $\bar{\mathbf{S}}$ in Eqs. (8-53*a*), (8-54*a*), and (8-55*a*). If $\bar{\mathbf{S}}$ and $\bar{\mathbf{x}}$ are expressed in real form [cf. Eq. (4-29)] by setting $\bar{\mathbf{S}} = \mathbf{S}^{\mathrm{r}} + j\mathbf{S}^{\mathrm{i}}$ and $\bar{\mathbf{x}} = \mathbf{x}^{\mathrm{r}} + j\mathbf{x}^{\mathrm{i}}$, we find that Eqs. (8-53*a*), (8-54*a*), and (8-55*a*) can be expressed in the form

$$\mathbf{S}\begin{bmatrix}\mathbf{x}^{\mathrm{r}}\\ \mathbf{x}^{\mathrm{i}}\end{bmatrix} = \begin{bmatrix}\mathbf{f}\\ \mathbf{0}\end{bmatrix}$$

where

$$\underset{2n}{\overset{2n}{[\mathbf{S}]}} = \left[\begin{array}{c|c}\mathbf{S}^{\mathrm{r}} & -\mathbf{S}^{\mathrm{i}}\\ \hline \mathbf{S}^{\mathrm{i}} & \mathbf{S}^{\mathrm{r}}\end{array}\right] \tag{8-57}$$

In Sec. 4-5 it was then shown that the inverse $\bar{\mathbf{S}}^{-1}$ may be written

$$\bar{\mathbf{S}}^{-1} = \mathbf{A} - j\mathbf{B}$$

where $$\mathbf{A} = [\mathbf{S}^r + \mathbf{S}^i(\mathbf{S}^r)^{-1}\mathbf{S}^i]^{-1} \qquad \text{and} \qquad \mathbf{B} = \mathbf{A}\mathbf{S}^i(\mathbf{S}^r)^{-1} \tag{8-58}$$

This means that an (n, n) complex matrix is inverted by means of the inversion of two (n, n) real matrices, although in its real form the (n, n) complex matrix appears as a $(2n, 2n)$ matrix.

For viscous damping (case a) $\mathbf{S}$ contains elements with Ω^2 as well as Ω, whereas for structural or hysteretic damping only Ω^2 appears in $\mathbf{S}$.

PROBLEMS

8-13. Establish the complex dynamic stiffness matrix $\bar{\mathbf{S}}$ for the system shown in Fig. P 8-13, which possesses structural damping. The floors may be taken to be rigid. Invert the stiffness matrix $\bar{\mathbf{S}}$ to find the response of the frame to the given forces when $\Omega = \sqrt{3EJ/2ml^3}$.

8-14. Compute the steady-state response of the system illustrated in Fig. P 8-14 when

$$m_1 = m \qquad m_2 = 2m \qquad I_2 = mr^2 \qquad k_1 = k \qquad k_2 = 2k$$

$$c_1 = c_2 = 0.2\sqrt{mk} \qquad \Omega = \sqrt{\frac{k}{m}}$$

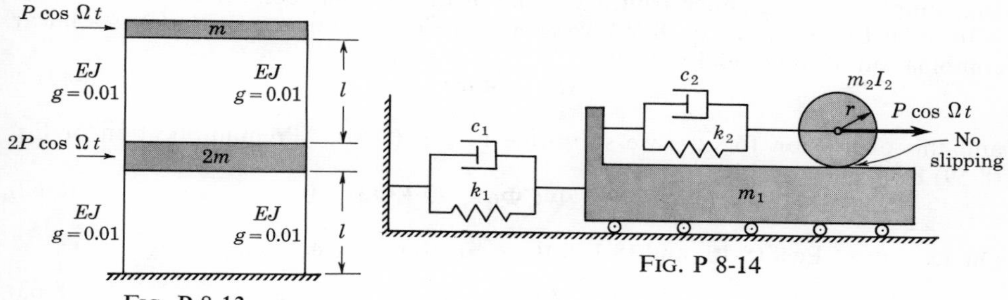

FIG. P 8-13

FIG. P 8-14

8-5. Free Damped Vibrations, Transients, and General Types of Damped Motions

Let us consider that the free damped motion of a system of n degrees of freedom is governed by the equation

$$\mathbf{M}\ddot{\mathbf{x}} + \mathbf{C}\dot{\mathbf{x}} + \mathbf{K}\mathbf{x}(t) = \mathbf{0} \tag{8-59}$$

The trial solution

$$\mathbf{x}(t) = \text{Re}\,(\bar{\mathbf{x}}e^{pt})$$

where p is a complex quantity, is substituted in Eq. (8-59) and yields the complex algebraic system of equations

$$(p^2\mathbf{M} + p\mathbf{C} + \mathbf{K})\bar{\mathbf{x}} = \mathbf{0} \tag{8-60}$$

which possesses a nontrivial solution for $\bar{\mathbf{x}}_0$ provided the complex eigenvalues p_i satisfy the condition

$$|p^2\mathbf{M} + p\mathbf{C} + \mathbf{K}| = 0 \tag{8-61}$$

Assuming that the n complex eigenvalues p_i have been found from Eq. (8-61), the complex eigenvectors $\bar{\mathbf{x}}_i$ can be determined by use of Eq. (8-60).

For a damped system of many degrees of freedom the necessary computational effort is enormous, and the practical solution of a damped multi-degree-of-freedom system is rarely attempted in this way. The situation, however, becomes quite simple if it is possible to uncouple the differential equation (8-59).

Conditions for Uncoupling of Vibration Modes. In Sec. 8-2 we have shown how the modal matrix $\mathbf{\Phi}$ of the undamped system was instrumental in diagonalizing the mass matrix $\mathbf{M}$ and the stiffness matrix $\mathbf{K}$ since

$$\mathbf{\Phi}'\mathbf{M}\mathbf{\Phi} = \bar{m}\mathbf{I} \tag{8-16}$$

and

$$\mathbf{\Phi}'\mathbf{K}\mathbf{\Phi} = \bar{m}\boldsymbol{\omega}^2 \tag{8-17}$$

With the help of these equations we found it possible to transform Eq. (8-30) into n uncoupled equations of motion of the type

$$\ddot{q}_i + \omega_i^2 q_i = F_{gi} \qquad \text{cf. Eq. (8-49)}$$

one such equation occurring for each normal mode and its associated natural circular frequency. This decoupling of the equations with the aid of the normal modes enabled us to transform the results gained for the case of one degree of freedom to multi-degree-of-freedom systems, so that it was relatively easy to determine the motion of the system under arbitrary initial conditions [cf. Eqs. (8-28) and (8-29)] for the general case of time-varying forces [cf. (Eq. 8-40)] and time-varying displacements [cf. Eqs. (8-45) and (8-46)]. Hence, it is worthwhile to investigate the conditions under which decoupling is also possible for free damped vibration, because there is no difficulty in determining the motion of a single-degree-of-freedom system with simple damping under arbitrary initial or time-varying conditions.

In order to uncouple Eq. (8-59) we express the displacement vector $\mathbf{x}(t)$ as a linear combination of the modal vectors:

$$\mathbf{x}(t) = \mathbf{\Phi}\mathbf{q}(t) \tag{8-47}$$

and this expression for $\mathbf{x}(t)$ we substitute in Eq. (8-59). Premultiplication of Eq. (8-59) by $\mathbf{\Phi}'$ then yields

$$\mathbf{\Phi}'\mathbf{M}\mathbf{\Phi}\ddot{\mathbf{q}} + \mathbf{\Phi}'\mathbf{C}\mathbf{\Phi}\dot{\mathbf{q}} + \mathbf{\Phi}'\mathbf{K}\mathbf{\Phi}\mathbf{q} = \mathbf{0} \tag{8-62}$$

On account of Eqs. (8-16) and (8-17), these equations become

$$\ddot{\mathbf{q}} + \mathbf{\Delta}\dot{\mathbf{q}} + \boldsymbol{\omega}^2\mathbf{q} = \mathbf{0} \tag{8-63}$$

where

$$\mathbf{\Delta} = \frac{1}{\bar{m}}\mathbf{\Phi}'\mathbf{C}\mathbf{\Phi}$$

If it should happen that $\mathbf{\Delta}$ is also a diagonal matrix, say

$$\mathbf{\Delta} = 2\boldsymbol{\zeta}\boldsymbol{\omega} = 2 \text{ diag } [\zeta_1\omega_1 \quad \zeta_2\omega_2 \quad \cdots \quad \zeta_n\omega_n] \tag{8-64}$$

($\boldsymbol{\zeta}$ must also be a diagonal matrix), then Eq. (8-63) represents n single-degree-of-freedom equations of motion expressed in the generalized coordinates $q_i(t)$. Each equation has the form

$$\ddot{q}_i + 2\zeta_i\omega_i\dot{q}_i + \omega_i^2 q_i(t) = 0 \qquad i = 1, 2, \ldots, n \tag{8-65}$$

Hence it may be stated generally that the diagonalization of the damping matrix $\mathbf{C}$ by means of the modal matrix $\mathbf{\Phi}$ of the undamped system is a necessary and sufficient condition† for uncoupling the damped motion of the system.

Discussion of Transformed Damping Matrix $\mathbf{\Delta}$. The reader may take note of the fact that, if $\mathbf{\Delta}$ is a diagonal matrix, then there is no restriction on the intensity of the damping. Furthermore, if

$$\boldsymbol{\zeta} = \frac{g}{2}\mathbf{I}$$

Eq. (8-63) may be written

$$\ddot{q}_i + g\omega_i\dot{q}_i + \omega_i^2 q_i(t) = 0 \tag{8-66}$$

† Caughey [45] has stated a sufficient, though not necessary, condition on the damping matrix which leads to a $\mathbf{\Delta}$ matrix proportional to the $\boldsymbol{\omega}$ matrix.

and we have a system that behaves very similarly to a system with structural damping, provided the damping is rather light. In this case the system possesses a constant percentage of critical damping in all n modes.

Often, however, the condition of Eq. (8-64) for uncoupling the vibration modes is not satisfied, so that

$$\mathbf{\Delta} = \begin{bmatrix} \Delta_{11} & \Delta_{12} & \cdots & \Delta_{1n} \\ \Delta_{21} & \Delta_{22} & \cdots & \Delta_{2n} \\ \cdot & \cdot & \cdot & \cdot \\ \Delta_{n1} & \Delta_{n2} & \cdots & \Delta_{nn} \end{bmatrix} \tag{8-67}$$

If the nondiagonal elements are small compared with the diagonal elements and if the natural frequencies are well separated, it is safe, by and large, to disregard the nondiagonal elements in Eq. (8-67) in order to obtain the uncoupled set of equations

$$\ddot{q}_i + \Delta_{ii}\dot{q}_i + \omega_i^2 q_i(t) = 0 \qquad \text{(8-68)†}$$

Initial Conditions. For the simple case of one-degree-of-freedom vibration with viscous damping we found that the motion was described by the equation

$$x(t) = e^{-\delta t}\left(x_0 \cos \nu t + \frac{\dot{x}_0 + \delta x_0}{\nu} \sin \nu t\right) \qquad \text{cf. Eqs. (4-13) and (4-19)}$$

where

$$\delta = \frac{c}{2m} \qquad \nu^2 = \frac{k}{m} - \left(\frac{c}{2m}\right)^2 = \omega^2 - \delta^2 \qquad \text{cf. Eqs. (4-17) and (4-18)}$$

This result can be applied immediately to Eq. (8-68), as soon as the initial values $\mathbf{x}_0$ and $\dot{\mathbf{x}}_0$ have been expressed in terms of the generalized coordinates $\mathbf{q}_0$ and $\dot{\mathbf{q}}_0$ [cf. Eqs. (8-51) and (8-52)]. Then the motion of the ith mode is

$$q_i(t) = e^{-\delta_i t}\left(q_i^0 \cos \nu_i t + \frac{\dot{q}_i^0 + \delta_i q_i^0}{\nu_i} \sin \nu_i t\right) \tag{8-69}$$

where

$$\delta_i = \frac{\Delta_{ii}}{2} \qquad \text{and} \qquad \nu_i^2 = \omega_i^2 - \delta_i^2 \tag{8-70}$$

In the case of Eq. (8-65) we have

$$\delta_i = \zeta_i \omega_i \qquad \text{and} \qquad \nu_i^2 = \omega_i^2(1 - \zeta_i^2) \tag{8-70a}$$

and in the special case of Eq. (8-66) we have

$$\delta_i = \frac{\omega_i g}{2} \qquad \text{and} \qquad \nu_i^2 = \omega_i^2\left(1 - \frac{g^2}{4}\right) \tag{8-70b}$$

Using notation similar to that of Eqs. (8-21) it is possible to express the n equations of type (8-69) according to the single matrix equation

$$\mathbf{q}(t) = \frac{1}{\overline{m}}\, \mathbf{E}\,[(\mathbf{Cos} + \boldsymbol{\delta\nu}^{-1}\,\mathbf{Sin})\,\mathbf{\Phi}'\mathbf{M}\mathbf{x}_0 + \boldsymbol{\nu}^{-1}\,\mathbf{Sin}\,\mathbf{\Phi}'\mathbf{M}\dot{\mathbf{x}}_0]$$

† A perturbation technique for the solution of the uncoupled equations for light damping is given by Lancaster [46].

where
$$\mathbf{E} = \text{diag}\ [e^{-\delta_i(t-t_0)}] \tag{8-71}$$
$$\boldsymbol{\nu} = \text{diag}\ [\nu_i] \tag{8-72}$$
$$\boldsymbol{\delta} = \text{diag}\ [\delta_i] \tag{8-73}$$
$$\mathbf{Sin} = \text{diag}\ [\sin \omega_i(t - t_0)] \tag{8-21a}$$
$$\mathbf{Cos} = \text{diag}\ [\cos \omega_i(t - t_0)] \tag{8-21b}$$

With $\mathbf{q}(t)$ found, the expression for $\mathbf{x}(t)$ is obtained by using the relation

$$\mathbf{x}(t) = \boldsymbol{\Phi}\mathbf{q}(t) \tag{8-47}$$

and hence

$$\mathbf{x}(t) = \frac{1}{\bar{m}}\boldsymbol{\Phi}\mathbf{E}\,[(\mathbf{Cos} + \boldsymbol{\delta\nu}^{-1}\,\mathbf{Sin})\,\boldsymbol{\Phi}'\mathbf{M}\mathbf{x}_0 + \boldsymbol{\nu}^{-1}\,\mathbf{Sin}\,\boldsymbol{\Phi}'\mathbf{M}\dot{\mathbf{x}}_0] \qquad \text{cf. Eq. (8-28)} \tag{8-74}$$

So, once the modal matrix $\boldsymbol{\Phi}$ is known for the undamped vibrations, it is a straightforward matter to compute the motion of the corresponding damped system under arbitrary initial conditions provided the damping matrix satisfies the conditions discussed under the previous heading. When the damping matrix is diagonalized by the modal matrix, heavy damping can also be handled in the same way.

Motion Due to Time-varying Forces. In Sec. 4-4 the motion of a one-degree-of-freedom system with viscous damping subjected to a time-varying force $P(t)$ was found to be ($x_0 = \dot{x}_0 = 0$)

$$x(t) = \frac{1}{m\nu}\int_0^t p(\tau)e^{-\delta(t-\tau)} \sin \nu(t - \tau)\, d\tau \tag{4-37}$$

The only difference between Eq. (4-37) and the corresponding equation (2-16) for the undamped case is the presence of the factor $e^{-\delta(t-\tau)}$ under the integral and, of course, the replacement of ω by ν.

The solution for the multi-degree-of-freedom system with damping subjected to time-varying forces can now be found with relative ease, as soon as the actual forces $\mathbf{f}(t)$ are transformed into the generalized forces $\mathbf{f}_g(t)$ by means of Eq. (8-48). For now we only have to find the solution for the n uncoupled differential equations

$$\ddot{q}_i + \Delta_{ii}\dot{q}_i + \omega_i^2 q_i(t) = F_{gi}(t) \qquad \text{cf. Eq. (8-49)} \tag{8-75}$$

By using the result (4-37) the solution of Eq. (8-75) is, for $q_{i0} = \dot{q}_{i0} = 0$,

$$q_i(t) = \frac{1}{\nu_i}\int_0^t F_{gi}(\tau)e^{-\delta_i(t-\tau)} \sin \nu_i(t - \tau)\, d\tau \tag{8-76}$$

where δ_i and ν_i are given by Eqs. (8-70). Hence

$$\mathbf{q}(t) = \frac{\boldsymbol{\nu}^{-1}}{\bar{m}}\int_0^t \mathbf{E}_\tau\, \mathbf{Sin}_\tau\, \boldsymbol{\Phi}'\mathbf{f}(\tau)\, d\tau$$

where
$$\mathbf{E}_\tau = \text{diag}\ [e^{-\delta_i(t-\tau)}]$$

Transforming back from generalized coordinates and forces to the given coordinates and forces then yields

$$\mathbf{x}(t) = \frac{\boldsymbol{\Phi}}{\bar{m}}\,\boldsymbol{\nu}^{-1}\int_0^t \mathbf{E}_\tau\, \mathbf{Sin}_\tau\, \boldsymbol{\Phi}'\mathbf{f}(\tau)\, d\tau \qquad \text{cf. Eq. (8-40)} \tag{8-77}$$

for
$$\mathbf{x}_0 = \dot{\mathbf{x}}_0 = \mathbf{0}$$

With initial conditions $\mathbf{x}_0 \neq \mathbf{0}$ and $\dot{\mathbf{x}}_0 \neq \mathbf{0}$ the expression for $\mathbf{x}(t)$ of Eq. (8-74) must be added to the above result.

Motion Due to Time-varying Displacement. In order to avoid unnecessary repetition of argument the reader is advised to study once more the corresponding discussion in Sec. 8-3. Using the notation employed there, we can, on account of the correspondence between Eqs. (8-40) and (8-77), immediately write in place of Eq. (8-45)

$$\mathbf{x}_s(t) = \frac{\mathbf{\Phi}_s}{\bar{m}} \boldsymbol{\nu}^{-1} \int_0^t \mathbf{E}_\tau \, \mathbf{Sin}_\tau \, \mathbf{\Phi}_s' \mathbf{f}(\tau) \, d\tau \qquad \mathbf{x}_0 = \dot{\mathbf{x}}_0 = \mathbf{0} \tag{8-78}$$

with $\mathbf{f}(t) = \mathbf{f}_s - (\mathbf{M}_3\ddot{\mathbf{x}}_f + \mathbf{C}_3\dot{\mathbf{x}}_f + \mathbf{K}_3\mathbf{x}_f)$.

PROBLEMS

8-15. Find the damping matrix for the system shown in Fig. P 8-15, and show that the modal matrix obtained in Prob. 8-5 also diagonalizes this damping matrix.

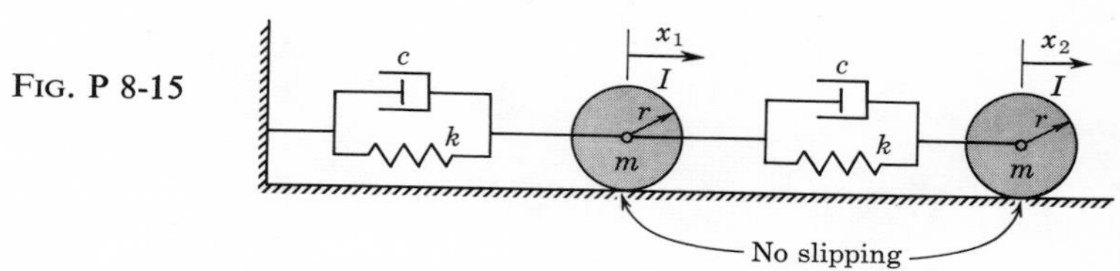

FIG. P 8-15

8-16. Find the response of the system in the previous problem to the initial conditions given in Prob. 8-6.

8-17. Use the modal matrix of Prob. 8-7 and note that it does not diagonalize the damping matrix for the system of Fig. P 8-17 if $c_1 \neq c_2$.

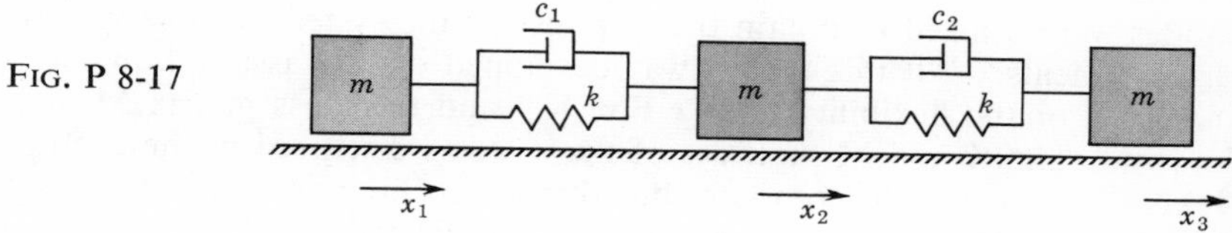

FIG. P 8-17

9 THE MATRIX FORCE METHOD

In Chap. 8 methods were developed for computing the natural frequencies and the normal modes of an elastic system, and furthermore the properties of the normal modes were utilized to obtain the response of the system to time-varying forces and displacements. All this theory was developed on the assumption that the stiffness matrix $\mathbf{K}$ or the flexibility matrix $\mathbf{F} = \mathbf{K}^{-1}$ and the mass matrix $\mathbf{M}$ of Eq. (8-3) are known. The $\mathbf{K}$ and $\mathbf{M}$ matrices of the systems discussed in the examples in Chap. 8 were in fact easy to compute, but this is—so far as the matrix $\mathbf{K}$ is concerned—seldom the case when the system is very complicated.

In this and the following chapter,† we shall consider the effect of external loading (either static or dynamic) on an elastic system which consists of an assembly of elastic elements connected at a finite number of joints (or nodal points). The system is said to be statically determinate when the forces acting on each of the elements can be determined by means of the equations of equilibrium. Should the system possess more elements or external supports than are necessary for stability, then it is described as being *statically indeterminate*. The excess forces carried by these elements and supports are described as *redundants*.‡

9-1. General Concepts and Theorems

We can be certain that the correct solution of our problem has been found if the following requirements are satisfied:

† In this section we follow closely the pioneering work by Argyris [48–50]. Since, throughout the text, we denoted vectors by lowercase boldface letters and rectangular as well as square matrices by capital boldface letters, some deviation from Argyris's notation is unavoidable in Chaps. 9 and 10.

‡ Methods of obtaining the number of redundancies in complex structures are described in Ref. 47. See also Additional Articles and Additional Textbooks for further work on general matrix methods by J. H. Argyris.

FIG. 9-1. Frame with two redundant members.

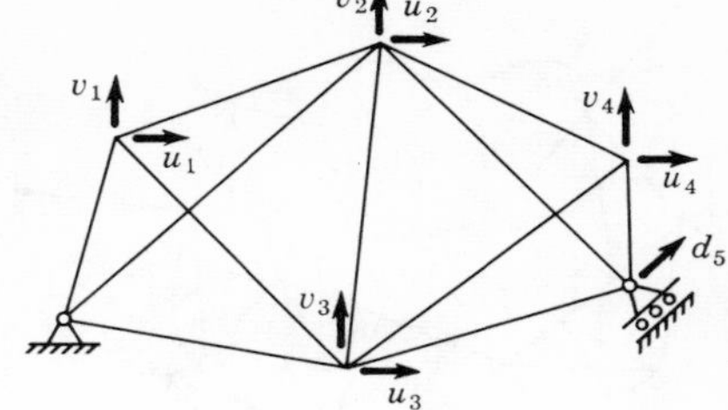

1. Equilibrium: The external forces and the internal forces they induce are in equilibrium at each joint.
2. Compatibility: The elements are so deformed that they can all fit together.
3. Force-deflection relationship: The internal forces and deformations satisfy the stress-strain relationship of the element. In our further considerations this relation will be assumed to be linear.

Two basic methods of analysis are available for solving the problem, and are referred to as the force method and the displacement method.

In the force method the redundant forces are taken as the unknowns of the problem, so that all the internal forces can be expressed in terms of the external and the redundant forces. Then by using the stress-strain relationship the deformations of the elements can also be expressed in terms of the external and redundant forces. Finally, by applying the compatibility criterion that the deformed elements must fit together, it is possible to formulate a set of linear simultaneous equations which yield the values of the redundant forces. We may then calculate the stresses in the elements of the structure as well as the displacements of its joints in the directions of the external forces which are related by the flexibility matrix **F**.

In the displacement method the displacements of the joints necessary to describe fully the deformed state of the structure are imposed on the structure. The deformations of the elements can then be calculated in terms of these displacements, and by use of the stress-strain relationship, so can the internal forces. Finally, by applying the equilibrium criterion at each joint, we obtain a set of linear simultaneous equations from which we can solve for the unknown forces necessary to cause the imposed displacements, thereby obtaining the stiffness matrix **K**.

In choosing the method most suited to a particular problem, one would certainly be influenced by the number of unknown quantities. For example, the pin-jointed frame shown in Fig. 9-1 has two unknown redundant forces F_1 and F_2 but nine displacements (u_1, v_1, u_2, v_2, u_3, v_3, u_4, v_4, d_5) have to be considered to determine fully the deformed state of the truss, so that the force method proves clearly superior in this case. However, the system shown in Fig. 9-2 has four redundant forces but only two unknown displacements, and consequently in this case we would favor the displacement method. The number of unknowns is not the only consideration, however, that

FIG. 9-2. Frame with four redundant members.

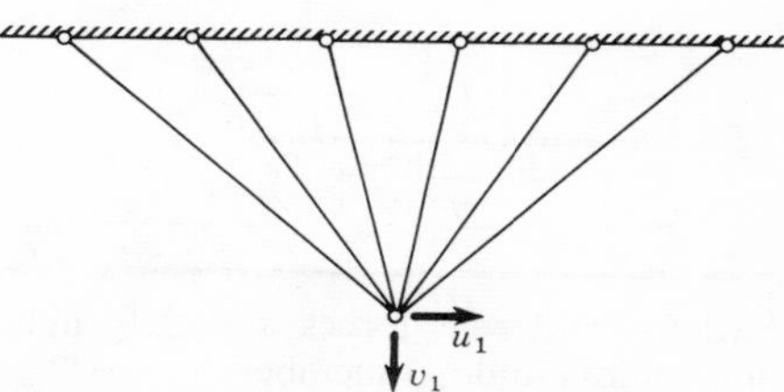

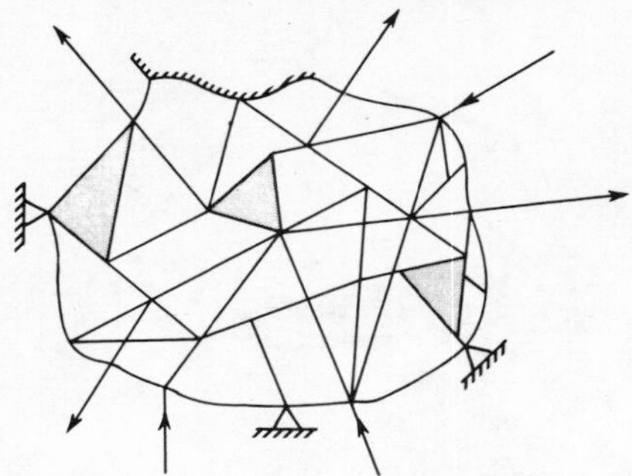

FIG. 9-3. System consisting of an assembly of elements.

dictates the advantage of one method over the other, but first we must develop each method before this question can be discussed more fully (cf. Sec. 10-4).

Internal Forces, Deformations, and Internal Energy. The system of Fig. 9-3, consisting of an assembly of elements, is subjected to external loading.† The state of stress in the gth element is defined by the internal forces $\mathbf{p}_g = \{P_{g1} \quad P_{g2} \quad \cdots \quad P_{gr}\}$, and its deformed shape by the associated deformations $\mathbf{v}_g = \{v_{g1} \quad v_{g2} \quad \cdots \quad v_{gr}\}$.

The convention for positive internal forces is the same as that defining positive forces on the positive face, as in transfer matrices. However, in contrast to the practice adopted in the transfer-matrix method, the forces acting on the negative face are also considered to be positive when they act in a positive direction (Figs. 9-4 and 9-5).

The relations between internal forces and deformations of the elastic element g are defined by

$$\mathbf{p}_g = \mathbf{K}_g\mathbf{v}_g \qquad \text{or} \qquad \mathbf{v}_g = \mathbf{F}_g\mathbf{p}_g \tag{9-1}$$

where the stiffness matrix $\mathbf{K}_g$ and the flexibility matrix $\mathbf{F}_g$ are square matrices of order r. From Eqs. (9-1) it is apparent that $\mathbf{K}_g$ and $\mathbf{F}_g$ are related according to the equation

$$\mathbf{K}_g\mathbf{F}_g = \mathbf{I} \tag{9-2}$$

When the element g is a member which carries only direct forces (Fig. 9-4), then on account of the equilibrium relation

$$N_g^L + N_g^R = 0$$

only one end force need be specified in order to determine the state of stress throughout the element. The associated deformation of the element is simply its elongation, so that in this case

† We confine our considerations to external loadings that are concentrated at points. Other types of loads can always be reduced to such point loads (cf. Sec. C-15). These points serve in our terminology also as joints of the structure. Thus, for example, a straight beam on two hinged supports loaded by a single force consists, from our point of view, of two elements joined at the point where the force is applied.

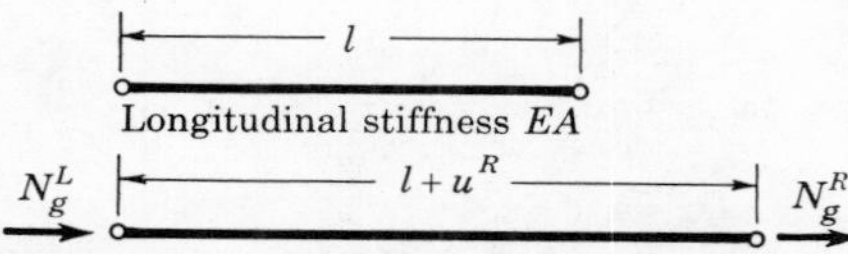

FIG. 9-4. Internal forces and deformation of longitudinal member.

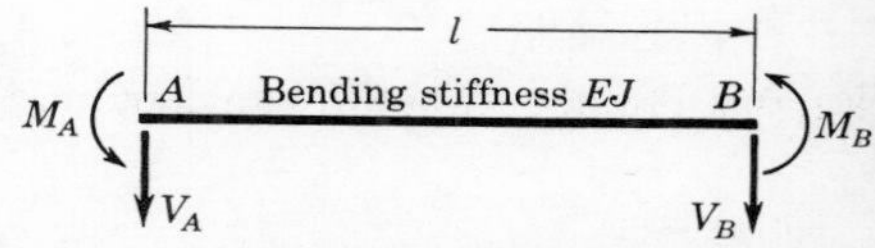

FIG. 9-5. Beam subjected to end forces.

FIG. 9-6. Deflected position of beam.

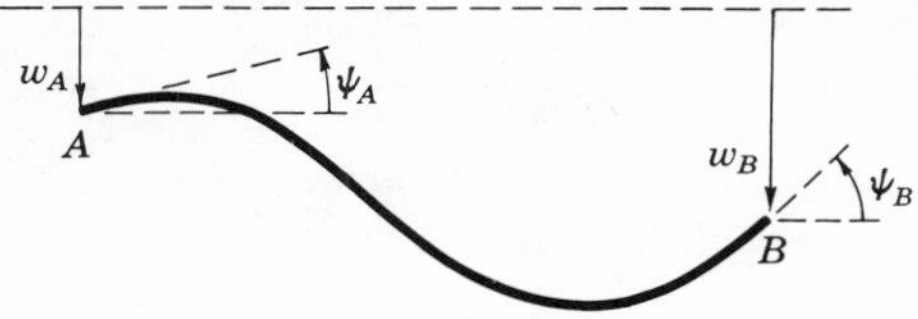

$$\mathbf{p}_g = N_g^R \qquad \text{and} \qquad \mathbf{v}_g = u_g^R$$

and since $N_g^R = u_g^R EA/l$, we have

$$\mathbf{K}_g = \frac{EA}{l} \qquad \text{and} \qquad \mathbf{F}_g = \frac{l}{EA}$$

When the element of the system is a uniform beam of length l and bending stiffness EJ, the internal forces and deformations can be expressed in different ways. The beam is subjected to the four end forces shown in Fig. 9-5, and the deflected position is shown in Fig. 9-6. On account of the equilibrium conditions

$$V_A + V_B = 0 \tag{9-3a}$$

and

$$M_A + M_B + V_A l = 0 \tag{9-3b}$$

we need only make a suitable choice of two of the end forces in order to define all the end forces, that is, $r = 2$. Possible choices for the internal forces $\mathbf{p}_g$ are then $\{M_B \quad V_B\}$, $\{M_A \quad V_A\}$, and $\{M_A \quad M_B\}$, since if the components of these vectors are known, the remaining two end forces can be calculated using Eqs. (9-3).

Next, we discuss the question of the associated deformations. The cantilever 01 of length l and flexural stiffness EJ is subjected to end moment M_1 and end shear V_1 (Fig. 9-7), which produce the slope ψ_1 and the deflection w_1 of end 1, respectively. If we let $M_1 = M_B$ and $V_1 = V_B$, then the cantilever 01 and the beam AB (Fig. 9-6) will have the same deformed shape and 01 may be moved bodily to coincide with AB. Since the end forces are in equilibrium, no work will be required for this body movement. The values of ψ_1 and w_1 may then be used to describe the deformed shape of the beam of Fig. 9-6.

Now, with $\mathbf{p}_g = \{M_B \quad V_B\} \equiv \{M_1 \quad V_1\}$ as the internal forces and $\mathbf{v}_g = \{\psi_1 \quad w_1\}$ as the associated deformations, it is relatively easy (cf. Sec. 5-5) to derive the relation [cf. Eqs. (9-1)]

$$\begin{bmatrix} M_1 \\ \\ V_1 \end{bmatrix} = \begin{bmatrix} \dfrac{4EJ}{l} & \dfrac{6EJ}{l^2} \\ \\ \dfrac{6EJ}{l^2} & \dfrac{12EJ}{l^3} \end{bmatrix} \cdot \begin{bmatrix} \psi_1 \\ \\ w_1 \end{bmatrix} \tag{9-4}$$

Another possible way of defining the deformed shape of the beam is to consider the

FIG. 9-7. Cantilever beam under the action of end moment and shear.

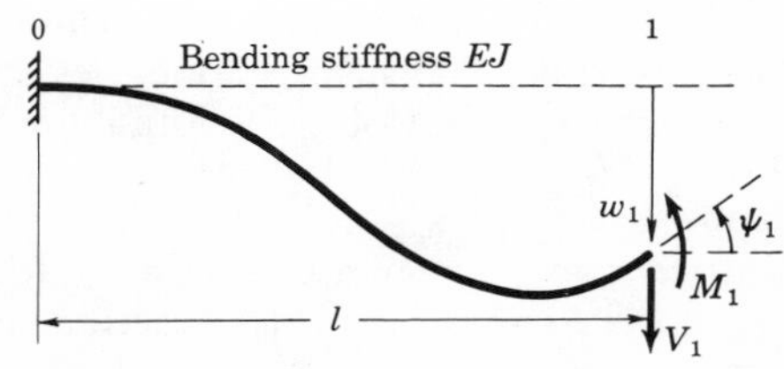

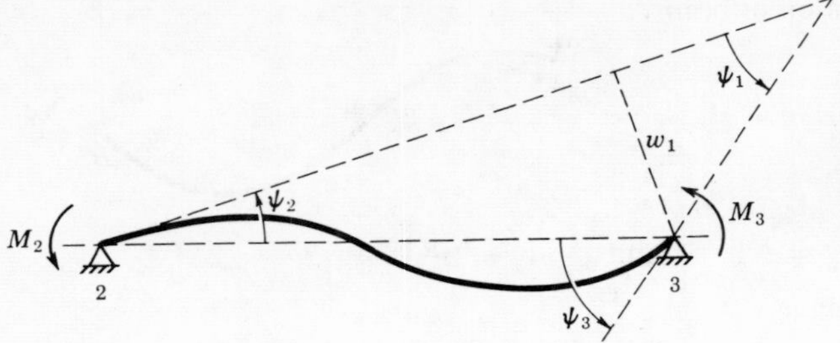

FIG. 9-8. Simply supported beam subjected to end moments.

simply supported beam 23 (Fig. 9-8) subjected to the end moments M_2 and M_3 which rotate through the angles ψ_2 and ψ_3. If we let $M_2 = M_A$ and $M_3 = M_B$, the deformed shape of 23 is then the same as that of AB. Using, for example, the conjugate-beam method [17], we find the relation [cf. Eqs. (9-1)]

$$\begin{bmatrix} M_2 \\ \\ M_3 \end{bmatrix} = \begin{bmatrix} \dfrac{4EJ}{l} & \dfrac{2EJ}{l} \\ \\ \dfrac{2EJ}{l} & \dfrac{4EJ}{l} \end{bmatrix} \cdot \begin{bmatrix} \psi_2 \\ \\ \psi_3 \end{bmatrix} \tag{9-4a}$$

In view of Eq. (9-2) the flexibility matrices corresponding to Eqs. (9-4) and (9-4*a*) are given by Eqs. (9-5) and (9-5*a*), respectively:

$$\mathbf{F}_g = \begin{bmatrix} \dfrac{l}{EJ} & \dfrac{-l^2}{2EJ} \\ \dfrac{-l^2}{2EJ} & \dfrac{l^3}{3EJ} \end{bmatrix} \tag{9-5}$$

$$\mathbf{F}_g = \begin{bmatrix} \dfrac{l}{3EJ} & \dfrac{-l}{6EJ} \\ \dfrac{-l}{6EJ} & \dfrac{l}{3EJ} \end{bmatrix} \tag{9-5a}$$

We should note that the stiffness and flexibility matrices are always symmetric on account of the Maxwell-Betti reciprocal theorem [17].

We can summarize the previous discussion by stating the following rules for determining the stiffness and flexibility matrices of structural elements: Choose a set of internal forces $\mathbf{p}_g$ sufficient to describe completely the state of stress in the element g (in the case of the straight beam element we learned that suitable choices are, for example, $\mathbf{p}_g = \{M_B \quad V_B\}$ or $\mathbf{p}_g = \{M_A \quad M_B\}$). Restrain the boundaries of the element in such a way that only the chosen internal forces $\mathbf{p}_g$ can do work (the boundary restraints corresponding to the above-mentioned choices of $\mathbf{p}_g$ are shown in Figs. 9-7 and 9-8, respectively). The deformations $\mathbf{v}_g$ are then the displacements of the unrestrained element boundaries in the direction of the chosen internal forces $\mathbf{p}_g$ (referring again to Figs. 9-7 and 9-8, the deformations associated with the internal forces $\{M_1 \quad V_1\}$ and $\{M_2 \quad M_3\}$ are, respectively, $\{\psi_1 \quad w_1\}$ and $\{\psi_2 \quad \psi_3\}$). Suitable combinations of $\mathbf{p}_g$ and $\mathbf{v}_g$ having been chosen, the element flexibility and stiffness matrices can be calculated according to the methods described in Sec. 8-1.

A special case of the rules described above, which is often useful, is the following: Restrain the element by completely clamping one end. The internal forces are then those forces which are applied at the other end, and the deformations are the displacements associated with these forces [the internal forces and deformations of the straight beam element when clamped at its left end (Fig. 9-7) are $\{M_1 \quad V_1\}$ and $\{\psi_1 \quad w_1\}$].

The internal energy stored in the gth element is given by the relation

$$U_g = \tfrac{1}{2}\mathbf{p}_g'\mathbf{v}_g = \tfrac{1}{2}\mathbf{v}_g'\mathbf{p}_g \tag{9-6}$$

For example, the internal energy stored in the cantilever beam of Fig. 9-7 is

$$U_g = \tfrac{1}{2}M_1\psi_1 + \tfrac{1}{2}V_1w_1 = \tfrac{1}{2}[M_1 \quad V_1]\begin{bmatrix}\psi_1\\ w_1\end{bmatrix} = \tfrac{1}{2}\mathbf{p}_g'\mathbf{v}_g$$

Using Eqs. (9-1), the internal energy can be expressed in terms of the internal forces or the deformations, so that

$$U_g = \tfrac{1}{2}\mathbf{p}_g'\mathbf{F}_g\mathbf{p}_g = \tfrac{1}{2}\mathbf{v}_g'\mathbf{K}_g\mathbf{v}_g \tag{9-7}$$

With the stiffness matrix of Eq. (9-4) the internal energy of a beam element is

$$2U_g = \begin{bmatrix}\psi_1 & w_1\end{bmatrix}\cdot\begin{bmatrix}\dfrac{4EJ}{l} & \dfrac{6EJ}{l^2}\\ \dfrac{6EJ}{l^2} & \dfrac{12EJ}{l^3}\end{bmatrix}\cdot\begin{bmatrix}\psi_1\\ w_1\end{bmatrix}$$

and if the stiffness matrix of Eq. (9-4*a*) is employed, the expression for the internal energy is

$$2U_g = \begin{bmatrix}\psi_2 & \psi_3\end{bmatrix}\cdot\begin{bmatrix}\dfrac{4EJ}{l} & \dfrac{2EJ}{l}\\ \dfrac{2EJ}{l} & \dfrac{4EJ}{l}\end{bmatrix}\cdot\begin{bmatrix}\psi_2\\ \psi_3\end{bmatrix}$$

Using the relations between the deformations $\{\psi_1 \quad w_1\}$ on the one hand and $\{\psi_2 \quad \psi_3\}$ on the other, it is easy to show that the two expressions for the internal energy agree with each other. Referring to Figs. 9-7 and 9-8, we obtain the relations

$$\psi_1 = \psi_3 - \psi_2 \qquad \text{and} \qquad w_1 = l\psi_2$$

so that

$$\begin{bmatrix}\psi_2\\ \psi_3\end{bmatrix} = \begin{bmatrix}0 & \dfrac{1}{l}\\ 1 & \dfrac{1}{l}\end{bmatrix}\cdot\begin{bmatrix}\psi_1\\ w_1\end{bmatrix}$$

With this relation the second expression for the internal energy, when transformed into terms of ψ_1 and w_1, becomes

$$2U_g = \begin{bmatrix}\psi_1 & w_1\end{bmatrix}\cdot\begin{bmatrix}0 & 1\\ \dfrac{1}{l} & \dfrac{1}{l}\end{bmatrix}\cdot\begin{bmatrix}\dfrac{4EJ}{l} & \dfrac{2EJ}{l}\\ \dfrac{2EJ}{l} & \dfrac{4EJ}{l}\end{bmatrix}\cdot\begin{bmatrix}0 & \dfrac{1}{l}\\ 1 & \dfrac{1}{l}\end{bmatrix}\cdot\begin{bmatrix}\psi_1\\ w_1\end{bmatrix}$$

$$= \begin{bmatrix}\psi_1 & w_1\end{bmatrix}\cdot\begin{bmatrix}\dfrac{4EJ}{l} & \dfrac{6EJ}{l^2}\\ \dfrac{6EJ}{l^2} & \dfrac{12EJ}{l^3}\end{bmatrix}\cdot\begin{bmatrix}\psi_1\\ w_1\end{bmatrix}$$

which, of course, is identical with the first expression for the internal energy.

Short Catalogue of Flexibility and Stiffness Matrices for Elastic Elements. A short catalogue of flexibility and stiffness matrices is included at this point. These matrices are used from time to time throughout the text and are also required in order to answer the problems. A general method of obtaining these matrices from the corresponding transfer matrices is given in Sec. C-15.

Rod with Longitudinal Load

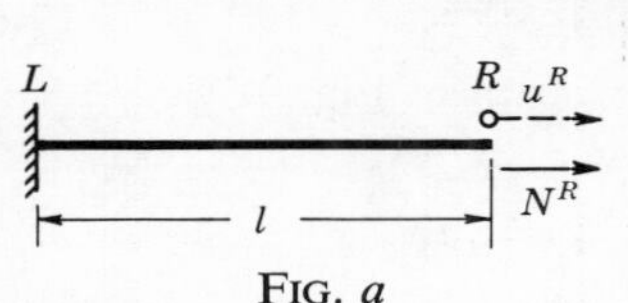

FIG. *a*

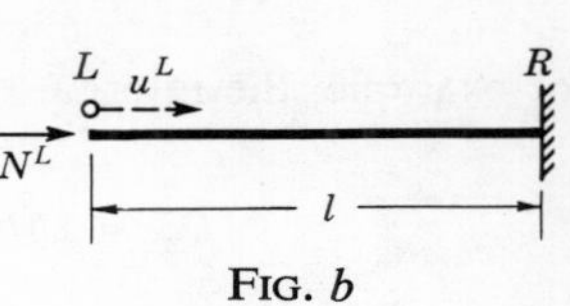

FIG. *b*

Longitudinal stiffness $= AE$

Chosen internal forces $\mathbf{p} = N^R$
Associated deformations $\mathbf{v} = u^R$
Flexibility-matrix relation

$$\mathbf{v} = \frac{l}{EA}\mathbf{p}$$

Stiffness-matrix relation

$$\mathbf{p} = \frac{EA}{l}\mathbf{v}$$

Chosen internal forces $\mathbf{p} = N^L$†
Associated deformations $\mathbf{v} = u^L$
Flexibility-matrix relation

$$\mathbf{v} = \frac{l}{EA}\mathbf{p}$$

Stiffness-matrix relation

$$\mathbf{p} = \frac{EA}{l}\mathbf{v}$$

Shaft in Torsion

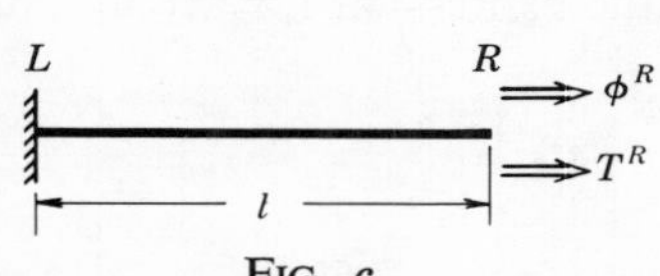

FIG. *c*

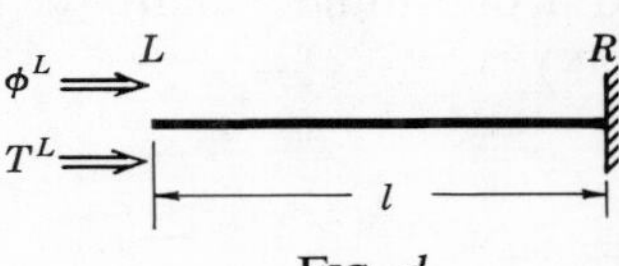

FIG. *d*

Torsional stiffness $= J_TG$

Chosen internal forces $\mathbf{p} = T^R$
Associated deformations $\mathbf{v} = \phi^R$
Flexibility-matrix relation

$$\mathbf{v} = \frac{l}{J_TG}\mathbf{p}$$

Stiffness-matrix relation

$$\mathbf{p} = \frac{J_TG}{l}\mathbf{v}$$

Chosen internal forces $\mathbf{p} = T^L$
Associated deformations $\mathbf{v} = \phi^L$
Flexibility-matrix relation

$$\mathbf{v} = \frac{l}{J_TG}\mathbf{p}$$

Stiffness-matrix relation

$$\mathbf{p} = \frac{J_TG}{l}\mathbf{v}$$

Beam in Bending

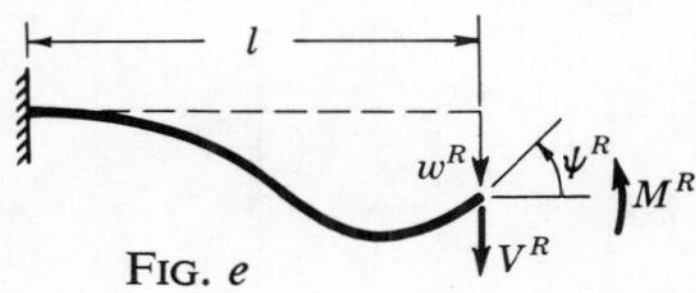

FIG. *e*

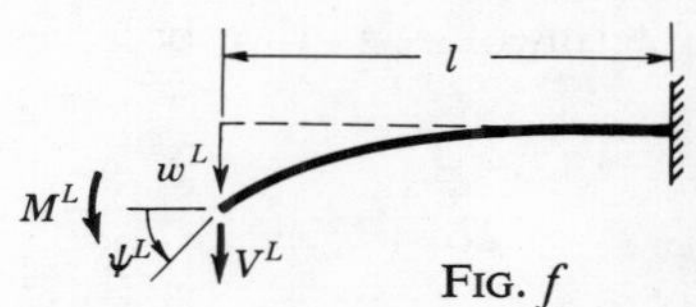

FIG. *f*

Bending stiffness $= EJ$

Chosen internal forces $\mathbf{p} = \{M^R \quad V^R\}$
Associated deformations $\mathbf{v} = \{\psi^R \quad w^R\}$

Chosen internal forces $\mathbf{p} = \{M^L \quad V^L\}$
Associated deformations $\mathbf{v} = \{\psi^L \quad w^L\}$

† Note that, if N^L is chosen as the internal force, then a positive N^L corresponds to compression of the member. Therefore we shall mostly use N^R as the chosen internal force and often just write N instead of N^R.

Flexibility-matrix relation

$$\mathbf{v} = \begin{bmatrix} \dfrac{l}{EJ} & \dfrac{-l^2}{2EJ} \\[2ex] \dfrac{-l^2}{2EJ} & \dfrac{l^3}{3EJ} \end{bmatrix} \mathbf{p}$$

Stiffness-matrix relation

$$\mathbf{p} = \begin{bmatrix} \dfrac{4EJ}{l} & \dfrac{6EJ}{l^2} \\[2ex] \dfrac{6EJ}{l^2} & \dfrac{12EJ}{l^3} \end{bmatrix} \mathbf{v}$$

Flexibility-matrix relation

$$\mathbf{v} = \begin{bmatrix} \dfrac{l}{EJ} & \dfrac{l^2}{2EJ} \\[2ex] \dfrac{l^2}{2EJ} & \dfrac{l^3}{3EJ} \end{bmatrix} \mathbf{p}$$

Stiffness-matrix relation

$$\mathbf{p} = \begin{bmatrix} \dfrac{4EJ}{l} & \dfrac{-6EJ}{l^2} \\[2ex] \dfrac{-6EJ}{l^2} & \dfrac{12EJ}{l^3} \end{bmatrix} \mathbf{v}$$

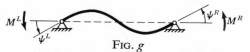

FIG. *g*

Chosen internal forces $\mathbf{p} = \{M^L \quad M^R\}$
Associated deformations $\mathbf{v} = \{\psi^L \quad \psi^R\}$

$$\text{Flexibility-matrix relation } \mathbf{v} = \begin{bmatrix} \dfrac{l}{3EJ} & \dfrac{-l}{6EJ} \\[2ex] \dfrac{-l}{6EJ} & \dfrac{l}{3EJ} \end{bmatrix} \mathbf{p}$$

$$\text{Stiffness-matrix relation } \mathbf{p} = \begin{bmatrix} \dfrac{4EJ}{l} & \dfrac{2EJ}{l} \\[2ex] \dfrac{2EJ}{l} & \dfrac{4EJ}{l} \end{bmatrix} \mathbf{v}$$

Degenerate Cases of a Beam in Bending

If it is known that a beam element is pinned at one end, then only one internal force is required to describe completely the state of stress of the element.

Right End Pinned

FIG. *h*

Chosen internal forces $\mathbf{p} = V^R$
Associated deformations $\mathbf{v} = w^R$
Flexibility-matrix relation

$$\mathbf{v} = \frac{l^3}{3EJ}\mathbf{p}$$

Stiffness-matrix relation

$$\mathbf{p} = \frac{3EJ}{l^3}\mathbf{v}$$

Left End Pinned

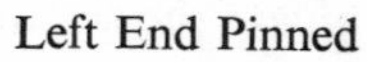

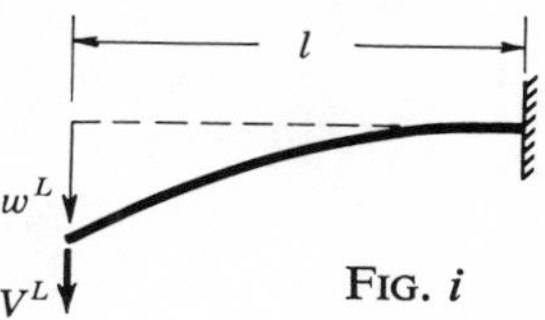

FIG. *i*

Chosen internal forces $\mathbf{p} = V^L$
Associated deformations $\mathbf{v} = w^L$
Flexibility-matrix relation

$$\mathbf{v} = \frac{l^3}{3EJ}\mathbf{p}$$

Stiffness-matrix relation

$$\mathbf{p} = \frac{3EJ}{l^3}\mathbf{v}$$

Right End Pinned

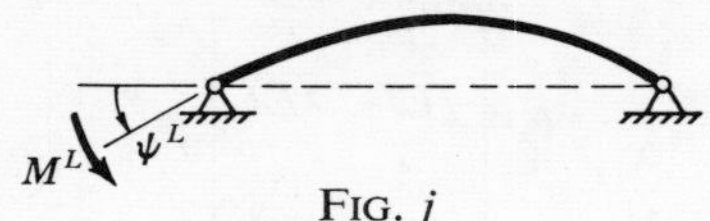

FIG. *j*

Chosen internal forces $\mathbf{p} = M^L$
Associated deformation $\mathbf{v} = \psi^L$
Flexibility-matrix relation

$$\mathbf{v} = \frac{l}{3EJ}\mathbf{p}$$

Stiffness-matrix relation

$$\mathbf{p} = \frac{3EJ}{l}\mathbf{v}$$

Left End Pinned

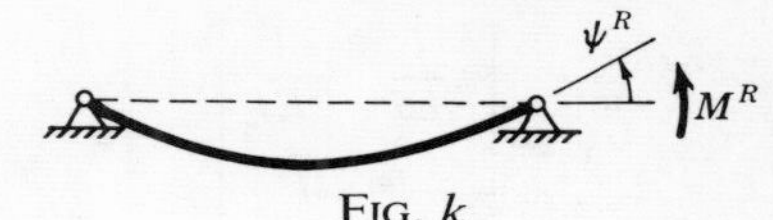

FIG. *k*

Chosen internal forces $\mathbf{p} = M^R$
Associated deformation $\mathbf{v} = \psi^R$
Flexibility-matrix relation

$$\mathbf{v} = \frac{l}{3EJ}\mathbf{p}$$

Stiffness-matrix relation

$$\mathbf{p} = \frac{3EJ}{l}\mathbf{v}$$

Some Comments on the Principle of Work. The principle of work proves to be a very powerful technique for deducing the conditions of compatibility and equilibrium. In its most general form the statement of the principle of work is as follows:

The work done by a set of external forces $\mathbf{f}$, acting on a structure, in moving through the associated displacements $\mathbf{d}$ is equal to the work done by some other set of forces $\mathbf{r}$, which is statically equivalent to the set $\mathbf{f}$, moving through associated displacements $\mathbf{e}$ which are compatible with $\mathbf{d}$. Associated forces and displacements have the same lines of action.†

In the development of the force and displacement methods we consider that the forces $\mathbf{r}$ are some set of internal forces $\mathbf{p}^*$ statically equivalent to the external forces $\mathbf{f}$ and that $\mathbf{e}$ is some set of deformations $\mathbf{v}^*$ compatible with the joint displacements $\mathbf{d}$.

Dummy-load Theorem.‡ We shall now discuss how to use this version of the principle of work to determine conditions of compatibility. This particular application of the principle is commonly referred to as the dummy-load method, or the method of virtual forces. Suppose that the deformed shape of all§ the elements of a system is known; then it is possible by using the principle of work to find the deflection of the system at any point. The procedure consists in applying a (dummy) load to the system, at the point and in the direction of the required displacement. Then we formulate the so-called dummy-load theorem as

$$\underbrace{\begin{pmatrix}\text{Applied}\\ \text{dummy}\\ \text{load}\end{pmatrix}}_{\substack{\text{usually}\\ \text{unity}}} \times \begin{pmatrix}\text{actual displacement of}\\ \text{structure at point of}\\ \text{application of dummy load}\end{pmatrix} = \begin{pmatrix}\text{internal forces statically}\\ \text{equivalent to the}\\ \text{applied dummy load}\end{pmatrix} \times \begin{pmatrix}\text{actual}\\ \text{deformation}\\ \text{of elements}\end{pmatrix} \tag{9-8}$$

It should be noted that the dummy-load theorem is a condition on the geometry of the structure. In fact, with the deformations of the elements known we could draw the deflected shape of the structure, and the results obtained for the deflections would agree with those of the dummy-load theorem.

† It is assumed that the forces remain constant during the displacement and that their direction relative to the structure does not change.

‡ In the original work by J. H. Argyris this theorem was introduced as unit load theorem.

§ If the structure is redundant, it is not necessary to know the deformations of all elements. It suffices to know the deformations of only those elements which are needed to support the applied dummy load (cf. Example 9-1).

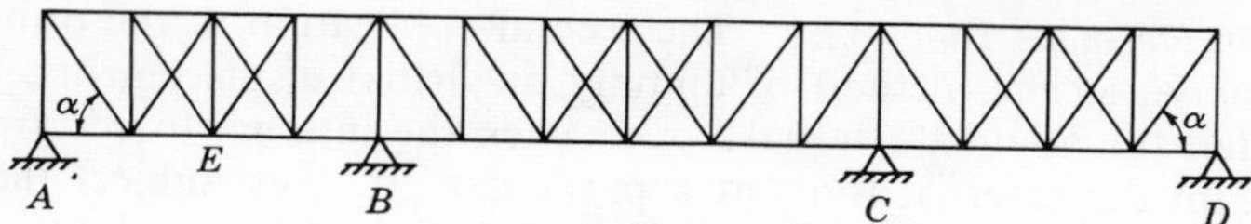

FIG. 9-9. Continuous truss on rigid supports.

Example 9-1. Figure 9-9 shows a continuous pin-jointed truss on four rigid supports. It is desired to measure the vertical deflection at E when the structure is subjected to a certain loading. One possible method of measuring the deflection is to measure the longitudinal deformations of certain members of the truss and then apply the dummy-load method. How many deformations should be measured in order that the deflection at E can be computed?

A unit load is applied at E, and a set of internal forces statically equivalent to the unit load is chosen. We have a wide choice open to us, since there are a large number of structural possibilities which could carry the load applied at point E. Several of these are shown in Fig. 9-10. Clearly, if we chose the redundant systems a and b, the calculation of the internal forces would entail a lot of work; the system c, however, is statically determinate, and here the calculation of the internal forces due to the dummy load presents no difficulty (Fig. 9-11). Hence, if the elongations of members 1 to 14 are measured and are found to be $e_1, e_2, \ldots, e_{14}$, then the dummy-load theorem gives the result ($\alpha = 45°$)

$$(\tfrac{1}{2})(0) + (1)(\delta) + (\tfrac{1}{2})(0) = \delta = -\tfrac{1}{2}e_1 + \frac{1}{\sqrt{2}}e_2 - \tfrac{1}{2}e_3 - \tfrac{1}{2}e_4 + \tfrac{1}{2}e_5 + \frac{1}{\sqrt{2}}e_6 - e_7 - e_8$$
$$+ \frac{1}{\sqrt{2}}e_9 + \tfrac{1}{2}e_{10} - \tfrac{1}{2}e_{11} - \tfrac{1}{2}e_{12} + \frac{1}{\sqrt{2}}e_{13} - \tfrac{1}{2}e_{14}$$

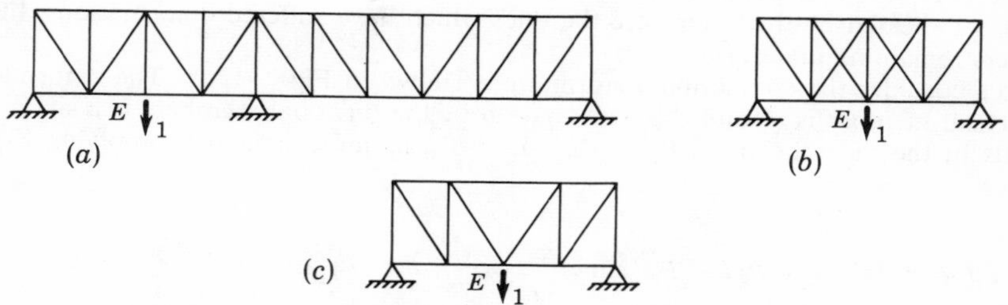

FIG. 9-10. Three systems capable of supporting the applied dummy load.

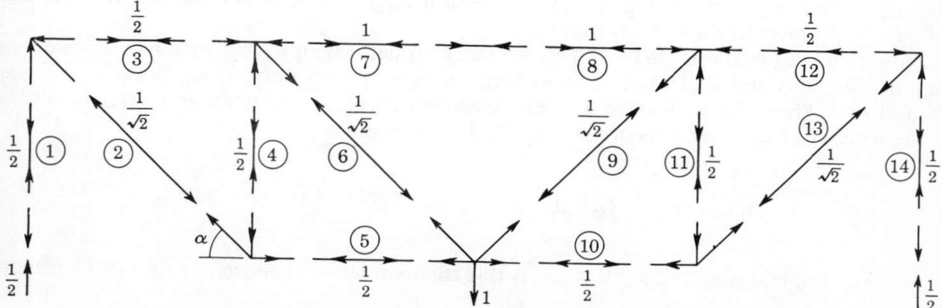

FIG. 9-11. Internal forces statically equivalent to applied dummy load.

Dummy-displacement Theorem.† The second application of the principle of work is usually known as the method of dummy or virtual displacements. We use this method to find the applied external forces when the internal forces are known. In order to obtain the external force at a particular point we subject the system to a unit displacement at that point in the direction of the force and choose any set of deformations compatible with the unit displacement. Then from the principle of work we have

$$\underbrace{\begin{pmatrix}\text{Dummy displacement applied}\\ \text{in direction of unknown}\\ \text{actual external force}\end{pmatrix}}_{\text{usually unity}} \times \begin{pmatrix}\text{actual}\\ \text{external}\\ \text{force}\end{pmatrix} = \begin{pmatrix}\text{deformation of elements}\\ \text{compatible with}\\ \text{dummy displacement}\end{pmatrix} \times \begin{pmatrix}\text{actual}\\ \text{internal}\\ \text{forces}\end{pmatrix} \tag{9-9}$$

Example 9-2. A vertical force is applied at point E of the continuous pin-jointed truss shown in Fig. 9-9. It is required to determine this load by measuring the internal forces in the members of the truss.

Clearly this could be done by determining the internal forces which act in the three elements at E which provide vertical force components. The sum of the three vertical components equals the applied load. However, it will be shown that the same end can be attained by measuring the internal forces of only two members and applying the dummy-displacement method.

It is assumed that the force F at E is given a virtual vertical displacement d downward. According to the dummy-displacement theorem we can use in Eq. (9-9) *any* set of deformations which can cause this displacement. Clearly the actual deformations would be a possibility, but these are extremely difficult to calculate for the structure. Much simpler possible compatible deformations are illustrated in Fig. 9-12*a* to *d*. In these figures the members indicated by thick lines are the ones which have suffered deformations, the other members remaining undeformed.

Let us consider the compatible deformations shown in Fig. 9-12*a*. The deformation of the vertical member is d, and the deformation of the diagonal members is $d \sin \alpha$. If the tensions in the member are $+P_1$, $+P_2$, and $+P_3$, as indicated, then, applying Eq. (9-9), we have

$$Fd = P_1 d \sin \alpha + P_2 d + P_3 d \sin \alpha \qquad \text{or} \qquad F = P_1 \sin \alpha + P_2 + P_3 \sin \alpha$$

This result contains no surprise, as we could have obtained it by resolving the forces P_1, P_2, and P_3 vertically at their common joint of attack. It is interesting to observe, however, that in order to compute the value of F, the three forces P_1, P_2, and P_3 must be known. The deformations shown in Fig. 9-12*b* involve four diagonal members, but the deformations of Fig. 9-12*c* involve three members.

Now if we look at Fig. 9-12*d*, it is necessary to deform only two members in order to obtain the deflection d at point E, and hence it is necessary only to know the two forces P_1 and P_2. The deformations of the deformed elements are $-3d \tan \alpha$ and $d \tan \alpha$, so that, if the forces in these elements are P_1 and P_2, Eq. (9-9) gives

$$dF = (-3d \tan \alpha)P_1 + (d \tan \alpha)P_2 \qquad \text{or} \qquad F = P_2 \tan \alpha - 3P_1 \tan \alpha$$

† In the original work by J. H. Argyris this theorem was introduced as unit displacement theorem.

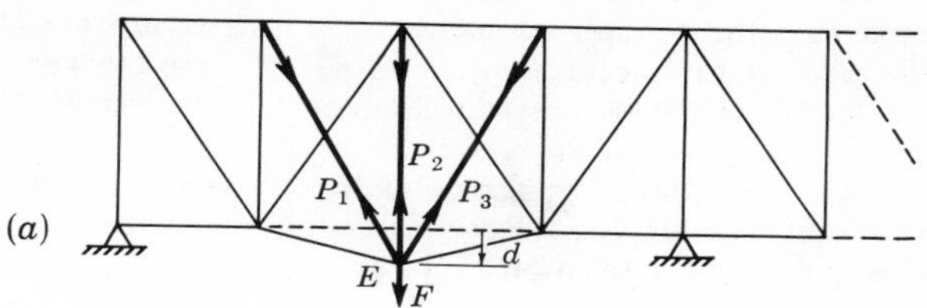

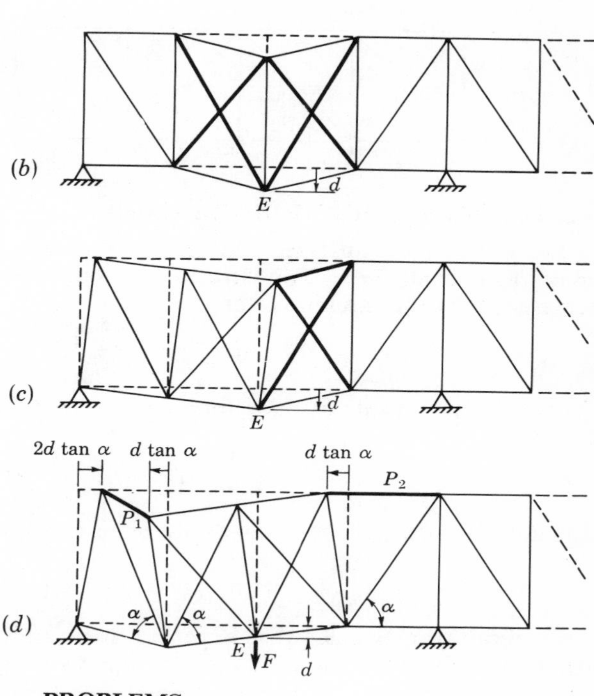

FIG. 9-12. Dummy displacement and compatible deformations.

PROBLEMS

9-1. Use the dummy-load theorem to find the deflection and slope at the mid-point of a uniform cantilever of length l and bending stiffness EJ, when it carries an end load W (Fig. P 9-1).

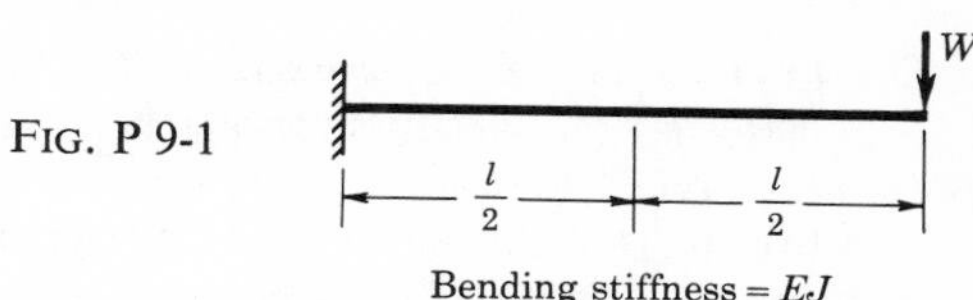

FIG. P 9-1

9-2. The bending-moment diagram of a continuous beam is shown in Fig. P 9-2. Compute with the help of the dummy-load theorem the deflection of the concentrated load W.

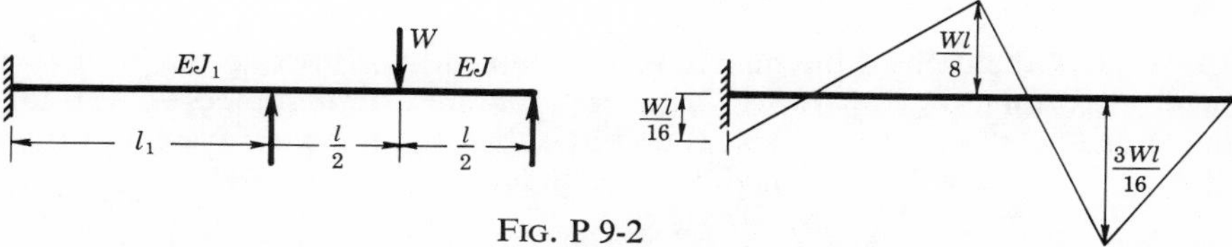

FIG. P 9-2

HINT: Divide the continuous beam into three beam elements. Show that the information regarding the bending moments in span l_1 is superfluous. For elements 2 and 3 use the flexibility matrix according to Fig. *g*. Observe the sign convention (Fig. 9-5).

9-3. Using the dummy-displacement theorem, find the reactions of the supports of the continuous beam of Prob. 9-2.

9-4. A pin-jointed girder is loaded in the manner shown in Fig. P 9-4. Measurements show that the member AB carries a compressive force of P. Using the dummy-displacement theorem, find the reactions at the supports.

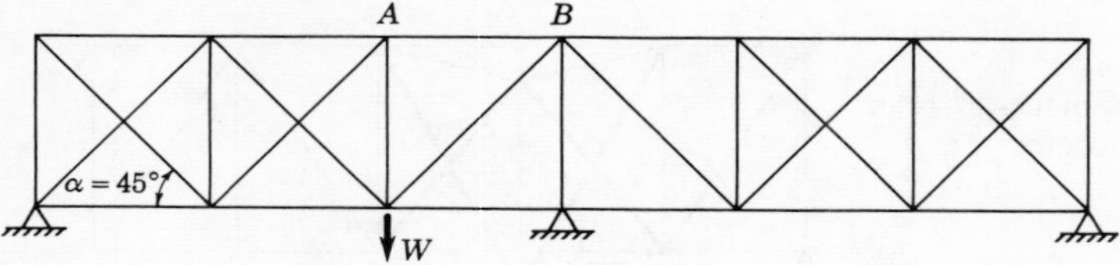

FIG. P 9-4

9-2. Basic Theory of the Matrix Force Method

The system to be analyzed consists of s individual elements that are assembled in some definite manner. This structure is subjected to a set of m external forces represented by the column vector

$$\overset{1}{{}^m\mathbf{f}} = \{F_1 \quad F_2 \quad \cdots \quad F_m\}$$

and the displacements of these forces along their lines of action are represented by the column vector

$$\overset{1}{{}^m\mathbf{d}} = \{d_1 \quad d_2 \quad \cdots \quad d_m\}$$

The internal forces of the elements are represented by the column vector

$$\overset{1}{{}^l\mathbf{p}} = \{P_1 \quad P_2 \quad \cdots \quad P_l\}$$

We recall from Sec. 9-1 that in general it requires more than one internal force to specify the state of stress of an element, and hence we conclude that $l \geq s$.

Finally the system is n times redundant, and the forces chosen as the redundancies are represented by the column vector

$$\overset{1}{{}^n\mathbf{x}} = \{X_1 \quad X_2 \quad \cdots \quad X_n\}$$

The Internal Forces Expressed in Terms of the External and Redundant Forces. Let the external redundant supports be removed and the structure be cut so that the system is reduced to a statically determinate structure that is called the basic system. In addition to the external forces **f**, the redundants **x** are applied at the cuts and the redundant supports. Then the internal forces **p** can be expressed in terms of the forces **f** and **x** according to the equation

$$\overset{1}{{}^l\mathbf{p}} = \overset{m}{{}^l\mathbf{B}_0}\, \overset{1}{{}^m\mathbf{f}} + \overset{n}{{}^l\mathbf{B}_1}\, \overset{1}{{}^n\mathbf{x}} \tag{9-10}$$

where the ith column of the matrix $\mathbf{B}_0$ is obtained by subjecting the basic system to the external force $F_i = 1$ $(i = 1, 2, \ldots, m)$, and all external forces $F_j = 0$ for $j \neq i$. Similarly, the ith column of $\mathbf{B}_1$ is found by subjecting the basic system to the redundant $X_i = 1$ $(i = 1, 2, \ldots, n)$, and all redundants $X_j = 0$ for $j \neq i$.

Example 9-3. For the sake of illustration consider the truss in Fig. 9-13*a*, where we have $s = 6$, $m = 5$, $n = 1$. Since the truss is pin-jointed, $l = s = 6$. Therefore

$\mathbf{p} = \{N_1 \ N_2 \ N_3 \ N_4 \ N_5 \ N_6\}$, $\mathbf{f} = \{F_1 \ F_2 \ F_3 \ F_4 \ F_5\}$, and $\mathbf{x} = \{X_1\}$. Thus the matrix $\mathbf{B}_0$ is of order (6, 5) and $\mathbf{B}_1$ is of order (6, 1). By cutting truss member 6 to obtain the statically determinate basic system, then, for example, the fourth column of matrix $\mathbf{B}_0$ is found by loading the basic system with $F_4 = 1$ (Fig. 9-13*b*), which yields the column $\{0 \ 0 \ -1 \ 0 \ \sqrt{2} \ 0\}$. As an exercise the reader may calculate the other four columns of $\mathbf{B}_0$. In the same way the one column of matrix $\mathbf{B}_1$ is determined by subjecting truss member 6 at both faces of the cut to tensional unit forces $X_1 = 1$ (Fig. 9-13*c*); thus we obtain $\mathbf{B}_1 = \{-1/\sqrt{2} \ -1/\sqrt{2} \ -1/\sqrt{2} \ -1/\sqrt{2} \ 1 \ 1\}$.

Since the structure is linearly elastic, a linear relation exists between the redundant forces $\mathbf{x}$ and the external forces $\mathbf{f}$. Hence, this relation can be written

$$ {}^{n}\overset{1}{\mathbf{x}} = {}^{n}\overset{m}{\mathbf{X}}\, {}^{m}\overset{1}{\mathbf{f}} \tag{9-11}$$

where ${}^{n}\overset{m}{\mathbf{X}}$ is a matrix that as yet we do not know. Using Eq. (9-11) in Eq. (9-10), we obtain

$$ {}^{l}\overset{1}{\mathbf{p}} = {}^{l}\overset{m}{\mathbf{B}_0}\, {}^{m}\overset{1}{\mathbf{f}} + {}^{l}\overset{n}{\mathbf{B}_1}\, {}^{n}\overset{1}{\mathbf{x}} = {}^{l}\overset{m}{\mathbf{B}_0}\, {}^{m}\overset{1}{\mathbf{f}} + {}^{l}\overset{n}{\mathbf{B}_1}\, {}^{n}\overset{m}{\mathbf{X}}\, {}^{m}\overset{1}{\mathbf{f}} = {}^{l}\overset{m}{\mathbf{B}}\, {}^{m}\overset{1}{\mathbf{f}} \tag{9-12}\dagger$$

where

$$\mathbf{B} = \mathbf{B}_0 + \mathbf{B}_1\mathbf{X} \tag{9-13}$$

The Relation between Internal Forces and Deformations. In Sec. 9-1 we discussed Eq. (9-1),

† In view of its definition the matrix **B** is also called the *influence matrix* of the system.

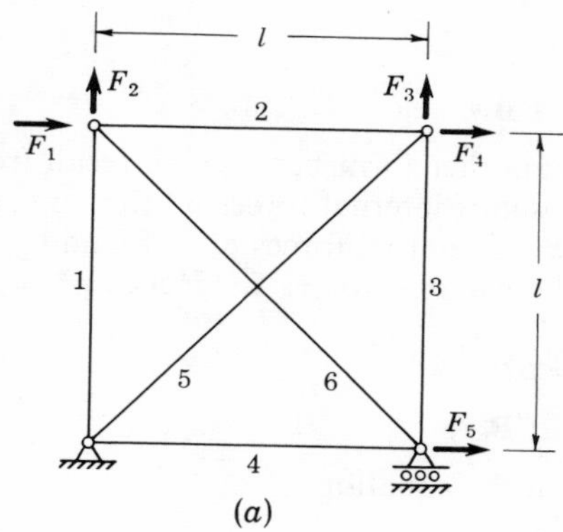

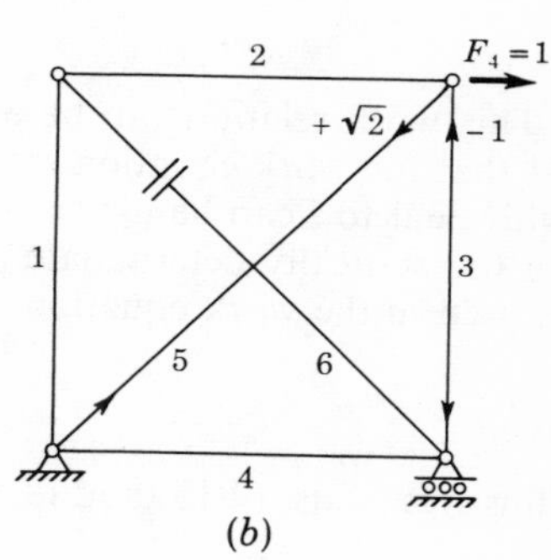

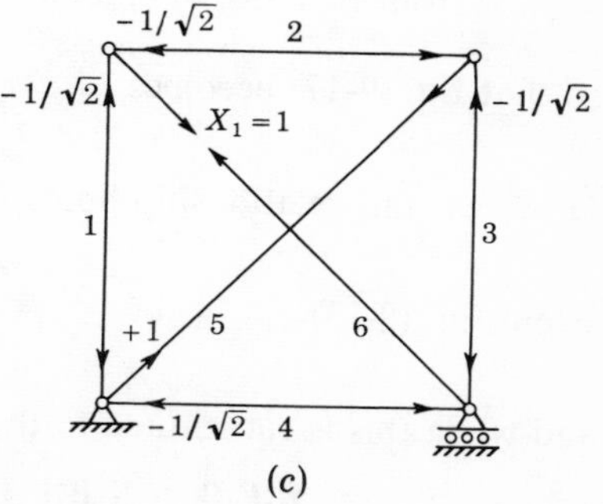

FIG. 9-13. (*a*) Statically indeterminate truss; (*b*) loading to determine the fourth column of $\mathbf{B}_0$; (*c*) loading to determine the only column of $\mathbf{B}_1$.

$$\overset{1}{{}^{r}\mathbf{v}_g} = \overset{r}{{}^{r}\mathbf{F}_g}\,\overset{1}{{}^{r}\mathbf{p}_g} \tag{9-1}$$

which relates the internal forces of the gth element $\mathbf{p}_g$ with the deformations $\mathbf{v}_g$.

The relation between the internal forces $\mathbf{p}$ and the deformations $\mathbf{v}$ then has the form

$$\overset{1}{{}^{l}\mathbf{v}} = \overset{l}{{}^{l}\mathbf{F}_v}\,\overset{1}{{}^{l}\mathbf{p}} \tag{9-14}$$

where

$$\mathbf{F}_v = \begin{bmatrix} \mathbf{F}_a & & & & & \\ & \mathbf{F}_b & & & & \\ & & \cdots & & & \\ & & & \mathbf{F}_g & & \\ & & & & \cdots & \\ & & & & & \mathbf{F}_s \end{bmatrix}$$

is a diagonally partitioned flexibility matrix made up of the flexibility matrices of the individual elements.

Example 9-3 (*continued*). In the illustrative example of Fig. 9-13 we obtain simply the diagonal matrix $\mathbf{F}_v = (l/EA)$ diag $[1 \quad 1 \quad 1 \quad 1 \quad \sqrt{2} \quad \sqrt{2}]$. Corresponding to $\mathbf{p}$ we have $\mathbf{v} = \{u_1 \quad u_2 \quad u_3 \quad u_4 \quad u_5 \quad u_6\}$.

Calculation of the Redundant Forces by Means of the Principle of Work. The work done by the external forces $\mathbf{f}$ in moving through the displacement $\mathbf{d}$ is $\mathbf{f}'\mathbf{d}$. The work done by the internal forces $\mathbf{p}$ in moving through the deformations $\mathbf{v}$ is $\mathbf{p}'\mathbf{v}$. Since $\mathbf{f}$ and $\mathbf{p}$ are statically equivalent and $\mathbf{d}$ and $\mathbf{v}$ are geometrically compatible, the work theorem can be used to yield

$$\mathbf{f}'\mathbf{d} = \mathbf{p}'\mathbf{v}$$

and from Eq. (9-12) this equation becomes

$$\mathbf{f}'\mathbf{d} = \mathbf{f}'\mathbf{B}'\mathbf{v} \tag{9-15}$$

This work relation can be expressed in another form because we recall from Sec. 9-1 that the work equation states that any set of internal forces $\mathbf{p}^*$ that are statically equivalent to $\mathbf{f}$ can be used. A suitable set of internal forces $\mathbf{p}^*$ is found by subjecting the statically determinate system to the external forces $\mathbf{f}$. Hence $\mathbf{p}^* = \mathbf{B}_0\mathbf{f}$ can be used in the work equation

$$\mathbf{f}'\mathbf{d} = \mathbf{p}^*\mathbf{v}$$

giving

$$\mathbf{f}'\mathbf{d} = \mathbf{f}'\mathbf{B}_0'\mathbf{v} \tag{9-16}$$

Thus from Eqs. (9-15) and (9-16) we obtain the equation

$$\mathbf{f}'\mathbf{B}'\mathbf{v} = \mathbf{f}'\mathbf{B}_0'\mathbf{v} \tag{9-17}$$

Now from Eqs. (9-14) and (9-12)

$$\mathbf{v} = \mathbf{F}_v\mathbf{B}\mathbf{f} \tag{9-18}$$

so that Eq. (9-17) becomes

$$\mathbf{f}'\mathbf{B}'\mathbf{F}_v\mathbf{B}\mathbf{f} = \mathbf{f}'\mathbf{B}_0'\mathbf{F}_v\mathbf{B}\mathbf{f}$$

However, this relationship holds for all values of $\mathbf{f}$, and hence it follows that

$$\mathbf{B}'\mathbf{F}_v\mathbf{B} = \mathbf{B}_0'\mathbf{F}_v\mathbf{B}$$

From Eq. (9-13)

$$\mathbf{B}' = \mathbf{B}_0' + \mathbf{X}'\mathbf{B}_1'$$

and when this is substituted in the left-hand side of the previous equation, then

$$\mathbf{B}_0'\mathbf{F}_v\mathbf{B} + \mathbf{X}'\mathbf{B}_1'\mathbf{F}_v\mathbf{B} = \mathbf{B}_0'\mathbf{F}_v\mathbf{B} \qquad \text{or} \qquad \mathbf{X}'\mathbf{B}_1'\mathbf{F}_v\mathbf{B} = \mathbf{0}$$

Substituting the expression for **B** of Eq. (9-13) gives

$$\mathbf{X}'(\mathbf{B}_1'\mathbf{F}_v\mathbf{B}_0 + \mathbf{B}_1'\mathbf{F}_v\mathbf{B}_1\mathbf{X}) = \mathbf{0}$$

The following substitutions are now made:

$$\mathbf{D}_{11} = \mathbf{B}_1'\mathbf{F}_v\mathbf{B}_1 \tag{9-19a}$$

$$\mathbf{D}_{10} = \mathbf{B}_1'\mathbf{F}_v\mathbf{B}_0 \tag{9-19b}$$

We notice on account of its formation that $\mathbf{D}_{11}$ is a square symmetric matrix† and can therefore be inverted. The equation now becomes

$$\mathbf{X}'(\mathbf{D}_{10} + \mathbf{D}_{11}\mathbf{X}) = \mathbf{0}$$

or

$$\mathbf{D}_{10} + \mathbf{D}_{11}\mathbf{X} = \mathbf{0}$$

and

$$\mathbf{X} = -\mathbf{D}_{11}^{-1}\mathbf{D}_{10} \tag{9-20}$$

The redundant forces **x** and the internal forces **p** can now be computed with the help of Eqs. (9-11) to (9-13).‡

The Flexibility Matrix. We now wish to find the expression for the flexibility matrix $\mathbf{F}_d$ which relates the applied forces **f** and their displacements **d** according to the equation

$$\mathbf{d} = \mathbf{F}_d\mathbf{f} \tag{9-21}$$

Premultiplying by **f**′ and using Eqs. (9-16) and (9-18) we obtain

$$\mathbf{f}'\mathbf{F}_d\mathbf{f} = \mathbf{f}'\mathbf{B}_0'\mathbf{v} = \mathbf{f}'\mathbf{B}_0'\mathbf{F}_v\mathbf{B}\mathbf{f}$$

Hence for the reason that **f** is arbitrary, the flexibility matrix is

$$\mathbf{F}_d = \mathbf{B}_0'\mathbf{F}_v\mathbf{B} = \mathbf{B}_0'\mathbf{F}_v(\mathbf{B}_0 + \mathbf{B}_1\mathbf{X})$$
$$= \mathbf{B}_0'\mathbf{F}_v(\mathbf{B}_0 - \mathbf{B}_1\mathbf{D}_{11}^{-1}\mathbf{D}_{10}) = \mathbf{B}_0'\mathbf{F}_v\mathbf{B}_0 - \mathbf{B}_0'\mathbf{F}_v\mathbf{B}_1\mathbf{D}_{11}^{-1}\mathbf{D}_{10}$$

From the property of a transposed matrix [cf. Eq. (1-19)]

$$\mathbf{D}_{10}' = \mathbf{B}_0'\mathbf{F}_v'\mathbf{B}_1 = \mathbf{B}_0'\mathbf{F}_v\mathbf{B}_1$$

since $\mathbf{F}_v$ is symmetric.

Therefore, the expression for the flexibility matrix becomes

$$\mathbf{F}_d = \mathbf{D}_{00} - \mathbf{D}_{10}'\mathbf{D}_{11}^{-1}\mathbf{D}_{10} \tag{9-22}$$

† Cf. Eq. (1-20).

‡ The reader is advised to work out as a simple exercise the illustrative Example 9-3. In order to reduce the computational labor, consider only the external forces F_3 and F_4. The following results are obtained:

$$\mathbf{D}_{11} = \left[2(1+\sqrt{2})\frac{l}{EA}\right] \qquad \mathbf{D}_{10} = \frac{l}{EA}\left[2+\frac{1}{\sqrt{2}} \quad -\frac{1}{\sqrt{2}}\right]$$

Furthermore

$$\mathbf{X} = [-0.560 \quad 0.146] \quad \text{and} \quad \mathbf{B} = \begin{bmatrix} 0.395 & -0.103 \\ 0.395 & -0.103 \\ -0.605 & 0.897 \\ 0.395 & -0.103 \\ 0.854 & 0.146 \\ -0.560 & 0.146 \end{bmatrix}$$

Table 9-1†

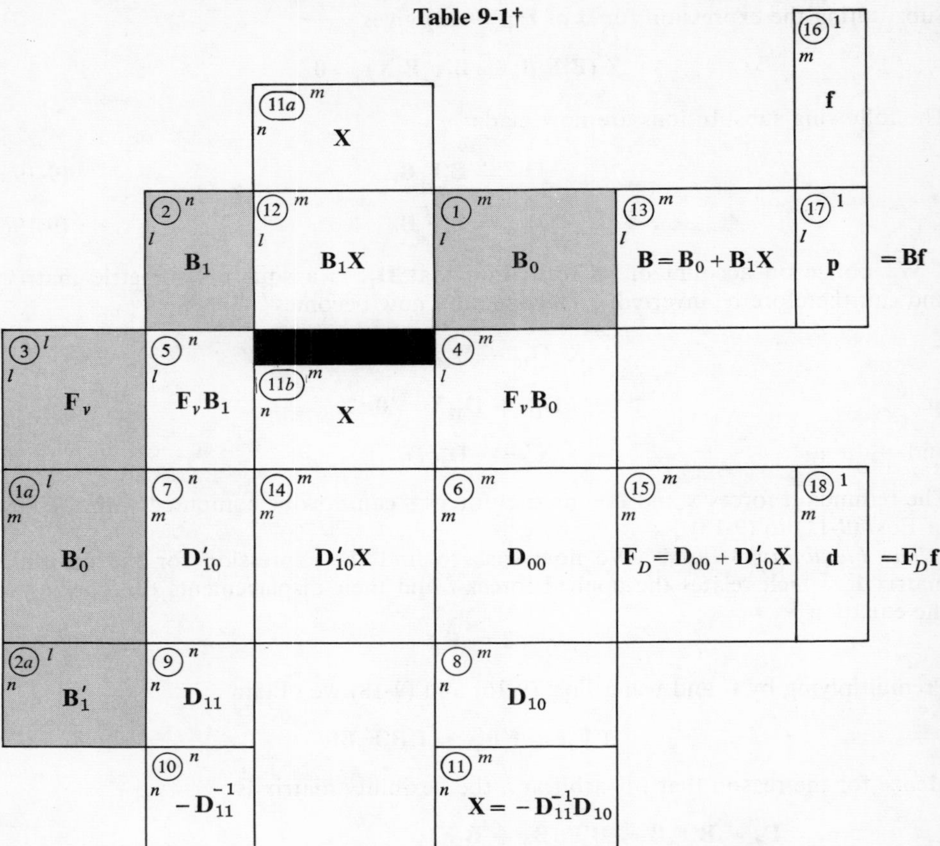

† Shading represents blocks into which initial information is fed. Circled numbers denote the sequence of the computational steps.

where
$$\mathbf{D}_{00} = \mathbf{B}_0'\mathbf{F}_v\mathbf{B}_0\dagger$$
so that the flexibility matrix $\mathbf{F}_d$ is symmetric.

Matrix Calculations in Tabular Form. The individual steps involved in the overall process can be very conveniently illustrated in the tabular form shown in Table 9-1. The matrices $\mathbf{B}_0$, $\mathbf{B}_1$, and $\mathbf{F}_v$ are placed in blocks 1, 2, and 3. The transposes of $\mathbf{B}_0$ and $\mathbf{B}_1$ are placed in blocks 1*a* and 2*a*. Blocks 1 and 3 are multiplied to give $\mathbf{F}_v\mathbf{B}_0$ in block 4,‡ and block 5 is filled by multiplying blocks 3 and 2. Now $\mathbf{D}_{00} = \mathbf{B}_0'\mathbf{F}_v\mathbf{B}_0$ (block 6) is found by multiplying blocks 1*a* and 4, and similarly $\mathbf{D}_{10}'$ (block 7) is formed by multiplying blocks 1*a* and 5. The matrices $\mathbf{D}_{10}$ in block 8 and $\mathbf{D}_{11}$ in block 9 are found by multiplying block 2*a* by block 4 and block 2*a* by block 5, respectively. Observe that block 7 is the transpose of block 8. The negative of the inverse of $\mathbf{D}_{11}$ is placed in block 10, and in block 11 is placed the product of blocks 10 and 8. Block 11 is repeated in blocks 11*a* and 11*b*. Block 12 is formed as the

† From Eq. (1-20) we deduce that $\mathbf{D}_{00}$ is symmetric. For the illustrative Example 9-3 we obtain, if we consider only F_3 and F_4,

$$\mathbf{D}_{00} = \begin{bmatrix} 2.121 & 0.707 \\ 0.707 & -0.707 \end{bmatrix} \quad \text{and} \quad \mathbf{F}_d = \begin{bmatrix} 0.611 & 1.102 \\ 1.102 & -0.810 \end{bmatrix}$$

‡ See multiplications in Chap. 1.

product of blocks 2 and 11*a*, and the matrix **B** in block 13 is then completed by adding blocks 1 and 12. Block 14 is formed as the product of blocks 7 and 11*b*, and the flexibility matrix in block 15 is formed by adding blocks 14 and 6. Finally the values of the external loads are placed in column 16, so that the values of the internal forces in column 17 are found by multiplying block 13 and column 16 and the values of the displacements in column 18 are found by multiplying block 15 and column 16.

Several points of interest should now be discussed. First of all, we notice that all the calculations are made using the basic matrices $\mathbf{B}_0$, $\mathbf{B}_1$, and $\mathbf{F}_v$. The external load matrix **f** comes into the calculation only at the very end, so that any change in the elements of **f** involves only the minor calculations indicated in blocks 17 and 18. Should we desire to apply an additional load at some point, the increase of computational labor is still not large as long as its point of application coincides with one of the joints of the structure. The matrix $\mathbf{B}_0$ is increased by an extra column from m to $m + 1$ columns. The modified matrix calculations are illustrated in Table 9-2, with the shaded parts remaining unchanged, while the additional columns and rows are completed according to the program previously described. The additional work involves no more than matrix multiplication. The most difficult operation involved in the calculation is the inversion of the $\mathbf{D}_{11}$ matrix. The order of this matrix is equal to the number of redundancies and is independent of the loading.

Table 9-2

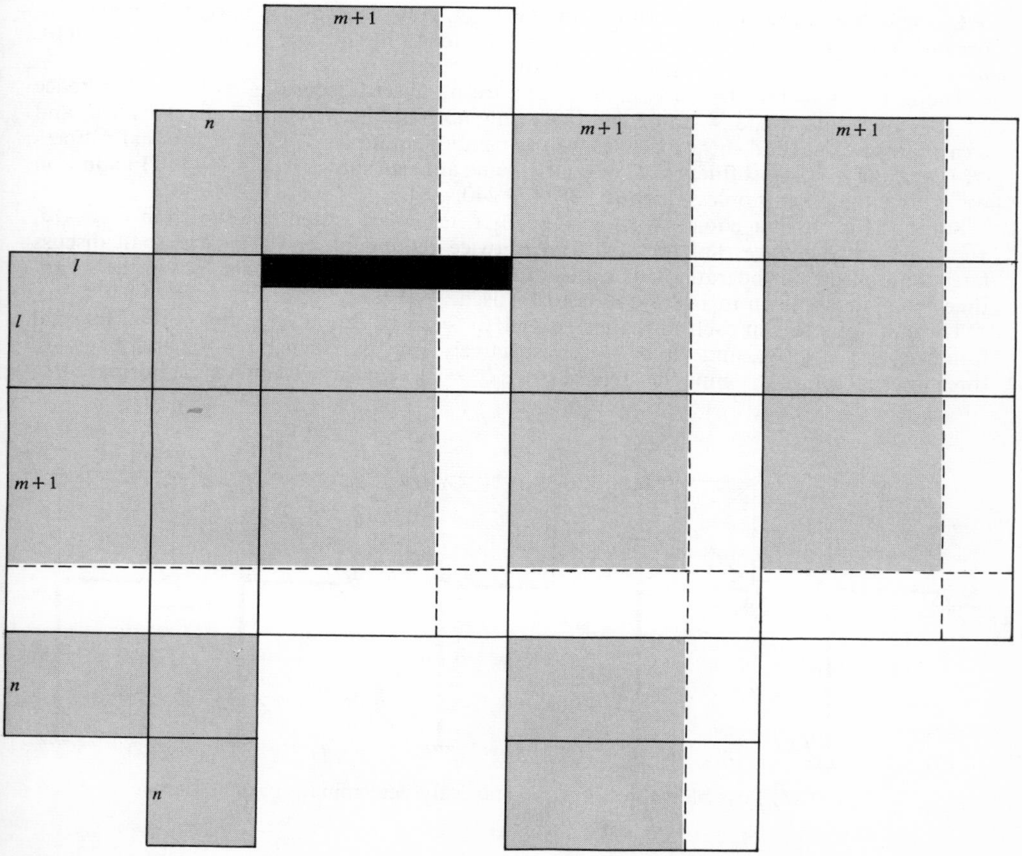

$m+1$

n

$m+1$

$m+1$

l

l

$m+1$

n

n

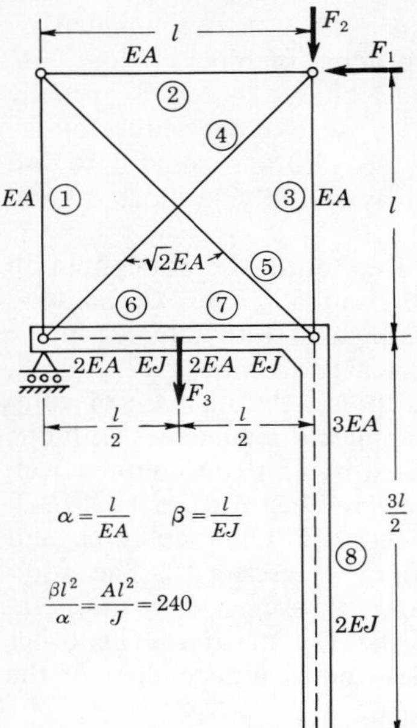

FIG. 9-14. Details of structure to be analyzed.

Example 9-4. The structure shown in Fig. 9-14, consisting of a pin-jointed frame connected to a right-angled bent, is subjected to the loads F_1, F_2, and F_3 ($m = 3$). We wish to determine the internal forces and the flexibility matrix.

The elements of the structure, eight in all, are numbered according to Fig. 9-14; hence $s = 8$. Elements 1, 2, 3, 4, and 5 can carry only normal forces, whereas elements 6, 7, and 8 can carry normal and shear forces as well as bending moments. The longitudinal stiffness (EA) and the bending stiffness (EJ) of the elements are also shown in Fig. 9-14. In addition we assume the dimensionless quantity $Al^2/J = 240$.

Some of the possible choices for the statically determinate system are shown in Fig. 9-15, and we readily deduce that the structure is twice redundant ($n = 2$). We shall discuss later some of the considerations that affect the choice of the basic system, but in the meantime the system shown in Fig. 9-15a is to be used.

The state of stress in each of the elements 1 to 5 can be found from the normal internal forces N_1, N_2, N_3, N_4, and N_5 ($r = 1$), respectively, and the elements 6, 7, and 8 require three internal forces to define the state of stress ($r = 3$). In these elements the normal force

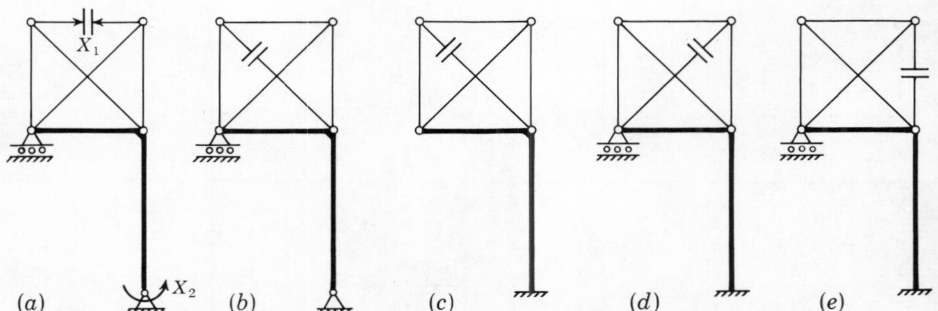

FIG. 9-15. Possible choices for the statically determinate basic systems.

FIG. 9-16. Internal forces and deformations of beam element.

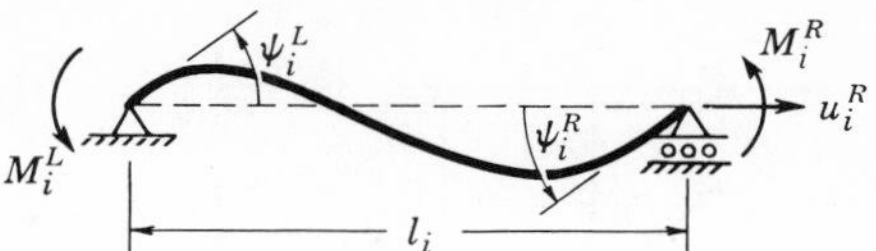

and the bending moments at the left and right end of the beam are to be used as the internal forces (Fig. 9-16) (cf. Sec. 9-1). The column vector $\mathbf{p}$ representing the internal forces is

$$\mathbf{p} = \{N_1 \quad N_2 \quad N_3 \quad N_4 \quad N_5 \quad N_6 \quad M_6^L \quad M_6^R \quad N_7 \quad M_7^L \quad M_7^R \quad N_8 \quad M_8^L \quad M_8^R\}$$

Hence $l = 14$.

For the calculation of the columns of the matrices $\mathbf{B}_0$ and $\mathbf{B}_1$ the internal forces are calculated when the unit loads shown in Fig. 9-17 act on the basic structure. The matrices $\mathbf{B}_0$ and $\mathbf{B}_1$ are shown in Table 9-3.

The flexibility matrices $\mathbf{F}_g$ for elements 1 to 5 consist of the single element l/EA, and the flexibility matrix $\mathbf{F}_g$ for each of the elements 6, 7, and 8 is a (3, 3) matrix relating three deformations to three internal forces:

$$\begin{bmatrix} u^R \\ \psi^L \\ \psi^R \end{bmatrix} = \begin{bmatrix} \dfrac{l}{EA} & 0 & 0 \\ 0 & \dfrac{l}{3EJ} & \dfrac{-l}{6EJ} \\ 0 & \dfrac{-l}{6EJ} & \dfrac{l}{3EJ} \end{bmatrix} \cdot \begin{bmatrix} N^R \\ M^L \\ M^R \end{bmatrix}$$

With the substitutions $\alpha = l/EA$ and $\beta = l/EJ$ the flexibility matrix $\mathbf{F}_v$ for the unassembled elements is (cf. the cross-sectional properties and lengths of the elements in Fig. 9-14)

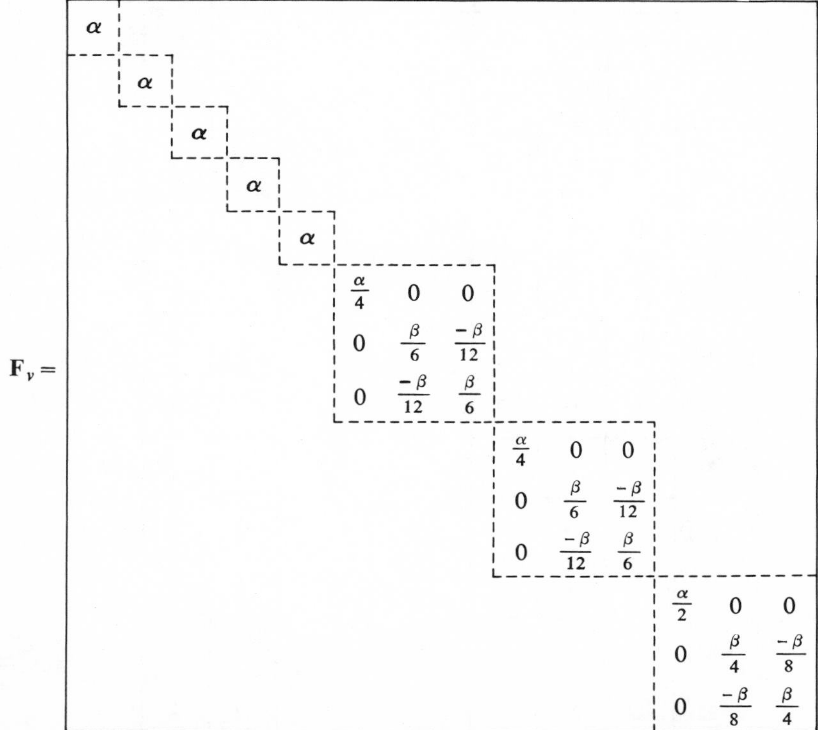

$$\mathbf{F}_v = \begin{bmatrix} \alpha & & & & & & & & & & & & & \\ & \alpha & & & & & & & & & & & & \\ & & \alpha & & & & & & & & & & & \\ & & & \alpha & & & & & & & & & & \\ & & & & \alpha & & & & & & & & & \\ & & & & & \frac{\alpha}{4} & 0 & 0 & & & & & & \\ & & & & & 0 & \frac{\beta}{6} & \frac{-\beta}{12} & & & & & & \\ & & & & & 0 & \frac{-\beta}{12} & \frac{\beta}{6} & & & & & & \\ & & & & & & & & \frac{\alpha}{4} & 0 & 0 & & & \\ & & & & & & & & 0 & \frac{\beta}{6} & \frac{-\beta}{12} & & & \\ & & & & & & & & 0 & \frac{-\beta}{12} & \frac{\beta}{6} & & & \\ & & & & & & & & & & & \frac{\alpha}{2} & 0 & 0 \\ & & & & & & & & & & & 0 & \frac{\beta}{4} & \frac{-\beta}{8} \\ & & & & & & & & & & & 0 & \frac{-\beta}{8} & \frac{\beta}{4} \end{bmatrix}$$

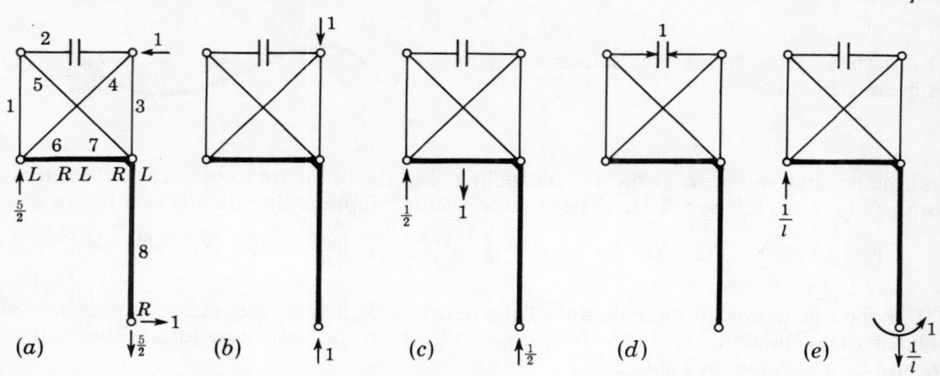

FIG. 9-17. Load systems for the evaluation of (a) first column of $\mathbf{B}_0$, (b) second column of $\mathbf{B}_0$, (c) third column of $\mathbf{B}_0$, (d) first column of $\mathbf{B}_1$, (e) second column of $\mathbf{B}_1$.

Table 9-3

	Matrix $\mathbf{B}_0$			Matrix $\mathbf{B}_1$	
	F_1	F_2	F_3	X_1	X_2
N_1	0	0	0	1	0
N_2	0	0	0	1	0
N_3	1	-1	0	1	0
N_4	$-\sqrt{2}$	0	0	$-\sqrt{2}$	0
N_5	0	0	0	$-\sqrt{2}$	0
N_6	1	0	0	1	0
M_6^L	0	0	0	0	0
M_6^R	$\frac{3l}{4}$	0	$\frac{l}{4}$	0	$\frac{1}{2}$
N_7	1	0	0	1	0
M_7^L	$\frac{-3l}{4}$	0	$\frac{-l}{4}$	0	$\frac{-1}{2}$
M_7^R	$\frac{3l}{2}$	0	0	0	1
N_8	$\frac{5}{2}$	-1	$\frac{-1}{2}$	0	$\frac{1}{l}$
M_8^L	$\frac{-3l}{2}$	0	0	0	-1
M_8^R	0	0	0	0	1

With the matrices $\mathbf{B}_0$, $\mathbf{B}_1$, and $\mathbf{F}_v$ found, the calculations now proceed as outlined in Table 9-1. Thus we obtain the matrices $\mathbf{B}$ and $\mathbf{F}_d$, as shown in Table 9-4.

All that now remains is to put in the values of the load matrix $\mathbf{f} = \{F_1 \quad F_2 \quad F_3\}$ and to multiply by the matrices $\mathbf{B}$ and $\mathbf{F}_d$ to give the internal forces and the displacements under the loading. It is clear that it involves very little labor to calculate the internal forces and the displacements for different values of $\mathbf{f}$.

Some Further Observations on the Matrix Force Method. Although the presentation of the basic theory is now completed, there are several points of interest that can be profitably brought to light.

By the application of the dummy-load theorem it is possible to find the relation that exists between the displacements $\mathbf{d}$ and the deformations of the elements $\mathbf{v}$. Under the action of the applied forces $\mathbf{f}$ the actual displacements are $\mathbf{d}$ and the deformations $\mathbf{v}$. Now apply dummy external forces $\mathbf{f}_d$, for which the corresponding internal forces are $\mathbf{p}_d$. Then from the dummy-load theorem

$$\mathbf{f}_d'\mathbf{d} = \mathbf{p}_d'\mathbf{v}$$

Table 9-4. Final Results in Tabular Form

$$\mathbf{B} = \begin{bmatrix} \frac{-7}{15} & \frac{2}{15} & 0 \\ \frac{-7}{15} & \frac{2}{15} & 0 \\ \frac{8}{15} & \frac{-13}{15} & 0 \\ \frac{-8\sqrt{2}}{15} & \frac{-2\sqrt{2}}{15} & 0 \\ \frac{7\sqrt{2}}{15} & \frac{-2\sqrt{2}}{15} & 0 \\ \frac{8}{15} & \frac{2}{15} & 0 \\ 0 & 0 & 0 \\ \frac{538l}{2{,}084} & \frac{l}{1{,}042} & \frac{462l}{2{,}084} \\ \frac{8}{15} & \frac{2}{15} & 0 \\ \frac{-538l}{2{,}084} & \frac{-l}{1{,}042} & \frac{-462l}{2{,}084} \\ \frac{538l}{1{,}042} & \frac{l}{521} & \frac{-59l}{1{,}042} \\ \frac{790}{521} & \frac{-520}{521} & \frac{-240}{521} \\ \frac{-538l}{1{,}042} & \frac{-l}{521} & \frac{59l}{1{,}042} \\ \frac{-1{,}025l}{1{,}042} & \frac{l}{521} & \frac{-59l}{1{,}042} \end{bmatrix} \qquad \mathbf{F}_d = \begin{bmatrix} 68.182\alpha & -1.292\alpha & 7.366\alpha \\ -1.292\alpha & 1.366\alpha & 0.278\alpha \\ 7.366\alpha & 0.278\alpha & 4.290\alpha \end{bmatrix}$$

But $$\mathbf{p}_d = \mathbf{B}\mathbf{f}_d$$

so that $$\mathbf{f}'_d\mathbf{d} = \mathbf{f}'_d\mathbf{B}'\mathbf{v}$$

However, since this equation must be satisfied for any choice of dummy load $\mathbf{f}_d$ (it is independent of $\mathbf{d}$ and $\mathbf{v}$!), it follows that

$$\mathbf{d} = \mathbf{B}'\mathbf{v} \tag{9-23}$$

The same process can be repeated, this time, however, using a set of internal dummy forces $\mathbf{p}_d^*$ that only has to be statically equivalent to the dummy load $\mathbf{f}_d$. This time the dummy-load theorem gives

$$\mathbf{f}'_d\mathbf{d} = \mathbf{p}_d^{*\prime}\mathbf{v}$$

A suitable set of internal dummy forces is given by loading the statically determinate structure so that

$$\mathbf{p}_d^* = \mathbf{B}_0\mathbf{f}_d$$

Substituting this in the dummy-load equation, we obtain

$$\mathbf{d} = \mathbf{B}'_0\mathbf{v} \tag{9-24}$$

Equations (9-23) and (9-24) give the rather surprising result that the displacements $\mathbf{d}$ can be obtained by premultiplying the deformations $\mathbf{v}$ by either $\mathbf{B}'$ or $\mathbf{B}'_0$. In fact, any $\mathbf{B}^*$ that corresponds to a statically equivalent set of internal forces will give the same result. Equating the displacements $\mathbf{d}$ of Eqs. (9-23) and (9-24) gives the result

$$\mathbf{B}'\mathbf{v} = \mathbf{B}'_0\mathbf{v} \tag{9-25}$$

From this equation it is possible to find the expression for $\mathbf{X}$, but it is left as an exercise for those who would like to do it.

However, let us continue with Eq. (9-25) by setting, from Eq. (9-13),

$$\mathbf{B}' = \mathbf{B}'_0 + \mathbf{X}'\mathbf{B}'_1$$

Then $$\mathbf{B}'_0\mathbf{v} + \mathbf{X}'\mathbf{B}'_1\mathbf{v} = \mathbf{B}'_0\mathbf{v}$$

from which $$\mathbf{X}'\mathbf{B}'_1\mathbf{v} = \mathbf{0} \tag{9-26}$$

However, since it is assumed that $\mathbf{X}' \neq \mathbf{0}$, it follows that, if Eq. (9-26) is to be satisfied for all $\mathbf{v}$, then the column vector resulting from the product $\mathbf{B}'_1\mathbf{v}$ must be zero, that is,

$$\mathbf{B}'_1\mathbf{v} = \mathbf{0} \tag{9-27}$$

From this result it can be shown that the relative displacements of the redundant forces at the cuts made in the redundant structure must be zero. When the redundant structure is loaded by the forces $\mathbf{f}$, the deformations of the elements are $\mathbf{v}$ and we assume that the relative displacements at the cuts are $\mathbf{e}$. Now apply dummy loads $\mathbf{x}_d$ at the cuts. Then the internal dummy forces are given by

$$\mathbf{p}_d = \mathbf{B}_1\mathbf{x}_d$$

Now the dummy-load theorem states that the work done by the dummy forces $\mathbf{x}_d$ in moving through the actual displacements $\mathbf{e}$ is equal to the work done by the dummy internal forces in moving through the deformations $\mathbf{v}$, that is,

$$\mathbf{p}'_d\mathbf{v} = \mathbf{x}'_d\mathbf{e} \qquad \text{or} \qquad \mathbf{x}'_d\mathbf{B}'_1\mathbf{v} = \mathbf{x}'_d\mathbf{e}$$

But since this must be true for all dummy loads $\mathbf{x}_d$, we conclude that the relative displacements at the cuts are zero [cf. Eq. (9-27)].

Besides the physical interpretation, the discussion of Eq. (9-27) shows how quickly we would have obtained this compatibility equation by means of the dummy-load theorem if we had started out with the condition that $\mathbf{e} = \mathbf{0}$.

Let us close our general remarks on the matrix force method by stating with reference to the first paragraph of Sec. 9-1 that the following three equations form the basis of this method:

$$\mathbf{p} = (\mathbf{B}_0 + \mathbf{B}_1\mathbf{X})\mathbf{f} \qquad \text{equilibrium} \qquad (9\text{-}12)$$
$$\mathbf{B}_1'\mathbf{v} = \mathbf{0} \qquad \text{compatibility} \qquad (9\text{-}27)$$
$$\mathbf{v} = \mathbf{F}_v\mathbf{p} \qquad \text{stress-strain relationship} \qquad (9\text{-}14)$$

PROBLEMS

9-5. Find the $\mathbf{B}_0$, $\mathbf{B}_1$, and $\mathbf{F}_v$ matrices for the pin-jointed truss when it is loaded as shown in Fig. P 9-5. The forces in members 15 and 06 should be used as the redundancies. All members of the truss are of longitudinal stiffness EA.

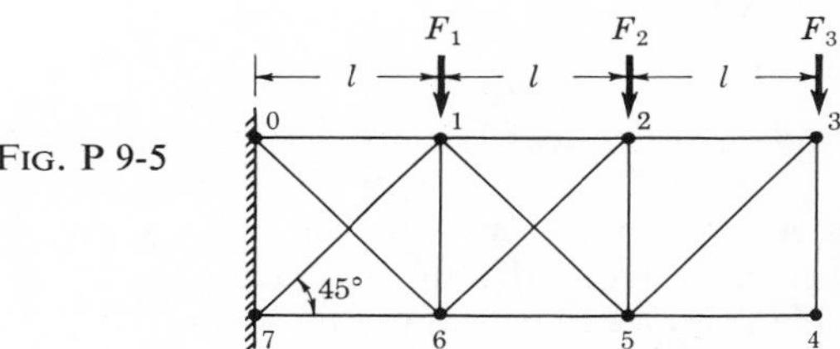

FIG. P 9-5

9-6. Compute the flexibility matrix $\mathbf{F}_d$ and the $\mathbf{B}$ matrix of the structure in Fig. P 9-5 using the matrix scheme of Table 9-1. If $F_1 = F_2 = F_3 = F$, find the deflections $\mathbf{d}$ in the direction of these forces, and verify the relations

$$\mathbf{d} = \mathbf{B}_0'\mathbf{v} = \mathbf{B}'\mathbf{v} \qquad \text{and} \qquad \mathbf{B}_1'\mathbf{v} = \mathbf{0}$$

9-7. Compute the new flexibility matrix $\mathbf{F}_d$ and the matrix $\mathbf{B}$ for the structure of Fig. P 9-5 when an additional vertical load F_5 is hung from point 5.

9-8. Find the flexibility matrix $\mathbf{F}_d$ for the propped cantilever beam of Fig. P 9-8 using the element flexibility matrices given under Fig. *e* of the flexibility-matrix catalogue in Sec. 9-1.

9-9. Repeat Prob. 9-8 using the element flexibility matrix under Fig. *g* of the catalogue.

9-10. Two concentrated masses, each of mass m, are attached at points 1 and 2 of the propped cantilever of Fig. P 9-8. From the mass matrix and the flexibility matrix obtained previously, determine the natural frequencies.

9-11. Determine the flexibility matrix $\mathbf{F}_d$ for the frame shown in Fig. P 9-11. Compute the reactions at points A and B (EJ = const, $EA \to \infty$).†

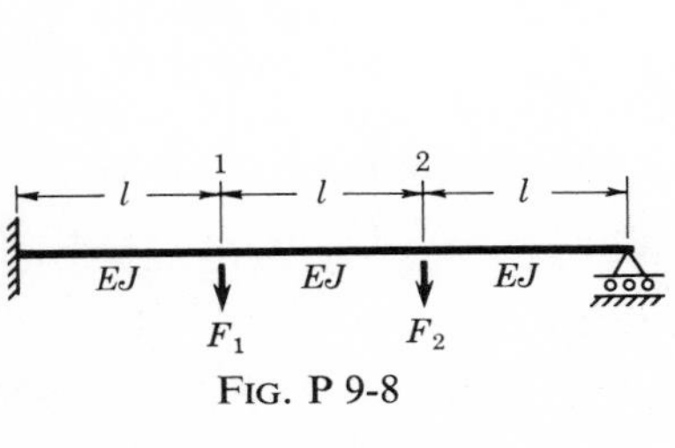

FIG. P 9-8

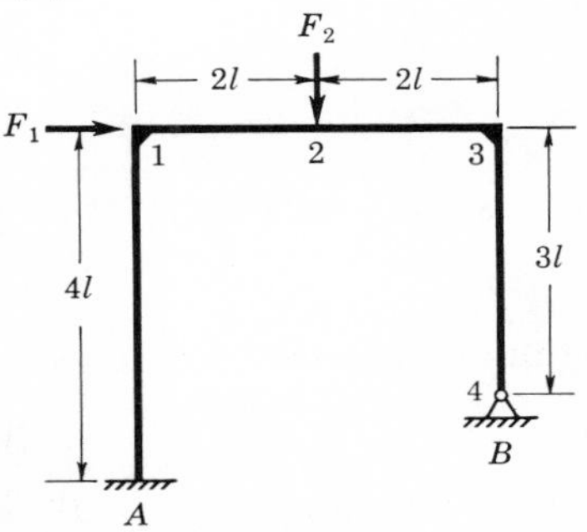

FIG. P 9-11

† R. Zurmühl, "Matrizen," 3d ed., Springer-Verlag, Berlin, 1958.

9-3. Stress Distribution Due to Thermal and/or Other Initial Strains†

We shall now consider how to calculate the stress distribution and the displacements that occur when the system is subjected to initial strains [50]. These strains can occur, for example, as a result of temperature changes and lack of fit of the elements during construction. The initial deformations of the s unassembled elements from their ideal shape are represented by the column matrix

$$\mathbf{h} = \{\mathbf{h}_1' \quad \mathbf{h}_2' \quad \cdots \quad \mathbf{h}_g' \quad \cdots \quad \mathbf{h}_s'\} \tag{9-28}$$

which is dimensionally equal to the deformation matrix $\mathbf{v}$ [Eq. (9-14)]. In fact, if the system is statically determinate and is unloaded, then the deformations of the elements are given by

$$\mathbf{v} = \mathbf{h} \tag{9-29}$$

For this simple case the displacements of the assembled structure are [from Eq. (9-24)]

$$\mathbf{d} = \mathbf{B}_0'\mathbf{h} \tag{9-30}$$

the displacements being in the direction of the loads used to determine $\mathbf{B}_0$.

Whereas no stresses are developed in a statically determinate system with initial deformations, this is not the case in a redundant system. Let the internal forces resulting from the initial deformations be represented by the column matrix $\mathbf{p}_h$. These internal forces modify the initial deformations $\mathbf{h}$, so that the total deformations of the assembled elements are now

$$\mathbf{v}_h = \mathbf{h} + \mathbf{F}_v\mathbf{p}_h \qquad \text{cf. Eq. (9-14)} \tag{9-31}$$

In the absence of external loads the internal forces are given by the equation [cf. Eq. (9-10)]

$$\mathbf{p}_h = \mathbf{B}_1\mathbf{x}_h \tag{9-32}$$

where $\mathbf{x}_h$ are the as yet unknown redundant forces caused by the initial strains. Equation (9-31) then becomes

$$\mathbf{v}_h = \mathbf{h} + \mathbf{F}_v\mathbf{B}_1\mathbf{x}_h \tag{9-33}$$

In this equation $\mathbf{h}$ is a known column vector and $\mathbf{F}_v$ and $\mathbf{B}_1$ are two matrices that were obtained for the structure in the previous section. The unknown redundant forces $\mathbf{x}_h$ can be computed by making use of Eq. (9-27), which implies that the relative displacements at the cuts made in the indeterminate structure are zero; that is,

$$\mathbf{B}_1'\mathbf{v} = \mathbf{B}_1'\mathbf{v}_h = \mathbf{0} \tag{9-27}$$

Substituting Eq. (9-33) into Eq. (9-27) gives

$$\mathbf{B}_1'\mathbf{h} + \mathbf{B}_1'\mathbf{F}_v\mathbf{B}_1\mathbf{x}_h = \mathbf{0}$$

If we recall the definition of $\mathbf{D}_{11}$ in Eq. (9-19*a*), the expression for $\mathbf{x}_h$ is

$$\mathbf{x}_h = -\mathbf{D}_{11}^{-1}\mathbf{B}_1'\mathbf{h} \tag{9-34}$$

Substituting this result in Eq. (9-32) gives the internal forces

$$\mathbf{p}_h = -\mathbf{B}_1\mathbf{D}_{11}^{-1}\mathbf{B}_1'\mathbf{h} \tag{9-35}$$

and substitution in Eq. (9-33) yields the deformations of the assembled elements

$$\mathbf{v}_h = \mathbf{h} - \mathbf{F}_v\mathbf{B}_1\mathbf{D}_{11}^{-1}\mathbf{B}_1'\mathbf{h} \tag{9-36}$$

† Cf. first footnote on p. 240.

The deflections are related to the deformations according to Eq. (9-24), so that by using Eq. (9-36) the expression for the deflections becomes

$$\mathbf{d}_h = \mathbf{B}_0'\mathbf{v}_h = [\mathbf{B}_0' - \mathbf{B}_0'\mathbf{F}_v\mathbf{B}_1\mathbf{D}_{11}^{-1}\mathbf{B}_1'] \cdot \mathbf{h}$$

This expression can be made more agreeable by using the transposed equivalent of the above matrix:

$$[\mathbf{B}_0' - \mathbf{B}_0'\mathbf{F}_v\mathbf{B}_1\mathbf{D}_{11}^{-1}\mathbf{B}_1'] = [\mathbf{B}_0 - \mathbf{B}_1\mathbf{D}_{11}^{-1}\mathbf{B}_1'\mathbf{F}_v\mathbf{B}_0]'$$

Note that $\mathbf{D}_{11}^{-1}$ and $\mathbf{F}_v$ are unaffected by the transposition since they are symmetric. Also we have $\mathbf{D}_{10} = \mathbf{B}_1'\mathbf{F}_v\mathbf{B}_0$ [Eq. (9-19*b*)], so that $\mathbf{d}_h$ becomes

$$\begin{aligned}\mathbf{d}_h &= [\mathbf{B}_0 - \mathbf{B}_1\mathbf{D}_{11}^{-1}\mathbf{D}_{10}]' \cdot \mathbf{h} \\ &= [\mathbf{B}_0 + \mathbf{B}_1\mathbf{X}]' \cdot \mathbf{h} \qquad \text{cf. Eq. (9-20)} \\ &= \mathbf{B}'\mathbf{h} \qquad \text{cf. Eq. (9-23)}\end{aligned} \tag{9-37}$$

The schematic layout for calculations involving initial strain is given in Table 9-5, the matrices $\mathbf{B}_1$, $\mathbf{B}_1'$, $-\mathbf{D}_{11}^{-1}$, and $\mathbf{B}'$ being carried over from Table 9-1.

Example 9-5. Find the internal forces that are induced when member 2 of the system shown in Fig. 9-14 before the assembly is of length $l + d$. The column vector $\mathbf{h}$ for this case is then

$$\mathbf{h} = \{0 \quad d \quad 0 \quad 0 \quad 0 \quad 0 \quad 0 \quad 0 \quad 0 \quad 0 \quad 0 \quad 0 \quad 0\}$$

and from the results of the calculations of Example 9-4, Table 9-6 can be completed. The reader should note how advantage is taken of the large number of zeros in reducing the amount of calculation.

Table 9-5

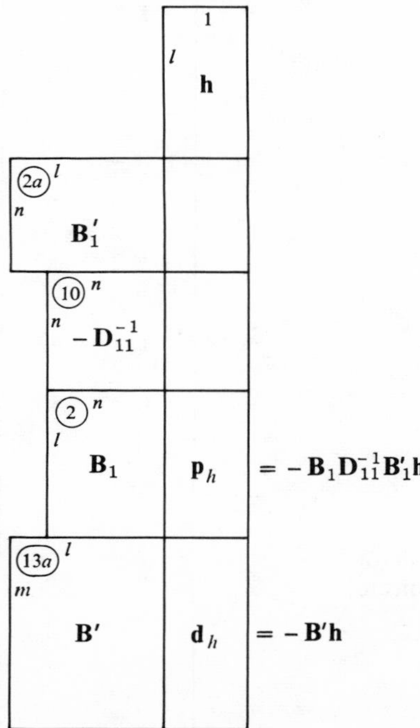

Table 9-6†

$$\mathbf{h} = \begin{bmatrix} 0 \\ d \\ 0 \\ 0 \\ 0 \\ 0 \\ 0 \\ 0 \\ 0 \\ 0 \\ 0 \\ 0 \\ 0 \\ 0 \end{bmatrix}$$

$$\mathbf{B}_1' = \begin{bmatrix} x & 1 & x & x & x & x & x & x & x & x & x & x & x & x \\ x & 0 & x & x & x & x & x & x & x & x & x & x & x & x \end{bmatrix} \begin{bmatrix} d \\ 0 \end{bmatrix}$$

$$-\mathbf{D}_{11}^{-1} = \begin{bmatrix} \dfrac{-2\alpha}{15} & 0 \\ 0 & \dfrac{-480}{521\beta} \end{bmatrix} \begin{bmatrix} \dfrac{-2\alpha d}{15} \\ 0 \end{bmatrix}$$

$$\mathbf{B}_1 = \begin{bmatrix} 1 & x \\ 1 & x \\ 1 & x \\ -\sqrt{2} & x \\ -\sqrt{2} & x \\ 1 & x \\ 0 & x \\ 0 & x \\ 1 & x \\ 0 & x \\ 0 & x \\ 0 & x \\ 0 & x \\ 0 & x \end{bmatrix} \begin{bmatrix} \dfrac{-2\alpha d}{15} \\ \dfrac{-2\alpha d}{15} \\ \dfrac{-2\alpha d}{15} \\ \dfrac{2\sqrt{2}\alpha d}{15} \\ \dfrac{2\sqrt{2}\alpha d}{15} \\ \dfrac{-2\alpha d}{15} \\ 0 \\ 0 \\ \dfrac{-2\alpha d}{15} \\ 0 \\ 0 \\ 0 \\ 0 \\ 0 \end{bmatrix} = \mathbf{p}_h$$

† Only the second column of $\mathbf{B}_1'$ is required. Crosses indicate elements not needed.

PROBLEMS

9-12. Before the assembly of the pin-jointed truss shown in Fig. P 9-5, the length of member 17 was found to be $\sqrt{2}l + d$ and that of member 35 was $\sqrt{2}l - d$. Find the internal forces due to the lack of fit of the two members. What is the horizontal displacement of point 3?

9-13. The beam shown in Fig. P 9-8 is subjected to a uniform temperature gradient θ/h through its depth h, the upper side being the cooler. Calculate the internal forces and the deflections at (1) and (2) due to this thermal load. What are the reactions of the supports?

9-4. Generalized Forces, Generalized Displacements, and Force Groups as Redundants

The work done by a force F in moving through a displacement d in the direction of the line of action of the force is described by the product Fd. Also, when a moment M is displaced (turned) through an angle ψ, the work done by the moment is $M\psi$. Frequently it proves advantageous to extend the idea of force, displacement, and work to groups of forces and moments. Such groups of forces and moments are referred to as generalized force groups, and the corresponding displacements as generalized displacements.

Generalized Force Group and Generalized Displacement. Figure 9-18*a* shows three parallel forces $\mathbf{f} = \{F_1 \quad F_2 \quad F_3\}$ and their corresponding displacements $\mathbf{d} = \{d_1 \quad d_2 \quad d_3\}$. The work done by the forces is $\mathbf{d}'\mathbf{f}$.

Now let us consider the three arbitrary (they must be linearly independent) groups of forces shown in Fig. 9-18*b*. The groups are known as the R_1, R_2, and R_3 groups, respectively, and by suitable combination of these three groups it is possible to obtain the forces $\mathbf{f}$. Referring again to Fig. 9-18, we obtain the equations relating $\mathbf{f}$ and $\mathbf{r}$:

$$\begin{aligned} F_1 &= R_1 - R_2 + R_3 \\ F_2 &= R_1 \qquad\quad - R_3 \\ F_3 &= R_1 + R_2 + R_3 \end{aligned} \qquad \text{or} \qquad \begin{bmatrix} F_1 \\ F_2 \\ F_3 \end{bmatrix} = \begin{bmatrix} 1 & -1 & 1 \\ 1 & 0 & -1 \\ 1 & 1 & 1 \end{bmatrix} \cdot \begin{bmatrix} R_1 \\ R_2 \\ R_3 \end{bmatrix}$$

That is,

$$\mathbf{f} = \mathbf{G}\mathbf{r} \tag{9-38}$$

where the matrix $\mathbf{G}$ is referred to as a load-transformation matrix. Hence

$$\mathbf{r} = \mathbf{G}^{-1}\mathbf{f} \qquad \text{or} \qquad \begin{bmatrix} R_1 \\ R_2 \\ R_3 \end{bmatrix} = \begin{bmatrix} \frac{1}{4} & \frac{1}{2} & \frac{1}{4} \\ -\frac{1}{2} & 0 & \frac{1}{2} \\ \frac{1}{4} & -\frac{1}{2} & \frac{1}{4} \end{bmatrix} \cdot \begin{bmatrix} F_1 \\ F_2 \\ F_3 \end{bmatrix}$$

The question now arises as to how the displacement $\mathbf{g} = \{g_1 \quad g_2 \quad g_3\}$ of the generalized force groups $\mathbf{r} = \{R_1 \quad R_2 \quad R_3\}$ can be defined. This is done by noting that the work done by the force groups $\mathbf{r}$ is $\mathbf{g}'\mathbf{r}$ and must equal $\mathbf{d}'\mathbf{f}$, that is,

$$\mathbf{g}'\mathbf{r} = \mathbf{d}'\mathbf{f}$$

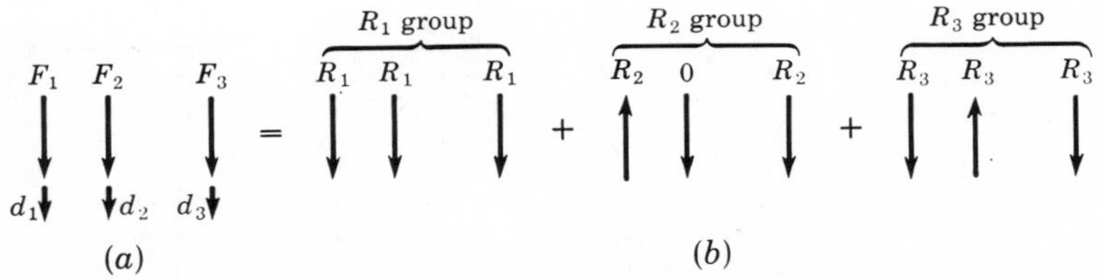

FIG. 9-18. Equivalence of three forces and three force groups.

Using Eq. (9-38) gives

$$\mathbf{g'r} = \mathbf{d'Gr} \qquad \text{so that } \mathbf{g'} = \mathbf{d'G}$$

Hence

$$\mathbf{g} = \mathbf{G'd} \tag{9-39}$$

and

$$\mathbf{d} = (\mathbf{G'})^{-1}\mathbf{g} \tag{9-40}$$

In the example under consideration, Eqs. (9-39) and (9-40) take the form

$$\begin{bmatrix} g_1 \\ g_2 \\ g_3 \end{bmatrix} = \begin{bmatrix} 1 & 1 & 1 \\ -1 & 0 & 1 \\ 1 & -1 & 1 \end{bmatrix} \cdot \begin{bmatrix} d_1 \\ d_2 \\ d_3 \end{bmatrix} \tag{9-41a}$$

and

$$\begin{bmatrix} d_1 \\ d_2 \\ d_3 \end{bmatrix} = \begin{bmatrix} \frac{1}{4} & -\frac{1}{2} & \frac{1}{4} \\ \frac{1}{2} & 0 & -\frac{1}{2} \\ \frac{1}{4} & \frac{1}{2} & \frac{1}{4} \end{bmatrix} \cdot \begin{bmatrix} g_1 \\ g_2 \\ g_3 \end{bmatrix} \tag{9-41b}$$

It is left to the reader to check that the work $\mathbf{d'f}$ done by the forces $\mathbf{f}$ in moving through the displacements $\mathbf{d}$ is equal to the work $\mathbf{g'r}$ done by the generalized force groups $\mathbf{r}$ moving through the generalized displacements $\mathbf{g}$.

With the help of Eq. (9-41*b*) we can compute the components in the directions of d_1, d_2, and d_3 of the generalized displacements. When $g_1 = 1$ and $g_2 = g_3 = 0$, then

$$\begin{bmatrix} d_1 \\ d_2 \\ d_3 \end{bmatrix} = \begin{bmatrix} \frac{1}{4} \\ \frac{1}{2} \\ \frac{1}{4} \end{bmatrix}$$

and similarly for $g_2 = 1$ $(g_1 = g_3 = 0)$ and $g_3 = 1$ $(g_1 = g_2 = 0)$ we obtain

$$\begin{bmatrix} d_1 \\ d_2 \\ d_3 \end{bmatrix} = \begin{bmatrix} -\frac{1}{2} \\ 0 \\ \frac{1}{2} \end{bmatrix} \quad \text{and} \quad \begin{bmatrix} d_1 \\ d_2 \\ d_3 \end{bmatrix} = \begin{bmatrix} \frac{1}{4} \\ -\frac{1}{2} \\ \frac{1}{4} \end{bmatrix}$$

These results are illustrated in Fig. 9-19.

Choice of Redundant Force Groups. In Example 9-4, several of the possible statically determinate systems were illustrated in Fig. 9-15. The question of the choice of the statically determinate system and thus of the redundancies will now be discussed further with reference to the continuous beam shown in Fig. 9-20. The four supports are rigid, the beam has a constant stiffness EJ throughout, and external moments M_1 and M_2 are applied as shown. The beam is subdivided into the three

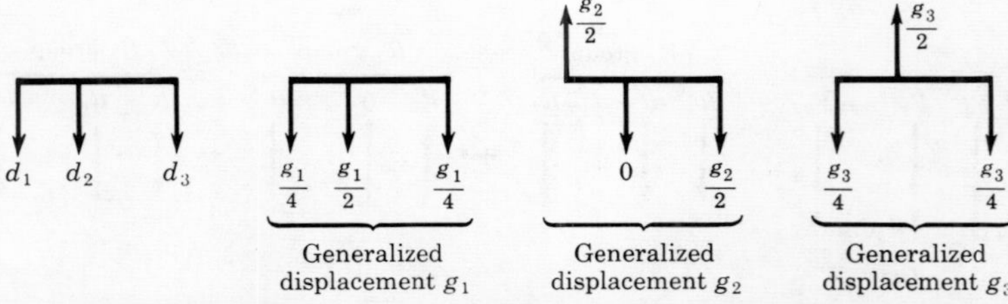

FIG. 9-19. Generalized displacements corresponding to the generalized forces.

FIG. 9-20. Continuous beam on rigid supports.

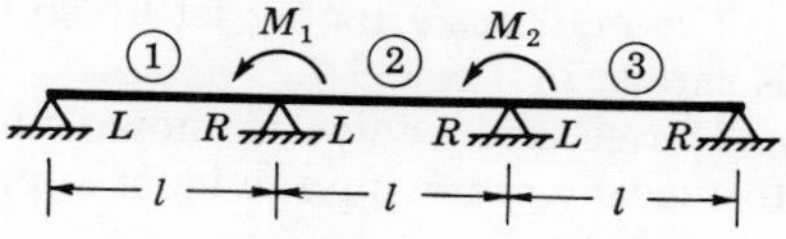

Bending stiffness EJ = constant throughout

beams 1, 2, and 3, each of length l and bending stiffness EJ. The bending moments at the left and right ends of the elements are used as the internal forces (cf. Fig. 9-8).

The first choice of a statically determinate system and suitable redundancies is shown in Fig. 9-21a. Hinges are formed at the rigid supports, the moment M_1 is applied at the right end of element 1, and the moment M_2 is applied at the right end of element 2. The matrix $\mathbf{B}_0$ calculated for this system is readily found to be

$$\begin{array}{c} \\ M_1^L \\ M_1^R \\ M_2^L \\ M_2^R \\ M_3^L \\ M_3^R \end{array} \begin{array}{c} \begin{array}{cc} M_1 & M_2 \end{array} \\ \begin{bmatrix} 0 & 0 \\ 1 & 0 \\ 0 & 0 \\ 0 & 1 \\ 0 & 0 \\ 0 & 0 \end{bmatrix} \end{array} = \mathbf{B}_0$$

Moment redundancies X_1 and X_2 must be introduced to provide the continuity at the supports. These are applied as shown in Fig. 9-21b and c, and the resulting matrix $\mathbf{B}_1$ is then

$$\begin{array}{c} \\ M_1^L \\ M_1^R \\ M_2^L \\ M_2^R \\ M_3^L \\ M_3^R \end{array} \begin{array}{c} \begin{array}{cc} X_1 & X_2 \end{array} \\ \begin{bmatrix} 0 & 0 \\ -1 & 0 \\ 1 & 0 \\ 0 & -1 \\ 0 & 1 \\ 0 & 0 \end{bmatrix} \end{array} = \mathbf{B}_1$$

The flexibility matrix $\mathbf{F}_g$ for each of the elements is

$$\begin{bmatrix} \dfrac{\beta}{3} & \dfrac{-\beta}{6} \\ \dfrac{-\beta}{6} & \dfrac{\beta}{3} \end{bmatrix}$$

where $\beta = l/EJ$ [cf. Eq. (9-5a)].

FIG. 9-21. First choice of basic system and redundants.

The matrices are now set up so that the regular procedure can be followed. This is shown in Table 9-7.

The second choice is shown in Fig. 9-22. The statically determinate system is formed by removing the inner supports. The matrix $\mathbf{B}_0$ is then

Table 9-7. Matrix Scheme for System of Fig. 9-21

								$\frac{8}{15}$	$\frac{2}{15}$					M_1
								$\frac{-2}{15}$	$\frac{7}{15}$					M_2
						0	0	0	0	0	0	0	0	
						-1	0	$\frac{-8}{15}$	$\frac{-2}{15}$	1	0	$\frac{7}{15}$	$\frac{-2}{15}$	
						1	0	$\frac{8}{15}$	$\frac{2}{15}$	0	0	$\frac{8}{15}$	$\frac{2}{15}$	**p**
						0	-1	$\frac{2}{15}$	$\frac{-7}{15}$	0	1	$\frac{2}{15}$	$\frac{8}{15}$	
						0	1	$\frac{-2}{15}$	$\frac{7}{15}$	0	0	$\frac{-2}{15}$	$\frac{7}{15}$	
						0	0	0	0	0	0	0	0	
$\frac{\beta}{3}$	$\frac{-\beta}{6}$					$\frac{\beta}{6}$	0			$\frac{-\beta}{6}$	0			
$\frac{-\beta}{6}$	$\frac{\beta}{3}$					$\frac{-\beta}{3}$	0			$\frac{\beta}{3}$	0			
		$\frac{\beta}{3}$	$\frac{-\beta}{6}$			$\frac{\beta}{3}$	$\frac{\beta}{6}$			0	$\frac{-\beta}{6}$			
		$\frac{-\beta}{6}$	$\frac{\beta}{3}$			$\frac{-\beta}{6}$	$\frac{-\beta}{3}$			0	$\frac{\beta}{3}$			
				$\frac{\beta}{3}$	$\frac{-\beta}{6}$	0	$\frac{\beta}{3}$	$\frac{8}{15}$	$\frac{2}{15}$	0	0			
				$\frac{-\beta}{6}$	$\frac{\beta}{3}$	0	$\frac{-\beta}{6}$	$\frac{-2}{15}$	$\frac{7}{15}$	0	0			
0	1	0	0	0	0	$\frac{-\beta}{3}$	0	$\frac{-8\beta}{45}$	$\frac{-2\beta}{45}$	$\frac{\beta}{3}$	0	$\frac{7\beta}{45}$	$\frac{-2\beta}{45}$	**d**
0	0	0	1	0	0	$\frac{-\beta}{6}$	$\frac{-\beta}{3}$	$\frac{-2\beta}{45}$	$\frac{-8\beta}{45}$	0	$\frac{\beta}{3}$	$\frac{-2\beta}{45}$	$\frac{7\beta}{45}$	
0	-1	1	0	0	0	$\frac{2\beta}{3}$	$\frac{\beta}{6}$			$\frac{-\beta}{3}$	$\frac{-\beta}{6}$			
0	0	0	-1	1	0	$\frac{\beta}{6}$	$\frac{2\beta}{3}$			0	$\frac{-\beta}{3}$			
						$\frac{-8}{5\beta}$	$\frac{2}{5\beta}$			$\frac{8}{15}$	$\frac{2}{15}$			
						$\frac{2}{5\beta}$	$\frac{-8}{5\beta}$			$\frac{-2}{15}$	$\frac{7}{15}$			

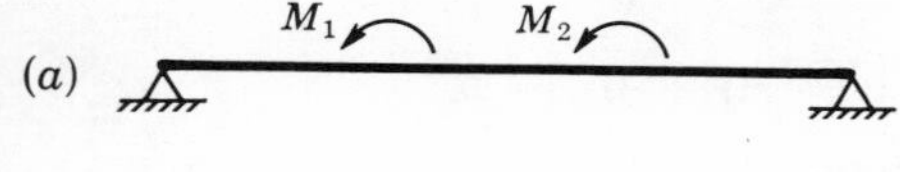

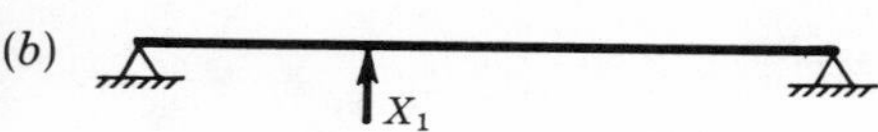

FIG. 9-22. Second choice of basic system and redundants.

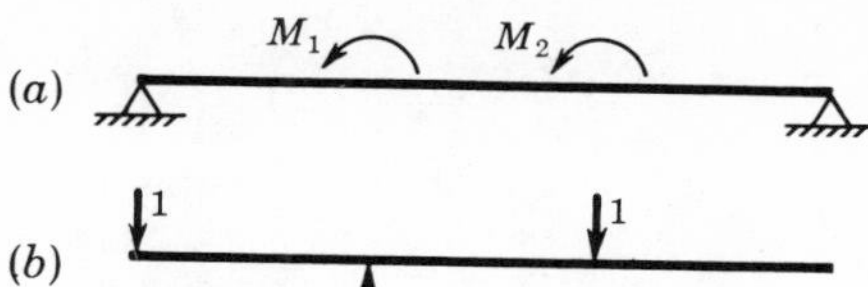

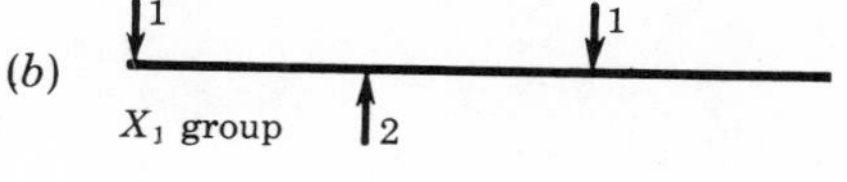

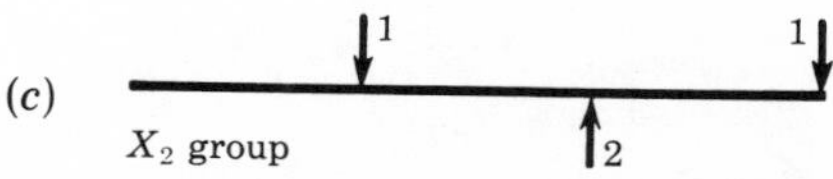

FIG. 9-23. Third choice of basic system and redundants.

$$\begin{array}{c} \\ M_1^L \\ M_1^R \\ M_2^L \\ M_2^R \\ M_3^L \\ M_3^R \end{array} \begin{array}{c} \begin{array}{cc} M_1 & M_2 \end{array} \\ \begin{bmatrix} 0 & 0 \\ \frac{1}{3} & \frac{1}{3} \\ \frac{2}{3} & -\frac{1}{3} \\ -\frac{1}{3} & \frac{2}{3} \\ \frac{1}{3} & \frac{1}{3} \\ 0 & 0 \end{bmatrix} \end{array} = \mathbf{B}_0$$

On this occasion the inner-support reactions are used as the redundancies. The matrix $\mathbf{B}_1$ for these redundancies is

$$\begin{array}{c} \\ M_1^L \\ M_1^R \\ M_2^L \\ M_2^R \\ M_3^L \\ M_3^R \end{array} \begin{array}{c} \begin{array}{cc} X_1 & X_2 \end{array} \\ \begin{bmatrix} 0 & 0 \\ \dfrac{-2l}{3} & \dfrac{-l}{3} \\ \dfrac{2l}{3} & \dfrac{l}{3} \\ \dfrac{-l}{3} & \dfrac{-2l}{3} \\ \dfrac{l}{3} & \dfrac{2l}{3} \\ 0 & 0 \end{bmatrix} \end{array} = \mathbf{B}_1$$

The flexibility matrix $\mathbf{F}_v$ remains unaltered, and the matrix calculations this time are as shown in Table 9-8. As a matter of course, the matrix **B** and the flexibility matrix $\mathbf{F}_d$ are found to be the same in both cases.

In the third choice (Fig. 9-23) the basic system is the same as for the second case (cf. Fig. 9-22*a*). The redundants are different, however, and consist of the self-equilibrating force groups shown in Fig. 9-23*b* and *c*. The matrices $\mathbf{B}_0$ and $\mathbf{B}_1$ in this case are

$$\begin{array}{c} \\ M_1^L \\ M_1^R \\ M_2^L \\ M_2^R \\ M_3^L \\ M_3^R \end{array}\begin{array}{c} \begin{array}{cc} M_1 & M_2 \end{array} \\ \left[\begin{array}{cc} 0 & 0 \\ \frac{1}{3} & \frac{1}{3} \\ \frac{2}{3} & -\frac{1}{3} \\ -\frac{1}{3} & \frac{2}{3} \\ \frac{1}{3} & \frac{1}{3} \\ 0 & 0 \end{array}\right] \end{array} = \mathbf{B}_0 \qquad \begin{array}{c} \\ M_1^L \\ M_1^R \\ M_2^L \\ M_2^R \\ M_3^L \\ M_3^R \end{array}\begin{array}{c} \begin{array}{cc} X_1 & X_2 \end{array} \\ \left[\begin{array}{cc} 0 & 0 \\ -l & 0 \\ l & 0 \\ 0 & -l \\ 0 & l \\ 0 & 0 \end{array}\right] \end{array} = \mathbf{B}_1$$

Table 9-8. Matrix Scheme for System of Fig. 9-22

								$\frac{1}{5l}$	$\frac{4}{5l}$					M_1
								$\frac{-4}{5l}$	$\frac{-1}{5l}$					M_2
						0	0	0	0	0	0	0	0	
						$\frac{-2l}{3}$	$\frac{-l}{3}$	$\frac{2}{15}$	$\frac{-7}{15}$	$\frac{1}{3}$	$\frac{1}{3}$	$\frac{7}{15}$	$\frac{-2}{15}$	
						$\frac{2l}{3}$	$\frac{l}{3}$	$\frac{-2}{15}$	$\frac{7}{15}$	$\frac{2}{3}$	$\frac{-1}{3}$	$\frac{8}{15}$	$\frac{2}{15}$	**p**
						$\frac{-l}{3}$	$\frac{-2l}{3}$	$\frac{7}{15}$	$\frac{-2}{15}$	$\frac{-1}{3}$	$\frac{2}{3}$	$\frac{2}{15}$	$\frac{8}{15}$	
						$\frac{l}{3}$	$\frac{2l}{3}$	$\frac{-7}{15}$	$\frac{2}{15}$	$\frac{1}{3}$	$\frac{1}{3}$	$\frac{-2}{15}$	$\frac{7}{15}$	
						0	0	0	0	0	0	0	0	
$\frac{\beta}{3}$	$\frac{-\beta}{6}$					$\frac{\beta l}{9}$	$\frac{\beta l}{18}$			$\frac{-\beta}{18}$	$\frac{-\beta}{18}$			
$\frac{-\beta}{6}$	$\frac{\beta}{3}$					$\frac{-2\beta l}{9}$	$\frac{-\beta l}{9}$			$\frac{\beta}{9}$	$\frac{\beta}{9}$			
		$\frac{\beta}{3}$	$\frac{-\beta}{6}$			$\frac{5\beta l}{18}$	$\frac{2\beta l}{9}$			$\frac{5\beta}{18}$	$\frac{-2\beta}{9}$			
		$\frac{-\beta}{6}$	$\frac{\beta}{3}$			$\frac{-2\beta l}{9}$	$\frac{5\beta l}{18}$			$\frac{-2\beta}{9}$	$\frac{5\beta}{18}$			
				$\frac{\beta}{3}$	$\frac{-\beta}{6}$	$\frac{\beta l}{9}$	$\frac{2\beta l}{9}$	$\frac{1}{5l}$	$\frac{4}{5l}$	$\frac{\beta}{9}$	$\frac{\beta}{9}$			
				$\frac{-\beta}{6}$	$\frac{\beta}{3}$	$\frac{-\beta l}{18}$	$\frac{-\beta l}{9}$	$\frac{-4}{5l}$	$\frac{-1}{5l}$	$\frac{-\beta}{18}$	$\frac{-\beta}{18}$			
0	$\frac{1}{3}$	$\frac{2}{3}$	$\frac{-1}{3}$	$\frac{1}{3}$	0	$\frac{2\beta l}{9}$	$\frac{5\beta l}{18}$	$\frac{8\beta}{45}$	$\frac{11\beta}{90}$	$\frac{\beta}{3}$	$\frac{-\beta}{6}$	$\frac{7\beta}{45}$	$\frac{-2\beta}{45}$	**d**
0	$\frac{1}{3}$	$\frac{-1}{3}$	$\frac{2}{3}$	$\frac{1}{3}$	0	$\frac{-5\beta l}{18}$	$\frac{-2\beta l}{9}$	$\frac{11\beta}{90}$	$\frac{-8\beta}{45}$	$\frac{-\beta}{6}$	$\frac{\beta}{3}$	$\frac{-2\beta}{45}$	$\frac{7\beta}{45}$	
0	$\frac{-2l}{3}$	$\frac{2l}{3}$	$\frac{-l}{3}$	$\frac{l}{3}$	0	$\frac{4\beta l^2}{9}$	$\frac{7\beta l^2}{18}$			$\frac{2\beta l}{9}$	$\frac{-5\beta l}{18}$			
0	$\frac{-l}{3}$	$\frac{l}{3}$	$\frac{-2l}{3}$	$\frac{2l}{3}$	0	$\frac{7\beta l^2}{18}$	$\frac{4\beta l^2}{9}$			$\frac{5\beta l}{18}$	$\frac{-2\beta l}{9}$			
						$\frac{-48}{5\beta l^2}$	$\frac{42}{5\beta l^2}$			$\frac{1}{5l}$	$\frac{4}{5l}$			
						$\frac{42}{5\beta l^2}$	$\frac{-48}{5\beta l^2}$			$\frac{-4}{5l}$	$\frac{-1}{5l}$			

and since the flexibility matrix $\mathbf{F}_v$ is the same as in the previous two cases, the matrix calculations take the form shown in Table 9-9.

The continuous beam of Fig. 9-20 has been analyzed using different basic systems and redundant groups. We shall now discuss the advantages and disadvantages of the three systems considered. Fundamentally it can be stated that a good choice has been made in the basic system if the matrix $\mathbf{B}_0$ is easy to calculate. We are readily convinced that the calculation of the matrix $\mathbf{B}_0$ for the system of Fig. 9-21*a* is easier than for the system of Figs. 9-22 and 9-23.

Table 9-9. Matrix Scheme for System of Fig. 9-23

								$\frac{-2}{15l}$	$\frac{7}{15l}$					M_1
								$\frac{-7}{15l}$	$\frac{2}{15l}$					M_2
						0	0	0	0	0	0	0	0	
						$-l$	0	$\frac{2}{15}$	$\frac{-7}{15}$	$\frac{1}{3}$	$\frac{1}{3}$	$\frac{7}{15}$	$\frac{-2}{15}$	
						l	0	$\frac{-2}{15}$	$\frac{7}{15}$	$\frac{2}{3}$	$\frac{-1}{3}$	$\frac{8}{15}$	$\frac{2}{15}$	**p**
						0	$-l$	$\frac{7}{15}$	$\frac{-2}{15}$	$\frac{-1}{3}$	$\frac{2}{3}$	$\frac{2}{15}$	$\frac{8}{15}$	
						0	l	$\frac{-7}{15}$	$\frac{2}{15}$	$\frac{1}{3}$	$\frac{1}{3}$	$\frac{-2}{15}$	$\frac{7}{15}$	
						0	0	0	0	0	0	0	0	
$\frac{\beta}{3}$	$\frac{-\beta}{6}$					$\frac{\beta l}{6}$	0			$\frac{\beta}{18}$	$\frac{-\beta}{18}$			
$\frac{-\beta}{6}$	$\frac{\beta}{3}$					$\frac{-\beta l}{3}$	0			$\frac{\beta}{9}$	$\frac{\beta}{9}$			
		$\frac{\beta}{3}$	$\frac{-\beta}{6}$			$\frac{\beta l}{3}$	$\frac{\beta l}{6}$			$\frac{5\beta}{18}$	$\frac{-2\beta}{9}$			
		$\frac{-\beta}{6}$	$\frac{\beta}{3}$			$\frac{-\beta l}{6}$	$\frac{-\beta l}{3}$			$\frac{-2\beta}{9}$	$\frac{5\beta}{18}$			
				$\frac{\beta}{3}$	$\frac{-\beta}{6}$	0	$\frac{\beta l}{3}$	$\frac{-2}{15l}$	$\frac{7}{15l}$	$\frac{\beta}{9}$	$\frac{\beta}{9}$			
				$\frac{-\beta}{6}$	$\frac{\beta}{3}$	0	$\frac{-\beta l}{6}$	$\frac{-7}{15l}$	$\frac{2}{15l}$	$\frac{-\beta}{18}$	$\frac{-\beta}{18}$			
0	$\frac{1}{3}$	$\frac{2}{3}$	$\frac{-1}{3}$	$\frac{1}{3}$	0	$\frac{\beta l}{6}$	$\frac{\beta l}{3}$	$\frac{-8\beta}{45}$	$\frac{11\beta}{90}$	$\frac{\beta}{3}$	$\frac{-\beta}{6}$	$\frac{7\beta}{45}$	$\frac{-2\beta}{45}$	**d**
0	$\frac{1}{3}$	$\frac{-1}{3}$	$\frac{2}{3}$	$\frac{1}{3}$	0	$\frac{-\beta l}{3}$	$\frac{-\beta l}{6}$	$\frac{11\beta}{90}$	$\frac{-8\beta}{45}$	$\frac{-\beta}{6}$	$\frac{\beta}{3}$	$\frac{-2\beta}{45}$	$\frac{7\beta}{45}$	
0	$-l$	l	0	0	0	$\frac{2\beta l^2}{3}$	$\frac{\beta l^2}{6}$			$\frac{\beta l}{6}$	$\frac{-\beta l}{3}$			
0	0	0	$-l$	l	0	$\frac{\beta l^2}{6}$	$\frac{2\beta l^2}{3}$			$\frac{\beta l}{3}$	$\frac{-\beta l}{6}$			
						$\frac{-8}{5\beta l^2}$	$\frac{2}{5\beta l^2}$			$\frac{-2}{15l}$	$\frac{7}{15l}$			
						$\frac{2}{5\beta l^2}$	$\frac{-8}{5\beta l^2}$			$\frac{-7}{15l}$	$\frac{2}{15l}$			

When choosing redundant force groups,† we should again be guided by the amount of effort involved in calculating the matrix $\mathbf{B}_1$. On this account we should choose redundancies that affect as few elements of the system as possible. In the case of Fig. 9-21 each moment redundancy affects only two members and the matrix $\mathbf{B}_1$ is very simple to calculate. In the case of Fig. 9-22 each of the redundancies X_1 and X_2 has an effect on all three members of the continuous beam. If it were longer and resting on a large number of supports, then a redundant force of this type would affect all its elements, and the formulation of the matrix $\mathbf{B}_1$ would be a lengthy procedure. However, if the self-equilibrating redundant groups that are shown in Fig. 9-23 are used, then only two elements are affected by each group, no matter how long the beam is. It is easy to appreciate this point by comparing the matrices $\mathbf{B}_1$ belonging to Figs. 9-22 and 9-23. Hence, in this problem, the basic system and redundancies of Fig. 9-21 would be the best choice, followed by those of Figs. 9-23 and 9-22. This is also evident from the matrix schemes of Tables 9-7 to 9-9.

9-5. The Effect of Modifications of the Elements on the Stress Distribution and the Flexibility

Very often it is necessary after initial design to modify certain elements of the original system, and the question then arises as to whether it is possible to find the new internal forces and flexibility without recomputing the modified structure.‡

Let us suppose that the analysis of the original system, when subjected to an external loading $\mathbf{f}$, has already been completed. Now let j of the total number of s elements be modified while i remain unchanged ($j + i = s$). As a result of the changes in the flexibility of the j elements, the new internal forces and deformations of the modified structure are $\mathbf{p}^*$ and $\mathbf{v}^*$. The flexibility matrix $\mathbf{F}_v^*$ of the unassembled elements of the modified structure is partitioned into the form

$$\mathbf{F}_v^* = \left[\begin{array}{c|c} \mathbf{F}_{vi}^* & \mathbf{0} \\ \hline \mathbf{0} & \mathbf{F}_{vj}^* \end{array}\right] = \left[\begin{array}{c|c} \mathbf{F}_{vi} & \mathbf{0} \\ \hline \mathbf{0} & \mathbf{F}_{vj} + \Delta\mathbf{F}_{vj} \end{array}\right] \tag{9-42}$$

where $\mathbf{F}_{vi}$ is the flexibility matrix of the i unmodified elements and $\Delta\mathbf{F}_{vj}$ is the change in the flexibility matrix of the modified elements. Partitioning the $\mathbf{p}^*$ and $\mathbf{v}^*$ columns into the i and j elements gives the relation

$$\left[\begin{array}{c} \mathbf{v}_i^* \\ \hline \mathbf{v}_j^* \end{array}\right] = \left[\begin{array}{c|c} \mathbf{F}_{vi} & \mathbf{0} \\ \hline \mathbf{0} & \mathbf{F}_{vj} + \Delta\mathbf{F}_{vj} \end{array}\right] \cdot \left[\begin{array}{c} \mathbf{p}_i^* \\ \hline \mathbf{p}_j^* \end{array}\right]$$

Hence
$$\mathbf{v}_i^* = \mathbf{F}_{vi}\mathbf{p}_i^* \tag{9-43}$$

and
$$\mathbf{v}_j^* = (\mathbf{F}_{vj} + \Delta\mathbf{F}_{vj})\mathbf{p}_j^* \tag{9-44}$$

In Sec. 9-3 we learned that, without changing the flexibility of the individual elements, the internal forces and deformations can also be modified by impressing initial deformations on some or all structural members. Let us therefore now return to the original structure, where we impose, in addition to the external loading $\mathbf{f}$, the initial deformations $\mathbf{h} = \left[\begin{array}{c} \mathbf{0} \\ \hline \mathbf{h}_j \end{array}\right]$ on the j elements that are altered in the modified

† Force groups that appear in aircraft structures are very fully discussed in Refs. 48 and 51.

‡ The analysis to be developed now is also very helpful in certain aircraft calculations [50].

structure. As a result of these initial deformations the internal forces $\bar{\mathbf{p}}$ and deformations $\bar{\mathbf{v}}$ are given by the relations [cf. Eqs. (9-35), (9-12), and (9-14)]

$$\bar{\mathbf{p}} = \mathbf{B}\mathbf{f} - \mathbf{B}_1\mathbf{D}_{11}^{-1}\mathbf{B}_1'\mathbf{h} \tag{9-45}$$

$$\bar{\mathbf{v}} = \mathbf{F}_v\bar{\mathbf{p}} + \mathbf{h} \tag{9-46}$$

The matrices $\mathbf{B}$, $\mathbf{B}_1$, and $\mathbf{F}_v$, which are known for the original structure, are partitioned into the form

$$\mathbf{B} = \begin{bmatrix} \mathbf{B}_i \\ \hline \mathbf{B}_j \end{bmatrix} \qquad \mathbf{B}_1 = \begin{bmatrix} \mathbf{B}_{1i} \\ \hline \mathbf{B}_{1j} \end{bmatrix} \qquad \mathbf{F}_v = \left[\begin{array}{c|c} \mathbf{F}_{vi} & \mathbf{0} \\ \hline \mathbf{0} & \mathbf{F}_{vj} \end{array}\right] \tag{9-47}$$

so that Eq. (9-45) becomes

$$\begin{bmatrix} \bar{\mathbf{p}}_i \\ \hline \bar{\mathbf{p}}_j \end{bmatrix} = \begin{bmatrix} \mathbf{B}_i \\ \hline \mathbf{B}_j \end{bmatrix} \mathbf{f} - \begin{bmatrix} \mathbf{B}_{1i} \\ \hline \mathbf{B}_{1j} \end{bmatrix} \mathbf{D}_{11}^{-1} \left[\mathbf{B}_{1i}' \;\middle|\; \mathbf{B}_{1j}'\right] \begin{bmatrix} \mathbf{0} \\ \hline \mathbf{h}_j \end{bmatrix}$$

which on expansion gives

$$\bar{\mathbf{p}}_i = \mathbf{B}_i\mathbf{f} - \mathbf{B}_{1i}\mathbf{D}_{11}^{-1}\mathbf{B}_{1j}'\mathbf{h}_j \tag{9-45a}$$

$$\bar{\mathbf{p}}_j = \mathbf{B}_j\mathbf{f} - \mathbf{B}_{1j}\mathbf{D}_{11}^{-1}\mathbf{B}_{1j}'\mathbf{h}_j \tag{9-45b}$$

Also from Eq. (9-46)

$$\bar{\mathbf{v}}_i = \mathbf{F}_{vi}\bar{\mathbf{p}}_i \tag{9-46a}$$

and

$$\bar{\mathbf{v}}_j = \mathbf{F}_{vj}\bar{\mathbf{p}}_j + \mathbf{h}_j \tag{9-46b}$$

We shall now let the deformations $\mathbf{h}_j$ be such that, together with the external forces $\mathbf{f}$, they produce in the original structure internal forces $\bar{\mathbf{p}}_j$ equal to the internal forces $\mathbf{p}_j^*$ of the modified system under the sole action of the load $\mathbf{f}$. Furthermore we make the demand that simultaneously the deformations $\bar{\mathbf{v}}_j$ are to be equal to $\mathbf{v}_j^*$. If we can do this, then the internal forces and deformations of the j modified elements of the modified system under the load $\mathbf{f}$ are exactly equal to the internal forces and deformations of these j elements of the original system under the load $\mathbf{f}$ and with the initial deformations $\mathbf{h}_j$, so that the elements of the two systems are indistinguishable from one another, and the two systems behave in an identical manner. Hence not only $\mathbf{p}_j^* = \bar{\mathbf{p}}_j$ and $\mathbf{v}_j^* = \bar{\mathbf{v}}_j$, but also $\mathbf{p}^* = \bar{\mathbf{p}}$ and $\mathbf{v}^* = \bar{\mathbf{v}}$.

Hence from Eqs. (9-45*b*) and (9-46*b*)

$$\bar{\mathbf{p}}_j = \mathbf{p}_j^* = \mathbf{B}_j\mathbf{f} - \mathbf{B}_{1j}\mathbf{D}_{11}^{-1}\mathbf{B}_{1j}'\mathbf{h}_j \tag{9-48}$$

and

$$\bar{\mathbf{v}}_j = \mathbf{v}_j^* = \mathbf{F}_{vj}\bar{\mathbf{p}}_j + \mathbf{h}_j \tag{9-49}$$

Equating $\mathbf{v}_j^*$ from Eqs. (9-44) and (9-49) gives

$$\mathbf{F}_{vj}\bar{\mathbf{p}}_j + \mathbf{h}_j = (\mathbf{F}_{vj} + \Delta\mathbf{F}_{vj})\mathbf{p}_j^*$$

$$\therefore\ \Delta\mathbf{F}_{vj}\mathbf{p}_j^* = \mathbf{h}_j \tag{9-50}$$

Then from Eq. (9-48)

$$\Delta\mathbf{F}_{vj}\,[\mathbf{B}_j\mathbf{f} - \mathbf{B}_{1j}\mathbf{D}_{11}^{-1}\mathbf{B}_{1j}'\mathbf{h}_j] = \mathbf{h}_j$$

from which

$$\mathbf{h}_j = [\mathbf{B}_{1j}\mathbf{D}_{11}^{-1}\mathbf{B}_{1j}' + \Delta\mathbf{F}_{vj}^{-1}]^{-1}\mathbf{B}_j\mathbf{f}$$

Then using Eq. (9-45) we obtain the internal forces in the modified structure:

$$\bar{\mathbf{p}} = \mathbf{p}^* = \{\mathbf{B} - \mathbf{B}_1\mathbf{D}_{11}^{-1}\mathbf{B}_{1j}'[\mathbf{B}_{1j}\mathbf{D}_{11}^{-1}\mathbf{B}_{1j}' + \Delta\mathbf{F}_{vj}^{-1}]^{-1}\mathbf{B}_j\}\mathbf{f} = (\mathbf{B} + \Delta\mathbf{B})\mathbf{f} = \mathbf{B}^*\mathbf{f} \tag{9-51}$$

This result is not so formidable as appears at first sight. The inversion of $\mathbf{D}_{11}$ has already been made, and the size of the matrix

$$[\mathbf{B}_{1j}\mathbf{D}_{11}^{-1}\mathbf{B}_{1j}' + \Delta\mathbf{F}_{vj}^{-1}]^{-1}$$

which depends on the number of modifications, will be small if the number of modifications is small.

The flexibility matrix $\mathbf{F}_d^*$ of the modified structure is readily found by adding the deflections $\mathbf{d}$ of the original system when subjected to forces $\mathbf{f}$ and the deflections $\mathbf{d}_h$ induced by the initial strains $\mathbf{h}$ [cf. Eq. (9-37)]:

$$\begin{aligned}\mathbf{d}^* &= \mathbf{F}_d\mathbf{f} + \mathbf{B}'\mathbf{h} = \mathbf{F}_d\mathbf{f} + \mathbf{B}_j'\mathbf{h}_j = \{\mathbf{F}_d + \mathbf{B}_j'[\mathbf{B}_{1j}\mathbf{D}_{11}^{-1}\mathbf{B}_{1j}' + \Delta\mathbf{F}_{vj}^{-1}]^{-1}\mathbf{B}_j\}\mathbf{f} \\ &= (\mathbf{F}_d + \Delta\mathbf{F}_d)\mathbf{f} = \mathbf{F}_d^*\mathbf{f}\end{aligned} \tag{9-52}$$

The matrix operations of Eqs. (9-51) and (9-52) are illustrated in Table 9-10.

It is worthwhile to state $\Delta\mathbf{F}_d$ for the two limiting cases:

Table 9-10

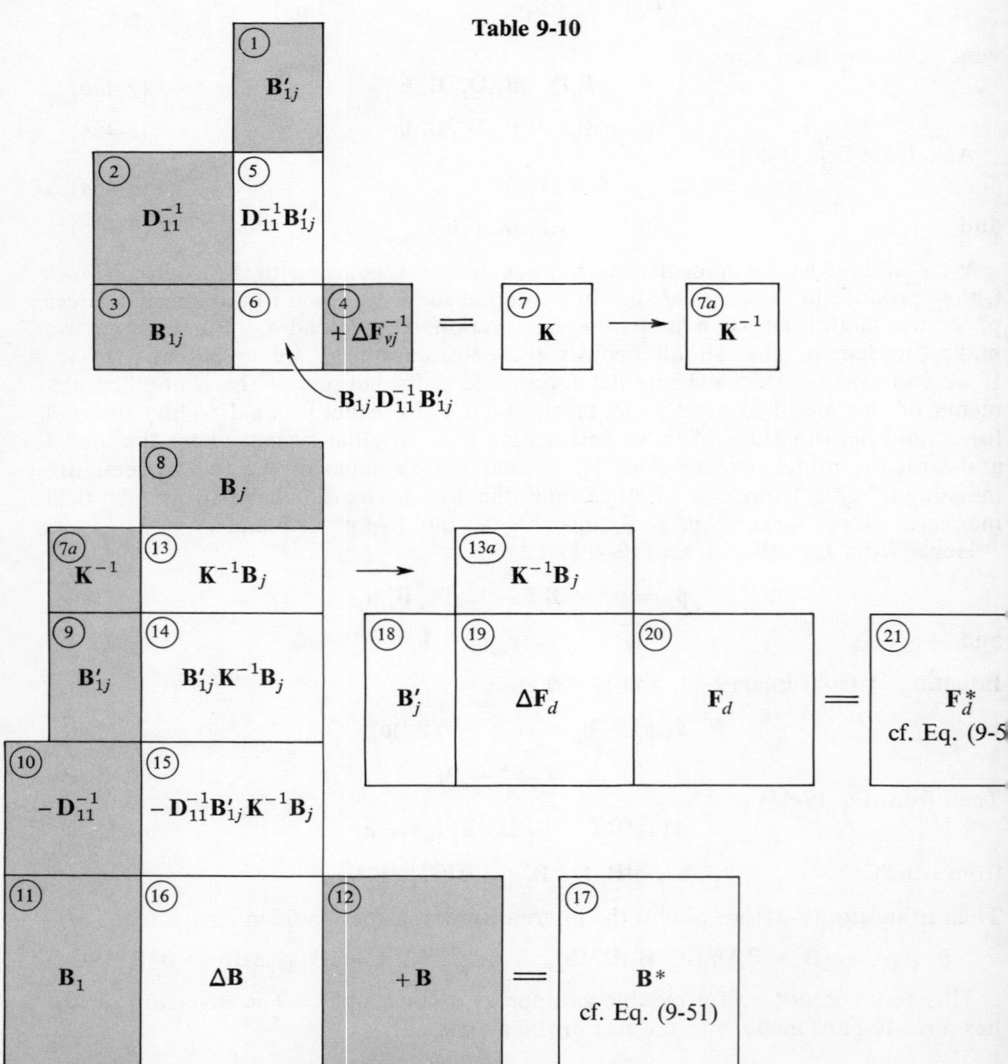

Elimination of j elements

$$\Delta\mathbf{F}_{vj} \to \infty \qquad \text{or} \qquad \Delta\mathbf{F}_{vj}^{-1} = \mathbf{0}$$

That is, block 4 drops out in the scheme of Table 9-10. Hence

$$\Delta\mathbf{F}_d = \mathbf{B}_j'[\mathbf{B}_{1j}\mathbf{D}_{11}^{-1}\mathbf{B}_{1j}']^{-1}\mathbf{B}_j \tag{9-53}$$

Rigidification of j elements

$$\mathbf{F}_{vj} + \Delta\mathbf{F}_{vj} = \mathbf{0} \qquad \text{or} \qquad \Delta\mathbf{F}_{vj} = -\mathbf{F}_{vj}$$

Hence

$$\Delta\mathbf{F}_d = \mathbf{B}_j'[\mathbf{B}_{1j}\mathbf{D}_{11}^{-1}\mathbf{B}_{1j}' - \mathbf{F}_{vj}^{-1}]^{-1}\mathbf{B}_j \tag{9-54}$$

Example 9-6. Compute the new matrix $\mathbf{B}^*$ and new flexibility matrix $\mathbf{F}_d^*$ when member 2 is removed from the structure of Fig. 9-14. In this case we have

$$\mathbf{B}_{1j} = [1 \quad 0]$$

which is the second row of $\mathbf{B}_1$ (cf. matrix $\mathbf{B}_1$ in Table 9-3). Also from previous calculations in Example 9-4 (cf. Table 9-6)

$$\mathbf{D}_{11}^{-1} = \begin{bmatrix} \dfrac{2}{15\alpha} & 0 \\ 0 & \dfrac{480}{521\beta} \end{bmatrix} \qquad \mathbf{B}_j = \begin{bmatrix} -\frac{7}{15} & \frac{2}{15} & 0 \end{bmatrix}$$

and hence from Eq. (9-53) the expression for $\Delta\mathbf{F}_d$ is obtained as shown in Table 9-11.

Table 9-11

$$\mathbf{B}_{1j}' = \begin{bmatrix} 1 \\ 0 \end{bmatrix}$$

$$\mathbf{D}_{11}^{-1} = \begin{bmatrix} \dfrac{2}{15\alpha} & 0 \\ 0 & \dfrac{480}{521\beta} \end{bmatrix} \begin{bmatrix} \dfrac{2}{15\alpha} \\ 0 \end{bmatrix}$$

$$\mathbf{B}_{1j} = \begin{bmatrix} 1 & 0 \end{bmatrix} \begin{bmatrix} \dfrac{2}{15\alpha} \end{bmatrix} = \mathbf{K} \qquad \mathbf{K}^{-1} = \begin{bmatrix} \dfrac{15\alpha}{2} \end{bmatrix}$$

$$\mathbf{B}_j = \begin{bmatrix} \dfrac{-7}{15} & \dfrac{2}{15} & 0 \end{bmatrix}$$

$$\mathbf{K}^{-1} = \begin{bmatrix} \dfrac{15\alpha}{2} \end{bmatrix} \begin{bmatrix} \dfrac{-7\alpha}{2} & \alpha & 0 \end{bmatrix}$$

$$\mathbf{B}_j' = \begin{bmatrix} \dfrac{-7}{15} \\ \dfrac{2}{15} \\ 0 \end{bmatrix} \underbrace{\begin{bmatrix} \dfrac{49\alpha}{30} & \dfrac{-7\alpha}{15} & 0 \\ \dfrac{-7\alpha}{15} & \dfrac{2\alpha}{15} & 0 \\ 0 & 0 & 0 \end{bmatrix}}_{\Delta\mathbf{F}_d} + \underbrace{\begin{bmatrix} 68.182\alpha & -1.292\alpha & 7.366\alpha \\ -1.292\alpha & 1.366\alpha & 0.278\alpha \\ 7.366\alpha & 0.278\alpha & 4.290\alpha \end{bmatrix}}_{\mathbf{F}_d}$$

$$= \begin{bmatrix} 69.815\alpha & -1.758\alpha & 7.366\alpha \\ -1.758\alpha & 1.499\alpha & 0.278\alpha \\ 7.366\alpha & 0.278\alpha & 4.290\alpha \end{bmatrix} = \mathbf{F}_d$$

Equally, with the aid of Table 9-10, we now compute matrix $\mathbf{B}^*$, as shown in Table 9-12. In the new structure the forces in the members 1, 3, 4, and 5 are easily determined by simple statics, and these are found to coincide with those obtained by the above calculations.

The Design of a Structure to Meet Certain Stress Conditions [53]. By a small extension the foregoing theory can be used to find the structural modifications that should be made in order that given stress conditions may prevail at certain points of

Table 9-12

$$\mathbf{B}_j = \begin{bmatrix} \frac{-7}{15} & \frac{2}{15} & 0 \end{bmatrix}$$

$$\mathbf{K}^{-1} = \begin{bmatrix} \frac{15\alpha}{2} \end{bmatrix} \begin{bmatrix} \frac{-7\alpha}{2} & \alpha & 0 \end{bmatrix}$$

$$\mathbf{B}'_{1j} = \begin{bmatrix} 1 \\ 0 \end{bmatrix} \begin{bmatrix} \frac{-7\alpha}{2} & \alpha & 0 \\ 0 & 0 & 0 \end{bmatrix}$$

$$-\mathbf{D}_{11}^{-1} = \begin{bmatrix} \frac{-2}{15\alpha} & 0 \\ 0 & \frac{-480}{521\beta} \end{bmatrix} \begin{bmatrix} \frac{7}{15} & \frac{-2}{15} & 0 \\ 0 & 0 & 0 \end{bmatrix}$$

$$\mathbf{B}_1 = \begin{bmatrix} 1 & 0 \\ 1 & 0 \\ 1 & 0 \\ -\sqrt{2} & 0 \\ -\sqrt{2} & 0 \\ 1 & 0 \\ 0 & 0 \\ 0 & \frac{1}{2} \\ 1 & 0 \\ 0 & \frac{-1}{2} \\ 0 & 1 \\ 0 & \frac{1}{l} \\ 0 & -1 \\ 0 & 1 \end{bmatrix} \underbrace{\begin{bmatrix} \frac{7}{15} & \frac{-2}{15} & 0 \\ \frac{7}{15} & \frac{-2}{15} & 0 \\ \frac{7}{15} & \frac{-2}{15} & 0 \\ \frac{-7\sqrt{2}}{15} & \frac{2\sqrt{2}}{15} & 0 \\ \frac{-7\sqrt{2}}{15} & \frac{2\sqrt{2}}{15} & 0 \\ \frac{7}{15} & \frac{-2}{15} & 0 \\ 0 & 0 & 0 \\ 0 & 0 & 0 \\ \frac{7}{15} & \frac{-2}{15} & 0 \\ 0 & 0 & 0 \\ 0 & 0 & 0 \\ 0 & 0 & 0 \\ 0 & 0 & 0 \\ 0 & 0 & 0 \end{bmatrix}}_{\Delta\mathbf{B}} + \underbrace{\begin{bmatrix} \frac{-7}{15} & \frac{2}{15} & 0 \\ \frac{-7}{15} & \frac{2}{15} & 0 \\ \frac{8}{15} & \frac{-13}{15} & 0 \\ \frac{-8\sqrt{2}}{15} & \frac{-2\sqrt{2}}{15} & 0 \\ \frac{7\sqrt{2}}{15} & \frac{-2\sqrt{2}}{15} & 0 \\ \frac{8}{15} & \frac{2}{15} & 0 \\ 0 & 0 & 0 \\ \frac{538l}{2{,}084} & \frac{l}{1{,}042} & \frac{462l}{2{,}084} \\ \frac{8}{15} & \frac{2}{15} & 0 \\ \frac{-538l}{2{,}084} & \frac{-l}{521} & \frac{-462l}{2{,}084} \\ \frac{538l}{1{,}042} & \frac{l}{521} & \frac{-59l}{1{,}042} \\ \frac{790}{521} & \frac{-520}{521} & \frac{-240}{521} \\ \frac{-538l}{1{,}042} & \frac{-l}{521} & \frac{59l}{1{,}042} \\ \frac{-1{,}025l}{1{,}042} & \frac{l}{521} & \frac{-59l}{1{,}042} \end{bmatrix}}_{\mathbf{B}} = \underbrace{\begin{bmatrix} 0 & 0 & 0 \\ 0 & 0 & 0 \\ 1 & -1 & 0 \\ -\sqrt{2} & 0 & 0 \\ 0 & 0 & 0 \\ 1 & 0 & 0 \\ 0 & 0 & 0 \\ \frac{538l}{2{,}084} & \frac{l}{1{,}042} & \frac{462l}{2{,}084} \\ 1 & 0 & 0 \\ \frac{-538l}{2{,}084} & \frac{-l}{521} & \frac{-462l}{2{,}084} \\ \frac{538l}{1{,}042} & \frac{l}{521} & \frac{-59l}{1{,}042} \\ \frac{790}{521} & \frac{-520}{521} & \frac{-240}{521} \\ \frac{-538l}{1{,}042} & \frac{-l}{521} & \frac{59l}{1{,}042} \\ \frac{-1{,}025l}{1{,}042} & \frac{l}{521} & \frac{-59l}{1{,}042} \end{bmatrix}}_{\mathbf{B}^*}$$

the structure. This is useful when after the first design it is found that some structural elements are overstressed or vice versa.

We suppose that the structure has been designed and that structural modifications are to be made to j elements in each of which at least one stress is to attain a given fixed value, and that i elements are to remain unaltered. Following the procedure of the previous section, we have from Eqs. (9-48) and (9-50) that

$$\mathbf{p}_j^* = \mathbf{B}_j\mathbf{f} - \mathbf{B}_{1j}\mathbf{D}_{11}^{-1}\mathbf{B}_{1j}'\mathbf{h}_j = \mathbf{B}_j\mathbf{f} - \mathbf{B}_{1j}\mathbf{D}_{11}^{-1}\mathbf{B}_{1j}'\,\Delta\mathbf{F}_{vj}\,\mathbf{p}_j^* = \mathbf{B}_j\mathbf{f} - \mathbf{B}_{1j}\mathbf{D}_{11}^{-1}\mathbf{B}_{1j}'(\mathbf{F}_{vj}^* - \mathbf{F}_{vj})\mathbf{p}_j^*$$

The product $\mathbf{F}_{vj}^*\mathbf{p}_j^*$ is equal to the deformations $\mathbf{v}_j^*$, which, in turn, are proportional to the stresses in the j modified elements of the structure. Let

$$\mathbf{F}_{vj}^*\mathbf{p}_j^* = \mathbf{v}_j^* = \mathbf{S}_j\boldsymbol{\sigma}_j^*$$

where the column matrix $\boldsymbol{\sigma}_j^*$ is composed of the stresses in the modified elements and $\mathbf{S}_j$ is the matrix that relates the deformations and the stresses of these elements. For example, consider the beam of Fig. 9-8. Its flexibility matrix is defined by the relation

$$\begin{bmatrix}\psi_2\\ \psi_3\end{bmatrix} = \begin{bmatrix}\dfrac{l}{3EJ} & \dfrac{-l}{6EJ}\\[2ex] \dfrac{-l}{6EJ} & \dfrac{l}{3EJ}\end{bmatrix}\cdot\begin{bmatrix}M_2\\ M_3\end{bmatrix}$$

The maximum bending stresses at the ends of the beam are obtained as

$$\sigma_2 = \frac{M_2}{J}\frac{d}{2} \qquad \text{and} \qquad \sigma_3 = \frac{M_3}{J}\frac{d}{2}$$

where d is the depth of the beam, so that

$$\begin{bmatrix}\psi_2\\ \psi_3\end{bmatrix} = \begin{bmatrix}\dfrac{2l}{3Ed} & \dfrac{-l}{3Ed}\\[2ex] \dfrac{-l}{3Ed} & \dfrac{2l}{3Ed}\end{bmatrix}\cdot\begin{bmatrix}\sigma_2\\ \sigma_3\end{bmatrix} \qquad \text{or} \qquad \mathbf{v} = \mathbf{S}\boldsymbol{\sigma}$$

Hence, provided the length and depth of the beam remain unaltered, $\mathbf{S}$ is a constant irrespective of the value of the moment of inertia J. With $\mathbf{F}_{vj}^*\mathbf{p}_j^* = \mathbf{S}_j\boldsymbol{\sigma}_j^*$ we may now rewrite the equation for $\mathbf{p}_j^*$:

$$\mathbf{p}_j^* = \mathbf{B}_j\mathbf{f} - \mathbf{B}_{1j}\mathbf{D}_{11}^{-1}\mathbf{B}_{1j}'\mathbf{S}_j\boldsymbol{\sigma}_j^* + \mathbf{B}_{1j}\mathbf{D}_{11}^{-1}\mathbf{B}_{1j}'\mathbf{F}_{vj}\mathbf{p}_j^*$$

In the column vector $\boldsymbol{\sigma}_j^*$ some, but not necessarily all, stress components are given. For the case where all components of $\boldsymbol{\sigma}_j^*$ are prescribed, the above equation can be solved directly according to the equation

$$\mathbf{p}_j^* = (\mathbf{I} - \mathbf{B}_{1j}\mathbf{D}_{11}^{-1}\mathbf{B}_{1j}'\mathbf{F}_{vj})^{-1}(\mathbf{B}_j\mathbf{f} - \mathbf{B}_{1j}\mathbf{D}_{11}^{-1}\mathbf{B}_{1j}'\mathbf{S}_j\boldsymbol{\sigma}_j^*) \tag{9-55}$$

Having found the internal forces $\mathbf{p}_j^*$ to which the elements to be modified are subjected, their cross-sectional properties are computed by dividing these internal forces by the associated given stresses. If not all components of $\boldsymbol{\sigma}_j^*$ are given, the process of finding $\mathbf{p}_j^*$ becomes more difficult and can be carried out only by means of iteration. An example for this procedure is given in Sec. 11-6.

PROBLEMS

9-14. Compute the new flexibility matrix $\mathbf{F}_d^*$ and the new matrix $\mathbf{B}^*$ for the structure of Fig. P 9-5, when the cross-sectional areas of members 15 and 26 are doubled. The results of Prob. 9-5 should be used.

9-15. Repeat Prob. 9-14 when member 26 is removed and member 15 is assumed rigid.

9-16. Compute the new flexibility matrix $\mathbf{F}_d^*$ and the new matrix $\mathbf{B}^*$ for the propped beam of Fig. P 9-8 when the bending stiffness of element 12 is trebled. Results of Prob. 9-8 should be used.

9-17. Recompute the modified structures of Probs. 9-14 and 9-16 from scratch and compare with the results of the previous two calculations.

9-18. For the truss of Fig. P 9-18 compute the matrices $\mathbf{F}_d$ and $\mathbf{B}$. Calculate the additional internal forces if truss member 4 experiences an initial temperature strain h_4. Furthermore determine the new matrix $\mathbf{F}_d^*$ if member 4 becomes rigid.† The longitudinal stiffness of all members is EA.

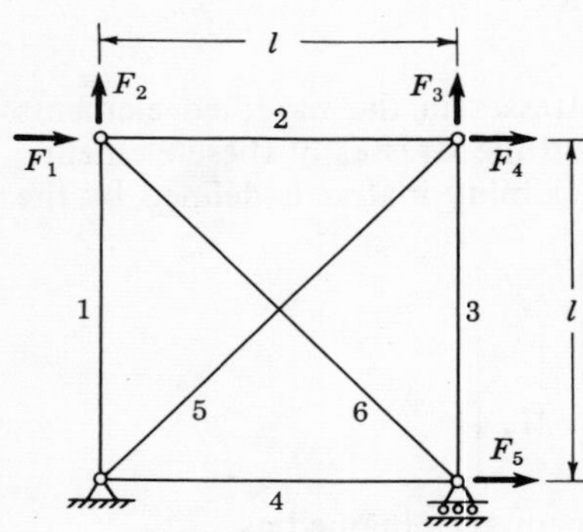

FIG. P 9-18

9-6. Recurrence Method for Highly Redundant Systems

We have seen before that the inversion of matrix $\mathbf{D}_{11}$ is necessary for the solution of a statically indeterminate structure problem. $\mathbf{D}_{11}$ is of the order n, where n denotes the number of redundant forces of the structure. In a highly redundant system the inversion of $\mathbf{D}_{11}$ may lead to considerable computational difficulties, especially in view of the always limited computer capacity. The method developed in this section shows a way to circumvent these difficulties. With its aid it is possible to split up the solution of the problem into an arbitrary number of successive steps. The magnitude of each step can be kept so small that the matrix inversion to be carried out in every step offers no difficulty. The method can therefore be very useful when a structure with quite a large number of redundancies is to be computed with the aid of a small electronic computer or even a desk computer.

As explained in Sec. 9-2, the redundant system is made statically determinate in the usual manner.‡ The n redundants $\mathbf{x} = \{X_1 \quad X_2 \quad \cdots \quad X_n\}$ are now subdivided into an arbitrary number of groups. Let us consider in the meantime that these statically indeterminate quantities are lumped into three separate groups, because this case is general enough to permit the formal extrapolation to larger numbers of such groups. Then the following sets of forces constitute the load of the statically determinate basic structure:

Redundants: $\mathbf{x}_\alpha$, $\mathbf{x}_\beta$, $\mathbf{x}_\gamma$, where subscripts α, β, and γ denote the number of components of the partitioned vectors of the redundants $\mathbf{x}$ ($\alpha + \beta + \gamma = n$)

$$\mathbf{x}_\alpha = \{X_1 \quad \cdots \quad X_\alpha\} \quad \mathbf{x}_\beta = \{X_{\alpha+1} \quad \cdots \quad X_{\alpha+\beta}\} \quad \mathbf{x}_\gamma = \{X_{\alpha+\beta+1} \quad \cdots \quad X_{\alpha+\beta+\gamma}\}$$

External load: $\mathbf{f} = \{F_1 \quad \cdots \quad F_m\}$

† R. Zurmühl, "Matrizen," 3d ed., Springer-Verlag, Berlin, 1958.

‡ See Sec. 9-4 for general rules to be observed when applying the "force method" to statically indeterminate systems.

In the first stage we consider the statically determinate basic structure to be loaded by the redundant forces $\mathbf{x}_\alpha$ and by the "external" forces $\mathbf{x}_\beta$, $\mathbf{x}_\gamma$, and $\mathbf{f}$. Hence the redundants are

$$\mathbf{x}_\alpha = \{X_1 \quad X_2 \quad \cdots \quad X_\alpha\}$$

and the "external" forces are

$$\mathbf{f}^{\mathrm{I}} = \{\mathbf{x}'_\beta \quad \mathbf{x}'_\gamma \quad \mathbf{f}'\}$$

As was demonstrated in Sec. 9-2, we compute for these sets of forces the matrices ${}_{l}\overset{\beta+\gamma+m}{\left[\mathbf{B}_0^{\mathrm{I}}\right]}$ and ${}_{l}\overset{\alpha}{\left[\mathbf{B}_1^{\mathrm{I}}\right]}$, of which $\mathbf{B}_0^{\mathrm{I}}$ can be partitioned as follows:

$$\mathbf{B}_0^{\mathrm{I}} = {}_{l}\left[\overset{\beta}{\mathbf{B}_{0\beta}^{\mathrm{I}}} \;\vdots\; \overset{\gamma}{\mathbf{B}_{0\gamma}^{\mathrm{I}}} \;\vdots\; \overset{m}{\mathbf{B}_{0m}^{\mathrm{I}}}\right] \tag{9-56}$$

The matrix ${}_{l}\overset{l}{\left[\mathbf{F}_v\right]}$ (diagonally partitioned) is determined in the usual way. Then, according to Eqs. (9-19), $\mathbf{D}_{11}^{\mathrm{I}}$ and $\mathbf{D}_{10}^{\mathrm{I}}$ are computed:

$${}_{\alpha}\overset{\alpha}{\left[\mathbf{D}_{11}^{\mathrm{I}}\right]} = {}_{\alpha}\overset{l}{\left[\mathbf{B}_1^{\mathrm{I}}\right]}' \cdot {}_{l}\overset{l}{\left[\mathbf{F}_v\right]} \cdot {}_{l}\overset{\alpha}{\left[\mathbf{B}_1^{\mathrm{I}}\right]} \tag{9-57}$$

$${}_{\alpha}\overset{\beta+\gamma+m}{\left[\mathbf{D}_{10}^{\mathrm{I}}\right]} = {}_{\alpha}\overset{l}{\left[\mathbf{B}_1^{\mathrm{I}}\right]}' \cdot {}_{l}\overset{l}{\left[\mathbf{F}_v\right]} \cdot {}_{l}\overset{\beta+\gamma+m}{\left[\mathbf{B}_0^{\mathrm{I}}\right]} \tag{9-58}$$

Hence from Eq. (9-20) we obtain

$${}_{\alpha}\overset{\beta+\gamma+m}{\left[\mathbf{X}^{\mathrm{I}}\right]} = {}_{\alpha}\left[\overset{\beta}{\mathbf{X}_\beta^{\mathrm{I}}} \;\vdots\; \overset{\gamma}{\mathbf{X}_\gamma^{\mathrm{I}}} \;\vdots\; \overset{m}{\mathbf{X}_m^{\mathrm{I}}}\right] = -{}_{\alpha}\overset{\alpha}{\left[\mathbf{D}_{11}^{\mathrm{I}}\right]}^{-1} \cdot {}_{\alpha}\overset{\beta+\gamma+m}{\left[\mathbf{D}_{10}^{\mathrm{I}}\right]} \tag{9-59}$$

It is noteworthy that the inversion of the matrix $\mathbf{D}_{11}^{\mathrm{I}}$ involves only an α-order matrix. We now obtain from Eq. (9-59) the expression for the redundants $\mathbf{x}_\alpha$ as a linear combination of $\mathbf{x}_\beta$, $\mathbf{x}_\gamma$, and $\mathbf{f}$:

$$\mathbf{x}_\alpha = \mathbf{X}^{\mathrm{I}}\mathbf{f}^{\mathrm{I}} = \mathbf{X}_\beta^{\mathrm{I}}\mathbf{x}_\beta + \mathbf{X}_\gamma^{\mathrm{I}}\mathbf{x}_\gamma + \mathbf{X}_m^{\mathrm{I}}\mathbf{f} \tag{9-60}$$

In the second stage our basic system is the statically indeterminate system containing the redundants $\mathbf{x}_\alpha$, which is now loaded by the "external" forces

$$\mathbf{f}^{\mathrm{II}} = \{\mathbf{x}'_\gamma \quad \mathbf{f}'\} \tag{9-61}$$

and the redundants $\mathbf{x}_\beta$. The internal forces are calculated from the usual formula [cf. Eq. (9-12)]

$$\mathbf{p} = \mathbf{B}_0^{\mathrm{II}}\begin{bmatrix}\mathbf{x}_\gamma \\ \hdashline \mathbf{f}\end{bmatrix} + \mathbf{B}_1^{\mathrm{II}}\mathbf{x}_\beta \tag{9-62}$$

The values for $\mathbf{B}_0^{\mathrm{II}}$ and $\mathbf{B}_1^{\mathrm{II}}$ are not yet known but are obtained in the following way. From the first system the internal forces are given by the relation

$$\mathbf{p} = \mathbf{B}_0^{\mathrm{I}}\begin{bmatrix}\mathbf{x}_\beta \\ \hdashline \mathbf{x}_\gamma \\ \hdashline \mathbf{f}\end{bmatrix} + \mathbf{B}_1^{\mathrm{I}}\mathbf{x}_\alpha$$

But $\mathbf{x}_\alpha$ is known from Eq. (9-60), and hence the previous equation can be written

$$\mathbf{p} = \left[\mathbf{B}_{0\beta}^{\mathrm{I}} \;\vdots\; \mathbf{B}_{0\gamma}^{\mathrm{I}} \;\vdots\; \mathbf{B}_{0m}^{\mathrm{I}}\right] \cdot \begin{bmatrix} \mathbf{x}_\beta \\ \hdashline \mathbf{x}_\gamma \\ \hdashline \mathbf{f} \end{bmatrix} + \mathbf{B}_1^{\mathrm{I}}\left[\mathbf{X}_\beta^{\mathrm{I}}\mathbf{x}_\beta + \mathbf{X}_\gamma^{\mathrm{I}}\mathbf{x}_\gamma + \mathbf{X}_m^{\mathrm{I}}\mathbf{f}\right]$$

$$= \left[\mathbf{B}_{0\gamma}^{\mathrm{I}} + \mathbf{B}_1^{\mathrm{I}}\mathbf{X}_\gamma^{\mathrm{I}} \;\vdots\; \mathbf{B}_{0m}^{\mathrm{I}} + \mathbf{B}_1^{\mathrm{I}}\mathbf{X}_m^{\mathrm{I}}\right] \cdot \begin{bmatrix} \mathbf{x}_\gamma \\ \hdashline \mathbf{f} \end{bmatrix} + \left[\mathbf{B}_{0\beta}^{\mathrm{I}} + \mathbf{B}_1^{\mathrm{I}}\mathbf{X}_\beta^{\mathrm{I}}\right]\mathbf{x}_\beta$$

Comparing this result with Eq. (9-62), we obtain

$$\mathbf{B}_0^{\mathrm{II}} = \left[\mathbf{B}_{0\gamma}^{\mathrm{I}} + \mathbf{B}_1^{\mathrm{I}}\mathbf{X}_\gamma^{\mathrm{I}} \;\vdots\; \mathbf{B}_{0m}^{\mathrm{I}} + \mathbf{B}_1^{\mathrm{I}}\mathbf{X}_m^{\mathrm{I}}\right] \tag{9-63}$$

and

$$\mathbf{B}_1^{\mathrm{II}} = \mathbf{B}_{0\beta}^{\mathrm{I}} + \mathbf{B}_1^{\mathrm{I}}\mathbf{X}_\beta^{\mathrm{I}} \tag{9-64}$$

Hence both $\mathbf{B}_0^{\mathrm{II}}$ and $\mathbf{B}_1^{\mathrm{II}}$ can be computed from the results obtained in stage I.

The procedure for the second stage now follows the usual pattern, so that we can compute $\mathbf{D}_{11}^{\mathrm{II}}$, $\mathbf{D}_{10}^{\mathrm{II}}$, $\mathbf{X}^{\mathrm{II}}$, and $\mathbf{x}_\beta$ from the formulas

$$\overset{\beta}{{}^{\beta}\left[\mathbf{D}_{11}^{\mathrm{II}}\right]} = \overset{l}{{}^{\beta}\left[\mathbf{B}_1^{\mathrm{II}}\right]'} \cdot \overset{l}{{}^{l}\left[\mathbf{F}_v\right]} \cdot \overset{\beta}{{}^{l}\left[\mathbf{B}_1^{\mathrm{II}}\right]} \tag{9-65}$$

$$\overset{\gamma+m}{{}^{\beta}\left[\mathbf{D}_{10}^{\mathrm{II}}\right]} = \overset{l}{{}^{\beta}\left[\mathbf{B}_1^{\mathrm{II}}\right]'} \cdot \overset{l}{{}^{l}\left[\mathbf{F}_v\right]} \cdot \overset{\gamma+m}{{}^{l}\left[\mathbf{B}_0^{\mathrm{II}}\right]} \tag{9-66}$$

$$\overset{\gamma+m}{{}^{\beta}\left[\mathbf{X}^{\mathrm{II}}\right]} = {}^{\beta}\left[\overset{\gamma}{\mathbf{X}_\gamma^{\mathrm{II}}} \;\vdots\; \overset{m}{\mathbf{X}_m^{\mathrm{II}}}\right] = -\overset{\beta}{{}^{\beta}\left[\mathbf{D}_{11}^{\mathrm{II}}\right]^{-1}} \cdot \overset{\gamma+m}{{}^{\beta}\left[\mathbf{D}_{10}^{\mathrm{II}}\right]} \tag{9-67}$$

$$\mathbf{x}_\beta = \mathbf{X}^{\mathrm{II}}\mathbf{f}^{\mathrm{II}} = \mathbf{X}_\gamma^{\mathrm{II}}\mathbf{x}_\gamma + \mathbf{X}_m^{\mathrm{II}}\mathbf{f} \tag{9-68}$$

Inserting the right side of Eq. (9-68) into Eq. (9-60) for $\mathbf{x}_\beta$, we obtain $\mathbf{x}_\alpha$ as a linear combination of $\mathbf{f}$ and $\mathbf{x}_\gamma$:

$$\mathbf{x}_\alpha = \mathbf{X}_m^{\mathrm{I}}\mathbf{f} + \mathbf{X}_\gamma^{\mathrm{I}}\mathbf{x}_\gamma + \mathbf{X}_\beta^{\mathrm{I}}(\mathbf{X}_m^{\mathrm{II}}\mathbf{f} + \mathbf{X}_\gamma^{\mathrm{II}}\mathbf{x}_\gamma) = (\mathbf{X}_m^{\mathrm{I}} + \mathbf{X}_\beta^{\mathrm{I}}\mathbf{X}_m^{\mathrm{II}})\mathbf{f} + (\mathbf{X}_\gamma^{\mathrm{I}} + \mathbf{X}_\beta^{\mathrm{I}}\mathbf{X}_\gamma^{\mathrm{II}})\mathbf{x}_\gamma \tag{9-69}$$

This completes the second step. We keep in mind that with Eqs. (9-68) and (9-69) we have the redundants $\mathbf{x}_\alpha$ and $\mathbf{x}_\beta$ expressed as linear combinations of the external forces $\mathbf{f}$ and the remaining redundants $\mathbf{x}_\gamma$.

So now we are ready to use as our basic system in the third and here the last stage of the computations the statically indeterminate system containing the redundants $\mathbf{x}_\alpha$ and $\mathbf{x}_\beta$, which is loaded by the external forces $\mathbf{f}^{\mathrm{III}} = \mathbf{f}$ and the redundants $\mathbf{x}_\gamma$.

From here on we proceed in the same manner as demonstrated previously. The internal forces are given by the relation

$$\mathbf{p} = \mathbf{B}_0^{\mathrm{III}}\mathbf{f} + \mathbf{B}_1^{\mathrm{III}}\mathbf{x}_\gamma \tag{9-70}$$

where $\mathbf{B}_0^{\mathrm{III}}$ and $\mathbf{B}_1^{\mathrm{III}}$ have yet to be calculated. The expression for the internal forces is also given in Eq. (9-62):

$$\mathbf{p} = [\mathbf{B}_{0\gamma}^{\mathrm{II}} \;\vdots\; \mathbf{B}_{0m}^{\mathrm{II}}] \cdot \begin{bmatrix} \mathbf{x}_\gamma \\ \hdashline \mathbf{f} \end{bmatrix} + \mathbf{B}_1^{\mathrm{II}}\mathbf{x}_\beta \tag{9-62a}$$

Eliminating $\mathbf{x}_\beta$ with the help of Eq. (9-68), $\mathbf{p}$ becomes

$$\mathbf{p} = (\mathbf{B}_{0m}^{\mathrm{II}} + \mathbf{B}_1^{\mathrm{II}}\mathbf{X}_m^{\mathrm{II}})\mathbf{f} + (\mathbf{B}_{0\gamma}^{\mathrm{II}} + \mathbf{B}_1^{\mathrm{II}}\mathbf{X}_\gamma^{\mathrm{II}})\mathbf{x}_\gamma$$

Table 9-13. Scheme of the Recurrence Method†

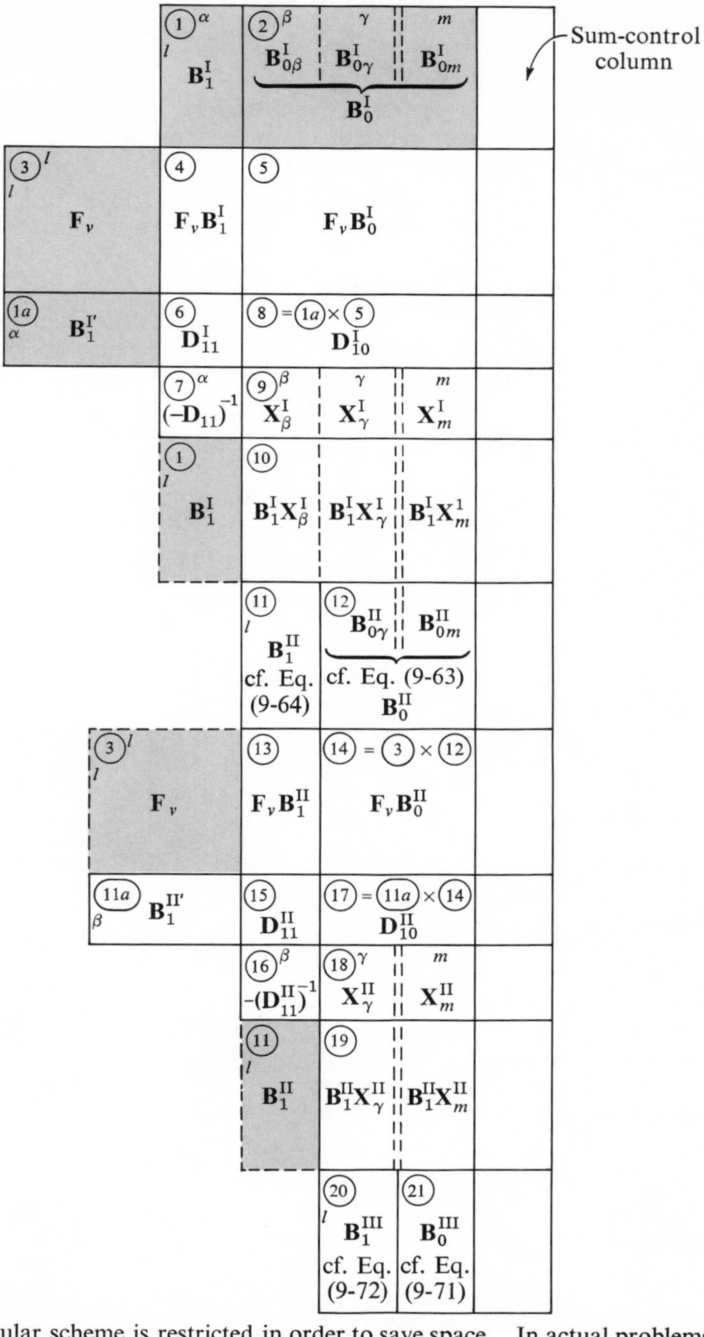

					Sum-control column
	(1) α, l, $\mathbf{B}_1^{\text{I}}$	(2) β, $\mathbf{B}_{0\beta}^{\text{I}}$	γ, $\mathbf{B}_{0\gamma}^{\text{I}}$	m, $\mathbf{B}_{0m}^{\text{I}}$ — together $\mathbf{B}_0^{\text{I}}$	
(3) l, l, $\mathbf{F}_\nu$	(4) $\mathbf{F}_\nu\mathbf{B}_1^{\text{I}}$	(5) $\mathbf{F}_\nu\mathbf{B}_0^{\text{I}}$			
(1a) α, $\mathbf{B}_1^{\text{I}'}$	(6) $\mathbf{D}_{11}^{\text{I}}$	(8) = (1a) × (5) $\mathbf{D}_{10}^{\text{I}}$			
	(7) α, $(-\mathbf{D}_{11})^{-1}$	(9) β, $\mathbf{X}_\beta^{\text{I}}$	γ, $\mathbf{X}_\gamma^{\text{I}}$	m, $\mathbf{X}_m^{\text{I}}$	
	(1) l, $\mathbf{B}_1^{\text{I}}$	(10) $\mathbf{B}_1^{\text{I}}\mathbf{X}_\beta^{\text{I}}$	$\mathbf{B}_1^{\text{I}}\mathbf{X}_\gamma^{\text{I}}$	$\mathbf{B}_1^{\text{I}}\mathbf{X}_m^{\text{I}}$	
		(11) l, $\mathbf{B}_1^{\text{II}}$ cf. Eq. (9-64)	(12) $\mathbf{B}_{0\gamma}^{\text{II}}$	$\mathbf{B}_{0m}^{\text{II}}$ — together cf. Eq. (9-63) $\mathbf{B}_0^{\text{II}}$	
(3) l, l, $\mathbf{F}_\nu$		(13) $\mathbf{F}_\nu\mathbf{B}_1^{\text{II}}$	(14) = (3) × (12) $\mathbf{F}_\nu\mathbf{B}_0^{\text{II}}$		
(11a) β, $\mathbf{B}_1^{\text{II}'}$		(15) $\mathbf{D}_{11}^{\text{II}}$	(17) = (11a) × (14) $\mathbf{D}_{10}^{\text{II}}$		
		(16) β, $-(\mathbf{D}_{11}^{\text{II}})^{-1}$	(18) γ, $\mathbf{X}_\gamma^{\text{II}}$	m, $\mathbf{X}_m^{\text{II}}$	
		(11) l, $\mathbf{B}_1^{\text{II}}$	(19) $\mathbf{B}_1^{\text{II}}\mathbf{X}_\gamma^{\text{II}}$	$\mathbf{B}_1^{\text{II}}\mathbf{X}_m^{\text{II}}$	
			(20) l, $\mathbf{B}_1^{\text{III}}$ cf. Eq. (9-72)	(21) $\mathbf{B}_0^{\text{III}}$ cf. Eq. (9-71)	

† The tabular scheme is restricted in order to save space. In actual problems l is mostly much larger than $\alpha + \beta + \gamma + m$. Shading represents blocks into which initial information is fed. Dashed outline represents repeated blocks. Circled numbers denote the sequence of the computational steps.

Table 9-14

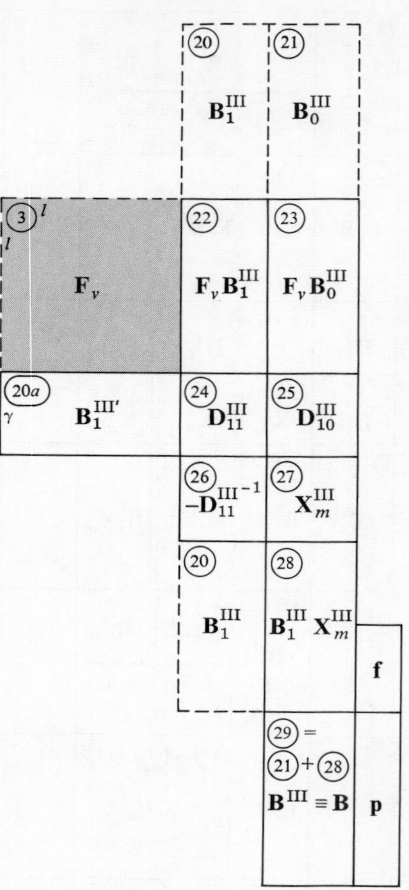

Hence, by comparison with Eq. (9-70),

$$ {}^{l}\overset{m}{\left[\mathbf{B}_0^{\mathrm{III}}\right]} = {}^{l}\overset{m}{\left[\mathbf{B}_{0m}^{\mathrm{II}}\right]} + {}^{l}\overset{\beta}{\left[\mathbf{B}_1^{\mathrm{II}}\right]} \cdot {}^{\beta}\overset{m}{\left[\mathbf{X}_m^{\mathrm{II}}\right]} \tag{9-71} $$

$$ {}^{l}\overset{\gamma}{\left[\mathbf{B}_1^{\mathrm{III}}\right]} = {}^{l}\overset{\gamma}{\left[\mathbf{B}_{0\gamma}^{\mathrm{II}}\right]} + {}^{l}\overset{\beta}{\left[\mathbf{B}_1^{\mathrm{II}}\right]} \cdot {}^{\beta}\overset{\gamma}{\left[\mathbf{X}_\gamma^{\mathrm{II}}\right]} \tag{9-72} $$

As before, we then find

$$ {}^{\gamma}\overset{\gamma}{\left[\mathbf{D}_{11}^{\mathrm{III}}\right]} = {}^{\gamma}\overset{l}{\left[\mathbf{B}_1^{\mathrm{III}}\right]}' \cdot {}^{l}\overset{l}{\left[\mathbf{F}_v\right]} \cdot {}^{l}\overset{\gamma}{\left[\mathbf{B}_1^{\mathrm{III}}\right]} \tag{9-73} $$

$$ {}^{\gamma}\overset{m}{\left[\mathbf{D}_{10}^{\mathrm{III}}\right]} = {}^{\gamma}\overset{l}{\left[\mathbf{B}_1^{\mathrm{III}}\right]}' \cdot {}^{l}\overset{l}{\left[\mathbf{F}_v\right]} \cdot {}^{l}\overset{m}{\left[\mathbf{B}_0^{\mathrm{III}}\right]} \tag{9-74} $$

$$ {}^{\gamma}\overset{m}{\left[\mathbf{X}^{\mathrm{III}}\right]} = -{}^{\gamma}\overset{\gamma}{\left[\mathbf{D}_{11}^{\mathrm{III}}\right]}^{-1} \cdot {}^{\gamma}\overset{m}{\left[\mathbf{D}_{10}^{\mathrm{III}}\right]} \tag{9-75} $$

$$ \mathbf{x}_\gamma = \mathbf{X}^{\mathrm{III}}\mathbf{f}^{\mathrm{III}} = \mathbf{X}^{\mathrm{III}}\mathbf{f} \tag{9-76} $$

Now, all l stresses $\mathbf{p}$ can be computed according to Eq. (9-12):

$$\mathbf{p} = \mathbf{B}^{\mathrm{III}}\mathbf{f} = (\mathbf{B}_0^{\mathrm{III}} + \mathbf{B}_1^{\mathrm{III}}\mathbf{X}^{\mathrm{III}})\mathbf{f} \tag{9-77}$$

The flexibility matrix $\mathbf{F}_d$ of the complete structure is

$$\mathbf{F}_d = [\mathbf{D}_{00}^{\mathrm{III}}] - [\mathbf{D}_{10}^{\mathrm{III}}]'[\mathbf{D}_{11}^{\mathrm{III}}]^{-1}[\mathbf{D}_{10}^{\mathrm{III}}] \tag{9-78}$$

where

$$\mathbf{D}_{00}^{\mathrm{III}} = [\mathbf{B}_0^{\mathrm{III}}]'[\mathbf{F}_v][\mathbf{B}_0^{\mathrm{III}}], \tag{9-79}$$

Finally we obtain

$$\mathbf{d} = \mathbf{F}_d\mathbf{f} \tag{9-80}$$

The procedure is presented in the scheme of Table 9-13, from which the extrapolation to an arbitrary number of groups will be immediately apparent.

From here on, the pattern of calculation is exactly like the one shown by the tabular scheme in Sec. 9-2, where $\mathbf{B}_1$ is replaced by $\mathbf{B}_1^{\mathrm{III}}$ and $\mathbf{B}_0$ by $\mathbf{B}_0^{\mathrm{III}}$, the flexibility matrix $\mathbf{F}_v$ remaining unchanged (see Tables 9-14 and 9-15).

Table 9-15

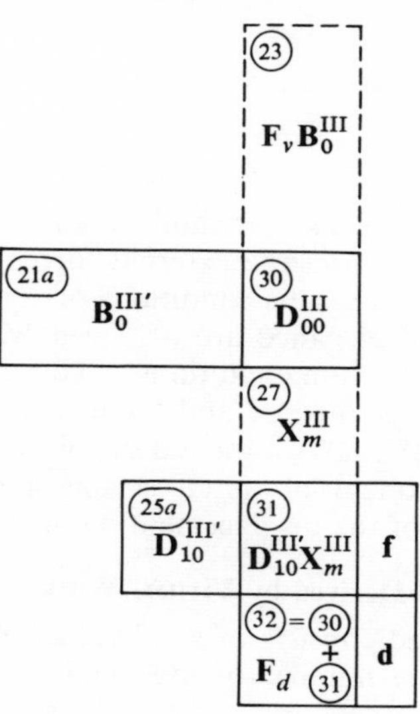

10 THE MATRIX DISPLACEMENT METHOD

In the displacement method, as commonly used in practice, joint displacements are imposed on the structure, and the external forces necessary to cause these displacements are found by applying the conditions of equilibrium at the joints. However, greater simplicity and elegance are achieved by employing the virtual-work principle instead of the equilibrium conditions. This also brings to light the analogy which exists between the force method and the displacement method and which was first exploited by Argyris [48]. With the aid of this analogy we can easily adapt the results found for the treatment of initial strains and structural modifications in Chap. 9 to the procedures of the displacement method.

10-1. Displacement Method Derived by Virtual Work

The system to be analyzed consists of s individual elements that are assembled in some definite manner. The number of independent displacements $\mathbf{d}$ of the joints necessary to determine uniquely the deformations $\mathbf{v}$ of all s elements is r. For example, in Fig. 9-1 we have $r = 9$, and in Fig. 9-2, $r = 2$. Hence

$$\mathbf{d} = \{d_1 \quad d_2 \quad \cdots \quad d_r\} \qquad \text{and} \qquad \mathbf{v} = \{v_1 \quad v_2 \quad \cdots \quad v_l\}$$

where $l \geq s$ (cf. Sec. 9-2).

The relations between the displacements $\mathbf{d}$ and the deformations $\mathbf{v}$ can then be expressed by the matrix equation

$$\mathbf{v} = \mathbf{A}\mathbf{d} \qquad \text{compatibility} \tag{10-1}$$

The ith column of the geometric matrix $\mathbf{A}$ is obtained by determining the deformations $\mathbf{v}$ after subjecting the system to the displacement $d_i = 1$; all other displacements $d_j = 0$ ($j = 1, 2, \ldots, r$) for $j \neq i$. The reader is advised to remember that the displacements $\mathbf{d}$ are measured with respect to a space-fixed coordinate system, whereas the deformations $\mathbf{v}_g$ are determined with respect to a coordinate system fixed in the element g.

In Sec. 9-1 we had shown that the relation between the deformations $\mathbf{v}_g$ of the gth structural element and its associated internal forces is described by

$$\mathbf{p}_g = \mathbf{K}_g\mathbf{v}_g \tag{9-1}$$

As was done in Eq. (9-14), we can establish this relation for the entire structure so that

$$\mathbf{p} = \mathbf{K}_p\mathbf{v} \qquad \text{stress-strain relationship} \tag{10-2}$$

where

$$\mathbf{K}_p = \begin{bmatrix} \mathbf{K}_a & & & & & \\ & \mathbf{K}_b & & & & \\ & & \cdots & & & \\ & & & \mathbf{K}_g & & \\ & & & & \cdots & \\ & & & & & \mathbf{K}_s \end{bmatrix} \tag{10-3}$$

combines the stiffness matrices of the s unassembled structural elements. We can now find the relation between the internal forces $\mathbf{p}$ and external forces $\mathbf{f}$ by using the dummy-displacement theorem (cf. Sec. 9-1). Giving the structure a set of dummy displacements $\mathbf{d}_d$ we have

$$\mathbf{d}'_d\mathbf{f} = \mathbf{v}'_d\mathbf{p} \tag{9-9}$$

and in view of the equation

$$\mathbf{v}'_d = \mathbf{d}'_d\mathbf{A}' \qquad \text{cf. Eq. (10-1)}$$

we may write

$$\mathbf{d}'_d\mathbf{f} = \mathbf{d}'_d\mathbf{A}'\mathbf{p}$$

Since this relation must hold for any set of dummy displacements $\mathbf{d}_d$, we have

$$\mathbf{f} = \mathbf{A}'\mathbf{p} \qquad \text{equilibrium}$$

which is the relation between the internal and applied forces. Using Eqs. (10-2) and (10-1),

$$\mathbf{f} = \mathbf{A}'\mathbf{K}_p\mathbf{v} = \mathbf{A}'\mathbf{K}_p\mathbf{A}\mathbf{d} \tag{10-4}$$

Defining the stiffness matrix $\mathbf{K}_f$ by the relation

$$\mathbf{f} = \mathbf{K}_f\mathbf{d} \tag{10-5}$$

we obtain

$$\mathbf{K}_f = \mathbf{A}'\mathbf{K}_p\mathbf{A} \tag{10-6}$$

$\mathbf{K}_f$ is a symmetric matrix, since $\mathbf{K}_p$ is symmetric [cf. Eq. (1-20)] on account of the Maxwell-Betti theorem (cf. Sec. 9-1). It is quite apparent that the use of the virtual (dummy) displacement theorem leads to an elegant and simple procedure.

Example 10-1. With the matrix displacement method we now compute for the frame of Fig. 10-1 the stiffness matrix $\mathbf{K}_f$, which here relates the forces

$$\mathbf{f} = \{F_{2H} \quad F_{2V} \quad C_2 \quad F_{3H} \quad F_{3V} \quad C_3 \quad C_4\}$$

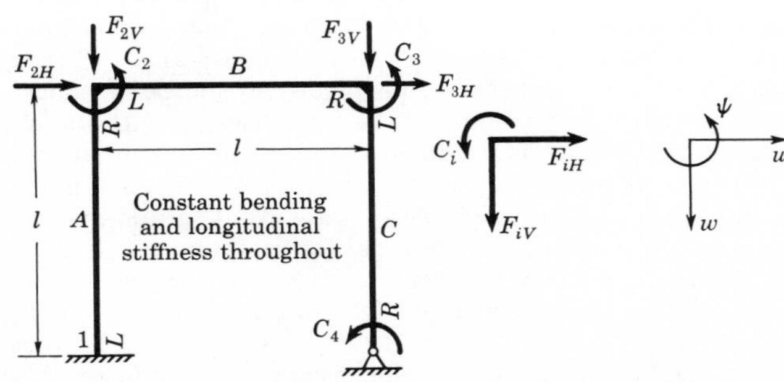

FIG. 10-1. Frame subjected to external forces. Convention for forces and displacement.

to the displacements

$$\mathbf{d} = \{u_2 \quad w_2 \quad \psi_2 \quad u_3 \quad w_3 \quad \psi_3 \quad \psi_4\}$$

which are necessary to describe all the possible displacements of the joints of the structure. After we label the elements *A*, *B*, and *C* of the frame in quite arbitrary fashion with the letters *L* and *R* (cf. Fig. 10-1), thereby denoting what we shall consider the left and right ends, respectively, of each element, we choose as the deformations (cf. Sec. 9-1)

$$\mathbf{v} = \{u_A^R \quad \psi_A^L \quad \psi_A^R \quad u_B^R \quad \psi_B^L \quad \psi_B^R \quad u_C^R \quad \psi_C^L \quad \psi_C^R\}$$

Using the sign convention of Fig. 10-3, we compose by inspection of Fig. 10-2 the geometric compatibility matrix **A** shown below. In Fig. 10-2 the heavy lines denote the deformed state of the structure, and the dashed lines indicate the undeformed frame. The thin unbroken lines are the auxiliary reference lines from which the deformations **v** are measured.

$$\begin{array}{c} \\ u_A^R \\ \psi_A^L \\ \psi_A^R \\ u_B^R \\ \psi_B^L \\ \psi_B^R \\ u_C^R \\ \psi_C^L \\ \psi_C^R \end{array}
\begin{array}{c} \begin{array}{ccccccc} u_2 & w_2 & \psi_2 & u_3 & w_3 & \psi_3 & \psi_4 \end{array} \\
\begin{bmatrix}
0 & -1 & 0 & 0 & 0 & 0 & 0 \\
\frac{1}{l} & 0 & 0 & 0 & 0 & 0 & 0 \\
\frac{1}{l} & 0 & 1 & 0 & 0 & 0 & 0 \\
-1 & 0 & 0 & 1 & 0 & 0 & 0 \\
0 & \frac{-1}{l} & 1 & 0 & \frac{1}{l} & 0 & 0 \\
0 & \frac{-1}{l} & 0 & 0 & \frac{1}{l} & 1 & 0 \\
0 & 0 & 0 & 0 & -1 & 0 & 0 \\
0 & 0 & 0 & \frac{1}{l} & 0 & 1 & 0 \\
0 & 0 & 0 & \frac{1}{l} & 0 & 0 & 1
\end{bmatrix} \end{array} = \mathbf{A}$$

For example, consider the horizontal displacement u_3 of joint 3 (cf. Fig. 10-2*d*). If all other displacements are kept zero, then the structure assumes the shape shown by the heavy lines. We recognize that on account of this displacement only frame elements *B* and *C* are deformed, since only they meet at joint 3. It is easily seen that the deformation of bar *B* is achieved by extending its right end through $u_B^R = 1$, while ψ_B^L and ψ_B^R both remain zero.

Somewhat more discussion is necessary with regard to the deformation of element *C*. Since we confine ourselves to the consideration of small displacements, member *C* is not extended; thus we have $u_C^R = 0$. How, then, do we bring member *C* into its deformed state by rotating its two ends through ψ_C^L and ψ_C^R? In order to do this we carry out two steps: (1) tilt bar *C* about joint 4 as a rigid body (see unbroken thin line connecting joint 4 with joint 3 in its displaced position); the internal forces acting on *C* being in equilibrium, no work is done by this rigid body movement; (2) rotate the left (upper) and the right (lower) ends of bar *C* through the angles $\psi_C^L = 1/l$ and $\psi_C^R = 1/l$, respectively, so that bar *C* assumes the shape shown by the heavy lines. It is step 2 which leads to work being done by the end moments M_C^L and M_C^R. It is self-evident that the chosen set of deformations **v** must be kept unchanged for all the successive displacements.

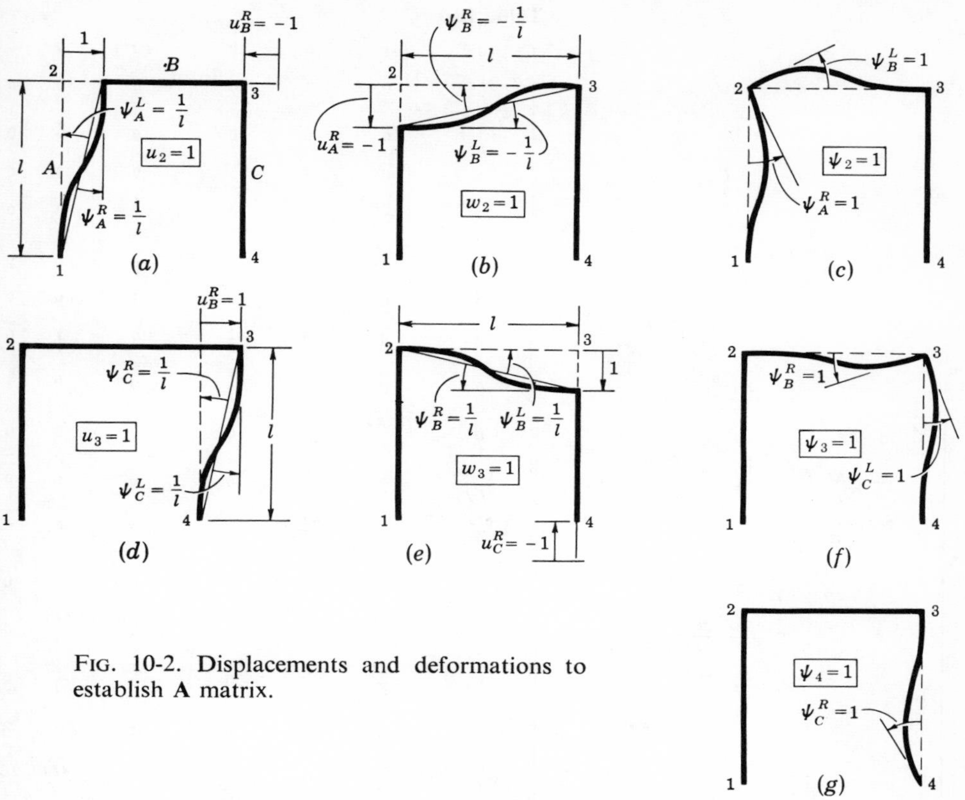

FIG. 10-2. Displacements and deformations to establish **A** matrix.

Referring to the Short Catalogue of flexibility and stiffness matrices in Sec. 9-1, our choice of the components of **v** leads us to use the stiffness matrices of cases *a* and *g*. Hence for each of the three structural elements we have to use the stiffness-matrix relation

$$\begin{bmatrix} N^R \\ M^L \\ M^R \end{bmatrix} = \begin{bmatrix} \dfrac{EA}{l} & 0 & 0 \\ 0 & \dfrac{4EJ}{l} & \dfrac{2EJ}{l} \\ 0 & \dfrac{2EJ}{l} & \dfrac{4EJ}{l} \end{bmatrix} \cdot \begin{bmatrix} u^R \\ \psi^L \\ \psi^R \end{bmatrix}$$

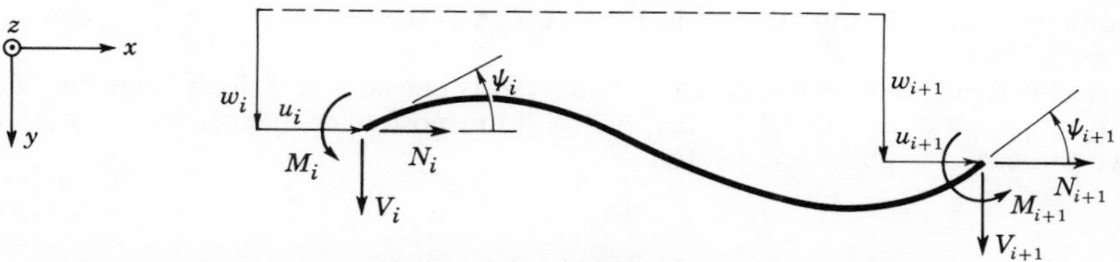

FIG. 10-3. End forces and displacements of beam element.

Table 10-1

$$
\mathbf{A} = \begin{bmatrix}
0 & -1 & 0 & 0 & 0 & 0 & 0 \\
\frac{1}{l} & 0 & 0 & 0 & 0 & 0 & 0 \\
\frac{1}{l} & 0 & 1 & 0 & 0 & 0 & 0 \\
-1 & 0 & 0 & 1 & 0 & 0 & 0 \\
0 & \frac{-1}{l} & 1 & 0 & \frac{1}{l} & 0 & 0 \\
0 & \frac{-1}{l} & 0 & 0 & \frac{1}{l} & 1 & 0 \\
0 & 0 & 0 & 0 & -1 & 0 & 0 \\
0 & 0 & 0 & \frac{1}{l} & 0 & 1 & 0 \\
0 & 0 & 0 & \frac{1}{l} & 0 & 0 & 1
\end{bmatrix}
$$

$$
\mathbf{K}_p = \begin{bmatrix}
\frac{EA}{l} & 0 & 0 & & & & & & \\
0 & \frac{4EJ}{l} & \frac{2EJ}{l} & & \mathbf{0} & & & \mathbf{0} & \\
0 & \frac{2EJ}{l} & \frac{4EJ}{l} & & & & & & \\
& & & \frac{EA}{l} & 0 & 0 & & & \\
& \mathbf{0} & & 0 & \frac{4EJ}{l} & \frac{2EJ}{l} & & \mathbf{0} & \\
& & & 0 & \frac{2EJ}{l} & \frac{4EJ}{l} & & & \\
& & & & & & \frac{EA}{l} & 0 & 0 \\
& \mathbf{0} & & & \mathbf{0} & & 0 & \frac{4EJ}{l} & \frac{2EJ}{l} \\
& & & & & & 0 & \frac{2EJ}{l} & \frac{4EJ}{l}
\end{bmatrix}
\qquad
\mathbf{K}_p\mathbf{A} = \begin{bmatrix}
0 & \frac{-EA}{l} & 0 & 0 & 0 & 0 & 0 \\
\frac{6EJ}{l^2} & 0 & \frac{2EJ}{l} & 0 & 0 & 0 & 0 \\
\frac{6EJ}{l^2} & 0 & \frac{4EJ}{l} & 0 & 0 & 0 & 0 \\
\frac{-EA}{l} & 0 & 0 & \frac{EA}{l} & 0 & 0 & 0 \\
0 & \frac{-6EJ}{l^2} & \frac{4EJ}{l} & 0 & \frac{6EJ}{l^2} & \frac{2EJ}{l} & 0 \\
0 & \frac{-6EJ}{l^2} & \frac{2EJ}{l} & 0 & \frac{6EJ}{l^2} & \frac{4EJ}{l} & 0 \\
0 & 0 & 0 & 0 & \frac{-EA}{l} & 0 & 0 \\
0 & 0 & 0 & \frac{6EJ}{l^2} & 0 & \frac{4EJ}{l} & \frac{2EJ}{l} \\
0 & 0 & 0 & \frac{6EJ}{l^2} & 0 & \frac{2EJ}{l} & \frac{4EJ}{l}
\end{bmatrix}
$$

$$
\mathbf{A}' = \begin{bmatrix}
0 & \frac{1}{l} & \frac{1}{l} & -1 & 0 & 0 & 0 & 0 & 0 \\
-1 & 0 & 0 & 0 & \frac{-1}{l} & \frac{-1}{l} & 0 & 0 & 0 \\
0 & 0 & 1 & 0 & 1 & 0 & 0 & 0 & 0 \\
0 & 0 & 0 & 1 & 0 & 0 & 0 & \frac{1}{l} & \frac{1}{l} \\
0 & 0 & 0 & 0 & \frac{1}{l} & \frac{1}{l} & -1 & 0 & 0 \\
0 & 0 & 0 & 0 & 0 & 1 & 0 & 1 & 0 \\
0 & 0 & 0 & 0 & 0 & 0 & 0 & 0 & 1
\end{bmatrix}
\qquad
\mathbf{K}_f = \begin{bmatrix}
\frac{12EJ}{l^3} + \frac{EA}{l} & 0 & \frac{6EJ}{l^2} & \frac{-EA}{l} & 0 & 0 & 0 \\
0 & \frac{12EJ}{l^3} + \frac{EA}{l} & \frac{-6EJ}{l^2} & 0 & \frac{-12EJ}{l^3} & \frac{-6EJ}{l^2} & 0 \\
\frac{6EJ}{l^2} & \frac{-6EJ}{l^2} & \frac{8EJ}{l} & 0 & \frac{6EJ}{l^2} & \frac{2EJ}{l} & 0 \\
\frac{-EA}{l} & 0 & 0 & \frac{12EJ}{l^3} + \frac{EA}{l} & 0 & \frac{6EJ}{l^2} & \frac{6EJ}{l^2} \\
0 & \frac{-12EJ}{l^3} & \frac{6EJ}{l^2} & 0 & \frac{12EJ}{l^3} + \frac{EA}{l} & \frac{6EJ}{l^2} & 0 \\
0 & \frac{-6EJ}{l^2} & \frac{2EJ}{l} & \frac{6EJ}{l^2} & \frac{6EJ}{l^2} & \frac{8EJ}{l} & \frac{2EJ}{l} \\
0 & 0 & 0 & \frac{6EJ}{l^2} & 0 & \frac{2EJ}{l} & \frac{4EJ}{l}
\end{bmatrix}
$$

Equation (10-6) for the stiffness matrix $\mathbf{K}_f = \mathbf{A}'\mathbf{K}_p\mathbf{A}$ is then evaluated in the matrix scheme shown in Table 10-1.

Let us also treat the case when beam element B is considered rigid. Then the displacements $\mathbf{d}_2 = \{u_2 \quad w_2 \quad \psi_2\}$ and $\mathbf{d}_3 = \{u_3 \quad w_3 \quad \psi_3\}$ are no longer independent of each other, since we can easily establish the relation

$$\begin{bmatrix} u \\ w \\ \psi \end{bmatrix}_3 = \begin{bmatrix} 1 & 0 & 0 \\ 0 & 1 & -l \\ 0 & 0 & 1 \end{bmatrix} \cdot \begin{bmatrix} u \\ w \\ \psi \end{bmatrix}_2 \qquad \text{or} \qquad \mathbf{d}_3 = \mathbf{T}\mathbf{d}_2$$

If we partition the matrix **A** we may write

$$\mathbf{v} = \mathbf{A}_2\mathbf{d}_2 + \mathbf{A}_3\mathbf{d}_3 + \mathbf{A}_4\mathbf{d}_4$$

or, using the above relation between $\mathbf{d}_3$ and $\mathbf{d}_2$,

$$\mathbf{v} = (\mathbf{A}_2 + \mathbf{A}_3\mathbf{T})\mathbf{d}_2 + \mathbf{A}_4\mathbf{d}_4$$

or with

$$\bar{\mathbf{d}} = \{\mathbf{d}_2' \;\; \mathbf{d}_4'\} = \{u_2 \;\; w_2 \;\; \psi_2 \;\; \psi_4\} \qquad \text{and} \qquad \bar{\mathbf{A}} = [\mathbf{A}_2 + \mathbf{A}_3\mathbf{T} \mid \mathbf{A}_4]$$

we have

$$\mathbf{v} = \bar{\mathbf{A}}\bar{\mathbf{d}}$$

The matrix $\bar{\mathbf{A}}$ is then easily found from the matrix **A** established above:

$$\begin{array}{c} \\ u_A^R \\ \psi_A^L \\ \psi_A^R \\ u_B^R \\ \psi_B^L \\ \psi_B^R \\ u_C^R \\ \psi_C^L \\ \psi_C^R \end{array} \begin{array}{c} \begin{array}{cccc} u_2 & w_2 & \psi_2 & \psi_4 \end{array} \\ \begin{bmatrix} 0 & -1 & 0 & 0 \\ \frac{1}{l} & 0 & 0 & 0 \\ \frac{1}{l} & 0 & 1 & 0 \\ 0 & 0 & 0 & 0 \\ 0 & 0 & 0 & 0 \\ 0 & 0 & 0 & 0 \\ 0 & -1 & l & 0 \\ \frac{1}{l} & 0 & 1 & 0 \\ \frac{1}{l} & 0 & 0 & 1 \end{bmatrix} \end{array} = \bar{\mathbf{A}}$$

We recognize immediately that all deformations of element B turn out to be zero, as ought to be the case in view of the assumed rigidity of this frame member. Therefore we may delete these three rows from matrix $\bar{\mathbf{A}}$.

Naturally matrix $\bar{\mathbf{A}}$ can be more quickly established "from scratch" without using the results found in the first part of this example. It is suggested that the reader do this as an exercise.

The stiffness matrix $\bar{\mathbf{K}}_f$ is then found by forming in accordance with Eq. (10-6) the product

$$\bar{\mathbf{K}}_f = \bar{\mathbf{A}}'\mathbf{K}_p\bar{\mathbf{A}}$$

where $\mathbf{K}_p$ contains only the individual stiffness matrices of elements A and C. Hence we obtain

$$\bar{\mathbf{K}}_f = \begin{bmatrix} \dfrac{24EJ}{l^3} & 0 & \dfrac{12EJ}{l^2} & \dfrac{6EJ}{l^2} \\ 0 & \dfrac{2EA}{l} & -EA & 0 \\ \dfrac{12EJ}{l^2} & -EA & \dfrac{8EJ}{l} + EAl & \dfrac{2EJ}{l} \\ \dfrac{6EJ}{l^2} & 0 & \dfrac{2EJ}{l} & \dfrac{4EJ}{l} \end{bmatrix}$$

Thus we have

$$\bar{\mathbf{f}} = \bar{\mathbf{K}}_f\bar{\mathbf{d}} \qquad \text{or} \qquad \bar{\mathbf{d}} = \bar{\mathbf{K}}_f^{-1}\bar{\mathbf{f}}$$

Generally, however, we are not given the force groups $\bar{\mathbf{f}}$ corresponding to $\bar{\mathbf{d}} = \{\mathbf{d}_2' \quad \mathbf{d}_4'\}$, but

$$\mathbf{f} = \{F_{2H} \quad F_{2V} \quad C_2 \quad F_{3H} \quad F_{3V} \quad C_3 \quad C_4\} = \{\mathbf{f}_2' \quad \mathbf{f}_3' \quad \mathbf{f}_4'\}$$

However, $\bar{\mathbf{f}}$ can be found by considering that it is statically equivalent to $\mathbf{f}$ if

$$\bar{\mathbf{f}}'\bar{\mathbf{d}} = \mathbf{f}'\mathbf{d}$$

since the displacements $\bar{\mathbf{d}}$ are compatible with $\mathbf{d}$ (cf. Principle of Work in Sec. 9-1).

If we partition the vectors $\bar{\mathbf{f}}$, $\bar{\mathbf{d}}$, $\mathbf{f}$, and $\mathbf{d}$ as shown above, we may write

$$\bar{\mathbf{f}}_2'\mathbf{d}_2 + \bar{\mathbf{f}}_4'\mathbf{d}_4 = \mathbf{f}_2'\mathbf{d}_2 + \mathbf{f}_3'\mathbf{d}_3 + \mathbf{f}_4'\mathbf{d}_4$$

or, with $\mathbf{d}_3 = \mathbf{T}\mathbf{d}_2$,

$$\bar{\mathbf{f}}_2'\mathbf{d}_2 = (\mathbf{f}_2' + \mathbf{f}_3'\mathbf{T})\mathbf{d}_2 \qquad \text{and} \qquad \bar{\mathbf{f}}_4'\mathbf{d}_4 = \mathbf{f}_4'\mathbf{d}_4$$

Thus we obtain

$$\bar{\mathbf{f}}_2 = \mathbf{f}_2 + \mathbf{T}'\mathbf{f}_3 \qquad \text{and} \qquad \bar{\mathbf{f}}_4 = \mathbf{f}_4$$

and hence

$$\bar{\mathbf{f}} = \{\bar{F}_{2H} \quad \bar{F}_{2V} \quad \bar{C}_2 \quad C_4\}$$

with

$$\bar{F}_{2H} = F_{2H} + F_{3H} \qquad \bar{F}_{2V} = F_{2V} + F_{3V} \qquad \bar{C}_2 = C_2 + C_3 - lF_{3V}$$

When member B is rigid, another interesting question arises, if we are dealing with the problem of free vibrations of the frame with masses—also having rotary inertia—concentrated in joints 2, 3, and 4. In order to establish the mass matrix corresponding to the displacements $\bar{\mathbf{d}} = \{\mathbf{d}_2' \quad \mathbf{d}_4'\}$, we apply the principle of work to the inertia forces and obtain

$$\omega^2(\overline{\mathbf{M}}_2\mathbf{d}_2)'\mathbf{d}_2 + \omega^2(\overline{\mathbf{M}}_4\mathbf{d}_4)'\mathbf{d}_4 = \omega^2(\mathbf{M}_2\mathbf{d}_2)'\mathbf{d}_2 + \omega^2(\mathbf{M}_3\mathbf{d}_3)'\mathbf{d}_3 + \omega^2(\mathbf{M}_4\mathbf{d}_4)'\mathbf{d}_4$$

which yields, with $\mathbf{d}_3 = \mathbf{T}\mathbf{d}_2$,

$$\overline{\mathbf{M}}_2 = \mathbf{M}_2 + \mathbf{T}'\mathbf{M}_3\mathbf{T} \qquad \text{and} \qquad \overline{\mathbf{M}}_4 = \mathbf{M}_4$$

Hence

$$\overline{\mathbf{M}} = \begin{bmatrix} \overline{\mathbf{M}}_2 & \\ & \overline{\mathbf{M}}_4 \end{bmatrix} = \begin{bmatrix} m_2 + m_3 & 0 & 0 & 0 \\ 0 & m_2 + m_3 & -m_3 l & 0 \\ 0 & -m_3 l & I_2 + I_3 + m_3 l^2 & 0 \\ 0 & 0 & 0 & I_4 \end{bmatrix}$$

We then have the frequency equation [cf. Eq. (8-6)]

$$|\bar{\mathbf{K}}_f - \omega^2\overline{\mathbf{M}}| = 0$$

Example 10-2. For the simple frame of Fig. 10-4 determine the stiffness matrix $\mathbf{K}_f$ for the displacements

FIG. 10-4. Simple frame.

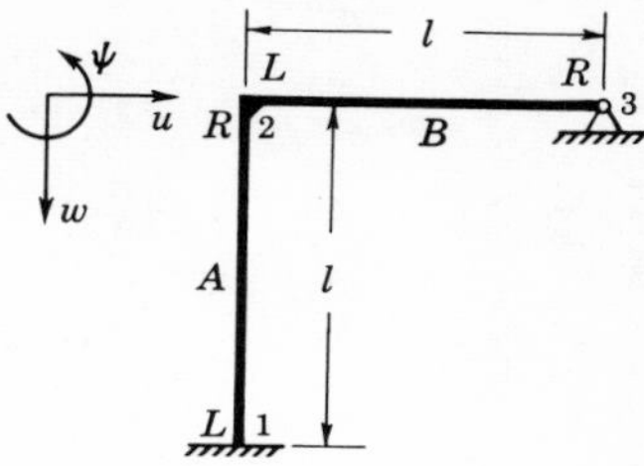

$$d = \{u_2 \quad w_2 \quad \psi_2\}$$

Referring to the Short Catalogue of flexibility and stiffness matrices in Sec. 9-1, it is advantageous to use for the structural element A cases a and e and for the horizontal bar B cases a and j, because its right end is pinned. Hence we have chosen the deformations

$$\mathbf{v} = \{u_A^R \quad w_A^R \quad \psi_A^R \qquad u_B^R \quad \psi_B^L\}$$

Inspection† of Fig. 10-5 then yields the matrix $\mathbf{A}$:

$$\begin{matrix} & u_2 & w_2 & \psi_2 \\ u_A^R \\ w_A^R \\ \psi_A^R \\ u_B^R \\ \psi_B^L \end{matrix} \begin{bmatrix} 0 & -1 & 0 \\ 1 & 0 & 0 \\ 0 & 0 & 1 \\ -1 & 0 & 0 \\ 0 & \dfrac{-1}{l} & 1 \end{bmatrix} = \mathbf{A}$$

We now obtain the stiffness matrix $\mathbf{K}_f = \mathbf{A}'\mathbf{K}_p\mathbf{A}$ [cf. Eq. (10-6)] by means of the matrix scheme of Table 10-2, in which the matrix $\mathbf{K}_p$ was compiled from the above-mentioned Short Catalogue.

Example 10-3. Let us now consider the same frame loaded by a vertical force P at point 2 (Fig. 10-6). As a first approximation we assume that the axial compressive force in column member A is equal to P and that the axial force in member B is equal to zero. At what load P does the frame become unstable?

† In Fig. 10-5*a* note the absence of a tilted reference line, as was used, for example, in Fig. 10-2*d*. For an explanation consider that in Example 10-2 the deformation of frame member A has to be carried out through the application of u_A^R, w_A^R, ψ_A^R, all being imposed on the right end of A. Therefore all these deformations are now measured with reference to the left end of A, which is then considered as being clamped in the displaced position.

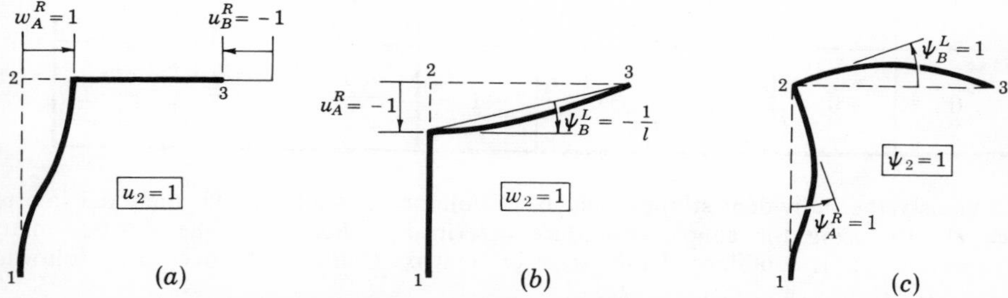

FIG. 10-5. Displacements and deformations to establish **A** matrix.

Table 10-2

						0	-1	0	
						1	0	0	
					A =	0	0	1	
						-1	0	0	
						0	$\frac{-1}{l}$	1	
	$\frac{EA}{l}$					0	$\frac{-EA}{l}$	0	
		$\frac{12EJ}{l^3}$	$\frac{6EJ}{l^2}$			$\frac{12EJ}{l^3}$	0	$\frac{6EJ}{l^2}$	
$\mathbf{K}_p=$		$\frac{6EJ}{l^2}$	$\frac{4EJ}{l}$			$\frac{6EJ}{l^2}$	0	$\frac{4EJ}{l}$	
				$\frac{EA}{l}$		$\frac{-EA}{l}$	0	0	
					$\frac{3EJ}{l}$	0	$\frac{-3EJ}{l^2}$	$\frac{3EJ}{l}$	
	0	1	0	-1	0	$\frac{EA}{l}+\frac{12EJ}{l^3}$	0	$\frac{6EJ}{l^2}$	
$\mathbf{A}'=$	-1	0	0	0	$\frac{-1}{l}$	0	$\frac{EA}{l}+\frac{3EJ}{l^3}$	$\frac{-3EJ}{l^2}$	$=\mathbf{K}_f$
	0	0	1	0	1	$\frac{6EJ}{l^2}$	$\frac{-3EJ}{l^2}$	$\frac{7EJ}{l}$	

Obviously the individual stiffness matrix of column A is affected by the axial internal force P. By using the simple procedure described in Sec. C-15 the stiffness matrix for member A is obtained from transfer matrix C-4b2 and gives the following ($\gamma^2 = Pl^2/EJ$):

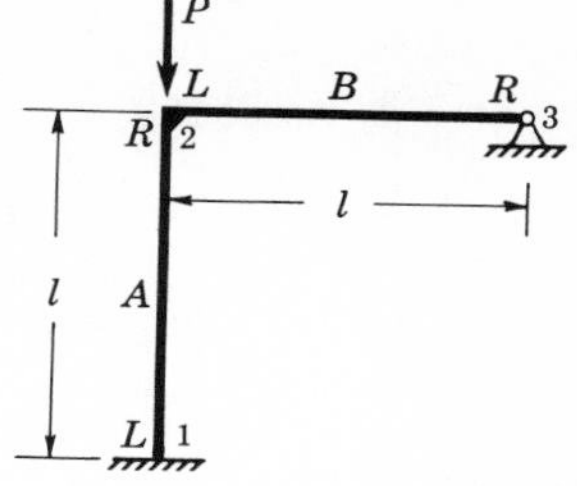

FIG. 10-6. Simple frame with compressed column.

$$\begin{bmatrix} \dfrac{EA}{l} & 0 & 0 \\ 0 & \dfrac{EJ\gamma^3 \sin\gamma}{l^3[2(1-\cos\gamma)-\gamma\sin\gamma]} & \dfrac{EJ\gamma^2(1-\cos\gamma)}{l^2[2(1-\cos\gamma)-\gamma\sin\gamma]} \\ 0 & \dfrac{EJ\gamma^2(1-\cos\gamma)}{l^2[2(1-\cos\gamma)-\gamma\sin\gamma]} & \dfrac{EJ\gamma(\sin\gamma-\gamma\cos\gamma)}{l[2(1-\cos\gamma)-\gamma\sin\gamma]} \end{bmatrix}$$

It is easily verified that for $\gamma \to 0$, that is, $P \to 0$, this stiffness matrix is reduced to the stiffness matrix $\mathbf{K}_p$ used in Example 10-2.

With the abbreviations

$$a = \frac{EJ\gamma^3 \sin\gamma}{l^3[2(1-\cos\gamma)-\gamma\sin\gamma]} \qquad b = \frac{EJ\gamma^2(1-\cos\gamma)}{l^2[2(1-\cos\gamma)-\gamma\sin\gamma]}$$

$$c = \frac{EJ\gamma(\sin\gamma-\gamma\cos\gamma)}{l[2(1-\cos\gamma)-\gamma\sin\gamma]}$$

the matrix scheme for the computation of the new stiffness matrix $\mathbf{K}_f$ is given in Table 10-3. Instability occurs when the flexibility of the structure in the presence of load P becomes infinite or, in other words, if

$$|\mathbf{K}_f| = 0$$

With the substitution $\beta = J/Al^2$ this stability equation yields

$$\left[1 + \frac{\beta\gamma^3 \sin\gamma}{2(1-\cos\gamma)-\gamma\sin\gamma}\right]\left[\frac{\beta\gamma(\sin\gamma-\gamma\cos\gamma)}{2(1-\cos\gamma)-\gamma\sin\gamma} + \frac{3\beta}{1+3\beta}\right] = \left[\frac{\beta\gamma^2(1-\cos\gamma)}{2(1-\cos\gamma)-\gamma\sin\gamma}\right]^2$$

In general, an iterative procedure is necessary for the solution of stability problems because first the longitudinal internal forces have to be determined for the given loading. Then the calculation is repeated with values for γ corresponding to the previously found longitudinal internal forces. If the new values of the longitudinal internal forces are markedly different, the computation has to be repeated with the new values for γ, and so on. In practice, however, no iteration is necessary in most cases, since usually the longitudinal internal forces are not greatly affected by the changed bending stiffness. Vice versa, their influence on the bending stiffness becomes very pronounced when the buckling load is approached.

Incidentally, it may be remarked that the basic eigenfrequency of a structure becomes zero, for whatever mass distribution, when the structure is prestressed to the buckling point.

Table 10-3

						0	−1	0	
						1	0	0	
						0	0	1	= **A**
						−1	0	0	
						0	$\frac{-1}{l}$	1	
	$\frac{EA}{l}$	0	0	0	0	0	$\frac{-EA}{l}$	0	
	0	a	b	0	0	a	0	b	
$\mathbf{K}_p =$	0	b	c	0	0	b	0	c	
	0	0	0	$\frac{EA}{l}$	0	$\frac{-EA}{l}$	0	0	
	0	0	0	0	$\frac{3EJ}{l}$	0	$\frac{-3EJ}{l^2}$	$\frac{3EJ}{l}$	
	0	1	0	−1	0	$\frac{EA}{l}+a$	0	b	
$\mathbf{A}' =$	−1	0	0	0	$\frac{-1}{l}$	0	$\frac{EA}{l}+\frac{3EJ}{l^3}$	$\frac{-3EJ}{l^2}$	$=\mathbf{K}_f=\mathbf{A}'\mathbf{K}_p\mathbf{A}$
	0	0	1	0	1	b	$\frac{-3EJ}{l^2}$	$c+\frac{3EJ}{l}$	

10-1. Find the stiffness matrix for the pin-jointed truss shown in Fig. P 10-1. The members are all of longitudinal stiffness EA. Express the displacements of the joints by the horizontal displacement u and the vertical displacement w.

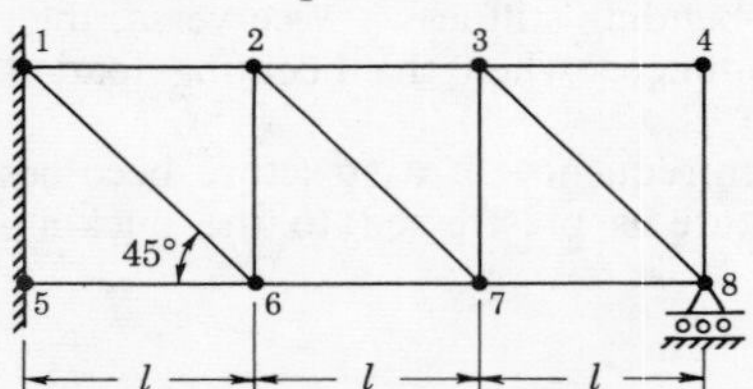

FIG. P 10-1

10-2. Find the stiffness matrix for the frame of Fig. P 10-2 which is built-in at point 1, has a rigid connection at point 2, and is simply supported at point 3. The displacements of each point are expressed in terms of the components shown in the figure.

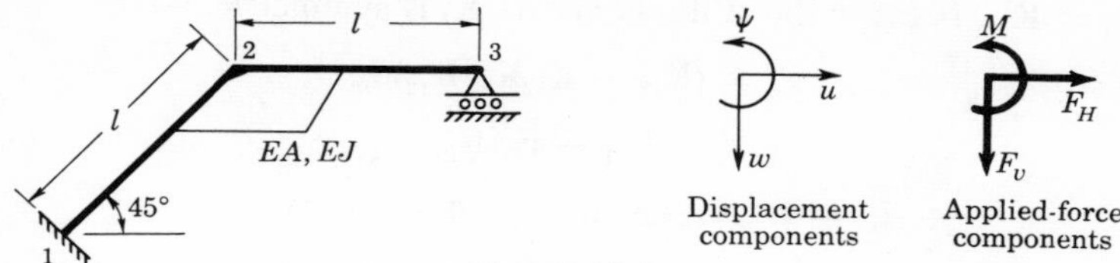

FIG. P 10-2

10-3. The built-in beam of Fig. P 10-3 is supported by two springs, each of stiffness k. Find the stiffness matrix $\mathbf{K}_f$ for the structure.

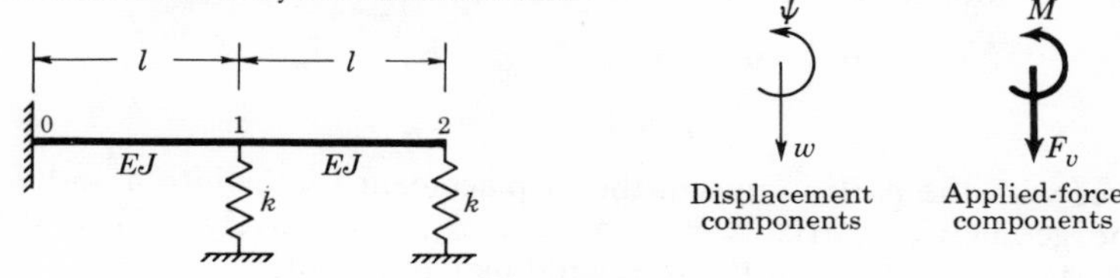

FIG. P 10-3

10-4. For the truss of Fig. P 10-4 compute the matrix **A** [49].

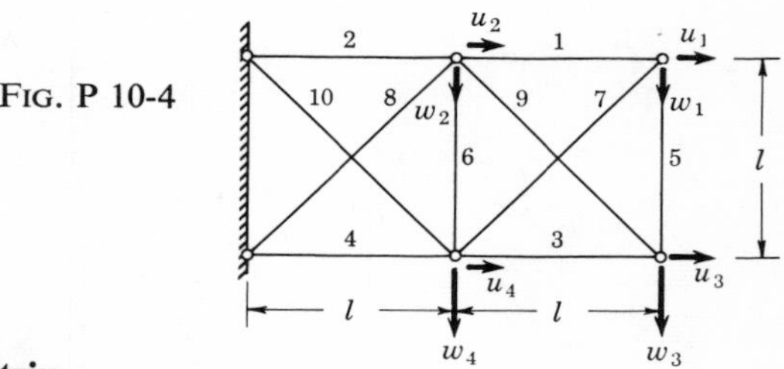

FIG. P 10-4

10-2. Condensation of the Stiffness Matrix

In Eq. (10-5) the applied forces and the displacements of these forces are related by means of the stiffness matrix. If the forces **f** are given, the values of the displacements **d** are found by inverting the stiffness matrix, so that

$$\mathbf{d} = \mathbf{K}_f^{-1}\mathbf{f}$$

However, if some of the forces are zero, the deflections can be found by the inversion of a smaller matrix. Suppose that the column matrix **f** contains $r = m + n$ elements, n of which are zero. Then Eq. (10-5) can be rewritten in the partitioned form

$$\begin{matrix} m \\ n \end{matrix}\begin{bmatrix} \mathbf{f}_m \\ \hline \mathbf{0} \end{bmatrix} = \begin{matrix} m \\ n \end{matrix}\overset{\begin{matrix} m & \quad n \end{matrix}}{\left[\begin{array}{c|c} \mathbf{K}_{11} & \mathbf{K}_{12} \\ \hline \mathbf{K}_{21} & \mathbf{K}_{22} \end{array}\right]} \cdot \begin{matrix} m \\ n \end{matrix}\begin{bmatrix} \mathbf{d}_m \\ \hline \mathbf{d}_n \end{bmatrix} \tag{10-7}$$

which on expansion gives

$$\mathbf{f}_m = \mathbf{K}_{11}\mathbf{d}_m + \mathbf{K}_{12}\mathbf{d}_n \qquad \mathbf{0} = \mathbf{K}_{21}\mathbf{d}_m + \mathbf{K}_{22}\mathbf{d}_n \tag{10-8}$$

From the second of these equations we obtain

$$\mathbf{d}_n = -\mathbf{K}_{22}^{-1}\mathbf{K}_{21}\mathbf{d}_m$$

so that the first equation becomes

$$\mathbf{f}_m = \mathbf{K}_{11}\mathbf{d}_m - \mathbf{K}_{12}\mathbf{K}_{22}^{-1}\mathbf{K}_{21}\mathbf{d}_m = (\mathbf{K}_{11} - \mathbf{K}_{12}\mathbf{K}_{22}^{-1}\mathbf{K}_{21})\mathbf{d}_m$$

or since $\mathbf{K}_{21} = \mathbf{K}'_{12}$, because the stiffness matrix $\mathbf{K}_f$ is symmetric,

$$\mathbf{f}_m = (\mathbf{K}_{11} - \mathbf{K}_{12}\mathbf{K}_{22}^{-1}\mathbf{K}'_{12})\mathbf{d}_m$$

and with

$$\mathbf{K}_{fm} = \mathbf{K}_{11} - \mathbf{K}_{12}\mathbf{K}_{22}^{-1}\mathbf{K}'_{12} \tag{10-9}$$

$$\mathbf{f}_m = \mathbf{K}_{fm}\mathbf{d}_m \qquad \text{and} \qquad \mathbf{d}_m = \mathbf{K}_{fm}^{-1}\mathbf{f}_m \tag{10-10}$$

The above reduction procedure will now be carried out using the displacement method based on the virtual-work principle.

In order to tie our notation to the one used in the analogy between the force and displacement methods in Sec. 10-3, we introduce the identities

$$\mathbf{d}_m = \mathbf{d} \qquad \mathbf{d}_n = \mathbf{y} \qquad \mathbf{K}_{fm} = \mathbf{K}_f \qquad \mathbf{f}_m = \mathbf{f} \tag{10-11}$$

so that

$$\mathbf{f} = \mathbf{K}_f\mathbf{d}$$

In accordance with the partitioning of the displacement vector into **d** and **y**, we also partition the geometric matrix **A** into $\mathbf{A}_0$ and $\mathbf{A}_1$, respectively. Then the matrix product $\mathbf{A}'\mathbf{K}_p\mathbf{A}$ is carried out in the following matrix scheme:

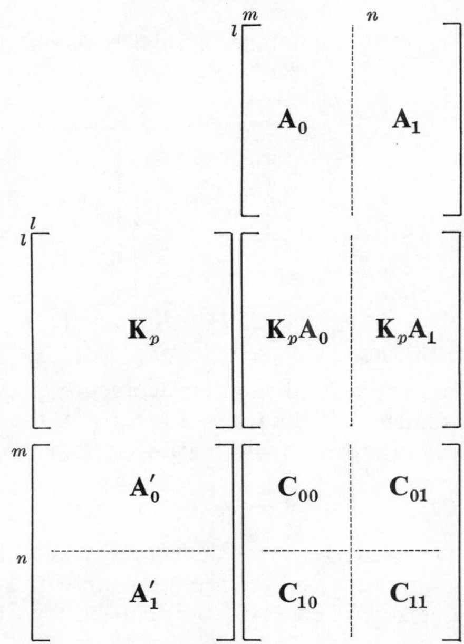

where $\mathbf{C}_{00} = \mathbf{A}'_0\mathbf{K}_p\mathbf{A}_0 \qquad \mathbf{C}_{01} = \mathbf{A}'_0\mathbf{K}_p\mathbf{A}_1 = \mathbf{C}'_{10} \qquad \mathbf{C}_{10} = \mathbf{C}'_{01} \qquad \mathbf{C}_{11} = \mathbf{A}'_1\mathbf{K}_p\mathbf{A}_1$

Comparison with Eq. (10-7) reveals that

$$\mathbf{C}_{00} \equiv \mathbf{K}_{11} \qquad \mathbf{C}_{01} \equiv \mathbf{K}_{12} \qquad \mathbf{C}_{10} \equiv \mathbf{K}_{21} = \mathbf{K}'_{12} \qquad \mathbf{C}_{11} \equiv \mathbf{K}_{22}$$

Therefore, in place of Eq. (10-9) we can write

$$\mathbf{K}_f = \mathbf{C}_{00} - \mathbf{C}'_{10}\mathbf{C}_{11}^{-1}\mathbf{C}_{10} \tag{10-12}$$

Remembering that the flexibility matrix of a structure was found to be

FIG. 10-7. Beam with discrete masses.

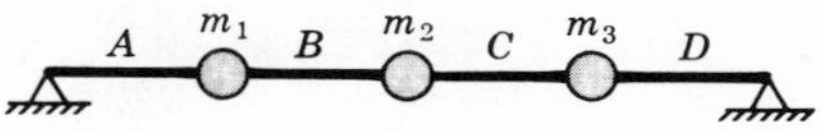

$$\mathbf{F}_d = \mathbf{D}_{00} - \mathbf{D}'_{10}\mathbf{D}_{11}^{-1}\mathbf{D}_{10} \tag{9-22}$$

we realize, by comparing Eqs. (10-12) and (9-22) and the expressions for matrices **C** and **D**, that a close analogy must exist between the displacement method and the force method. This analogy is further set forth in Sec. 10-3.

The above reduction of the stiffness matrix is of special importance in the vibration theory of structures. For example, consider the free vibration of the beam in Fig. 10-7, where the rotary inertia of the masses has been neglected, so that we have only three degrees of freedom instead of six. The matrix equation describing this problem is

$$\mathbf{M}\ddot{\mathbf{d}} + \mathbf{K}\mathbf{d} = \mathbf{0} \tag{10-13}$$

or, in expanded form,

$$\begin{bmatrix} m_1 & 0 & 0 \\ 0 & m_2 & 0 \\ 0 & 0 & m_3 \end{bmatrix} \cdot \begin{bmatrix} \ddot{w}_1 \\ \ddot{w}_2 \\ \ddot{w}_3 \end{bmatrix} + \begin{bmatrix} k_{11} & k_{12} & k_{13} \\ k_{21} & k_{22} & k_{23} \\ k_{31} & k_{32} & k_{33} \end{bmatrix} \cdot \begin{bmatrix} w_1 \\ w_2 \\ w_3 \end{bmatrix} = \begin{bmatrix} 0 \\ 0 \\ 0 \end{bmatrix}$$

The deflections w_1, w_2, and w_3 are, however, insufficient to describe completely the possible displacements of the five joints of the beam. In order to do this, we also have to know the five slopes ψ_0, ψ_1, ψ_2, ψ_3, and ψ_4. So in this case we have

$$\mathbf{d} = \{w_1 \quad w_2 \quad w_3\} \qquad \text{and} \qquad \mathbf{y} = \{\psi_0 \quad \psi_1 \quad \psi_2 \quad \psi_3 \quad \psi_4\}$$

The five components of **y** could be reduced to three if we apply to beam members A and D the degenerate cases k and j, respectively, of Sec. 9-1.

Since in our problem the displacements **d** are deficient by the displacements **y**, in order to describe completely all possible displacements of the joints, we call the displacements **y** the *kinematic deficiencies* of the problem. We shall see in Sec. 10-3 that the kinematic deficiencies **y** are exactly analogous to the force redundants **x**.† Hence in order to compute the stiffness matrix **K** in Eq. (10-13), we have to form both the matrix $\mathbf{A}_0$ for the "given" displacements **d** and the matrix $\mathbf{A}_1$ for the kinematic deficiencies **y** [49].

Example 10-4. Let us repeat Example 10-2 from a different point of view. In Example 10-2 we were able to solve the problem by using the special element stiffness matrix j (Short Catalogue of Sec. 9-1) for member B. This time, however, we do not use the special form of the stiffness matrix and so we choose the deformations

$$\mathbf{v} = \{u_A^R \quad w_A^R \quad \psi_A^R \qquad u_B^R \quad w_B^R \quad \psi_B^R\}$$

The displacements $\mathbf{d} = \{u_2 \quad w_2 \quad \psi_2\}$ are then deficient by the slope ψ_3, because the displacements u_2, w_2, ψ_2, and ψ_3 are necessary to describe all possible displacements of the frame. Thus our problem now possesses the one kinematic deficiency $\mathbf{y} = \{\psi_3\}$.

Inspection of Fig. 10-8 yields the matrices $\mathbf{A}_0$ and $\mathbf{A}_1$, and $\mathbf{K}_p$ is readily compiled from the Short Catalogue in Sec. 9-1 (cases a and e).

† For this reason, apparently, Argyris calls them *kinematic redundants*.

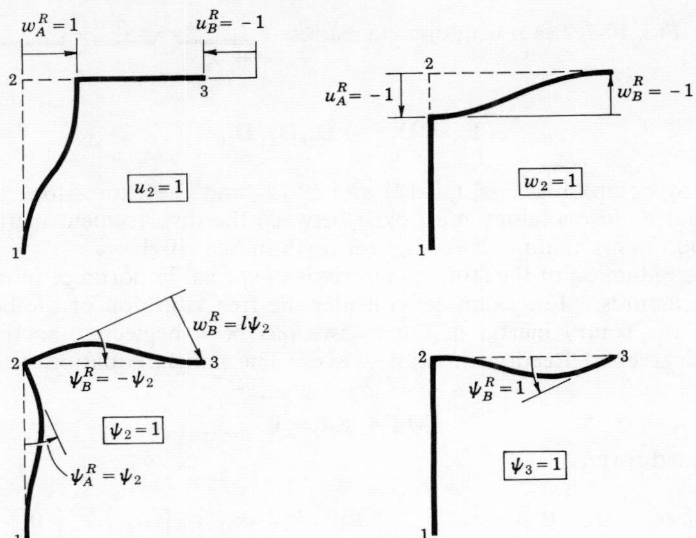

FIG. 10-8. Displacements and deformations to establish matrices $\mathbf{A}_0$ and $\mathbf{A}_1$.

$$
\begin{array}{c} \\ u_A^R \\ w_A^R \\ \psi_A^R \\ u_B^R \\ w_B^R \\ \psi_B^R \end{array}
\begin{array}{c} \begin{array}{ccc} u_2 & w_2 & \psi_2 \end{array} \\ \begin{bmatrix} 0 & -1 & 0 \\ 1 & 0 & 0 \\ 0 & 0 & 1 \\ -1 & 0 & 0 \\ 0 & -1 & l \\ 0 & 0 & -1 \end{bmatrix} \end{array} = \mathbf{A}_0
\qquad
\begin{array}{c} \\ u_A^R \\ w_A^R \\ \psi_A^R \\ u_B^R \\ w_B^R \\ \psi_B^R \end{array}
\begin{array}{c} \psi_3 \\ \begin{bmatrix} 0 \\ 0 \\ 0 \\ 0 \\ 0 \\ 1 \end{bmatrix} \end{array} = \mathbf{A}_1
$$

In view of the fact that Eqs. (10-12) and (9-22) revealed the analogy between the displacement method and the force method, it may be expected that a matrix scheme analogous to the one in Table 9-1 can be employed for the computation of the stiffness matrix $\mathbf{K}_f$. This matrix scheme is given in Table 10-4, and it is easily seen that it serves to evaluate Eq. (10-12) as soon as $\mathbf{A}_0$, $\mathbf{A}_1$, and $\mathbf{K}_p$ are known.

This table is employed in the computation, which of course yields the same result for $\mathbf{K}_f$, though a bit more clumsily than the computations in Example 10-2, where the case of a kinematic deficiency was avoided.

PROBLEMS

10-5. For the truss shown in Fig. P 10-4 calculate the stiffness matrix $\mathbf{K}_f$ associated with all vertical displacements and the horizontal displacements u_1 and u_3. EA = const.

10-6. The system shown in Fig. P 10-2 has a point mass m attached to point 2. Find the mass and stiffness matrices from which the two natural frequencies and the normal modes can be determined.

10-7. From the stiffness matrix obtained for the structure of Fig. P 10-3, use the condensation technique to find the stiffness matrix $\mathbf{K}_f$ required in solving the vibration problem displayed in Fig. P 10-7. Repeat the computation by first determining the matrices $\mathbf{A}_0$ and $\mathbf{A}_1$ and then using the matrix scheme of Table 10-4.

10-8. How many kinematic deficiencies exist when the frame of Fig. P 10-8 is loaded in the manner shown? Form the matrices $\mathbf{A}_0$, $\mathbf{A}_1$, and $\mathbf{K}_p$.

10-9. Find the matrices $\mathbf{A}_0$, $\mathbf{A}_1$, and $\mathbf{K}_p$ when the frame of Fig. P 10-8 is pinned at points 4, 5, and 6.

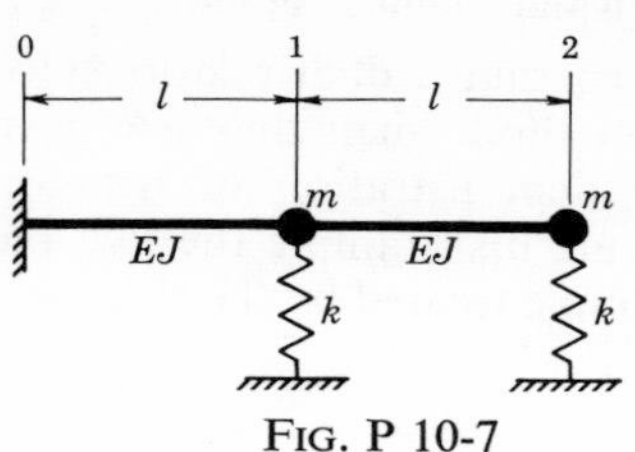

FIG. P 10-7

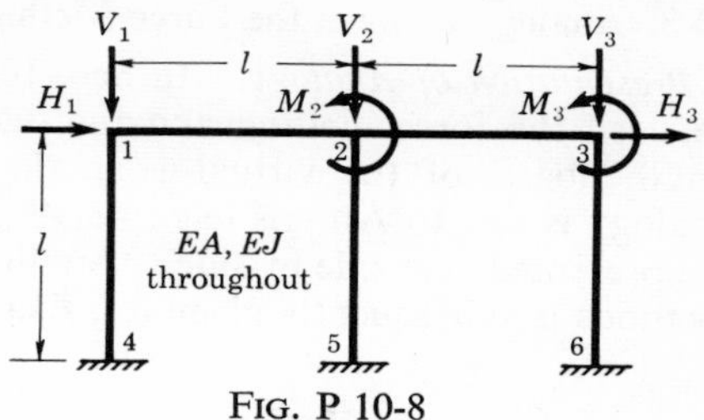

FIG. P 10-8

10-10. Calculate the internal forces and the reactions of the circular arch shown in Fig. P 10-10 if its left support is moved horizontally to the right, so that $u_0/r = 0.001$. Neglect the axial deformation of the arch and assume constant bending stiffness EJ. HINT: Calculate the individual stiffness matrices $\mathbf{K}_p$ from the corresponding transfer matrix (cf. Secs. C-7 and C-15).

FIG. P 10-10

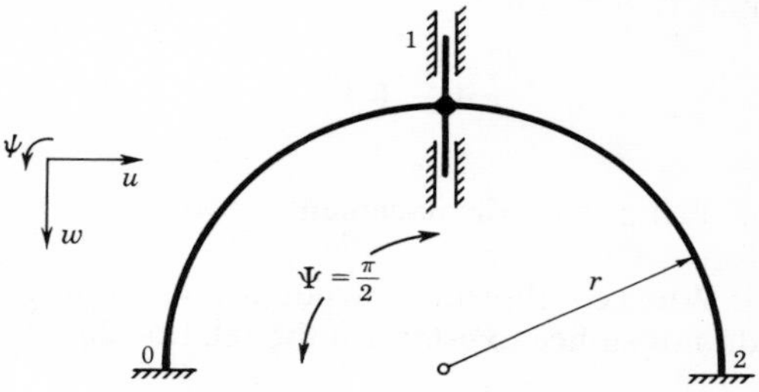

Table 10-4†

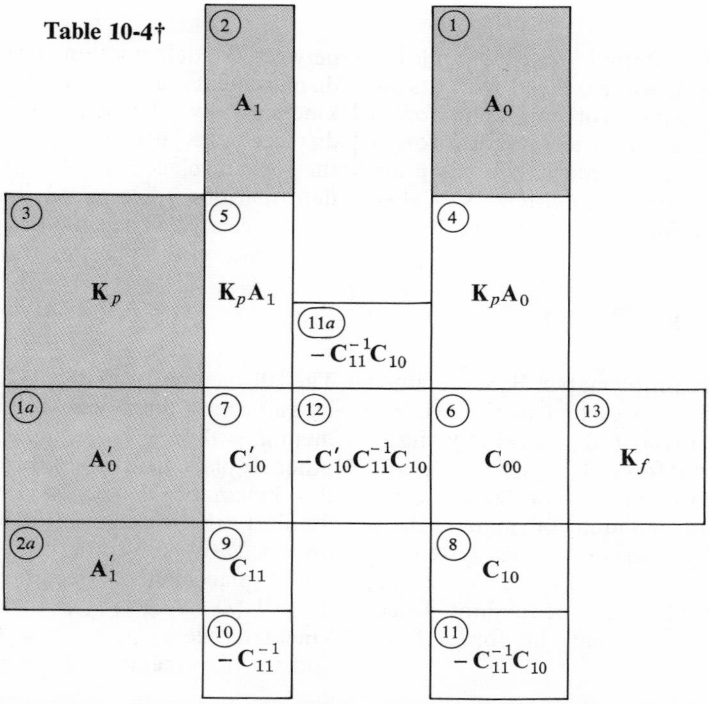

	(2) $\mathbf{A}_1$		(1) $\mathbf{A}_0$	
(3) $\mathbf{K}_p$	(5) $\mathbf{K}_p\mathbf{A}_1$	(11a) $-\mathbf{C}_{11}^{-1}\mathbf{C}_{10}$	(4) $\mathbf{K}_p\mathbf{A}_0$	
(1a) $\mathbf{A}'_0$	(7) $\mathbf{C}'_{10}$	(12) $-\mathbf{C}'_{10}\mathbf{C}_{11}^{-1}\mathbf{C}_{10}$	(6) $\mathbf{C}_{00}$	(13) $\mathbf{K}_f$
(2a) $\mathbf{A}'_1$	(9) $\mathbf{C}_{11}$		(8) $\mathbf{C}_{10}$	
	(10) $-\mathbf{C}_{11}^{-1}$		(11) $-\mathbf{C}_{11}^{-1}\mathbf{C}_{10}$	

† The matrices into which initial information is fed are indicated by shading. Circled numbers denote the sequence of the computational steps.

10-3. Analogy between the Force Method and the Displacement Method

Presentation of Analogy. In Sec. 10-2 we realized that a dual relationship exists between the force method and the displacement method when they are developed on the basis of the virtual-work theorem. The demonstration of the complete analogy is due to Argyris [e.g., 48, 49], and following his example the two methods are presented here side by side. An illustrative example treated by the two associated methods is subsequently given (cf. Example 10-5).

Force Method

Forces $\mathbf{f}$ are applied to an elastic system. It is required to find the internal forces $\mathbf{p}$ and the flexibility-matrix relation

$$\mathbf{d} = \mathbf{F}_d\mathbf{f}$$

$\mathbf{d}$ being the displacements caused by forces $\mathbf{f}$.

When equilibrium considerations alone do not suffice to establish the relationship

$$\mathbf{p} = \mathbf{B}\mathbf{f}$$

between the internal forces $\mathbf{p}$ and the given forces $\mathbf{f}$, we are faced with a statically redundant problem. The forces necessary in addition to the given forces $\mathbf{f}$ to determine the internal forces $\mathbf{p}$ are called the redundant forces $\mathbf{x}$. Then the internal forces $\mathbf{p}$ are found by the relation

$$\mathbf{p} = \mathbf{B}_0\mathbf{f} + \mathbf{B}_1\mathbf{x} \qquad (a)$$

The ith column of matrix $\mathbf{B}_0$ is obtained by subjecting the system to the external force $F_i = 1$ $(i = 1, 2, \ldots, m)$,† while all other external forces $F_j = 0$ for $j \neq i$ and the redundant forces $\mathbf{x}$ are zero. Similarly the ith column of matrix $\mathbf{B}_1$ is obtained by subjecting the system to the redundant force $X_i = 1$ $(i = 1, 2, \ldots, n)$,† while all other redundant forces $X_j = 0$ for $j \neq i$ and the forces $\mathbf{f}$ are zero.

Displacement Method

Displacements $\mathbf{d}$ are impressed on an elastic system. It is required to find the deformations $\mathbf{v}$ of the elements and the stiffness-matrix relation

$$\mathbf{f} = \mathbf{K}_f\mathbf{d}$$

$\mathbf{f}$ being the external forces required to produce the displacements $\mathbf{d}$.

When compatibility considerations alone do not suffice to establish the relationship

$$\mathbf{v} = \mathbf{A}\mathbf{d}$$

between the deformations $\mathbf{v}$ and the given displacements $\mathbf{d}$, we are faced with a kinematically deficient problem. The displacements necessary in addition to the given displacements $\mathbf{d}$ to determine the deformations $\mathbf{v}$ are called the kinematic deficiencies $\mathbf{y}$. Then the deformations $\mathbf{v}$ are found by the relation

$$\mathbf{v} = \mathbf{A}_0\mathbf{d} + \mathbf{A}_1\mathbf{y} \qquad (a)$$

The ith column of matrix $\mathbf{A}_0$ is obtained by subjecting the system to the displacement $d_i = 1$ $(i = 1, 2, \ldots, m)$,† while all other displacements $d_j = 0$ for $j \neq i$ and the kinematic deficiencies $\mathbf{y}$ are zero. Similarly the ith column of matrix $\mathbf{A}_1$ is obtained by subjecting the system to the displacement (kinematic deficiency) $Y_i = 1$ $(i = 1, 2, \ldots, n)$,† while all other kinematic deficiencies $Y_j = 0$ for $j \neq i$ and the displacements $\mathbf{d}$ are zero.

† For the same elastic system, $m(n)$, as used in the force method, denotes, in general, a different number $m(n)$ than when used in the displacement method (cf. also Example 10-5).

Force Method

Since we consider the system to be linear, the relationship between the redundant forces **x** and the applied forces **f** has the form

$$\mathbf{x} = \mathbf{X}\mathbf{f} \tag{b}$$

Hence Eq. (*a*) can be written

$$\mathbf{p} = \mathbf{B}_0\mathbf{f} + \mathbf{B}_1\mathbf{X}\mathbf{f} = \mathbf{B}\mathbf{f} \tag{c}$$

Matrix **B** is still unknown, because matrix **X** has yet to be determined.

The internal forces **p** are related to the deformations **v** by means of the equation

$$\mathbf{v} = \mathbf{F}_v\mathbf{p} \tag{d}$$

where $\mathbf{F}_v$ is a diagonally partitioned matrix made up of the flexibility matrices of the individual elements:

$$\mathbf{F}_v = \begin{bmatrix} \mathbf{F}_a & & & \\ & \mathbf{F}_b & & \\ & & \cdots & \\ & & & \mathbf{F}_s \end{bmatrix} \tag{e}$$

The relation between the external displacements **d** and deformations **v** is found by applying the dummy-load theorem so that

$$\mathbf{f}'\mathbf{d} = \mathbf{p}'\mathbf{v} \tag{f}$$

Using Eq. (*c*) in (*f*), we obtain the relation

$$\mathbf{d} = \mathbf{B}'\mathbf{v} \tag{g}$$

Actually, any set of internal forces $\mathbf{p}^*$ statically equivalent to the applied forces **f** can be used in Eq. (*f*). Hence $\mathbf{p}^* = \mathbf{B}_0\mathbf{f}$ is a suitable set of internal forces.

Replacing $\mathbf{p}^*$ for **p** in Eq. (*f*), we obtain instead of Eq. (*g*) the relation

$$\mathbf{d} = \mathbf{B}_0'\mathbf{v} \tag{h}$$

The redundant forces **x** are calculated by equating the expressions for **d** given by Eqs. (*g*) and (*h*), that is,

$$\mathbf{B}'\mathbf{v} = \mathbf{B}_0'\mathbf{v}$$

Substituting the expression for **B** from Eq. (*c*) into this equation gives the result

$$\mathbf{B}_1'\mathbf{v} = \mathbf{0} \tag{i}$$

Displacement Method

Since we consider the system to be linear, the relationship between the kinematic deficiencies **y** and the applied displacements **d** has the form

$$\mathbf{y} = \mathbf{Y}\mathbf{d} \tag{b}$$

Hence Eq. (*a*) can be written

$$\mathbf{v} = \mathbf{A}_0\mathbf{d} + \mathbf{A}_1\mathbf{Y}\mathbf{d} = \mathbf{A}\mathbf{d} \tag{c}$$

Matrix **A** is still unknown, because matrix **Y** has yet to be determined.

The deformations **v** are related to the internal forces **p** by means of the equation

$$\mathbf{p} = \mathbf{K}_p\mathbf{v} \tag{d}$$

where $\mathbf{K}_p$ is a diagonally partitioned matrix made up of the stiffness matrices of the individual elements:

$$\mathbf{K}_p = \begin{bmatrix} \mathbf{K}_a & & & \\ & \mathbf{K}_b & & \\ & & \cdots & \\ & & & \mathbf{K}_s \end{bmatrix} \tag{e}$$

The relation between the external forces **f** and internal forces **p** is found by applying the dummy-displacement theorem so that

$$\mathbf{d}'\mathbf{f} = \mathbf{v}'\mathbf{p} \tag{f}$$

Using Eq. (*c*) in (*f*), we obtain the relation

$$\mathbf{f} = \mathbf{A}'\mathbf{p} \tag{g}$$

Actually, any set of deformations $\mathbf{v}^*$ compatible with the deformations **d** can be used in Eq. (*f*). Hence $\mathbf{v}^* = \mathbf{A}_0\mathbf{d}$ is a suitable set of deformations.

Replacing $\mathbf{v}^*$ for **v** in Eq. (*f*), we obtain instead of Eq. (*g*) the relation

$$\mathbf{f} = \mathbf{A}_0'\mathbf{p} \tag{h}$$

The kinematic deficiencies **y** are calculated by equating the expressions for **f** given by Eqs. (*g*) and (*h*), that is,

$$\mathbf{A}'\mathbf{p} = \mathbf{A}_0'\mathbf{p}$$

Substituting the expression for **A** from Eq. (*c*) into this equation gives the result

$$\mathbf{A}_1'\mathbf{p} = \mathbf{0} \tag{i}$$

Force Method

Using Eqs. (*d*) and (*a*) in Eq. (*i*) yields the expression for the redundant forces:

$$\mathbf{x} = -\mathbf{D}_{11}^{-1}\mathbf{D}_{10}\mathbf{f} \qquad (j)$$

where $\mathbf{D}_{11} = \mathbf{B}_1'\mathbf{F}_v\mathbf{B}_1$

and $\mathbf{D}_{10} = \mathbf{B}_1'\mathbf{F}_v\mathbf{B}_0$

Hence the internal forces are given by the relation [cf. Eq. (*a*)]

$$\mathbf{p} = (\mathbf{B}_0 - \mathbf{B}_1\mathbf{D}_{11}^{-1}\mathbf{D}_{10})\,\mathbf{f} = \mathbf{B}\mathbf{f} \qquad (k)$$

The flexibility matrix $\mathbf{F}_d$ for the entire system is formed by starting from Eq. (*h*) and using Eqs. (*d*) and (*k*), so that

$$\mathbf{d} = \mathbf{B}_0'\mathbf{F}_v\mathbf{p} = \mathbf{B}_0'\mathbf{F}_v\mathbf{B}\mathbf{f} = \mathbf{F}_d\mathbf{f} \qquad (l)$$

where $\mathbf{F}_d = \mathbf{B}_0'\mathbf{F}_v[\mathbf{B}_0 - \mathbf{B}_1\mathbf{D}_{11}^{-1}\mathbf{D}_{10}]$
$= \mathbf{D}_{00} - \mathbf{D}_{10}'\mathbf{D}_{11}^{-1}\mathbf{D}_{10}$

Displacement Method

Using Eqs. (*d*) and (*a*) in Eq. (*i*) yields the expression for the kinematic deficiencies:

$$\mathbf{y} = -\mathbf{C}_{11}^{-1}\mathbf{C}_{10}\mathbf{d} \qquad (j)$$

where $\mathbf{C}_{11} = \mathbf{A}_1'\mathbf{K}_p\mathbf{A}_1$

and $\mathbf{C}_{10} = \mathbf{A}_1'\mathbf{K}_p\mathbf{A}_0$

Hence the deformations are given by the relation [cf. Eq. (*a*)]

$$\mathbf{v} = (\mathbf{A}_0 - \mathbf{A}_1\mathbf{C}_{11}^{-1}\mathbf{C}_{10})\,\mathbf{d} = \mathbf{A}\mathbf{d} \qquad (k)$$

The stiffness matrix $\mathbf{K}_f$ for the entire system is found by starting from Eq. (*h*) and using Eqs. (*d*) and (*k*), so that

$$\mathbf{f} = \mathbf{A}_0'\mathbf{K}_p\mathbf{v} = \mathbf{A}_0'\mathbf{K}_p\mathbf{A}\mathbf{d} = \mathbf{K}_f\mathbf{d} \qquad (l)$$

where $\mathbf{K}_f = \mathbf{A}_0'\mathbf{K}_p[\mathbf{A}_0 - \mathbf{A}_1\mathbf{C}_{11}^{-1}\mathbf{C}_{10}]$
$= \mathbf{C}_{00} - \mathbf{C}_{10}'\mathbf{C}_{11}^{-1}\mathbf{C}_{10}$

The same tabular form (cf. Table 9-1) of the calculations for the force method can clearly be used in the displacement method (cf. Table 10-5).

Finally we want to point out that Eqs. (*c*) and (*g*) reveal the striking fact that the equilibrium conditions and the compatibility conditions are not independent of each other:

$\mathbf{d} = \mathbf{B}'\mathbf{v}$	Compatibility	$\mathbf{v} = \mathbf{A}\mathbf{d}$
$\mathbf{p} = \mathbf{B}\mathbf{f}$	Equilibrium	$\mathbf{f} = \mathbf{A}'\mathbf{p}$

From these equations we furthermore realize that for the same structure, where **d** and **f** are taken to be associated with each other, we have

$$\mathbf{A}'\mathbf{B} = \mathbf{B}'\mathbf{A} = \mathbf{I}$$

Also, in view of Eqs. (*h*),

$$\mathbf{A}_0'\mathbf{B} = \mathbf{B}_0'\mathbf{A} = \mathbf{I}$$

Example 10-5

Figure 10-9*a* shows a propped cantilever beam subjected to a force F_1 and a moment F_2. It is required to find the internal forces and the flexibility matrix $\mathbf{F}_d$.

Figure 10-9*b* shows a propped cantilever beam subjected to a deflection d_1 and a rotation d_2. It is required to find the deformations and the stiffness matrix $\mathbf{K}_f$.

In these problems we choose the end moments acting on a simply supported beam as the internal forces **p** and the associated end rotations ψ^L and ψ^R as the deformations **v** (see Fig. 10-10 and the Short Catalogue, case *g*, in Sec. 9-1).

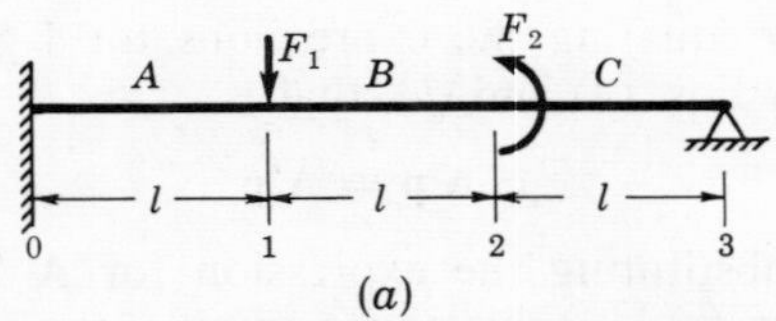

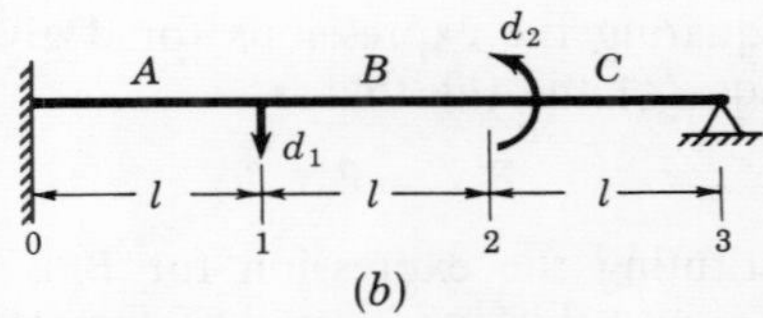

FIG. 10-9. (*a*) Propped cantilever with applied external forces F_1 and F_2; (*b*) propped cantilever with applied deflections d_1 and d_2.

Table 10-5†

		(11a) $n \times m$: $\mathbf{Y}$			(16) $m \times 1$: $\mathbf{d}$	
	(2) $l \times n$: $\mathbf{A}_1$	(12) $l \times m$: $\mathbf{A}_1\mathbf{Y}$	(1) $l \times m$: $\mathbf{A}_0$	(13) $l \times m$: $\mathbf{A}=\mathbf{A}_0+\mathbf{A}_1\mathbf{Y}$	(17) $l \times 1$: $\mathbf{v}$	$=\mathbf{Ad}$
(3) $l \times l$: $\mathbf{K}_p$	(5) $l \times n$: $\mathbf{K}_p\mathbf{A}_1$	(11b) $n \times m$: $\mathbf{Y}$	(4) $l \times m$: $\mathbf{K}_p\mathbf{A}_0$			
(1a) $m \times l$: $\mathbf{A}_0'$	(7) $m \times n$: $\mathbf{C}_{10}'$	(14) $m \times m$: $\mathbf{C}_{10}'\mathbf{Y}$	(6) $m \times m$: $\mathbf{C}_{00}$	(15) $m \times m$: $\mathbf{K}_f=\mathbf{C}_{00}+\mathbf{C}_{10}'\mathbf{Y}$	(18) $m \times 1$: $\mathbf{f}$	$=\mathbf{K}_f\mathbf{d}$
(2a) $n \times l$: $\mathbf{A}_1'$	(9) $n \times n$: $\mathbf{C}_{11}$		(8) $n \times m$: $\mathbf{C}_{10}$			
	(10) $n \times n$: $-\mathbf{C}_{11}^{-1}$		(11) $n \times m$: $\mathbf{Y}=-\mathbf{C}_{11}^{-1}\mathbf{C}_{10}$			

† Shaded blocks represent matrices into which initial information is fed. Circled numbers denote the sequence of the computational steps.

Force Method

The problem of Fig. 10-9*a* has a single force redundancy. Let the force at the prop be chosen as the redundancy (Fig. 10-11*a*).

Displacement Method

The problem of Fig. 10-9*b* has the three kinematic deficiencies Y_1, Y_2, and Y_3, which are the rotation at point 1, the deflection at point 2, and the rotation at point 3, respectively (Fig. 10-11*b*), because they have to be known in addition to the impressed displacements d_1 and d_2 to determine the deformations **v** of the structural elements *A*, *B*, *C* of the propped cantilever.

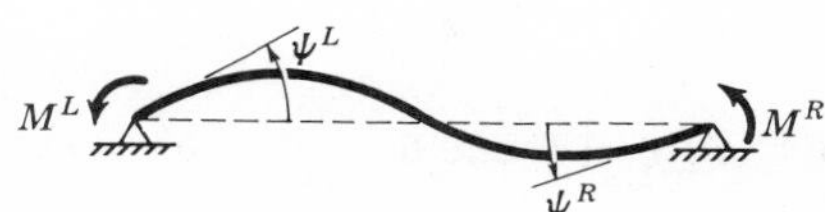

FIG. 10-10. End forces and deformations of beam element.

X_1

(*a*)

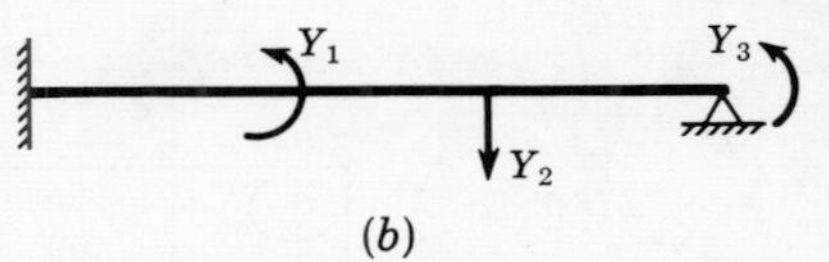

(*b*)

FIG. 10-11. (*a*) Redundant force; (*b*) kinematic deficiencies.

Force Method

Matrix $\mathbf{B}_0$ is found by computing the end moments, i.e., the internal forces, when the basic system (cantilever beam) is subjected to the external forces F_1 and F_2 in turn, the redundant force being zero (Fig. 10-12*a*).

$$\mathbf{B}_0 = \begin{bmatrix} l & -1 \\ 0 & 1 \\ 0 & -1 \\ 0 & 1 \\ 0 & 0 \\ 0 & 0 \end{bmatrix} \begin{matrix} M_A^L \\ M_A^R \\ M_B^L \\ M_B^R \\ M_C^L \\ M_C^R \end{matrix} \qquad (\text{columns } F_1,\ F_2)$$

Displacement Method

Matrix $\mathbf{A}_0$ is found by computing the deformations when the system is subjected to the displacements d_1 and d_2 in turn, the kinematic deficiencies being zero (Fig. 10-12*b*).

$$\mathbf{A}_0 = \begin{bmatrix} \frac{1}{l} & 0 \\ \frac{1}{l} & 0 \\ \frac{-1}{l} & 0 \\ \frac{-1}{l} & 1 \\ 0 & 1 \\ 0 & 0 \end{bmatrix} \begin{matrix} \psi_A^L \\ \psi_A^R \\ \psi_B^L \\ \psi_B^R \\ \psi_C^L \\ \psi_C^R \end{matrix} \qquad (\text{columns } d_1,\ d_2)$$

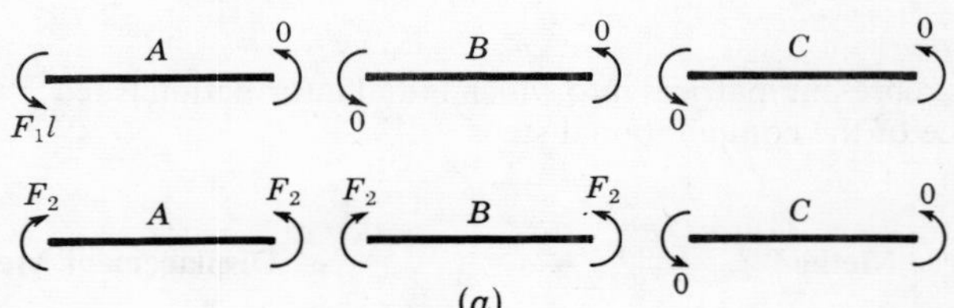

(*a*)

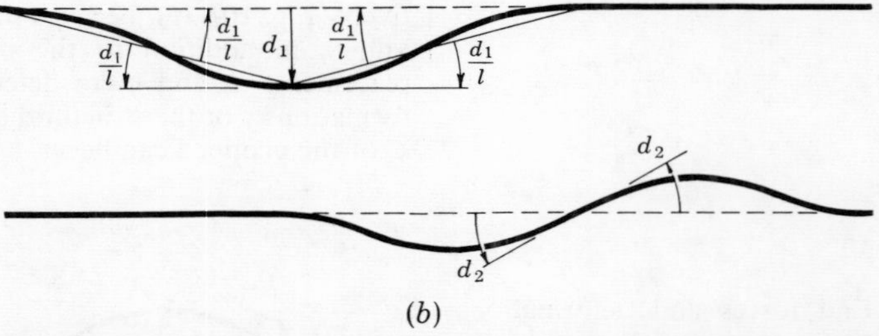

(*b*)

FIG. 10-12. (*a*) End forces due to F_1 and F_2; (*b*) deformations due to displacements d_1 and d_2.

Force Method

Matrix $\mathbf{B}_1$ is formed by computing the internal forces when the system is subjected to the redundant force, the forces F_1 and F_2 being zero (Fig. 10-13*a*).

$$\mathbf{B}_1 = \begin{array}{c} X_1 \\ \left[\begin{array}{c} -3l \\ 2l \\ -2l \\ l \\ -l \\ 0 \end{array}\right] \end{array} \begin{array}{c} \\ M_A^L \\ M_A^R \\ M_B^L \\ M_B^R \\ M_C^L \\ M_C^R \end{array}$$

Displacement Method

Matrix $\mathbf{A}_1$ is formed by computing the deformations when the system is subjected to the kinematic deficiencies Y_1, Y_2, and Y_3 in turn, the displacements d_1 and d_2 being zero (Fig. 10-13*b*).

$$\mathbf{A}_1 = \begin{array}{c} \begin{array}{ccc} Y_1 & Y_2 & Y_3 \end{array} \\ \left[\begin{array}{ccc} 0 & 0 & 0 \\ 1 & 0 & 0 \\ 1 & \frac{1}{l} & 0 \\ 0 & \frac{1}{l} & 0 \\ 0 & \frac{-1}{l} & 0 \\ 0 & \frac{-1}{l} & 1 \end{array}\right] \end{array} \begin{array}{c} \\ \psi_A^L \\ \psi_A^R \\ \psi_B^L \\ \psi_B^R \\ \psi_C^L \\ \psi_C^R \end{array}$$

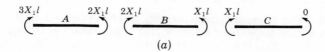

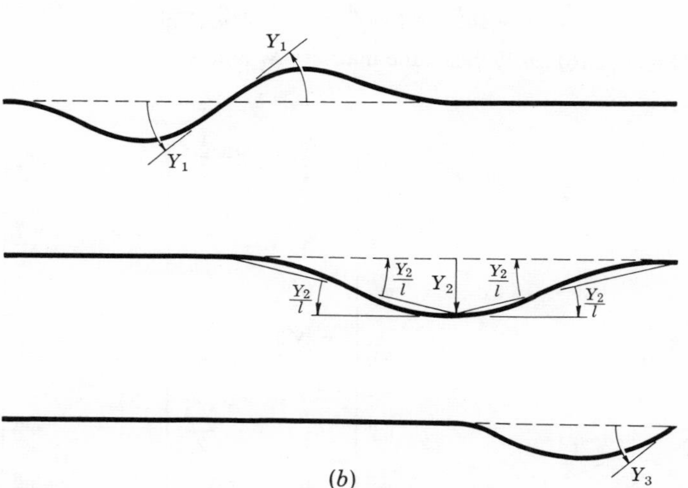

FIG. 10-13. (*a*) End forces due to X_1; (*b*) deformations due to kinematic deficiencies Y_1, Y_2, and Y_3.

Force Method

Finally the flexibility matrix $\mathbf{F}_v$ for the unassembled beam elements is

$$\mathbf{F}_v = \begin{bmatrix} \frac{g}{3} & \frac{-g}{6} & & & & \\ \frac{-g}{6} & \frac{g}{3} & & \mathbf{0} & & \mathbf{0} \\ & & \frac{g}{3} & \frac{-g}{6} & & \\ & \mathbf{0} & \frac{-g}{6} & \frac{g}{3} & & \mathbf{0} \\ & & & & \frac{g}{3} & \frac{-g}{6} \\ & \mathbf{0} & & \mathbf{0} & \frac{-g}{6} & \frac{g}{3} \end{bmatrix}$$

where $g = l/EJ$.

The matrix calculations are given in Table 10-6 according to the scheme in Table 9-1.

Displacement Method

Finally the stiffness matrix $\mathbf{K}_p$ for the unassembled beam elements is

$$\mathbf{K}_p = \begin{bmatrix} \frac{4}{g} & \frac{2}{g} & & & & \\ \frac{2}{g} & \frac{4}{g} & & \mathbf{0} & & \mathbf{0} \\ & & \frac{4}{g} & \frac{2}{g} & & \\ & \mathbf{0} & \frac{2}{g} & \frac{4}{g} & & \mathbf{0} \\ & & & & \frac{4}{g} & \frac{2}{g} \\ & \mathbf{0} & & \mathbf{0} & \frac{2}{g} & \frac{4}{g} \end{bmatrix}$$

where $g = l/EJ$.

The matrix calculations are given in Table 10-7 according to the scheme in Table 10-5.

Notice that the flexibility matrix $\mathbf{F}_d$ and the stiffness matrix $\mathbf{K}_f$ satisfy the relation $\mathbf{F}_d\mathbf{K}_f = \mathbf{I}$ and that furthermore $\mathbf{A}'\mathbf{B} = \mathbf{B}'\mathbf{A} = \mathbf{I}$, which is a check on our work.

Example 10-6. The symmetric frame of Fig. 10-14 is subjected to the force F at the stiff joint 2. Determine the stiffness matrix $\mathbf{K}_f$, the displacements u_2 and w_2, and the internal forces $\mathbf{p}$. The stiffness matrix $\mathbf{K}_f$ has to be determined for the displacements $\mathbf{d} = \{u_2 \quad w_2\}$ (Fig. 10-15). Since the displacement ψ_2 is wanting to describe completely the possible displacements of joint 2, we have the one kinematic deficiency $\mathbf{y} = \{\psi_2\}$. For the vector $\mathbf{v}$ of the deformations we choose

$$\mathbf{v} = \{u_A^R \quad w_A^R \quad \psi_A^R \qquad u_B^R \quad w_B^R \quad \psi_B^R\}$$

Inspection of Fig. (10-16) easily yields the matrices $\mathbf{A}_0$ and $\mathbf{A}_1$:

$$\begin{array}{c} \\ u_A^R \\ w_A^R \\ \psi_A^R \\ u_B^R \\ w_B^R \\ \psi_B^R \end{array} \begin{array}{c} \quad u_2 \qquad\quad w_2 \\ \begin{bmatrix} \frac{\sqrt{3}}{2} & -\frac{1}{2} \\ \frac{1}{2} & \frac{\sqrt{3}}{2} \\ 0 & 0 \\ -\frac{\sqrt{3}}{2} & -\frac{1}{2} \\ \frac{1}{2} & -\frac{\sqrt{3}}{2} \\ 0 & 0 \end{bmatrix} \end{array} = \mathbf{A}_0 \qquad \begin{array}{c} \\ u_A^R \\ w_A^R \\ \psi_A^R \\ u_B^R \\ w_B^R \\ \psi_B^R \end{array} \begin{array}{c} \psi_2 \\ \begin{bmatrix} 0 \\ 0 \\ 1 \\ 0 \\ l \\ -1 \end{bmatrix} \end{array} = \mathbf{A}_1$$

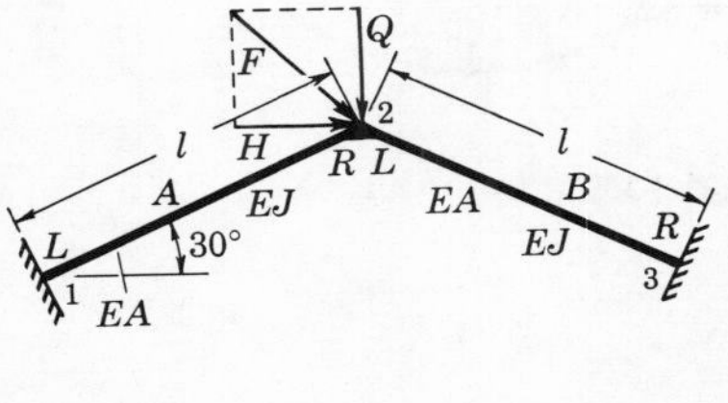

FIG. 10-14. Symmetric frame.

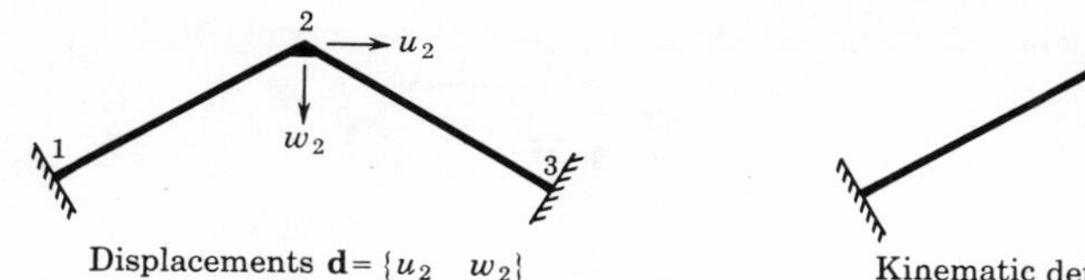

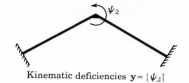

Displacements $\mathbf{d} = \{u_2 \quad w_2\}$

Kinematic deficiencies $\mathbf{y} = \{\psi_2\}$

FIG. 10-15. Displacements and kinematic deficiencies.

Table 10-6. Force-method Calculations for Example 10-5

													F_1
							$\frac{4}{27}$	$\frac{-4}{9l}$					F_2
						$-3l$	$\frac{-4l}{9}$	$\frac{4}{3}$	l	-1	$\frac{5l}{9}$	$\frac{1}{3}$	
						$2l$	$\frac{8l}{27}$	$\frac{-8}{9}$	0	1	$\frac{8l}{27}$	$\frac{1}{9}$	
						$-2l$	$\frac{-8l}{27}$	$\frac{8}{9}$	0	-1	$\frac{-8l}{27}$	$\frac{-1}{9}$	**p**
						l	$\frac{4l}{27}$	$\frac{-4}{9}$	0	1	$\frac{4l}{27}$	$\frac{5}{9}$	
						$-l$	$\frac{-4l}{27}$	$\frac{4}{9}$	0	0	$\frac{-4l}{27}$	$\frac{4}{9}$	
						0	0	0	0	0	0	0	
$\frac{g}{3}$	$\frac{-g}{6}$	**0**		**0**		$\frac{-4gl}{3}$			$\frac{gl}{3}$	$\frac{-g}{2}$			
$\frac{-g}{6}$	$\frac{g}{3}$					$\frac{7gl}{6}$			$\frac{-gl}{6}$	$\frac{g}{2}$			
0		$\frac{g}{3}$	$\frac{-g}{6}$	**0**		$\frac{-5gl}{6}$			0	$\frac{-g}{2}$			
		$\frac{-g}{6}$	$\frac{g}{3}$			$\frac{2gl}{3}$			0	$\frac{g}{2}$			
0		**0**		$\frac{g}{3}$	$\frac{-g}{6}$	$\frac{-gl}{3}$			0	0			
				$\frac{-g}{6}$	$\frac{g}{3}$	$\frac{g}{6}$	$\frac{4}{27}$	$\frac{-4}{9l}$	0	0			
l	0	0	0	0	0	$\frac{-4gl^2}{3}$	$\frac{-16gl^2}{81}$	$\frac{16gl}{27}$	$\frac{gl^2}{3}$	$\frac{-gl}{2}$	$\frac{11gl^2}{81}$	$\frac{5gl}{54}$	**d**
-1	1	-1	1	0	0	$4gl$	$\frac{16gl}{27}$	$\frac{-16g}{9}$	$\frac{-gl}{2}$	$2g$	$\frac{5gl}{54}$	$\frac{2g}{9}$	
$-3l$	$2l$	$-2l$	l	$-l$	0	$9gl^2$			$\frac{-4gl^2}{3}$	$4gl$			
						$\frac{-1}{9gl^2}$			$\frac{4}{27}$	$\frac{-4}{9l}$			

Table 10-7. Displacement-method Calculations for Example 10-5

									$\frac{-6}{7l}$	$\frac{-1}{7}$					
									$\frac{8}{7}$	$\frac{-l}{7}$					d_1
									$\frac{12}{7l}$	$\frac{-5}{7}$					d_2
						0	0	0	0	0	$\frac{1}{l}$	0	$\frac{1}{l}$	0	
						1	0	0	$\frac{-6}{7l}$	$\frac{-1}{7}$	$\frac{1}{l}$	0	$\frac{1}{7l}$	$\frac{-1}{7}$	
						1	$\frac{1}{l}$	0	$\frac{2}{7l}$	$\frac{-2}{7}$	$\frac{-1}{l}$	0	$\frac{-5}{7l}$	$\frac{-2}{7}$	
						0	$\frac{1}{l}$	0	$\frac{8}{7l}$	$\frac{-1}{7}$	$\frac{-1}{l}$	1	$\frac{1}{7l}$	$\frac{6}{7}$	**v**
						0	$\frac{-1}{l}$	0	$\frac{-8}{7l}$	$\frac{1}{7}$	0	1	$\frac{-8}{7l}$	$\frac{8}{7}$	
						0	$\frac{-1}{l}$	1	$\frac{4}{7l}$	$\frac{-4}{7}$	0	0	$\frac{4}{7l}$	$\frac{-4}{7}$	
$\frac{4}{g}$	$\frac{2}{g}$					$\frac{2}{g}$	0	0			$\frac{6}{gl}$	0			
$\frac{2}{g}$	$\frac{4}{g}$			**0**		$\frac{4}{g}$	0	0			$\frac{6}{gl}$	0			
		$\frac{4}{g}$	$\frac{2}{g}$			$\frac{4}{g}$	$\frac{6}{gl}$	0			$\frac{-6}{gl}$	$\frac{2}{g}$			
		$\frac{2}{g}$	$\frac{4}{g}$			$\frac{2}{g}$	$\frac{6}{gl}$	0	$\frac{-6}{7l}$	$\frac{-1}{7}$	$\frac{-6}{gl}$	$\frac{4}{g}$			
	0			$\frac{4}{g}$	$\frac{2}{g}$	0	$\frac{-6}{gl}$	$\frac{2}{g}$	$\frac{8}{7}$	$\frac{-l}{7}$	0	$\frac{4}{g}$			
				$\frac{2}{g}$	$\frac{4}{g}$	0	$\frac{-6}{gl}$	$\frac{4}{g}$	$\frac{12}{7l}$	$\frac{-5}{7}$	0	$\frac{2}{g}$			
$\frac{1}{l}$	$\frac{1}{l}$	$\frac{-1}{l}$	$\frac{-1}{l}$	0	0	0	$\frac{-12}{gl^2}$	0	$\frac{-96}{7gl^2}$	$\frac{12}{7gl}$	$\frac{24}{gl^2}$	$\frac{-6}{gl}$	$\frac{72}{7gl^2}$	$\frac{-30}{7gl}$	**f**
0	0	0	1	1	0	$\frac{2}{g}$	0	$\frac{2}{g}$	$\frac{12}{7gl}$	$\frac{-12}{7g}$	$\frac{-6}{gl}$	$\frac{8}{g}$	$\frac{-30}{7gl}$	$\frac{44}{7g}$	
0	1	1	0	0	0	$\frac{8}{g}$	$\frac{6}{gl}$	0			0	$\frac{2}{g}$			
0	0	$\frac{1}{l}$	$\frac{1}{l}$	$\frac{-1}{l}$	$\frac{-1}{l}$	$\frac{6}{gl}$	$\frac{24}{gl^2}$	$\frac{-6}{gl}$			$\frac{-12}{gl^2}$	0			
0	0	0	0	0	1	0	$\frac{-6}{gl}$	$\frac{4}{g}$			0	$\frac{2}{g}$			
						$\frac{-5g}{28}$	$\frac{gl}{14}$	$\frac{3g}{28}$			$\frac{-6}{7l}$	$\frac{-1}{7}$			
						$\frac{gl}{14}$	$\frac{-2gl^2}{21}$	$\frac{-gl}{7}$			$\frac{8}{7}$	$\frac{-l}{7}$			
						$\frac{3g}{28}$	$\frac{-gl}{7}$	$\frac{-13g}{28}$			$\frac{12}{7l}$	$\frac{-5}{7}$			

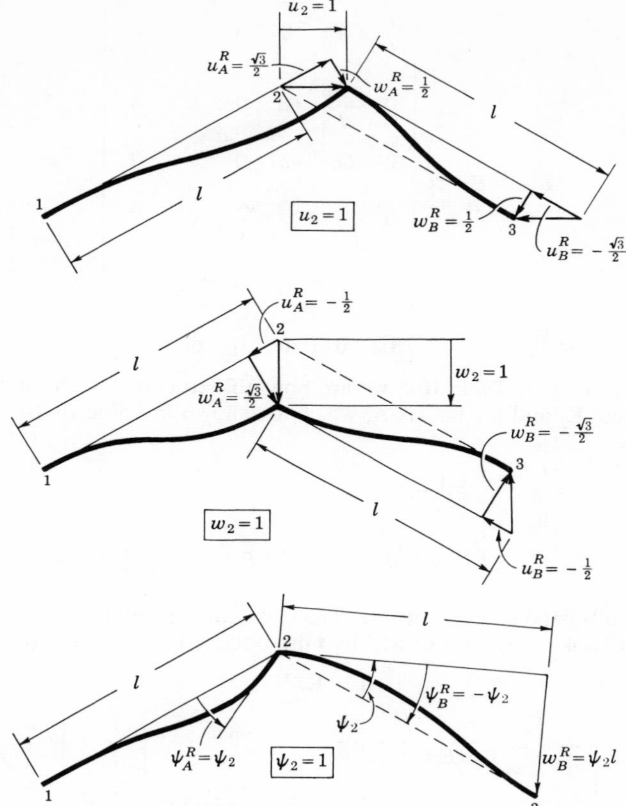

FIG. 10-16. Displacements and deformations.

and for the matrix $\mathbf{K}_p$ we have

$$\mathbf{K}_p = \begin{bmatrix} \frac{EA}{l} & 0 & 0 & 0 & 0 & 0 \\ 0 & \frac{12EJ}{l^3} & \frac{6EJ}{l^2} & 0 & 0 & 0 \\ 0 & \frac{6EJ}{l^2} & \frac{4EJ}{l} & 0 & 0 & 0 \\ 0 & 0 & 0 & \frac{EA}{l} & 0 & 0 \\ 0 & 0 & 0 & 0 & \frac{12EJ}{l^3} & \frac{6EJ}{l^2} \\ 0 & 0 & 0 & 0 & \frac{6EJ}{l^2} & \frac{4EJ}{l} \end{bmatrix}$$

or, with $a = J/Al^2$,

$$\mathbf{K}_p = EA \times \begin{bmatrix} \frac{1}{l} & 0 & 0 & 0 & 0 & 0 \\ 0 & \frac{12a}{l} & 6a & 0 & 0 & 0 \\ 0 & 6a & 4al & 0 & 0 & 0 \\ 0 & 0 & 0 & \frac{1}{l} & 0 & 0 \\ 0 & 0 & 0 & 0 & \frac{12a}{l} & 6a \\ 0 & 0 & 0 & 0 & 6a & 4al \end{bmatrix}$$

With the matrix scheme of Table 10-5 we are now able to compute the stiffness matrix of the complete system $\mathbf{K}_f$ and the matrix $\mathbf{A}$, which are shown in Table 10-8.

Hence we have

$$\mathbf{K}_f = \begin{bmatrix} \frac{3}{2l}\left(EA + \frac{EJ}{l^2}\right) & 0 \\ 0 & \frac{1}{2l}\left(EA + \frac{36EJ}{l^2}\right) \end{bmatrix}$$

The fact that the off-diagonal elements are zero is due to the symmetry of the system.

The displacements $\mathbf{d} = \{u_2 \quad w_2\}$ caused by $\mathbf{f}$ are obtained with the aid of Eq. (l):

$$\mathbf{d} = \mathbf{K}_f^{-1}\mathbf{f}$$

or

$$\begin{bmatrix} u_2 \\ w_2 \end{bmatrix} = \begin{bmatrix} \frac{2l}{3(EA + EJ/l^2)} & 0 \\ 0 & \frac{2l}{EA + 36EJ/l^2} \end{bmatrix} \cdot \begin{bmatrix} H \\ Q \end{bmatrix}$$

Table 10-8

$\mathbf{A} =$

$\frac{\sqrt{3}}{2}$	$\frac{-1}{2}$
$\frac{1}{2}$	$\frac{\sqrt{3}}{2}$
$\frac{-3}{4l}$	0
$\frac{-\sqrt{3}}{2}$	$\frac{-1}{2}$
$\frac{-1}{4}$	$\frac{-\sqrt{3}}{2}$
$\frac{3}{4l}$	0

$\mathbf{K}_f = EA \times$

$\frac{3}{2l}(1+a)$	0
0	$\frac{1}{2l}(1+36a)$

Hence, as was to be expected from the symmetry of the structure,

$$u_2 = \frac{2lH}{3[EA + (EJ/l^2)]} \qquad \text{and} \qquad w_2 = \frac{2lQ}{EA + (36EJ/l^2)}$$

Knowing **d**, we obtain by means of Eqs. (*k*) and (*d*) the internal forces

$$\mathbf{p} = \mathbf{K}_p\mathbf{A}\mathbf{d} = \mathbf{K}_p\mathbf{A}\mathbf{K}_f^{-1}\mathbf{f}$$

or

$$N_A^R = \frac{\sqrt{3}H}{3(1+a)} - \frac{Q}{1+36a} \qquad V_A^R = \frac{4aH}{1+a} + \frac{12\sqrt{3}aQ}{1+36a} \qquad M_A^R = \frac{6\sqrt{3}alQ}{1+36a}$$

$$N_B^R = -\frac{\sqrt{3}H}{3(1+a)} - \frac{Q}{1+36a} \qquad V_B^R = \frac{aH}{1+a} - \frac{12\sqrt{3}aQ}{1+36a} \qquad M_B^R = \frac{alH}{1+a} - \frac{6\sqrt{3}alQ}{1+36a}$$

Initial Stresses. In Sec. 9-3 we used the force method to compute the effect of initial strains **h** applied to the unassembled elements of the elastic system. We shall now demonstrate how the displacement method is applied to the associated problem of the effect of initial stresses **i** on the elements of the structure [49]. We define initial stresses as those internal forces which must be impressed on the ends of the structural elements in order to maintain the elements in their undeformed shape. Consider, for example, a straight bar of length l, cross-sectional area A, and Young's modulus E and with a coefficient of thermal expansion α that is subjected to a temperature change θ. Then a normal force $N^R = -EA\alpha\theta$ is necessary to hold the bar to its original length. Hence the initial stress vector $\mathbf{i}_g$ consists of this single component, which corresponds directly to the initial strain vector $\mathbf{h}_g = \{\alpha\theta l\}$. We therefore recognize that the initial stresses are the internal forces necessary to remove the initial strains **h** of the unassembled elements brought about by temperature changes, lack of fit, and similar causes.

Again we assemble all the initial stresses of the s elements of the structure in the column vector

$$\mathbf{i} = \{\mathbf{i}_1' \quad \mathbf{i}_2' \quad \cdots \quad \mathbf{i}_g' \quad \cdots \quad \mathbf{i}_s'\} \tag{10-14}$$

and the release of the joints of the structure will cause displacements and internal forces in addition to those due to the external forces applied to the structure. The analysis of the problem can be readily performed if we follow the analogy that exists between the force and displacement methods. The correspondence table is given as follows:

$$\mathbf{d} \leftrightarrow \mathbf{f} \qquad \mathbf{v} \leftrightarrow \mathbf{p} \qquad \mathbf{F}_v \leftrightarrow \mathbf{K}_p \qquad \mathbf{F}_d \leftrightarrow \mathbf{K}_f \qquad \mathbf{B} \leftrightarrow \mathbf{A} \qquad \mathbf{D} \leftrightarrow \mathbf{C} \qquad \mathbf{h} \leftrightarrow \mathbf{i}$$

The relation between the joint displacements $\mathbf{d}_h$ and the initial strains **h** with $\mathbf{f} = \mathbf{0}$ (i.e., the applied forces are zero) is [cf. Eq. (9-37)]

$$\mathbf{d}_h = \mathbf{B}'\mathbf{h}$$

By analogy the relationship between the initial stresses **i** and the forces $\mathbf{f}_i$ that must be applied, in order that the displacements of the points of application of the forces $\mathbf{f}_i$ in the presence of the initial stresses **i** may be zero, that is, $\mathbf{d}_i = \mathbf{0}$, is

$$\mathbf{f}_i = \mathbf{A}'\mathbf{i}$$

Clearly, if these forces $\mathbf{f}_i$ are "removed" by applying, in addition, the forces $-\mathbf{f}_i$, the displacements are, according to Eq. (9-21),

$$\mathbf{d}_i = -\mathbf{F}_d\mathbf{f}_i = -\mathbf{K}_f^{-1}\mathbf{f}_i = -\mathbf{K}_f^{-1}\mathbf{A}'\mathbf{i} \tag{10-15}$$

If the deformations of the elements are represented by $\mathbf{v}_i$, then the internal forces are given by the relation

$$\mathbf{p}_i = \mathbf{i} + \mathbf{K}_p\mathbf{v}_i \tag{10-16}$$

Also, by definition,

$$\mathbf{v}_i = \mathbf{A}_0\mathbf{d}_i + \mathbf{A}_1\mathbf{y}_i \tag{10-17}$$

where $\mathbf{y}_i$ are the kinematic deficiencies. Now we use Eq. (*i*),

$$\mathbf{A}_1'\mathbf{p}_i = \mathbf{0} \tag{10-18}$$

which expresses the fact that the forces associated with the kinematic deficiencies $\mathbf{y}_i$ are zero [cf. Eq. (9-27)].

Substituting Eqs. (10-16), (10-17), and (10-15) into Eq. (10-18),

$$(\mathbf{A}_1' - \mathbf{A}_1'\mathbf{K}_p\mathbf{A}_0\mathbf{K}_f^{-1}\mathbf{A}')\mathbf{i} + \mathbf{A}_1'\mathbf{K}_p\mathbf{A}_1\mathbf{y}_i = \mathbf{0}$$

and using the expressions for $\mathbf{C}_{11}$ and $\mathbf{C}_{10}$,

$$(\mathbf{A}_1' - \mathbf{C}_{10}\mathbf{K}_f^{-1}\mathbf{A}')\mathbf{i} + \mathbf{C}_{11}\mathbf{y}_i = \mathbf{0} \tag{10-19}$$

If we substitute the expressions for $\mathbf{y}_i$ and $\mathbf{d}_i$ of Eqs. (10-19) and (10-15) into Eq. (10-17), the solution for $\mathbf{v}_i$ is

$$\begin{aligned}\mathbf{v}_i &= \mathbf{A}_1\mathbf{C}_{11}^{-1}(\mathbf{C}_{10}\mathbf{K}_f^{-1}\mathbf{A}' - \mathbf{A}_1')\mathbf{i} - \mathbf{A}_0\mathbf{K}_f^{-1}\mathbf{A}'\mathbf{i}\\ &= -\mathbf{A}_1\mathbf{C}_{11}^{-1}\mathbf{A}_1'\mathbf{i} - (\mathbf{A}_0 - \mathbf{A}_1\mathbf{C}_{11}^{-1}\mathbf{C}_{10})\mathbf{K}_f^{-1}\mathbf{A}'\mathbf{i} = -(\mathbf{A}_1\mathbf{C}_{11}^{-1}\mathbf{A}_1' + \mathbf{A}\mathbf{K}_f^{-1}\mathbf{A}')\mathbf{i}\end{aligned} \tag{10-20}$$

Substituting Eq. (10-20) in Eq. (10-16), we obtain the internal forces $\mathbf{p}_i$ due to the initial stresses $\mathbf{i}$:

$$\mathbf{p}_i = \mathbf{P}\mathbf{i} \tag{10-21}$$

with

$$\mathbf{P} = -\mathbf{K}_p(\mathbf{A}_1\mathbf{C}_{11}^{-1}\mathbf{A}_1' + \mathbf{A}\mathbf{K}_f^{-1}\mathbf{A}') + \mathbf{I} \tag{10-22}$$

Example 10-7. Considering the frame shown in Fig. 10-14, determine the internal forces and the displacements $\mathbf{d}_i = \{u_2 \quad w_2\}_i$ caused by the temperature rise θ in element *B*. It is easily seen that the initial stress vector is

$$\mathbf{i} = \{0 \quad 0 \quad 0 \quad -EA\alpha\theta \quad 0 \quad 0\}$$

In order to obtain the internal forces $\mathbf{p}_i$ caused by $\mathbf{i}$, we have to evaluate Eqs. (10-21) and (10-22). On account of the fact that all components of $\mathbf{i}$ but the fourth are zero, we need only calculate the fourth column of $\mathbf{P}$. Besides, the fourth column of $\mathbf{A}_1'\mathbf{C}_{11}^{-1}\mathbf{A}_1'$ contains only zeros, since the fourth element of $\mathbf{A}_1$ is zero (cf. p. 308). Therefore only the fourth column of $-\mathbf{K}_p\mathbf{A}\mathbf{K}_f^{-1}\mathbf{A}'$ has to be computed, yielding

$$\begin{bmatrix} -\dfrac{1}{4l}(-3k_1 + k_2) \\[2ex] \dfrac{\sqrt{3}a}{4l}(3k_1 + 12k_2) \\[2ex] \dfrac{3\sqrt{3}a}{2}k_2 \\[2ex] -\dfrac{1}{4l}(3k_1 + k_2) \\[2ex] \dfrac{3\sqrt{3}a}{l}\left(\dfrac{k_1}{4} - k_2\right) \\[2ex] \dfrac{3\sqrt{3}a}{4}(k_1 - 2k_2) \end{bmatrix}$$

where
$$k_1 = \frac{2lEA}{3(1 + a)} \qquad k_2 = \frac{2lEA}{1 + 36a}$$

Hence, the internal forces are

$$N_A^R = -\frac{1}{4l}(-3k_1 + k_2)(-EA\alpha\theta) = -\frac{EA\alpha\theta}{2}\left(\frac{1}{1 + a} - \frac{1}{1 + 36a}\right)$$

$$V_A^R = -\sqrt{3}aEA\alpha\theta\left[\frac{1}{2(1 + a)} + \frac{6}{1 + 36a}\right]$$

$$M_A^R = -3\sqrt{3}al\frac{EA\alpha\theta}{1 + 36a}$$

$$N_B^R = -EA\alpha\theta\left[1 - \frac{1}{2}\left(\frac{1}{1 + a} + \frac{1}{1 + 36a}\right)\right]$$

$$V_B^R = -\sqrt{3}aEA\alpha\theta\left[\frac{1}{2(1 + a)} - \frac{6}{1 + 36a}\right]$$

$$M_B^R = -\frac{3\sqrt{3}al}{2}EA\theta\left[\frac{1}{3(1 + a)} - \frac{2}{1 + 36a}\right]$$

The displacements $\mathbf{d}_i = -\mathbf{K}_f^{-1}\mathbf{A}'\mathbf{i}$ [cf. Eq. (10-15)] are also found easily:

$$u_2 = -\frac{\sqrt{3}l}{3(1 + a)}\alpha\theta \qquad \text{and} \qquad w_2 = -\frac{l}{1 + 36a}\alpha\theta$$

Modified Structure. The effect of modifications of the elements of a structure on the stress distribution and the flexibility was thoroughly discussed in Sec. 9-5 under the aspect of the force method. We shall now—again by analogy—deduce the corresponding results for the displacement method. Let the stiffness matrix $\mathbf{K}_f$ of the unmodified original structure be known and let us denote by $\mathbf{K}_f^*$ the stiffness matrix of the structure, in which j elements are modified and i elements remain unchanged. Then we have, by analogy with Eq. (9-52),

$$\mathbf{K}_f^* = \mathbf{K}_f + \Delta\mathbf{K}_f = \mathbf{K}_f + \mathbf{A}_j'(\mathbf{A}_{1j}\mathbf{C}_{11}^{-1}\mathbf{A}_{1j}' + \Delta\mathbf{K}_{pj}^{-1})^{-1}\mathbf{A}_j \tag{10-23}$$

where $\mathbf{A}_j$ and $\mathbf{A}_{1j}$ are the submatrices analogous to the submatrices $\mathbf{B}_j$ and $\mathbf{B}_{1j}$, as shown in Eqs. (9-47), and $\Delta\mathbf{K}_{pj}$ [cf. Eq. (9-42)] describes the changes in the stiffness of the unassembled modified elements. We then have

$$\mathbf{f}^* = \mathbf{K}_f^*\mathbf{d} \tag{10-24}$$

Similarly we find, by analogy with Eq. (9-51), that the relation between the internal deformations $\mathbf{v}^*$ of the modified structure and the impressed joint displacements $\mathbf{d}$ is

$$\mathbf{v}^* = [\mathbf{A} - \mathbf{A}_1\mathbf{C}_{11}^{-1}\mathbf{A}_{1j}'(\mathbf{A}_{1j}\mathbf{C}_{11}^{-1}\mathbf{A}_{1j}' + \Delta\mathbf{K}_{pj}^{-1})^{-1}\mathbf{A}_j]\,\mathbf{d} = \mathbf{A}^*\mathbf{d} \tag{10-25}$$

and hence the internal forces are

$$\mathbf{p}^* = (\mathbf{K}_p + \Delta\mathbf{K}_p)\mathbf{v}^* = \mathbf{K}_p^*\mathbf{v}^* \tag{10-26}$$

where
$$\mathbf{K}_p^* = \begin{bmatrix} \mathbf{K}_{pi} & \mathbf{0} \\ \mathbf{0} & \mathbf{K}_{pj} + \Delta\mathbf{K}_{pj} \end{bmatrix} \qquad \text{cf. Eq. (9-42)} \tag{10-27}$$

The tabular scheme of calculation is displayed in Table 10-9, where again the matrices which are known from the calculation of the original system or which contain given information are shaded.

Table 10-9

	① $\mathbf{A}'_{1j}$			
② $\mathbf{C}_{11}^{-1}$	⑤ $\mathbf{C}_{11}^{-1}\mathbf{A}'_{1j}$			
③ $\mathbf{A}_{1j}$	⑥ ($\mathbf{A}_{1j}\mathbf{C}_{11}^{-1}\mathbf{A}'_{1j}$)	④ $\Delta\mathbf{K}_{pj}^{-1}$	= ⑦ $\mathbf{F}$	→ ⑦a $\mathbf{F}^{-1}$

	⑧ $\mathbf{A}_j$					
⑦a $\mathbf{F}^{-1}$	⑬ $\mathbf{F}^{-1}\mathbf{A}_j$	→	⑬a $\mathbf{F}^{-1}\mathbf{A}_j$			
⑨ $\mathbf{A}'_{1j}$	⑭ $\mathbf{A}'_{1j}\mathbf{F}^{-1}\mathbf{A}_j$	⑱ $\mathbf{A}'_j$	⑲ $\Delta\mathbf{K}_f$	⑳ $\mathbf{K}_f$	=	㉑ $\mathbf{K}_f^*$ cf. Eq. (10-23)
⑩ $-\mathbf{C}_{11}^{-1}$	⑮ $-\mathbf{C}_{11}^{-1}\mathbf{A}'_{1j}\mathbf{F}^{-1}\mathbf{A}_j$					
⑪ $\mathbf{A}_1$	⑯ $\Delta\mathbf{A}$	⑫ $+\mathbf{A}$	=	⑰ $\mathbf{A}^*$		

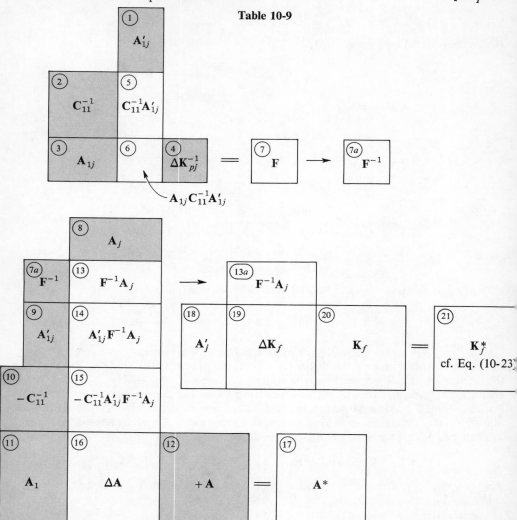

From Eqs. (10-23) to (10-27) the results for the two limiting cases are easily deduced:

1. Rigidification† of j elements: $\Delta\mathbf{K}_{pj} \to \infty$ or $\Delta\mathbf{K}_{pj}^{-1} = \mathbf{0}$; that is, block 4 in the scheme of Table 10-9 drops out.
2. Elimination of j elements: $\Delta\mathbf{K}_{pj} = -\mathbf{K}_{pj}$.

Example 10-8. The stiffness matrix for the displacements $\mathbf{d} = \{u_2 \quad w_2 \quad \psi_2\}$ of the frame shown in Fig. 10-17 is to be computed. Since members B and C are hinged together at point 3, we apply to these frame members the degenerate cases h and i, respectively, of Sec. 9-1 and so we have only the two kinematic deficiencies

$$\mathbf{y} = \{u_3 \quad w_3\}$$

We choose as internal deformations

$$\mathbf{v} = \{u_A^R \quad \psi_A^L \quad \psi_A^R \qquad u_B^R \quad w_B^R \qquad u_C^R \quad w_C^L\}$$

† Rigidification can obviously be taken into account by this method only if it concerns members that are affected by kinematic deficiencies, so that $\mathbf{A}'_{1j}\mathbf{C}_{11}^{-1}\mathbf{A}_{1j}$ is not singular.

Then by inspection of Fig. 10-18 we obtain the matrices $\mathbf{A}_0$ and $\mathbf{A}_1$:

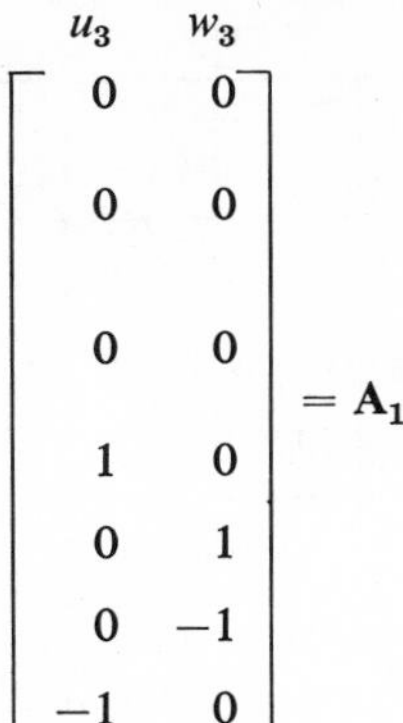

$$\begin{array}{c} \\ u_A^R \\ \psi_A^L \\ \psi_A^R \\ u_B^R \\ w_B^R \\ u_C^R \\ w_C^L \end{array}
\begin{array}{c} \begin{array}{ccc} u_2 & w_2 & \psi_2 \end{array} \\ \begin{bmatrix} 0 & -1 & 0 \\ \frac{1}{l} & 0 & 0 \\ \frac{1}{l} & 0 & 1 \\ -1 & 0 & 0 \\ 0 & -1 & l \\ 0 & 0 & 0 \\ 0 & 0 & 0 \end{bmatrix} \end{array} = \mathbf{A}_0
\qquad
\begin{array}{c} \begin{array}{cc} u_3 & w_3 \end{array} \\ \begin{bmatrix} 0 & 0 \\ 0 & 0 \\ 0 & 0 \\ 1 & 0 \\ 0 & 1 \\ 0 & -1 \\ -1 & 0 \end{bmatrix} \end{array} = \mathbf{A}_1$$

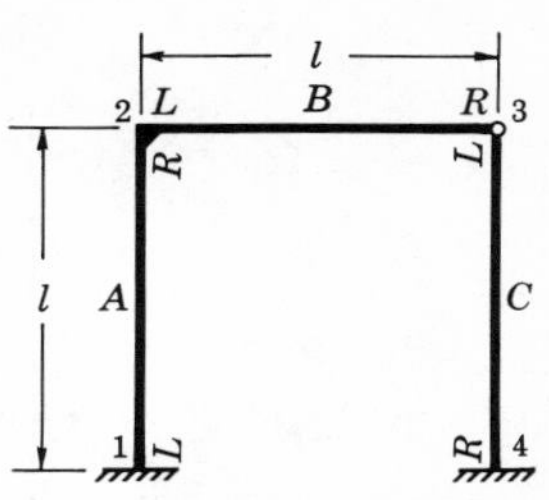

FIG. 10-17. Portal frame with hinge.

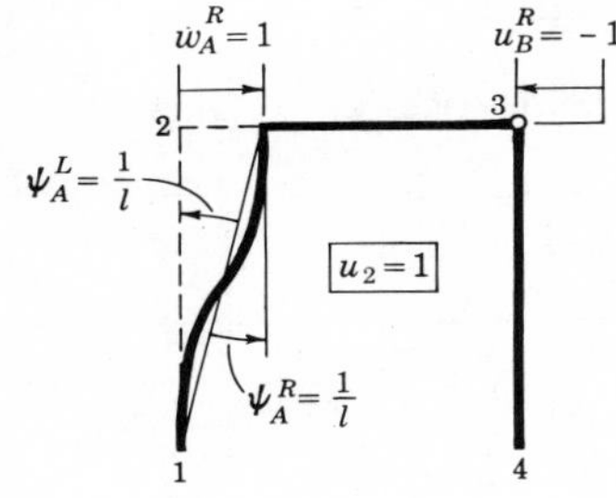

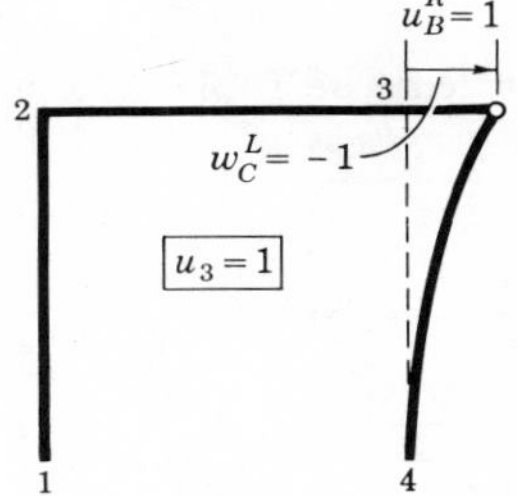

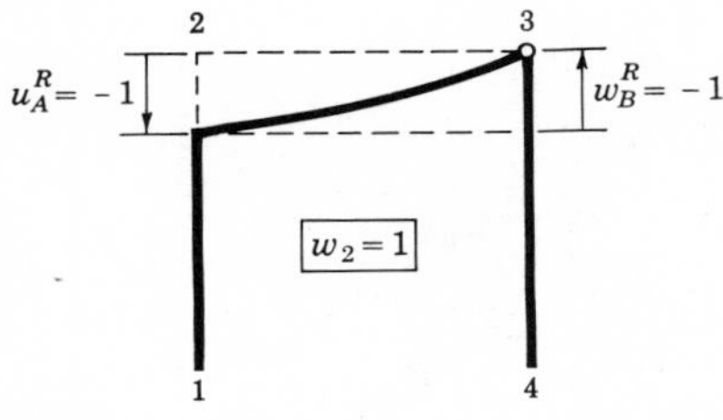

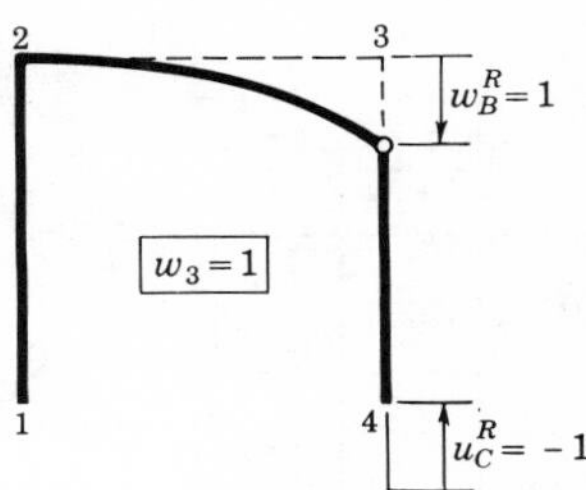

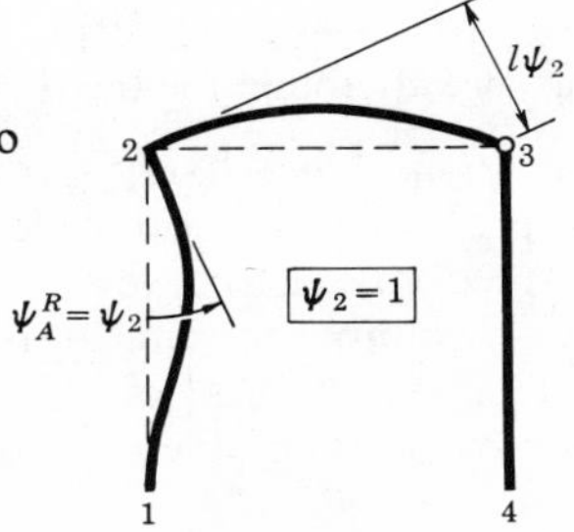

FIG. 10-18. Displacements and deformations to establish matrices $\mathbf{A}_0$ and $\mathbf{A}_1$.

The individual stiffness matrices are again taken from the Short Catalogue in Sec. 9-1. Hence

$$\mathbf{K}_v = \begin{bmatrix} \frac{EA}{l} & & & & & & \\ & \frac{4EJ}{l} & \frac{2EJ}{l} & & & & \\ & \frac{2EJ}{l} & \frac{4EJ}{l} & & & & \\ & & & \frac{EA}{l} & & & \\ & & & & \frac{3EJ}{l^3} & & \\ & & & & & \frac{EA}{l} & \\ & & & & & & \frac{3EJ}{l^3} \end{bmatrix}$$

Using the scheme of Table 10-5, we now compute the matrices ($a = J/Al^2$)

$$\mathbf{A} = \begin{bmatrix} 0 & -1 & 0 \\ \frac{1}{l} & 0 & 0 \\ \frac{1}{l} & 0 & 1 \\ \frac{-3a}{1+3a} & 0 & 0 \\ 0 & \frac{-1}{1+3a} & \frac{l}{1+3a} \\ 0 & \frac{-3a}{1+3a} & \frac{3al}{1+3a} \\ \frac{-1}{1+3a} & 0 & 0 \end{bmatrix}$$

$$\mathbf{K}_f = \begin{bmatrix} \frac{12EJ}{l^3} + \frac{EA}{l}\,\frac{3a}{1+3a} & 0 & \frac{6EJ}{l^2} \\ 0 & \frac{EA}{l} + \frac{3EJ}{l^3}\,\frac{1}{1+3a} & \frac{-3EJ}{l^2}\,\frac{1}{1+3a} \\ \frac{6EJ}{l^2} & \frac{-3EJ}{l^2}\,\frac{1}{1+3a} & \frac{EJ}{l}\left(7 - \frac{9a}{1+3a}\right) \end{bmatrix}$$

$$\mathbf{C}_{11}^{-1} = \begin{bmatrix} \frac{l^3}{E(Al^2+3J)} & 0 \\ 0 & \frac{l^3}{E(Al^2+3J)} \end{bmatrix}$$

Now the frame is modified so that member C becomes rigid. Stiffness matrix $\mathbf{K}_f^*$ is then determined from Eq. (10-23) with $\Delta\mathbf{K}_{pj}^{-1} = \mathbf{0}$, which means that block 4 in the matrix scheme of Table 10-9 drops out. The computation is shown in Table 10-10, and yields the result that was already found for the frame of Fig. 10-4 in Example 10-2.

Recurrence Method for Highly Kinematically Deficient Problems. In static as well as in kinetic problems, it is often desirable to reduce the number of displacements (degrees of freedom) to the lowest possible value compatible with the required accuracy. For example, in vibration problems it is often permissible to neglect the rotary inertia of the masses; all rotations of the points at which masses are concentrated thereby become kinematic deficiencies.

Table 10-10

u_C^R			0	-1				$=\mathbf{A}'_{1j}$
w_C^L			-1	0				
$\mathbf{C}_{11}^{-1}=$	$\frac{l}{EA(1+3a)}$	0	0	$\frac{-l}{EA(1+3a)}$				
	0	$\frac{l}{EA(1+3a)}$	$\frac{-l}{EA(1+3a)}$	0				$=\mathbf{F}$ (pointing to the block below)
$\mathbf{A}_{1j}=$	0	-1	$\frac{l}{EA(1+3a)}$	0	0	$\frac{-3a}{1+3a}$	$\frac{3al}{1+3a}$	
	-1	0	0	$\frac{l}{EA(1+3a)}$	$\frac{-1}{1+3a}$	0	0	$=\mathbf{A}_j$
$\mathbf{F}^{-1}=(\mathbf{A}_{1j}\mathbf{C}_{11}^{-1}\mathbf{A}'_{1j})^{-1}=$			$\frac{EA(1+3a)}{l}$	0	0	$\frac{-3EAa}{l}$	$3EAa$	
			0	$\frac{EA(1+3a)}{l}$	$\frac{-EA}{l}$	0	0	
			0	$\frac{-1}{1+3a}$	$\frac{EA}{l}\,\frac{1}{1+3a}$	0	0	
$\mathbf{A}'_j=$			$\frac{-3a}{1+3a}$	0	0	$\frac{9EAa^2}{l(1+3a)}$	$\frac{-9EAa^2}{1+3a}$	$=\Delta\mathbf{K}_f$
			$\frac{3al}{1+3a}$	0	0	$\frac{-9EAa^2}{1+3a}$	$\frac{9EAa^2 l}{1+3a}$	
					$\frac{12EJ}{l^3}+\frac{EA}{l}\,\frac{3a}{1+3a}$	0	$\frac{6EJ}{l^2}$	
					0	$\frac{EA}{l}+\frac{3EJ}{l^3}\,\frac{1}{1+3a}$	$\frac{-3EJ}{l^2(1+3a)}$	$=\mathbf{K}_f$
					$\frac{6EJ}{l^2}$	$\frac{-3EJ}{l^2(1+3a)}$	$\frac{EJ}{l}\left(7-\frac{9a}{1+3a}\right)$	
					$\frac{EA}{l}+\frac{12EJ}{l^3}$	0	$\frac{6EJ}{l^2}$	
					0	$\frac{EA}{l}+\frac{3EJ}{l^3}$	$\frac{-3EJ}{l^2}$	$=\mathbf{K}_f^*$
					$\frac{6EJ}{l^2}$	$\frac{-3EJ}{l^2}$	$\frac{7EJ}{l}$	

Table 10-11. Scheme of the Recurrence Method†

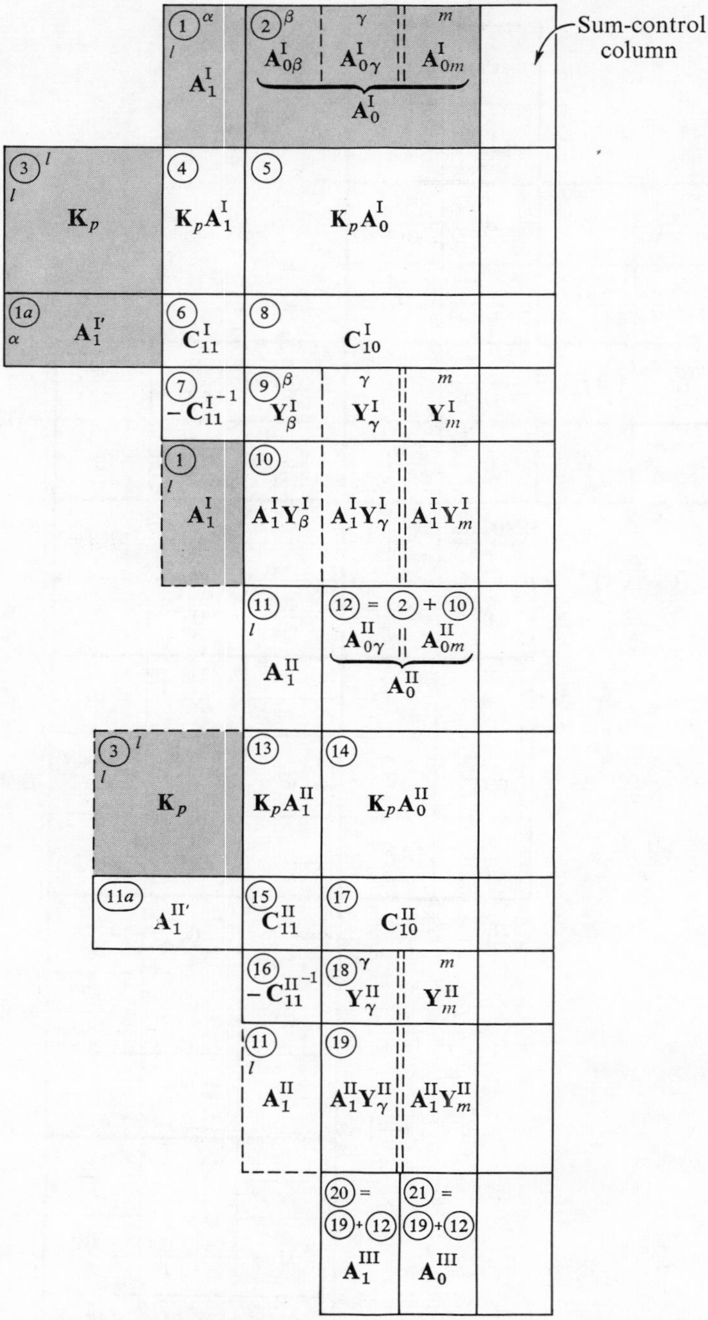

					Sum-control column
	(1) α l $\mathbf{A}_1^{\mathrm{I}}$	(2) β $\mathbf{A}_{0\beta}^{\mathrm{I}}$	γ $\mathbf{A}_{0\gamma}^{\mathrm{I}}$	m $\mathbf{A}_{0m}^{\mathrm{I}}$ ($\mathbf{A}_0^{\mathrm{I}}$)	
(3) l l $\mathbf{K}_p$	(4) $\mathbf{K}_p\mathbf{A}_1^{\mathrm{I}}$	(5) $\mathbf{K}_p\mathbf{A}_0^{\mathrm{I}}$			
(1a) α $\mathbf{A}_1^{\mathrm{I}'}$	(6) $\mathbf{C}_{11}^{\mathrm{I}}$	(8) $\mathbf{C}_{10}^{\mathrm{I}}$			
	(7) $-\mathbf{C}_{11}^{\mathrm{I}-1}$	(9) β $\mathbf{Y}_\beta^{\mathrm{I}}$	γ $\mathbf{Y}_\gamma^{\mathrm{I}}$	m $\mathbf{Y}_m^{\mathrm{I}}$	
	(1) l $\mathbf{A}_1^{\mathrm{I}}$	(10) $\mathbf{A}_1^{\mathrm{I}}\mathbf{Y}_\beta^{\mathrm{I}}$	$\mathbf{A}_1^{\mathrm{I}}\mathbf{Y}_\gamma^{\mathrm{I}}$	$\mathbf{A}_1^{\mathrm{I}}\mathbf{Y}_m^{\mathrm{I}}$	
		(11) l $\mathbf{A}_1^{\mathrm{II}}$	(12) = (2) + (10) $\mathbf{A}_{0\gamma}^{\mathrm{II}}$	$\mathbf{A}_{0m}^{\mathrm{II}}$ ($\mathbf{A}_0^{\mathrm{II}}$)	
	(3) l l $\mathbf{K}_p$	(13) $\mathbf{K}_p\mathbf{A}_1^{\mathrm{II}}$	(14) $\mathbf{K}_p\mathbf{A}_0^{\mathrm{II}}$		
	(11a) $\mathbf{A}_1^{\mathrm{II}'}$	(15) $\mathbf{C}_{11}^{\mathrm{II}}$	(17) $\mathbf{C}_{10}^{\mathrm{II}}$		
		(16) $-\mathbf{C}_{11}^{\mathrm{II}-1}$	(18) γ $\mathbf{Y}_\gamma^{\mathrm{II}}$	m $\mathbf{Y}_m^{\mathrm{II}}$	
		(11) l $\mathbf{A}_1^{\mathrm{II}}$	(19) $\mathbf{A}_1^{\mathrm{II}}\mathbf{Y}_\gamma^{\mathrm{II}}$	$\mathbf{A}_1^{\mathrm{II}}\mathbf{Y}_m^{\mathrm{II}}$	
			(20) = (19)+(12) $\mathbf{A}_1^{\mathrm{III}}$	(21) = (19)+(12) $\mathbf{A}_0^{\mathrm{III}}$	

† The tabular scheme is restricted in order to save space. In actual problems l is mostly much larger than $\alpha + \beta + \gamma + m$. Shading represents blocks into which initial information is fed. Dashed outline represents repeated blocks. Circled numbers denote the sequence of the computational steps.

The immediate consequence of such procedure is a corresponding increase in the order of the matrix $\mathbf{C}_{11}$ that has to be inverted in order to obtain the stiffness matrix $\mathbf{K}_f$. If we wish to carry out this inversion in successive steps, the same procedure may be adopted as was described in Sec. 9-6. So if the computer capacity limits the order of a matrix to be inverted to α, then not more than α kinematic deficiencies are introduced in the first step; that is, $\mathbf{A}_1^{\mathrm{I}}$ has at most α columns. In the second step $\mathbf{A}_1^{\mathrm{II}}$ is again limited to α columns, and so on. The computation is best carried out in a matrix scheme as shown in Tables 10-11 to 10-13 (cf. Tables 9-13 to 9-15).

PROBLEMS

10-11. Using Table 10-5 compute the matrix $\mathbf{A}$ for Prob. 10-7. Determine the internal forces if the members B and D (the spring supports) are too long, both exceeding their proper length by d.

10-12. With the information obtained in Prob. 10-6, determine the deflections u_2 and w_2 of the frame shown in Fig. P 10-2 when member 23 is subjected to a uniform temperature gradient θ/h through its depth h, the upper side being the cooler.

10-13. Compute the deflections w_1 and w_2 and the internal forces at points 0, 1, and 2 of the beam shown in Fig. P 10-3 (cf. also Probs. 10-7 and 10-11), if section 01 has, before assembly, an initial curvature of $10^{-2}l^{-1}$.

Table 10-12

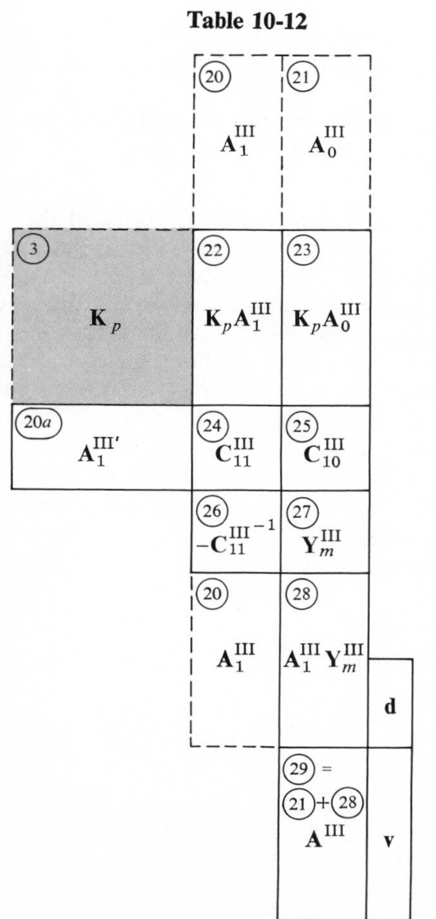

Table 10-13

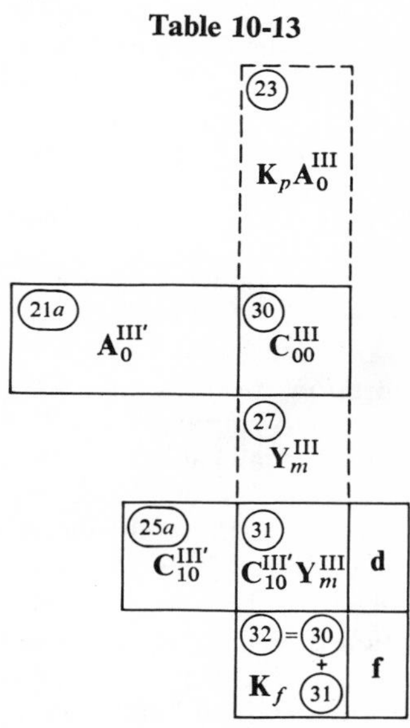

10-14. Repeat Prob. 10-7 if the spring support at point 1 (*a*) assumes the stiffness $2k$, (*b*) is eliminated. (*c*) Would it be possible to obtain the effect of rigidification of the spring support by using the same scheme?

10-15. Repeat Prob. 10-7 if member 12 is rigidified.

10-4. Some Remarks about the Matrix Force Method and the Matrix Displacement Method

The force method has been traditionally favored by engineers because the systems formerly occurring in practice could mostly be idealized to possess only a few force redundancies. With the availability of digital computers, much more complicated systems can now be analyzed, and a comparison of the number of unknown redundancies with the number of kinematic deficiencies is seldom of overriding importance in deciding which of the two methods is to be used. The various factors affecting this decision are now discussed.

As mentioned earlier, the force method is to be preferred when the number of unknown redundancies is much smaller than the number of kinematic deficiencies, and vice versa. One clear advantage of the force method, when applied to the static problems, can be seen from the following discussion.

The expressions obtained from the force method are

$$\mathbf{d} = \mathbf{F}_d\mathbf{f} \qquad \text{and} \qquad \mathbf{p} = \mathbf{B}\mathbf{f}$$

That is, the displacements and internal forces are expressed in terms of the applied forces. This is an advantage of the force method because usually the applied forces are given.

In the displacement method, on the other hand, the corresponding expressions obtained are

$$\mathbf{f} = \mathbf{K}_f\mathbf{d} \qquad \text{and} \qquad \mathbf{v} = \mathbf{A}\mathbf{d}$$

That is, the applied forces and internal deformations are given in terms of the displacements **d**, which are normally unknown. In order to determine the displacements when the forces are given, it is necessary to invert the stiffness matrix $\mathbf{K}_f$. However, in vibration problems (cf. Chap. 8) this inversion is unnecessary, since there it is customary to employ the stiffness matrix $\mathbf{K}_f$ rather than the flexibility matrix $\mathbf{F}_d$.

A severe drawback of the force method must be seen in the fact that considerable skill is needed in choosing the best redundant force groups, the best groups being those which cause only local effects and do not diffuse into the system (cf., for example, [48]). This can be a real disadvantage when the system is one of great complexity. The displacement method does not suffer from this defect since the selection of displacements is usually obvious. Furthermore the effects of impressing one displacement on the structure at a time—with the others kept zero—are purely local. Because of this advantage there appears to be a definite swing in practice toward the use of the displacement method.

11 MISCELLANEOUS APPLICATIONS

11-1. Bending Vibrations and Whirling Speeds of a Machine Shaft

A continuous shaft (Fig. 11-1) rests on three elastic bearings. The bearings are considered to be elastic in order to account for the deformability of the oil film in the bearings. It is required to find the first five bending frequencies and the first five whirling speeds. For the purpose of analysis the shaft is replaced by the substitute shaft shown in Fig. 11-2, in which the mass of the shaft is concentrated at discrete points. The shaft is divided into a number of equal lengths, and the mass

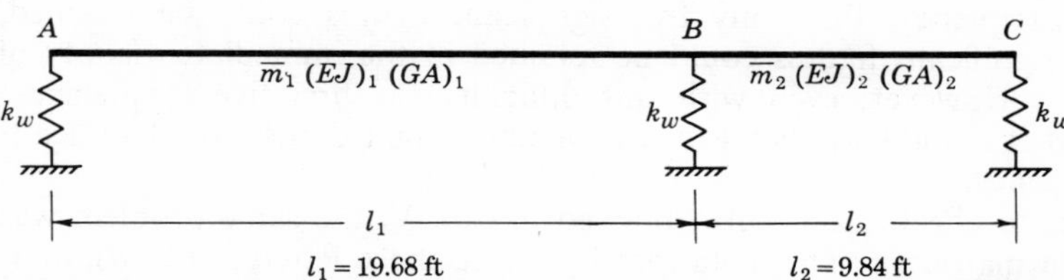

FIG. 11-1. Shaft on oil-film supports. Total mass between A and B is $\bar{m}_1 = 1{,}135$ lb-sec^2/ft; between B and C, $\bar{m}_2 = 291$ lb-sec^2/ft. $(EJ)_1 = 4.910 \times 10^9$ lb-ft^2; $(EJ)_2 = 1.285 \times 10^9$ lb-ft^2. $(GA)_1 = 6.27 \times 10^9$ lb; $(GA)_2 = 3.22 \times 10^9$ lb. Stiffness of oil film is $k_w = 1.345 \times 10^8$ lb/ft.

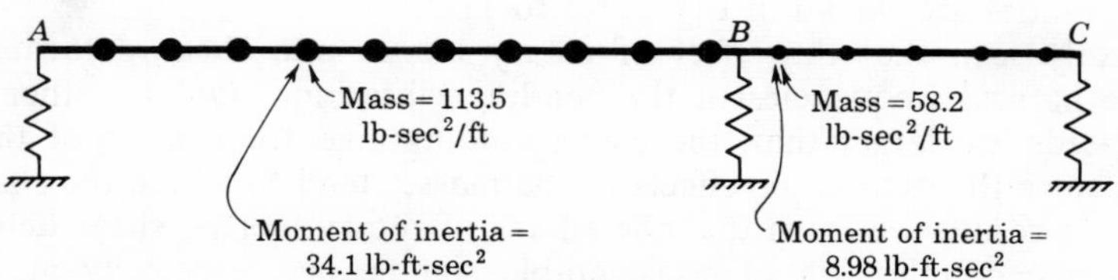

FIG. 11-2. Substitute shaft.

of each length is concentrated at its center. In addition, the mass has rotary inertia, its radius of gyration being that of the cross section of the shaft. In order to study the effect of various parameters, different cases are investigated. These are:

I. Bending vibrations, assuming that the effects of rotary inertia and shear deformation can be neglected and that the oil-film stiffness k_w is so large that the shaft may be considered to be rigidly supported at A, B, and C

II. The same as case I but including the effect of rotary inertia

III. The same as case I but including the effect of shear deformation

IV. Whirling, including the gyroscopic effect of the masses but neglecting shear deformation and assuming rigid supports at A, B, and C

V. The same as case I except that the supports are elastic

VI. The same as case V but using delta matrices

For case I the required field transfer matrix appears in Sec. C-3*c*. Since shear deformations are neglected, $1/GA_s$ is taken to be zero. The appropriate point matrix is C-3*f* in the Catalogue, with $k = 0$, $k^* = 0$, and $I = 0$. The transfer matrices are multiplied in the usual way, with the slope and shear at A as the initial unknowns. Following the procedure of elimination described in Sec. 6-2, the unknown shear V_A can be eliminated by using the fact that the deflection at B is zero. The process of matrix multiplication then continues with the slope at A and the reaction at B as the unknown vector (cf. again Sec. 6-2).

Case II is treated by the same procedure as in case I, except that in the point matrix (C-3*f*) the value of the rotary inertia I must be included. Since bending vibrations are under consideration, the value for h in the point matrix is -1.

For case III, the effect of shear deformation is included in the field matrix (C-3*c*), noting that the form factor κ for a circular cross section is 1.185.

The calculation of the whirling speeds of the shaft (case IV) follows the same procedure as for case II except that the value of h in the point matrix (C-3*f*) is $+1$.

The effect of the spring supports (case V) is introduced by spring point matrices C-3*f*, with $m = 0$, $k^* = 0$, $I = 0$, and $k = k_w$. In view of the fact that the spring stiffness is very large, we would expect to have numerical difficulties (cf. Sec. 7-1) in calculating the value of the frequency determinant, and this is indeed the case. With an eight-figure accuracy in the calculations it was found, while searching for the first eigenfrequency, that only five significant figures could be retained, whereas only two significant figures could be retained in the immediate vicinity of the fifth frequency. However, even with this difficulty the first five frequencies could be found, but it is unlikely that with this method eight digits would suffice to find the sixth frequency.

In order to check the results obtained in case V, the same problem was repeated using delta matrices. The delta matrices were those lettered (*b*), (*d*), and (*e*) in the catalogue of reduced delta matrices of Sec. 7-2. No numerical difficulties arose, and it was possible to maintain eight significant figures in the calculations.

The values for the natural circular frequencies, in reciprocal seconds, obtained for cases I to III and the whirling speeds of case IV are given in Table 11-1, and the normal modes are shown in Figs. 11-3 to 11-7.

It is readily seen that the effect of rotary inertia and shear deformation is to depress the natural frequencies of the bending vibration. On the other hand, the whirling speeds are larger than the corresponding eigenfrequencies of the bending vibrations, since the gyroscopic effects of the masses tend to stiffen the shaft.

From these results we learn that the effects of rotary inertia, shear deformations, and gyroscopic couples are of considerable significance, especially at the higher frequencies.

Table 11-1

	Case			
	I	II	III	IV
ω_1	262.0	260.8	257.5	262.9
ω_2	859.1	848.8	824.0	868.8
ω_3	1,117.0	1,102.6	1,040.0	1,131.6
ω_4	2,164.0	2,092.0	1,943.0	2,239.3
ω_5	3,235.0	3,121.0	2,781.0	3,355.0

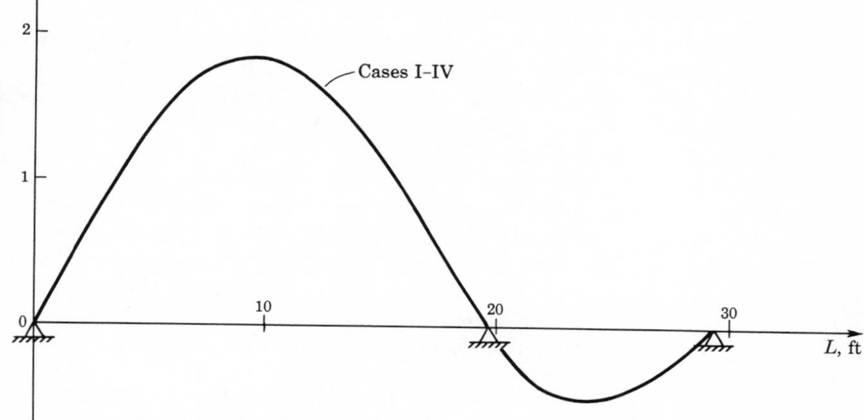

FIG. 11-3. Normal mode for ω_1.

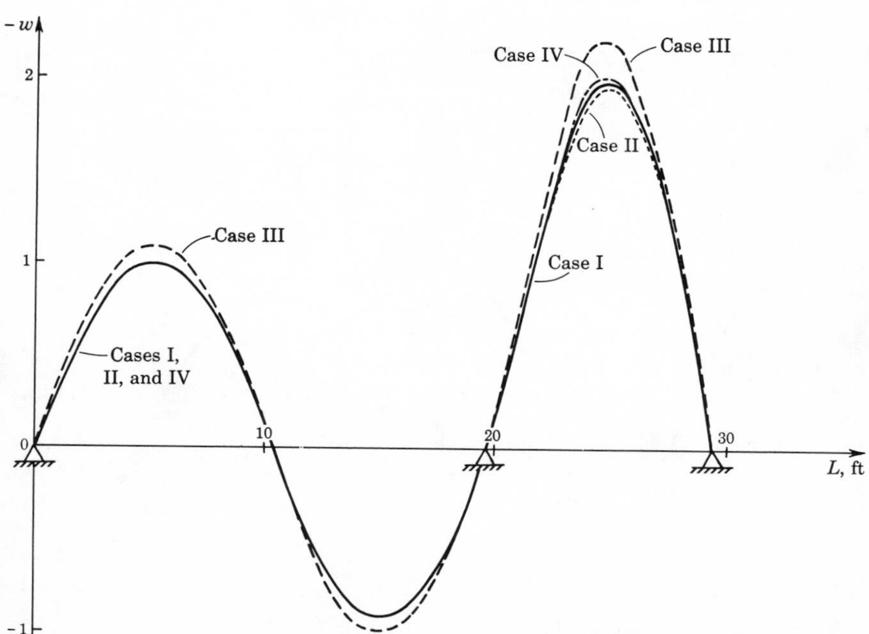

FIG. 11-4. Normal mode for ω_2.

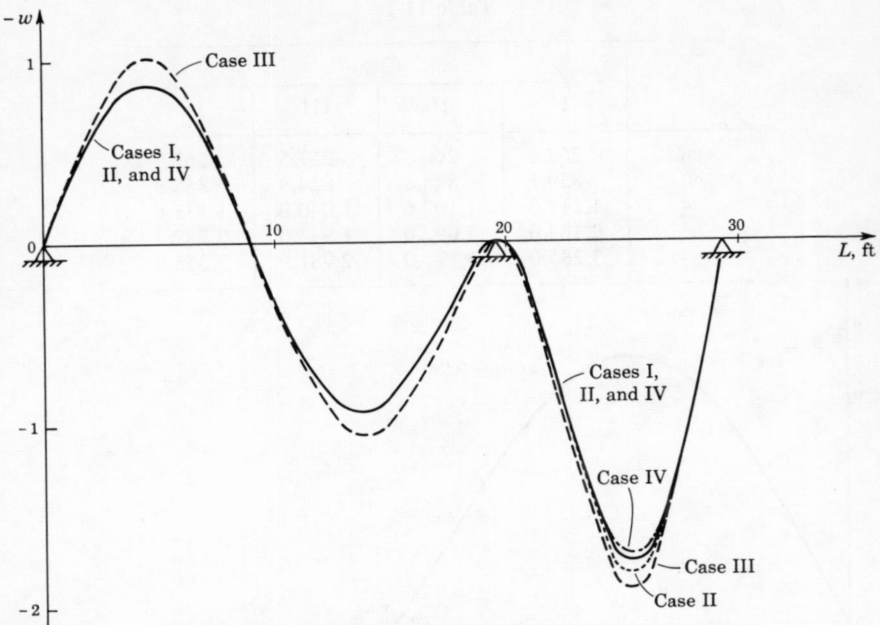

FIG. 11-5. Normal mode for ω_3.

In spite of the loss of significant figures in case V it was found that the first five frequencies differed only insignificantly from those obtained by the delta matrices of case VI. The natural circular frequencies are given below, and the normal modes are shown in Figs. 11-8 to 11-12.

ω_1	ω_2	ω_3	ω_4	ω_5
230.2	574.8	724.1	1,165.7	1,631.1

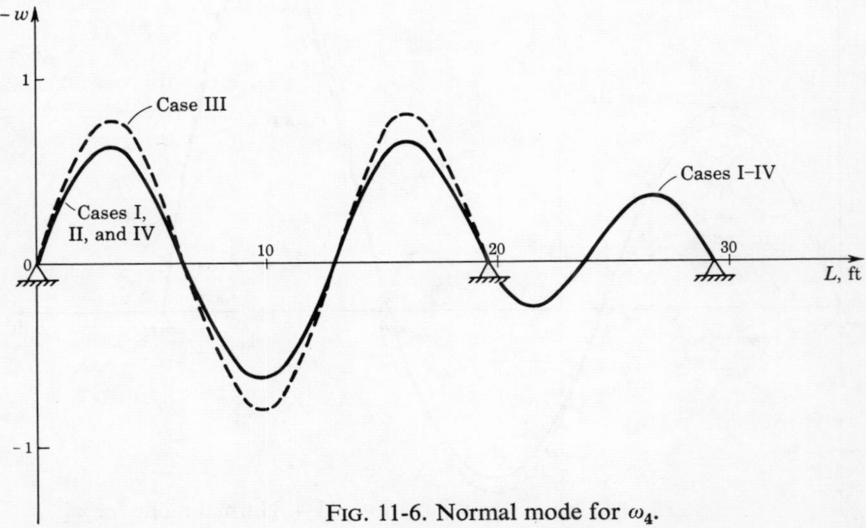

FIG. 11-6. Normal mode for ω_4.

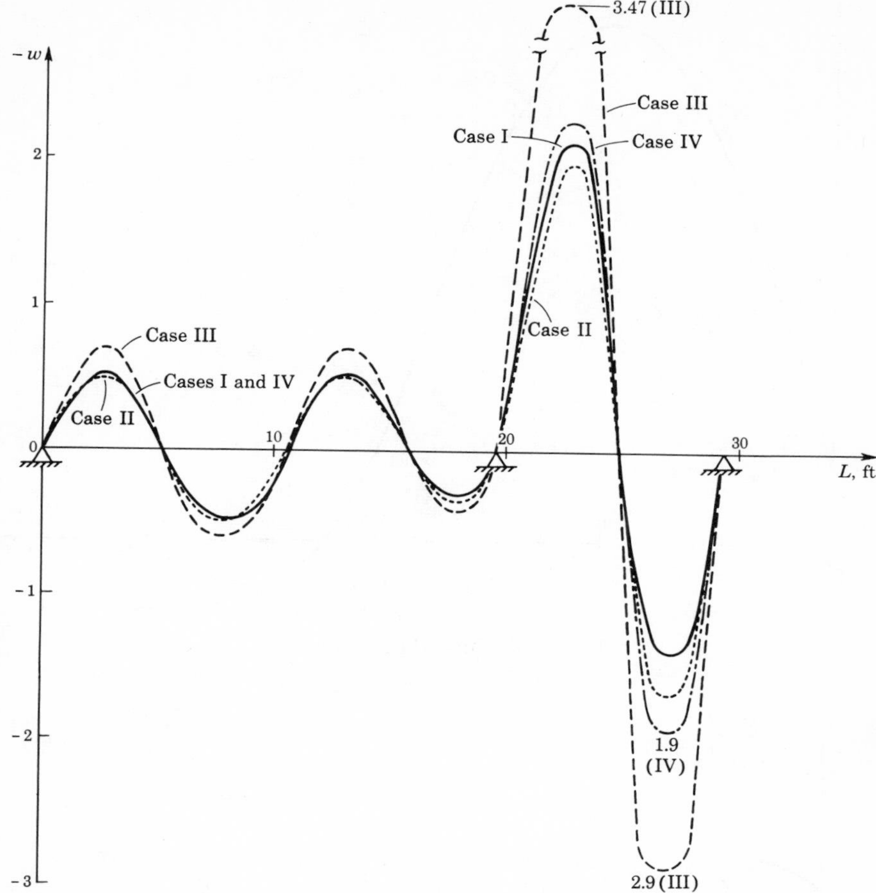

FIG. 11-7. Normal mode for ω_5.

As would be expected, the effect of the elasticity of the oil film in the bearings is to reduce the natural frequencies. However, the effect is very marked, and clearly caution must be exercised before assuming that an extremely stiff spring can be considered to be rigid.

11-2. Coupled Bending and Longitudinal Vibrations of a Circular Arch [18]

We shall consider the vibrations of the circular arch, shown in Fig. 11-13, in the plane of its central axis when it is constrained by various boundary conditions. For the application of the transfer-matrix method it is convenient to employ a substitute arch whose mass is concentrated at equidistant points along its length. Two such substitute systems are used (Figs. 11-14 and 11-15) for the arch described by the following data:

$$\alpha = \frac{\pi}{3} \qquad \frac{J_y}{A} = i_y^2 = \frac{1}{400} \qquad R = 1 \qquad \mu = 1 \qquad \frac{1}{EJ_y} = 1$$

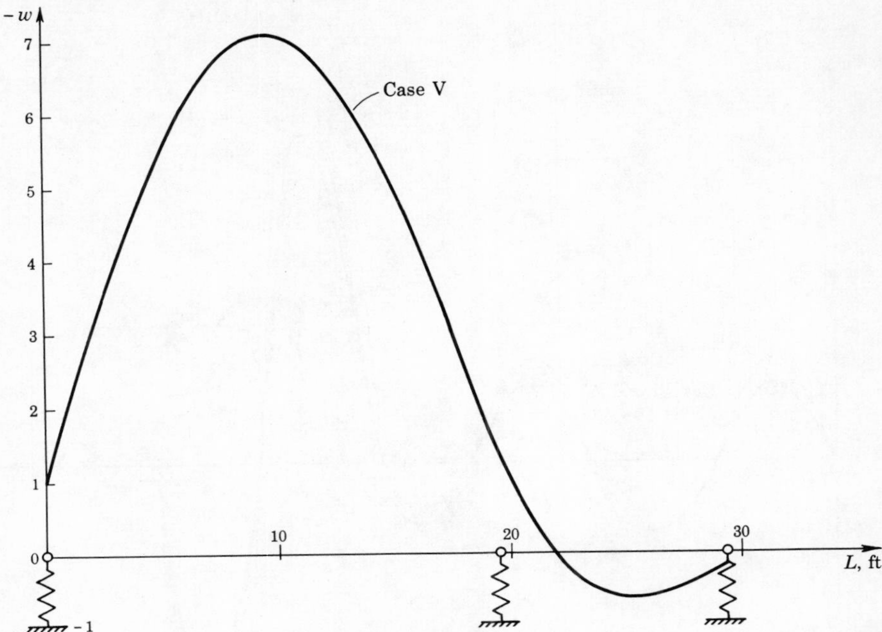

FIG. 11-8. Normal mode for ω_1.

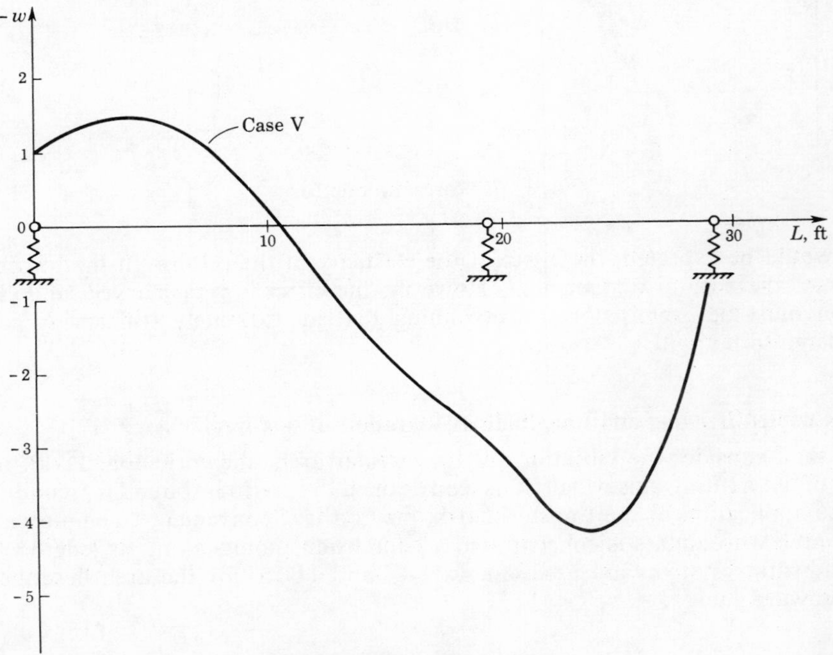

FIG. 11-9. Normal mode for ω_2.

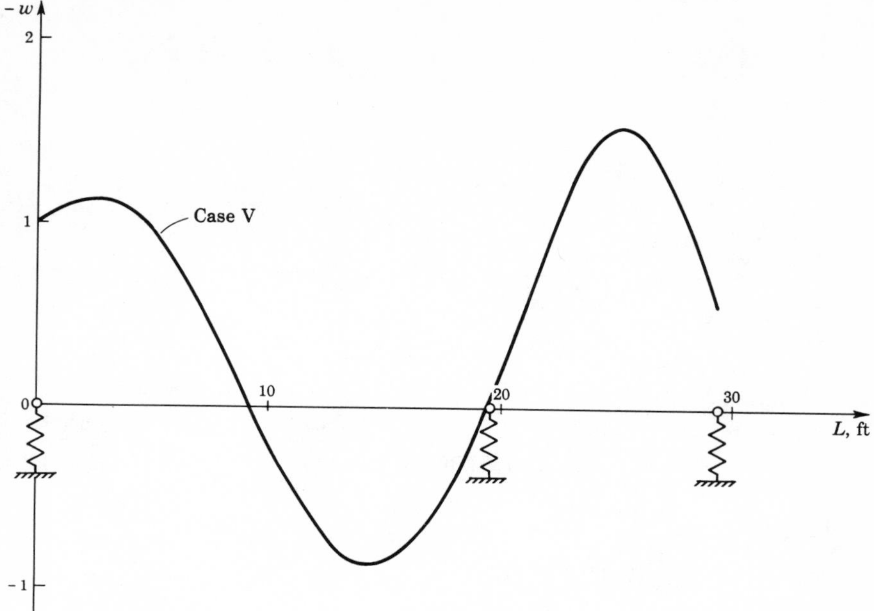

FIG. 11-10. Normal mode for ω_3.

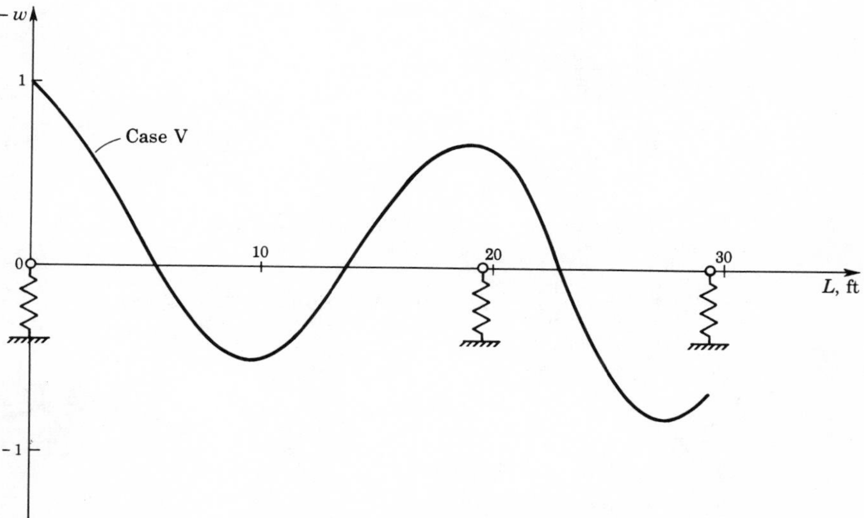

FIG. 11-11. Normal mode for ω_4.

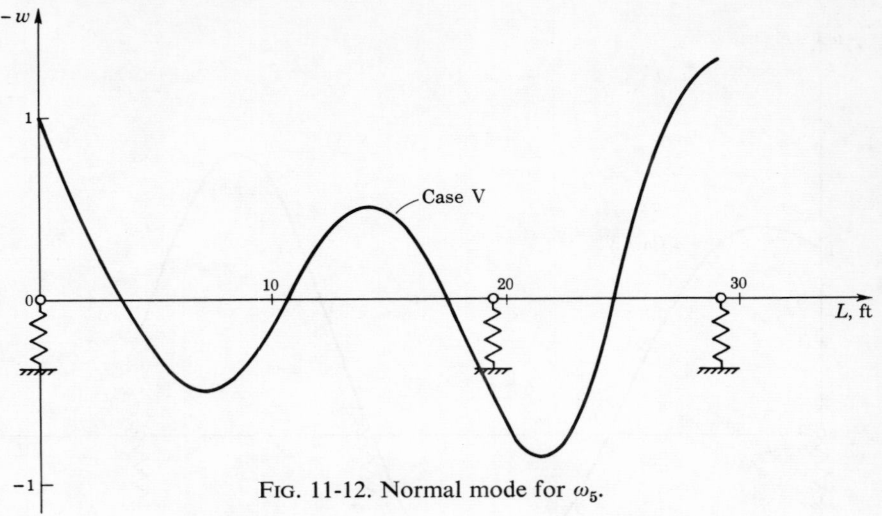

FIG. 11-12. Normal mode for ω_5.

Then we have

For substitute system I (Fig. 11-14):

$$\Psi = \frac{\pi}{12}$$

$$m = \begin{cases} \dfrac{\pi}{12} & \text{at inner points 1, 2, 3} \\ \dfrac{\pi}{24} & \text{at boundary points 0, 4} \end{cases}$$

For substitute system II (Fig. 11-15):

$$\Psi = \frac{\pi}{18}$$

$$m = \begin{cases} \dfrac{\pi}{18} & \text{at inner points 1, 2, 3, 4, 5} \\ \dfrac{\pi}{36} & \text{at boundary points 0, 6} \end{cases}$$

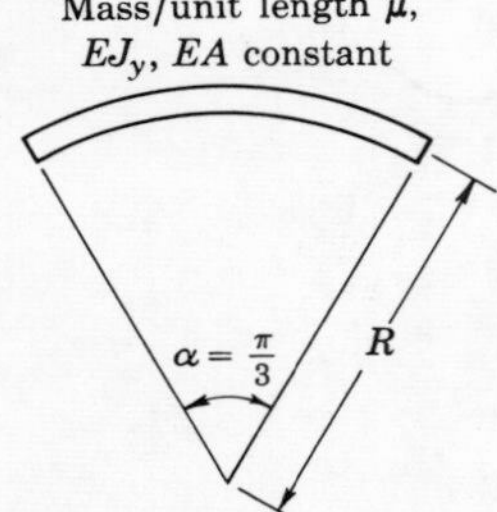

FIG. 11-13. Arch of constant cross section.

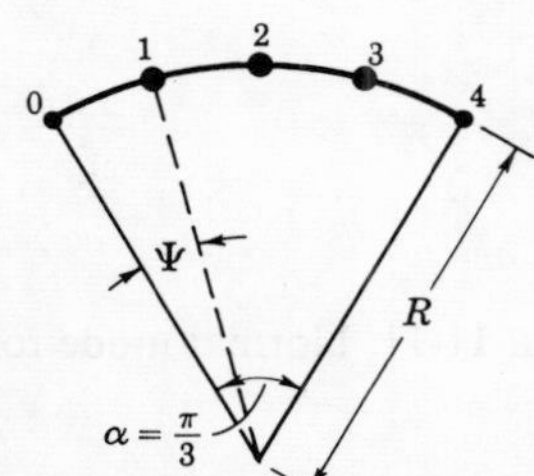

FIG. 11-14. Substitute arch I.

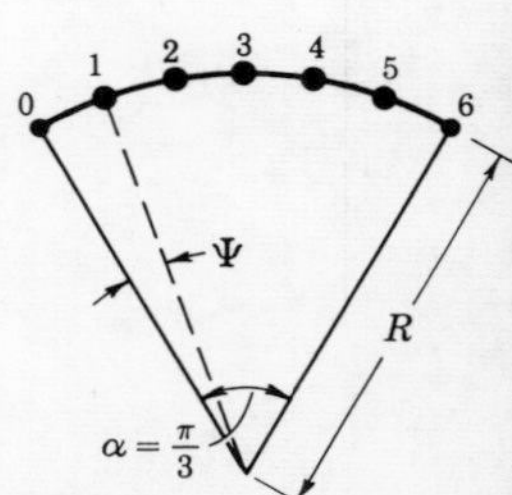

FIG. 11-15. Substitute arch II.

In both cases the effect of the axial elasticity has been included. In case I, however, the rotary inertia has been neglected, whereas it is considered in system II.

The transfer matrices to be used are given in Sec. C-7*c* and *d*. Considering system I, we have the following matrix relation between the state vectors $\mathbf{z}_0^L$ and $\mathbf{z}_4^R$:

$$\mathbf{z}_4^R = \mathbf{P}_4\mathbf{F}_4\mathbf{P}_3\mathbf{F}_3\mathbf{P}_2\mathbf{F}_2\mathbf{P}_1\mathbf{F}_1\mathbf{P}_0\mathbf{z}_0^L$$

where $\mathbf{P}$ stands for point matrix and $\mathbf{F}$ for field matrix. Since we shall consider only boundary conditions in which $w = u = 0$, the point matrices $\mathbf{P}_0$ and $\mathbf{P}_4$ may be dropped, because in case I the rotary inertia of the masses is neglected. Therefore

$$\mathbf{z}_4^R = \mathbf{F}_4\mathbf{P}_3\mathbf{F}_3\mathbf{P}_2\mathbf{F}_2\mathbf{P}_1\mathbf{F}_1\mathbf{z}_0^L = \mathbf{E}\mathbf{z}_0^L \tag{11-1}$$

In dealing with system II, however, where the rotary inertia of the masses is considered, the point matrices $\mathbf{P}_0$ and $\mathbf{P}_6$ have to be included when ψ_0 and ψ_6, respectively, are not zero on account of the boundary conditions. The computation of the matrix $\mathbf{E}$ is carried out along the usual lines and will not be repeated here. However, we shall indicate the frequency determinants that must be computed for the various boundary conditions.

For the case where both ends are pinned, we have the boundary conditions†

$$u_0 = w_0 = M_{y0}^L = u_4 = w_4 = M_{y4}^R = 0$$

from which we obtain the frequency determinant

$$\Delta_1 = \begin{vmatrix} e_{13} & e_{15} & e_{16} \\ e_{23} & e_{25} & e_{26} \\ e_{43} & e_{45} & e_{46} \end{vmatrix} = 0$$

If both ends are built-in ($u_0 = w_0 = \psi_0 = u_4 = w_4 = \psi_4 = 0$), the frequency determinant is

$$\Delta_2 = \begin{vmatrix} e_{14} & e_{15} & e_{16} \\ e_{24} & e_{25} & e_{26} \\ e_{34} & e_{35} & e_{36} \end{vmatrix} = 0$$

Finally, we shall consider the case of one end built-in, the other being pinned. The boundary conditions are then

$$u_0 = w_0 = \psi_0 = u_4 = w_4 = M_{y4}^R = 0$$

and thus the frequency determinant is

$$\Delta_3 = \begin{vmatrix} e_{14} & e_{15} & e_{16} \\ e_{24} & e_{25} & e_{26} \\ e_{44} & e_{45} & e_{46} \end{vmatrix} = 0$$

For substitute systems I and II the values of the determinants Δ_1, Δ_2, and Δ_3 are plotted in Figs. 11-16 and 11-17, respectively, after they have been computed for the frequency values $\omega = 15, 20, 25, 30, 35, 40, 45, 50$. Within this range we find from the crossover points the first two eigenfrequencies. The results are compiled in Tables 11-2*a* and *b*. There is only little difference in the results for the two substitute systems, since even in substitute system I the number of masses is more than twice the order of the highest calculated eigenfrequency and, furthermore, the effect of the rotary inertia becomes noticeable only for higher frequencies.

† For substitute system II the subscript 4 is to be replaced by the subscript 6.

Table 11-2

a

	Case 1 ω_1	Case 1 ω_2	Case 2 ω_1	Case 2 ω_2
Ritz method	19.8	33.6	26.0	53.8
Transfer-matrix method: system I	19.8	32.5	25.5	48.9
Transfer-matrix method: system II	19.7	31.6	25.4	48.6

b

	Case 3 ω_1	Case 3 ω_2
Transfer-matrix method: system I	21.5	40.7
Transfer-matrix method: system II	21.2	40.2

The eigenfrequencies of the arch shown in Fig. 11-13 under the symmetric boundary conditions (cases 1 and 2) have also been computed, using the Ritz method. These results are included in Table 11-2*a*. The fact that here the axial elasticity was excluded is mainly responsible for the higher values of the frequencies (note especially ω_2 in boundary case 2). For comparison, the transfer-matrix calculation (substitute system I) was repeated under the assumption of axial rigidity, yielding $\omega_2 = 52.4$, which is only slightly below the value obtained by the Ritz method.

It is interesting to note that for nonsymmetrical boundary conditions the Ritz method is rather inconvenient, whereas such boundary conditions do not cause any trouble in the application of the transfer-matrix method.

11-3. Symmetric Bending Vibrations of Turbine-Generator Shaft on Elastic Steel Foundation

The turbine-generator set and its steel foundation, which are treated in this section, are illustrated in Fig. 11-18. For the purpose of our investigation, which is limited

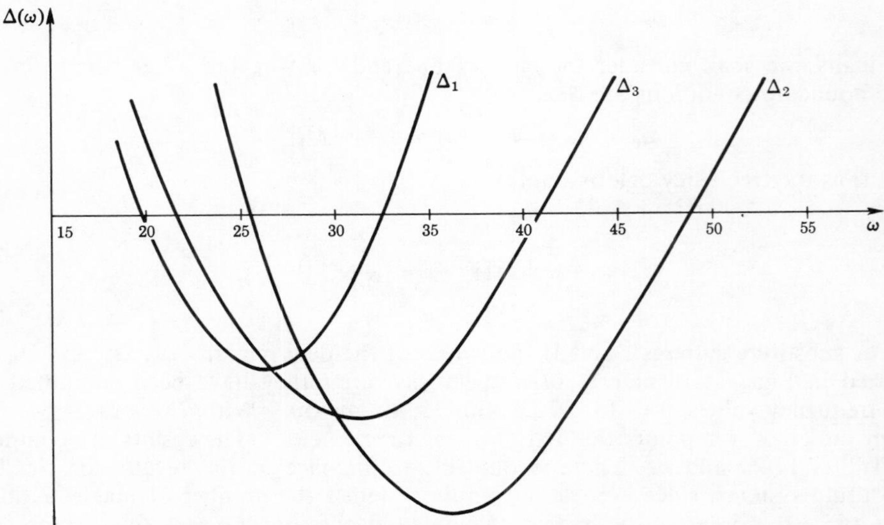

FIG. 11-16. Plot of frequency determinants Δ_1, Δ_2, and Δ_3 for substitute system I.

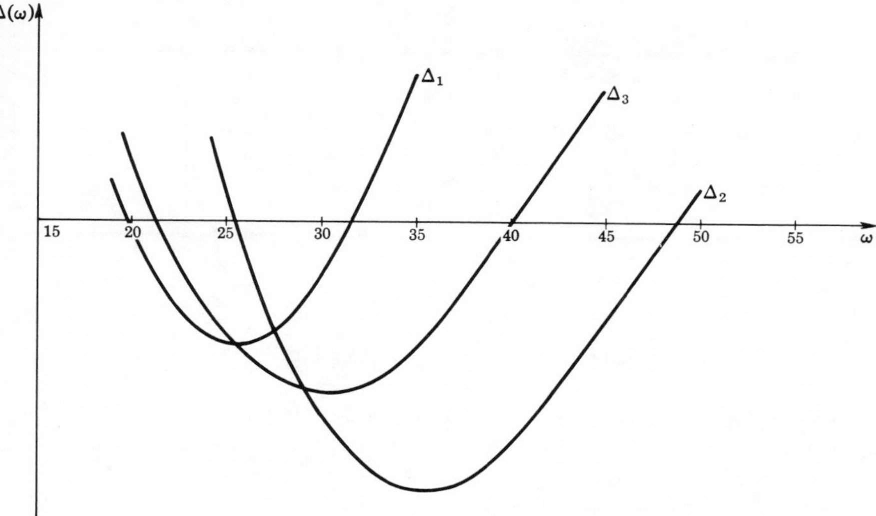

FIG. 11-17. Plot of frequency determinants Δ_1, Δ_2, and Δ_3 for substitute system II.

to the bending vibrations in the symmetry plane, the system can be reduced to two coupled beams. This substitute system, shown in Fig. 11-19, was derived from the shaft and foundation data, neglecting the stiffness contributed by the casings of the turbine and the generator. Two cases were treated:

1. Including the oil-film elasticity by means of springs, which couple shaft and foundation (Fig. 11-20)
2. Rigid coupling between shaft and foundation (Fig. 11-21)

Since the application of the normal transfer-matrix method led to insurmountable numerical difficulties at the higher frequencies,† the modified transfer-matrix method

† Even the use of 18 digits failed to yield satisfactory results for the first five eigenfrequencies. Cf. also Ref. 54, where 44 digits were employed.

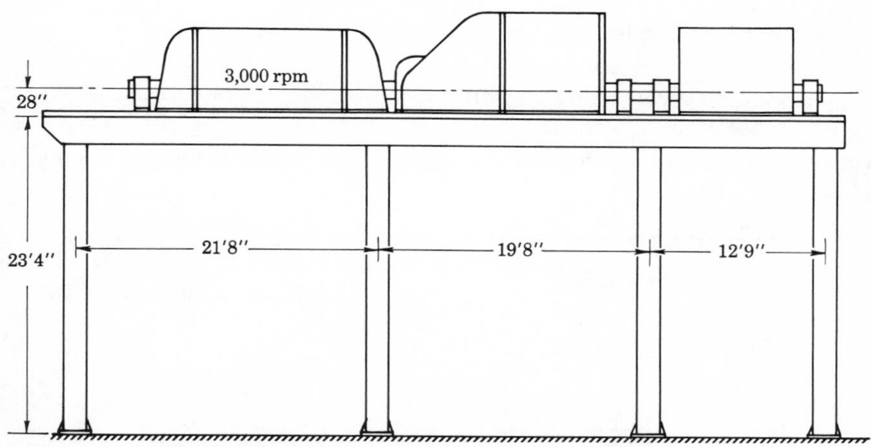

FIG. 11-18. Turbine-generator set on steel foundation.

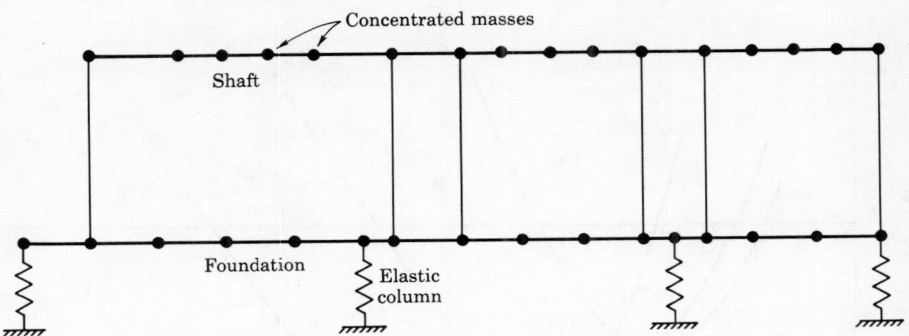

FIG. 11-19. Substitute system of Fig. 11-18.

developed in Sec. 7-3† was used. Although only eight digits were employed, no difficulties were encountered at a trial calculation with frequencies up to $\omega = 2{,}160$ sec^{-1}, corresponding to 20,650 rpm, where the calculation was stopped because this was already far beyond the interesting frequency range. Before the results are recorded, let us discuss the methods used for the two cases.

Procedure for Elastic Coupling. For the sake of illustrating the procedure let us deal with the rather simpler example shown in Fig. 11-22, where the transfer matrix **A** links the state vectors $\overset{\mathrm{I}}{\mathbf{z}}{}_0^R$ and $\overset{\mathrm{I}}{\mathbf{z}}{}_1^L$ and **B** links the state vectors $\overset{\mathrm{II}}{\mathbf{z}}{}_0^R$ and $\overset{\mathrm{II}}{\mathbf{z}}{}_1^L$. For $m\omega^2 = 1$ the transfer matrices are found to be

$$\mathbf{A} = \begin{bmatrix} 55 & 14 & 66 & 44 \\ 85 & 22 & 99 & 66 \\ 18 & 5 & 22 & 14 \\ 69 & 18 & 84 & 55 \end{bmatrix} \quad \text{and} \quad \mathbf{B} = \begin{bmatrix} -33 & 14 & 66 & 44 \\ -48 & 22 & 99 & 66 \\ -10 & 5 & 22 & 14 \\ 25 & -10 & -48 & -33 \end{bmatrix}$$

The boundary conditions are clearly

$$\overset{\mathrm{I}}{M}{}_0^L = \overset{\mathrm{II}}{M}{}_0^L = \overset{\mathrm{I}}{V}{}_0^L = \overset{\mathrm{II}}{V}{}_0^L = 0 \qquad \text{and} \qquad \overset{\mathrm{I}}{M}{}_1^R = \overset{\mathrm{II}}{M}{}_1^R = \overset{\mathrm{I}}{V}{}_1^R = \overset{\mathrm{II}}{V}{}_1^R = 0$$

Hence the initial state vector is

$$\mathbf{z}_0^L = \{-\overset{\mathrm{I}}{w}_0 \quad \overset{\mathrm{I}}{\psi}_0 \quad 0 \quad 0 \quad -\overset{\mathrm{II}}{w}_0 \quad \overset{\mathrm{II}}{\psi}_0 \quad 0 \quad 0\} \tag{11-2}$$

† The reader is advised to familiarize himself with this section before proceeding.

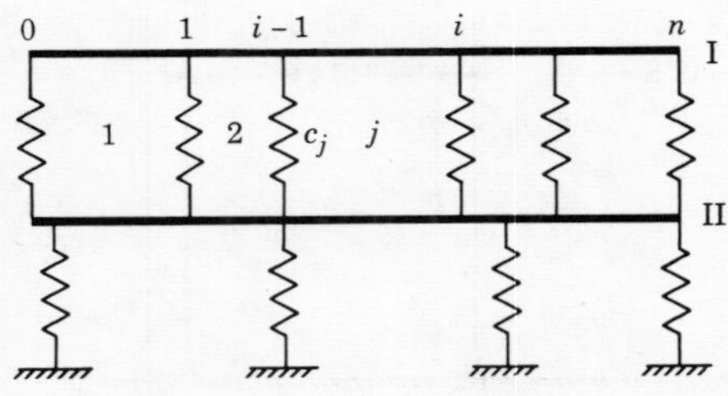

FIG. 11-20. Elastic coupling of shaft and foundation.

The point matrix for the coupling springs is easily found to be

$$\mathbf{K} = \left[\begin{array}{cccc|cccc} 1 & 0 & 0 & 0 & 0 & 0 & 0 & 0 \\ 0 & 1 & 0 & 0 & 0 & 0 & 0 & 0 \\ 0 & 0 & 1 & 0 & 0 & 0 & 0 & 0 \\ -k & 0 & 0 & 1 & k & 0 & 0 & 0 \\ \hline 0 & 0 & 0 & 0 & 1 & 0 & 0 & 0 \\ 0 & 0 & 0 & 0 & 0 & 1 & 0 & 0 \\ 0 & 0 & 0 & 0 & 0 & 0 & 1 & 0 \\ k & 0 & 0 & 0 & -k & 0 & 0 & 1 \end{array}\right]$$

and the field matrix for the coupled shaft and beam is

$$\mathbf{C} = \left[\begin{array}{c|c} \mathbf{A} & \mathbf{O} \\ \hline \mathbf{O} & \mathbf{B} \end{array}\right] \tag{11-3}$$

We now form the product

$$\mathbf{z}_1^R = \mathbf{K}_1\mathbf{C}\mathbf{K}_0\mathbf{z}_0^L$$

where in accordance with Eq. (7-10) the initial state vector $\mathbf{z}_0^L$ is chosen as

$$\mathbf{z}_0^L = \begin{bmatrix} \lambda_1 \\ \lambda_2 \\ 0 \\ 0 \\ \lambda_3 \\ 1 \\ 0 \\ 0 \end{bmatrix} + \kappa_1 \begin{bmatrix} 1 \\ 0 \\ 0 \\ 0 \\ 0 \\ 0 \\ 0 \\ 0 \end{bmatrix} + \kappa_2 \begin{bmatrix} 0 \\ 1 \\ 0 \\ 0 \\ 0 \\ 0 \\ 0 \\ 0 \end{bmatrix} + \kappa_3 \begin{bmatrix} 0 \\ 0 \\ 0 \\ 0 \\ 1 \\ 0 \\ 0 \\ 0 \end{bmatrix} \tag{11-4}$$

Here λ_1 is our first guess for $-\overset{\mathrm{I}}{w}_0$, λ_2 for $\overset{\mathrm{I}}{\psi}_0$, and λ_3 for $-\overset{\mathrm{II}}{w}_0$. For the sake of simplicity the calculation in Table 11-3 is carried out with $\lambda_1 = \lambda_2 = \lambda_3 = 1$. Disregard column 5 in Table 11-3 for the time being.

In view of the right-hand boundary conditions we may now extract from columns

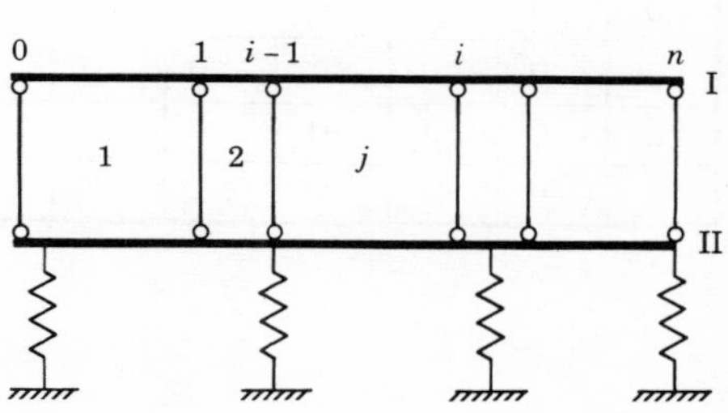

FIG. 11-21. Rigid coupling of shaft and foundation.

Table 11-3

									1	2	3	4	5	
									1	1	0	0	−1.0893	
									1	0	1	0	1.5738	
									0	0	0	0	0	
									0	0	0	0	0	$=\mathbf{z}_0^L$
									1	0	0	1	−0.6706	
									1	0	0	0	1	
									0	0	0	0	0	
									0	0	0	0	0	
	1	0	0	0	0	0	0	0	1	1	0	0	−1.0893	
	0	1	0	0	0	0	0	0	1	0	1	0	1.5738	
	0	0	1	0	0	0	0	0	0	0	0	0	0	
$\mathbf{K}_0=$	−2	0	0	1	2	0	0	0	0	−2	0	2	0.8374	$=\mathbf{z}_0^R$
	0	0	0	0	1	0	0	0	1	0	0	1	−0.6706	
	0	0	0	0	0	1	0	0	1	0	0	0	1	
	0	0	0	0	0	0	1	0	0	0	0	0	0	
	2	0	0	0	−2	0	0	1	0	2	0	−2	−0.8374	
	55	14	66	44	0	0	0	0	69	−33	14	88	−1.0327	
	84	22	99	66	0	0	0	0	106	−48	22	132	−1.6092	
	18	5	22	14	0	0	0	0	23	−10	5	28	−0.0148	
$\mathbf{C}=$	69	18	84	55	0	0	0	0	87	−41	18	110	−0.7763	$=\mathbf{z}_1^L$
	0	0	0	0	−33	14	66	44	−19	88	0	−121	−0.7158	
	0	0	0	0	−48	22	99	66	−26	132	0	−180	−1.0796	
	0	0	0	0	−10	5	22	14	−5	28	0	−38	−0.0176	
	0	0	0	0	25	−10	−48	−33	15	−66	0	91	0.8692	
	1	0	0	0	0	0	0	0	69	−33	14	88	−1.0327	
	0	1	0	0	0	0	0	0	106	−48	22	132	−1.6092	
	0	0	1	0	0	0	0	0	23	−10	5	28	−0.0148	
$\mathbf{K}_1=$	−2	0	0	1	2	0	0	0	−89	201	−10	−308	−0.1425	$=\mathbf{z}_1^R$
	0	0	0	0	1	0	0	0	−19	88	0	−121	−0.7158	
	0	0	0	0	0	1	0	0	−26	132	0	−180	−1.0796	
	0	0	0	0	0	0	1	0	−5	28	0	−38	−0.0176	
	2	0	0	0	−2	0	0	1	191	−308	28	509	0.2354	

1 to 4 the following system of four equations for the correction factors κ_1, κ_2, and κ_3:

$$23 - 10\kappa_1 + 5\kappa_2 + 28\kappa_3 = 0 \qquad (1)$$

$$-89 + 201\kappa_1 - 10\kappa_2 - 308\kappa_3 = 0 \qquad (2)$$

$$-5 + 28\kappa_1 + 0\kappa_2 - 38\kappa_3 = 0 \qquad (3)$$

$$191 - 308\kappa_1 + 28\kappa_2 + 509\kappa_3 = 0 \qquad (4)$$

If all four equations were satisfied by the same values κ_1, κ_2, and κ_3, then the equations would be linearly dependent and the chosen ω would coincide with an eigenfrequency ω_E of the system. This, however, is generally not the case. Let us first solve the last three equations, which yield

$$\kappa_1 = -2.0893 \qquad \kappa_2 = 0.5738 \qquad \kappa_3 = x_3 = -1.6711$$

Substituting κ_1 and κ_2 into the first equation, we obtain

$$\kappa_3 = y_3 = -1.6700$$

Since $x_3 - y_3 = R_3 \neq 0$, we have $\omega \neq \omega_E$. In the present case we have

$$R_3 = -1.6711 + 1.6700 = -0.0011$$

We now form the arithmetic mean of the two values found for κ_3:

$$\bar{\kappa}_3 = \frac{x_3 + y_3}{2} = -1.6706$$

and then compute the following new values:

$$\lambda_1' = \lambda_1 - 2.0893 = -1.0893 \qquad \lambda_2' = \lambda_2 + 0.5738 = 1.5738$$

$$\lambda_3' = \lambda_3 - 1.6706 = -0.6706$$

which are placed in column 5 of Table 11-3.

Let us now repeat the calculation for the same value of ω with the new initial state vector (cf. columns 5, 2, 3, and 4 of Table 11-3)

$$\mathbf{z}_0^L = \begin{bmatrix} -1.0893 \\ 1.5738 \\ 0 \\ 0 \\ -0.6706 \\ 1 \\ 0 \\ 0 \end{bmatrix} + \kappa_1' \begin{bmatrix} 1 \\ 0 \\ 0 \\ 0 \\ 0 \\ 0 \\ 0 \\ 0 \end{bmatrix} + \kappa_2' \begin{bmatrix} 0 \\ 1 \\ 0 \\ 0 \\ 0 \\ 0 \\ 0 \\ 0 \end{bmatrix} + \kappa_3' \begin{bmatrix} 0 \\ 0 \\ 0 \\ 0 \\ 1 \\ 0 \\ 0 \\ 0 \end{bmatrix} \qquad (11\text{-}4a)$$

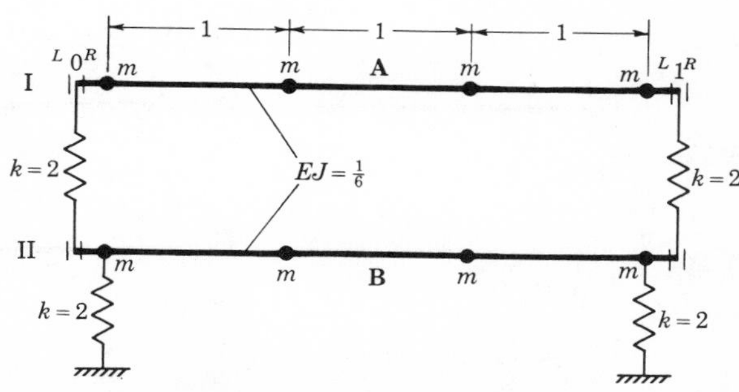

FIG. 11-22. Two beams coupled by springs.

and obtain the following system of four equations for κ_1', κ_2', and κ_3':

$$-0.0148 - 10\kappa_1' + 5\kappa_2' + 28\kappa_3' = 0$$
$$-0.1425 + 201\kappa_1' - 10\kappa_2' - 308\kappa_3' = 0$$
$$-0.0176 + 28\kappa_1' + 0\kappa_2' - 38\kappa_3' = 0$$
$$0.2354 - 308\kappa_1' + 28\kappa_2' + 509\kappa_3' = 0$$

the last three of which yield

$$\kappa_1' = 0.00001558 \qquad \kappa_2' = -0.00002455 \qquad \kappa_3' = x_3' = -0.0004517$$

Substituting the values for κ_1' and κ_2' into the first equation, we obtain

$$\kappa_3' = y_3' = 0.0005385$$

Hence $R_3' = x_3' - y_3' = -0.0009902$ and $\bar{\kappa}_3' = \dfrac{x_3' + y_3'}{2} = 0.0000434$

We therefore recognize that κ_1', κ_2', and $\bar{\kappa}_3'$ are practically zero, as they should be according to the theory developed in Sec. 7-3, the deviations being due to rounding-off errors. Furthermore we see that

$$R_3 \approx R_3' \approx -0.001$$

According to the theory we should have obtained $R_3 = R_3'$. Instead of x_3 and y_3, and thus instead of R_3, we could also have computed R_1 or R_2. For the case where $\omega = \omega_E$ all $R_1 = R_2 = R_3 = 0$. In general, one will plot a certain R_p over ω. It is possible, however, that in a certain frequency range this R_p might "jump" (cf. Fig. 11-26). Then another R_q has to be used in this frequency range.

The calculation is carried out in such a way that the values λ_1', λ_2', and λ_3' are employed as λ_1, λ_2, and λ_3 for the calculation with the next higher ω, as was shown for a simple example in Sec. 7-3. It is furthermore pointed out that the state vectors displayed in the fifth column of Table 11-3 can be used immediately for the plot of the vibration modes.

Procedure for Rigid Coupling. Figure 11-23 shows two beams, I and II, linked together by rigid rods at points along their lengths. The transfer matrices relating the state vectors at 0^R and 1^L are $\mathbf{A}_1$ and $\mathbf{B}_1$ for beams I and II respectively. According to Fig. 11-23 the left-hand boundary conditions are the same as in the case of elastic coupling (Fig. 11-22). So we use the same initial state vector as displayed in Eqs. (11-2) and (11-4). Because of the rigid coupling we have, however,

$$-\overset{\mathrm{I}}{w}{}_0^L = -\overset{\mathrm{II}}{w}{}_0^L$$

or in terms of the state vector of Eq. (11-4)

$$\lambda_1 + \kappa_1 = \lambda_3 + \kappa_3$$

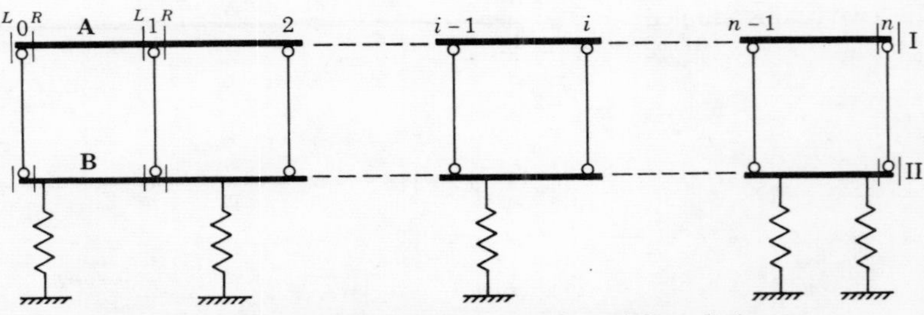

FIG. 11-23. Rigid coupling of shaft and foundation.

Hence we can eliminate λ_1 and κ_1 and write, instead of Eq. (11-4),

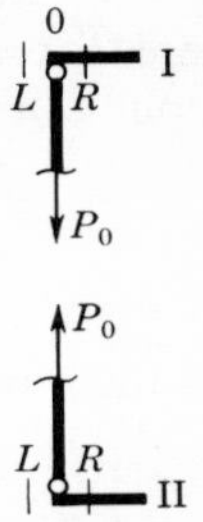

$$\mathbf{z}_0^L = \begin{bmatrix} \lambda_3 \\ \lambda_2 \\ 0 \\ 0 \\ \lambda_3 \\ 1 \\ 0 \\ 0 \end{bmatrix} + \kappa_2 \begin{bmatrix} 0 \\ 1 \\ 0 \\ 0 \\ 0 \\ 0 \\ 0 \\ 0 \end{bmatrix} + \kappa_3 \begin{bmatrix} 1 \\ 0 \\ 0 \\ 0 \\ 1 \\ 0 \\ 0 \\ 0 \end{bmatrix} \qquad (11\text{-}5)$$

FIG. 11-24. Force in rigid bar linking beams I and II.

In view of Fig. 11-24 we may write the following relations:

$$-\overset{\mathrm{I}}{w}{}_0^R = -\overset{\mathrm{I}}{w}{}_0^L \qquad \overset{\mathrm{I}}{\psi}{}_0^R = \overset{\mathrm{I}}{\psi}{}_0^L \qquad \overset{\mathrm{I}}{M}{}_0^R = \overset{\mathrm{I}}{M}{}_0^L \qquad \overset{\mathrm{I}}{V}{}_0^R = \overset{\mathrm{I}}{V}{}_0^L - P_0 \qquad (11\text{-}6)$$

$$-\overset{\mathrm{II}}{w}{}_0^R = -\overset{\mathrm{II}}{w}{}_0^L \qquad \overset{\mathrm{II}}{\psi}{}_0^R = \overset{\mathrm{II}}{\psi}{}_0^L \qquad \overset{\mathrm{II}}{M}{}_0^R = \overset{\mathrm{II}}{M}{}_0^L \qquad \overset{\mathrm{II}}{V}{}_0^R = \overset{\mathrm{II}}{V}{}_0^L + P_0 \qquad (11\text{-}7)$$

where P_0 is the force in the rigid rod connecting the points 0 in beams I and II. Therefore we obtain for the state vector on the right side of point 0, by use of Eqs. (11-5) to (11-7),

$$\mathbf{z}_0^R = \mathbf{z}_0^L + P_0 \begin{bmatrix} 0 \\ 0 \\ 0 \\ -1 \\ 0 \\ 0 \\ 0 \\ 1 \end{bmatrix} = \begin{bmatrix} \lambda_3 \\ \lambda_2 \\ 0 \\ 0 \\ \lambda_3 \\ 1 \\ 0 \\ 0 \end{bmatrix} + \kappa_2 \begin{bmatrix} 0 \\ 1 \\ 0 \\ 0 \\ 0 \\ 0 \\ 0 \\ 0 \end{bmatrix} + \kappa_3 \begin{bmatrix} 1 \\ 0 \\ 0 \\ 0 \\ 1 \\ 0 \\ 0 \\ 0 \end{bmatrix} + P_0 \begin{bmatrix} 0 \\ 0 \\ 0 \\ -1 \\ 0 \\ 0 \\ 0 \\ 1 \end{bmatrix} \qquad (11\text{-}8)$$

which we now multiply by the field matrix $\mathbf{C}_1$ [cf. Eq. (11-3)] to obtain the state vector $\mathbf{z}_1^L$:

$$\mathbf{z}_1^L = \begin{bmatrix} \alpha_1 \\ \alpha_2 \\ \alpha_3 \\ \alpha_4 \\ \beta_1 \\ \beta_2 \\ \beta_3 \\ \beta_4 \end{bmatrix} + \kappa_2 \begin{bmatrix} a_{12} \\ a_{22} \\ a_{32} \\ a_{42} \\ 0 \\ 0 \\ 0 \\ 0 \end{bmatrix} + \kappa_3 \begin{bmatrix} a_{11} \\ a_{21} \\ a_{31} \\ a_{41} \\ b_{11} \\ b_{21} \\ b_{31} \\ b_{41} \end{bmatrix} + P_0 \begin{bmatrix} -a_{14} \\ -a_{24} \\ -a_{34} \\ -a_{44} \\ b_{14} \\ b_{24} \\ b_{34} \\ b_{44} \end{bmatrix} = \begin{bmatrix} -\overset{\mathrm{I}}{w} \\ \overset{\mathrm{I}}{\psi} \\ \overset{\mathrm{I}}{M} \\ \overset{\mathrm{I}}{V} \\ -\overset{\mathrm{II}}{w} \\ \overset{\mathrm{II}}{\psi} \\ \overset{\mathrm{II}}{M} \\ \overset{\mathrm{II}}{V} \end{bmatrix}_1^L \qquad (11\text{-}9)$$

where, for example, $\alpha_1 = a_{11}\lambda_3 + a_{12}\lambda_2$. Since $-\overset{\text{I}}{w_1^L} = -\overset{\text{II}}{w_1^L}$ on account of the rigid coupling, it is possible to eliminate P_0. Thus

$$P_0 = \frac{(\alpha_1 - \beta_1) + \kappa_2 a_{12} + \kappa_3(a_{11} - b_{11})}{a_{14} + b_{14}} \tag{11-10}$$

and therefore we can write for Eq. (11-9)

$$\mathbf{z}_1^L = \begin{bmatrix} \alpha_1 - a_{14}\dfrac{\alpha_1 - \beta_1}{a_{14} + b_{14}} \\ \alpha_2 - a_{24}\dfrac{\alpha_1 - \beta_1}{a_{14} + b_{14}} \\ \alpha_3 - a_{34}\dfrac{\alpha_1 - \beta_1}{a_{14} + b_{14}} \\ \alpha_4 - a_{44}\dfrac{\alpha_1 - \beta_1}{a_{14} + b_{14}} \\ \beta_1 + b_{14}\dfrac{\alpha_1 - \beta_1}{a_{14} + b_{14}} \\ \beta_2 + b_{24}\dfrac{\alpha_1 - \beta_1}{a_{14} + b_{14}} \\ \beta_3 + b_{34}\dfrac{\alpha_1 - \beta_1}{a_{14} + b_{14}} \\ \beta_4 + b_{44}\dfrac{\alpha_1 - \beta_1}{a_{14} + b_{14}} \end{bmatrix} + \kappa_2 \begin{bmatrix} a_{12} - \dfrac{a_{14}a_{12}}{a_{14} + b_{14}} \\ a_{22} - \dfrac{a_{24}a_{12}}{a_{14} + b_{14}} \\ a_{32} - \dfrac{a_{34}a_{12}}{a_{14} + b_{14}} \\ a_{42} - \dfrac{a_{44}a_{12}}{a_{14} + b_{14}} \\ \dfrac{b_{14}a_{12}}{a_{14} + b_{14}} \\ \dfrac{b_{24}a_{12}}{a_{14} + b_{14}} \\ \dfrac{b_{34}a_{12}}{a_{14} + b_{14}} \\ \dfrac{b_{44}a_{12}}{a_{14} + b_{14}} \end{bmatrix} + \kappa_3 \begin{bmatrix} a_{11} - a_{14}\dfrac{a_{11} - b_{11}}{a_{14} + b_{14}} \\ a_{21} - a_{24}\dfrac{a_{11} - b_{11}}{a_{14} + b_{14}} \\ a_{31} - a_{34}\dfrac{a_{11} - b_{11}}{a_{14} + b_{14}} \\ a_{41} - a_{44}\dfrac{a_{11} - b_{11}}{a_{14} + b_{14}} \\ b_{11} + b_{14}\dfrac{a_{11} - b_{11}}{a_{14} + b_{14}} \\ b_{21} + b_{24}\dfrac{a_{11} - b_{11}}{a_{14} + b_{14}} \\ b_{31} + b_{34}\dfrac{a_{11} - b_{11}}{a_{14} + b_{14}} \\ b_{41} + b_{44}\dfrac{a_{11} - b_{11}}{a_{14} + b_{14}} \end{bmatrix} \tag{11-11}$$

Now we write for point 1 two sets of equations analogous to Eqs. (11-6) and (11-7) and obtain similarly, as in Eq. (11-8), the state vector to the right of point 1:

$$\mathbf{z}_1^R = \mathbf{z}_1^L + P_1 \begin{bmatrix} 0 \\ 0 \\ 0 \\ -1 \\ 0 \\ 0 \\ 0 \\ 1 \end{bmatrix} \tag{11-12}$$

which is then multiplied by the field matrix $\mathbf{C}_2$ to yield $\mathbf{z}_2^L$, where again the equation

$$-\overset{\text{I}}{w_2^L} = -\overset{\text{II}}{w_2^L}$$

serves to eliminate P_1, and so on.

In this fashion we finally arrive at the left of point n, where

$$\mathbf{z}_n^L = \begin{bmatrix} p_1 \\ p_2 \\ p_3 \\ p_4 \\ q_1 \\ q_2 \\ q_3 \\ q_4 \end{bmatrix} + \kappa_2 \begin{bmatrix} p_{12} \\ p_{22} \\ p_{32} \\ p_{42} \\ q_{12} \\ q_{22} \\ q_{32} \\ q_{42} \end{bmatrix} + \kappa_3 \begin{bmatrix} p_{13} \\ p_{23} \\ p_{33} \\ p_{43} \\ q_{13} \\ q_{23} \\ q_{33} \\ q_{43} \end{bmatrix} \tag{11-13}$$

Again we can write two sets of equations analogous to Eqs. (11-6) and (11-7) and obtain, as in Eq. (11-8),

$$\mathbf{z}_n^R = \begin{bmatrix} p_1 \\ p_2 \\ p_3 \\ p_4 \\ q_1 \\ q_2 \\ q_3 \\ q_4 \end{bmatrix} + \kappa_2 \begin{bmatrix} p_{12} \\ p_{22} \\ p_{32} \\ p_{42} \\ q_{12} \\ q_{22} \\ q_{32} \\ q_{42} \end{bmatrix} + \kappa_3 \begin{bmatrix} p_{13} \\ p_{23} \\ p_{33} \\ p_{43} \\ q_{13} \\ q_{23} \\ q_{33} \\ q_{43} \end{bmatrix} + P_n \begin{bmatrix} 0 \\ 0 \\ 0 \\ -1 \\ 0 \\ 0 \\ 0 \\ 1 \end{bmatrix} = \begin{bmatrix} -\overset{\text{I}}{w} \\ \overset{\text{I}}{\psi} \\ \overset{\text{I}}{M} = 0 \\ \overset{\text{I}}{V} = 0 \\ -\overset{\text{II}}{w} \\ \overset{\text{II}}{\psi} \\ \overset{\text{II}}{M} = 0 \\ \overset{\text{II}}{V} = 0 \end{bmatrix}_n^R \tag{11-14}$$

The right-hand boundary conditions [cf. Eq. (11-14)] yield the following four equations:

$$\begin{aligned} p_3 + p_{32}\kappa_2 + p_{33}\kappa_3 \qquad &= 0 \\ p_4 + p_{42}\kappa_2 + p_{43}\kappa_3 - P_n &= 0 \\ q_3 + q_{32}\kappa_2 + q_{33}\kappa_3 \qquad &= 0 \\ q_4 + q_{42}\kappa_2 + q_{43}\kappa_3 + P_n &= 0 \end{aligned} \tag{11-15}$$

Let us take the first three equations of Eqs. (11-15) and solve for P_n, κ_3, and $\kappa_2 = x_2$. Then substitute P_n and κ_3 into the fourth equation and obtain another value $\kappa_2 = y_2$.

Again, if $x_2 - y_2 = R_2 = 0$, then the value ω used in the computation corresponds to an eigenfrequency ω_E of the system. Generally this is not the case. We then proceed to repeat the calculation with a new value for ω, usually somewhat higher than the previous one. Again we use the initial state vector as shown in Eq. (11-5). In the first column, however, we replace λ_3 by $\lambda_3' = \lambda_3 + \kappa_3$ and λ_2 by $\lambda_2' = \lambda_2 + (x_2 + y_2)/2$, where λ_3 and λ_2 are taken from the first column in Eq. (11-5) and κ_3 and also x_2 and y_2 are the values gained from Eqs. (11-15). Thus we have, as our initial state vector for the calculation with the new value of ω,

$$\mathbf{z}_0^L = \begin{bmatrix} \lambda_3 + \kappa_3 \\ \lambda_2 + \dfrac{x_2 + y_2}{2} \\ 0 \\ 0 \\ \lambda_3 + \kappa_3 \\ 1 \\ 0 \\ 0 \end{bmatrix} + \kappa_2' \begin{bmatrix} 0 \\ 1 \\ 0 \\ 0 \\ 0 \\ 0 \\ 0 \\ 0 \end{bmatrix} + \kappa_3' \begin{bmatrix} 1 \\ 0 \\ 0 \\ 0 \\ 1 \\ 0 \\ 0 \\ 0 \end{bmatrix}$$

where κ_2' and κ_3' are the unknown correction factors that are associated with the computation with the new value of ω. Then, normally, no numerical difficulties are to be expected as we go on to ever rising values of ω; that is to say, $R_p = x_p - y_p$ always remains a small difference of small numbers, whereas in the normal transfer-matrix method the frequency determinant becomes, with rising values of ω in the vicinity of an eigenfrequency, an increasingly unreliable small difference of large numbers.

In some problems we encounter the situation that at point 0 we have only beam II, as shown in Fig. 11-25, where matrix $\mathbf{B}_1$ links the state vectors $\overset{\text{II}}{\mathbf{z}_0^L}$ and $\overset{\text{II}}{\mathbf{z}_1^L}$. In this case we start with the state vector

$$\overset{\text{II}}{\mathbf{z}_0^L} = \begin{bmatrix} \lambda_3 \\ 1 \\ 0 \\ 0 \end{bmatrix} + \kappa_3 \begin{bmatrix} 1 \\ 0 \\ 0 \\ 0 \end{bmatrix}$$

and obtain, after multiplication by matrix $\mathbf{B}_1$, the state vector

$$\overset{\text{II}}{\mathbf{z}_1^L} = \begin{bmatrix} \beta_1 \\ \beta_2 \\ \beta_3 \\ \beta_4 \end{bmatrix} + \kappa_3 \begin{bmatrix} b_{11} \\ b_{21} \\ b_{31} \\ b_{41} \end{bmatrix}$$

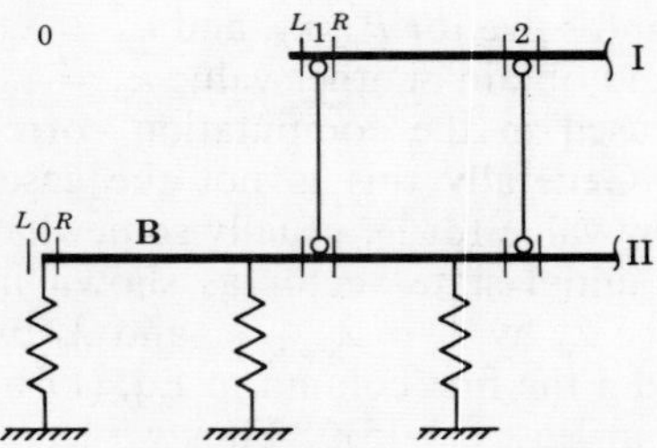

FIG. 11-25. Beam I recessed.

Then we can write for the complete state vector to the left of point 1

$$\mathbf{z}_1^L = \begin{bmatrix} \overset{\text{I}}{\mathbf{z}} \\ \overset{\text{II}}{\mathbf{z}} \end{bmatrix}_1^L = \begin{bmatrix} \lambda_1 \\ \lambda_2 \\ 0 \\ 0 \\ \beta_1 \\ \beta_2 \\ \beta_3 \\ \beta_4 \end{bmatrix} + \kappa_1 \begin{bmatrix} 1 \\ 0 \\ 0 \\ 0 \\ 0 \\ 0 \\ 0 \\ 0 \end{bmatrix} + \kappa_2 \begin{bmatrix} 0 \\ 1 \\ 0 \\ 0 \\ 0 \\ 0 \\ 0 \\ 0 \end{bmatrix} + \kappa_3 \begin{bmatrix} 0 \\ 0 \\ 0 \\ 0 \\ b_{11} \\ b_{21} \\ b_{31} \\ b_{41} \end{bmatrix} \tag{11-16}$$

and with

$$-\overset{\text{I}}{w}{}_1^L = -\overset{\text{II}}{w}{}_1^L$$

we obtain from Eq. (11-16)

$$\lambda_1 + \kappa_1 = \beta_1 + \kappa_3 b_{11}$$

and hence we can eliminate λ_1 and κ_1 and write for Eq. (11-16)

$$\mathbf{z}_1^L = \begin{bmatrix} \beta_1 \\ \lambda_2 \\ 0 \\ 0 \\ \beta_1 \\ \beta_2 \\ \beta_3 \\ \beta_4 \end{bmatrix} + \kappa_2 \begin{bmatrix} 0 \\ 1 \\ 0 \\ 0 \\ 0 \\ 0 \\ 0 \\ 0 \end{bmatrix} + \kappa_3 \begin{bmatrix} b_{11} \\ 0 \\ 0 \\ 0 \\ b_{11} \\ b_{21} \\ b_{31} \\ b_{41} \end{bmatrix} \tag{11-17}$$

Equation (11-17) is analogous to Eq. (11-5), and from here on the computation is carried out in the same way as demonstrated earlier.

Results of the Calculation for the Substitute System of Fig. 11-19. The substitute system represents the shaft of a 34-Mw turbine-generator set mounted on a steel foundation with slender columns. In both cases of elastic and rigid coupling the frequency range between 900 and 3,500 rpm was investigated. In order to take into account the oil-film elasticity, the coupling springs were given a spring constant $k = 1.345 \times 10^8$ lb/ft. From the plots of the differences R_p over the frequency in rpm the eigenfrequencies were determined as shown in Figs. 11-26 and 11-27. From these graphs the reader will see that all values R_p ($p = 1, 2, 3$) go simultaneously through zero if $\omega = \omega_E$ and furthermore that it is sometimes necessary to change, for example, from R_1 to R_2 if R_1 "jumps."† The calculated first six eigenmodes for both cases are shown side by side in Figs. 11-28 to 11-33. The mode shapes differ only slightly except when generator shaft and foundation table are in opposite phase, as seen from Figs. 11-30 and 11-31. All eigenmodes were found to satisfy the condition of orthogonality.

† For an explanation of this "phenomenon" see Ref. 67.

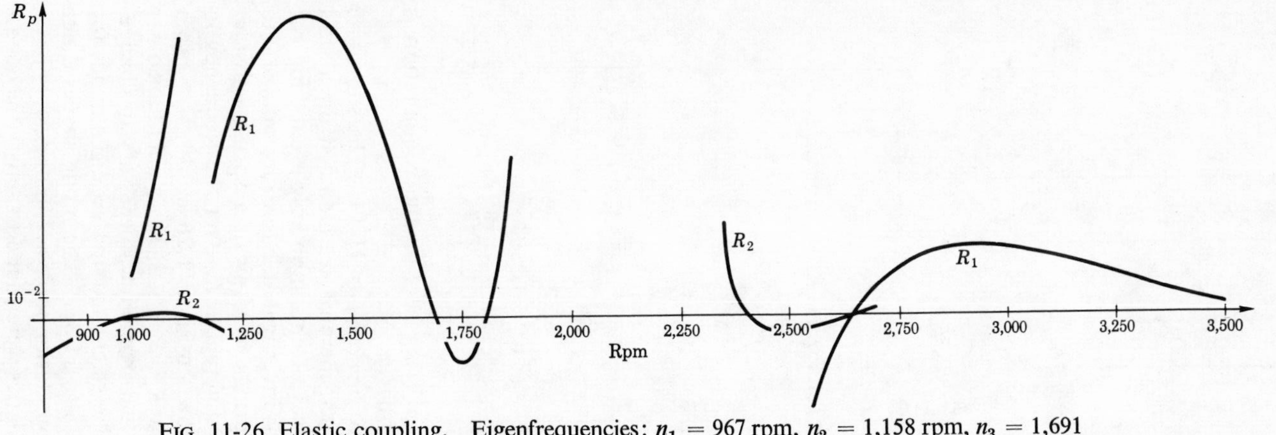

FIG. 11-26. Elastic coupling. Eigenfrequencies: $n_1 = 967$ rpm, $n_2 = 1{,}158$ rpm, $n_3 = 1{,}691$ rpm, $n_4 = 1{,}805$ rpm, $n_5 = 2{,}406$ rpm, $n_6 = 2{,}646$ rpm.

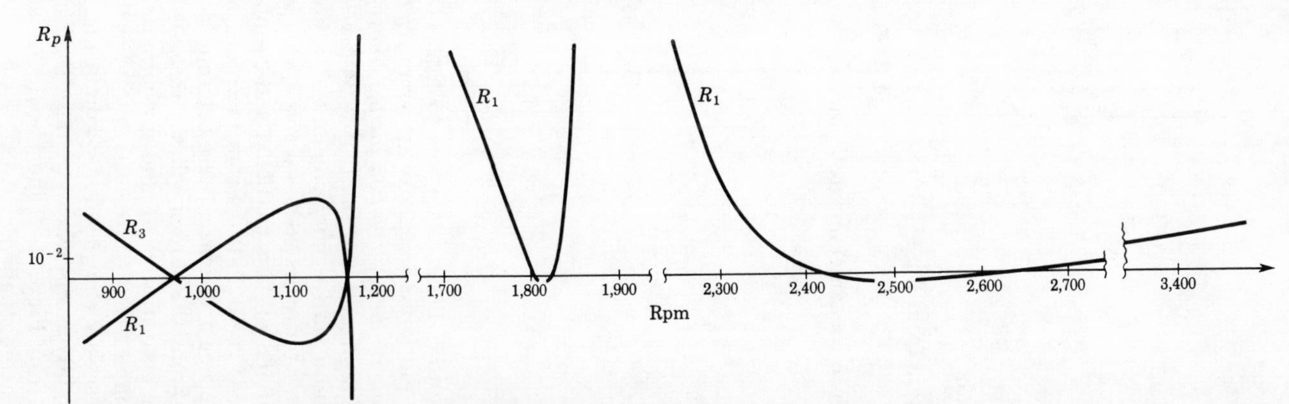

FIG. 11-27. Rigid coupling. Eigenfrequencies: $n_1 = 970$ rpm, $n_2 = 1{,}166$ rpm, $n_3 = 1{,}804$ rpm, $n_4 = 1{,}824$ rpm, $n_5 = 2{,}423$ rpm, $n_6 = 2{,}652$ rpm.

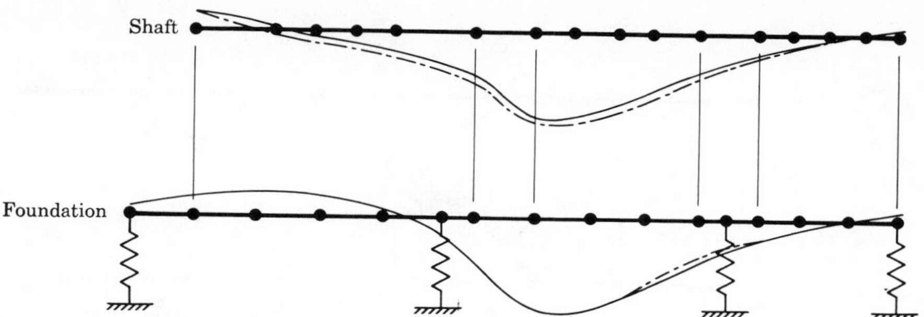

FIG. 11-28. Eigenmode for rigid coupling (solid line), $n_1 = 970$ rpm, $\omega_1 = 102$ sec^{-1}, and for elastic coupling (broken line), $n_1 = 967$ rpm, $\omega_1 = 101$ sec^{-1}.

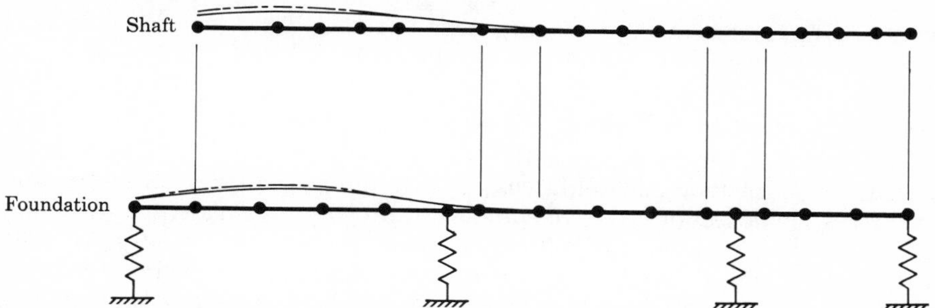

FIG. 11-29. Eigenmode for rigid coupling (solid line), $n_2 = 1{,}166$ rpm, $\omega_2 = 122$ sec^{-1}, and for elastic coupling (broken line), $n_2 = 1{,}158$ rpm, $\omega_2 = 121$ sec^{-1}.

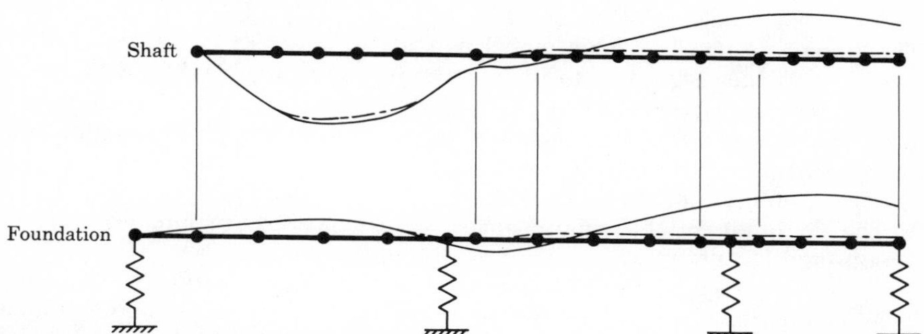

FIG. 11-30. Eigenmode for rigid coupling (solid line), $n_3 = 1{,}804$ rpm, $\omega_3 = 189$ sec^{-1}, and for elastic coupling (broken line), $n_3 = 1{,}691$ rpm, $\omega_3 = 177$ sec^{-1}.

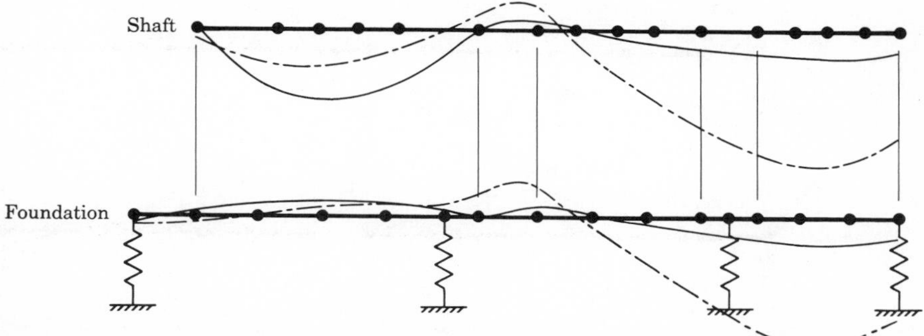

FIG. 11-31. Eigenmode for rigid coupling (solid line), $n_4 = 1{,}824$ rpm, $\omega_4 = 191$ sec^{-1}, and for elastic coupling (broken line), $n_4 = 1{,}805$ rpm, $\omega_4 = 189$ sec^{-1}.

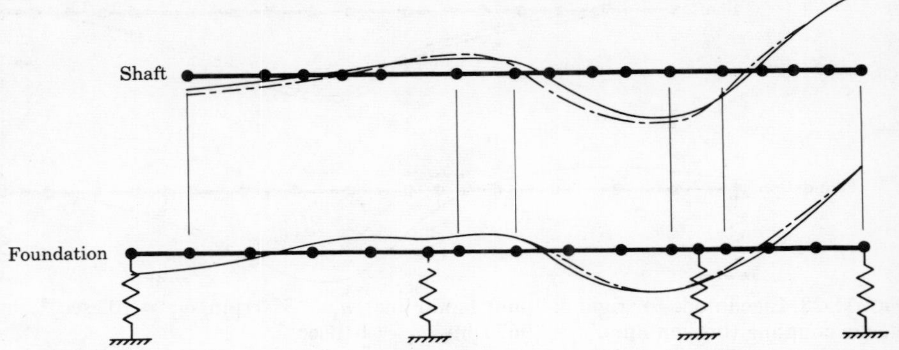

FIG. 11-32. Eigenmode for rigid coupling (solid line), $n_5 = 2{,}423$ rpm, $\omega_5 = 254\ \text{sec}^{-1}$, and for elastic coupling (broken line), $n_5 = 2{,}406$ rpm, $\omega_5 = 252\ \text{sec}^{-1}$.

11-4. The Application of Transfer Matrices to Plate Vibrations

The numerical approach normally adopted when attacking plate problems is the finite-difference method due to Marcus [55]. In this method derivatives are expressed in terms of the deflections of selected points throughout the plate, but it suffers from the disadvantage that it is difficult to formulate the boundary conditions with sufficient accuracy [56]. Furthermore one is committed with this method to developing the stiffness matrix for the entire plate, and thereby it does not lend itself to the transfer-matrix treatment. Instead, the plate is replaced by the model suggested by Hrennikoff [57] which in common with the Marcus method reduces the problem to one with finite degrees of freedom.

The Hrennikoff Model. This model consists of a lattice of beams rigidly connected at the nodes according to the form indicated in Fig. 11-34. The method of obtaining the properties of the beams is fully explained in the original paper [57], but briefly the argument runs as follows. In deriving the plate equation the two basic considerations are:

1. The equilibrium of the plate element
2. The deflection of the plate element when subjected to pure bending in two directions and to pure twist

The equations of equilibrium are independent of the properties of the plate, and it is by comparing the effect of pure bending and twist on the model and on an element of the plate of the same size that the moments of inertia J_1 and J_2 can be computed. Applying two of the three demands required by (2), one obtains

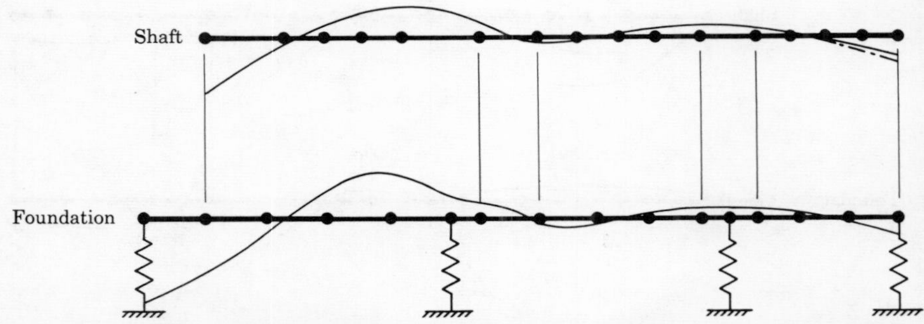

FIG. 11-33. Eigenmode for rigid coupling (solid line), $n_6 = 2{,}652$ rpm, $\omega_6 = 277\ \text{sec}^{-1}$, and for elastic coupling (broken line), $n_6 = 2{,}646$ rpm, $\omega_6 = 277\ \text{sec}^{-1}$.

FIG. 11-34. Hrennikoff model with square elements. h = plate thickness.

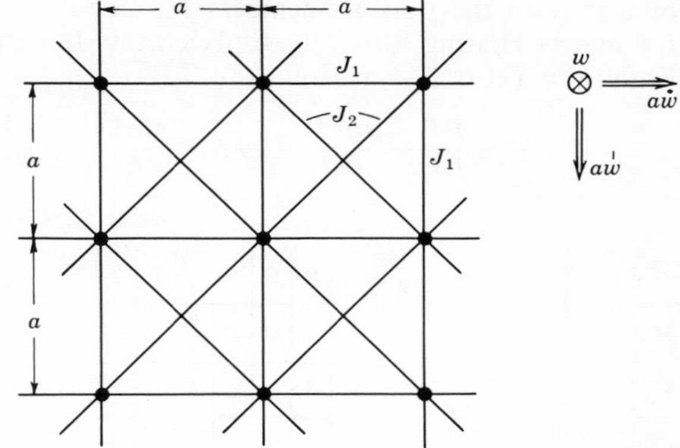

expressions for J_1 and J_2, and finally applying the third demand gives the condition that Poisson's ratio is $\frac{1}{3}$. For the square model† shown in Fig. 11-34 we obtain the following:

$$J_1 = \frac{ah^3}{16} \qquad J_2 = \frac{ah^3}{16\sqrt{2}} \qquad \nu = \tfrac{1}{3}$$

It is possible, by choosing more complicated models, to have a free choice of Poisson's ratio, but since $\frac{1}{3}$ is a reasonable value, the simple model is regarded as being suitable. It should be noted that the moments of inertia of edge members are half of those cited above.

If the distributed mass of the plate is replaced by discrete masses attached at the nodal points of the model, then the dynamic-stiffness matrix for the model can be formulated according to the displacement method of Chap. 10. In the case of the Hrennikoff model the vertical displacement w and the two rotations $\dot{w}$ and $\overset{|}{w}$ (positive sign convention shown in Fig. 11-34) of each node are regarded as the unknowns.

Although the application of the displacement method to the Hrennikoff model is absolutely straightforward, we take a different approach and apply the transfer-matrix procedure. The reason for this is that the size of the matrices in the displacement method can become very large and severely test the storage capacity of computers, whereas this is unlikely to happen with the transfer-matrix method. In fact, it can be said that even large problems often come within the range of hand computation when transfer matrices are used (cf. Sec. 11-5).

The Transfer-matrix Method.‡ A section is made at the nodes across the full width of the plate, the state vector consisting of all the displacements and forces at this section. The structure is divided as shown in Fig. 11-35, the vertical members being designated by $j - 1$, j, $j + 1$, etc., and the horizontal members by $i - 1$, i, $i + 1$, etc. The vertical and diagonal members make up the field, and the horizontal members with the point masses attached give rise to the point matrix **P**.

The field matrix **F** is most readily computed by first formulating the stiffness matrix, a process that can be achieved with relative ease.§ On noting that the moments

† For rectangular elements of arbitrary aspect ratio, cf. Ref. 57.

‡ For another transfer-matrix method, see the paper by F. A. Leckie in Ref. 59, first report.

§ A more general procedure for setting up the stiffness matrix for plate and shell problems in order to derive the associated transfer matrix is described in Ref. 64, where the reader will also find a simple technique to invert submatrix **B** of the stiffness matrix, a necessary prerequisite for the establishment of the transfer matrix of Eq. (11-20).

of inertia of the outside members are one-half of those of the internal members, the matrix relating forces to displacements for a plate with four vertical members† is given in Table 11-4, where

$$\bar{T} = \frac{Ta^2}{EJ_1} = \frac{16aT}{Eh^3} \qquad \bar{M} = \frac{Ma^2}{EJ_1} = \frac{16aM}{Eh^3} \qquad \bar{V} = \frac{Va^3}{EJ_1} = \frac{16a^2V}{Eh^3}$$

Table 11-4

$-\bar{T}_3$								0	0	0	$\frac{-3}{2}$	1	1				0	0	0	$\frac{3}{2}$	$\frac{1}{2}$	$\frac{1}{2}$	0	0	0		$-w_0$	
$\bar{M}_3$								0	0	0	$\frac{9}{2}$	−3	−1				0	0	0	$\frac{-3}{2}$	$\frac{-1}{2}$	$\frac{-1}{2}$	−3	−1	0		$a\dot{w}_0$	
$\bar{V}_3$								0	0	0	9	$\frac{-9}{2}$	$\frac{-3}{2}$				0	0	0	−3	$\frac{-3}{2}$	$\frac{-3}{2}$	−6	−3	0		aw_0'	
$-\bar{T}_2$				**0**				0	0	2	0	0	0		**0**		$\frac{3}{2}$	$\frac{1}{2}$	$\frac{1}{2}$	0	0	0	$\frac{-3}{2}$	$\frac{-1}{2}$	$\frac{1}{2}$		$-w_1$	
$\bar{M}_2$								9	−6	0	0	0	0				$\frac{-3}{2}$	$\frac{-1}{2}$	$\frac{-1}{2}$	−6	−2	0	$\frac{-3}{2}$	$\frac{-1}{2}$	$\frac{1}{2}$		$a\dot{w}_1$	
$\bar{V}_2$								18	−9	0	0	0	0				−3	$\frac{-3}{2}$	$\frac{-3}{2}$	−12	−6	0	−3	$\frac{-3}{2}$	$\frac{3}{2}$		aw_1'	
$-\bar{T}_1$		0	0	0	0	0	2							$\frac{3}{2}$	$\frac{1}{2}$	$\frac{1}{2}$	0	0	0	$\frac{-3}{2}$	$\frac{-1}{2}$	$\frac{1}{2}$					$-w_2$	
$\bar{M}_1$		0	0	0	9	−6	0							$\frac{-3}{2}$	$\frac{-1}{2}$	$\frac{-1}{2}$	−6	−2	0	$\frac{-3}{2}$	$\frac{-1}{2}$	$\frac{1}{2}$					$a\dot{w}_2$	
$\bar{V}_1$		0	0	0	18	−9	0							−3	$\frac{-3}{2}$	$\frac{-3}{2}$	−12	−6	0	−3	$\frac{-3}{2}$	$\frac{3}{2}$					aw_2'	
$-\bar{T}_0$		$\frac{3}{2}$	−1	1	0	0	0			**0**				0	0	0	$\frac{-3}{2}$	$\frac{-1}{2}$	$\frac{1}{2}$	0	0	0		**0**			$-w_3$	
$\bar{M}_0$		$\frac{9}{2}$	−3	1	0	0	0							−3	−1	0	$\frac{-3}{2}$	$\frac{-1}{2}$	$\frac{1}{2}$	0	0	0					$a\dot{w}_3$	
$\bar{V}_0$	$_{i-1}=$	9	$\frac{-9}{2}$	$\frac{3}{2}$	0	0	0							−6	−3	0	−3	$\frac{-3}{2}$	$\frac{3}{2}$	0	0	0				·	aw_3'	$_{i-}$
$-\bar{T}_3$					0	0	0	$\frac{-3}{2}$	$\frac{1}{2}$	$\frac{-1}{2}$	0	0	0							0	0	0	$\frac{3}{2}$	1	−1		$-w_0$	
$\bar{M}_3$					0	0	0	$\frac{-3}{2}$	$\frac{1}{2}$	$\frac{-1}{2}$	−3	1	0							0	0	0	$\frac{9}{2}$	3	−1		$a\dot{w}_0$	
$\bar{V}_3$					0	0	0	3	$\frac{-3}{2}$	$\frac{3}{2}$	6	−3	0							0	0	0	−9	$\frac{-9}{2}$	$\frac{3}{2}$		aw_0'	
$-\bar{T}_2$			**0**		$\frac{-3}{2}$	$\frac{1}{2}$	$\frac{-1}{2}$	0	0	0	$\frac{3}{2}$	$\frac{-1}{2}$	$\frac{-1}{2}$				**0**			0	0	−2	0	0	0		$-w_1$	
$\bar{M}_2$					$\frac{-3}{2}$	$\frac{1}{2}$	$\frac{-1}{2}$	−6	2	0	$\frac{-3}{2}$	$\frac{1}{2}$	$\frac{1}{2}$							9	6	0	0	0	0		$a\dot{w}_1$	
$\bar{V}_2$					3	$\frac{-3}{2}$	$\frac{3}{2}$	12	−6	0	3	$\frac{-3}{2}$	$\frac{-3}{2}$							−18	−9	0	0	0	0		aw_1'	
$-\bar{T}_1$		$\frac{-3}{2}$	$\frac{1}{2}$	$\frac{-1}{2}$	0	0	0	$\frac{3}{2}$	$\frac{-1}{2}$	$\frac{-1}{2}$				0	0	0	0	0	−2								$-w_2$	
$\bar{M}_1$		$\frac{-3}{2}$	$\frac{1}{2}$	$\frac{-1}{2}$	−6	2	0	$\frac{-3}{2}$	$\frac{1}{2}$	$\frac{1}{2}$				0	0	0	9	6	0								$a\dot{w}_2$	
$\bar{V}_1$		3	$\frac{-3}{2}$	$\frac{3}{2}$	12	−6	0	3	$\frac{-3}{2}$	$\frac{-3}{2}$				0	0	0	−18	−9	0								aw_2'	
$-\bar{T}_0$		0	0	0	$\frac{3}{2}$	$\frac{-1}{2}$	$\frac{-1}{2}$	0	0	0		**0**		$\frac{-3}{2}$	−1	−1	0	0	0			**0**					$-w_3$	
$\bar{M}_0$		−3	1	0	$\frac{-3}{2}$	$\frac{1}{2}$	$\frac{1}{2}$	0	0	0				$\frac{9}{2}$	3	1	0	0	0								$a\dot{w}_3$	
$\bar{V}_0$	$_i$	6	−3	0	3	$\frac{-3}{2}$	$\frac{-3}{2}$	0	0	0				−9	$\frac{-9}{2}$	$\frac{-3}{2}$	0	0	0								aw_3'	$_i$

† For the more general case, see Refs. 58 and 59.

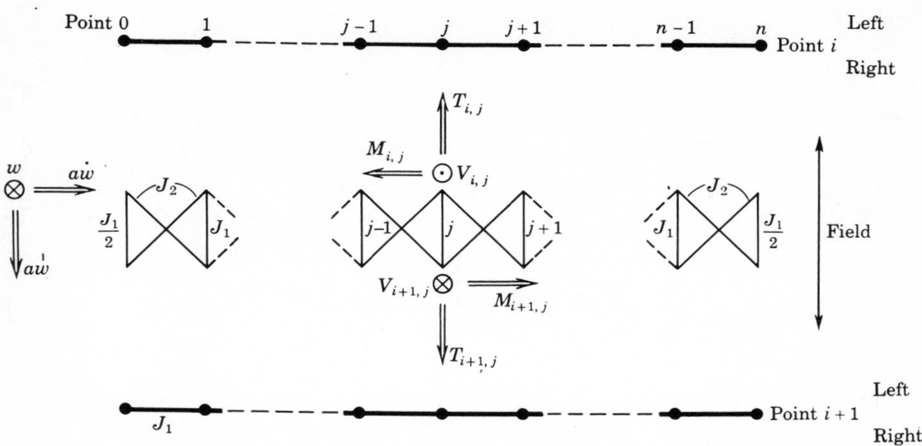

FIG. 11-35. Division into field and point transfer matrices.

Written in a shortened form, this matrix relation is

$$\begin{bmatrix} \mathbf{p}_{i-1} \\ \hline \mathbf{p}_i \end{bmatrix} = \left[\begin{array}{c|c} \mathbf{A} & \mathbf{B} \\ \hline \mathbf{C} & \mathbf{D} \end{array}\right] \cdot \begin{bmatrix} \mathbf{d}_{i-1} \\ \hline \mathbf{d}_i \end{bmatrix}$$

where $\mathbf{p}_i$ is the column vector representing the internal forces and $\mathbf{d}_i$ is the column vector representing the displacements at section i. Expanding the above equation gives

$$\mathbf{p}_{i-1} = \mathbf{A}\mathbf{d}_{i-1} + \mathbf{B}\mathbf{d}_i \tag{11-18}$$

$$\mathbf{p}_i = \mathbf{C}\mathbf{d}_{i-1} + \mathbf{D}\mathbf{d}_i \tag{11-19}$$

From Eq. (11-18)

$$\mathbf{d}_i = \mathbf{B}^{-1}\mathbf{p}_{i-1} - \mathbf{B}^{-1}\mathbf{A}\mathbf{d}_{i-1}$$

and then, using Eq. (11-19),

$$\mathbf{p}_i = (\mathbf{C} - \mathbf{D}\mathbf{B}^{-1}\mathbf{A})\mathbf{d}_{i-1} + \mathbf{D}\mathbf{B}^{-1}\mathbf{p}_{i-1}$$

The field-transfer-matrix relation is then

$$\begin{bmatrix} \mathbf{d} \\ \hline \mathbf{p} \end{bmatrix}_i^L = \left[\begin{array}{c|c} -\mathbf{B}^{-1}\mathbf{A} & \mathbf{B}^{-1} \\ \hline \mathbf{C} - \mathbf{D}\mathbf{B}^{-1}\mathbf{A} & \mathbf{D}\mathbf{B}^{-1} \end{array}\right] \cdot \begin{bmatrix} \mathbf{d} \\ \hline \mathbf{p} \end{bmatrix}_{i-1}^R \tag{11-20}$$

The point matrix, which can be computed directly, is found to be

$$\begin{bmatrix} \mathbf{d} \\ \hline \mathbf{p} \end{bmatrix}_i^R = \left[\begin{array}{c|c} \mathbf{I} & \mathbf{0} \\ \hline \mathbf{K} & \mathbf{I} \end{array}\right] \cdot \begin{bmatrix} \mathbf{d} \\ \hline \mathbf{p} \end{bmatrix}_i^L$$

where

$$\mathbf{K} = \begin{bmatrix} & & & & & & -6 & 0 & -2 & 6 & 0 & -4 \\ & & & & & & 0 & 0 & 0 & 0 & 0 & 0 \\ & \mathbf{0} & & & & & 12 & 0 & 6 & -12+\frac{\kappa}{2} & 0 & 6 \\ & & & -6 & 0 & -2 & 0 & 0 & -8 & 6 & 0 & -2 \\ & & & 0 & 0 & 0 & 0 & 0 & 0 & 0 & 0 & 0 \\ & & & 12 & 0 & 6 & -24+\kappa & 0 & 0 & 12 & 0 & -6 \\ -6 & 0 & -2 & 0 & 0 & -8 & 6 & 0 & -2 & & & \\ 0 & 0 & 0 & 0 & 0 & 0 & 0 & 0 & 0 & & & \\ 12 & 0 & 6 & -24+\kappa & 0 & 0 & 12 & 0 & -6 & & & \\ -6 & 0 & -4 & 6 & 0 & -2 & & & & & \mathbf{0} & \\ 0 & 0 & 0 & 0 & 0 & 0 & & & & & & \\ -12+\frac{\kappa}{2} & 0 & -6 & 12 & 0 & -6 & & & & & & \end{bmatrix}$$

and
$$\kappa = \frac{ma^3\omega^2}{EJ_1} = \frac{16ma^2\omega^2}{Eh^3}$$

Illustrative Example. With the field and point matrices found, they can now be used in accordance with the transfer-matrix procedure. One simple illustrative example is the cantilever plate of Fig. 11-36. If in this example use is made of symmetry and antimetry, the computation of the matrices of Eq. (11-20) is simple and yields the following results.

The field matrices are

$$\begin{bmatrix} -w \\ a\dot{w} \\ a\overset{|}{w} \\ -\bar{T} \\ \bar{M} \\ \bar{V} \end{bmatrix}_i^L = \begin{bmatrix} 1 & -1 & \frac{1}{3} & 0 & -\frac{2}{3} & \frac{2}{9} \\ 0 & 1 & -1 & 1 & 1 & -\frac{2}{3} \\ 0 & 0 & 2 & -3 & 1 & 0 \\ 0 & 0 & -1 & 2 & -1 & \frac{1}{3} \\ 0 & 0 & 0 & 0 & 1 & -1 \\ 0 & 0 & 0 & 0 & 0 & 1 \end{bmatrix} \cdot \begin{bmatrix} -w \\ a\dot{w} \\ a\overset{|}{w} \\ -\bar{T} \\ \bar{M} \\ \bar{V} \end{bmatrix}_{i-1}^R \qquad \text{symmetric modes}$$

$$\begin{bmatrix} -w \\ a\dot{w} \\ a\overset{|}{w} \\ -\bar{T} \\ \bar{M} \\ \bar{V} \end{bmatrix}_i^L = \begin{bmatrix} 3 & -3 & 1 & 0 & -2 & \frac{2}{3} \\ -6 & 7 & -3 & 1 & 5 & -2 \\ -6 & 4 & -2 & 1 & 1 & 0 \\ 6 & -6 & 3 & -2 & -3 & 1 \\ -12 & 12 & -6 & 4 & 7 & -3 \\ 12 & -12 & 6 & -6 & -6 & 3 \end{bmatrix} \cdot \begin{bmatrix} -w \\ a\dot{w} \\ a\overset{|}{w} \\ -\bar{T} \\ \bar{M} \\ \bar{V} \end{bmatrix}_{i-1}^R \qquad \text{antimetric modes}$$

FIG. 11-36. Cantilever plate with edge stiffening beam and its substitute model. $J = ah^3/16$, $m = \mu a^2/2$.

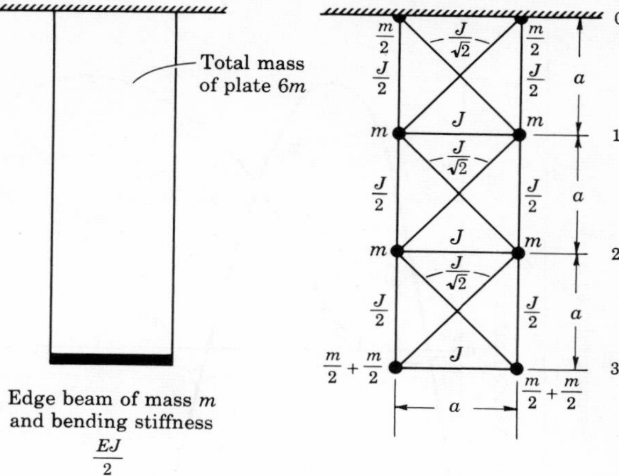

and the **K** matrices that appear in the point matrix are

$$\begin{bmatrix} 0 & 0 & -2 \\ 0 & 0 & 0 \\ \kappa & 0 & 0 \end{bmatrix} \qquad \text{for symmetric modes}$$

and

$$\begin{bmatrix} -12 & 0 & -6 \\ 0 & 0 & 0 \\ -24+\kappa & 0 & -12 \end{bmatrix} \qquad \text{for antimetric modes}$$

The state vectors $\mathbf{z}_0$ and $\mathbf{z}_3^R$ are related by the equation

$$\mathbf{z}_3^R = \mathbf{PFPFPFz}_0$$

and noting that the boundary conditions are

$$w_0 = a\dot{w}_0 = a\overset{|}{w}_0 = 0 \qquad \text{and} \qquad \bar{M}_3^R = \bar{T}_3^R = \bar{V}_3^R = 0$$

one can then form the frequency determinant. The plot of the frequency determinant against the circular frequency is shown in Fig. 11-37.

11-5. Shear-lag Problem

The shear sheet panel with stiffeners shown in Fig. 11-38 is subjected to a centrally applied end load of $4P_0$, and it is required to find the diffusion of the load into the panel. In common with usual aircraft practice the following assumptions are made:

1. The shear panels can take shear stress but no direct stress.
2. The cross stiffeners are assumed to be rigid.
3. The shear stress in any one panel is constant, and from this assumption it follows that the direct stress distribution in the main stiffeners is linear.

The problem will be treated in two ways, first by transfer matrices and second by the matrix force method.

Transfer-matrix Method. By using the principle of superposition the problem may be separated into two parts, as shown in Fig. 11-39. The solution of the first

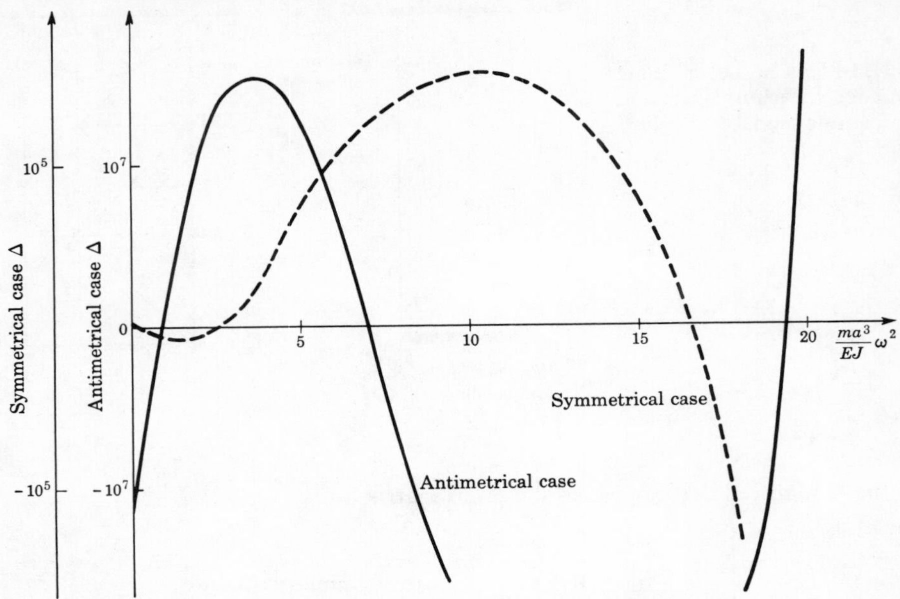

FIG. 11-37. Graph of frequency determinant.

part is trivial, the boom forces being carried through from one end to the other without any shear being introduced into the shear panels. Each boom will stretch by an identical amount, so that plane sections through the structure remain plane. The second loading is self-equilibrating with two outer compression forces and a single central tensile force. This force group will distort the structure, so that shears are introduced into the panel.

Let us remove the panel between the points $i - 1$ and i. Acting on the face $i - 1$ we have the equilibrium force group $(-P_{i-1}, 2P_{i-1}, -P_{i-1})$, and on the face i we have the force group $(-P_i, 2P_i, -P_i)$ (Fig. 11-40). Under the action of these force groups at section $i - 1$ the booms will be displaced relative to one another by an amount u_{i-1}, and at section i the relative displacement will be u_i. The displacements u_{i-1} and u_i can also be described as the generalized displacements u_{i-1} and u_i corresponding to the generalized force groups P_{i-1} and P_i.

Now making use of assumptions 1 to 3, we can find the stresses and strains present in the element under consideration:

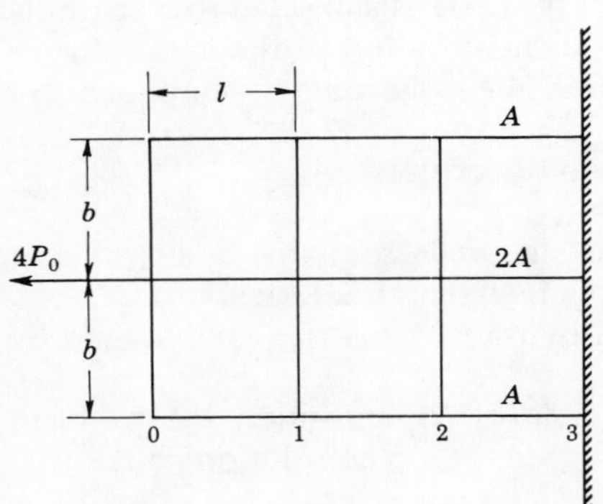

FIG. 11-38. Shear panel.

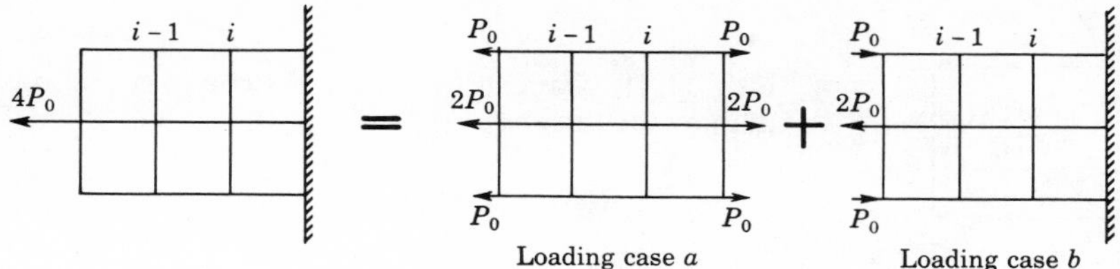

FIG. 11-39. Superposition of forces.

Direct stress in the booms

$$\sigma = \pm \frac{1}{A}\left(P_i \frac{l-x}{l} + P_{i-1}\frac{x}{l}\right) \qquad \begin{matrix}\text{inner boom } + \\ \text{outer boom } -\end{matrix}$$

Direct strain in the booms

$$\epsilon = \pm \frac{1}{AE}\left(P_i \frac{l-x}{l} + P_{i-1}\frac{x}{l}\right) \qquad \begin{matrix}\text{inner boom } + \\ \text{outer boom } -\end{matrix}$$

Shear stress in the shear panel (11-21)

$$\tau = \frac{P_{i-1} - P_i}{lt}$$

Shear strain in the shear panel

$$\gamma = \frac{P_{i-1} - P_i}{Glt}$$

In order to find the displacement u_{i-1}, we impress a unit dummy force group at the point $i-1$ and apply the principle of virtual work. We recall (cf. Sec. 9-1) that the principle of virtual work states that the work done by the unit dummy load in moving through the corresponding actual displacement of the structure is equal to the work done by any internal forces that are statically equivalent to the dummy group multiplied by the actual deformations of the elements of the structure. In this case we shall take internal forces equivalent to the unit force group that extends

FIG. 11-40. Details of ith panel.

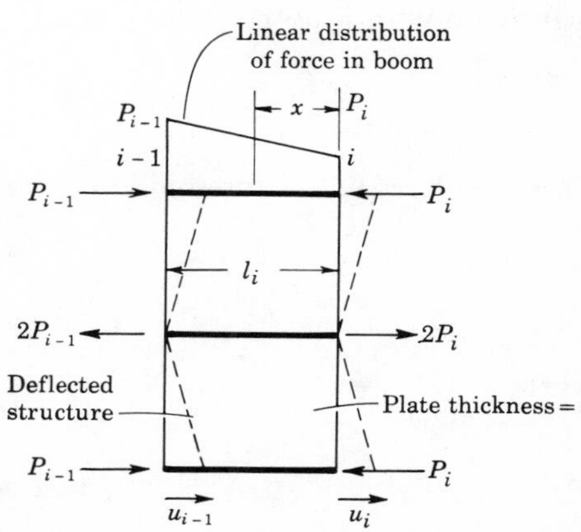

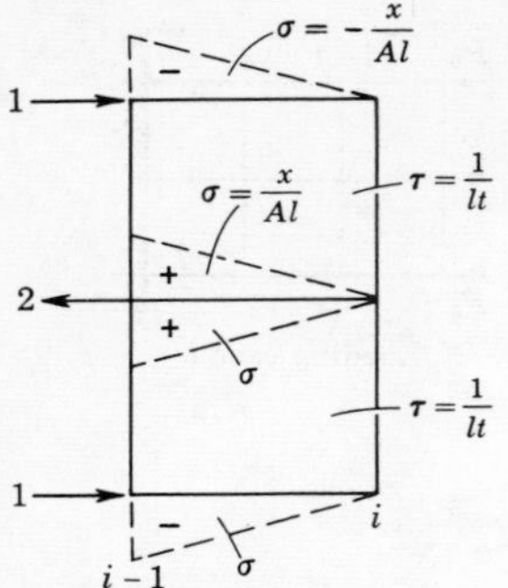

FIG. 11-41. Statically equivalent stress distribution due to dummy loading.

over only one element of the structure, as indicated in Fig. 11-41. Then Eqs. (11-21) yield the stresses

$$\sigma = \pm \frac{1}{A}\frac{x}{l} \qquad \tau = \frac{1}{lt}$$

We shall now apply the principle of virtual work, and since the structure is symmetrical to the center line we need consider only the lower or the upper half:

$$\underset{\substack{\text{unit}\\\text{dummy}\\\text{load}}}{(1)} \quad \underset{\substack{\text{true}\\\text{displace-}\\\text{ment}}}{(u_{i-1})} = \underset{\substack{\text{dummy}\\\text{shear}\\\text{stress}}}{\left(\frac{1}{lt}\right)} \underset{\substack{\text{true shear}\\\text{strain}}}{\left[\frac{1}{Glt}(P_{i-1} - P_i)\right]} \underset{\substack{\text{vol-}\\\text{ume}}}{(blt)}$$

$$+ 2\int_0^l \underset{\substack{\text{dummy}\\\text{direct}\\\text{stress}}}{\left[\pm\frac{1}{A}\left(\frac{x}{l}\right)\right]} \underset{\text{true direct strain}}{\left[\pm\frac{1}{AE}\left(P_i\frac{l-x}{l} + P_{i-1}\frac{x}{l}\right)\right]} \underset{\text{volume}}{A\,dx}$$

$$\therefore \quad u_{i-1} = \frac{b}{Glt}(P_{i-1} - P_i) + \frac{2}{AEl^2}\int_0^l [P_i x(l-x) + P_{i-1}x^2]\,dx$$

$$= P_{i-1}\left(\frac{b}{Glt} + \frac{2l}{3AE}\right) - P_i\left(\frac{b}{Glt} - \frac{l}{3AE}\right) \tag{11-22}$$

In the same way, if we apply a unit dummy force group at points i, we shall find that the result for displacement u_i is

$$u_i = P_{i-1}\left(\frac{b}{Glt} - \frac{l}{3AE}\right) - P_i\left(\frac{b}{Glt} + \frac{2l}{3AE}\right)$$

These results may be expressed in the form

$$u_{i-1} = \alpha P_{i-1} - \beta P_i \tag{11-23}$$

$$u_i = \beta P_{i-1} - \alpha P_i \tag{11-24}$$

where

$$\alpha = \frac{b}{Glt} + \frac{2l}{3AE} \tag{11-25}$$

and

$$\beta = \frac{b}{Glt} - \frac{l}{3AE} \tag{11-26}$$

Solving Eqs. (11-23) and (11-24) for u_i and P_i in terms of u_{i-1} and P_{i-1}, we obtain

$$u_i = \frac{\alpha}{\beta} u_{i-1} + \frac{\beta^2 - \alpha^2}{\beta} P_{i-1} \tag{11-27}$$

$$P_i = -\frac{u_i}{\beta} + \frac{\alpha}{\beta} P_{i-1} \tag{11-28}$$

The two components of the state vector at $i - 1$ are P_{i-1} and u_{i-1}, and expressing Eqs. (11-27) and (11-28) in matrix form, we have the result

$$\begin{bmatrix} u \\ P \end{bmatrix}_i = \begin{bmatrix} \dfrac{\alpha}{\beta} & \dfrac{\beta^2 - \alpha^2}{\beta} \\ -\dfrac{1}{\beta} & \dfrac{\alpha}{\beta} \end{bmatrix} \cdot \begin{bmatrix} u \\ P \end{bmatrix}_{i-1} \tag{11-29}$$

If the sheet has the following dimensions and properties:

$$A = 1 \text{ in.}^2 \qquad l = 40 \text{ in.} \qquad b = 20 \text{ in.} \qquad t = 0.03 \text{ in.}$$

and

$$\frac{G}{E} = \frac{1}{2(1 + \nu)} = \frac{1}{2.6}$$

then

$$\alpha = \frac{b}{Glt}\left(1 + \frac{2Gl^2t}{3EAb}\right) = 1.615 \frac{b}{Glt} = \frac{1.615}{k}$$

and

$$\beta = \frac{b}{Glt}\left(1 - \frac{Gl^2t}{3EAb}\right) = 0.692 \frac{b}{Glt} = \frac{0.692}{k} \qquad \text{when } k = \frac{Glt}{b}$$

The transfer-matrix calculation is then

$$\begin{bmatrix} 2.333 & -3.076 \\ -1.445 & 2.333 \end{bmatrix} \cdot \begin{bmatrix} u \\ \dfrac{P}{k} \end{bmatrix}_0 = \mathbf{z}_1$$

$$\begin{bmatrix} 2.333 & -3.076 \\ -1.445 & 2.333 \end{bmatrix} \begin{bmatrix} 9.888 & -14.353 \\ -6.742 & 9.888 \end{bmatrix} \cdot \begin{bmatrix} u \\ \dfrac{P}{k} \end{bmatrix}_0 = \mathbf{z}_2$$

$$\begin{bmatrix} 2.333 & -3.076 \\ -1.445 & 2.333 \end{bmatrix} \begin{bmatrix} 43.807 & -63.901 \\ -30.017 & 43.808 \end{bmatrix} \cdot \begin{bmatrix} u \\ \dfrac{P}{k} \end{bmatrix}_0 = \begin{bmatrix} 0 \\ \dfrac{P}{k} \end{bmatrix}_3$$

From the final product

$$43.807 u_0 - 63.901 \frac{P_0}{k} = 0$$

we obtain

$$u_0 = \frac{63.901}{43.807} \frac{P_0}{k} = 1.45865 \frac{P_0}{k}$$

The intermediate state vectors give

$$P_1 = -1.445 \times 1.45865 P_0 + 2.333 P_0 = 0.225 P_0$$

$$P_2 = -6.742 \times 1.45865 P_0 + 9.888 P_0 = 0.054 P_0$$

$$P_3 = -30.017 \times 1.45865 P_0 + 43.808 P_0 = 0.024 P_0$$

The shear flows in the panels are therefore

$$q_1 = \frac{P_0 - P_1}{l} = \frac{P_0(1 - 0.225)}{40} = 0.0194P_0$$

$$q_2 = \frac{P_1 - P_2}{l} = \frac{P_0(0.225 - 0.054)}{40} = 0.0043P_0$$

$$q_3 = \frac{P_2 - P_3}{l} = \frac{P_0(0.054 - 0.024)}{40} = 0.00075P_0$$

These shear flows stem from loading case 2, no shear flows resulting from loading case 1. However, in order to determine the loads in the booms, we must add the results of case 1 and case 2. Hence the total boom forces of the outside booms are 0, $0.775P_0$, $0.944P_0$, and $0.976P_0$, and the inner-boom forces for each half of the boom are $2P_0$, $1.225P_0$, $1.056P_0$, and $1.024P_0$.

Matrix Force Method. For this method the structure is disassembled into its component parts, as shown in Fig. 11-42, where the internal forces required to determine the state of stress throughout the structure are also shown. The state of stress in the panel is defined by the shear flow q, and since the boom members are subjected to these constant shear flows, the forces P in the booms vary linearly along their length. Hence, in order to define the stress in the booms, it is necessary that the two end forces P^L and P^R be known. Because the structure and the loading are symmetric, only one-half of the system need be considered. Therefore the structure has three redundancies, for which we choose the shear forces q_1l, q_2l, and q_3l. Then the basic system is such that the applied load $4P_0$ is carried entirely by the central boom. Hence the matrix $\mathbf{B}_0$ is found to be (cf. Sec. 9-2)

$$\begin{bmatrix} q_1l \\ q_2l \\ q_3l \\ P_1^L \\ P_1^R \\ P_2^L \\ P_2^R \\ P_3^L \\ P_3^R \\ P_4^L \\ P_4^R \\ P_5^L \\ P_5^R \\ P_6^L \\ P_6^R \end{bmatrix} = \begin{bmatrix} 0 \\ 0 \\ 0 \\ 1 \\ 1 \\ 1 \\ 1 \\ 1 \\ 1 \\ 0 \\ 0 \\ 0 \\ 0 \\ 0 \\ 0 \end{bmatrix} \cdot \begin{bmatrix} 2P_0 \end{bmatrix} \qquad \text{or} \qquad \mathbf{p}_0 = \mathbf{B}_0\mathbf{f}$$

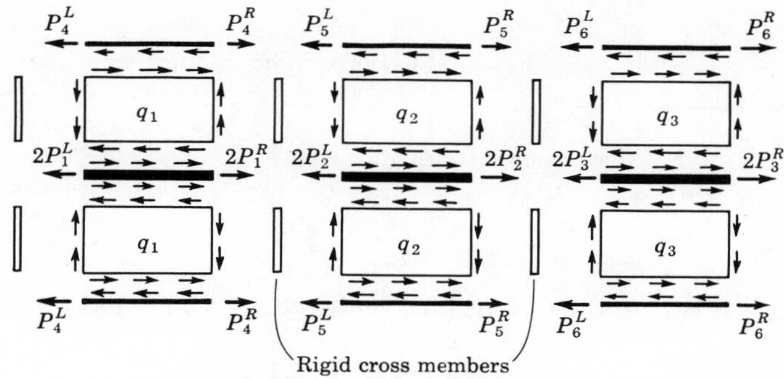

FIG. 11-42. Shear panel and its component parts.

The matrix $\mathbf{B}_1$ is obtained by subjecting the structure to the redundant forces $\mathbf{x} = \{q_1 l \quad q_2 l \quad q_3 l\}$:

$$\begin{bmatrix} q_1 l \\ q_2 l \\ q_3 l \\ P_1^L \\ P_1^R \\ P_2^L \\ P_2^R \\ P_3^L \\ P_3^R \\ P_4^L \\ P_4^R \\ P_5^L \\ P_5^R \\ P_6^L \\ P_6^R \end{bmatrix} = \begin{bmatrix} 1 & 0 & 0 \\ 0 & 1 & 0 \\ 0 & 0 & 1 \\ 0 & 0 & 0 \\ -1 & 0 & 0 \\ -1 & 0 & 0 \\ -1 & -1 & 0 \\ -1 & -1 & 0 \\ -1 & -1 & -1 \\ 0 & 0 & 0 \\ 1 & 0 & 0 \\ 1 & 0 & 0 \\ 1 & 1 & 0 \\ 1 & 1 & 0 \\ 1 & 1 & 1 \end{bmatrix} \cdot \begin{bmatrix} q_1 l \\ q_2 l \\ q_3 l \end{bmatrix} \qquad \text{or} \qquad \mathbf{p}_1 = \mathbf{B}_1 \mathbf{x}$$

Finally we must determine the flexibility matrices for each of the elements. The internal energy for the gth component is [cf. Eq. (9-7)]

$$u_g = \tfrac{1}{2}\mathbf{p}_g' \mathbf{F}_g \mathbf{p}_g$$

where $\mathbf{p}_g$ are the internal forces and $\mathbf{F}_g$ is the flexibility matrix.

The internal energy for one of the shear panels is

$$u = \tfrac{1}{2}(ql)^2 \frac{b}{ltG} = \tfrac{1}{2}(ql) \frac{b}{ltG} (ql)$$

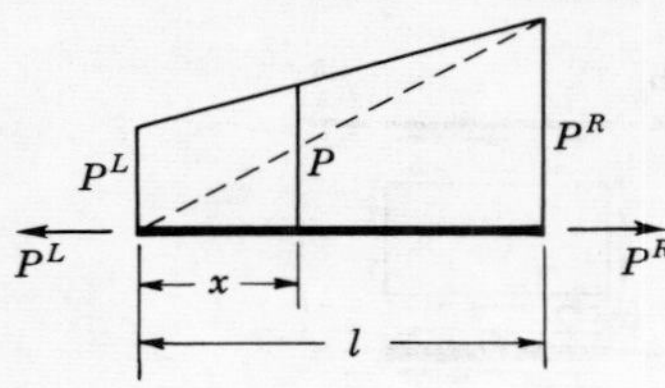

FIG. 11-43. Force in boom member.

so that

$$\mathbf{F}_g = \frac{b}{ltG} = \xi$$

The internal energy of a boom member with end forces P^L and P^R is (Fig. 11-43)

$$u = \frac{1}{2AE}\int_0^l \left(P^L \frac{l-x}{l} + P^R \frac{x}{l}\right)^2 dx$$

$$= \frac{l}{6AE}[(P^L)^2 + P^L P^R + (P^R)^2]$$

$$= \tfrac{1}{2}\begin{bmatrix} P^L & P^R \end{bmatrix} \cdot \begin{bmatrix} \dfrac{2l}{6AE} & \dfrac{l}{6AE} \\ \dfrac{l}{6AE} & \dfrac{2l}{6AE} \end{bmatrix} \cdot \begin{bmatrix} P^L \\ P^R \end{bmatrix}$$

and hence

$$\mathbf{F}_g = \frac{l}{6AE}\begin{bmatrix} 2 & 1 \\ 1 & 2 \end{bmatrix} = \eta \begin{bmatrix} 2 & 1 \\ 1 & 2 \end{bmatrix}$$

where

$$\eta = \frac{l}{6AE}$$

The flexibility matrix for the unassembled elements is therefore

$$\mathbf{F}_v = \eta \begin{bmatrix} \frac{\xi}{\eta} & & & & & & & & \\ & \frac{\xi}{\eta} & & & & & & & \\ & & \frac{\xi}{\eta} & & & & & & \\ & & & \begin{matrix} 2 & 1 \\ 1 & 2 \end{matrix} & & & & & \mathbf{0} \\ & & & & \begin{matrix} 2 & 1 \\ 1 & 2 \end{matrix} & & & & \\ & & & & & \begin{matrix} 2 & 1 \\ 1 & 2 \end{matrix} & & & \\ & & & & & & \begin{matrix} 2 & 1 \\ 1 & 2 \end{matrix} & & \\ & & & \mathbf{0} & & & & \begin{matrix} 2 & 1 \\ 1 & 2 \end{matrix} & \\ & & & & & & & & \begin{matrix} 2 & 1 \\ 1 & 2 \end{matrix} \end{bmatrix}$$

With the matrices $\mathbf{B}_0$, $\mathbf{B}_1$, and $\mathbf{F}_v$ known, we calculate the column vector $\mathbf{p}$ (internal forces) using the scheme of Table 9-1:

$$\mathbf{p} = \{0.774 \quad 0.174 \quad 0.030 \quad 2.00 \quad 1.226 \quad 1.226 \quad 1.052 \quad 1.052 \quad 1.022 \quad 0 \quad 0.774 \quad 0.774 \quad 0.948 \quad 0.948 \quad 0.978\}P_0$$

The shear flows in the panels are therefore

$$q_1 = \frac{0.774}{40} P_0 = 0.0194P_0 \qquad q_2 = \frac{0.174}{40} P_0 = 0.00435P_0 \qquad q_3 = \frac{0.030}{40} P_0 = 0.00075P_0$$

These results practically coincide with those obtained by means of the transfer-matrix method.

11-6. The Analysis of a Box Beam and the Effect of Structural Modification†

The box girder is shown in Fig. 11-44, and its component parts of Fig. 11-45 are

† This problem has been taken from the paper by Poppleton [53], and the authors express their gratitude for permission to draw freely on this work.

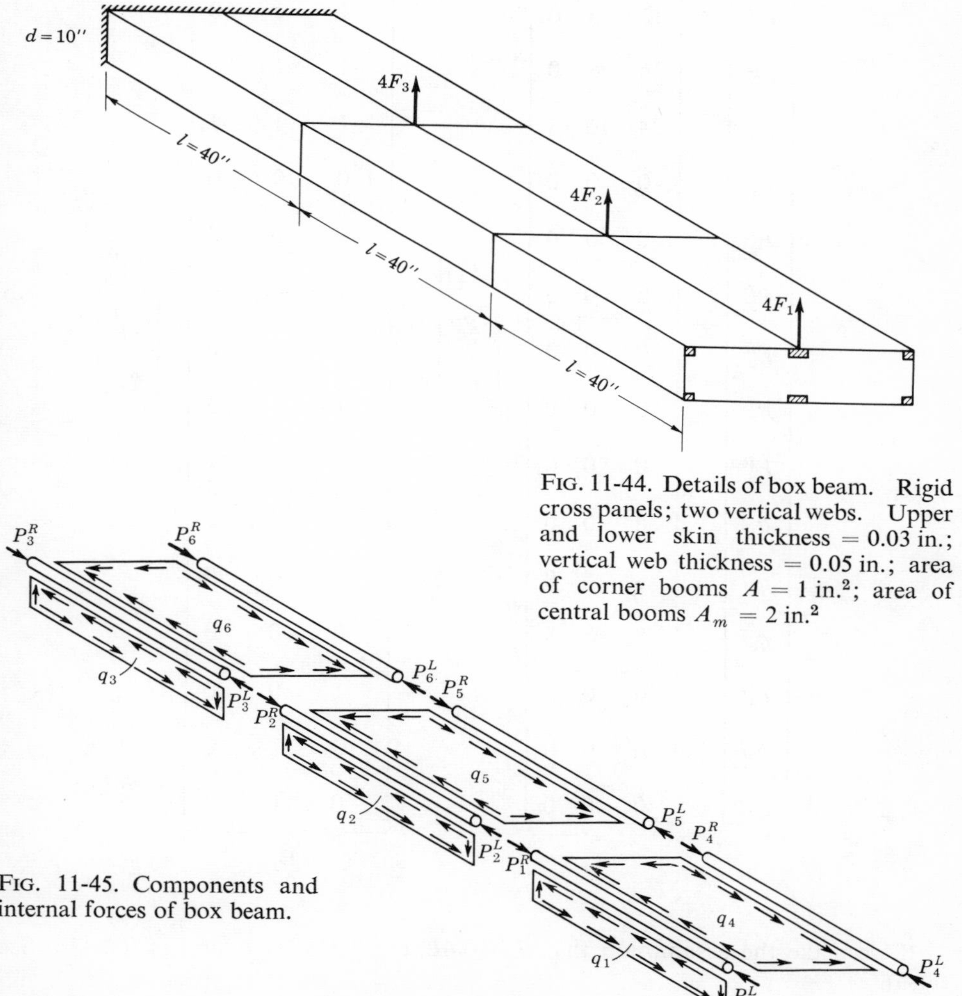

FIG. 11-44. Details of box beam. Rigid cross panels; two vertical webs. Upper and lower skin thickness = 0.03 in.; vertical web thickness = 0.05 in.; area of corner booms $A = 1$ in.^{2}; area of central booms $A_m = 2$ in.^{2}

FIG. 11-45. Components and internal forces of box beam.

similar to those of the shear panel of the previous section (cf. Fig. 11-42). On account of the symmetry of the structure and the loading, the internal forces in only one-fourth of the structure need be calculated. Therefore, for the calculation of the internal forces, it is necessary to consider only one-fourth of the structure.

The load can be carried by the basic structure, which consists of the four outer booms, the two vertical webs, and the rigid cross panels, so that the redundant forces are the shears q_4l, q_5l, and q_6l. Hence the matrix equation for the expression of the internal forces $\mathbf{p} = \mathbf{B}_0\mathbf{f} + \mathbf{B}_1\mathbf{x}$ is obtained by simple statics in the following manner:

$$\mathbf{p} = \begin{bmatrix} P_1^L \\ P_1^R \\ P_2^L \\ P_2^R \\ P_3^L \\ P_3^R \\ P_4^L \\ P_4^R \\ P_5^L \\ P_5^R \\ P_6^L \\ P_6^R \\ q_1l \\ q_2l \\ q_3l \\ q_4l \\ q_5l \\ q_6l \end{bmatrix} = \underbrace{\begin{bmatrix} 0 & 0 & 0 \\ 8 & 0 & 0 \\ 8 & 0 & 0 \\ 16 & 8 & 0 \\ 16 & 8 & 0 \\ 24 & 16 & 8 \\ 0 & 0 & 0 \\ 0 & 0 & 0 \\ 0 & 0 & 0 \\ 0 & 0 & 0 \\ 0 & 0 & 0 \\ 0 & 0 & 0 \\ 8 & 0 & 0 \\ 8 & 8 & 0 \\ 8 & 8 & 8 \\ 0 & 0 & 0 \\ 0 & 0 & 0 \\ 0 & 0 & 0 \end{bmatrix}}_{\mathbf{B}_0} \cdot \begin{bmatrix} F_1 \\ F_2 \\ F_3 \end{bmatrix} + \underbrace{\begin{bmatrix} 0 & 0 & 0 \\ -1 & 0 & 0 \\ -1 & 0 & 0 \\ -1 & -1 & 0 \\ -1 & -1 & 0 \\ -1 & -1 & -1 \\ 0 & 0 & 0 \\ 1 & 0 & 0 \\ 1 & 0 & 0 \\ 1 & 1 & 0 \\ 1 & 1 & 0 \\ 1 & 1 & 1 \\ 0 & 0 & 0 \\ 0 & 0 & 0 \\ 0 & 0 & 0 \\ 1 & 0 & 0 \\ 0 & 1 & 0 \\ 0 & 0 & 1 \end{bmatrix}}_{\mathbf{B}_1} \cdot \begin{bmatrix} q_4l \\ q_5l \\ q_6l \end{bmatrix}$$

If we make the assumption that $G = 0.4E$, the flexibility matrix is (cf. also Sec. 11-5)

$$
\mathbf{F}_v = \frac{l}{6AE} \times \begin{bmatrix}
2 & 1 & & & & & & & & & & & & & & & & \\
1 & 2 & & & & & & & & & & & & & & & & \\
 & & 2 & 1 & & & & & & & & & & & & & & \\
 & & 1 & 2 & & & & & & & & & & & & & & \\
 & & & & 2 & 1 & & & & & & & & & & & & \\
 & & & & 1 & 2 & & & & & & & & & & & & \\
 & & & & & & 2 & 1 & & & & & & & & & & \\
 & & & & & & 1 & 2 & & & & & & & & & & \\
 & & & & & & & & 2 & 1 & & & & & & & & \\
 & & & & & & & & 1 & 2 & & & & & & & & \\
 & & & & & & & & & & 2 & 1 & & & & & & \\
 & & & & & & & & & & 1 & 2 & & & & & & \\
 & & & & & & & & & & & & 0.9375 & & & & & \\
 & & & & & & & & & & & & & 0.9375 & & & & \\
 & & & & & & & & & & & & & & 0.9375 & & & \\
 & & & & & & & & & & & & & & & 6.25 & & \\
 & & & & & & & & & & & & & & & & 6.25 & \\
 & & & & & & & & & & & & & & & & & 6.25
\end{bmatrix}
$$

With the matrices $\mathbf{B}_0$, $\mathbf{B}_1$, and $\mathbf{F}_v$ found, the computations follow the standard pattern (cf. Sec. 9-2). The matrix $\mathbf{B}$ is found to be

$$
\mathbf{B} = \begin{bmatrix}
0 & 0 & 0 \\
4.12 & -1.16 & -0.17 \\
4.12 & -1.16 & -0.17 \\
8.56 & 4.29 & -0.82 \\
8.56 & 4.29 & -0.82 \\
14.68 & 10.56 & 6.10 \\
0 & 0 & 0 \\
3.88 & 1.16 & 0.17 \\
3.88 & 1.16 & 0.17 \\
7.42 & 3.71 & 0.82 \\
7.42 & 3.71 & 0.82 \\
9.32 & 5.44 & 1.90 \\
8.00 & 0 & 0 \\
8.00 & 8.00 & 0 \\
8.00 & 8.00 & 8.00 \\
3.88 & 1.16 & 0.17 \\
3.54 & 2.55 & 0.65 \\
1.90 & 1.73 & 1.08
\end{bmatrix}
$$

and the matrix $\mathbf{B}_1\mathbf{D}_{11}^{-1}\mathbf{B}_1'$ is given on the next page.

Matrix $\mathbf{B}_1\mathbf{D}_{11}^{-1}\mathbf{B}_1'$

$$
\frac{6AE}{3{,}752l} \times
\begin{bmatrix}
0 & 0 & 0 & 0 & 0 & 0 & 0 & 0 & 0 & 0 & 0 & 0 & 0 & 0 & 0 & 0 & 0 & 0 \\
0 & 192 & 192 & 44 & 44 & 18 & 0 & -192 & -192 & -44 & -44 & -18 & 0 & 0 & 0 & -192 & 149 & 26 \\
0 & 192 & 192 & 44 & 44 & 18 & 0 & -192 & -192 & -44 & -44 & -18 & 0 & 0 & 0 & -192 & 149 & 26 \\
0 & 44 & 44 & 210 & 210 & 87 & 0 & -44 & -44 & -210 & -210 & -87 & 0 & 0 & 0 & -44 & -167 & 123 \\
0 & 44 & 44 & 210 & 210 & 87 & 0 & -44 & -44 & -210 & -210 & -87 & 0 & 0 & 0 & -44 & -167 & 123 \\
0 & 18 & 18 & 87 & 87 & 402 & 0 & -18 & -18 & -87 & -87 & -402 & 0 & 0 & 0 & -18 & -69 & -315 \\
0 & 0 & 0 & 0 & 0 & 0 & 0 & 0 & 0 & 0 & 0 & 0 & 0 & 0 & 0 & 0 & 0 & 0 \\
0 & -192 & -192 & -44 & -44 & -18 & 0 & 192 & 192 & 44 & 44 & 18 & 0 & 0 & 0 & 192 & -149 & 26 \\
0 & -192 & -192 & -44 & -44 & -18 & 0 & 192 & 192 & 44 & 44 & 18 & 0 & 0 & 0 & 192 & -149 & 26 \\
0 & -44 & -44 & -210 & -210 & -87 & 0 & 44 & 44 & 210 & 210 & 87 & 0 & 0 & 0 & 44 & 167 & -123 \\
0 & -44 & -44 & -210 & -210 & -87 & 0 & 44 & 44 & 210 & 210 & 87 & 0 & 0 & 0 & 44 & 167 & -123 \\
0 & -18 & -18 & -87 & -87 & -402 & 0 & 18 & 18 & 87 & 87 & 402 & 0 & 0 & 0 & 18 & 69 & 315 \\
0 & 0 & 0 & 0 & 0 & 0 & 0 & 0 & 0 & 0 & 0 & 0 & 0 & 0 & 0 & 0 & 0 & 0 \\
0 & 0 & 0 & 0 & 0 & 0 & 0 & 0 & 0 & 0 & 0 & 0 & 0 & 0 & 0 & 0 & 0 & 0 \\
0 & 0 & 0 & 0 & 0 & 0 & 0 & 0 & 0 & 0 & 0 & 0 & 0 & 0 & 0 & 0 & 0 & 0 \\
0 & -192 & -192 & -44 & -44 & -18 & 0 & 192 & 192 & 44 & 44 & 18 & 0 & 0 & 0 & 192 & -149 & -26 \\
0 & 149 & 149 & -167 & -167 & -69 & 0 & -149 & -149 & 167 & 167 & 69 & 0 & 0 & 0 & -149 & 315 & -98 \\
0 & 26 & 26 & 123 & 123 & -315 & 0 & -26 & -26 & -123 & -123 & 315 & 0 & 0 & 0 & -26 & -98 & 438
\end{bmatrix}
$$

When $F_1 = 500$ lb, $F_2 = 1{,}500$ lb, and $F_3 = 2{,}000$ lb, then the internal forces are

$$\mathbf{p} = \begin{bmatrix} 0 \\ -0.02 \\ -0.02 \\ 9.09 \\ 9.09 \\ 35.38 \\ 0 \\ 4.02 \\ 4.02 \\ 10.92 \\ 10.92 \\ 16.62 \\ 4 \\ 16 \\ 32 \\ 4.02 \\ 6.90 \\ 5.71 \end{bmatrix} \times 10^3 \text{ lb}$$

From these results we find that the maximum direct stress in member 3 is 35,380 lb/in.^{2} and the shear stresses in panels 5 and 6 are 4,910 and 4,760 lb/in.^{2}, respectively. Suppose these are rather high and we wish to limit these stresses to 30,000, 4,000, and 4,000 lb/in.^{2}, respectively. In Sec. 9-5 we developed the equation

$$\mathbf{p}_j^* = \mathbf{B}_j\mathbf{f} - \mathbf{B}_{1j}\mathbf{D}_{11}^{-1}\mathbf{B}_{1j}'\mathbf{S}_j\boldsymbol{\sigma}_j^* + \mathbf{B}_{1j}\mathbf{D}_{11}^{-1}\mathbf{B}_{1j}'\mathbf{F}_{vj}\mathbf{p}_j^* \tag{11-30}$$

The internal forces $\mathbf{p}_j^*$ are

$$\mathbf{p}_j^* = \{P_3^{*L} \quad P_3^{*R} \quad q_5^*l \quad q_6^*l\}$$

so that from the matrix $\mathbf{B}_1\mathbf{D}_{11}^{-1}\mathbf{B}_1'$ we extract the matrix

$$\mathbf{B}_{1j}\mathbf{D}_{11}^{-1}\mathbf{B}_{1j}' = \frac{6AE}{3{,}752l} \times \begin{bmatrix} 210 & 87 & -167 & 123 \\ 87 & 402 & -69 & -315 \\ -167 & -69 & 315 & -98 \\ 123 & -315 & -98 & 438 \end{bmatrix}$$

Also $$\mathbf{F}_{vj} = \frac{l}{6AE} \times \begin{bmatrix} 2 & 1 & & \\ 1 & 2 & & \\ & & 6.25 & \\ & & & 6.25 \end{bmatrix}$$

The matrix $\mathbf{S}_j$ is given by the relation

$$\mathbf{F}^*_{vj}\mathbf{p}^*_j = \mathbf{S}_j\boldsymbol{\sigma}^*_j$$

or

$$\begin{bmatrix} \frac{2l}{6EA_3} & \frac{l}{6EA_3} & & \\ \frac{l}{6EA_3} & \frac{2l}{6EA_3} & & \\ & & \frac{d}{G(lt)_5} & \\ & & & \frac{d}{G(lt)_6} \end{bmatrix} \cdot \begin{bmatrix} P_3^{*L} \\ P_3^{*R} \\ q_5^* l \\ q_6^* l \end{bmatrix} = \begin{bmatrix} \frac{2l}{6E} & \frac{l}{6E} & & \\ \frac{l}{6E} & \frac{2l}{6E} & & \\ & & \frac{d}{G} & \\ & & & \frac{d}{G} \end{bmatrix} \cdot \begin{bmatrix} \sigma_3^{*L} \\ \sigma_3^{*R} \\ \tau_5^* \\ \tau_6^* \end{bmatrix}$$

Hence

$$\mathbf{S}_j = \frac{l}{6E} \times \begin{bmatrix} 2 & 1 & & \\ 1 & 2 & & \\ & & \frac{6Ed}{Gl} & \\ & & & \frac{6Ed}{Gl} \end{bmatrix} = \frac{l}{6E} \times \begin{bmatrix} 2 & 1 & & \\ 1 & 2 & & \\ & & 7.5 & \\ & & & 7.5 \end{bmatrix}$$

With $\mathbf{f} = \{500 \quad 1{,}500 \quad 2{,}000\}$ lb, the governing equation (11-30) becomes

$$\begin{bmatrix} P_3^{*L} \\ P_3^{*R} \\ q_5^* l \\ q_6^* l \end{bmatrix} = \begin{bmatrix} 9.09 \\ 35.38 \\ 6.90 \\ 5.71 \end{bmatrix} \times 10^3 - \begin{bmatrix} 0.1352 & 0.1025 & -0.3330 & 0.2459 \\ 0.1536 & 0.2376 & -0.1381 & -0.6298 \\ -0.1072 & -0.0812 & 0.6298 & -0.1949 \\ -0.0184 & -0.1352 & -0.1949 & 0.8757 \end{bmatrix} \cdot \begin{bmatrix} \sigma_3^{*L} \\ \sigma_3^{*R} \\ \tau_5^* \\ \tau_6^* \end{bmatrix}$$
$$+ \begin{bmatrix} 0.1352 & 0.1025 & -0.2775 & 0.2049 \\ 0.1536 & 0.2376 & -0.1150 & -0.5248 \\ -0.1072 & -0.0812 & 0.5248 & -0.1624 \\ -0.0184 & -0.1352 & -0.1624 & 0.7297 \end{bmatrix} \cdot \begin{bmatrix} P_3^{*L} \\ P_3^{*R} \\ q_5^* l \\ q_6^* l \end{bmatrix}$$

and with $\boldsymbol{\sigma}^*_j = \{\sigma_3^{*L} \quad 30{,}000 \quad 4{,}000 \quad 4{,}000\}$

$$\begin{bmatrix} P_3^{*L} \\ P_3^{*R} \\ q_5^* l \\ q_6^* l \end{bmatrix} = \begin{bmatrix} 6.36 \\ 31.32 \\ 7.60 \\ 7.04 \end{bmatrix} \times 10^3 - \begin{bmatrix} 0.1352 \\ 0.1536 \\ -0.1072 \\ -0.0184 \end{bmatrix} \times \sigma_3^{*L}$$
$$+ \begin{bmatrix} 0.1352 & 0.1025 & -0.2775 & 0.2049 \\ 0.1536 & 0.2376 & -0.1150 & -0.5248 \\ -0.1072 & -0.0821 & 0.5248 & -0.1624 \\ -0.0184 & -0.1352 & -0.1624 & 0.7297 \end{bmatrix} \cdot \begin{bmatrix} P_3^{*L} \\ P_3^{*R} \\ q_5^* l \\ q_6^* l \end{bmatrix} \qquad (11\text{-}31)$$

In this equation $\mathbf{p}^*_j$ and σ_3^{*L} are unknown, but σ_3^{*L} is related to $\mathbf{p}^*_j$, its value depending on the cross section of the boom. It is solved by iteration, choosing, first of all, $\mathbf{p}_j^* = \{9.09 \quad 35.38 \quad 6.90 \quad 5.71\} \times 10^3$ lb, which is the value of $\mathbf{p}_j$ obtained for the unmodified structure. With this choice and using the sections of the unmodified structure, σ_3^{*L} can also be calculated to give $\sigma_3^{*L} = 9{,}090$ lb/in.^{2} These values are now put into the right-hand side of Eq. (11-31) to give a new value of $\mathbf{p}_j^*$ on the left-hand side. With these new internal end forces the new sections can be calculated which give the required stresses. With the new values for $\mathbf{p}_j^*$ and σ_3^{*L} the process is continued until convergence is attained. After six such iterations it was found that $\mathbf{p}_j^*$ converged to the values

$$\mathbf{p}_j^* = \{8.74 \quad 39.62 \quad 8.33 \quad 1.12\} \times 10^3 \text{ lb} \tag{11-32}$$

Hence we find the cross-sectional areas to be

$$A_3 = \frac{39.62 \times 10^3}{30 \times 10^3} = 1.32 \text{ in.}^2$$

$$A_5 = t_5 l = \frac{8.33 \times 10^3}{4 \times 10^3} = 2.08 \text{ in.}^2 \rightarrow t_5 = 0.052 \text{ in.}$$

$$A_6 = t_6 l = \frac{1.12 \times 10^3}{4 \times 10^3} = 0.28 \text{ in.}^2 \rightarrow t_6 = 0.007 \text{ in.}$$

For a further discussion of this problem the reader is referred to the original paper [53].

11-7. Calculation of Stresses and Strains in Rotating Disks

The transfer-matrix method can readily be applied to the calculation of stresses and strains in rotating disks if the following assumptions are justified:

1. Rotational symmetry of the disk
2. Plane of symmetry perpendicular to shaft axis
3. Gradual change of disk thickness (plane state of stress)
4. Small deformations
5. Hooke's law

In addition, the real disk (Fig. 11-46) is replaced by the substitute disk of Fig. 11-47. With these assumptions a straightforward derivation [60] of the transfer

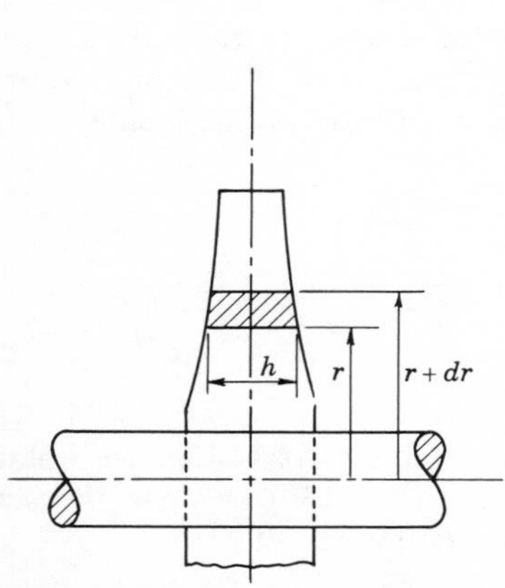

FIG. 11-46. Axial section through circular disk.

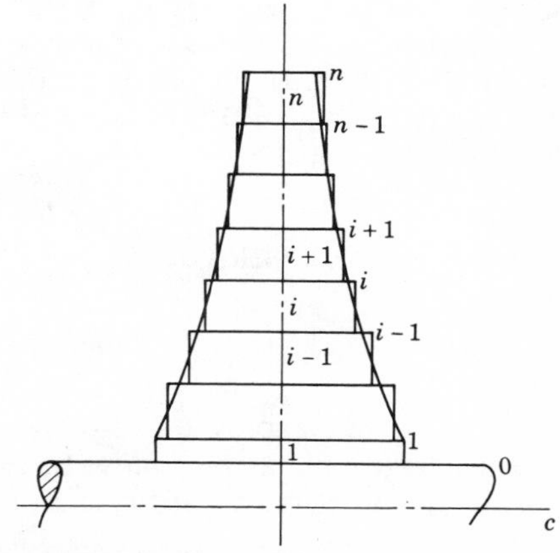

FIG. 11-47. Axial section through substitute disk.

matrix leads to the extended transfer matrix $\tilde{\mathbf{U}}_i$ displayed in the Catalogue (Sec. C-13*a*).

The relation between the state vectors at the inner radius (subscript 0) and the outer radius (subscript *n*) of the disk is obtained by multiplying all extended transfer matrices $\tilde{\mathbf{U}}_i$ as follows:

$$\tilde{\mathbf{z}}_n = \tilde{\mathbf{U}}_n\tilde{\mathbf{U}}_{n-1}\tilde{\mathbf{U}}_{n-2}\cdots\tilde{\mathbf{U}}_i\cdots\tilde{\mathbf{U}}_2\tilde{\mathbf{U}}_1\tilde{\mathbf{z}}_0 = \tilde{\mathbf{P}}\tilde{\mathbf{z}}_0 \tag{11-33}$$

which reads, in "long hand" (cf. Fig. C-16),

$$\begin{aligned} S_{r_n} &= p_{11}S_{r_0} + p_{12}u_0 + p_{13} \\ u_n &= p_{21}S_{r_0} + p_{22}u_0 + p_{23} \\ 1 &= 0 \qquad + 0 \qquad + 1 \end{aligned} \tag{11-34}$$

From transfer matrix C-13*a* we realize that the elements p_{ik} of the first two columns do not contain the angular velocity Ω of the rotating disk. For the special case ($\Omega = 0$), therefore, these elements remain unchanged, and p_{13} and p_{23} become zero. This fact proves advantageous later in the determination of the shrink fit.

In Eqs. (11-34) the radial force per unit length S_{r_n} is usually known because it stems from the centrifugal force caused by the blading. S_{r_0} denotes the shrink-fit force per unit length for which a certain negative value is prescribed while disk and shaft are rotating. With S_{r_0} and S_{r_n} known, the radial shifts u_0 and u_n can be found by Eqs. (11-34). After that, all state vectors $\mathbf{z}_i$ at the points *i* between 0 and *n* can be determined. Then it is also possible to compute all hoop forces $S_{\theta i}$:

$$S_{\theta i} = \mathbf{H}_i\mathbf{z}_i$$

with

$$\mathbf{H}_i = \begin{bmatrix} \nu & E\dfrac{h_i}{r_i} \end{bmatrix}$$

where h_i is the thickness of the disk at radius r_i.

Calculation of the Shrink Fit. Because of the forces induced by the shrink fit the outer radius of the shaft is changed. Since the determination of the three-dimensional state of stress and strain in the shaft is extremely complicated, the influence of the shaft on the state of stress and strain in the disk is considered only approximately, by regarding the part of the shaft that is surrounded by the shrink fit as a disk without a hole, of constant thickness equal to that of the root of the disk.† Since the inner radius of a disk without a hole is equal to zero, the transfer matrix $\tilde{\mathbf{U}}$ (Sec. C-13*a*) cannot be used, because the elements of the second column go to infinity for $r_{i-1} \to 0$. Because of the fact that equilibrium at the center of the disk is satisfied only if

$$h\sigma_r = h\sigma_\theta = S_c$$

the relation $\varepsilon_\theta = u/r$ yields, for $r_{i-1} \to 0$,

$$\lim_{r_{i-1}\to 0} h\frac{u}{r_{i-1}} = \frac{S_c}{E}(1 - \nu)$$

Substituting this expression into the extended transfer matrix C-13*a*, we obtain, after some regrouping, the following relation (cf. matrix C-13*b*) between the state vectors at the outer radius of the shaft and the center (subscript *c*):

† For the case where the shaft has been bored hollow (concentric), the difficulties discussed hereafter do not occur.

$$\begin{bmatrix} S_{r_0} \\ u_S \\ 1 \end{bmatrix} = \begin{bmatrix} 1 & 0 & q_{13} \\ q_{21} & 0 & q_{23} \\ 0 & 0 & 1 \end{bmatrix} \begin{bmatrix} S_c \\ u_c = 0 \\ 1 \end{bmatrix} \tag{11-35}$$

$$\tilde{\mathbf{z}}_0 = \tilde{\mathbf{U}}_0 \tilde{\mathbf{z}}_c$$

with $q_{13} = -\dfrac{\rho h_0 \Omega^2}{8} r_0^2(3 + \nu) \qquad q_{21} = \dfrac{1}{Eh_0}(1 - \nu) r_0 \qquad q_{23} = -\dfrac{\rho\Omega^2}{8}\dfrac{r_0^3}{E}(1 - \nu^2)$

When the stress and strain in a rotating disk without a hole is to be determined, Eq. (11-33) has to be extended as follows:

$$\tilde{\mathbf{z}}_n = \tilde{\mathbf{P}} \tilde{\mathbf{U}}_0 \tilde{\mathbf{z}}_c \tag{11-36}$$

We now turn to the determination of $\Delta r = r_S - r_D$, where r_S denotes the radius of the shaft and r_D denotes the inner radius of the disk hole before shrinking the disk onto the shaft. Δr is to be determined in such a way that during rotation with the angular velocity Ω a shrink-fit force S_{r_0} is present.

Figure 11-48 shows the validity of the following relation:

$$\Delta r = u_0 - u_S = \bar{u}_0 - \bar{u}_S \tag{11-37}$$

where the case $\Omega = 0$ is indicated by the bar. Now the first of Eqs. (11-34) yields

$$u_0 = \frac{1}{p_{12}}(S_{rn} - p_{11} S_{r_0} - p_{13})$$

and u_S is found from Eq. (11-35) as follows:

$$S_{r_0} = S_c + q_{13} \qquad u_S = q_{21} S_c + q_{23} = q_{21}(S_{r_0} - q_{13}) + q_{23}$$

Thus Δr is found for a prescribed shrink-fit force S_{r_0} during rotation as

$$\Delta r = u_0 - u_S = -\left(\frac{p_{11}}{p_{12}} + q_{21}\right) S_{r_0} + \frac{1}{p_{12}}(S_{rn} - p_{13}) + q_{21} q_{13} - q_{23}$$

We are interested also in the shrink-fit force $\bar{S}_{r_0}$ for $\Omega = 0$. Then $S_{r_n} = 0$ and $p_{13} = 0$ yield [cf. remarks after Eqs. (11-34)]

$$0 = p_{11} \bar{S}_{r_0} + p_{12} \bar{u}_0$$

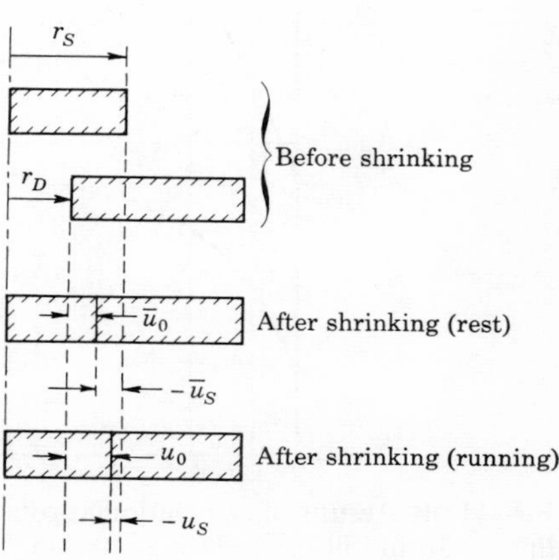

FIG. 11-48. Shrink-fit deformations.

Hence

$$\bar{u}_0 = -\frac{p_{11}}{p_{12}}\bar{S}_{r_0}$$

Correspondingly Eq. (11-35) gives for $\Omega = 0$ ($q_{13} = q_{23} = 0$)

$$\bar{S}_{r_0} = \bar{S}_c$$

and thus

$$\bar{u}_S = q_{21}\bar{S}_{r_0}$$

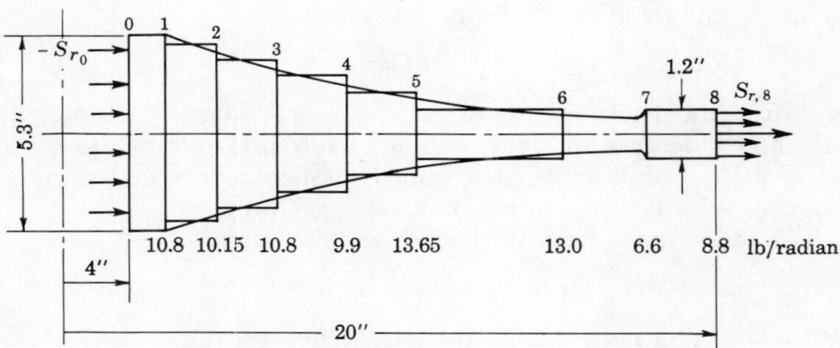

FIG. 11-49. Disk and substitute system.

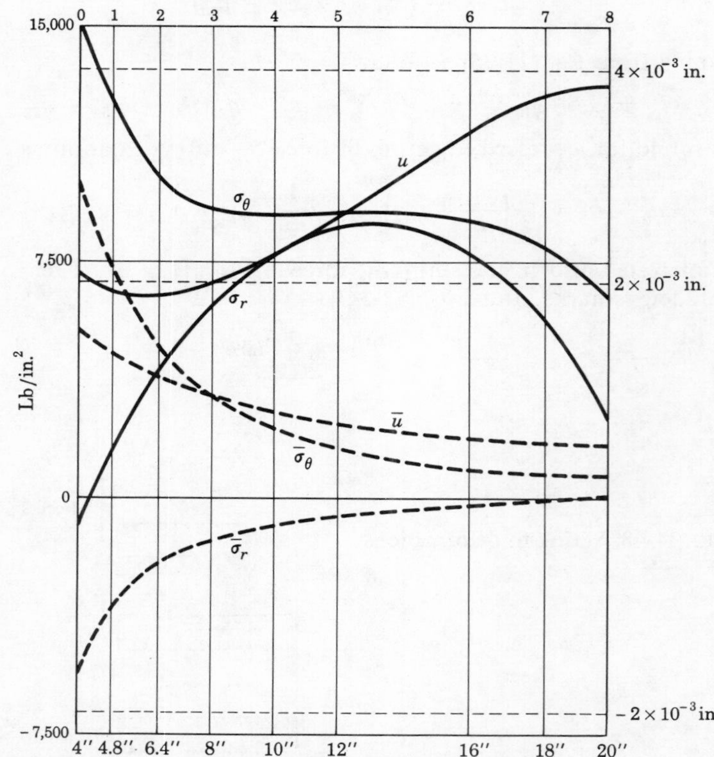

FIG. 11-50. Results of calculation at rotational speed of 3,000 rpm (solid line), at rest (broken line). Shrink fit $\Delta r = 2.09 \times 10^{-3}$ in.

Therefore, with the aid of Eq. (11-37), we obtain

$$\bar{S}_{r_0} = \frac{-\Delta r}{p_{11}/p_{12} + q_{21}}$$

Hence the determination of the stresses and strain in the disk at rest is also done in the same manner as before.

Numerical Example. The steel disk [38, 60] whose cross section is shown in Fig. 11-49 is running at 3,000 rpm. It is required that at this speed the pressure between disk and shaft be $S_{r_0} = -5{,}580$ lb/in., and that the blading exert on the outer rim of the disk a radial force per unit length of $S_{r_8} = 3{,}360$ lb/in. Determine the shrink fit Δr, the stress distribution, and the radial displacement in the disk at rest and the above rotational speed.

First we choose the substitute system shown in Fig. 11-49, where the weight $W_i/2\pi$ of each ring mass in pounds per radian is also indicated, which was computed for the specific weight $\gamma = 0.284$ lb/in.^{3} The application of the transfer-matrix method as developed above yields easily the results that are plotted in Fig. 11-50 ($E = 30 \times 10^6$ lb/in.^{2} and $\nu = 0.3$).

11-8. Simultaneous Bending and Buckling of Multisectional Straight Beams

Derivation of Extended Transfer Matrix. Let us first derive the differential equation for the beam element (Fig. 11-51) which is loaded in vertical and horizontal directions, so that simultaneous bending and buckling occurs. Inspection of Fig. 11-51 yields

$$\frac{dH}{dx} = +h \tag{11-38a}$$

$$\frac{dV}{dx} = -q \tag{11-38b}$$

$$\frac{dM}{dx} = V - H\psi \tag{11-38c}$$

$$\frac{d\psi}{dx} = \frac{M}{EJ} \tag{11-38d}$$

$$-\frac{dw}{dx} = \psi \tag{11-38e}$$

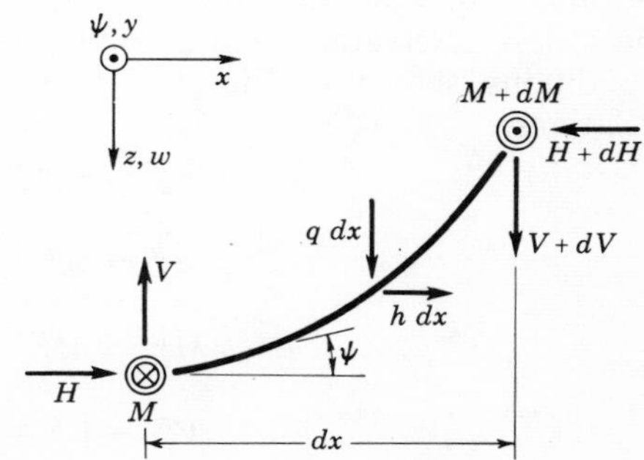

FIG. 11-51. Beam element under compression and bending.

Hence we obtain, after eliminating all dependent variables but w,

$$EJw^{\text{iv}} + Hw'' + hw' = q \tag{11-39}$$

Whereas the transfer matrices given in Sec. C-4 were found on the basis of Eq. (11-39) for $h = q = 0$, we shall now derive the extended transfer matrix for the special case $h = 0$, $q = \text{const}$, $H = P_c$:

$$w^{\text{iv}} + \frac{P_c}{EJ} w'' = \frac{q}{EJ} \tag{11-40}$$

With the abbreviation $\varepsilon^2 = P_c/EJ$ the general solution of Eq. (11-40) is given as follows:

$$w(x) = C_1 + C_2 x + C_3 \sin \varepsilon x + C_4 \cos \varepsilon x + \frac{q}{2P_c} x^2$$

Using the procedure demonstrated in Sec. 5-1, we obtain the extended-transfer-matrix relation ($\gamma^2 = \varepsilon^2 l^2$)

$$\begin{bmatrix} -w \\ \psi \\ M \\ V \\ \hline 1 \end{bmatrix}_i = \left[\begin{array}{ccccc|c} 1 & l\dfrac{\sin\gamma}{\gamma} & \dfrac{l^2}{EJ}\dfrac{1-\cos\gamma}{\gamma^2} & \dfrac{l^3}{EJ}\dfrac{\gamma-\sin\gamma}{\gamma^3} & & \dfrac{ql^4}{EJ}\dfrac{1-\cos\gamma-\gamma^2/2}{\gamma^4} \\ 0 & \cos\gamma & \dfrac{l}{EJ}\dfrac{\sin\gamma}{\gamma} & \dfrac{l^2}{EJ}\dfrac{1-\cos\gamma}{\gamma^2} & & \dfrac{ql^3}{EJ}\dfrac{\sin\gamma-\gamma}{\gamma^3} \\ 0 & -P_c l\dfrac{\sin\gamma}{\gamma} & \cos\gamma & l\dfrac{\sin\gamma}{\gamma} & & ql^2\dfrac{\cos\gamma-1}{\gamma^2} \\ 0 & 0 & 0 & 1 & & -ql\dfrac{\sin\gamma}{\gamma} \\ \hline 0 & 0 & 0 & 0 & & 1 \end{array}\right]_i \cdot \begin{bmatrix} -w \\ \psi \\ M \\ V \\ \hline 1 \end{bmatrix}_{i-1} \tag{11-41}$$

Corresponding to the forcing functions listed in the table in Sec. C-6, it is not difficult to establish Table 11-5 of forcing functions, with the assumption that $H = P_c = \text{const}$.

Shifted-Matrix Multiplication. In Sec. 3-4 we introduced shifted-matrix multiplication [9], which is quite useful when the numerical calculations are carried out on a desk calculator. We use this procedure here to take care of the intermediate conditions shown in Fig. 11-52. Inspection of this figure yields the following relations:

$$-w_i^R = -w_i^L$$

$$\psi_i^R = \psi_i^L$$

$$M_i^R = M_i^L + k_\psi \psi_i - C_i$$

$$V_i^R = V_i^L + k_w w_i - P_{zi}$$

Table 11-5

	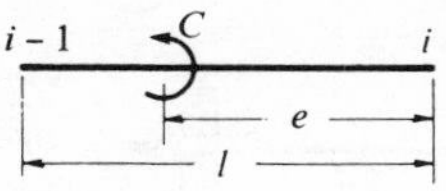 $i-1$, C, i; e; l	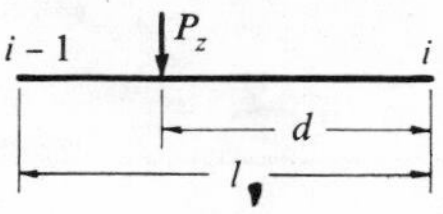 $i-1$, P_z, i; d; l	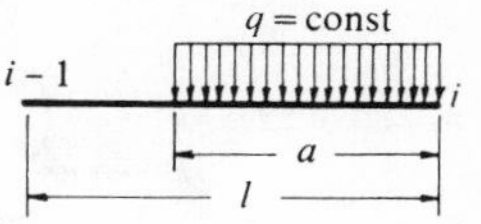 $q=\text{const}$; $i-1$, i; a; l
$r_1 = -\tilde{w}$	$-\dfrac{Cl^2}{EJ}\dfrac{1-\cos(e\gamma/l)}{\gamma^2}$	$-\dfrac{P_z l^3}{EJ}\dfrac{\gamma d/l - \sin(\gamma d/l)}{\gamma^3}$	$\dfrac{ql^4}{EJ}\dfrac{1-\cos(a\gamma/l)-(a\gamma/l)^2/2}{\gamma^4}$
$r_2 = \tilde{\psi}$	$-\dfrac{Cl}{EJ}\dfrac{\sin(e\gamma/l)}{\gamma}$	$-\dfrac{P_z l^2}{EJ}\dfrac{1-\cos(\gamma d/l)}{\gamma^2}$	$\dfrac{ql^3}{EJ}\dfrac{\sin(a\gamma/l)-a\gamma/l}{\gamma^3}$
$r_3 = \tilde{M}$	$-C\cos\dfrac{e\gamma}{l}$	$\dfrac{P_z l}{\gamma}\sin\dfrac{\gamma d}{l}$	$ql^2\dfrac{\cos(a\gamma/l)-1}{\gamma^2}$
$r_4 = \tilde{Q}$	$\dfrac{C\gamma}{l}\sin\dfrac{e\gamma}{l}$	$-P_z\cos\dfrac{\gamma d}{l}$	$-ql\dfrac{\sin(a\gamma/l)}{\gamma}$

On the basis of Fig. 11-53 the matrix relation for the shifted-matrix multiplication is

$$\begin{bmatrix} -w \\ \psi \\ M \\ V \\ 1 \end{bmatrix}_{i-1}^{R} = \mathbf{z}_{i-1}^{R}$$

$$\mathbf{L}_i = \left[\begin{array}{c|c|cc} & \dfrac{ql^4}{EJ}\dfrac{1-\cos\gamma-\gamma^2/2}{\gamma^4} & 0 & 0 \\ \text{cf. Eq.} & \dfrac{ql^3}{EJ}\dfrac{\sin\gamma-\gamma}{\gamma^3} & 0 & 0 \\ \text{(11-41)} & ql^2\dfrac{\cos\gamma-1}{\gamma^2}-C & 0 & k_\psi \\ & -ql\dfrac{\sin\gamma}{\gamma}-P_z & -k_w & 0 \\ \hline 0\quad 0\quad 0\quad 0 & 1 & 0 & 0 \end{array}\right]_i = \begin{bmatrix} -w \\ \psi \\ M \\ V \\ \hline 1 \end{bmatrix}_i^{R} = \mathbf{z}_i^{R} \tag{11-42}$$

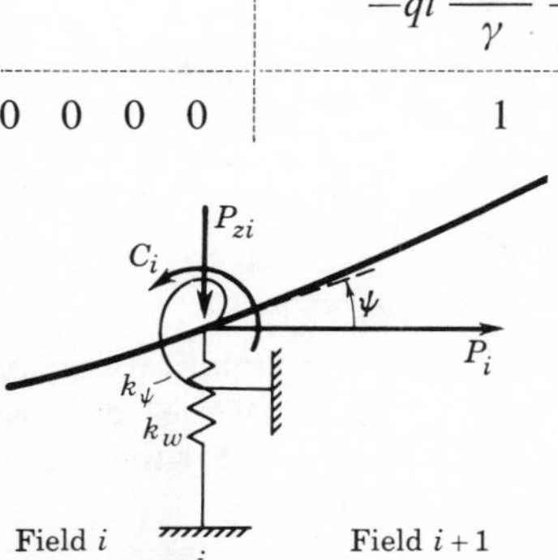

FIG. 11-52

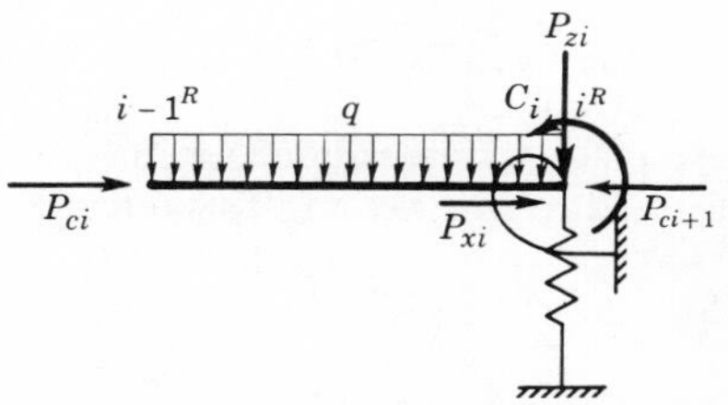

FIG. 11-53

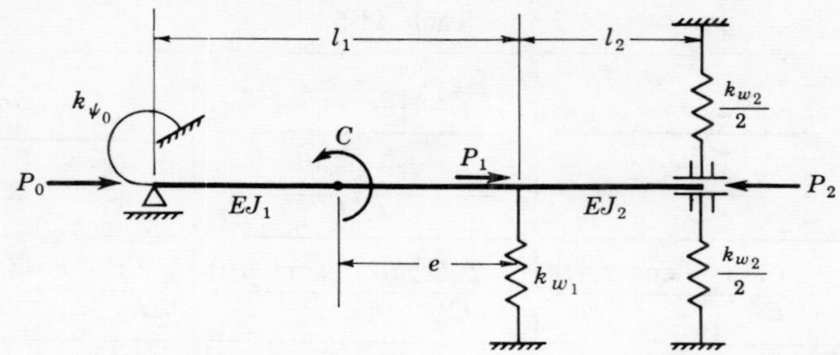

FIG. 11-54. Beam in bending and buckling. $P_0 = P_1 = 2{,}000$ lb; $P_2 = 4{,}000$ lb. $l_1 = 200$ in.; $l_2 = 100$ in. $e = 100$ in. $k_{\psi_0} = 10{,}000$ lb-in.; $k_{w_1} = 100$ lb/in.; $k_{w_2} = 25$ lb/in. $C = 50{,}000$ lb-in. $EJ_1 = 8 \times 10^7$ lb-in.^{2}; $EJ_2 = 16 \times 10^7$ lb-in.^{2}

First Illustrative Example. Let us now apply the results obtained above to the simple example depicted in Fig. 11-54 [61], the data of which yield immediately

$$P_{c1} = 2{,}000 \text{ lb} \qquad \text{and thus} \qquad \gamma_1 = \sqrt{\frac{P_{c1}l_1^2}{EJ_1}} = 1$$

and

$$P_{c2} = 4{,}000 \text{ lb} \qquad \text{and thus} \qquad \gamma_2 = \sqrt{\frac{P_{c2}l_2^2}{EJ_2}} = 0.5$$

With the left-hand boundary conditions $w_0 = 0$ and $M_0^R = k_{\psi_0}\psi_0$ we may write, for the initial extended state vector, $\mathbf{z}_0^R = \{0 \quad \psi_0 \quad k_{\psi_0}\psi_0 \quad V_0^R \mid 1\}$ and then form the matrix product

$$\tilde{\mathbf{z}}_2^R = \mathbf{L}_2\mathbf{L}_1\tilde{\mathbf{z}}_0^R$$

The matrices $\mathbf{L}_1$ and $\mathbf{L}_2$ are taken from Eq. (11-42). However, because of the transverse load (cf. Fig. 11-54), in $\mathbf{L}_1$ the fifth column of Eq. (11-42) is replaced by the first column of Table 11-5, and in $\mathbf{L}_2$ the fifth column is zero.

The right-hand boundary conditions $\psi_2 = 0$ and $V_2^R = 0$ then yield

$$\psi_0 = 0.00643 \text{ radian} \qquad \text{and} \qquad V_0^R = 249.37 \text{ lb}$$

Now we may compute the components of all state vectors and obtain

$$\mathbf{z}_0^R = \begin{bmatrix} 0 \\ 0.00643 \text{ radian} \\ 64.32 \text{ lb-in.} \\ 249.37 \text{ lb} \end{bmatrix} \qquad \mathbf{z}_1^R = \begin{bmatrix} 1.9902 \text{ in.} \\ 0.00100 \text{ radian} \\ -4{,}039.7 \text{ lb-in.} \\ 50.35 \text{ lb} \end{bmatrix} \qquad \mathbf{z}_2^R = \begin{bmatrix} 2.0145 \text{ in.} \\ 0 \text{ radians} \\ 899.36 \text{ lb-in.} \\ 0 \text{ lb} \end{bmatrix}$$

These results are easily checked by means of the equilibrium equations. The reader is advised to do this and to sketch the shape of the deflection of the beam.

Second Illustrative Example [61]. We seek the safety factor α for the beam of Fig. 11-55 under the given load:

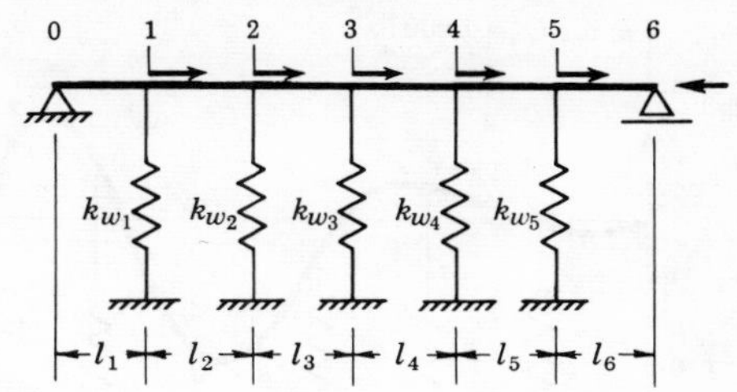

FIG. 11-55. Girder in compression on elastic intermediate supports.

$$P_0 = 300 \times 10^3 \text{ lb}$$
$$P_1 = 290 \times 10^3 \text{ lb}$$
$$P_2 = 290 \times 10^3 \text{ lb}$$
$$P_3 = 275 \times 10^3 \text{ lb}$$
$$P_4 = 315 \times 10^3 \text{ lb}$$
$$P_5 = 645 \times 10^3 \text{ lb}$$
$$P_6 = -2{,}110 \times 10^3 \text{ lb}$$

This example refers to a steel girder in the airport roof at Berlin-Tempelhof, described by the following data:

$$J_1 = 1{,}045 \text{ in.}^4 \qquad k_{w_1} = 84.6 \times 10^3 \text{ lb/in.}$$
$$J_2 = 1{,}045 \text{ in.}^4 \qquad k_{w_2} = 57.6 \times 10^3 \text{ lb/in.}$$
$$J_3 = 1{,}565 \text{ in.}^4 \qquad k_{w_3} = 42.3 \times 10^3 \text{ lb/in.}$$
$$J_4 = 2{,}230 \text{ in.}^4 \qquad k_{w_4} = 32.3 \times 10^3 \text{ lb/in.}$$
$$J_5 = 2{,}230 \text{ in.}^4 \qquad k_{w_5} = 96.3 \times 10^3 \text{ lb/in.}$$
$$J_6 = 2{,}690 \text{ in.}^4$$
$$l_1 = l_2 = l_3 = l_4 = l_5 = l_6 = 20 \text{ ft} \qquad E = 30 \times 10^6 \text{ lb/in.}^2$$

The smallest factor α by which the horizontal forces P_i have to be multiplied in order to bring about buckling was found, after 20 min computing time on a small computer (Zuse Z22), to be

$$\alpha = 5.86$$

Since this is a case of pure buckling (no load perpendicular to the beam), the fifth column and row of Eq. (11-42) are abolished. The procedure is then as follows:

Beginning with $\alpha = 1$ (actual loading), all values γ_i are computed in order to obtain the elements in the transfer matrices. Then the matrix multiplication is carried out, observing that on account of the left-hand boundary conditions solely $\psi_0^L \neq 0$ and $V_0^L \neq 0$. So the right-hand boundary conditions $w = M = 0$ yield

$$p_{11}\psi_0^L + p_{12}V_0^L = 0 \qquad p_{31}\psi_0^L + p_{32}V_0^L = 0$$

Only if

$$\Delta(\alpha) = \begin{vmatrix} p_{11} & p_{12} \\ p_{31} & p_{32} \end{vmatrix} = 0$$

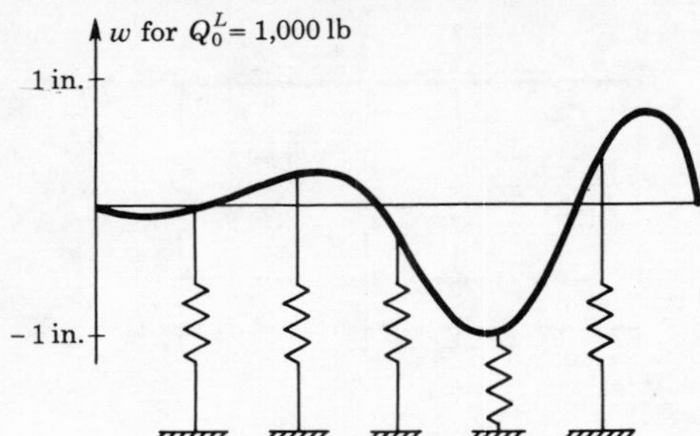

FIG. 11-56. Deflection of buckled girder shown in Fig. 11-55.

do we obtain a nontrivial solution for ψ_0^L and V_0^L; that is, the beam is then also in equilibrium under the given loading in a configuration other than its original straight shape, or, in other words, the critical buckling load is reached. If $\Delta \neq 0$, as is usually the case, we multiply the given loads by a somewhat larger factor α and then determine the new values for γ_i, after which the elements of the transfer matrices are computed, etc. This procedure is continued for ever-increasing values α until the determinant Δ changes its sign for the first time. The value α for which $\Delta = 0$ is called the safety factor because it indicates the factor by which the given loads must be multiplied in order to cause buckling. If for the critical value of α ($\Delta = 0$) V_0^L is taken as 1,000 lb, the buckling shape of the girder is obtained as shown in Fig. 11-56.

If in the present example the spring supports are replaced by rigid bearings ($k_{wi} = \infty$), the safety factor attains the value

$$\alpha = 8.10$$

In stability problems the rigid intermediate conditions are taken care of in exactly the same way as explained in Chap. 6 for the cases of statics and vibrations.

CATALOGUE OF TRANSFER MATRICES

Straight beams
1. Longitudinal vibration
2. Torsional vibration
3. Bending vibration in xz or xy plane
4. Bending vibration under constant axial stress
5. Miscellaneous cases
6. Forcing functions

Curved and twisted beams

7. Deformation in the plane of the central axis
8. Deformation perpendicular to the plane of the central axis
9. Straight twisted beam
10. Coordinate transformations
11. General case
12. Forcing functions

Rotating disks

13. Stresses and deformation caused by centrifugal forces and thermal loading
14. Bending vibrations of thick rotating disks (Reissner's theory)
15. The derivation of flexibility and stiffness matrices from the transfer matrix and remarks on various load conditions

In all transfer matrices in this catalogue it is assumed that elastic and mass-centroidal axes coincide (with the exception of Sec. C-5). They are therefore called central axes.

STRAIGHT BEAMS

Symbols used (Fig. C-1):

x, y, z — Cartesian right-handed coordinate system, with x axis coinciding with central axis of beam and y and z axes coinciding with principal axes of inertia of cross-sectional area

u, v, w — Displacements in x, y, and z directions, respectively

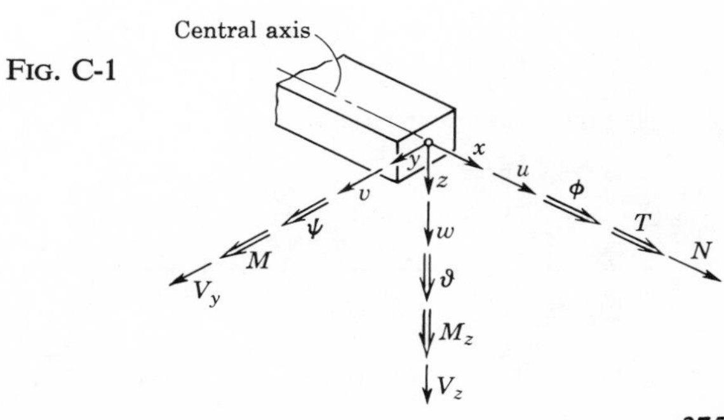

Fig. C-1

ϕ, ψ, ϑ Rotations around x, y, and z axes, respectively
M_y, M_z Bending moment about y and z axes, respectively
N Longitudinal force in x direction
T Torsional moment about x axis
V_y, V_z Shear in y and z directions, respectively
E Young's modulus
G Shear modulus
EA Longitudinal stiffness
$GA_s = \dfrac{GA}{K_s}$ Shear stiffness in y or z direction (K_s = form factor)
EJ Bending stiffness about y or z axis
GJ_T Torsional stiffness
ρ Specific mass
μ Mass per unit length
m Point mass
i_x Radius of gyration of cross-sectional area about x axis
i Radius of gyration of cross-sectional area about y or z axis
I_x Moment of inertia about x axis
I Moment of inertia about y or z axis
l Length of field
Γ Distributed foundation stiffness, lb/in.^{2}, against translatory displacement of beam
Γ^* Distributed foundation stiffness, lb, against rotations of beam due to bending
k_u, k_v, k_w Longitudinal spring stiffness, lb/in. (subscript on k denotes the displacement with which k has to be multiplied to yield the spring force)
k Stands for k_v or k_w
k_ϕ^*, k_ψ^*, k_ϑ^* Rotary spring stiffness, lb-in. (subscript on k^* denotes the rotation with which k^* has to be multiplied to yield the spring moment)
k^* Stands for k_ψ^* or k_ϑ^*
ω Circular frequency of free vibration
$\mathbf{A}$ Matrix of coefficients of system of first-order differential equations
$\mathbf{U}$ Transfer matrix

C-1. Longitudinal Vibration

$$\mathbf{z} = \{u \quad N\}$$

(*a*) Elastic field with distributed mass

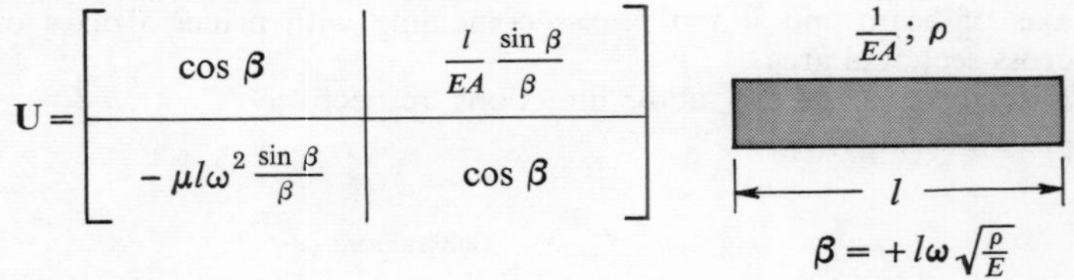

(*b*) Rigid field (also point mass)

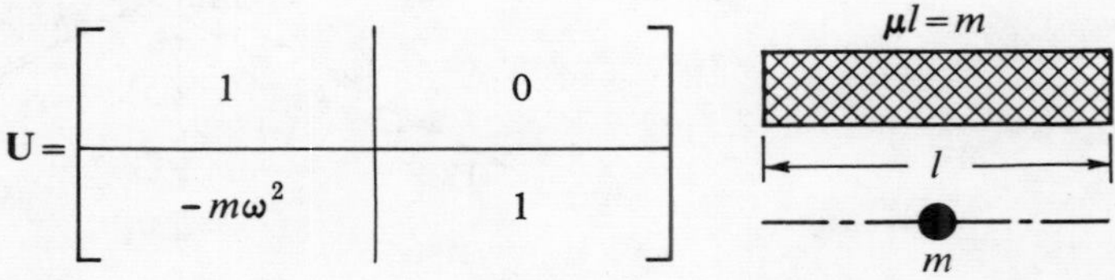

(*c*) Elastic massless field

$$\mathbf{U} = \left[\begin{array}{c|c} 1 & \frac{l}{EA} \\ \hline 0 & 1 \end{array}\right]$$

$\frac{1}{EA}$

l

(*d*) Longitudinal spring

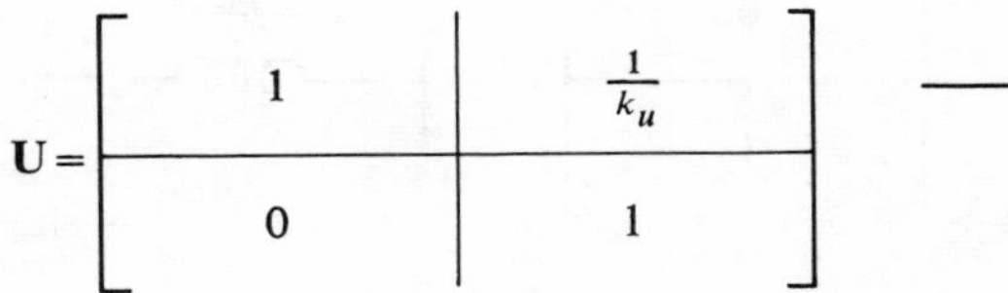

$$\mathbf{U} = \left[\begin{array}{c|c} 1 & \frac{1}{k_u} \\ \hline 0 & 1 \end{array}\right]$$

k_u

$l \longrightarrow 0$

$\frac{l}{EA} \longrightarrow \frac{1}{k_u}$

(*e*) Linear spring support

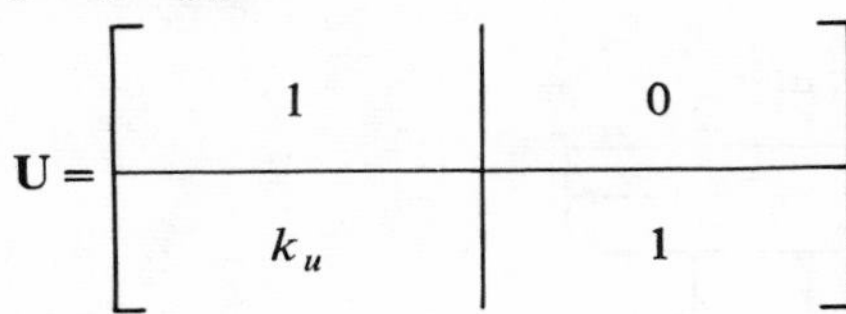

$$\mathbf{U} = \left[\begin{array}{c|c} 1 & 0 \\ \hline k_u & 1 \end{array}\right]$$

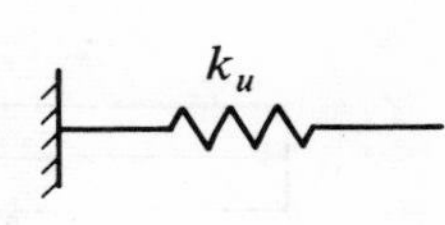

C-2. Torsional Vibration

$$\mathbf{z} = \{\phi \quad T\}$$

(*a*) Elastic field with distributed mass

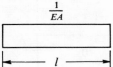

$$\mathbf{U} = \left[\begin{array}{c|c} \cos\beta & \frac{l}{GJ_T}\frac{\sin\beta}{\beta} \\ \hline -\mu l i_x^2 \omega^2 \frac{\sin\beta}{\beta} & \cos\beta \end{array}\right]$$

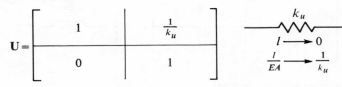

$\frac{1}{GJ_T}$; μi_x^2

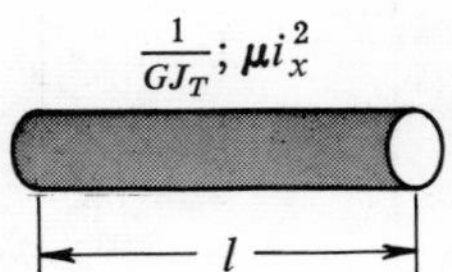

$\beta = +l\omega\sqrt{\frac{\mu i_x^2}{GJ_T}}$

For circular cross section, $\beta = +l\omega\sqrt{\frac{\rho}{G}}$

(*b*) Rigid field (also rotary point mass)

$$\mathbf{U} = \left[\begin{array}{c|c} 1 & 0 \\ \hline -I_x\omega^2 & 1 \end{array}\right]$$

$I_x = \mu i_x^2 l$

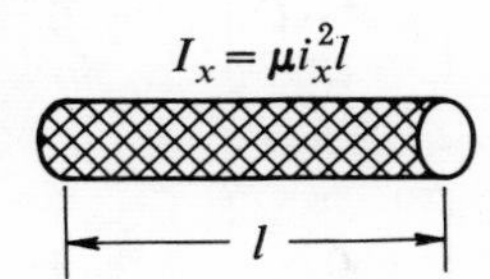

(*c*) Elastic massless field

$$\mathbf{U} = \left[\begin{array}{c|c} 1 & \frac{l}{GJ_T} \\ \hline 0 & 1 \end{array}\right]$$

$\frac{1}{GJ_T}$

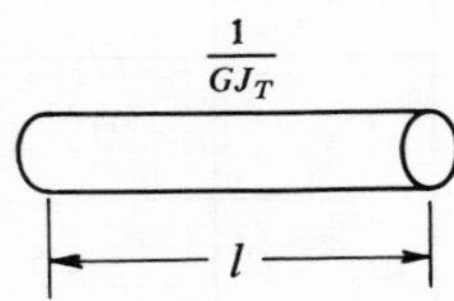

(*d*) Rotary spring

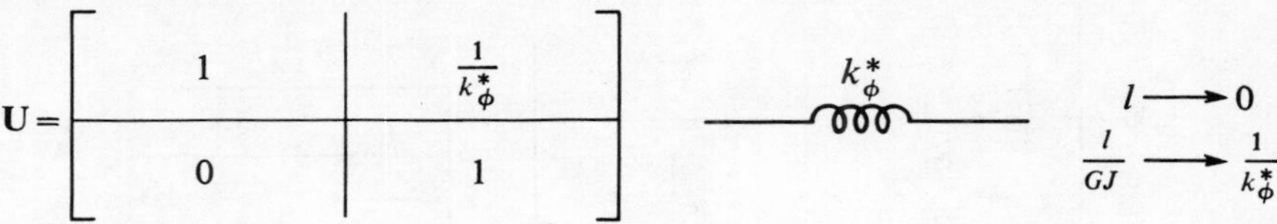

(*e*) Rotary spring support

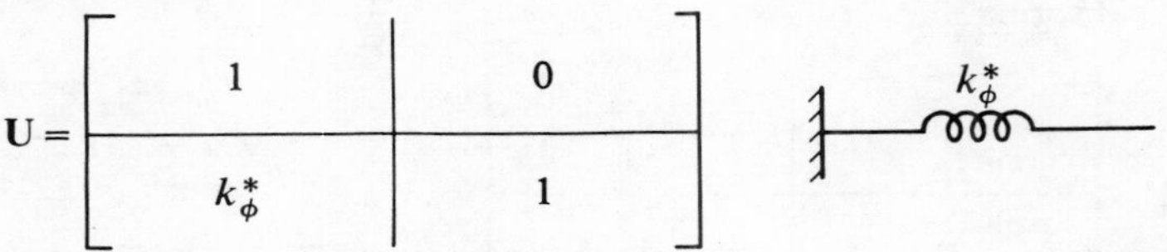

C-3. Bending Vibration in *xz* or *xy* Plane

(*a*) Homogeneous field with shear deformation, rotary inertia, and elasticity of foundation

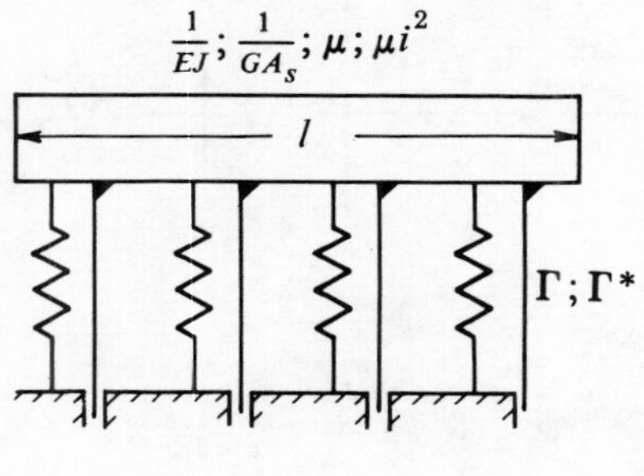

$$\mathbf{z} = \{-w \quad \psi \quad M_y \quad V_z\}$$
or
$$\mathbf{z} = \{v \quad \vartheta \quad M_z \quad V_y\}$$

$$\mathbf{A} = \begin{bmatrix} 0 & 1 & 0 & \dfrac{-1}{GA_s} \\ 0 & 0 & \dfrac{1}{EJ} & 0 \\ 0 & -\mu i^2\omega^2 + \Gamma^* & 0 & 1 \\ \mu\omega^2 - \Gamma & 0 & 0 & 0 \end{bmatrix}$$

Bending vibration

$$\mathbf{A} = \begin{bmatrix} 0 & 1 & 0 & \dfrac{-1}{GA_s} \\ 0 & 0 & \dfrac{1}{EJ} & 0 \\ 0 & \mu\omega^2(i_x^2 - i^2) + \Gamma^* & 0 & 1 \\ \mu\omega^2 - \Gamma & 0 & 0 & 0 \end{bmatrix}$$

Rotating shaft

If we limit our considerations for the rotating shaft to the case where $i_y^2 = i_z^2 = i^2 = i_x^2/2$ (e.g., a beam with circular cross section), then the matrix **A** for bending vibration as well as for the rotating shaft can be written as follows:

$$\mathbf{A} = \begin{bmatrix} 0 & 1 & 0 & \frac{-1}{GA_s} \\ 0 & 0 & \frac{1}{EJ} & 0 \\ 0 & h\mu i^2\omega^2 + \Gamma^* & 0 & 1 \\ \mu\omega^2 - \Gamma & 0 & 0 & 0 \end{bmatrix}$$

where

$$h = \begin{cases} -1 & \text{for bending vibration} \\ +1 & \text{for rotating shaft (equal angular direction of whirl and rotation)} \\ -3 & \text{for rotating shaft (opposite angular direction† of whirl and rotation)} \end{cases}$$

$$\mathbf{U} = \begin{bmatrix} c_0 - \sigma c_2 & l[c_1 - (\sigma+\tau)c_3] & a c_2 & \frac{al}{\beta^4}[-\sigma c_1 + (\beta^4+\sigma^2)c_3] \\ \frac{\beta^4}{l} c_3 & c_0 - \tau c_2 & \frac{a}{l}(c_1 - \tau c_3) & a c_2 \\ \frac{\beta^4}{a} c_2 & \frac{l}{a}[-\tau c_1 + (\beta^4+\tau^2)c_3] & c_0 - \tau c_2 & l[c_1 - (\sigma+\tau)c_3] \\ \frac{\beta^4}{al}(c_1 - \sigma c_3) & \frac{\beta^4}{a} c_2 & \frac{\beta^4}{l} c_3 & c_0 - \sigma c_2 \end{bmatrix}$$

where

$$a = \frac{l^2}{EJ} \qquad c_0 = \Lambda(\lambda_2^2 \cosh \lambda_1 + \lambda_1^2 \cos \lambda_2)$$

$$\beta^4 = \frac{\mu\omega^2 - \Gamma}{EJ} l^4 \qquad c_1 = \Lambda\left(\frac{\lambda_2^2}{\lambda_1} \sinh \lambda_1 + \frac{\lambda_1^2}{\lambda_2} \sin \lambda_2\right)$$

$$\sigma = \frac{\mu\omega^2 - \Gamma}{GA_s} l^2 \qquad c_2 = \Lambda(\cosh \lambda_1 - \cos \lambda_2)$$

$$\tau = -\frac{l^2}{EJ}(h\mu i^2\omega^2 + \Gamma^*) \qquad c_3 = \Lambda\left(\frac{1}{\lambda_1} \sinh \lambda_1 - \frac{1}{\lambda_2} \sin \lambda_2\right)$$

$$\lambda_{\frac{1}{2}} = +\sqrt{\sqrt{\beta^4 + \tfrac{1}{4}(\sigma - \tau)^2} \mp \tfrac{1}{2}(\sigma + \tau)} \qquad \Lambda = \frac{1}{\lambda_1^2 + \lambda_2^2}$$

† For this phenomenon to happen it is necessary that, besides $I_y = I_z$, the shaft be absolutely straight, with no eccentricity of mass [38].

(*b*) Homogeneous field on elastic foundation

$$\mathbf{U} = \begin{bmatrix} c_0 & lc_1 & ac_2 & alc_3 \\ \frac{\beta^4}{l} c_3 & c_0 & \frac{a}{l} c_1 & ac_2 \\ \frac{\beta^4}{a} c_2 & \frac{\beta^4 l}{a} c_3 & c_0 & lc_1 \\ \frac{\beta^4}{al} c_1 & \frac{\beta^4}{a} c_2 & \frac{\beta^4}{l} c_3 & c_0 \end{bmatrix}$$

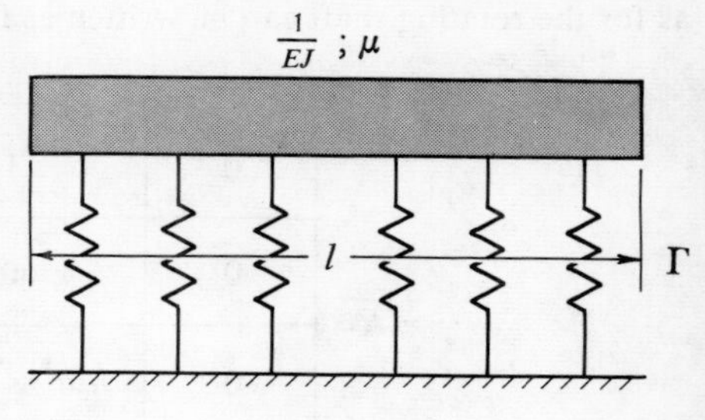

where

$$c_0 = \tfrac{1}{2}(\cosh\beta + \cos\beta)$$

$$c_1 = \frac{1}{2\beta}(\sinh\beta + \sin\beta)$$

$$c_2 = \frac{1}{2\beta^2}(\cosh\beta - \cos\beta)$$

$$c_3 = \frac{1}{2\beta^3}(\sinh\beta - \sin\beta)$$

$$a = \frac{l^2}{EJ}$$

$$\beta^4 = \frac{\mu\omega^2 - \Gamma}{EJ} l^4$$

(*c*) Elastic massless field

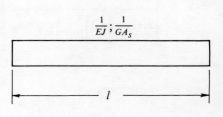

$$\mathbf{U} = \begin{bmatrix} 1 & l & \frac{l^2}{2EJ} & \frac{l^3}{6EJ} - \frac{l}{GA_s} \\ 0 & 1 & \frac{l}{EJ} & \frac{l^2}{2EJ} \\ 0 & 0 & 1 & l \\ 0 & 0 & 0 & 1 \end{bmatrix}$$

$\frac{1}{EJ}$; $\frac{1}{GA_s}$

l

(*d*) Rigid field

$$\mathbf{U} = \begin{bmatrix} 1 & l & 0 & 0 \\ 0 & 1 & 0 & 0 \\ \frac{ml\omega^2}{2} & m\omega^2\left(\frac{l^2}{6} + hi^2\right) & 1 & l \\ m\omega^2 & \frac{ml\omega^2}{2} & 0 & 1 \end{bmatrix}$$

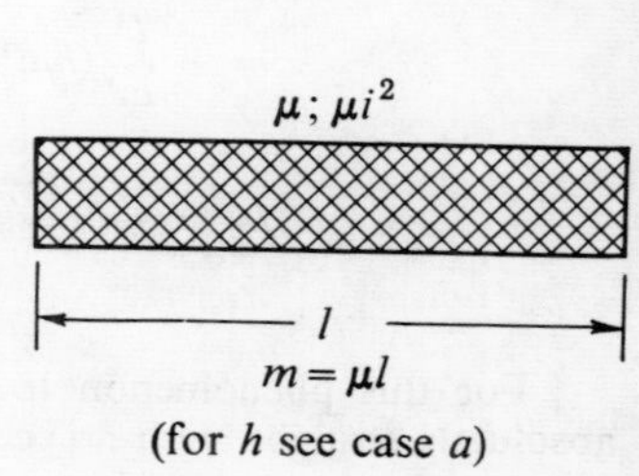

(*e*) Rigid field on elastic foundation

$$\mathbf{U} = \begin{bmatrix} 1 & l & 0 & 0 \\ 0 & 1 & 0 & 0 \\ \dfrac{ml\omega^2 - \Gamma l^2}{2} & \dfrac{(m\omega^2 - \Gamma l)l^2}{6} + hmi^2\omega^2 + \Gamma^* l & 1 & l \\ m\omega^2 - \Gamma l & \dfrac{m\omega^2 l - \Gamma l^2}{2} & 0 & 1 \end{bmatrix}$$

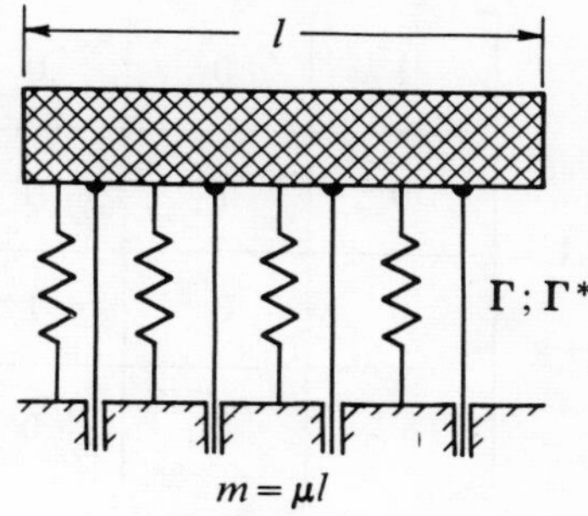

(for h see case a)

(*f*) Point mass with rotary inertia on spring (linear and rotary)

$$\mathbf{U} = \begin{bmatrix} 1 & 0 & 0 & 0 \\ 0 & 1 & 0 & 0 \\ 0 & hI\omega^2 + k^* & 1 & 0 \\ m\omega^2 - k & 0 & 0 & 1 \end{bmatrix}$$

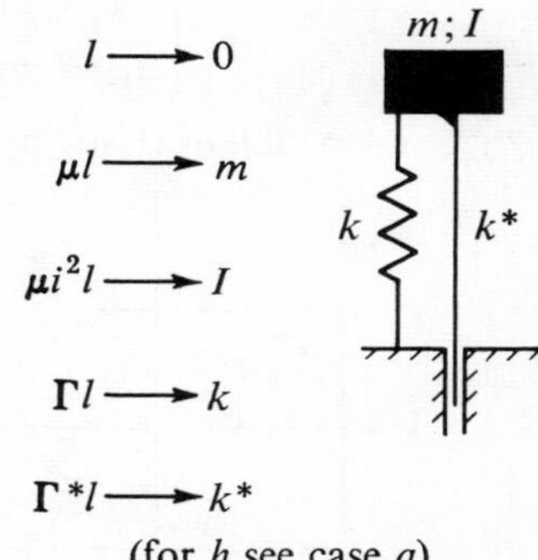

(for h see case a)

(*g*) Elastic hinge (rotary)

$$\mathbf{U} = \begin{bmatrix} 1 & 0 & 0 & 0 \\ 0 & 1 & \dfrac{1}{k^*} & 0 \\ 0 & 0 & 1 & 0 \\ 0 & 0 & 0 & 1 \end{bmatrix}$$

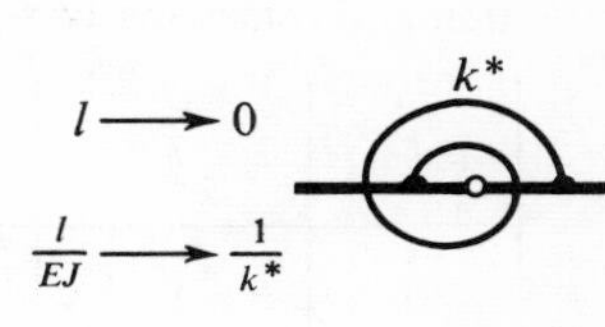

(*h*) Elastic hinge (linear)

$$\mathbf{U} = \begin{bmatrix} 1 & 0 & 0 & \dfrac{-1}{k} \\ 0 & 1 & 0 & 0 \\ 0 & 0 & 1 & 0 \\ 0 & 0 & 0 & 1 \end{bmatrix}$$

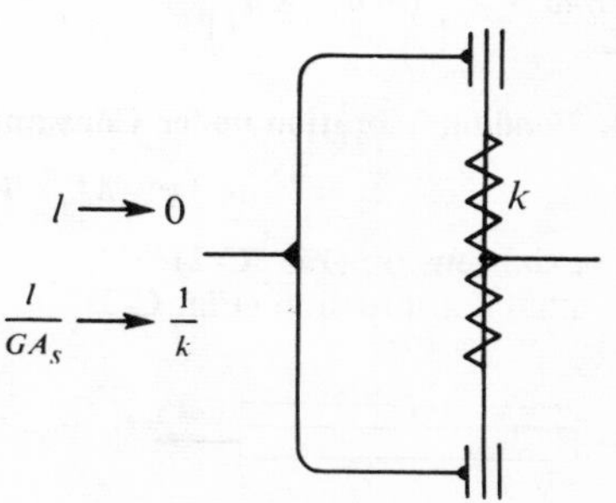

(*i, j*) Spring-coupled mass

$$\mathbf{U} = \begin{bmatrix} 1 & 0 & 0 & 0 \\ 0 & 1 & 0 & 0 \\ 0 & 0 & 1 & 0 \\ K_d & 0 & 0 & 1 \end{bmatrix}$$

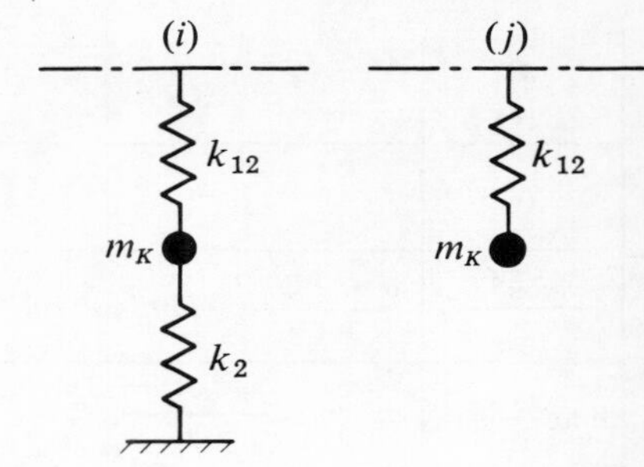

where $K_d = \begin{cases} -\dfrac{k_{12}(k_2 - m_K\omega^2)}{k_{12} + k_2 - m_K\omega^2} & \text{case } i \\ \dfrac{k_{12}m_K\omega^2}{k_{12} - m_K\omega^2} & \text{case } j \end{cases}$ K_d = dynamic stiffness

(*k*) Combination of elastic field and point mass

$$\mathbf{U} = \begin{bmatrix} 1 & l & \dfrac{l^2}{2EJ} & \dfrac{l^3}{6EJ} \\ 0 & 1 & \dfrac{l}{EJ} & \dfrac{l^2}{2EJ} \\ 0 & 0 & 1 & l \\ m\omega^2 & ml\omega^2 & \dfrac{ml^2\omega^2}{2EJ} & 1 + \dfrac{ml^3\omega^2}{6EJ} \end{bmatrix}$$

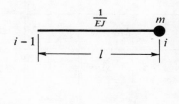

$\frac{1}{EJ}$ m $i-1$ i l

(*l*) Combination of elastic field with single mass and linear spring support (shear deformation and rotary inertia)

$$\mathbf{U} = \begin{bmatrix} 1 & l & \dfrac{l^2}{2EJ} & \dfrac{l^3}{6EJ} - \dfrac{l}{GA_s} \\ 0 & 1 & \dfrac{l}{EJ} & \dfrac{l^2}{2EJ} \\ 0 & hI\omega^2 & 1 + \dfrac{hI\omega^2 l}{EJ} & l + \dfrac{hI\omega^2 l^2}{2EJ} \\ m\omega^2 - k & (m\omega^2 - k)l & \dfrac{(m\omega^2 - k)l^2}{2EJ} & 1 + (m\omega^2 - k)\left(\dfrac{l^3}{6EJ} - \dfrac{l}{GA_s}\right) \end{bmatrix}$$

m, I l i $i-1$ $\frac{1}{EJ}$; $\frac{1}{GA_s}$ k

(For h see case *a*)

C-4. Bending Vibration under Constant Axial Stress

$$\mathbf{z} = \{-w \quad \psi \quad M_y \quad V_z\} \qquad \text{or} \qquad \mathbf{z} = \{v \quad \vartheta \quad M_z \quad -V_y\}$$

P_T axial tension (Fig. C-2)
P_C axial compression (Fig. C-3)

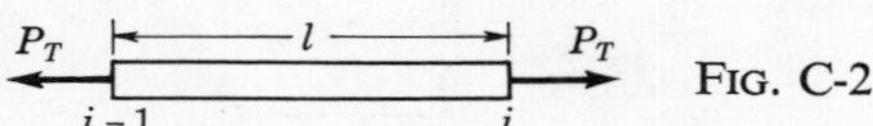

FIG. C-2

FIG. C-3

P_C ⟵ l ⟶ P_C

$i-1$ i

(*a*) General case (homogeneous field with shear deformation, rotary inertia, and elasticity of foundation)

$$\mathbf{U}=\begin{bmatrix} c_0-\sigma c_2 & l[c_1-(\sigma+\tau^*)c_3] & ac_2 & \frac{al}{\beta^4}[-\sigma c_1+(\beta^4+\sigma^2)c_3] \\ \frac{\beta^4}{l}c_3 & c_0-\tau^*c_2 & \frac{a}{l}(c_1-\tau^*c_3) & ac_2 \\ \frac{\beta^4}{a}c_2 & \frac{l}{a}[-\tau^*c_1+(\beta^4+\tau^{*2})c_3] & c_0-\tau^*c_2 & l[c_1-(\sigma+\tau^*)c_3] \\ \frac{\beta^4}{al}(c_1-\sigma c_3) & \frac{\beta^4}{a}c_2 & \frac{\beta^4}{l}c_3 & c_0-\sigma c_2 \end{bmatrix}$$

Use expressions c_0, c_1, c_2, and c_3 as given in Sec. C-3*a*. In expressions for λ replace τ by τ^*.

$$\tau^*=\begin{cases} \tau-\dfrac{P_Tl^2}{EJ} & \text{for tension} \\ \tau+\dfrac{P_Cl^2}{EJ} & \text{for compression} \end{cases}$$

For the other symbols used, see Sec. C-3*a*.

(*b*) Elastic massless field

(1) Tension

$$\mathbf{U}=\begin{bmatrix} 1 & l\dfrac{\sinh\gamma}{\gamma} & \dfrac{l^2}{EJ}\dfrac{\cosh\gamma-1}{\gamma^2} & \dfrac{l^3}{EJ}\dfrac{\sinh\gamma-\gamma}{\gamma^3} \\ 0 & \cosh\gamma & \dfrac{l}{EJ}\dfrac{\sinh\gamma}{\gamma} & \dfrac{l^2}{EJ}\dfrac{\cosh\gamma-1}{\gamma^2} \\ 0 & P_Tl\dfrac{\sinh\gamma}{\gamma} & \cosh\gamma & l\dfrac{\sinh\gamma}{\gamma} \\ 0 & 0 & 0 & 1 \end{bmatrix}$$

$\frac{1}{EJ}$, P_T, P_T, l

$$\gamma=+\sqrt{\frac{P_Tl^2}{EJ}}$$

(2) Compression

$$\mathbf{U}=\begin{bmatrix} 1 & l\dfrac{\sin\gamma}{\gamma} & \dfrac{l^2}{EJ}\dfrac{1-\cos\gamma}{\gamma^2} & \dfrac{l^3}{EJ}\dfrac{\gamma-\sin\gamma}{\gamma^3} \\ 0 & \cos\gamma & \dfrac{l}{EJ}\dfrac{\sin\gamma}{\gamma} & \dfrac{l^2}{EJ}\dfrac{1-\cos\gamma}{\gamma^2} \\ 0 & -P_Cl\dfrac{\sin\gamma}{\gamma} & \cos\gamma & l\dfrac{\sin\gamma}{\gamma} \\ 0 & 0 & 0 & 1 \end{bmatrix}$$

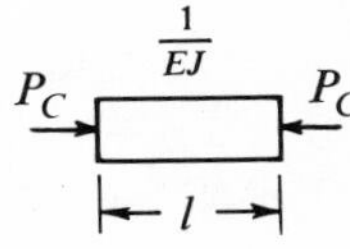

$$\gamma=+\sqrt{\frac{P_Cl^2}{EJ}}$$

(*c*) Combination of elastic field with single mass

(1) Tension

$$
\mathbf{U}=\begin{bmatrix}
1 & l\dfrac{\sinh\gamma}{\gamma} & \dfrac{l^2}{EJ}\dfrac{\cosh\gamma-1}{\gamma^2} & \dfrac{l^3}{EJ}\dfrac{\sinh\gamma-\gamma}{\gamma^3}\\
0 & \cosh\gamma & \dfrac{l}{EJ}\dfrac{\sinh\gamma}{\gamma} & \dfrac{l^2}{EJ}\dfrac{\cosh\gamma-1}{\gamma^2}\\
0 & P_T\,l\dfrac{\sinh\gamma}{\gamma} & \cosh\gamma & l\dfrac{\sinh\gamma}{\gamma}\\
m\omega^2 & m\omega^2 l\dfrac{\sin\gamma}{\gamma} & \dfrac{m\omega^2 l^2}{EJ}\dfrac{1-\cos\gamma}{\gamma^2} & 1+\dfrac{m\omega^2 l^3}{EJ}\dfrac{\gamma-\sin\gamma}{\gamma^3}
\end{bmatrix}
$$

P_T $\frac{1}{EJ}$ m P_T

$i \leftarrow l \rightarrow i-1$

$$\gamma=+\sqrt{\frac{P_T l^2}{EJ}}$$

(2) Compression

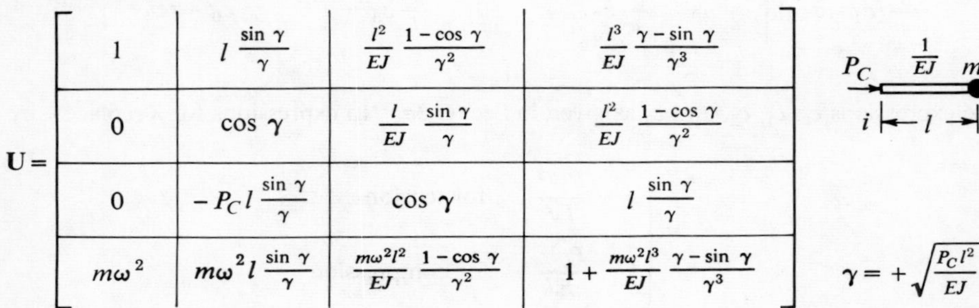

$$
\mathbf{U}=\begin{bmatrix}
1 & l\dfrac{\sin\gamma}{\gamma} & \dfrac{l^2}{EJ}\dfrac{1-\cos\gamma}{\gamma^2} & \dfrac{l^3}{EJ}\dfrac{\gamma-\sin\gamma}{\gamma^3}\\
0 & \cos\gamma & \dfrac{l}{EJ}\dfrac{\sin\gamma}{\gamma} & \dfrac{l^2}{EJ}\dfrac{1-\cos\gamma}{\gamma^2}\\
0 & -P_C\,l\dfrac{\sin\gamma}{\gamma} & \cos\gamma & l\dfrac{\sin\gamma}{\gamma}\\
m\omega^2 & m\omega^2 l\dfrac{\sin\gamma}{\gamma} & \dfrac{m\omega^2 l^2}{EJ}\dfrac{1-\cos\gamma}{\gamma^2} & 1+\dfrac{m\omega^2 l^3}{EJ}\dfrac{\gamma-\sin\gamma}{\gamma^3}
\end{bmatrix}
$$

P_C $\frac{1}{EJ}$ m P_C

$i \leftarrow l \rightarrow i-1$

$$\gamma=+\sqrt{\frac{P_C l^2}{EJ}}$$

C-5. Miscellaneous Cases

$$\mathbf{z}=\{u \quad N \quad \phi \quad T \quad v \quad \vartheta \quad M_z \quad -V_y \quad -w \quad \psi \quad M_y \quad V_z\}$$

(*a*) Three-dimensional field matrix (e.g., vibration of straight bars in frames)

$$
\mathbf{U}=\begin{bmatrix}
\mathbf{A}^* & 0 & 0 & 0\\
0 & \mathbf{B}^* & 0 & 0\\
0 & 0 & \mathbf{C}^* & 0\\
0 & 0 & 0 & \mathbf{D}^*
\end{bmatrix}
$$

For **A*** see Sec. C-1; for example,

$$
\mathbf{A}^*=\begin{bmatrix}
\cos\beta & \dfrac{l}{EA}\dfrac{\sin\beta}{\beta}\\
-\mu l\omega^2\dfrac{\sin\beta}{\beta} & \cos\beta
\end{bmatrix}
$$

For **B*** see Sec. C-2; for example,

$$\mathbf{B}^* = \left[\begin{array}{c|c} \cos\beta & \dfrac{l}{GJ_T}\dfrac{\sin\beta}{\beta} \\ \hline -\mu l i_x^2 \omega^2 \dfrac{\sin\beta}{\beta} & \cos\beta \end{array}\right]$$

For **C*** and **D*** see Sec. C-3; for example,

$$\left.\begin{matrix}\mathbf{C}^* \\ \mathbf{D}^*\end{matrix}\right\} = \left[\begin{array}{c|c|c|c} c_0 - \sigma c_2 & l[c_1 - (\sigma+\tau)c_3] & ac_2 & \dfrac{al}{\beta^4}[-\sigma c_1 + (\beta^4+\sigma^2)c_3] \\ \hline \dfrac{\beta^4}{l}c_3 & c_0 - \tau c_2 & \dfrac{a}{l}(c_1 - \tau c_3) & ac_2 \\ \hline \dfrac{\beta^4}{a}c_2 & \dfrac{l}{a}[-\tau c_1 + (\beta^4+\tau^2)c_3] & c_0 - \tau c_2 & l[c_1 - (\sigma+\tau)c_3] \\ \hline \dfrac{\beta^4}{al}(c_1 - \sigma c_3) & \dfrac{\beta^4}{a}c_2 & \dfrac{\beta^4}{l}c_3 & c_0 - \sigma c_2 \end{array}\right]$$

For **C***

$$a = \frac{l^2}{EJ_z}$$

$$\beta^4 = \frac{\mu\omega^2 - \Gamma}{EJ_z} l^4$$

$$\sigma = \frac{\mu\omega^2 - \Gamma}{GA_{sy}} l^2$$

$$\tau = -\frac{l^2}{EJ_z}(h\mu i^2\omega^2 + \Gamma^*)$$

For **D***

$$a = \frac{l^2}{EJ_y}$$

$$\beta^4 = \frac{\mu\omega^2 - \Gamma}{EJ_y} l^4$$

$$\sigma = \frac{\mu\omega^2 - \Gamma}{GA_{sz}} l^2$$

$$\tau = -\frac{l^2}{EJ_y}(h\mu i^2\omega^2 + \Gamma^*)$$

For the other symbols used in **C*** and **D***, see Sec. C-3*a*.

(*b*) Point matrix for eccentric mass

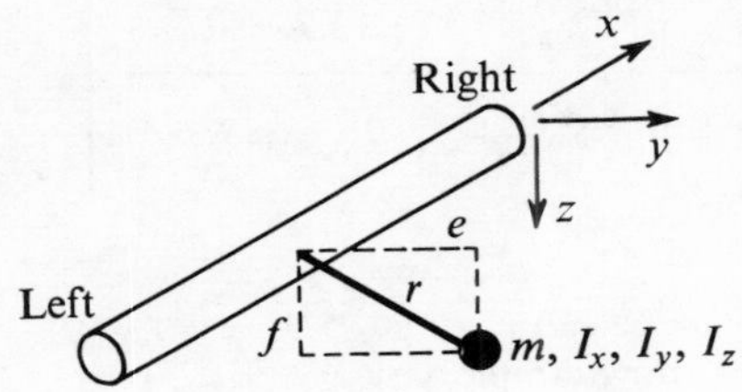

$$
\mathbf{U}=\begin{bmatrix}
1 & & & & & & & & & & & \\
-m\omega^2 & 1 & & & & m\omega^2 e & & & & -m\omega^2 f & & \\
 & & 1 & & & & & & & & & \\
 & & -(mr^2+I_x)\omega^2 & 1 & m\omega^2 f & & & & m\omega^2 e & & & \\
 & & & & 1 & & & & & & & \\
 & & & & & 1 & & & & & & \\
m\omega^2 e & & & & & -(me^2+I_z)\omega^2 & 1 & & & m\omega^2 fe & & \\
 & & -m\omega^2 f & & m\omega^2 & & & 1 & & & & \\
 & & & & & & & & 1 & & & \\
 & & & & & & & & & 1 & & \\
-m\omega^2 f & & & & & m\omega^2 ef & & & & -(mf^2+I_y)\omega^2 & 1 & \\
 & & -m\omega^2 e & & & & & & m\omega^2 & & & 1
\end{bmatrix}
$$

(*c*) Combination of (*a*) and (*b*)

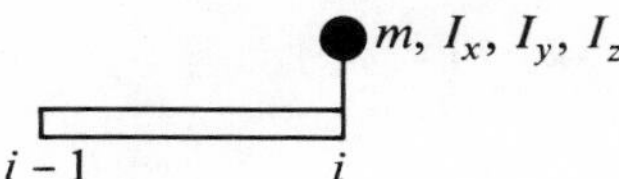

U =

$\mathbf{A}_1^*$			
$-m\omega^2\mathbf{A}_1^*+\mathbf{A}_2^*$		$m\omega^2 e\mathbf{C}_2^*$	$-m\omega^2 f\mathbf{D}_2^*$
	$\mathbf{B}_1^*$		
	$-(mr^2+I_x)\omega^2\mathbf{B}_1^*+\mathbf{B}_2^*$	$m\omega^2 f\mathbf{C}_1^*$	$m\omega^2 e\mathbf{D}_1^*$
		$\mathbf{C}_1^*$	
		$\mathbf{C}_2^*$	
$m\omega^2 e\mathbf{A}_1^*$		$-(me^2+I_z)\omega^2\mathbf{C}_2^*+\mathbf{C}_3^*$	$m\omega^2 fe\mathbf{D}_2^*$
	$-m\omega^2 f\mathbf{B}_1^*$	$m\omega^2\mathbf{C}_1^*+\mathbf{C}_4^*$	
			$\mathbf{D}_1^*$
			$\mathbf{D}_2^*$
$-m\omega^2 f\mathbf{A}_1^*$		$m\omega^2 ef\mathbf{C}_2^*$	$-(mf^2+I_y^2)\omega^2\mathbf{D}_2^*+\mathbf{D}_3^*$
	$-m\omega^2 e\mathbf{B}_1^*$		$m\omega^2\mathbf{D}_1^*+\mathbf{D}_4^*$

$\mathbf{A}_i^*$, $\mathbf{B}_i^*$, $\mathbf{C}_i^*$, $\mathbf{D}_i^*$: row i of matrix $\mathbf{A}^*$, $\mathbf{B}^*$, $\mathbf{C}^*$, and $\mathbf{D}^*$, respectively.
For $\mathbf{A}^*$, $\mathbf{B}^*$, $\mathbf{C}^*$, and $\mathbf{D}^*$, see (*a*).

C-6. Forcing Functions

Massless span in forced bending vibration or under static load.
Load vector **r** (fifth column in extended transfer matrix $\tilde{\mathbf{U}}$).

$$\mathbf{r} = \{r_1 \quad r_2 \quad r_3 \quad r_4\}$$

$$r_1 = -\tilde{w} = \int_{x_{i-1}}^{x_i} \tilde{\psi}(\xi)\,d\xi \qquad r_2 = \tilde{\psi} = \int_{x_{i-1}}^{x_i} \frac{\tilde{M}(\xi)}{EJ(\xi)}\,d\xi$$

$$r_3 = \tilde{M} = \int_{x_{i-1}}^{x_i} \tilde{V}(\xi)\,d\xi \qquad r_4 = \tilde{V} = -\int_{x_{i-1}}^{x_i} q(\xi)\,d\xi$$

Table of Special Cases for EJ = const

	$i-1$, P, i, d, l_i	$i-1$, C, i, e, l_i	$i-1$, q, i, l_i	$i-1$, q_1, i, q_2, l_i
$r_1 = -\tilde{w}$	$\frac{-Pd^3}{6EJ}$	$\frac{-Ce^2}{2EJ}$	$\frac{-ql_i^4}{24EJ}$	$\frac{-(4q_1+q_2)l_i^4}{120EJ}$
$r_2 = \tilde{\psi}$	$\frac{-Pd^2}{2EJ}$	$\frac{-Ce}{EJ}$	$\frac{-ql_i^3}{6EJ}$	$\frac{-(3q_1+q_2)l_i^3}{24EJ}$
$r_3 = \tilde{M}$	$-Pd$	$-C$	$\frac{-ql_i^2}{2}$	$\frac{-(2q_1+q_2)l_i^2}{6}$
$r_4 = \tilde{V}$	$-P$	0	$-ql_i$	$\frac{-(q_1+q_2)l_i^2}{2}$

CURVED AND TWISTED BEAMS

Symbols used (Fig. C-4) (besides the symbols used in Secs. C-1 to C-6):

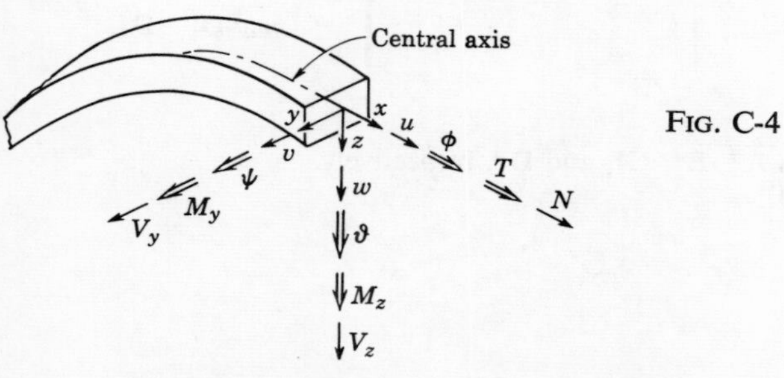

FIG. C-4

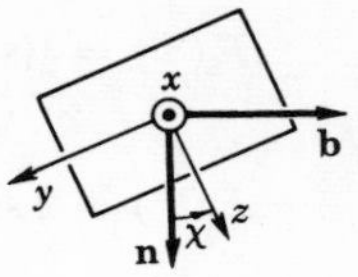

s Length of arch

$\mathbf{n}$ Unit principal normal of central axis

$\mathbf{b}$ Unit binormal of central axis

τ Torsion of central axis ($d\mathbf{b}/ds = -\tau\mathbf{n}$; see Fig. C-5)

χ Twisting angle of principal axis of inertia of cross section relative to principal normal $\mathbf{n}$ and binormal $\mathbf{b}$ of central axis of beam (Fig. C-5)

FIG. C-5

$\sigma = \tau + \dfrac{d\chi}{ds}$ Effective twist

$\kappa = \dfrac{1}{R}$ Curvature of central axis

$\left.\begin{aligned}\kappa_y &= \kappa \cos \chi \\ \kappa_z &= \kappa \sin \chi\end{aligned}\right\}$ Components of curvature in xz and xy planes, respectively

Ψ Central arc

In Secs. C-7 and C-8 we limit our consideration to the plane curved beam, where the central axis is located in the xz plane (Fig. C-6). Here we have

$$\kappa_y = \kappa \qquad \kappa_z = 0 \qquad \chi = 0 \qquad \tau = 0 \qquad \sigma = 0$$

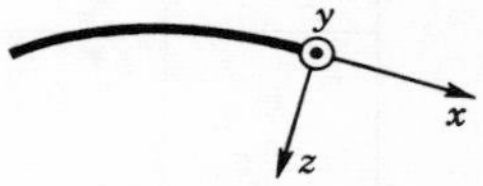

FIG. C-6

Vibrations in and perpendicular to the plane of the central axis are uncoupled. The following transfer matrices are valid for the case where the z axis points to the center of curvature. In the opposite case the matrix elements x, which effect the coupling between

	x	x	x	x	
x					x
x					x
x					x
x					x
	x	x	x	x	

bending and longitudinal vibrations and the coupling between bending and torsional vibrations, take on opposite signs.

We use the following abbreviations:

$$F_1(\Psi) = \tfrac{1}{2}(\Psi \cos \Psi + \sin \Psi) = \Psi - \frac{2}{3!}\Psi^3 + \frac{3}{5!}\Psi^5 - \frac{4}{7!}\Psi^7 + \frac{5}{9!}\Psi^9 - \cdots$$

$$F_2(\Psi) = \Psi \sin \Psi + \cos \Psi - 1 = \frac{1}{2!}\Psi^2 - \frac{3}{4!}\Psi^4 + \frac{5}{6!}\Psi^6 - \frac{7}{8!}\Psi^8 + \cdots$$

$$F_3(\Psi) = \tfrac{1}{2}(\sin \Psi - \Psi \cos \Psi) = \frac{1}{3!}\Psi^3 - \frac{2}{5!}\Psi^5 + \frac{3}{7!}\Psi^7 - \frac{4}{9!}\Psi^9 + \cdots$$

$$F_4(\Psi) = 2 \sin \Psi - \Psi \cos \Psi - \Psi = \frac{1}{3!}\Psi^3 - \frac{3}{5!}\Psi^5 + \frac{5}{7!}\Psi^7 - \frac{7}{9!}\Psi^9 + \cdots$$

$$F_5(\Psi) = \tfrac{1}{2}(2 - 2 \cos \Psi - \Psi \sin \Psi) = \frac{1}{4!}\Psi^4 - \frac{2}{6!}\Psi^6 + \frac{3}{8!}\Psi^8 - \frac{4}{10!}\Psi^{10} + \cdots$$

$$F_6(\Psi) = \tfrac{1}{2}(2\Psi + \Psi \cos \Psi - 3 \sin \Psi) = \frac{1}{5!}\Psi^5 - \frac{2}{7!}\Psi^7 + \frac{3}{9!}\Psi^9 - \frac{4}{11!}\Psi^{11} + \cdots$$

C-7. Deformation in the Plane of the Central Axis

$$\mathbf{z} = \{u \quad -w \quad \psi \qquad M_y \quad V_z \quad N\}$$

(*a*) Elastic circular arch with distributed mass

$$\mathbf{A} = \begin{bmatrix} 0 & -\kappa & 0 & 0 & 0 & \frac{1}{EA} \\ \kappa & 0 & 1 & 0 & 0 & 0 \\ 0 & 0 & 0 & \frac{1}{EJ_y} & 0 & 0 \\ 0 & 0 & -\mu\omega^2 i_y^2 & 0 & 1 & 0 \\ 0 & \mu\omega^2 & 0 & 0 & 0 & -\kappa \\ -\mu\omega^2 & 0 & 0 & 0 & \kappa & 0 \end{bmatrix}$$

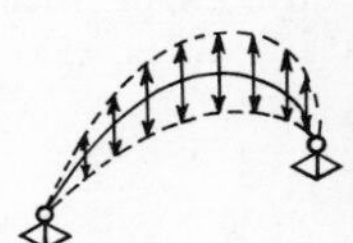

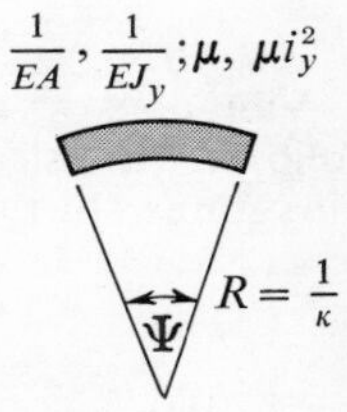

(*b*) Rigid circular arch with distributed mass

$$\mathbf{U} = \begin{bmatrix} \cos\Psi & -\sin\Psi & -R(1-\cos\Psi) & 0 & 0 & 0 \\ \sin\Psi & \cos\Psi & R\sin\Psi & 0 & 0 & 0 \\ 0 & 0 & 1 & 0 & 0 & 0 \\ 2\mu\omega^2 R^2 F_3 & \mu\omega^2 R^2 F_2 & u_{43} & 1 & R\sin\Psi & -R(1-\cos\Psi) \\ \mu\omega^2 R\Psi\sin\Psi & \mu\omega^2 R\Psi\cos\Psi & \mu\omega^2 R^2 F_2 & 0 & \cos\Psi & -\sin\Psi \\ -\mu\omega^2 R\Psi\cos\Psi & \mu\omega^2 R\Psi\sin\Psi & 2\mu\omega^2 R^2 F_3 & 0 & \sin\Psi & \cos\Psi \end{bmatrix}$$

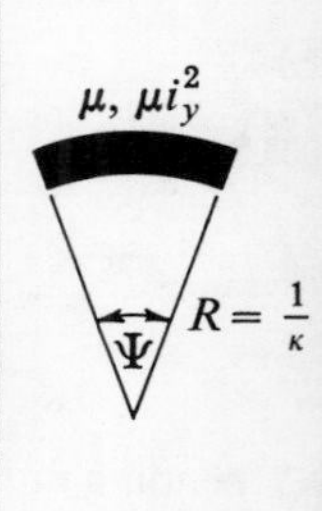

$$u_{43} = -\mu\omega^2 R i_y^2 \Psi + \mu\omega^2 R^3 F_4$$

(*c*) Elastic massless circular arch

$$\mathbf{U}=\begin{bmatrix} \cos\Psi & -\sin\Psi & -R(1-\cos\Psi) & \frac{-R^2}{EJ_y}(\Psi-\sin\Psi) & u_{15} & \frac{RF_1}{EA}+\frac{R^3F_6}{EJ_y} \\ \sin\Psi & \cos\Psi & R\sin\Psi & \frac{R^2}{EJ_y}(1-\cos\Psi) & \left(\frac{1}{EA}+\frac{R^2}{EJ_y}\right)RF_3 & u_{26} \\ 0 & 0 & 1 & \frac{R}{EJ_y}\Psi & \frac{R^2}{EJ_y}(1-\cos\Psi) & \frac{-R^2}{EJ_y}(\Psi-\sin\Psi) \\ 0 & 0 & 0 & 1 & R\sin\Psi & -R(1-\cos\Psi) \\ 0 & 0 & 0 & 0 & \cos\Psi & -\sin\Psi \\ 0 & 0 & 0 & 0 & \sin\Psi & \cos\Psi \end{bmatrix}$$

$\frac{1}{EA}, \frac{1}{EJ_y}$ $\quad R=\frac{1}{\kappa}$ $\quad \Psi$

$$u_{15}=u_{26}=\frac{R}{2EA}\Psi\sin\Psi-\frac{R^3F_5}{EJ_y}$$

(*d*) Single mass

$$\mathbf{U}=\begin{bmatrix} 1 & 0 & 0 & 0 & 0 & 0 \\ 0 & 1 & 0 & 0 & 0 & 0 \\ 0 & 0 & 1 & 0 & 0 & 0 \\ 0 & 0 & -I_y\omega^2 & 1 & 0 & 0 \\ 0 & m\omega^2 & 0 & 0 & 1 & 0 \\ -m\omega^2 & 0 & 0 & 0 & 0 & 1 \end{bmatrix}$$

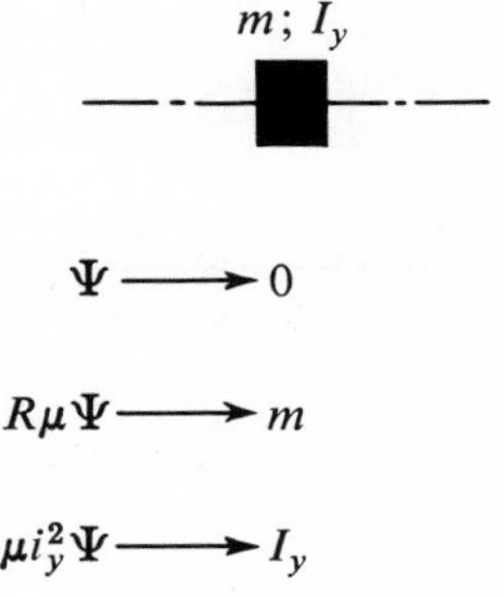

(*e*) Point elasticity

$$\mathbf{U}=\begin{bmatrix} 1 & 0 & 0 & 0 & 0 & \frac{1}{k_u} \\ 0 & 1 & 0 & 0 & 0 & 0 \\ 0 & 0 & 1 & \frac{1}{k_\psi^*} & 0 & 0 \\ 0 & 0 & 0 & 1 & 0 & 0 \\ 0 & 0 & 0 & 0 & 1 & 0 \\ 0 & 0 & 0 & 0 & 0 & 1 \end{bmatrix}$$

$k_u;\ k_\psi^*$

$\Psi \longrightarrow 0$

$\frac{R\Psi}{EJ_y} \longrightarrow \frac{1}{k_\psi^*}$

$\frac{R\Psi}{EA} \longrightarrow \frac{1}{k_u}$

(*f*) Stiff corner

$$\mathbf{U}=\begin{bmatrix} \cos\Psi & -\sin\Psi & 0 & 0 & 0 & 0 \\ \sin\Psi & \cos\Psi & 0 & 0 & 0 & 0 \\ 0 & 0 & 1 & 0 & 0 & 0 \\ 0 & 0 & 0 & 1 & 0 & 0 \\ 0 & 0 & 0 & 0 & \cos\Psi & -\sin\Psi \\ 0 & 0 & 0 & 0 & \sin\Psi & \cos\Psi \end{bmatrix}$$

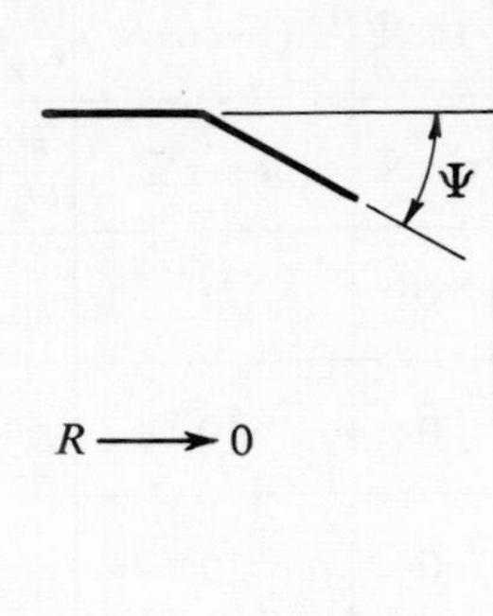

(*g*) Elastic support

$$\mathbf{U}=\begin{bmatrix} 1 & 0 & 0 & 0 & 0 & 0 \\ 0 & 1 & 0 & 0 & 0 & 0 \\ 0 & 0 & 1 & 0 & 0 & 0 \\ 0 & 0 & k_\psi^* & 1 & 0 & 0 \\ 0 & -k_w & 0 & 0 & 1 & 0 \\ k_u & 0 & 0 & 0 & 0 & 1 \end{bmatrix}$$

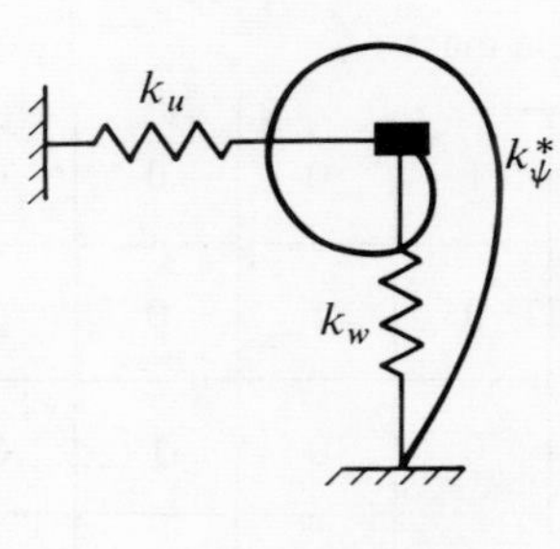

C-8. Deformation Perpendicular to the Plane of the Central Axis

$$\mathbf{z} = \{\phi \quad v \quad \vartheta \quad M_z \quad -V_y \quad T\}$$

(*a*) Elastic circular arch with distributed mass

$$\mathbf{A}=\begin{bmatrix} 0 & 0 & \kappa & 0 & 0 & \frac{1}{GJ_T} \\ 0 & 0 & 1 & 0 & 0 & 0 \\ -\kappa & 0 & 0 & \frac{1}{EJ_z} & 0 & 0 \\ 0 & 0 & -\mu\omega^2 i_z^2 & 0 & 1 & -\kappa \\ 0 & \mu\omega^2 & 0 & 0 & 0 & 0 \\ -\mu\omega^2 i_x^2 & 0 & 0 & \kappa & 0 & 0 \end{bmatrix}$$

$\frac{1}{EJ_z}; \frac{1}{GJ_T}; \mu; \mu i_x^2; \mu i_z^2$

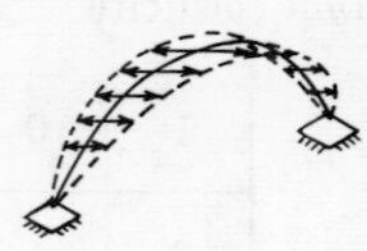

Ψ $R=\frac{1}{\kappa}$

(*b*) Rigid circular arch with distributed mass

$$
\mathbf{U} = \begin{bmatrix}
\cos\Psi & 0 & \sin\Psi & 0 & 0 & 0 \\
-R(1-\cos\Psi) & 1 & R\cos\Psi & 0 & 0 & 0 \\
-\sin\Psi & 0 & \cos\Psi & 0 & 0 & 0 \\
u_{41} & \mu\omega^2 R^2(1-\cos\Psi) & u_{43} & \cos\Psi & R\sin\Psi & -\sin\Psi \\
-\mu\omega^2 R^2(\Psi-\sin\Psi) & \mu\omega^2 R\Psi & \mu\omega^2 R^2(1-\cos\Psi) & 0 & 1 & 0 \\
u_{61} & \mu\omega^2 R^2(\Psi-\sin\Psi) & u_{63} & \sin\Psi & R(1-\cos\Psi) & \cos\Psi
\end{bmatrix}
$$

$\mu;\ \mu i_x^2;\ \mu i_z^2$

Ψ

$R = \frac{1}{\kappa}$

where

$$u_{61} = -\mu\omega^2 R i_x^2 F_1 + \mu\omega^2 R i_z^2 F_3 - \mu\omega^2 R^3 F_6$$

$$u_{63} = -u_{41} = \mu\omega^2 R^3 F_5 - \mu\omega^2 R(i_x^2 + i_z^2)\tfrac{1}{2}\Psi \sin\Psi$$

$$u_{43} = -\mu\omega^2 R i_z^2 F_1 + \mu\omega^2 R(i_x^2 + R^2)F_3$$

(*c*) Elastic massless circular arch

$$
\mathbf{U} = \begin{bmatrix}
\cos\Psi & 0 & \sin\Psi & \left(\frac{1}{GJ_T}+\frac{1}{EJ_z}\right)\frac{R\Psi}{2}\sin\Psi & \left(\frac{1}{GJ_T}+\frac{1}{EJ_z}\right)R^2F_3 & \frac{RF_1}{GJ_T}-\frac{RF_3}{EJ_z} \\
-R(1-\cos\Psi) & 1 & R\sin\Psi & u_{24} & u_{25} & -\left(\frac{1}{GJ_T}+\frac{1}{EJ_z}\right)R^2F_3 \\
-\sin\Psi & 0 & \cos\Psi & u_{34} & u_{35} & -\left(\frac{1}{GJ_T}+\frac{1}{EJ_z}\right)\frac{R\Psi}{2}\sin\Psi \\
0 & 0 & 0 & \cos\Psi & R\sin\Psi & -\sin\Psi \\
0 & 0 & 0 & 0 & 1 & 0 \\
0 & 0 & 0 & \sin\Psi & R(1-\cos\Psi) & \cos\Psi
\end{bmatrix}
$$

where

$$u_{24} = u_{35} = \frac{R^2}{2EJ_z}\Psi\sin\Psi - \frac{R^2}{GJ_T}F_5$$

$$u_{25} = \frac{R^3}{EJ_z}F_3 - \frac{R^3}{GJ_T}F_6$$

$$u_{34} = \frac{R}{EJ_z}F_1 - \frac{R}{GJ_T}F_3$$

(*d*) Single mass

$$\mathbf{U}=\begin{bmatrix} 1 & 0 & 0 & 0 & 0 & 0 \\ 0 & 1 & 0 & 0 & 0 & 0 \\ 0 & 0 & 1 & 0 & 0 & 0 \\ 0 & 0 & -I_z\omega^2 & 1 & 0 & 0 \\ 0 & m\omega^2 & 0 & 0 & 1 & 0 \\ -I_x\omega^2 & 0 & 0 & 0 & 0 & 1 \end{bmatrix}$$

$m;\ I_x;\ I_z$

$\Psi \longrightarrow 0$

$\mu R\Psi \longrightarrow m$

$\mu Ri^2\Psi \longrightarrow I$

(*e*) Point elasticity

$$\mathbf{U}=\begin{bmatrix} 1 & 0 & 0 & 0 & 0 & \frac{1}{k_\phi^*} \\ 0 & 1 & 0 & 0 & 0 & 0 \\ 0 & 0 & 1 & \frac{1}{k_\vartheta^*} & 0 & 0 \\ 0 & 0 & 0 & 1 & 0 & 0 \\ 0 & 0 & 0 & 0 & 1 & 0 \\ 0 & 0 & 0 & 0 & 0 & 1 \end{bmatrix}$$

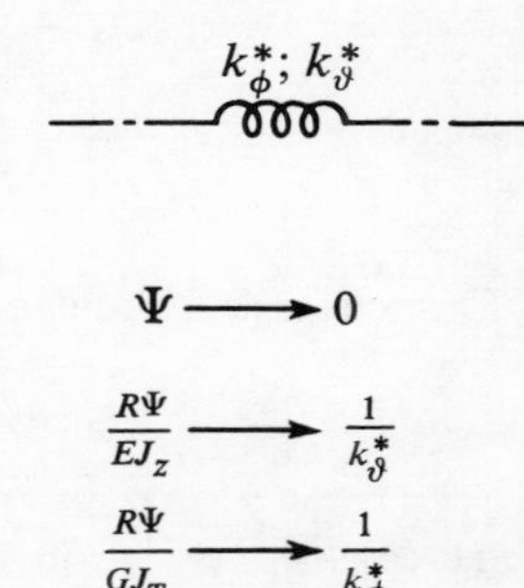

$\Psi \longrightarrow 0$

$\frac{R\Psi}{EJ_z} \longrightarrow \frac{1}{k_\vartheta^*}$

$\frac{R\Psi}{GJ_T} \longrightarrow \frac{1}{k_\phi^*}$

(*f*) Stiff corner

$$\mathbf{U}=\begin{bmatrix} \cos\Psi & 0 & \sin\Psi & 0 & 0 & 0 \\ 0 & 1 & 0 & 0 & 0 & 0 \\ -\sin\Psi & 0 & \cos\Psi & 0 & 0 & 0 \\ 0 & 0 & 0 & \cos\Psi & 0 & -\sin\Psi \\ 0 & 0 & 0 & 0 & 1 & 0 \\ 0 & 0 & 0 & \sin\Psi & 0 & \cos\Psi \end{bmatrix}$$

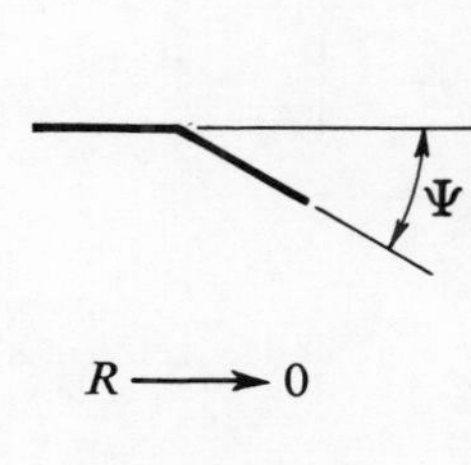

$R \longrightarrow 0$

(*g*) Elastic support

$$\mathbf{U} = \begin{bmatrix} 1 & 0 & 0 & 0 & 0 & 0 \\ 0 & 1 & 0 & 0 & 0 & 0 \\ 0 & 0 & 1 & 0 & 0 & 0 \\ 0 & 0 & k_{\vartheta}^{*} & 1 & 0 & 0 \\ 0 & -k_v & 0 & 0 & 1 & 0 \\ k_{\phi}^{*} & 0 & 0 & 0 & 0 & 1 \end{bmatrix}$$

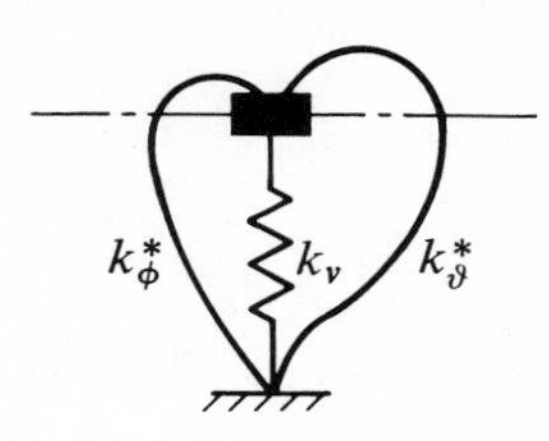

C-9. Straight Twisted Beam (Fig. C-7)

$$\kappa_y = \kappa_z = 0$$

$$\tau = 0$$

$$\sigma = \frac{d\chi}{ds} \neq 0$$

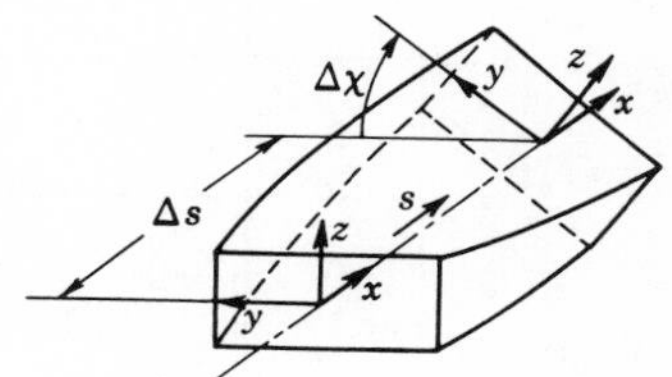

FIG. C-7

(*a*) General case

$$\mathbf{z} = \{v \quad -w \quad \psi \quad \vartheta \qquad M_z \quad M_y \quad V_z \quad -V_y\}$$

$$\mathbf{A} = \begin{bmatrix} 0 & -\sigma & 0 & 1 & 0 & 0 & 0 & 0 \\ \sigma & 0 & 1 & 0 & 0 & 0 & 0 & 0 \\ 0 & 0 & 0 & \sigma & 0 & \frac{1}{EJ_y} & 0 & 0 \\ 0 & 0 & -\sigma & 0 & \frac{1}{EJ_z} & 0 & 0 & 0 \\ 0 & 0 & 0 & -\mu\omega^2 i_z^2 & 0 & -\sigma & 0 & 1 \\ 0 & 0 & -\mu\omega^2 i_y^2 & 0 & \sigma & 0 & 1 & 0 \\ 0 & \mu\omega^2 & 0 & 0 & 0 & 0 & 0 & \sigma \\ \mu\omega^2 & 0 & 0 & 0 & 0 & 0 & -\sigma & 0 \end{bmatrix}$$

(*b*) Twist discontinuity (Fig. C-8)

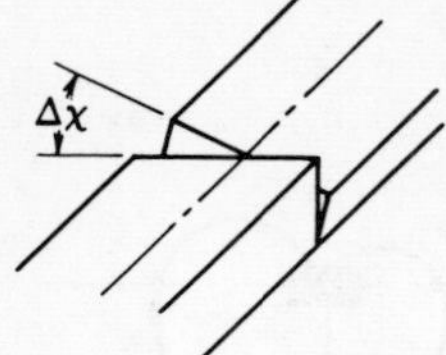

FIG. C-8

$$\Delta s \to 0$$
$$\sigma\,\Delta s \to \Delta\chi$$

$$\mathbf{U} = \begin{bmatrix} \cos\Delta\chi & -\sin\Delta\chi & 0 & 0 & 0 & 0 & 0 & 0 \\ \sin\Delta\chi & \cos\Delta\chi & 0 & 0 & 0 & 0 & 0 & 0 \\ 0 & 0 & \cos\Delta\chi & \sin\Delta\chi & 0 & 0 & 0 & 0 \\ 0 & 0 & -\sin\Delta\chi & \cos\Delta\chi & 0 & 0 & 0 & 0 \\ 0 & 0 & 0 & 0 & \cos\Delta\chi & -\sin\Delta\chi & 0 & 0 \\ 0 & 0 & 0 & 0 & \sin\Delta\chi & \cos\Delta\chi & 0 & 0 \\ 0 & 0 & 0 & 0 & 0 & 0 & \cos\Delta\chi & \sin\Delta\chi \\ 0 & 0 & 0 & 0 & 0 & 0 & -\sin\Delta\chi & \cos\Delta\chi \end{bmatrix}$$

C-10. Coordinate Transformations

$$\mathbf{z} = \{u \quad v \quad -w \qquad \phi \quad \psi \quad \vartheta \qquad M_z \quad M_y \quad T \qquad V_z \quad -V_y \quad N\} \qquad \mathbf{z}_i = \mathbf{G}\mathbf{z}_{i-1}$$

(*a*) Rotation about x axis (Fig. C-9) (observe direction of angle; right-hand-screw rule); *top, facing page*

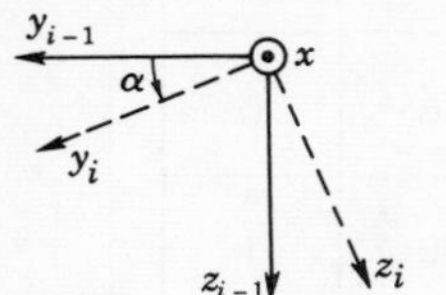

FIG. C-9

(*b*) Rotation about y axis (Fig. C-10); *bottom, facing page*

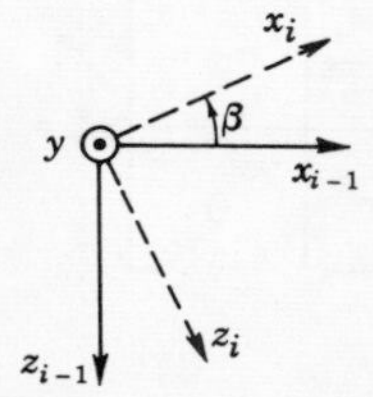

FIG. C-10

$$
\mathbf{G}=\begin{bmatrix}
1 & 0 & 0 & 0 & 0 & 0 & 0 & 0 & 0 & 0 & 0 & 0\\
0 & \cos\alpha & -\sin\alpha & 0 & 0 & 0 & 0 & 0 & 0 & 0 & 0 & 0\\
0 & \sin\alpha & \cos\alpha & 0 & 0 & 0 & 0 & 0 & 0 & 0 & 0 & 0\\
0 & 0 & 0 & 1 & 0 & 0 & 0 & 0 & 0 & 0 & 0 & 0\\
0 & 0 & 0 & 0 & \cos\alpha & \sin\alpha & 0 & 0 & 0 & 0 & 0 & 0\\
0 & 0 & 0 & 0 & -\sin\alpha & \cos\alpha & 0 & 0 & 0 & 0 & 0 & 0\\
0 & 0 & 0 & 0 & 0 & 0 & \cos\alpha & -\sin\alpha & 0 & 0 & 0 & 0\\
0 & 0 & 0 & 0 & 0 & 0 & \sin\alpha & \cos\alpha & 0 & 0 & 0 & 0\\
0 & 0 & 0 & 0 & 0 & 0 & 0 & 0 & 1 & 0 & 0 & 0\\
0 & 0 & 0 & 0 & 0 & 0 & 0 & 0 & 0 & \cos\alpha & \sin\alpha & 0\\
0 & 0 & 0 & 0 & 0 & 0 & 0 & 0 & 0 & -\sin\alpha & \cos\alpha & 0\\
0 & 0 & 0 & 0 & 0 & 0 & 0 & 0 & 0 & 0 & 0 & 1
\end{bmatrix}
$$

$$
\mathbf{G}=\begin{bmatrix}
\cos\beta & 0 & \sin\beta & 0 & 0 & 0 & 0 & 0 & 0 & 0 & 0 & 0\\
0 & 1 & 0 & 0 & 0 & 0 & 0 & 0 & 0 & 0 & 0 & 0\\
-\sin\beta & 0 & \cos\beta & 0 & 0 & 0 & 0 & 0 & 0 & 0 & 0 & 0\\
0 & 0 & 0 & \cos\beta & 0 & -\sin\beta & 0 & 0 & 0 & 0 & 0 & 0\\
0 & 0 & 0 & 0 & 1 & 0 & 0 & 0 & 0 & 0 & 0 & 0\\
0 & 0 & 0 & \sin\beta & 0 & \cos\beta & 0 & 0 & 0 & 0 & 0 & 0\\
0 & 0 & 0 & 0 & 0 & 0 & \cos\beta & 0 & \sin\beta & 0 & 0 & 0\\
0 & 0 & 0 & 0 & 0 & 0 & 0 & 1 & 0 & 0 & 0 & 0\\
0 & 0 & 0 & 0 & 0 & 0 & -\sin\beta & 0 & \cos\beta & 0 & 0 & 0\\
0 & 0 & 0 & 0 & 0 & 0 & 0 & 0 & 0 & \cos\beta & 0 & \sin\beta\\
0 & 0 & 0 & 0 & 0 & 0 & 0 & 0 & 0 & 0 & 1 & 0\\
0 & 0 & 0 & 0 & 0 & 0 & 0 & 0 & 0 & -\sin\beta & 0 & \cos\beta
\end{bmatrix}
$$

(*c*) Rotation about *z* axis (Fig. C-11)

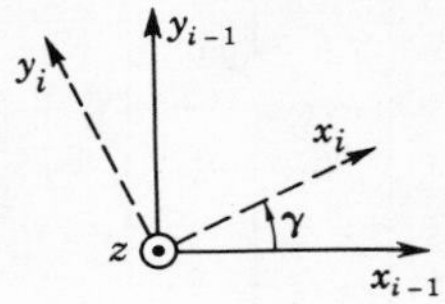

FIG. C-11

$$
\mathbf{G} = \begin{bmatrix}
\cos\gamma & \sin\gamma & 0 & 0 & 0 & 0 & 0 & 0 & 0 & 0 & 0 & 0 \\
-\sin\gamma & \cos\gamma & 0 & 0 & 0 & 0 & 0 & 0 & 0 & 0 & 0 & 0 \\
0 & 0 & 1 & 0 & 0 & 0 & 0 & 0 & 0 & 0 & 0 & 0 \\
0 & 0 & 0 & \cos\gamma & \sin\gamma & 0 & 0 & 0 & 0 & 0 & 0 & 0 \\
0 & 0 & 0 & -\sin\gamma & \cos\gamma & 0 & 0 & 0 & 0 & 0 & 0 & 0 \\
0 & 0 & 0 & 0 & 0 & 1 & 0 & 0 & 0 & 0 & 0 & 0 \\
0 & 0 & 0 & 0 & 0 & 0 & 1 & 0 & 0 & 0 & 0 & 0 \\
0 & 0 & 0 & 0 & 0 & 0 & 0 & \cos\gamma & -\sin\gamma & 0 & 0 & 0 \\
0 & 0 & 0 & 0 & 0 & 0 & 0 & \sin\gamma & \cos\gamma & 0 & 0 & 0 \\
0 & 0 & 0 & 0 & 0 & 0 & 0 & 0 & 0 & 1 & 0 & 0 \\
0 & 0 & 0 & 0 & 0 & 0 & 0 & 0 & 0 & 0 & \cos\gamma & \sin\gamma \\
0 & 0 & 0 & 0 & 0 & 0 & 0 & 0 & 0 & 0 & -\sin\gamma & \cos\gamma
\end{bmatrix}
$$

(*d*) Space corner [62]

Additional symbols:

X, Y, Z Right-handed coordinate system (fixed in space) (Fig. C-12)

ξ, η, ζ Right-handed coordinate system (attached to beam) (Fig. C-12); the coordinate axes are defined as follows:

- ξ axis: coinciding with beam axis
- η axis: perpendicular to beam axis, parallel to XY plane; in the special case where the beam axis is parallel to the Z axis, the η axis is chosen so as to have the direction of the Y axis
- ζ axis: perpendicular to beam and η axes, its positive direction pointing into the same half-space as the Z axis

χ^* Angle through which the $\xi\eta\zeta$ system is turned to coincide with the xyz system (Fig. C-13)

P, Q, R Three adjacent points (Fig. C-14) to fix the space corner in the XYZ space:

$$P = \{p_X \quad p_Y \quad p_Z\} \qquad Q = \{q_X \quad q_Y \quad q_Z\} \qquad R = \{r_X \quad r_Y \quad r_Z\}$$

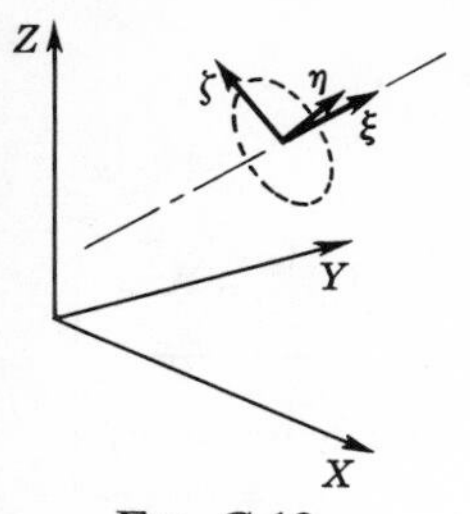

FIG. C-12

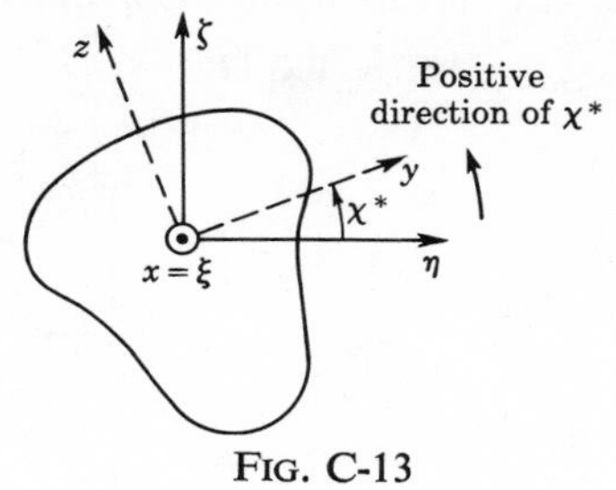

FIG. C-13

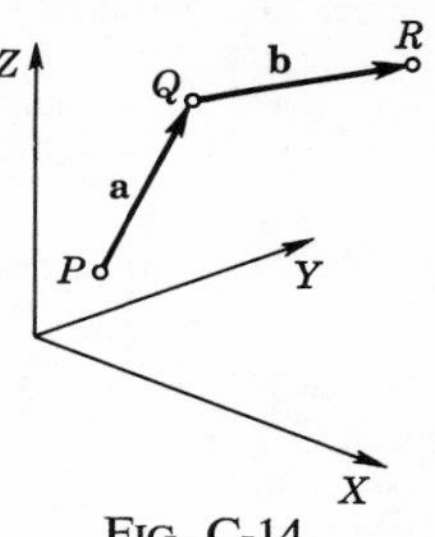

FIG. C-14

a, b Vectors connecting points P, Q, and R:

$$\mathbf{a} = \overrightarrow{PQ} = \{a_X \quad a_Y \quad a_Z\} \qquad \mathbf{b} = \overrightarrow{QR} = \{b_X \quad b_Y \quad b_Z\}$$

$$a_X = q_X - p_X \qquad\qquad b_X = r_X - q_X$$

$$\cdots\cdots \qquad\qquad \cdots\cdots$$

To simplify the formulation of the transfer matrix, we use the following state vector:

$$\mathbf{z}^* = \{u \quad v \quad w \qquad \phi \quad \psi \quad \vartheta \qquad T \quad M_y \quad M_z \qquad N \quad V_y \quad V_z\}$$

which is related to the state vector $\mathbf{z}$ otherwise used (cf. Sec. C-5) as follows:

$$\mathbf{z} = \mathbf{S}\mathbf{z}^* \qquad \text{or} \qquad \mathbf{z}^* = \mathbf{S}'\mathbf{z}\dagger$$

where

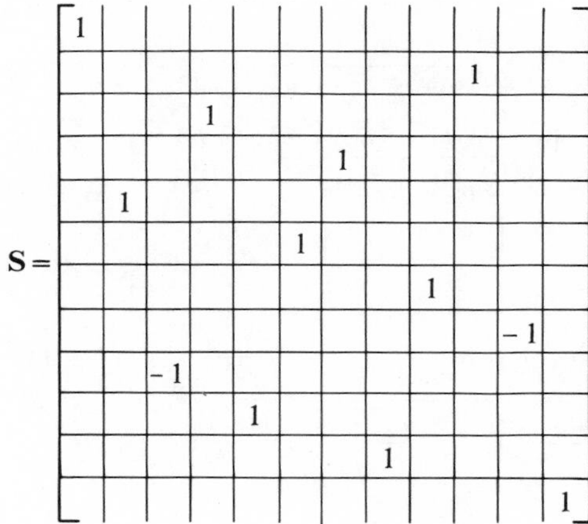

$$\mathbf{S} = \begin{bmatrix}
1 & & & & & & & & & & & \\
 & & & & & & & & & 1 & & \\
 & & & 1 & & & & & & & & \\
 & & & & & & 1 & & & & & \\
 & 1 & & & & & & & & & & \\
 & & & & & 1 & & & & & & \\
 & & & & & & & & 1 & & & \\
 & & & & & & & & & & -1 & \\
 & & -1 & & & & & & & & & \\
 & & & & 1 & & & & & & & \\
 & & & & & & & 1 & & & & \\
 & & & & & & & & & & & 1
\end{bmatrix}$$

Then the transfer matrix $\mathbf{U}^*$ is given by

$$\mathbf{U}^* = \begin{bmatrix}
\mathbf{G} & \mathbf{0} & \mathbf{0} & \mathbf{0} \\
\mathbf{0} & \mathbf{G} & \mathbf{0} & \mathbf{0} \\
\mathbf{0} & \mathbf{0} & \mathbf{G} & \mathbf{0} \\
\mathbf{0} & \mathbf{0} & \mathbf{0} & \mathbf{G}
\end{bmatrix}$$

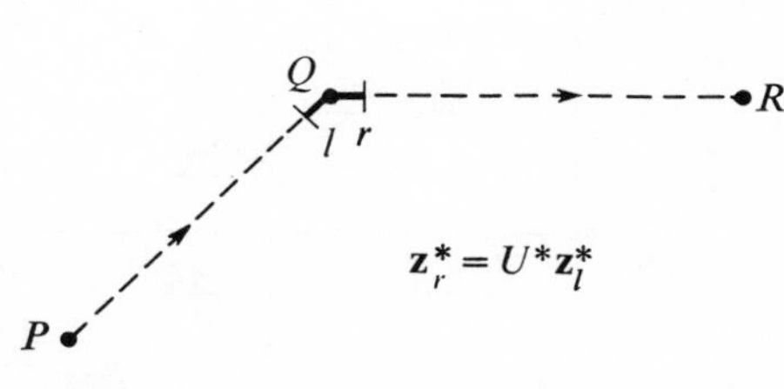

† $\mathbf{S}'$ is the transpose of $\mathbf{S}$. The reader will easily verify that in this case $\mathbf{S}' = \mathbf{S}^{-1}$.

where $\mathbf{G}$ represents a (3, 3) matrix of the following composition:

$$\mathbf{G} = \mathbf{T}_r \mathbf{G}^* \mathbf{T}_l'$$

with

$$\mathbf{T}_r = \begin{bmatrix} 1 & 0 & 0 \\ 0 & \cos\chi_r^* & \sin\chi_r^* \\ 0 & -\sin\chi_r^* & \cos\chi_r^* \end{bmatrix} \qquad \mathbf{T}_l' = \begin{bmatrix} 1 & 0 & 0 \\ 0 & \cos\chi_l^* & -\sin\chi_l^* \\ 0 & \sin\chi_l^* & \cos\chi_l^* \end{bmatrix}$$

With regard to $\mathbf{G}^*$ we have to distinguish between the following three cases:

(1) **a** as well as **b** not parallel to Z axis

$$\mathbf{G}^* = \begin{bmatrix} \frac{1}{ab}(a_X b_X + a_Y b_Y + a_Z b_Z) & \frac{1}{a^* b}(a_X b_Y - a_Y b_X) & \frac{1}{ab}\left[\frac{-a_Z}{a^*}(a_X b_X + a_Y b_Y) + a^* b_Z\right] \\ \frac{-1}{ab^*}(a_X b_Y - a_Y b_X) & \frac{1}{a^* b^*}(a_X b_X + a_Y b_Y) & \frac{a_Z}{a a^* b^*}(a_X b_Y - a_Y b_X) \\ \frac{1}{ab}\left[\frac{-b_Z}{b^*}(a_X b_X + a_Y b_Y) + a_Z b^*\right] & \frac{-b_Z}{a^* b^* b}(a_X b_Y - a_Y b_X) & \frac{1}{ab}\left[\frac{a_Z b_Z}{a^* b^*}(a_X b_X + a_Y b_Y) + a^* b^*\right] \end{bmatrix}$$

where

$$a = |\mathbf{a}| = \overset{+}{\sqrt{a_X^2 + a_Y^2 + a_Z^2}} \qquad a^* = \overset{+}{\sqrt{a_X^2 + a_Y^2}}$$

$$b = |\mathbf{b}| = \overset{+}{\sqrt{b_X^2 + b_Y^2 + b_Z^2}} \qquad b^* = \overset{+}{\sqrt{b_X^2 + b_Y^2}}$$

(2) **b** parallel to Z axis ($b_x = b_y = 0$)

$$\mathbf{G}^* = \begin{bmatrix} \frac{a_Z b_Z}{ab} & 0 & \frac{a^* b_Z}{ab} \\ \frac{a_Y}{a} & \frac{a_X}{a^*} & \frac{-a_Y a_Z}{a a^*} \\ \frac{-a_X b_Z}{ab} & \frac{a_Y b_Z}{a^* b} & \frac{a_X a_Z b_Z}{a^* ab} \end{bmatrix}$$

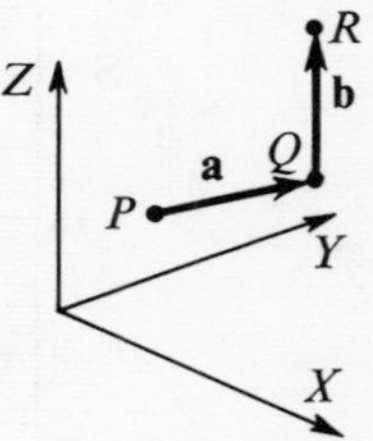

For a, a^* see (1). $b = \overset{+}{\sqrt{b_Z^2}} = |b_Z|$.

(3) **a** parallel to Z axis ($a_x = a_y = 0$)

$$\mathbf{G}^* = \begin{bmatrix} \frac{a_Z b_Z}{ab} & \frac{b_Y}{b} & \frac{-a_Z b_X}{ab} \\ 0 & \frac{b_X}{b^*} & \frac{a_Z b_Y}{ab^*} \\ \frac{a_Z b^*}{ab} & \frac{-b_Y b_Z}{bb^*} & \frac{a_Z b_Z b_X}{abb^*} \end{bmatrix}$$

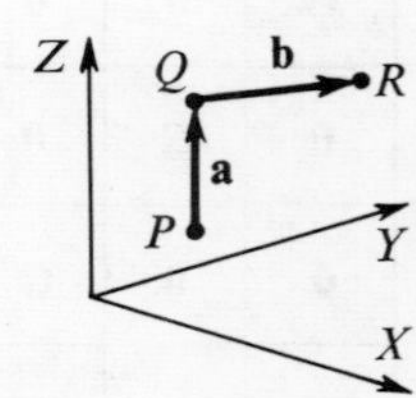

For b, b^* see (1). $a = \overset{+}{\sqrt{a_Z^2}} = |a_Z|$.

C-11. General Case

$$\mathbf{z} = \{u \quad v \quad -w \qquad \phi \quad \psi \quad \vartheta \qquad M_z \quad M_y \quad T \qquad V_z \quad -V_y \quad N\}$$

$$\mathbf{A} = \begin{bmatrix}
0 & \kappa_z & -\kappa_y & 0 & 0 & 0 & 0 & 0 & 0 & 0 & 0 & \frac{1}{EA} \\
-\kappa_z & 0 & -\sigma & 0 & 0 & 1 & 0 & 0 & 0 & 0 & 0 & 0 \\
\kappa_y & \sigma & 0 & 0 & 1 & 0 & 0 & 0 & 0 & 0 & 0 & 0 \\
0 & 0 & 0 & 0 & \kappa_z & \kappa_y & 0 & 0 & \frac{1}{GJ_T} & 0 & 0 & 0 \\
0 & 0 & 0 & -\kappa_z & 0 & \sigma & 0 & \frac{1}{EJ_y} & 0 & 0 & 0 & 0 \\
0 & 0 & 0 & -\kappa_y & -\sigma & 0 & \frac{1}{EJ_z} & 0 & 0 & 0 & 0 & 0 \\
0 & 0 & 0 & 0 & 0 & \mu i_z^2\omega^2 & 0 & -\sigma & -\kappa_y & 0 & 1 & 0 \\
0 & 0 & 0 & 0 & -\mu i_y^2\omega^2 & 0 & \sigma & 0 & -\kappa_z & 1 & 0 & 0 \\
0 & 0 & 0 & -\mu i_x^2\omega^2 & 0 & 0 & \kappa_y & \kappa_z & 0 & 0 & 0 & 0 \\
0 & 0 & \mu\omega^2 & 0 & 0 & 0 & 0 & 0 & 0 & 0 & \sigma & -\kappa_y \\
0 & \mu\omega^2 & 0 & 0 & 0 & 0 & 0 & 0 & 0 & -\sigma & 0 & \kappa_z \\
-\mu\omega^2 & 0 & 0 & 0 & 0 & 0 & 0 & 0 & 0 & \kappa_y & -\kappa_z & 0
\end{bmatrix}$$

C-12. Forcing Functions

Massless circular arch in forced vibration or under static loading (Fig. C-15):

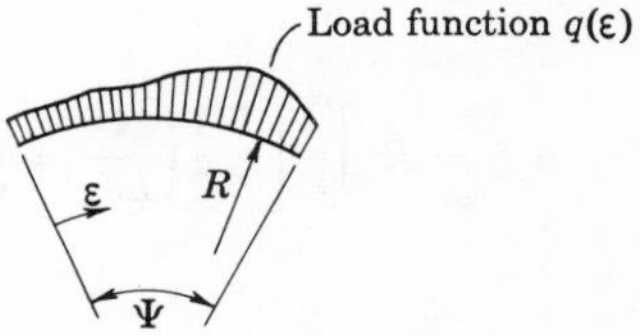

Load function $q(\varepsilon)$

ε R Ψ

FIG. C-15

(*a*) Load acting in plane of arch

$$q_x(\varepsilon) = \text{distributed load in } x \text{ direction}$$
$$q_z(\varepsilon) = \text{distributed load in } z \text{ direction}$$
$$m_y(\varepsilon) = \text{distributed moment about } y \text{ axis}$$

Load column vector **r** (seventh column in extended transfer matrix $\tilde{\mathbf{U}}$):

$$\mathbf{r} = \mathbf{U}(\Psi)\{r_1 \quad r_2 \quad r_3 \quad r_4 \quad r_5 \quad r_6\}$$

$$r_1 = \tilde{u} = R^2 \int_0^{\Psi} \left[q_x \left(\frac{1}{EA} F_1 + \frac{1}{EJ_y} R^2 F_6 \right) + m_y \frac{1}{EJ_y} R(\varepsilon - \sin \varepsilon) - q_z \left(\frac{1}{2} \frac{1}{EA} \varepsilon \sin \varepsilon - \frac{1}{EJ_y} R^2 F_5 \right) \right] d\varepsilon$$

$$r_2 = -\tilde{w} = R^2 \int_0^{\Psi} \left[q_x \left(\frac{1}{2} \frac{1}{EA} \sin \varepsilon - \frac{1}{EJ_y} R^2 F_5 \right) - m_y \frac{1}{EJ_y} R(1 - \cos \varepsilon) - q_z \left(\frac{1}{EA} + \frac{1}{EJ_y} R^2 \right) F_3 \right] d\varepsilon$$

$$r_3 = \tilde{\psi} = R^2 \int_0^{\Psi} \left[q_x \frac{1}{EJ_y} R(\varepsilon - \sin \varepsilon) + m_y \frac{1}{EJ_y} \varepsilon + q_z \frac{1}{EJ_y} R(1 - \cos \varepsilon) \right] d\varepsilon$$

$$r_4 = \tilde{M}_y = R \int_0^{\Psi} [-q_x R(1 - \cos \varepsilon) - m_y - q_z R \sin \varepsilon] \, d\varepsilon$$

$$r_5 = \tilde{V}_z = R \int_0^{\Psi} (q_x \sin \varepsilon + q_z \cos \varepsilon) \, d\varepsilon$$

$$r_6 = \tilde{N} = R \int_0^{\Psi} (-q_x \cos \varepsilon + q_z \sin \varepsilon) \, d\varepsilon$$

(*b*) Load acting perpendicular to plane of arch

$q_y(\varepsilon)$ = distributed load in y direction
$t_x(\varepsilon)$ = distributed torque about x axis
$m_z(\varepsilon)$ = distributed moment about z axis

Load column vector **r** (seventh column in extended transfer matrix $\tilde{\mathbf{U}}$):

$$\mathbf{r} = \mathbf{U}(\Psi)\{r_1 \quad r_2 \quad r_3 \quad r_4 \quad r_5 \quad r_6\}$$

$$r_1 = \tilde{\phi} = R^2 \int_0^{\Psi} \left[t_x \left(\frac{1}{GJ_T} F_1 - \frac{1}{EJ_z} F_3 \right) - m_z \frac{1}{2} \left(\frac{1}{EJ_z} + \frac{1}{GJ_T} \right) \varepsilon \sin \varepsilon - q_y R \left(\frac{1}{EJ_z} + \frac{1}{GJ_T} \right) F_3 \right] d\varepsilon$$

$$r_2 = \tilde{v} = R^3 \int_0^{\Psi} \left[-t_x \left(\frac{1}{EJ_z} + \frac{1}{GJ_T} \right) F_3 - m_z \left(\frac{1}{2} \frac{1}{EJ_z} \varepsilon \sin \varepsilon - \frac{1}{GJ_T} F_5 \right) - q_y R \left(\frac{1}{EJ_z} F_3 - \frac{1}{GJ_T} F_6 \right) \right] d\varepsilon$$

$$r_3 = \tilde{\vartheta} = R^2 \int_0^{\Psi} \left[t_x \frac{1}{2} \left(\frac{1}{EJ_z} + \frac{1}{GJ_T} \right) \varepsilon \sin \varepsilon + m_z \left(\frac{1}{EJ_z} F_1 - \frac{1}{GJ_T} F_3 \right) + q_y R \left(\frac{1}{2} \frac{1}{EJ_z} \varepsilon \sin \varepsilon - \frac{1}{GJ_T} F_5 \right) \right] d\varepsilon$$

$$r_4 = \tilde{M}_z = R \int_0^{\Psi} (-t_x \sin \varepsilon - m_z \cos \varepsilon - q_y R \sin \varepsilon) \, d\varepsilon$$

$$r_5 = -\tilde{V}_y = R \int_0^{\Psi} q_y \, d\varepsilon$$

$$r_6 = \tilde{T} = R \int_0^{\Psi} [-t_x \cos \varepsilon + m_z \sin \varepsilon + q_y R(1 - \cos \varepsilon)] \, d\varepsilon$$

ROTATING DISKS

C-13. Stresses and Deformation Caused by Centrifugal Forces and Thermal Loading [60]

Symbols used (Fig. C-16):

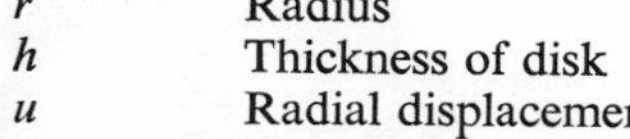

r	Radius
h	Thickness of disk
u	Radial displacement
$S_r = \sigma_r h$	Normal force per unit length on r face, lb/in.
$S_\theta = \sigma_\theta h$	Normal force per unit length on θ face, lb/in.
Ω	Angular velocity of disk
E	Young's modulus of disk material
ν	Poisson's ratio of disk material
ρ	Specific mass of disk material
α	Thermal-expansion coefficient
Δt	Change of temperature

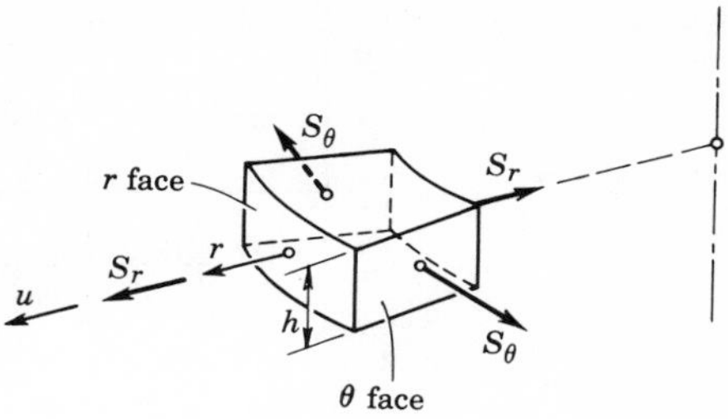

FIG. C-16

Extended state vector:

$$\tilde{\mathbf{z}} = \{S_r \quad u \qquad 1\}$$

If desired, the force per unit length $S_{\theta i}$ at concentric line i is calculated as follows:

$$S_{\theta i} = \mathbf{H}_i \tilde{\mathbf{z}}_i$$

where $\mathbf{H}_i$ is a row vector.

(*a*) Disk with concentric hole (Fig. C-17)

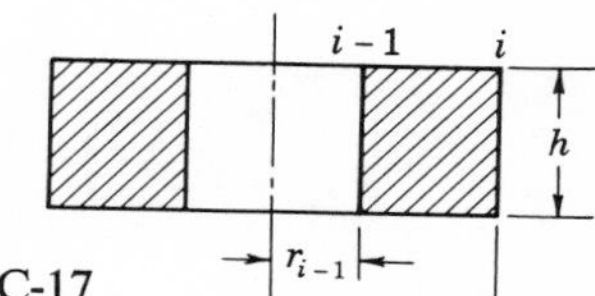

FIG. C-17

$$= \begin{bmatrix} 1 - \frac{1-\nu}{2}\left[1 - \left(\frac{r_{i-1}}{r_i}\right)^2\right] & \frac{Eh}{2r_{i-1}}\left[1 - \left(\frac{r_{i-1}}{r_i}\right)^2\right] & \frac{-h}{2}\left[1 - \left(\frac{r_{i-1}}{r_i}\right)^2\right]\left(\frac{\rho\Omega^2 r_i^2}{2}\left\{1 + \nu + \frac{1-\nu}{2}\left[1 + \left(\frac{r_{i-1}}{r_i}\right)^2\right]\right\} + E\alpha\,\Delta t\right) \\ \frac{r_i}{Eh}\,\frac{1-\nu^2}{2}\left[1 - \left(\frac{r_{i-1}}{r_i}\right)^2\right] & \frac{r_i}{r_{i-1}}\left\{1 - \frac{1+\nu}{2}\left[1 - \left(\frac{r_{i-1}}{r_i}\right)^2\right]\right\} & \frac{-r_i}{2}\left[1 - \left(\frac{r_{i-1}}{r_i}\right)^2\right]\left\{\frac{1-\nu^2}{4}\,\frac{\rho\Omega^2 r_i^2}{E}\left[1 - \left(\frac{r_{i-1}}{r_i}\right)^2\right] - (1+\nu)\alpha\,\Delta t\right\} \\ 0 & 0 & 1 \end{bmatrix}$$

$$\mathbf{H}_i = \left[\nu \quad E\frac{h_i}{r_i} \qquad 0\right]^\dagger$$

(*b*) Disk without hole (Fig. C-18)

FIG. C-18

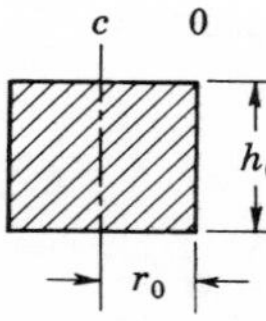

FIG. C-19

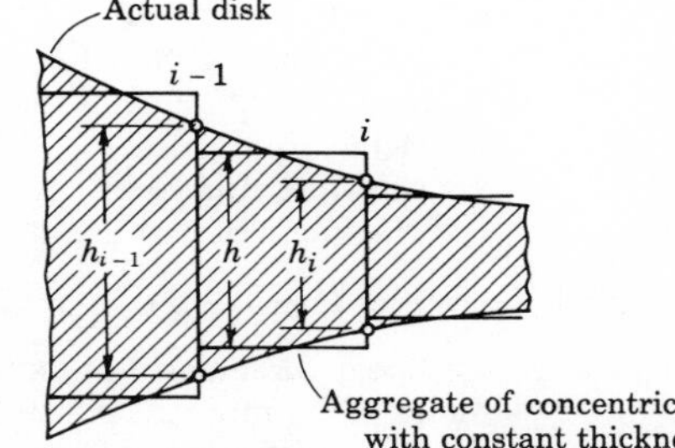

† If the disk is of variable thickness, $h = h(r)$, it is replaced by an aggregate of concentric rings, each ring being of constant thickness $h = h(r)$, with r chosen somewhere between r_i and r_{i-1} (Fig. C-19). However, $h_i = h(r_i)$.

$$
\mathbf{U} = \begin{bmatrix} 1 & 0 & -(3+\nu)\dfrac{\rho h\Omega^2 r_0^2}{8} \\ \dfrac{r_0}{Eh}(1-\nu) & 0 & -(1-\nu^2)\dfrac{\rho\Omega^2 r_0^3}{8E} + r_0\alpha\,\Delta t \\ 0 & 0 & 1 \end{bmatrix}
$$

$$
\mathbf{H}_c = [1 \quad 0 \quad 0]
$$

$$
\mathbf{H}_0 = \left[\nu \quad E\frac{h_0}{r_0} \quad 0\right]^{\dagger}
$$

C-14. Bending Vibrations of Thick Rotating Disks (Reissner's Theory) [63]

Symbols used:

1. Geometric quantities (Fig. C-20)

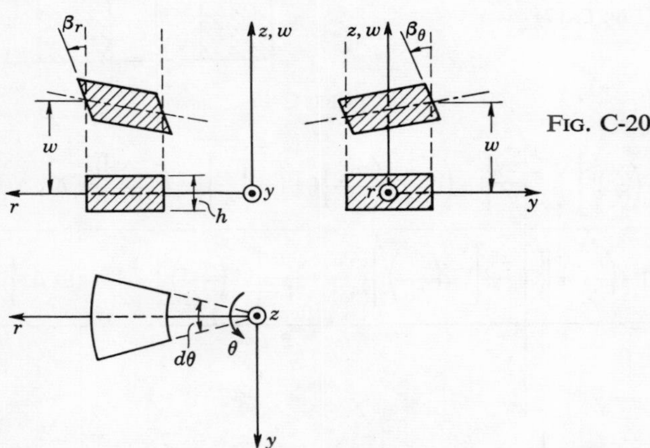

FIG. C-20

r, y, z	Right-handed coordinate system
r, θ	Polar coordinates in middle surface of disk
w	Deflection of disk
β_r, β_θ	Absolute rotation of concentric and radial sections
h	Thickness of disk

2. Dynamic quantities (Fig. C-21)

V_r, V_θ	Shear force per unit length on r or θ face, lb/in.
M_r, M_θ	Bending moment per unit length on r or θ face, lb
H	Torsional moment per unit length, lb

† Cf. previous footnote.

FIG. C-21

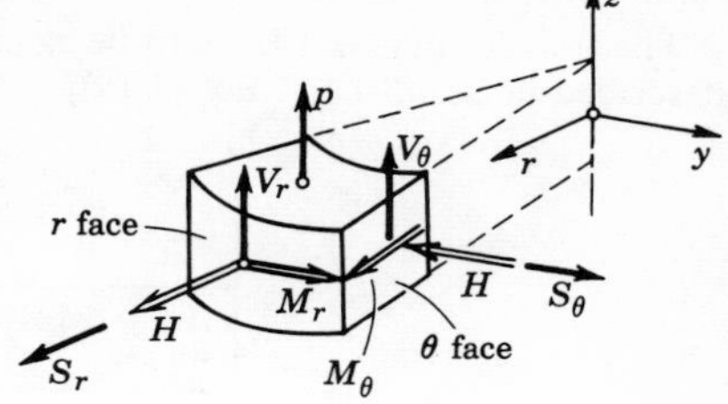

p	Distributed load normal to disk per unit area, lb/in.²
S_r, S_θ	Normal force per unit length on r or θ face, lb/in.

3. Material constants

E, ν, ρ	See Sec. C-13
G	Shear modulus

4. Miscellaneous quantities

n	Number of nodal diameters of vibrating disk
$D = \dfrac{Eh^3}{12(1-\nu^2)}$	Flexural stiffness of disk
m	Mass of disk ring
ω	Natural frequency of bending vibration
a	$\dfrac{\sqrt{10}}{h}$
r^*	$\dfrac{\sqrt{10}}{h}\,r$
r_0	Suitable basic length
I_n, K_n	So-called modified Bessel functions

5. State vector

$$\mathbf{z} = \{w^* \quad \beta_r^* \quad \beta_\theta^* \qquad H^* \quad M_r^* \quad V_r^*\}$$

Here the asterisk denotes the amplitudes of concentric sine waves:

$$w(r,\theta) = w^*(r)\cos n\theta$$

$$\beta_r(r,\theta) = \beta_r^*(r)\cos n\theta$$

$$\beta_\theta(r,\theta) = \beta_\theta^*(r)\begin{cases}1 & \text{for } n = 0\\ \sin n\theta & \text{for } n = 1, 2, 3, \ldots\end{cases}$$

$$H(r,\theta) = H^*(r)\begin{cases}1 & \text{for } n = 0\\ \sin n\theta & \text{for } n = 1, 2, 3, \ldots\end{cases}$$

$$M_r(r,\theta) = M_r^*(r)\cos n\theta$$

$$V_r(r,\theta) = V_r^*(r)\cos n\theta$$

(*a*) Elastic massless field of constant thickness

The transfer matrix $\mathbf{U}(r)$ is to be calculated from the matrix $\mathbf{B}(r)$ according to the method described in Sec. 5-1 [cf. Eq. (5-18)].

$n=0$

$\mathbf{B}(r) =$

1	$\ln \frac{r}{r_0}$	r^2
0	$-r^{-1}$	$-2r$
0	0	0
0	0	0
0	$(1-\nu)r^{-2}$	$-2(1+\nu)$
0	0	0

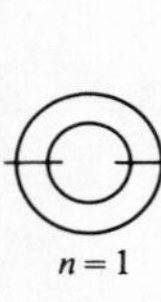

$\mathbf{B}(r) =$

r^{-1}	r	$r \ln \frac{r}{r_0}$
r^{-2}	-1	$-1-\ln \frac{r}{r_0} + 2r^{-2}\frac{h^2}{5(1-\nu)}$
$-r^{-2}$	-1	$-\ln \frac{r}{r_0} - 2r^{-2}\frac{h^2}{5(1-\nu)}$
$2(1-\nu)r^{-3}$	0	$\frac{4}{5}h^2r^{-3}-(1-\nu)r^{-1}$
$-2(1-\nu)r^{-3}$	0	$\frac{-4}{5}h^2r^{-3}-(1+\nu)r^{-1}$
0	0	$2r^{-2}$

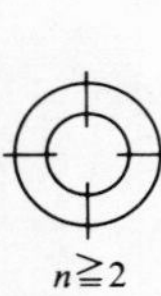

$\mathbf{B}(r) =$

r^{-n}	r^{n}	r^{2-n}
nr^{-n-1}	$-nr^{n-1}$	$(n-2)r^{1-n}-\frac{h^2}{5(1-\nu)}4n(n-1)r^{-1-n}$
$-nr^{-n-1}$	$-nr^{n-1}$	$-nr^{1-n}+\frac{h^2}{5(1-\nu)}4n(n-1)r^{-n-1}$
$n(n+1)(1-\nu)r^{-n-2}$	$-n(n-1)(1-\nu)r^{n-2}$	$\left[\frac{-4}{5}h^2(n+1)r^{-n-2}+(1-\nu)r^{-n}\right]n(n-1)$
$-n(n+1)(1-\nu)r^{-n-2}$	$-n(n-1)(1-\nu)r^{n-2}$	$(n-1)\left\{\frac{4}{5}h^2n(n+1)r^{-n-2}-[n-2-\nu(n+2)]r^{-}\right.$
0	0	$-4n(n-1)r^{-n-1}$

$r^2 \ln \frac{r}{r_0}$	0	0
$-r(2 \ln \frac{r}{r_0} + 1) - 4r^{-1} \frac{h^2}{5(1-\nu)}$	0	0
0	$\frac{h^2}{5(1-\nu)} a\dot{I}_0(r^*)$	$\frac{h^2}{5(1-\nu)} aK_0(r^*)$
0	$\frac{h^2}{10}[-ar^{-1}\dot{I}_0(r^*) + a^2\ddot{I}_0(r^*)]$	$\frac{h^2}{10}[-ar^{-1}\dot{K}_0(r^*) + a^2\ddot{K}_0(r^*)]$
$\frac{4}{5} h^2 r^{-2} - 3 - \nu - 2(1+\nu) \ln \frac{r}{r_0}$	0	0
$-4r^{-1}$	0	0

r^3	0	0
$-3r^2 - 8 \frac{h^2}{5(1-\nu)}$	$\frac{h^2}{5(1-\nu)} r^{-1} I_1(r^*)$	$\frac{h^2}{5(1-\nu)} r^{-1} K_1(r^*)$
$-r^2 - 8 \frac{h^2}{5(1-\nu)}$	$\frac{h^2}{5(1-\nu)} a\dot{I}_1(r^*)$	$\frac{h^2}{5(1-\nu)} a\dot{K}_1(r^*)$
$-2(1-\nu)r$	$\frac{h^2}{10}[r^{-2}I_1(r^*) - ar^{-1}\dot{I}_1(r^*) + a^2\ddot{I}_1(r^*)]$	$\frac{h^2}{10}[r^{-2}K_1(r^*) - ar^{-1}\dot{K}_1(r^*) + a^2\ddot{K}_1(r^*)]$
$-2(3+\nu)r$	$\frac{h^2}{5}[-r^{-2}I_1(r^*) + ar^{-1}\dot{I}_1(r^*)]$	$\frac{h^2}{5}[-r^{-2}K_1(r^*) + ar^{-1}\dot{K}_1(r^*)]$
-8	$r^{-1}I_1(r^*)$	$r^{-1}K_1(r^*)$

r^{2+n}	0	0
$-(n+2)r^{1+n} - \frac{h^2}{5(1-\nu)} 4n(n+1)r^{n-1}$	$\frac{h^2}{5(1-\nu)} nr^{-1} I_n(r^*)$	$\frac{h^2}{5(1-\nu)} nr^{-1} K_n(r^*)$
$-nr^{1+n} - \frac{h^2}{5(1-\nu)} 4n(n+1)r^{n-1}$	$\frac{h^2}{5(1-\nu)} a\dot{I}_n(r^*)$	$\frac{h^2}{5(1-\nu)} a\dot{K}_n(r^*)$
$n(n+1)\left[\frac{4}{5} h^2(n-1)r^{n-2} + (1-\nu)r^n\right]$	$\frac{h^2}{10}[n^2 r^{-2} I_n(r^*) - ar^{-1}\dot{I}_n(r^*) + a^2\ddot{I}_n(r^*)]$	$\frac{h^2}{10}[n^2 r^{-2} K_n(r^*) - ar^{-1}\dot{K}_n(r^*) + a^2\ddot{K}_n(r^*)]$
$1)\left\{\frac{4}{5} h^2 n(n-1)r^{n-2} + [n+2-\nu(n-2)]r^n\right\}$	$n \frac{h^2}{5}[-r^{-2}I_n(r^*) + ar^{-1}\dot{I}_n(r^*)]$	$n \frac{h^2}{5}[-r^{-2}K_n(r^*) + ar^{-1}\dot{K}_n(r^*)]$
$-4n(n+1)r^{n-1}$	$nr^{-1}I_n(r^*)$	$nr^{-1}K_n(r^*)$

(*b*) Transfer matrix across concentric line where the mass of the respective rings is concentrated

In this transfer matrix is also concentrated the influence of the normal forces per unit length S_r and S_θ, which are calculated in accordance with Sec. C-13. S_r^* and S_θ^* denote average values of S_r and S_θ in the respective rings.

$$
\mathbf{U} = \left[\begin{array}{c|c|c|c|c|c}
1 & 0 & 0 & 0 & 0 & 0 \\
\hline
\frac{-\nu}{1-\nu}\frac{h^2\omega^2}{60D}\frac{m}{2\pi r} & 1 & 0 & 0 & 0 & 0 \\
\hline
0 & 0 & 1 & 0 & 0 & 0 \\
\hline
\frac{-n}{D}\left(\frac{S_\theta^*}{r} + \nu\frac{h^2\omega^2}{60D}\frac{m}{2\pi r^2}\right) & 0 & \frac{-h^2\omega^2}{12D}\frac{m}{2\pi r} & 1 & 0 & 0 \\
\hline
\begin{array}{c}\nu\frac{h^2\omega^2}{60D}\frac{m}{2\pi r^2}\left[1 + \frac{1}{2D(1-\nu)}\left(\frac{h^2\omega^2}{12}\frac{m}{2\pi} - rS_r^*\right)\right] \\ \frac{+1}{2}\frac{6}{5Gh}\frac{\omega^2}{D}S_r^*\frac{m}{2\pi r}\end{array} & \frac{-1}{D}\left(\frac{h^2\omega^2}{12}\frac{m}{2\pi r} - S_r^*\right) & 0 & 0 & 1 & \frac{-6}{5Gh}S_r^* \\
\hline
\frac{-\omega^2}{D}\frac{m}{2\pi r} & 0 & 0 & 0 & 0 & 1
\end{array}\right]
$$

C-15. The Derivation of Flexibility and Stiffness Matrices from the Transfer Matrix and Remarks on Various Load Conditions

By means of a few matrix operations, it is possible to obtain the flexibility and stiffness matrices (cf. Sec. 9-1) required in Chaps. 9 and 10 from the transfer matrix of the given element. It should be noted that, although the illustrative examples given in this section are completed in closed form, in practice the values of the parameters of the elements will be inserted in the transfer matrix and that the matrix operations required to obtain the flexibility and stiffness matrices will be carried out numerically.

It was explained in Sec. 9-1 that for a given element the deformations can be expressed in different ways. Normally, however, it proves more convenient to regard the deformations as the displacements of the right end when the left end is clamped. In this case the stiffness and flexibility matrices can be easily obtained from the partitioned transfer-matrix relation

$$
\left[\begin{array}{c}\mathbf{v}_i \\ \hdashline \mathbf{p}_i\end{array}\right] = \left[\begin{array}{c:c}\mathbf{A} & \mathbf{B} \\ \hdashline \mathbf{C} & \mathbf{D}\end{array}\right] \cdot \left[\begin{array}{c}\mathbf{v}_{i-1} \\ \hdashline \mathbf{p}_{i-1}\end{array}\right]
$$

With $\mathbf{v}_{i-1}$ set equal to zero (since the element is clamped at $i - 1$), we have

$$
\mathbf{v}_i = \mathbf{B}\mathbf{p}_{i-1} \qquad \text{and} \qquad \mathbf{p}_i = \mathbf{D}\mathbf{p}_{i-1}
$$

Eliminating $\mathbf{p}_{i-1}$, we obtain the stiffness-matrix relation

$$
\mathbf{p}_i = \mathbf{D}\mathbf{B}^{-1}\mathbf{v}_i = \mathbf{K}_p\mathbf{v}_i
$$

that is,

$$\mathbf{K}_p = \mathbf{DB}^{-1} \tag{a}$$

The flexibility matrix is given by the relation

$$\mathbf{v}_i = \mathbf{BD}^{-1}\mathbf{p}_i = \mathbf{F}_v\mathbf{p}_i$$

that is,

$$\mathbf{F}_v = \mathbf{BD}^{-1} \tag{b}$$

For example, referring to the case of a homogeneous beam, we have the transfer-matrix relation†

$$\begin{bmatrix} \psi \\ w \\ \hdashline M \\ V \end{bmatrix}_i = \left[\begin{array}{cc:cc} 1 & 0 & -\dfrac{l}{EJ} & -\dfrac{l^2}{2EJ} \\ -l & 1 & \dfrac{l^2}{2EJ} & \dfrac{l^3}{6EJ} \\ \hdashline 0 & 0 & -1 & -l \\ 0 & 0 & 0 & -1 \end{array}\right] \cdot \begin{bmatrix} \psi \\ w \\ \hdashline M \\ V \end{bmatrix}_{i-1}$$

so that

$$\mathbf{B} = \begin{bmatrix} -\dfrac{l}{EJ} & -\dfrac{l^2}{2EJ} \\ \dfrac{l^2}{2EJ} & \dfrac{l^3}{6EJ} \end{bmatrix} \quad \text{and} \quad \mathbf{D} = \begin{bmatrix} -1 & -l \\ 0 & -1 \end{bmatrix}$$

Then Eq. (*a*) yields

$$\mathbf{K}_p = \begin{bmatrix} \dfrac{4EJ}{l} & \dfrac{6EJ}{l^2} \\ \dfrac{6EJ}{l^2} & \dfrac{12EJ}{l^3} \end{bmatrix} \qquad \text{cf. Eq. (9-4)}$$

and Eq. (*b*) yields

$$\mathbf{F}_v = \begin{bmatrix} \dfrac{l}{EJ} & -\dfrac{l^2}{2EJ} \\ -\dfrac{l^2}{2EJ} & \dfrac{l^3}{3EJ} \end{bmatrix} \qquad \text{cf. Eq. (9-5)}$$

The extended transfer matrix (cf. Secs. 3-5 and 5-3) can be used to take care of various load conditions, such as are shown, in the case of straight beams, for example, in the table in Sec. C-6, where the load is not applied at either joint $i-1$ or i of the individual beam element (cf. also Sec. C-12 for curved beams). The expansion of the extended-transfer-matrix† relation

$$\begin{bmatrix} \mathbf{v}_i \\ \hdashline \mathbf{p}_i \\ \hdashline 1 \end{bmatrix} = \left[\begin{array}{c:c:c} \mathbf{A} & \mathbf{B} & \mathbf{r}_v \\ \hdashline \mathbf{C} & \mathbf{D} & \mathbf{r}_p \\ \hdashline \multicolumn{2}{c:}{\mathbf{0}} & 1 \end{array}\right] \cdot \begin{bmatrix} \mathbf{v}_{i-1} \\ \hdashline \mathbf{p}_{i-1} \\ \hdashline 1 \end{bmatrix}$$

yields

$$\mathbf{v}_i = \mathbf{Av}_{i-1} + \mathbf{Bp}_{i-1} + \mathbf{r}_v \qquad \mathbf{p}_i = \mathbf{Cv}_{i-1} + \mathbf{Dp}_{i-1} + \mathbf{r}_p$$

Following the same procedure as above, we reduce these two equations to the following relation:

$$\mathbf{p}_i = \mathbf{DB}^{-1}\mathbf{v}_i + \mathbf{r}_p - \mathbf{DB}^{-1}\mathbf{r}_v = \mathbf{K}_p\mathbf{v}_i + \mathbf{r}_p - \mathbf{K}_p\mathbf{r}_v$$

† Note that the sequence of the components in the state vectors as well as the signs of the forces at face $i-1$ has been changed compared with the usual transfer-matrix relation, in order to comply with the conventions introduced in Sec. 9-1.

The term $\mathbf{r}_p - \mathbf{K}_p\mathbf{r}_v$ represents the change in the internal forces at joint i caused by the loading on field i.

Hence, by applying at point i the external load described by the vector

$$\mathbf{f}_i = -\mathbf{r}_p + \mathbf{K}_p\mathbf{r}_v \tag{c}$$

we achieve the same effect at this point i as the actual loading of the span i. The force $\mathbf{f}_{i-1}$ that has to be applied at point $i - 1$ is then found considering that $\mathbf{f}_{i-1}$ and $\mathbf{f}_i$ together must be statically equivalent to the actual load.

As an example, let us consider that the straight beam element i of length l and constant bending stiffness EJ is loaded by the uniform continuous load q; then from the fourth column of the table in Sec. C-6 we have, upon proper change of sequence and sign,

$$\mathbf{r}_v = \left\{\frac{-ql^3}{6EJ} \quad \frac{ql^4}{24EJ}\right\} \qquad \text{and} \qquad \mathbf{r}_p = \left\{\frac{-ql^2}{2} \quad -ql\right\}$$

Hence the evaluation of Eq. (c) yields easily

$$\mathbf{f}_i = \left\{\frac{ql^2}{12} \quad \frac{ql}{2}\right\}$$

Since the resultant of the total actual load of the span is located at the center of the beam, we have

$$\mathbf{f}_{i-1} = \left\{\frac{-ql^2}{12} \quad \frac{ql}{2}\right\}$$

So the load vectors $\mathbf{f}_{i-1}$ and $\mathbf{f}_i$ take the place of the continuous load, because they achieve the same effect, not only so far as the relative deformation of joints $i - 1$ and i is concerned, but also, on account of their static equivalence, for the whole structure. The reader is cautioned against assuming that in the absence of couples in the actual load the substitute couples at both ends are always equal and opposite. This is the case only for symmetric loading. For example, if the homogeneous beam is loaded by a single force so that $d = l/4$ (cf. second column in the table in Sec. C-6), then we obtain, following the above procedure,

$$\mathbf{f}_i = \left\{\frac{9Pl}{64} \quad \frac{54P}{64}\right\} \qquad \text{and} \qquad \mathbf{f}_{i-1} = \left\{\frac{-3Pl}{64} \quad \frac{10P}{64}\right\}$$

which can be easily verified as statically equivalent to P.

In conclusion we might state that with this method we need no longer make a joint in the structure wherever a force or couple is applied; thereby we gain the advantage of reducing the numbers of the elements into which the structure is decomposed when the matrix force method is applied. The reader may convince himself of the fact that in the case of straight beams the same results are obtained in the following way: The beam element is put on two simple supports. Then the slopes at both ends caused by the actual loading are determined. Thereafter we determine the two end couples that would produce the same slopes, and finally we compute the two end forces that together with the substitute end couples yield the same resultant as the actual load.

REFERENCES

1. Aitken, A. C.: "Determinants and Matrices," Oliver & Boyd, Ltd., Edinburgh, 1958.
2. Falk, S.: Ein uebersichtliches Schema fuer die Matrizenmultiplikation, *Z. angew. Math. u. Mech.*, vol. 31, pp. 152–153, 1951.
3. Frazer, R. A., W. J. Duncan, and A. R. Collar: "Elementary Matrices and Some Applications to Dynamics and Differential Equations," Cambridge University Press, New York, 1938.
4. Lanczos, C.: "Applied Analysis," Sir Isaac Pitman & Sons, Ltd., London, 1957.
5. Bodewig, E.: "Matrix Calculus," 2d ed., Interscience Publishers, Inc., New York, 1959.
6. Den Hartog, J. P.: "Mechanical Vibrations," 4th ed., McGraw-Hill Book Company, Inc., New York, 1956.
7. Thomson, W. T.: "Mechanical Vibrations," Prentice-Hall, Inc., Englewood Cliffs, N.J., 1953.
8. Myklestad, N. O.: A New Method of Calculating Natural Modes of Uncoupled Bending Vibrations, *J. Aeronaut. Sci.*, April, 1944, p. 153.
9. Falk, S.: Die Berechnung des beliebig gestützten Durchlaufträgers nach dem Reduktionsverfahren, *Ingr.-Arch.*, vol. 24, p. 216, 1956.
10. Fraeijs de Veubeke, B. M.: Influence of Internal Damping on Aircraft Resonance, "Manual on Aeroelasticity," vol. I, chap. 3, North Atlantic Treaty Organization, Advisory Group for Aeronautical Research and Development.
11. Bishop, R. E. D., and G. M. L. Gladwell: An Investigation into the Theory of Resonance Testing, *Phil. Trans. Roy. Soc. London*, ser. A, vol. 255, pp. 241–280, Jan. 17, 1963.
12. Bishop, R. E. D., and D. C. Johnson: "The Mechanics of Vibration," Cambridge University Press, New York, 1960.
13. Hansen, H. M., and P. F. Chenea: "Mechanics of Vibration," John Wiley & Sons, Inc., New York, 1952.
14. Pestel, E., and E. Kollmann: "Grundlagen der Regelungstechnik," Vieweg-Verlag, Brunswick, Germany, 1961.
15. Truxal, J. G.: "Automatic Feedback Control System Synthesis," McGraw-Hill Book Company, Inc., New York, 1955.
16. Benz, W.: Zur Berechnung erzwungener gedämpfter Schwingungen, *VDI-Ber.*, no. 35, pp. 123–134, 1959.
17. Shanley, F. R.: "Strength of Materials," McGraw-Hill Book Company, Inc., New York, 1957.
18. Schumpich, G.: Beitrag zur Kinetik und Statik ebener Stabwerke mit gekrümmten Stäben, *Österr. Ingr.-Arch.*, vol. 11, pp. 194–225, 1957.
19. Thomson, W. T.: Matrix Solution for the Vibration of Non-uniform Beams, *J. Appl. Mech.*, September, 1950, pp. 337–339.
20. Pestel, E., G. Schumpich, and S. Spierig: Katalog von Übertragungsmatrizen zur Berechnung technischer Schwingungsprobleme, *VDI-Ber.*, no. 35, pp. 11–28, 1959.

21. Okumura, A.: On a Method of Analysis for Vibration and Stability Problems of Linear Mechanical Systems or Structures, *Mem. Fac. Sci. & Eng., Waseda Univ.*, no. 21, 1957.
22. Zurmühl, R.: "Praktische Mathematik für Ingenieure und Physiker," 3d ed., Springer-Verlag, Berlin, 1961.
23. Falk, S.: Die Berechnung offener Rahmentragwerke nach dem Reduktionsverfahren, *Ingr.-Arch.*, vol. 26, pp. 61–80, 1958.
24. Leckie, F. A., and E. Pestel: Transfer Matrix Fundamentals, *Intern. J. Mech. Sci.*, vol. 2, pp. 137–167, 1960.
25. Pestel, E.: Ein allgemeines Verfahren zur Berechnung freier und erzwungener Schwingungen von Stabwerken, *Abhandl. braunschweig. wiss. Ges.*, vol. 6, pp. 227–242, 1954.
26. Pestel, E., and G. Schumpich: Beitrag zur Schwingungsberechnung einfacher und gekoppelter Stabzüge, *Schiffstechnik*, vol. 4, pp. 55–61, 1957.
27. Pestel, E., and G. Schumpich: Berechnung des Schwingungsverhaltens gekoppelter paralleler Stabzüge mit Hilfe von Übertragungsmatrizen, *VDI-Ber.*, no. 30, pp. 41–44, 1958.
28. Marguerre, K.: Vibration and Stability Problems of Beams Treated by Matrices, *J. Math. and Phys.*, vol. 15, pp. 27–43, 1956.
29. Fuhrke, H.: Bestimmung von Balkenschwingungen mit Hilfe des Matrizenkalküls, *Ingr.-Arch.*, vol. 23, pp. 329–384, 1955.
30. Fuhrke, H.: Bestimmung von Rahmenschwingungen mit Hilfe des Matrizenkalküls, *Ingr.-Arch.*, vol. 24, pp. 27–42, 1956.
31. Fuhrke, H.: Eigenwert-Bestimmungen mit Hilfe von abgeleiteten Übertragungsmatrizen, *VDI-Ber.*, no. 30, pp. 34–40, 1958.
32. Schnell, W.: Zur Berechnung der Beulwerte von längs- und querversteiften Platten unter Drucklast, *Z. angew. Math. u. Mech.*, vol. 36, pp. 36–51, 1956.
33. Schnell, W.: Berechnung der Stabilität mehrfeldriger Stäbe mit Hilfe von Matrizen, *Z. angew. Math. u. Mech.*, vol. 35, pp. 269–284, 1955.
34. Marguerre, K.: "Matrices of Transmission in Beam Problems. Progress in Solid Mechanics," vol. 1, pp. 61–82, North-Holland Publishing Company, Amsterdam, 1960.
35. Marguerre, K.: Abriss der Schwingungslehre, "Stahlbau, Handbuch für Studium und Praxis," vol. 1, Stahlbau Verlag, Cologne, 1960.
36. Pestel, E.: Anwendung der Delta-Matrizen auf inhomogene Probleme, *Ingr.-Arch.*, vol. 27, pp. 250–254, 1959.
37. Fuhrke, H.: Eigenwertbestimmung mit Hilfe von abgeleiteten Übertragungsmatrizen, *VDI-Ber.*, no. 35, pp. 29–32, 1959.
38. Biezeno, C. B., and R. Grammel: "Technische Dynamik," 2d ed., vol. 2, Springer-Verlag, Berlin, 1953.
39. Tong, K. N.: "Theory of Mechanical Vibration," John Wiley & Sons, Inc., New York, 1960.
40. Pestel, E., and O. Mahrenholtz: Zum numerischen Problem der Eigenwertbestimmung mit Übertragungsmatrizen, *Ingr.-Arch.*, vol. 28, pp. 255–262, 1959.
41. Dinamika i Protchnost Mashin, *Rept. Polytech. Inst. Leningrad*, no. 210, 1960; cf. contributions by B. A. Troitski, pp. 220–255, and B. A. Palmov and A. A. Pervozvanski, pp. 199–212.
42. Norris, C. H., and J. B. Wilbur: "Elementary Structural Analysis," McGraw-Hill Book Company, Inc., New York, 1960.
43. Klotter, K.: "Technische Schwingungslehre," 2d ed., vol. 2, Springer-Verlag, Berlin, 1960.
44. Young, D.: Response of Structural Systems to Ground Shock, in M. V. Barton (ed.), "Shock and Structural Response," American Society of Mechanical Engineers, New York, 1960.
45. Caughey, T. K.: Classical Normal Modes in Damped Linear Dynamic Systems, *J. Appl. Mech.*, vol. 27, pp. 269–271, 1960.
46. Lancaster, P.: Free Vibrations of Lightly Damped Systems by Perturbation Methods, *Quart. J. Mech. Appl. Math.*, vol. 13, 1960.
47. Morice, P. B.: "Linear Structural Analysis," The Ronald Press Company, New York, 1959.

48. Argyris, J. H.: Energy Theorems and Structural Analysis, *Aircraft Eng.*, vol. 27, p. 347, 1955, and subsequent issues.
49. Argyris, J. H.: Die Matrizentheorie der Statik, *Ingr.-Arch.*, vol. 25, p. 174, 1957.
50. Argyris, J. H., and S. Kelsey: Structural Analysis by the Matrix Force Method with Applications to Aircraft Wings, "Jahrbuch wissenschaftliche Gesellschaft für Luftfahrt," pp. 78–98, Vieweg-Verlag, Brunswick, Germany, 1956.
51. Argyris, J. H., and S. Kelsey: The Analysis of Fuselages of Arbitrary Cross-section and Taper, *Aircraft Eng.*, vol. 31, p. 62, 1959; vol. 33, p. 34, 1961; and subsequent issues.
52. Livesley, R. K.: Analysis of Large Structural Systems, *Computer J.*, vol. 3, no. 1, 1960.
53. Poppleton, E. D.: Note on the Design of Redundant Structures, *UTIA Tech. Note* 36, July, 1960.
54. Weber, H.: Über das gemeinsame Schwingungsverhalten von Welle und Fundament bei Turbinenanlagen, *VDI-Ber.*, no. 48, pp. 55–62, 1961.
55. Marcus, H.: Die Theorie elastischer Gewebe und ihre Anwendung auf die Berechnung biegsamer Platten, Springer-Verlag, Berlin, 1924.
56. Fox, L.: *Phil. Trans. Roy. Soc. London*, ser. A, vol. 242, 1950.
57. Hrennikoff, A.: Solution of Problems of Elasticity by the Framework Method, *J. Appl. Mech.*, December, 1941.
58. Leckie, F. A.: The Application of Transfer Matrices to Plate Vibration, *Ingr.-Arch.*, vol. 30, 1962.
59. Pestel, E.: Dynamics of Structures by Transfer Matrices, EOARDC [two reports under contracts AF 61 (052)-33, 1959, and AF 61 (052)-302, 1960].
60. Pestel, E., G. Schumpich, and S. Spierig: Berechnung rotierender Scheiben mit Hilfe von Übertragungsmatrizen, *VDI-Ber.*, no. 30, pp. 55–64, 1958.
61. Borgwardt, F.: Die Knickbiegung des mehrfeldrigen geraden Balkens mit feldweise konstanten Feldgrössen, *Abhandl. braunschweig. wiss. Ges.*, vol. 12, pp. 77–94, 1960.
62. Schumpich, G., and S. Spierig: Zur Praxis der Berechnung von räumlichen Stabwerken mit Hilfe von Übertragungsmatrizen, *Abhandl. braunschweig. wiss. Ges.*, vol. 13, pp. 193–213, 1961.
63. Reissner, E.: The Effect of Transverse Shear Deformation on the Bending of Elastic Plates, *J. Appl. Mech.*, vol. 67, pp. A69–A77, 1945.
64. Pestel, E.: Application of the Transfer Matrix Method to Cylindrical Shells, *Intern. J. Mech. Sci.*, vol. 5, 1963 (in press).
65. Rubin, S.: On Transmission Matrices for Vibration and Their Relation to Admittance and Impedance, *J. Appl. Mech.*, 1963 (in press).
66. Pestel, E.: Note on Rectangular Transfer Matrices, *Intern. J. Mech. Sci.*, vol. 5, 1963 (in press).
67. Marguerre, K., and R. Uhrig: Das Uebertragungsverfahren und seine Grenzen, *Z. angew. Math. u. Mech.*, vol. 43, 1963 (in press).
68. Prentice, J. M., and F. A. Leckie: "Mechanical Vibrations: An Introduction to Matrix Methods," Longmans, Green & Co., Ltd., London, 1963.

ADDITIONAL ARTICLES

Transfer Matrices

Bergmann, H., and E. Pestel: Die Anwendung von Übertragungsmatrizen auf die Untersuchung mehrzelliger Kastenträger, *Z. Flugwiss.*, vol. 9, pp. 239–253, 1961.

——— and ———: Die Anwendung von Übertragungsmatrizen auf die Untersuchung von Deltaflügeln, *Z. Flugwiss.*, vol. 10, pp. 73–83, 1962.

Cremer, L., and H. O. Leilich: Zur Theorie der Biegekettenleiter, *Arch. elek. Übertragung*, vol. 7, pp. 261–270, 1953.

Ehrich, F. F.: A Matrix Solution for the Vibration of Non-uniform Disks, *J. Appl. Mech.*, vol. 23, pp. 109–115, 1956.

Falk, S.: Biegen, Knicken und Schwingen des mehrfeldrigen geraden Balkens, *Abhandl. braunschweig. wiss. Ges.*, vol. 7, pp. 74–92, 1955.

———: Die Knickformeln für den Stab mit Teilstücken konstanter Biegesteifigkeit, *Ingr.-Arch.*, vol. 24, pp. 85–91, 1956.

Falk, S.: Die Biegeschwingungen ebener Rahmentragwerke mit unverschieblichen Knoten, *Abhandl. braunschweig. wiss. Ges.*, vol. 9, pp. 1–17, 1957.

———: Die Berechnung von Rahmentragwerken mit Hilfe von Übertragungsmatrizen, *Z. angew. Math. u. Mech.*, vol. 37, pp. 269–270, 1957.

———: Die Berechnung geschlossener Rahmentragwerke nach dem Reduktionsverfahren, *Ingr.-Arch.*, vol. 26, pp. 96–109, 1958.

———: Die Berechnung von Kurbelwellen mit Hilfe von digitalen Rechenautomaten, *VDI-Ber.*, no. 30, pp. 65–69, 1958.

Hasselgruber, H.: Die Berechnung von erzwungenen gedämpften Drehschwingungsketten mit Hilfe von Übertragungsmatrizen, *Forsch. Gebiete Ingenieurw.*, vol. 26, pp. 69–79, 1960.

Jäger, B.: Die Eigenfrequenzen verwundener Schaufeln, *Ingr.-Arch.*, vol. 29, pp. 280–290, 1960.

———: Eigenfrequenzen von Stahltriebwerken, *VDI-Ber.*, no. 48, pp. 47–53, 1961.

Krämer, E.: Dynamik rotierender Wellen bei Berücksichtigung von Unwucht- und Dämpfungskräften, *VDI-Ber.*, no. 30, pp. 49–53, 1958.

Okumura, A.: On a Method for Eigenvalue Problems of Multiply-connected Systems (four reports), *Trans. Japan Soc. Mech. Engrs.*, vol. 17, no. 64, 1951.

———: On a Method for Vibration Problems of Branch-type Systems, *Proc. 2d Japan. Natl. Congr. Appl. Mech.*, 1952.

———: On a Method for Vibration Problems of Ring-type Systems, *Proc. 4th Japan. Natl. Congr. Appl. Mech.*, 1954.

Pestel, E.: Matrix Methods in the Dynamics of Machines and Structures, Lecture Notes, Engineering Extension, UCLA, Los Angeles, 1958.

———: Anwendung von Übertragungsmatrizen auf die Torsion eines Kastenprofils, *Z. angew. Math. u. Mech.*, vol. 38, pp. 465–466, 1958.

——— and W. T. Thomson: Frequenzgangmethode fuer stochastische Vorgaenge, *VDI-Ber.*, no. 66, pp. 25–29, 1962.

Pipes, L. A.: The Matrix Theory of Torsional Oscillations, *Appl. Phys.*, vol. 13, pp. 434–444, 1942.

Prohl, M. A.: A General Method for Calculating Critical Speeds of Flexible Rotors, *Trans. ASME*, vol. 67, pp. A142–A148, 1945.†

———: A Method for Calculating Vibration Frequency and Stress of a Banded Group of Turbine Buckets, Paper 56-A-116, *Trans. ASME*, 1957.†

Schnell, W.: Krafteinleitung in versteifte Zylinderschalen, *Z. Flugwiss.*, vol. 3, pp. 385–399, 1955.

Targoff, W. P.: The Associated Matrices of Bending and Coupled Bending-Torsion Vibrations, *J. Aeronaut. Sci.*, 1947, pp. 579–582.

Thomson, W. T.: Matrix Solution for the *n*-section Column, *J. Aeronaut. Sci.*, vol. 16, pp. 623ff., 1949.

Unger, H.: Matrizenverfahren bei linearen Differentialgleichungsproblemen, *Intern. Colloq. Problem. Rechentechnik*, *Dresden*, 1955, pp. 141–149.

Weaver, F. L., and M. A. Prohl: High-frequency Vibration of Steam-turbine Buckets, Paper 56-A-119, *Trans. ASME*, 1957.†

Woernle, H.: Eine Matrizenmethode für mehrfeldrige Balken, *Stahlbau*, vol. 25, pp. 140–145, 1956.

Zurmühl, R.: Die Berechnung von Biegeschwingungen abgesetzter Wellen mit Zwischenbedingungen mittels Übertragungsmatrizen, *Ingr.-Arch.*, vol. 26, pp. 398-407, 1958.

General Matrix Methods

Archer, J. S.: Stiffness Matrix Analysis of Structures, *Convair–Fort Worth SDG-64 Rept.*, December, 1957.

Argyris, J. H.: Thermal Stress Analysis and Energy Theorems, Aeronautical Research Council, no. 16,489, December, 1953.

† Not in matrix notation.

Argyris, J. H.: On the Analysis of Complex Elastic Structures, *Appl. Mech. Revs.*, vol. 11, no. 7, 1958.

———: Some Further Developments of Matrix Methods of Structural Analysis, I and II, Advisory Group for Aeronautical Research and Development, September, 1959, and July, 1962.

——— and S. Kelsey: The Matrix Force Method of Structural Analysis and Some New Applications, Aeronautical Research Council, R and M no. 3034, February, 1956.

——— and ———: Note on the Theory of Aircraft Structures, *Z. Flugwiss.*, vol. 7, pp. 73–77, 1959.

Benscotter, S. U.: Matrix Analysis of Continuous Beams, *Trans. ASCE*, vol. 112, pp. 1109ff., 1947.

Brock, J. E.: A Matrix Method for Flexibility Analysis of Piping Systems, *Trans. ASME, J. Appl. Mech.*, vol. 74, pp. 501–516, 1952.

———: Matrix Analysis of Flexible Filaments, *Proc. 1st Natl. Congr. Appl. Mech.*, 1953, pp. 285–289.

———: Matrix Analysis of Piping Flexibility, Paper 55-S-5, *J. Appl. Mech.*, 1955.

Clough, R. W.: Matrix Analysis of Beams, *J. Eng. Mech. Div., ASCE*, vol. 84, no. EM 1, 1958.

———: Use of Modern Computers in Structural Analysis, *J. Structural Div., ASCE*, vol. 84, no. ST 3, 1958.

Denke, P. H.: A Matrix Method of Structural Analysis, *Proc. 2d Natl. Congr. Appl. Mech.*, 1954.

———: The Matrix Solution of Certain Nonlinear Problems in Structural Analysis, *J. Aeronaut. Sci.*, vol. 23, no. 3, March, 1956.

Falkenheiner, H.: Le Calcul systématique des charactéristiques elastiques des systèmes hyperstatiques, *Recherche aéronaut.*, no. 17, pp. 17–31, 1950.

Klein, B.: A Simple Method of Matrix Structural Analysis, *J. Aeronaut. Sci.*, vol. 25, 1958.

Kron, G.: Tensorial Analysis of Elastic Structures, *J. Franklin Inst.*, vol. 238, 1944.

Langefors, B.: Analysis of Elastic Structures by Matrix Transformation with Special Regard to Semimonocoque Structures, *J. Aeronaut. Sci.*, vol. 19, pp. 451–458, 1952.

Livesley, R. K.: The Application of an Electronic Digital Computer to Some Problems of Structural Analysis, *Structural Engr.*, vol. 34, pp. 1–12, 1956.

Poppleton, E. D.: Note on the Matrix Analysis of Non-linear Structures, *UTIA Tech. Note* 46, March, 1961.

Przemieniecki, J. S.: Matrix Analysis of Shell Structures with Flexible Frames, *Aeronaut. Quart.*, vol. 9, p. 361, 1958.

Steinbacher, F. R., C. N. Gaylord, and W. K. Rey: Method for Analyzing Indeterminate Structures, Stress above Proportional Limit, *NACA Tech. Note* 2376, June, 1951.

Turner, M. J., R. W. Clough, H. C. Martin, and L. J. Topp: Stiffness and Deflection Analysis of Complex Structures, *J. Aeronaut. Sci.*, vol. 23, pp. 805–824, 1956.

ADDITIONAL TEXTBOOKS

Apart from the textbooks specifically mentioned in the preceding References, the following are recommended for general background reading:

Matrices and Determinants

Collatz, L.: "Eigenwertaufgaben mit technischen Anwendungen," Akademische Verlagsanstalt, Leipzig, 1949. (For advanced readers interested in matrix formulation of Rayleigh-Ritz method, etc.)

Pipes, L. A.: "Applied Mathematics for Engineers and Physicists," 2d ed., chap. 4, McGraw-Hill Book Company, Inc., New York, 1958.

———: "Matrix Methods for Engineering," Prentice-Hall, Inc., Englewood Cliffs, N.J., 1963.

Zurmühl, R.: "Matrizen," 3d ed., Springer-Verlag, Berlin, 1958. (Well illustrated with engineering applications.)

Theory of Vibrations

Crede, C. E.: "Vibration and Shock Isolation," John Wiley & Sons, Inc., New York, 1951.

Gardner, M. F., and J. L. Barnes: "Transients in Linear Systems," John Wiley & Sons, Inc., New York, 1942.

Jacobsen, L. S., and R. S. Ayre: "Engineering Vibrations," McGraw-Hill Book Company, Inc., New York, 1958.

Klotter, K.: "Technische Schwingungslehre," 2 vols., Springer-Verlag, Berlin, 1957, 1960.

Myklestad, N. O.: "Fundamentals of Vibration Analysis," McGraw-Hill Book Company, Inc., New York, 1956.

Prager, W., and K. Hohenemser: "Dynamik der Stabwerke," Springer-Verlag, Berlin, 1933.

Timoshenko, S.: "Vibration Problems in Engineering," 3d ed., D. Van Nostrand Company, Inc., Princeton, N.J., 1955.

Theory of Structures

Argyris, J. H.: "The Elastic Aircraft and Modern Fuselage Analysis," Butterworth & Co. (Publishers) Ltd., London, 1962.

——— and S. Kelsey: "Energy Theorems and Structural Analysis," Butterworth & Co. (Publishers) Ltd., London, 1960.

Hall, A. S., and R. W. Woodhead: "Frame Analysis," John Wiley & Sons, Inc., New York, 1961.

Hoff, N. J.: "The Analysis of Structures," John Wiley & Sons, Inc., New York, 1956.

Kersten, R., and S. Falk: "Das Reduktionsverfahren der Baustatik, Verfahren der Übertragungsmatrizen," Springer-Verlag, Berlin, 1962.

McMinn, S. J.: "Matrices for Structural Analysis," E. & F. N. Spon, Ltd., London, 1962.

Matheson, J. L.: "Hyperstatic Structures," Butterworth & Co. (Publishers) Ltd., London, 1959.

Timoshenko, S. P., and D. H. Young: "Theory of Structures," McGraw-Hill Book Company, Inc., New York, 1945.

ANSWERS TO SELECTED PROBLEMS

1-1. $|\mathbf{A}| = 70$; $|\mathbf{A}| = 5$; $|\mathbf{A}| = \frac{16}{10}$; $|\mathbf{A}| = 1$

1-3. $x_1 = 1$; $x_2 = \dfrac{-1}{2}$; $x_3 = \frac{3}{8}$; $r = 2$

1-4. $r = 2$

1-5. $|\mathbf{D}| = 108$

1-6. $|\mathbf{B}| = 125$

1-7. $\mathbf{D} = \begin{bmatrix} 17 & 35 \\ 35 & 104 \end{bmatrix}$

1-8. $\mathbf{D} = \mathbf{ACB}$

1-12. $\mathbf{A}^{-1} = \begin{bmatrix} 0.4 & 0.1 \\ -0.2 & -0.3 \end{bmatrix}$; $\mathbf{B}^{-1} = \begin{bmatrix} \frac{2}{3} & 1 \\ 1 & 2 \end{bmatrix}$

$$\mathbf{C}^{-1} = \begin{bmatrix} \dfrac{1}{9} & \dfrac{-1}{12} & \dfrac{1}{18} \\[2ex] \dfrac{-5}{18} & \dfrac{5}{24} & \dfrac{13}{36} \\[2ex] \dfrac{-1}{18} & \dfrac{7}{24} & \dfrac{-1}{36} \end{bmatrix}; \quad \mathbf{D}^{-1} = \begin{bmatrix} \dfrac{3}{11} & \dfrac{4}{11} & 0 & 0 & 0 \\[2ex] \dfrac{-2}{11} & \dfrac{1}{11} & 0 & 0 & 0 \\[2ex] 0 & 0 & \dfrac{12}{76} & 0 & \dfrac{-8}{76} \\[2ex] 0 & 0 & \dfrac{-4}{76} & 0 & \dfrac{28}{76} \\[2ex] 0 & 0 & \dfrac{1}{76} & \dfrac{19}{76} & \dfrac{-7}{76} \end{bmatrix}$$

1-15. (*a*) $\mathbf{x} = \left\{\dfrac{-1}{18} \quad \dfrac{-49}{36} \quad \dfrac{1}{36}\right\}$; (*b*) $\mathbf{x} = \left\{\dfrac{-1}{2} \quad \dfrac{7}{4} \quad \dfrac{5}{4}\right\}$

1-17. $\lambda_1 = 1$; $\lambda_2 = 2 + \sqrt{13}$; $\lambda_3 = 2 - \sqrt{13}$

$$\mathbf{x}_1 = \left\{\frac{1}{\sqrt{3}} \quad -\sqrt{\frac{2}{3}} \quad 0\right\}; \quad \mathbf{x}_2 = \left\{\frac{2}{(13 + \sqrt{13})^{\frac{1}{2}}} \quad \frac{\sqrt{2}}{(13 + \sqrt{13})^{\frac{1}{2}}} \quad \frac{(7 + \sqrt{13})^{\frac{1}{2}}}{(13 + \sqrt{13})^{\frac{1}{2}}}\right\}$$

$$\mathbf{x}_3 = \left\{\frac{2}{(13 - \sqrt{13})^{\frac{1}{2}}} \quad \frac{\sqrt{2}}{(13 - \sqrt{13})^{\frac{1}{2}}} \quad \frac{(7 - \sqrt{13})^{\frac{1}{2}}}{(13 - \sqrt{13})^{\frac{1}{2}}}\right\}$$

1-18. $\mathbf{x}_2 = \left\{\frac{-1}{\sqrt{5}} \quad \sqrt{\frac{3}{5}} \quad \frac{1}{\sqrt{5}}\right\}; \ \mathbf{x}_3 = \left\{\frac{-7}{4\sqrt{5}} \quad \frac{-3\sqrt{3}}{4\sqrt{5}} \quad \frac{2}{4\sqrt{5}}\right\}$

1-22. $\mathbf{x} = \{e^t \quad -e^t\}$

1-24. $\mathbf{x} = \left\{e^t(t-1) - \frac{4}{5}e^{6t} \quad e^t(\frac{2}{5} - t) - \frac{e^{6t}}{5}\right\}$

2-1. $x = \frac{W_2}{k}(1 - \cos \omega t) + \sqrt{\frac{2h}{k}}\frac{W_2}{\sqrt{W_1 + W_2}} \sin \omega t$, where $\omega^2 = \frac{k}{m_1 + m_2}$

2-3. $\omega^2 = \frac{k}{m} - \frac{g}{l}$

2-5. $\omega^2 = \frac{4T}{lm}$

2-6. $A = \frac{T}{kr^2 - Wr \sin \alpha - \Omega_1^2 r^2(m/2 + W/g)}$

2-7. $x = \frac{P}{k}\frac{\Omega}{\omega}\frac{1}{1 - (\Omega/\omega)^2}\left[\sin \omega\left(t - \frac{2\pi}{\Omega}\right) - \sin \omega t\right]$ for $t \geq \frac{2\pi}{\Omega}$

2-9. $\omega_{1,2}^2 = \frac{1}{4}\left[3\frac{g}{l} + \frac{k}{m} \mp \sqrt{\left(3\frac{g}{l}\right)^2 - 2\frac{k}{m}\frac{g}{l} + \left(\frac{k}{m}\right)^2}\right]$

For $\frac{k}{m}\frac{l}{g} = 2$, $\omega_1^2 = \frac{1}{2}\frac{g}{l}$; $\omega_2^2 = 2\frac{g}{l}$; $\left(\frac{\phi l}{x}\right)_1 = 1$; $\left(\frac{\phi l}{x}\right)_2 = -2$

2-11. $\omega_{1,2}^2 = \frac{(5 \mp \sqrt{17})3EJ}{2ml^3}$; $\mathbf{x}_1 = \left\{1 \quad \frac{2}{\sqrt{17} - 3}\right\}$; $\mathbf{x}_2 = \left\{1 \quad \frac{-2}{\sqrt{17} + 3}\right\}$

2-12. $\omega_{1,2}^2 = \frac{3T}{mL}(2 \mp 1)$

2-13. $\omega_{1,2}^2 = \frac{2}{7}\frac{k}{m}(3 \mp \sqrt{2})$; $\left(\frac{X_1}{X_2}\right)_1 = \frac{1}{\sqrt{2}}$; $\left(\frac{X_1}{X_2}\right)_2 = -\frac{1}{\sqrt{2}}$

2-16. $\Omega^2 = \frac{k}{2m}$; $X_2 = \frac{-F}{k}$

2-17. $X = \frac{F}{2k - \Omega^2\left[2m - \frac{m(k - \Omega^2 m/2)}{\Omega^2 3m/2 - k}\right]}$

3-1. See Secs. C-3*d* and C-3*f*.

3-2. See Sec. C-3*f*.

3-3. $\omega^2 = \frac{k_1 k_2}{m(k_1 + k_2)}$

3-4. $\omega_{1,2}^2 = \frac{8EJ}{mr^2 l}\left[1 + \frac{3}{4}\left(\frac{r}{l}\right)^2 \mp \sqrt{1 + \frac{3}{4}\left(\frac{r}{l}\right)^2 + \left(\frac{3}{4}\right)^2\left(\frac{r}{l}\right)^4}\right]$

3-6. $\omega^2 = \frac{k_w k_\varphi}{m(k_\varphi + k_w l^2 + k_w k_\varphi l^3/3EJ)}$

3-9. (*a*) $\omega_{1,2}^2 = \dfrac{k}{m}\dfrac{3 \mp \sqrt{5}}{3}$; (*b*) $\omega^2 = \dfrac{10}{3}\dfrac{k}{m}$; (*c*) $\omega_1^2 = 0$; $\omega_2^2 = \dfrac{7}{6}\dfrac{k}{m}$

3-11. (*a*) $\omega^2 = \dfrac{24EJ}{ml^3}$; (*b*) $\omega^2 = \dfrac{96EJ}{7ml^3}$; (*c*) $\omega^2 = \dfrac{EJ}{ml^3}\dfrac{72 + 48kl^3/EJ}{15 + 2kl^3/EJ}$

3-12. $\mathbf{x}_1 = \left\{1 \quad \dfrac{1+\sqrt{5}}{2}\right\}$; $\mathbf{x}_2 = \left\{1 \quad \dfrac{1-\sqrt{5}}{2}\right\}$

3-14. $x_1 = \dfrac{g}{2}\sin\alpha\left[t^2 - \dfrac{4}{3}\dfrac{m}{k}\left(\cos\sqrt{\dfrac{3k}{m}}\,t - 1\right)\right]$; $x_2 = \dfrac{g}{2}\sin\alpha\left[t^2 + \dfrac{2}{3}\dfrac{m}{k}\left(\cos\sqrt{\dfrac{3k}{m}}\,t - 1\right)\right]$

3-16. Approximate values: $f_1 = 16$ cps, $f_2 = 50$ cps, $f_3 = 86$ cps

3-17. See Prob. 3-12.

3-18. $X_1 = \dfrac{X_2}{2} + \dfrac{F}{2k}$; $X_2 = \dfrac{F}{k}\dfrac{1}{1 - 2m\Omega^2/k}$

$X_1 \to \infty$ for $\Omega = \sqrt{\dfrac{k}{2m}}$; $X_1 \to 0$ for $\Omega = \sqrt{\dfrac{k}{m}}$

3-20. $$w_{\max} = M\frac{24EJ/(lmr)^2}{\Omega^4 - \Omega^2(16EJ/lmr^2)[1 + \frac{3}{4}(r/l)^2] + 48(EJ/l^2mr)^2}$$

$$\psi_{\max} = M\frac{-(12EJ/l^3 - m\Omega^2)(2/mr)^2}{\Omega^4 - \Omega^2(16EJ/lmr^2)[1 + \frac{3}{4}(r/l)^2] + 48(EJ/l^2mr)^2}$$

3-21. $X_1 = \delta\left(1 - \dfrac{k}{k_1}\right)$; $X_2 = \dfrac{X_1 k_2}{k_2 - m_2\Omega^2}$

$$F_0 = \delta k;\ k = \frac{\Omega^2[m_1 m_2\Omega^2/k_2 - (m_1 + m_2)]}{1 - \Omega^2[(m_1 + m_2)/k_1 + m_2(1 - m_1\Omega^2/k_1)/k_2]}$$

3-22. (*a*) $V_0^R = \dfrac{ql}{6}$; $V_1^L = \dfrac{-5ql}{6}$; $V_2^L = V_1^R = \dfrac{-ql}{3}$

$M_0^R = M_2^L = 0$; $M_1^L = \dfrac{-ql^2}{3}$; $M_1^R = \dfrac{2ql^2}{3}$

(*b*) $V_0^R = \dfrac{7ql}{54}$; $V_1^L = \dfrac{-47ql}{54}$; $V_2^L = V_1^R = \dfrac{-17ql}{54}$

$M_0^R = M_2^L = 0$; $M_1^L = \dfrac{-10ql^2}{27}$; $M_1^R = \dfrac{17ql^2}{27}$

3-24. $\phi_0 = 0.941 \times 10^{-6}T_1 \sin 300t$; $\phi_1 = 0.377 \times 10^{-6}T_1 \sin 300t$

$\phi_2 = 0.125 \times 10^{-6}T_1 \sin 300t$; $\phi_3 = -0.023 \times 10^{-6}T_1 \sin 300t$

$\phi_4 = -0.232 \times 10^{-6}T_1 \sin 300t$

3-26. $\psi_{0,\max} = \dfrac{0.768Pl^2}{EJ}$

3-27. (*a*) $p_1^2 = 0.235$; $p_2^2 = 4.265$, where $p^2 = m\omega^2/k$

(*b*) $\mathbf{x}_1 = \{1 \quad 0.53\}$; $\mathbf{x}_2 = \{1 \quad -7.53\}$

3-28. $\begin{bmatrix} 1 & 0 \\ -m\left(\omega^2 + \dfrac{g}{l}\right) & 1 \end{bmatrix}$

3-30. (*a*) $\begin{bmatrix} 1 & 0 \\ -\omega^2\left(M + \dfrac{mk}{k - m\omega^2}\right) & 1 \end{bmatrix}$; (*b*) $\begin{bmatrix} 1 & 0 \\ -\omega^2\left[M + \dfrac{m(k - \omega^2 I/r^2)}{k - \omega^2(m + I/r^2)}\right] & 1 \end{bmatrix}$

(*c*) $\begin{bmatrix} 1 & 0 \\ -\omega^2\left(M + m\dfrac{k - m\omega^2 \sin^2\alpha}{k - m\omega^2}\right) & 1 \end{bmatrix}$

3-32. $X = \dfrac{\delta}{2}\dfrac{1}{1 - m\Omega^2/2k}$

3-33. $\phi_2 = \Phi_1\dfrac{2(1 - p^2)\cos\Omega t}{2 - 4p^2 + p^4}$; $\phi_3 = \Phi_1\dfrac{2\cos\Omega t}{2 - 4p^2 + p^4}$

$T = k\Phi_1\dfrac{4(1 - 3p^2 + p^4)}{2 - 4p^2 + p^4}$; $p^2 = \dfrac{I\Omega^2}{k}$

3-34. $V_0 = \dfrac{13ql}{16}$; $V_1 = \dfrac{-3ql}{16}$; $V_2 = \dfrac{-3ql}{16}$

$M_0 = \dfrac{-11ql^2}{48}$; $M_2 = \dfrac{-5ql^2}{48}$

$M_{\max} = \dfrac{155}{1{,}536}ql^2$ at $\dfrac{13}{16}l$ from left support

$M = 0$ at $\dfrac{(13 - \sqrt{155/3})l}{16}$ from left support and at $\dfrac{5l}{9}$ from right support

3-36. $\omega = \sqrt{\dfrac{k}{m}}$

3-37. $p_1^2 = 0$; $p_2^2 = \dfrac{4 - \sqrt{7}}{3}$; $p_3^2 = 4$; $p_4^2 = \dfrac{4 + \sqrt{7}}{3}$, where $p^2 = \dfrac{I\omega^2}{k}$

$\phi_1 = (1 - p^2)\phi_0$; $\phi_2 = (1 - 3p^2 + p^4)\phi_0$; $\phi_3 = (1 - 4.5p^2 + 3p^4 - 0.5p^6)\phi_0$

3-38. $p_1^2 = 0$; $p_2^2 = 1$; $p_3^2 = 1.9$, where $p^2 = \dfrac{I\omega^2}{k}$

$\phi_{11} = (1 - p^2)\phi_0$; $\phi_{21} = (2 - 4.75p^2 + 2.5p^4)\phi_0$

4-1. $\nu^2 = \dfrac{k + 3EJ/l^3}{m} - \left(\dfrac{c}{2m}\right)^2$; $\delta = \dfrac{c}{2m}$

4-2. $\dfrac{k_2(k_1 + jc_1\omega)}{k_1 + k_2 + jc_1\omega}$

4-3. $\dfrac{k_\varphi/h^2 + 3EJ/h^3 + k_w + j\omega c}{(k_\varphi/h^2 + 3EJ/h^3)(k_w + j\omega c)}$

4-4. $\nu^2 = \dfrac{10k}{3m} - \left(\dfrac{5c}{3m}\right)^2$; $\delta = \dfrac{5c}{3m}$

4-5. $\zeta = \dfrac{c}{2\sqrt{mk}} = \dfrac{c}{2\sqrt{96mEJ/7l^3}}$

4-6. $\nu^2 = \dfrac{3k}{2m} - \left(\dfrac{3c}{4m}\right)^2$

4-9. (*a*) $$\begin{bmatrix} 1 & 0 \\ p^2\left[M + \dfrac{m(k + cp)}{k + cp + mp^2}\right] & 1 \end{bmatrix}$$

(*b*) $$\begin{bmatrix} 1 & 0 \\ p^2\left[M + \dfrac{m(k + cp + Ip^2/r^2)}{k + cp + (m + I/r^2)p^2}\right] & 1 \end{bmatrix}$$

4-11. $\omega^2 = \dfrac{24EJ}{ml^3}$

$$x = \frac{P \sin(\Omega t - \alpha)}{[(m\Omega^2 - 24EJ/l^3)^2 + c^2\Omega^2]^{\frac{1}{2}}}; \ \alpha = \tan^{-1}\frac{2\zeta\Omega/\omega}{1 - (\Omega/\omega)^2}$$

$$\zeta = \frac{c}{2}\sqrt{\frac{l^3}{24EJm}}; \ E = \frac{\pi c\Omega P^2}{(m\Omega^2 - 24EJ/l^3)^2 + c^2\Omega^2}$$

4-13. $\bar{x} = \dfrac{P(1 - g/l\Omega^2 - jc/m_2\Omega)}{(k_1 + k_2 - m_1\Omega^2)(1 - g/l\Omega^2 - jc/m_2\Omega) + m_2 g/l + jc\Omega}$

For $\Omega^2 = k/m = g/l$, $m_2 = m_1 = m$, $k_1 = k_2 = k/2$, and $c = \sqrt{km}$, we have

$$\bar{x} = -\frac{P}{2k}(1 + j)$$

4-15. $$\left[\begin{array}{c|c|c} 1 & 0 & 0 \\ \hline -m_1\Omega^2 + \dfrac{m_2 g/l + jc\Omega}{1 - g/l\Omega^2 - jc/m_2\Omega} & 1 & -P \\ \hline 0 & 0 & 1 \end{array}\right] \left[\begin{array}{cc|cc|c} 1 & 0 & 0 & 0 & 0 \\ A^r & 1 & -A^i & 0 & -P \\ \hline 0 & 0 & 1 & 0 & 0 \\ A^i & 0 & A^r & 1 & -P^i \\ \hline 0 & 0 & 0 & 0 & 1 \end{array}\right]$$

where $A^r = \dfrac{[-m_1\Omega^2 + (m_1 + m_2)g/l](1 - g/l\Omega^2) - c^2(1 + m_1/m_2)/m_2}{(1 - g/l\Omega^2)^2 + (c/m_2\Omega)^2}$

$A^i = \dfrac{[-m_1\Omega^2 + (m_1 + m_2)g/l]c/m_2\Omega + c\Omega(1 + m_1/m_2)(1 - g/l\Omega^2)}{(1 - g/l\Omega^2)^2 + (c/m_2\Omega)^2}$

4-17. $x_1^r = 0.40 \times 10^{-5}$ ft; $x_2^r = -5.27 \times 10^{-5}$ ft

$x_1^i = 0.017 \times 10^{-5}$ ft; $x_2^i = -0.072 \times 10^{-5}$ ft

4-19. Displacement of mass $2m$ is described by

$$x^r = -1.20 \times 10^{-3}P \qquad x^i = -4.01 \times 10^{-5}P$$

4-21. The displacement and slope at mass m are

$$\left\{\frac{-w}{l} \quad \psi \quad \frac{v}{l} \quad \vartheta\right\} = 10^{-5}\{-0.0160 \quad -0.0189 \quad -0.120 \quad 0.113\}$$

5-17.
$$\left[\begin{array}{ccccc|c} 1 & l & \dfrac{l^2}{2EJ} & \dfrac{l^3}{6EJ} & & 0 \\ 0 & 1 & \dfrac{l}{EJ} & \dfrac{l^2}{2EJ} & & 0 \\ 0 & 0 & 1 & l & & 0 \\ m\Omega^2 & ml\Omega^2 & \dfrac{ml^2\Omega^2}{2EJ} & 1+\dfrac{ml^3\Omega^2}{6EJ} & & -P \\ \hline 0 & 0 & 0 & 0 & & 1 \end{array}\right]$$

5-20. $M_{x0} = -\left(\dfrac{\pi}{2} - \dfrac{4}{\pi}\right)9R^2;\ M_{z0} = 9R^2;\ V_{y0} = \dfrac{\pi}{2}9R$

6-1. $$\mathbf{S} = \begin{bmatrix} \dfrac{6EJ}{l^2}\sin\alpha & -\dfrac{6EJ}{l^2}\cos\alpha & \dfrac{4EJ}{l} \\ \left(\dfrac{12EJ}{l^3} - \dfrac{EA}{l}\right)\sin\alpha\cos\alpha & -\dfrac{12EJ}{l^3}\cos^2\alpha - \dfrac{EA}{l}\sin^2\alpha & \dfrac{6EJ}{l^2}\cos\alpha \\ \dfrac{12EJ}{l^3}\sin^2\alpha + \dfrac{EA}{l}\cos^2\alpha & -\left(\dfrac{12EJ}{l^3} - \dfrac{EA}{l}\right)\sin\alpha\cos\alpha & \dfrac{6EJ}{l^2}\sin\alpha \end{bmatrix}$$

6-2. $$\begin{bmatrix} \dfrac{-2}{3} & 0 \\ \omega^2\left[\frac{2}{3}I_3 + \frac{3}{2}\left(I_1 + \dfrac{I_2}{1-\omega^2 I_2/k_2}\right)\right] & \dfrac{-3}{2} \end{bmatrix}$$

6-3. $\mathbf{P}_1 = \begin{bmatrix} 1 & 0 \\ \dfrac{k(1-p^2)}{2-p^2} & 1 \end{bmatrix};\ p_1^2 = \dfrac{5-\sqrt{5}}{2};\ p_2^2 = \dfrac{5+\sqrt{5}}{2}$

Main system: $\mathbf{x}_1 = \{0 \quad 1 \quad 0\}$; $\mathbf{x}_2 = \{0 \quad 1 \quad 0\}$
Branch: $\hat{\mathbf{x}}_1 = \{0 \quad 1.618 \quad 1\}$; $\hat{\mathbf{x}}_2 = \{0 \quad -0.618 \quad 1\}$

Note that for $p^2 = 2$, we have $\mathbf{P}_1 = \begin{bmatrix} 1 & 0 \\ \infty & 1 \end{bmatrix}$. $p^2 = 2$ corresponds to the natural frequency of the branch when ends 3 and 1 are fixed; therefore the branch acts like a rigid support when the main branch is excited with this frequency.

6-4. $\Omega_1^2 = \dfrac{k_2}{I_2};\ \Omega_{2,3}^2 = \dfrac{1}{2}\left(\dfrac{k_3+k_4}{I_4} + \dfrac{k_4}{I_5}\right) \mp \sqrt{\dfrac{1}{4}\left[\left(\dfrac{k_3+k_4}{I_4}\right)^2 + \left(\dfrac{k_4}{I_5}\right)^2\right] + \dfrac{1}{2}\dfrac{k_4(k_4-k_3)}{I_4 I_5}}$

6-6. (*a*) $\dfrac{\sin\beta}{\beta} = 0$, with $\beta = \omega l\sqrt{\dfrac{\mu}{EA}}$

(*b*) $\cosh\lambda\cos\lambda = 1$, with $\lambda = \dfrac{\mu\omega^2 l^4}{EJ}$

6-8. $$\mathbf{S} = \begin{bmatrix} 0 & 0 & 0 \\ 0 & \dfrac{-EA}{l} & 0 \\ 0 & 0 & 0 \end{bmatrix}$$

6-9. $\mathbf{S} = \begin{bmatrix} 0 & 0 & \frac{EJ}{l} \\ 0 & \frac{-EA}{l} & 0 \\ 0 & 0 & 0 \end{bmatrix}$

6-10. $\omega^2 = \frac{12}{7}\frac{EJ}{ml^3}$

6-11. $\omega^2 = \frac{3}{2}\frac{EJ}{ml^3}$

6-12. $w = -1.3158\frac{Ml^2}{EJ}\sin\Omega t$, for $\Omega = 0.9\omega$; $w = 1.1905\frac{Ml^2}{EJ}\sin\Omega t$, for $\Omega = 1.1\omega$

6-14. $M_0 = \frac{Pl}{12}$; $M_1 = \frac{-Pl}{6}$; $M_2 = \frac{13Pl}{48}$; $M_3 = \frac{-7Pl}{24}$

$V_0^R = V_1^L = \frac{-P}{4}$; $V_1^R = V_2^L = \frac{7P}{16}$; $V_2^R = V_3^L = \frac{-9P}{16}$

6-15. $M_0 = \frac{-9Pl}{40}$; $M_1 = \frac{3Pl}{20}$; $M_2 = \frac{3Pl}{160}$; $M_3 = \frac{-9Pl}{80}$

$V_0^R = V_1^L = \frac{3P}{8}$; $V_1^R = V_2^L = \frac{-21P}{160}$; $V_2^R = V_3^L = \frac{-21P}{160}$

6-16. (*a*) $\begin{bmatrix} \psi \\ M \end{bmatrix}_i = \begin{bmatrix} \frac{1}{l} & \frac{l^2}{3EJ} \\ 0 & l \end{bmatrix} \cdot \begin{bmatrix} -w \\ V \end{bmatrix}_{i-1}$; (*b*) $M_n = 0 = \begin{bmatrix} \frac{-6EJ}{l} & -2 \end{bmatrix} \cdot \begin{bmatrix} \psi \\ M \end{bmatrix}_{n-1}$

(*c*) $\begin{bmatrix} \psi \\ M \end{bmatrix}_i = \begin{bmatrix} -2 & \frac{-l}{2EJ} \\ \frac{-6EJ}{l} & -2 \end{bmatrix} \cdot \begin{bmatrix} \psi \\ M \end{bmatrix}_{i-1}$

6-17. $(\beta^4 c_3^2 - c_1^2)(c_3c_1 - c_2^2) + (c_3c_0 - c_2c_1)^2 = 0$

6-19. $\beta^4(c_1^2 - \beta^4 c_3^2)(c_2^2 - c_1c_3) - (\beta^4 c_3c_2 - c_0c_1)^2 = 0$

6-21. $k_{\text{II}} = \frac{6p^2 - 17.5p^4 + 10p^6 - 1.5p^8}{1 - 4.5p^2 + 3p^4 - 0.5p^6}$; $k_{\text{III}} = \frac{-19p^2 + 29p^4 - 10p^6}{2 - 4.75p^2 + 2.5p^4}$

$$k = k_{\text{II}}\left(\frac{r_{32}}{r_{31}}\right)^2 + k_{\text{III}}\left(\frac{r_{23}}{r_{21}}\right)^2$$

7-1. $\omega^2 = \frac{12}{7}\frac{EJ}{ml^3}$

7-3. 38 cps, or 2,280 rpm
7-4. 37 cps, or 2,220 rpm
7-5. See Example 3-7.
7-8. In your choice of numerical values for ω^2 consider that the exact values for the two eigenfrequencies are found from

$$\frac{\omega^2 ml^3}{EJ} = \frac{451}{1{,}016} \mp \sqrt{\left(\frac{451}{1{,}016}\right)^2 - \frac{13}{508}}$$

8-1. $\mathbf{M} = I\begin{bmatrix} 1 & 0 & 0 \\ 0 & 2 & 0 \\ 0 & 0 & 1 \end{bmatrix}$; $\mathbf{K} = k\begin{bmatrix} 2 & -1 & 0 \\ -1 & 5 & 2 \\ 0 & 2 & 1 \end{bmatrix}$

8-4. $\mathbf{F} = \dfrac{l^3}{9EJ}\begin{bmatrix} 4 & \frac{7}{2} \\ \frac{7}{2} & 4 \end{bmatrix}$; $\mathbf{M} = m\begin{bmatrix} 1 & 0 \\ 0 & 2 \end{bmatrix}$

8-5. $\boldsymbol{\omega}^2 = \dfrac{k}{m}\begin{bmatrix} \dfrac{3-\sqrt{5}}{3} & 0 \\ 0 & \dfrac{3+\sqrt{5}}{3} \end{bmatrix}$; $\boldsymbol{\Phi} = \begin{bmatrix} \dfrac{2}{\sqrt{3(5+\sqrt{5})}} & \dfrac{2}{\sqrt{3(5-\sqrt{5})}} \\ \dfrac{1+\sqrt{5}}{\sqrt{3(5+\sqrt{5})}} & \dfrac{1-\sqrt{5}}{\sqrt{3(5-\sqrt{5})}} \end{bmatrix}$

8-7. $\boldsymbol{\Phi} = \begin{bmatrix} \dfrac{1}{\sqrt{3}} & \dfrac{1}{\sqrt{2}} & \dfrac{1}{\sqrt{6}} \\ \dfrac{1}{\sqrt{3}} & 0 & \dfrac{-2}{\sqrt{6}} \\ \dfrac{1}{\sqrt{3}} & \dfrac{-1}{\sqrt{2}} & \dfrac{1}{\sqrt{6}} \end{bmatrix}$; $\boldsymbol{\omega}^2 = \dfrac{k}{m}\begin{bmatrix} 0 & 0 & 0 \\ 0 & 1 & 0 \\ 0 & 0 & 3 \end{bmatrix}$

8-9. $\mathbf{x}(t) = \dfrac{mg}{k}\begin{bmatrix} \dfrac{5}{3} - \dfrac{3}{2}\cos\omega_1 t - \dfrac{1}{6}\cos\omega_2 t + \dfrac{kt^2}{2m} \\ \dfrac{-1}{3} + \dfrac{1}{3}\cos\omega_2 t + \dfrac{kt^2}{2m} \\ \dfrac{-4}{3} + \dfrac{3}{2}\cos\omega_1 t - \dfrac{1}{6}\cos\omega_2 t + \dfrac{kt^2}{2m} \end{bmatrix}$

The displacements are measured from the positions of static equilibrium: $\omega_1^2 = k/m$; $\omega_2^2 = 3k/m$.

8-11. $\mathbf{x}(t) = \alpha\begin{bmatrix} \dfrac{3+\sqrt{5}}{5+\sqrt{5}}\left(t - \dfrac{\sin\omega_1 t}{\omega_1}\right) + \dfrac{3-\sqrt{5}}{5-\sqrt{5}}\left(t - \dfrac{\sin\omega_2 t}{\omega_2}\right) \\ \dfrac{3+\sqrt{5}}{2\sqrt{5}}\left(t - \dfrac{\sin\omega_1 t}{\omega_1}\right) - \dfrac{3-\sqrt{5}}{2\sqrt{5}}\left(t - \dfrac{\sin\omega_2 t}{\omega_2}\right) \end{bmatrix}$

$$\omega_1^2 = \frac{k}{m}\,\frac{3-\sqrt{5}}{2}; \quad \omega_2^2 = \frac{k}{m}\,\frac{3+\sqrt{5}}{2}$$

8-13. $\mathbf{x}^{\mathrm{r}} = \dfrac{Pl^3}{EJ}\begin{bmatrix} 0.158 \\ 0.213 \end{bmatrix}$; $\mathbf{x}^{\mathrm{i}} = -\dfrac{Pl^3}{EJ}\begin{bmatrix} 0.00200 \\ 0.00272 \end{bmatrix}$

8-14. $\mathbf{x}^{\mathrm{r}} = -\dfrac{P}{k}\begin{bmatrix} 0.477 \\ 0.504 \end{bmatrix}$; $\mathbf{x}^{\mathrm{i}} = \dfrac{P}{k}\begin{bmatrix} 0.0423 \\ -0.0477 \end{bmatrix}$

8-15. $\mathbf{C} = c\begin{bmatrix} 2 & -1 \\ -1 & 1 \end{bmatrix}$

8-17. $\mathbf{C} = \begin{bmatrix} c_1 & -c_1 & 0 \\ -c_1 & c_1 + c_2 & -c_2 \\ 0 & -c_2 & c_2 \end{bmatrix}$

9-1. $\dfrac{5Wl^3}{48EJ}$

9-2. $\dfrac{5Wl^3}{384EJ}$

9-3. $\dfrac{3W}{8}; \dfrac{13W}{16}; \dfrac{-3W}{16}$

9-4. $\dfrac{P}{2}; \dfrac{P}{2} - \dfrac{W}{3}; \dfrac{4W}{3} - P$

9-5.

$$\mathbf{B}_0 = \begin{array}{c} \\ \left[\begin{array}{ccc} P_1 & P_2 & P_3 \\ \hline 1 & 2 & 3 \\ 0 & 1 & 2 \\ 0 & 0 & 1 \\ 0 & 0 & 0 \\ 0 & 0 & 0 \\ 0 & 0 & -1 \\ 0 & -1 & -2 \\ -\sqrt{2} & -\sqrt{2} & -\sqrt{2} \\ 0 & 0 & 0 \\ 0 & 1 & 1 \\ 0 & -\sqrt{2} & -\sqrt{2} \\ 0 & 0 & 0 \\ 0 & 0 & 1 \\ 0 & 0 & -\sqrt{2} \end{array}\right] \end{array} \qquad \mathbf{B}_1 = \left[\begin{array}{cc|c} X_1 & X_2 & \\ \hline \frac{-1}{\sqrt{2}} & 0 & 01 \\ 0 & \frac{-1}{\sqrt{2}} & 12 \\ 0 & 0 & 23 \\ 0 & 0 & 34 \\ 0 & 0 & 45 \\ 0 & \frac{-1}{\sqrt{2}} & 56 \\ \frac{-1}{\sqrt{2}} & 0 & 67 \\ 1 & 0 & 17 \\ 1 & 0 & 06 \\ \frac{-1}{\sqrt{2}} & \frac{-1}{\sqrt{2}} & 16 \\ 0 & 1 & 62 \\ 0 & 1 & 15 \\ 0 & \frac{-1}{\sqrt{2}} & 25 \\ 0 & 0 & 35 \end{array}\right]$$

$$\mathbf{F}_v = \frac{l}{EA}\,\text{diag}\,[1 \;\; 1 \;\; 1 \;\; 1 \;\; 1 \;\; 1 \;\; 1 \;\; \sqrt{2} \;\; \sqrt{2} \;\; 1 \;\; \sqrt{2} \;\; \sqrt{2} \;\; 1 \;\; \sqrt{2}]$$

9-8. $\mathbf{F}_d = \dfrac{l^3}{162EJ}\begin{bmatrix} 22 & 23 \\ 23 & 40 \end{bmatrix}$

9-10. $p_{1,2}^2 = \dfrac{31 \mp \sqrt{610}}{351}$; $p^2 = \dfrac{m\omega^2 l^3}{162EJ}$

9-13. $\mathbf{d} = \{\frac{1}{6} \quad \frac{1}{3}\}\dfrac{l^2\alpha\theta}{h}$. Reaction at right-hand support is $X = \dfrac{\theta\alpha EJ}{2hl}$.

9-18. $$\mathbf{F}_d = \frac{l}{4EA} \times \begin{bmatrix} 4+4\sqrt{2} & 2 & 2+4\sqrt{2} & -2 & 2 \\ 2 & 5-\sqrt{2} & 3-\sqrt{2} & 1-\sqrt{2} & 1-\sqrt{2} \\ 2+4\sqrt{2} & 3-\sqrt{2} & 5+3\sqrt{2} & -1-\sqrt{2} & 3-\sqrt{2} \\ -2 & 1-\sqrt{2} & -1-\sqrt{2} & 5-\sqrt{2} & 1-\sqrt{2} \\ 2 & 1-\sqrt{2} & 3-\sqrt{2} & 1-\sqrt{2} & 5-\sqrt{2} \end{bmatrix}$$

$$\mathbf{B} = \tfrac{1}{4} \times \begin{bmatrix} 2 & 5-\sqrt{2} & 3-\sqrt{2} & 1-\sqrt{2} & 1-\sqrt{2} \\ -2 & 1-\sqrt{2} & 3-\sqrt{2} & 1-\sqrt{2} & 1-\sqrt{2} \\ -2 & 1-\sqrt{2} & -1-\sqrt{2} & 5-\sqrt{2} & 1-\sqrt{2} \\ 2 & 1-\sqrt{2} & 3-\sqrt{2} & 1-\sqrt{2} & 5-\sqrt{2} \\ 2\sqrt{2} & 2-\sqrt{2} & 2+\sqrt{2} & 2-\sqrt{2} & 2-\sqrt{2} \\ -2\sqrt{2} & 2-\sqrt{2} & 2-3\sqrt{2} & 2-\sqrt{2} & 2-\sqrt{2} \end{bmatrix}$$

$$p_4 = -(\sqrt{2}-1)\frac{EAh_4}{4l}\{1 \quad 1 \quad 1 \quad 1 \quad -\sqrt{2} \quad -\sqrt{2}\}$$

$$\mathbf{F}_d^* = \frac{l}{23EA} \times \begin{bmatrix} 18+22\sqrt{2} & 10+2\sqrt{2} & 5+24\sqrt{2} & -13+2\sqrt{2} & 0 \\ 10+2\sqrt{2} & 26-4\sqrt{2} & 13-2\sqrt{2} & 3-4\sqrt{2} & 0 \\ 5+24\sqrt{2} & 13-2\sqrt{2} & 18+22\sqrt{2} & -10-2\sqrt{2} & 0 \\ -13+2\sqrt{2} & 3-4\sqrt{2} & -10-2\sqrt{2} & 26-4\sqrt{2} & 0 \\ 0 & 0 & 0 & 0 & 0 \end{bmatrix}$$

10-2. Using $\mathbf{d} = \{u_2 \quad w_2 \quad \psi_2 \quad u_3\}$ and $\mathbf{v} = \{u_A^R \quad \psi_A^R \quad w_A^R \quad \psi_B^L \quad u_B^R\}$, we obtain

$$\mathbf{A} = \begin{bmatrix} \frac{1}{\sqrt{2}} & \frac{-1}{\sqrt{2}} & 0 & 0 \\ 0 & 0 & 1 & 0 \\ \frac{1}{\sqrt{2}} & \frac{1}{\sqrt{2}} & 0 & 0 \\ 0 & \frac{-1}{l} & 1 & 0 \\ -1 & 0 & 0 & 1 \end{bmatrix} \qquad \mathbf{K}_p = \begin{bmatrix} \frac{EA}{l} & 0 & 0 & 0 & 0 \\ 0 & \frac{4EJ}{l} & \frac{6EJ}{l^2} & 0 & 0 \\ 0 & \frac{6EJ}{l^2} & \frac{12EJ}{l^3} & 0 & 0 \\ 0 & 0 & 0 & \frac{3EJ}{l} & 0 \\ 0 & 0 & 0 & 0 & \frac{EA}{l} \end{bmatrix}$$

10-3. $\mathbf{d} = \{w_1 \quad \psi_1 \quad w_2 \quad \psi_2\}$; $\mathbf{v} = \{\psi_A^R \quad w_A^R \quad u_B^R \quad \psi_C^R \quad w_C^R \quad u_D^R\}$

$$\mathbf{A} = \begin{bmatrix} 0 & 1 & 0 & 0 \\ 1 & 0 & 0 & 0 \\ -1 & 0 & 0 & 0 \\ 0 & -1 & 0 & 1 \\ -1 & l & 1 & 0 \\ 0 & 0 & -1 & 0 \end{bmatrix} \qquad \mathbf{K}_p = \begin{bmatrix} \frac{4EJ}{l} & \frac{6EJ}{l^2} & 0 & 0 & 0 & 0 \\ \frac{6EJ}{l^2} & \frac{12EJ}{l^3} & 0 & 0 & 0 & 0 \\ 0 & 0 & k & 0 & 0 & 0 \\ 0 & 0 & 0 & \frac{4EJ}{l} & \frac{6EJ}{l^2} & 0 \\ 0 & 0 & 0 & \frac{6EJ}{l^2} & \frac{12EJ}{l^3} & 0 \\ 0 & 0 & 0 & 0 & 0 & k \end{bmatrix}$$

10-4.

$$\mathbf{A} = \begin{array}{c} \begin{matrix} w_1 & w_2 & w_3 & w_4 & u_1 & u_2 & u_3 & u_4 \end{matrix} \quad u^R \\ \left[\begin{matrix} 0 & 0 & 0 & 0 & 1 & -1 & 0 & 0 \\ 0 & 0 & 0 & 0 & 0 & 1 & 0 & 0 \\ 0 & 0 & 0 & 0 & 0 & 0 & 1 & -1 \\ 0 & 0 & 0 & 0 & 0 & 0 & 0 & 1 \\ 1 & 0 & -1 & 0 & 0 & 0 & 0 & 0 \\ 0 & 1 & 0 & -1 & 0 & 0 & 0 & 0 \\ \frac{1}{\sqrt{2}} & 0 & 0 & \frac{-1}{\sqrt{2}} & \frac{1}{\sqrt{2}} & 0 & 0 & \frac{-1}{\sqrt{2}} \\ 0 & \frac{1}{\sqrt{2}} & 0 & 0 & 0 & \frac{1}{\sqrt{2}} & 0 & 0 \\ 0 & \frac{1}{\sqrt{2}} & \frac{-1}{\sqrt{2}} & 0 & 0 & \frac{-1}{\sqrt{2}} & \frac{1}{\sqrt{2}} & 0 \\ 0 & 0 & 0 & \frac{-1}{\sqrt{2}} & 0 & 0 & 0 & \frac{1}{\sqrt{2}} \end{matrix}\right] \begin{matrix} 1 \\ 2 \\ 3 \\ 4 \\ 5 \\ 6 \\ 7 \\ 8 \\ 9 \\ 10 \end{matrix} \end{array}$$

$$\mathbf{K}_p = \frac{EA}{l} \operatorname{diag} \left[1 \quad 1 \quad 1 \quad 1 \quad 1 \quad 1 \quad \frac{1}{\sqrt{2}} \quad \frac{1}{\sqrt{2}} \quad \frac{1}{\sqrt{2}} \quad \frac{1}{\sqrt{2}} \right]$$

10-5. Form vectors $\mathbf{d} = \{w_1 \quad w_2 \quad w_3 \quad w_4 \quad u_1 \quad u_3\}$ and $\mathbf{y} = \{u_2 \quad u_4\}$, and split matrix **A** of Prob. 10-4 accordingly. Then use scheme of Table 10-4.

10-6. Form vectors $\mathbf{d} = \{u_2 \quad w_2\}$ and $\mathbf{y} = \{\psi_2 \quad u_3\}$, and split matrix **A** of Prob. 10-2 accordingly. Then use scheme of Table 10-4.

10-7.

$$\mathbf{K}_f = \begin{bmatrix} \frac{96EJ}{7l^3} + k & \frac{-30EJ}{7l^3} \\ \frac{-30EJ}{7l^3} & \frac{12EJ}{7l^3} + k \end{bmatrix}$$

10-8. $n = 2$; $\mathbf{d} = \{u_1 \quad w_1 \quad w_2 \quad \psi_2 \quad u_3 \quad w_3 \quad \psi_3\}$; $\mathbf{y} = \{\psi_1 \quad u_2\}$

$\mathbf{v} = \{u_A^R \quad \psi_A^L \quad \psi_A^R \quad \cdots \quad u_E^R \quad \psi_E^L \quad \psi_E^R\}$

$$\mathbf{K}_p = \text{diag}\,[\mathbf{K} \quad \mathbf{K} \quad \mathbf{K} \quad \mathbf{K} \quad \mathbf{K} \quad \mathbf{K}], \text{ with } \mathbf{K} = \begin{bmatrix} \frac{EA}{l} & 0 & 0 \\ 0 & \frac{4EJ}{l} & \frac{2EJ}{l} \\ 0 & \frac{2EJ}{l} & \frac{4EJ}{l} \end{bmatrix}$$

$$\mathbf{A}_0 = \begin{bmatrix} 0 & -1 & 0 & 0 & 0 & 0 & 0 \\ \frac{1}{l} & 0 & 0 & 0 & 0 & 0 & 0 \\ \frac{1}{l} & 0 & 0 & 0 & 0 & 0 & 0 \\ -1 & 0 & 0 & 0 & 0 & 0 & 0 \\ 0 & \frac{-1}{l} & \frac{1}{l} & 0 & 0 & 0 & 0 \\ 0 & \frac{-1}{l} & \frac{1}{l} & 1 & 0 & 0 & 0 \\ 0 & 0 & -1 & 0 & 0 & 0 & 0 \\ 0 & 0 & 0 & 0 & 0 & 0 & 0 \\ 0 & 0 & 0 & 1 & 0 & 0 & 0 \\ 0 & 0 & 0 & 0 & 1 & 0 & 0 \\ 0 & 0 & \frac{-1}{l} & 1 & 0 & \frac{1}{l} & 0 \\ 0 & 0 & \frac{-1}{l} & 0 & 0 & \frac{1}{l} & 1 \\ 0 & 0 & 0 & 0 & 0 & -1 & 0 \\ 0 & 0 & 0 & 0 & \frac{1}{l} & 0 & 0 \\ 0 & 0 & 0 & 0 & \frac{1}{l} & 0 & 1 \end{bmatrix} \qquad \mathbf{A}_1 = \begin{bmatrix} 0 & 0 \\ 0 & 0 \\ 1 & 0 \\ 0 & 1 \\ 1 & 0 \\ 0 & 0 \\ 0 & 0 \\ 0 & \frac{1}{l} \\ 0 & \frac{1}{l} \\ 0 & -1 \\ 0 & 0 \\ 0 & 0 \\ 0 & 0 \\ 0 & 0 \\ 0 & 0 \end{bmatrix}$$

10-10. Internal forces:

$\bar{V}_A^L = 0.0248 \qquad \bar{M}_A^L = -0.00864 \qquad \bar{N}_A^L = 0.0197$

$\bar{V}_A^R = 0.0197 \qquad \bar{M}_A^R = 0.00353 \qquad \bar{N}_A^R = -0.0248$

$\bar{V}_B^L = -0.0197 \qquad \bar{M}_B^L = 0.00597 \qquad \bar{N}_B^L = -0.0181$

$\bar{V}_B^R = -0.0181 \qquad \bar{M}_B^R = -0.00436 \qquad \bar{N}_B^R = 0.0197$

10-14. (*a*) $\mathbf{K}_f = \begin{bmatrix} \dfrac{96EJ}{7l^3} + 2k & \dfrac{-30EJ}{7l^3} \\ \dfrac{-30EJ}{7l^3} & \dfrac{12EJ}{7l^3} + k \end{bmatrix}$; (*b*) $\mathbf{K}_f = \begin{bmatrix} \dfrac{96EJ}{7l^3} & \dfrac{-30EJ}{7l^3} \\ \dfrac{-30EJ}{7l^3} & \dfrac{12EJ}{7l^3} + k \end{bmatrix}$; (*c*) no.

10-15. $\mathbf{K}_f^* = \dfrac{EJ}{l^3}\begin{bmatrix} 28 + \dfrac{kl^3}{EJ} & -10 \\ -10 & 4 + \dfrac{kl^3}{EJ} \end{bmatrix}$

INDEX

Amplitude, 30
Amplitude matrix, 219
Amplitude resonance, 106
Arch, coupled bending and longitudinal vibration of, 327
  vibrating, frequency determinant for, 331
Associative law, 13

Beam, box, analysis of, 359
  buckling of, 369
  flexural vibration of, 55, 86, 323
    shear and rotary inertia effects from, 132, 324
Bearings, isotropic, 124, 125, 127
  oil film in, 323, 333
Bilinear form, 15
Bode diagram, 107
Box beam, analysis of, 359
Branched systems, 153
  forced vibration of, 161
Buckling of a beam, 369

Catalogue, of flexibility matrices, 246
  of reduced delta matrices, 200
  of stiffness matrices, 246
  of transfer matrices, 375–410
Cayley-Hamilton theorem, 22
  applied to derivation of transfer matrix, 137
Characteristic equation, 18, 19, 22, 38, 98
Closed systems, 90
Compatibility, 241, 248, 254, 263, 302–304
Compatibility matrix, 288
Compatible deformations, 251
Complex admittance, 111
Complex amplitude, 98, 234
Complex dynamic stiffness matrix, 234
Complex eigenvalue, 98, 235
Complex impedance, 96, 111
Complex receptance, 111
Complex shear modulus, 97
Complex state vector, 100
Complex stiffness, 111
Complex transfer matrix, 100, 109
Complex Young's modulus, 97
Condensation (*see* Stiffness matrix)
Coordinate system, 52
Coupled system, 187
Coupling, elastic, 334
  rigid, 333, 338
Coupling matrix, 188
Coupling spring with release, 190
Cramer's rule, 6
Cross-symmetric matrix, 4

D'Alembert's principle, 29, 218
Damped vibrations, 95, 97, 109, 233
Damper, vibration, 46, 163
Damping, hysteretic, 233
  rotating shaft with, 124
  steady-state motion with, 104, 106, 233
  structural, 96, 106, 233
  viscous, 95, 104, 233
Damping factor, 105
Damping matrix, 233, 236–238
Damping models, 95
Deficiencies (*see* Kinematic deficiencies)
Deformations, 242–244, 253, 286
  initial, 274
Degrees of freedom, 28, 37
Delta matrix, 194, 324

Delta matrix, boundary conditions, 197
 catalogue of, 200
 reduced, 200
Dependence, linear, 5, 6
Determinant, frequency (*see* Frequency Determinant)
 rules for evaluation of, 4
 shorthand notation for, 166
 subdeterminant, 6
Determinant matrices, 194
Diagonal, cross, 3
 main, 3, 215
Diagonal matrix, 3, 218, 225
Diagonally partitioned matrix, 4, 17
Differential equations, 25
 constant coefficients of, 137
 derivation of transfer matrix from, 130
 solution of, 141, 145
Differentiation of a matrix, 25
Disk, rotating, 165
Displacement, dummy, 251
 generalized, 267, 268, 352
 time-varying, 49, 230, 239
Displacement method, 241
 matrix, 286, 302, 322
  tabular calculation, 305
Distributive law, 13
Division, matrix, 15
 (*See also* Inversion of a matrix)
Dummy displacement, 251
Dummy-displacement theorem, 250, 287, 303
Dyadic product, 17
Dynamic magnification factor, 105

Eccentricity of mass on rotating shaft, 124
Eigenvalue, 18, 38
 complex, 98, 235
 multiple, 23, 139
Eigenvector, 20–22, 221
Elastic coupling, 334
Elimination, transfer matrices as means of, 60
Elimination technique for intermediate conditions, 169, 172
Equation of motion in matrix form, 214, 217
 uncoupled, 236
Equilibrium conditions, 241, 263, 302, 304
Euler's relation, 29, 98
Excitation, harmonic, 34
Extended point matrix, 83
Extended state vector, 82, 83
Extended transfer matrix, 82
 derivation of, for bending and buckling of straight beam, 369

Face, positive and negative, 52
Field matrix, 53
Flexibility matrix, 214–218, 240, 241, 255
 catalogue of, 246
 sign convention for, 242
Flow, shear, 356
Force, generalized, 232, 238, 267, 352
 internal, 242, 243, 252, 253
 time-varying, 32, 104, 228, 238
Force-deflection relationship, 241
Force group, 268, 322
 redundant (*see* Redundant force groups)
 self-equilibrating, 271
Force method, 241, 286, 302, 322
 matrix, 240, 261, 356
  basic theory of, 252
  comparison with matrix displacement method, 322
  tabular calculation, 256
Forced vibration (*see* Vibration)
Form factor, 133, 324
Free vibration, 28, 219, 225, 235
Frequency, natural, 28, 30, 98
Frequency determinant, 61, 90, 102, 206, 219
 difficulties of computing, 193, 204
 for vibrating arch, 331
Frequency response, 115

Generalized displacements, 267, 268, 352
Generalized forces, 232, 238, 267, 352

Harmonic excitation, 34
Harmonic motion, 30, 42
Homogeneous algebraic equations, 6
 solution of, 7
Hrennikoff model, 346

Impedance, complex, 96, 111
Impulse, 32, 33, 104
 effect of, on multi-degree-of-freedom systems, 228
Independence, linear, 7
Initial conditions, 28, 237

Initial conditions, for multi-degree-of-freedom systems, 224, 225
  for systems with two degrees of freedom, 41
Initial deformations, 274
Initial strains, 264, 276
Initial stress, 313
Integration of a matrix, 25
Intermediate conditions, 153
  rigid, 169
    elimination of, 169, 172
    modified transfer matrix applied to, 338
Internal energy, 242, 245, 357
Internal force, 242, 243, 252, 253
Inversion of a matrix, 15
  formulas for, 16
  in highly redundant structures, 280
  properties of inverse matrix, 16
Isotropic bearings, 124, 125
  point matrix for, 127
Iteration, 295, 364
  Picard, 146

Kinematic deficiencies, 299, 302, 303, 306, 314
  recurrence method for large numbers of, 318, 320

Lag, shear, 351
Left inverse, 151
Linear dependence, 5, 6
Linear independence, 7

Magnification factor, dynamic, 105
Mass matrix, 217
Matrix, amplitude, 219
  coupling, 188
  cross-symmetric, 4
  damping, 233, 236–238
  delta (*see* Delta matrix)
  diagonal, 3, 218, 225
  differentiation of, 25
  eigenvalues of (*see* Eigenvalue)
  field, 53
  flexibility (*see* Flexibility matrix)
  integration of, 25
  inverse (*see* Inversion of a matrix)
  mass, 217
  modal, 221, 222
Matrix, null, 3
  partitioned, 3
    diagonally, 4, 17
  point (*see* Point matrix)
  rank of, 7
  real symmetric, 19
  rearrangement of transfer matrices, 173
  reduction, 176
  singular, 7, 14, 227
  skew-symmetric, 17
  spring, 155, 157, 163
  stiffness (*see* Stiffness matrix)
  symmetric, 4, 215, 244, 255
  trace of, 19
  transfer (*see* Transfer matrix)
  transformations, 158, 188, 267
  transposed, 4
  unit, 3
Matrix addition, 8
Matrix algebra, 8
Matrix displacement method (*see* Displacement method)
Matrix division, 15
Matrix force method (*see* Force method)
Matrix multiplication, checks, 10
  by a parameter, 9
  of partitioned matrices, 12
  transfer-, 62
Matrix product, properties of, 13
Matrix subtraction, 8
Matrizant, 147
Maxwell-Betti reciprocal theorem, 215, 244, 287
Modal matrix, 221
  properties of, 222
Modal vector, 221
  orthogonality of, 222
Modes (*see* Normal modes)
Modified method of transfer matrices, 204, 333
  fourth-order, 205
  general theory, 211
  sixth-order, 210
Multiple eigenvalue, 23, 139

Natural frequency, 28, 30, 98
Normal modes, 37, 39
  as coordinates, 231
  orthogonality of, 40, 41, 76, 221, 222
Notation for determinant, shorthand, 166
Null matrix, 3

Numerical difficulties of transfer-matrix calculations, 192, 324

Oil film in bearings, 323, 333
Orthogonality, eigenvectors of, 20
  of normal modes, 40, 41, 76, 221, 222

Particular integral, 34
Partitioned matrix, 3, 4, 17
Period of vibration, 30
Phase angle, 30, 35, 105
Phase plane, 233
Phase resonance, 106
Picard iteration, 146
Plate vibration, 346
Point matrix, 54
  extended, 83
  for isotropic bearings, 127
Postmultiplication, 14
Premultiplication, 14
Principle, D'Alembert's, 29, 218
  of work, 248, 250
Product, dyadic, 17
  matrix, properties of, 13
  scalar, 2

Quadratic form, 15

Rank of a matrix, 7
Real symmetric matrix, 19
Receptance, complex, 111
Reciprocal theorem, Maxwell-Betti, 215, 244, 287
Recurrence method, 280
Reduced delta matrix, 200
Reduced transfer matrix, 176, 179–181
Reduction method in presence of rigidities and releases, 176
Redundant force groups, 267
  choice of, 268
  self-equilibrating, 274
Redundant forces, 240
Redundants, many, recurrence method for, 280
Release, 165, 169
  coupling spring with, 190
  reduction in presence of, 176
Resonance, phase, 106
Response, frequency, 115
Rigid coupling, 333, 338
Rigidity, reduction in presence of, 176
  (*See also* Intermediate conditions)
Rotating disk, 165
Rotating shaft with damping, 124
Runge-Kutta method, 145

Scalar product, 2
Self-equilibrating force group, 271
  redundant, 274
Shaft, rotating, with damping, 124
Shear flow, 356
Shear lag, 351
Shear modulus, complex, 97
Shifted-matrix method, 72, 74, 78, 370
Shrink fit, calculation of, 366
Sign convention, for flexibility and stiffness matrices, 242
  for transfer matrices, 52
Skew-symmetric matrix, 17
Spring matrix, 155, 157
  singularities of, 163
State vector, 51
  complex, 100
  extended, 82, 83
  intermediate, elimination of, 60
Statically determinate system, 240, 258, 262, 269, 270
Statically equivalent forces, 248, 303
Statically indeterminate system, 240
Steady-state forced vibration, 35, 82, 227
Steady-state motion with damping, 104, 106, 233
Stiff supports and numerical difficulties of transfer-matrix calculations, 192, 324
Stiffness, complex, 111
Stiffness matrix, 214, 215, 240
  catalogue of, 246
  complex dynamic, 234
  condensation of, 297
  derivation of transfer matrix from, 148
  diagonal, 218
  sign convention for, 242
  of structural element, 244
Strains, initial, 264, 276
Stress, initial, 313
Stress-strain relationship, 263
Structural damping, 96, 106, 233
Structural modifications, 274, 315, 359
  elimination of element, 277, 316

Structural modifications, to meet certain stress conditions, 278
  rigidification of element, 277, 316
Subdeterminant, 6
Symmetric matrix, 4, 215, 244, 255

Thermal strain, 264
Time-varying displacement, 49, 230, 239
Time-varying force, 32, 104, 228, 238
Trace of matrix, 19
Transfer matrix, 51
  catalogue of, 375–410
  complex, 100, 109
  derivation of, 130
    Cayley-Hamilton theorem applied to, 137
    from differential equations, 130
    from stiffness matrix, 148
  dimensionless, 76
  elimination by, 60
  extended, 82, 369
  imaginary part of, 101
  modified method (*see* Modified method of transfer matrices)
  multiplication of, 62
  numerical calculation with, 71
    difficulties in, 192, 324
  real part of, 101
  rearrangement of columns, 173
  rectangular, 151
  reduced, 176, 179–181
  variations of method, 192
Transformations, 158, 188, 267
Transposed matrices, 4
Turbine-generator shaft, bending vibrations of, 332

Undamped vibration, 28, 227
Unit matrix, 3

Vector, column, 2, 51, 252
  modal, 221, 222
  row, 2
  state (*see* State vector)
Vibration, bending, of turbine-generator shaft, 332
  coupled bending and longitudinal, of circle, 327
  damped, 95, 97, 109, 233
  flexural, of beam (*see* Beam)
  forced, 32, 45, 82, 109, 227, 233
    of branched systems, 161
    steady-state, 35, 82, 227
  free, 28, 219, 225, 235
  general theory of, 214
  period of, 30
  plate, 346
  undamped, 28, 227
Vibration damper, 46, 163

Whirling speed, 323
Work principle, 248, 250

Young's modulus, complex, 97